PLANT SCIENCE MONOGRAPHS

Edited by

Professor Nicholas Polunin

———————

WEEDS OF THE WORLD

BIOLOGY AND CONTROL

PLANT SCIENCE MONOGRAPHS

Uniform with this volume:

Biology of Mycorrhiza . . . . J. L. Harley

Microbiology of the Atmosphere . . . . . . P. H. Gregory

Plant Growth Substances . . . . L. J. Audus

Salt Marshes and Salt Deserts of the World . . . V. J. Chapman

Seed Preservation and Longevity . . . . . . L. V. Barton

FURTHER TITLES ARE UNDER CONSIDERATION

THE feeding and clothing of the world's teeming millions can continue to keep abreast of population increases through the help of effective application of research in the plant sciences. The publication of this research, by which means a scientist or technologist makes his findings known to workers elsewhere, tends to be scattered in literally hundreds of botanical and agricultural journals emanating from most of the countries of the world. Often it appears in such polyglot arrays of fragments that it is extremely difficult to bring together even in some narrow 'line' of endeavour. Consequently advances are slowed and interests unnecessarily divided, scientific and human progress being thereby retarded.

The present series of 'monographs' is designed to remedy these deficiencies in especially important or attractive specialities, by publishing individual book-length accounts of the entire background and current progress in their fields. Such detailed surveys, being fully documented and plentifully illustrated, should prove of real value to the world at large in constituting the bases for further advances on the ever-expanding horizons of scientific research, and so lead to improved productivity and, ultimately, standards of living. They are prepared by specialists usually of international reputation for their work in the field chosen, and often culminate a lifetime of active investigation. Being as up-to-date as possible, they will often embody significant advances not previously published.

PLANT SCIENCE MONOGRAPHS
Edited by
Professor Nicholas Polunin

WEEDS OF THE WORLD

Biology and Control

By

LAWRENCE J. KING

M.S., Ph.D. (Chicago)
Dept. of Biology, State University College,
Genesco, New York

LONDON
LEONARD HILL

INTERSCIENCE PUBLISHERS, INC.
NEW YORK
1966

LONDON
A Leonard Hill Book Published by the Book Division, Grampian Press Ltd.,
8/10 King Street, Hammersmith, London, W.6.
NEW YORK
Interscience Publishers Inc.
250 Fifth Avenue, New York 1

FIRST PUBLISHED IN GREAT BRITAIN 1966

PRINTED IN GREAT BRITAIN AT
THE UNIVERSITY PRESS
ABERDEEN

TO CYNTHIA, JOYCE AND LAURIE
AND TO THE MEMORY OF
DOROTHY ROWE KING

CONTENTS

		PAGE
FIGURES IN TEXT		xi
LIST OF TABLES		xiv
LIST OF PLATES		xv
PREFACE		xvi
General aspects		xvi
Common names		xviii
Technical names		xviii
Poisonous plants		xx
Legal aspects		xx
Control methods		xx
The bibliographies		xxii
Acknowledgements		xxvi

CHAPTER

I	AN INTRODUCTION TO WEEDS	1
	History of the term 'weed'	1
	Definitions of 'weed'	6
	Ancient weed records	10
	The origins of weeds	14
	Bibliography	24

II	THE CLASSIFICATION OF WEEDS	32
	The various systems	32
	The types of weeds	34
	Bibliography	46

III	THE PARASITIC WEEDS	49
	Cuscutaceae	49
	Lauraceae	51
	Loranthaceae	52
	Santalaceae	60
	Orobanchaceae	61
	Scrophulariaceae	64
	Bibliography	68

CHAPTER   PAGE

IV   THE USES OF WEEDS 79
     Utilization as food for animals 79
     The value of weeds as food for humans 80
     Medical uses of wild plants 81
     Some general uses 82
     Examples of plant usage by the Indian tribes of northern
       California 83
     The contributions of ethnobotanical studies 85
     Weeding operations in primitive agriculture 86
     Bibliography 88

V   HARMFUL ASPECTS OF WEEDS 91
     Poisonous plants 91
     Food-tainting weeds 93
     Poisonous and fetish plants used by primitive peoples . . 94
     Weeds as hosts for fungus and bacterial diseases . . . 95
     Weeds as hosts of virus diseases 97
     Weeds as hosts for nematodes 98
     Pollinosis and related allergies 99
     Problems of malaria control 102
     Vegetation control and the tsetse fly 103
     Miscellaneous harmful plants 103
     Weeds and associated insects 105
     Bibliography 107

VI   THE ESTABLISHMENT OF WEEDS: SEED STRUCTURE, GERMINATION
    AND SEEDLING ECESIS 115
     The angiosperm seed 115
     The types of dormancy of weed seeds 119
     The weed seed populations of soil 128
     Condition and longevity of weed seeds in the soil . . . 129
     Germination 130
     Factors involved in the germination of weed seeds under field
       conditions 134
     Factors in seedling establishment 144
     Bibliography 154

VII   THE GROWTH AND DEVELOPMENT OF WEEDS 162
     General growth aspects 162
     Root systems 162
     Depth and extent of root development 166
     Physiology of root growth 167
     General soil factors and the growth of weeds . . . 169
     Nutrient absorption and weed growth 173
     Nitrogen relationships 175
     Nitrate content and toxicity to animals 178
     The water relations of weeds 180

CONTENTS

CHAPTER   PAGE

        Temperature and weed growth 185
        The response of day-length—photoperiodism . . . 187
        Life-forms and growth-forms 191
        Bibliography 192

VIII THE REPRODUCTION AND DISPERSAL OF WEEDS . . . 203
        Flowering and seed production of weeds 203
        Phenology 208
        The propagation of weeds 212
        Dispersal of weeds 216
        Bibliography 220

IX GENETIC ASPECTS OF THE ORIGIN AND EVOLUTION OF WEEDS 226
        Interspecific hybridization 226
        Introgressive hybridization 230
        Apomixis 232
        Ecotypes 233
        Agricultural ecotypes 234
        The origin of some crop plants from weeds 235
        Development of resistance to herbicides 238
        Bibliography 239

X INJURIOUS INTERACTIONS OF WEEDS AND CROP PLANTS . . 243
        Injurious effects of weeds on crops 243
        The influence of one plant upon another 248
        Bibliography 254

XI THE PHYTOSOCIOLOGY AND WORLD DISTRIBUTION OF WEEDS . 260
        Introduction and phytosociology 260
        World aspects of weed distribution 270
        Bibliography 276

XII THE CLASSIFICATION AND MODE OF ACTION OF HERBICIDES . 284
        Introduction 284
        Classification of herbicides 287
        Contact herbicides 289
        Inhibitors of cell growth 290
        'Auxin-type' growth-regulating chemicals 294
        Inhibitors of growth and of tropic responses . . . 301
        Inhibitors of chlorophyll formation and of photosynthesis . 302
        Other translocated herbicides 306
        Bibliography 307

XIII APPLICATION, ENTRY, AND ACTIVITY OF HERBICIDES . . 314
        Formulation 314
        Application, coverage, and spray retention 316
        Mode of entry into plants 325

CHAPTER   PAGE

      The plasma membrane 330
      Movement of herbicides in plants 331
      Fate of 2,4-D and other herbicides within plant tissues . . 333
      Physiological effects following herbicidal applications . . 335
      The selectivity of herbicides 336
      Fate of herbicides applied to the soil 338
      Bibliography 341

XIV THE USES OF HERBICIDES 349
      Introduction 349
      International progress in chemical weed control . . . 350
      Introduction to chemical methods 352
      Herbicides for field crops 352
      Herbicides for vegetable crops 359
      Herbicides for ornamental, fruit, and nursery crops . . 360
      Weed control in forage crops, pastures, and rangelands . . 361
      Control of herbaceous perennial weeds 369
      The control of aquatic plants 372
      Herbicides for lawns and sports areas 378
      The use of soil sterilants 380
      The control of special groups of weeds 381
      The use of growth suppressants 382
      Herbicides and the environment 383
      Bibliography 384

XV NON-CHEMICAL METHODS FOR THE CONTROL OF WEEDS . . 402
      Control by soil cultivation 402
      Mechanical clearing of land 405
      Control by flooding 408
      Control by fire 408
      Prevention of weed infestations by the use of clean crop seed 409
      Ecological control of weeds 409
      The biological control of weeds by insects . . . 411
      Control by fungal or other diseases, or parasitic seed plants . 416
      Control by animal feeding 417
      Competitive cropping 418
      Bibliography 420

APPENDIX I: Properties and Uses of Herbicides 438

APPENDIX II: Supplementary Data on Recently Introduced Herbicides 450

APPENDIX III: Chemical Weed Control Suggestions for Vegetable Crops,
      State of Wisconsin, U.S.A. 453

APPENDIX IV: Choosing the Correct Spray Nozzle Tip . . . 459

CONVERSION FACTORS 460

SUBJECT INDEX 463

AUTHOR INDEX 504

FIGURES IN TEXT

FIG.   PAGE

1. Dyer's woad 3
2. The Chinese and Japanese ideographs for 'tza tsao' or 'weed' . 5
3. Seeds and fruits principally of weeds 11
4. Diagrams showing the many and diverse paths which may lead to the development of present-day weeds 21
5. Wild plant regions of the world 22
6. Cultivated plant regions of the world 23
7. Semi-diagrammatic drawing of a portion of a dwarf-mistletoe shoot 56
8. Stages in pollen release of the common ragweed 100
9. Diagram showing the daily collections of atmospheric pollen etc. at Utica, New York 101
10. Outline drawings of crop seed or fruit, and of similarly-shaped weed seeds or fruits associated with these crops, illustrating the voilure principle 116
11. Drawing of crop seeds or fruits, together with the associated weed ones 118
12. Drawings of crop seeds or fruits, together with the associated weed ones 119
13. Drawings of crop seeds or fruits, together with the associated weed ones 120
14. *Xanthium* fruits showing positions of normal seeds . . . 123
15. Germination and emergence from the soil of some dicotyledonous plants 132
16. Germination and emergence from the soil of some monocotyledon-ous plants 133
17. Germination curves, lowest soil temperature, and rainfall in stubble cultivation experiment 135
18. Germination curves of *Sinapis arvensis* seeds 136
19. The effect of day-length on the percentage of germination of various seeds 136
20. Seedlings of some weedy members of the Cruciferae . . . 145
21. Seedlings of some weedy members of the Compositae . . . 146
22. Schematic drawing of a young grass seedling 147
23. Seedlings of members of the Gramineae, and of a species of *Yucca* 148
24. Underground growth of *Alopecurus myosuroides* 149
25. The ten types of root systems 163
26. Diagrams of the root system and vegetative reproduction of cut sections of a dandelion 168
27. Variation in day-length throughout the year at four latitudes in North America 188

FIG.   PAGE

28. Cross-section of a flower head (capitulum) 204
29. Seed weight and habitat 206
30. Heteromorphic propagules 207
31. Growth-development curve of Dakold winter rye . . . 210
32. Accumulated degree days from 1st May to the date when crabgrass had from two to four leaves 211
33. Period of growth, throughout one year, of a series of annual weeds 213
34. Some major representative dispersal types 214
35. Examples of the seven kinds of propagules in three climatic regions 215
36. Semi-diagrammatic representation of a plant of *Ranunculus repens* 216
37. Chromosome evolution in the family Proteaceae 228
38. Diagram of geographical expansion of species under extreme circumstances 235
39. Weeds represented as having greater mineral content than their associated cultivated plants 245
40. Yields of corn (maize) grown alone, and grown with weeds . . 245
41. Amount of average growth for the important ruderal associations of the southern area of the lower Balkans 260
42A. Development of the different associations considered during the formation of the rice field 262
42B. Development of the main associations composing the biocoenosis of the rice field during the summer 263
43. Distribution of the weed associations in the cereal-growing areas around Pavia, Italy 264
44. The development of weed associations in an open courtyard, Budapest, Hungary 265
45. The relative importance, and the distribution of a group of weeds in six different habitats in Quebec 266
46. Map of part of the artillery field at Uppsala, Sweden, showing the distribution of several species etc. of plants 268
47. Soil profiles along one of the diagonals shown in the preceding figure 269
48. Graph showing the average per cent germination obtained through-out a 100-day period from ecotypes of *Stellaria media* . . 271
49. Principal ocean currents of the world 275
50. Effect of isopropyl N-phenylcarbamate (IPC) and its mono-chlorinated derivatives on the Hill reaction of chloroplasts . 292
51. Commercial production in the United States of the acid and ester derivatives of 2,4-dichlorophenoxyacetic acid (2,4-D) . . 295
52. Length of time required for conversion of sodium 2-(2,4-dichloro-phenoxy)ethyl sulphate to an active form in soil . . . 300
53. Evaporation of n-butyl ester of 2,4-D from nickel-plated planchets at room temperature 316
54. Evaporation of the 2-ethylhexyl and the 2-(2-ethoxyethoxy)propyl esters of 2,4-D from nickel-plated planchets at room temperature . 317
55. Effect of relative humidity on $t^{\frac{1}{2}}$ for three formulations of maleic hydrazide 317

FIG.   PAGE

56. Three-dimensional response surfaces for two maleic hydrazide formulations 318
57. The outlines of a liquid drop on the surface of a pea, and on a leaf of *Sinapis arvensis* 320
58. Computed paths of spray droplets of various sizes . . . 323
59. The effect of a cross-wind of up to 8 miles per hour upon a trapezoidal spray distribution pattern applied from an aircraft . . 324
60. Diagrammatic representation of a leaf's outer epidermal cell-wall and cuticle 326
61. An ontogenetic study of the development of cuticular wax on fibre flax 327
62. Spectrophotometric determination of the decomposition in a soil culture medium 339
63. Herbicides for selective weed-control in cereal crops, and situations in which they may be used 353
64. Three-year average number of kernels per head and yield in bushels per acre of Pawnee winter wheat 354
65. The effect of several phenoxyalkylcarboxylic acids at $\frac{1}{2}$ lb per acre on flax 355
66. Relationship of yield of weed to the resulting corn yield reductions 356
67. Illustration of *Echinochloa crusgalli* 357
68. Yield of weedy grasses as affected by chemical treatment at three stages of the growth of alfalfa 362
69. Total yield per acre from areas renovated with different chemical and tillage treatments 363
70. Average percentage survival of two age-classes of big sage-brush one year after being sprayed with 2,4-D 364
71. Percentage of big sage-brush controlled with one application . . 365
72. 1953-4 average air-dry grass production and utilization of grasses on control plots sprayed in 1952-3 366
73. Average total carbohydrate content of mesquite root tissues . . 367
74. Influence of mesquite control on gain in weight of yearling steers . 367
75. Canada thistle stand after successive treatments with 2,4-D and 2,4,5-T 370
76. Toxicity of MCPB, 2,4-D and 2,4-DB as compared with the toxicity of MCPA 371
77. Beneficial effects of the herbicide Acrolein 375
78. Examples of land-clearing equipment 406
79. Growth regions of members of the grass family 407
80. Controlled vegetation zones along power-lines in Connecticut . 411

LIST OF TABLES

TABLE   PAGE

I   Biological characteristics of weeds, their expression and suggested control measures 8, 9

II   Details of the more important *Striga* species 67

III   Voilure coefficients for the seeds of a number of common weeds   117

IV   Compiled data on the 1000-seed weight, the optimum and maximum depths of emergence from soil, and the number of seeds per plant, for various common weeds 139

V   Absorption of nutrients by weeds 174

VI   Coefficients of transpiration and efficiencies of transpiration of important weeds and crop plants 180

VII   Origins of crops from weeds 237

VIII   Chemical composition of maize grown alone, of maize grown with weeds, and of different weeds grown with maize . . . 246

IX   Comparisons of relative yields and of plant nutrient uptake by maize alone, maize with weeds, and different weeds grown alone . . 246

X   Substances from plant parts, chiefly roots, believed to be associated with teletoxicity 252

XI   A chemical classification of the principal organic herbicides . . 288

XII   The nine most important substituted s-triazine herbicides . . 306

XIII   Surface-tension values and contact angles of pure water, and as modified by the addition of surface-active agents, or by a herbicide at several concentrations, obtained for various leaf surfaces . . 321

XIV   Responses of some woody species of the temperate zone of the northern United States to either foliage or basal applications of hormone herbicides 369

XV   Rates of aromatic solvent usually needed to control different species of submerged aquatic weeds 374

XVI   Turf-grass survey of Los Angeles County, California . . . 379

LIST OF PLATES

(Between pages 224-225)

PLATE

1. Illustration of darnel
2. (a) Witches'-brooms caused by a dwarf-mistletoe
   (b) Lodgepole pine killed by a dwarf-mistletoe
3. (a) Features of the dwarf-mistletoe plant
   (b) Features of the dwarf-mistletoe plant
4. (a) Features of the dwarf-mistletoe plant
   (b) Features of the dwarf-mistletoe plant
5. (a) Four-branched broomrape (*Orobanche ramosa*) clusters
   (b) Plants of witchweed (*Striga asiatica*)
6. (a) Coins of the ancient city of Cyrene
   (b) Illustration of *Tlalquequetzal* from an Aztec herbal
7. (a) Branches of ragweed showing the abundance of pollen-producing flowers
   (b) Giant ragweed growing along a highway
8. Turkish women winnowing grain
9. (a) Competition between Marquis wheat and wild mustard
   (b) Competition between Marquis wheat and wild oats
10. Effect of two different photoperiods upon the growth and flowering of low ragweed (*Ambrosia artemisiifolia*)
11. Contrast between large and depauperate plants of *Saxifraga tridactylites*
12. (a) Foxtail grass (*Setaria viridis*) and the cultivated common millet (*S. italica*)
    (b) Brilliant fluorescence of five-day old seedling roots of cultivated oats under ultra-violet radiation
13. Influence of apple root-bark on the growth of apple seedlings in water culture
14. Paper chromatographic separation of materials in a soil extract
15. 2,4-D activity on tomato plants
16. Infestations of Johnson grass (*Sorghum halepense*) in test cotton plots
17. Pre-emergence weed control with the herbicide Sesone
18. (a) Water-hyacinths being sprayed with a 40 per cent preparation of 2,4-D
    (b) Aerial view of the same area seven weeks later
19. (a) Isolated disks of cuticle from the leaves of *Gardenia*
    (b) Photomicrographs of cuticles from upper and lower surfaces of *Gardenia*
20. (a) Sub-surface soil applicator for more volatile herbicides
    (b) Early post-emergence tillage in a soybean field
21. Piles of weed seeds after removal from wheat
22. Power-line right-of-way through a forested area cleared of brush by the use of 2,4-D and 2,4,5-T
23. Fumigant action of Mylone in soil

PREFACE

General Aspects

WEED science involves the study and control of the more aggressive and troublesome elements of the world's vegetation, and accordingly constitutes parts of such subjects as plant ecology and plant geography. This relatively new science also encompasses the other plant-science disciplines, in addition to certain of the chemical, zoological, and earth sciences. Thus, with the present work listing nearly 5,000 references, in this and the two volumes to follow weed science is no small subject.

Although it is convenient at times to have a topic treated on a world-wide basis within the plan of a few volumes, this can commonly be achieved only at the price of considerable compression. As our knowledge of any special subject grows and changes, condensation, 'pruning', and abbreviated treatment are permissible. More often, and justifiably so the minutiae have engaged biologists, but the broader aspects should also receive due attention. It is certainly desirable to outline the details of past and contemporary work, and, what is perhaps more important, to suggest or imply new avenues of approach in the light of this survey of existing information. Naturally, not all of the weeds or the weed problems occurring in the world can be covered here. For some areas detailed lists are available, and these are presented; but for many areas of the world only brief lists of major weeds, or a few scattered papers, provide our current knowledge of indigenous weed problems. Yet even such limited surveys are valuable, as they indicate where additional knowledge may be needed.

Weeds in these volumes are treated *in sensu lato* as including the principal vascular plants which are considered troublesome, harmful, or otherwise annoying to man and to his agriculture.

Most of the groupings employed here are determined by country or continent, although the weed lists have often been grouped together so that large areas embracing several countries are covered at once. The weed check-lists have been prepared from a few selected publications, deemed both important and extensive, that have appeared to represent the weeds of the region concerned. These publications are indicated in the introductory section to each regional treatment; and the country in which the species is considered a weed—in these publications only—is given after the name. The species may occur, or be considered a weed, in countries adjacent to those cited, but only this type-location could be used in such

xvi

an abbreviated treatment. While one might question this procedure for listing species of the entire natural flora, with weeds—which are far more widespread—it seems appropriate. Many more weed lists may be found in the respective bibliographies, whose contents have not been specifically utilized in the present lists. The bibliographies associated with each of the gross regions are grouped by country to assist readers in readily finding the weed publications for the smaller and more local areas.

References to floras of specific regions have not been made, as, although they may be valuable for identification and related data, they frequently include too little that is of value with regard to the agricultural environments; furthermore, an excellent guide to the floras of the world has been prepared by Blake & Atwood (1942), and Blake (1961)*, although it does not include special publications on weeds and related subjects. Such references as are made to species numbers for any specific region in the present work are taken from the data provided in the most recent and complete flora of the region as indicated by Blake & Atwood. For areas not at present covered by these authors, such data are taken from a standard flora of the region concerned, or from other sources. The species numbers given are, of course, only approximate, but they do serve to show the magnitude of the floristic complement of the region under consideration.

It is recognized that the compiler of regional weed lists is beset with many problems, and the results of his labour may be the subject of some controversy. Usually, however, there are a considerable number of plants in any given region that are considered sufficiently troublesome to be classed as weeds. It is concerning the fringe areas, where ruderals (broadly speaking, weeds) of cities and habitations occur as well as wayside and other plants, that controversy arises as to which are to be included as weeds. Accepting these disputes as inevitable, it is considered that the greatest value will come from an emphasis of the more troublesome elements of the vegetation. The present author's opinion has not entered into the selection of the weeds given in the lists for the majority of areas covered; rather, such lists were compiled from specialists' studies of the respective regions. Of course, authors have differed regarding the extent of coverage.

Often rather old weed lists are available for many countries. If these are the sole existing sources of information, they have been included, but with the place and date of publication indicated. In making use of older data it should always be kept in mind that, while the weed flora as a whole may not change appreciably, the relative balance and importance of individual species may be affected by changing crops, by many phases of agricultural cropping methods (such as tillage, fertilizer practice, crop seed source and cleanliness), and, of course, by invasion of new weed species as well as by the application of newer chemical or other control

* References given in the Preface are to be found listed in the Bibliography to Chapter I.

methods. The dominance and recession of certain weeds may also be related to weather cycles. Caution should be exercised in inter-relating or comparing data listed for the same species in two different countries or regions, for although the name applied to the weeds may be the same in each case, the plants may represent different ecotypes or physiological races. It is hoped that the present work will enable the researcher to probe into, and follow, any particular phase in more detail.

One final aspect should be considered. Much of what is reviewed here concerning the successful growth and establishment of weeds, together with the many species involved throughout the world, should be useful and illustrative to the agriculturist and other specialists in their labours of improving the growth, nature, and range of crops and other useful plants. By one who scans the weed lists, many relatives of cultivated plants may be noted—and not a few cultivated plants, too. Much use has already been made of the wild relatives of cultivated plants in breeding programmes, but the weedy relatives may also provide some valuable germ-plasm.

COMMON NAMES

Common names for the various weeds may be found in the principal floras of the countries concerned. For North America, the several regional floras (e.g. Gleason's *Illustrated Flora of the Northeastern United States and Adjacent Canada*, 3 vols., New York, 1952)*; for the U.S.S.R., Komarov's *Flora U.R.R.S.* is perhaps the best; and for the Arabic, Armenian, and Turkish names, Bedevian's *Illustrated Polyglot Dictionary of Plant Names* (Cairo, 1936) is recommended. One good general work is Gerth van Wijk's *A Dictionary of Plant Names* (2 vols., The Hague, 1911–16). Emil Korsmo's *Weed Seeds* (1935), gives the weed's name in English, Danish, French, Dutch, German, Italian, Swedish, Norwegian, and Russian. Brouwer & Stählin's illustrated *Handbuch der Samenkunde* (1955) provides German and English common names for the 2,512 plant species represented. In the present work, English common names are given principally in the North American, Australian, and European sections. In the Central American section the Spanish common names are given when known, as are the Argentinian and Brazilian names in the South American section. For the other areas, the regional floras or the books just listed should be consulted.†

TECHNICAL NAMES

No area of modern botanical study presents a subject so complex, and at times so controversial, as plant nomenclature. In any check-list given in the present work, an attempt has been made to follow the technical

* References given in the Preface are to be found listed in the Bibliography to Chapter I.

† *See also* R. Kwizda, *Vocabularium Nocentium Florae*, Springer, Berlin. Vierte Auflage, 1963, 128 pp.

nomenclature of the more important and comprehensive weed study, or studies, that are cited for the region concerned. Where differences occurred among these works, the usage employed in the *Index Kewensis* has generally been followed; in cases where the name used in the *Index Kewensis* has not been employed, this name is generally listed in the synonymy following the more acceptable name.   In this matter of multiplicity of technical names for the same plant, it is sometimes forgotten that any established name pin-points the plant in question and serves to identify it for all time. It is in relationships within or between genera and allied species concerning which opinions differ, that newer names may serve to document the opinion held at the time.

The writer takes no responsibility for the accuracy of the scientific names applied to specific weeds. In a work of this scope, the original scientist's determination has to be accepted, and the references are cited to enable any specialist to carry out such checking as may be deemed necessary. Thus, this work rests on the taxonomic efforts of others and makes no original contributions in this area—for it is primarily concerned with the biology and control of weeds.

In conformity with the recommendation of the latest editions of the *International Code of Botanical Nomenclature*, all specific names are de-capitalized—a procedure practised in zoological nomenclature since 1926.

The authority citations have generally been omitted or abbreviated, as authorities' names have sometimes appeared to be considered of greater significance than the technical names proper. It appears to the present author that this is a highly undesirable development, and so in the textual portions of this work no authority citations are employed—they may in any case generally be found in the appropriate weed check-list. Unfortunately, the manner and form of authority citations following the technical names of plants are not consistently followed by taxonomists, and few specialists appear to agree on any standard usage. In fact, it would seem desirable to omit authority citations entirely where the floristic source is cited, and a number of recent publications in plant biology do just this (Polunin, 1948; Darlington & Wylie, 1956). In view of this variability of treatment, the authority citations in the present work generally follow the form of the major source work for the region concerned. Meanwhile it may be noted that some sections have been reviewed by specialists in the respective geographical areas, and it is hoped that any marked errors and omissions have been corrected.

To anyone examining this work, or indeed any flora, it is all too evident how important a knowledge of plant systematics is to the student and investigator alike in weed science. It is the foundation upon which much of plant knowledge rests, for it is the cataloguing and filing system by which order and relationship are established among the myriads of plants inhabiting the earth. Instead of reducing instruction in this field, greater efforts will have to be made if workers in weed science and allied subjects are to know the plants with which they work, and if they are to provide the necessary advances in basic research.

POISONOUS PLANTS

As will be pointed out in the text, most weed definitions encompass the poisonous plants. While many of these plants have been included, no attempt has been made to cover completely either them or their extensive literature. Generally, those plants that have a high toxicity to the grazing animal are included. In most cases, one or more of the recent and leading works on this group of plants has been included for the principal countries of the world. However, the coverage is by no means complete, and for more exhaustive studies other bibliographies should be consulted. L. H. Pammel (1911) included about 2,457 vascular species in his catalogue of the poisonous plants of the world, which likewise included an extensive bibliography. In an early work, Duchesne (1836) surveyed the poisonous as well as the useful plants of the entire world.*

LEGAL ASPECTS

This phase of the weed problem consists of a highly-flexible and diverse group of regulations depending upon the area, the crops concerned, and the type of chemicals involved at the moment. The seed laws for the United States are generally reproduced in the *Seed World*, a trade annual (cf. the issue for 1958). Long (1910), in an appendix, listed legislation enforcing the destruction of noxious weeds in the chief agricultural countries of the world, while Julien-Dannfelt (1919) has reviewed the weed laws of different countries. In the United States, chemicals sold for pesticide use must be certified by the U.S. Department of Agriculture; and the Food and Drug Administration determines the degree of toxicity of the pesticide in relation to its possible harmful effects on man, and legislates accordingly. These requirements are covered in the Miller Amendment of 1954 (cf. Haller, 1958). The tolerances of pesticide residues permissible on agricultural produce as officially determined by the Food and Drug Administration (FDA) and originally published in the *Federal Register* are summarized annually (*see* the 11th annual revision in *National Agricultural Chemicals Ass. News and Pesticide Review*, **23** (3), 3–23, 1965). No attempt, however, has been made in the present work to cover the legal aspects, or to include pertinent literature. This is an area in definite need of a survey and special study.

CONTROL METHODS

The control measures given for the various weeds are those recommended in the respective area by the authorities generally cited. For many parts of the world, such information is lacking for specific weeds,

---

* *See* the recent work of Kingsbury (1964, ref. p. 392); the study of Ragonese (1956, ref. p. 111) on the plants of central Argentina toxic to cattle; also Ch. V, pp. 91–93.

or is not readily available in published form, and cannot, therefore, be included here. Sometimes only certain early cultivation methods are known, and occasionally some of the older chemical techniques have been given. A considerable time must elapse before the newer organic selective herbicides will have been tried on a large number of the weeds included in this work. However, the ambitious reader may see effective control of a species in one country and apply such knowledge to a closely allied type—or possibly to one merely in the same genus—in an adjacent country.

It is also felt that a need probably exists for a presentation of the principal weeds and the problems encountered therefrom, together with an adequate bibliography. Weeds and weed problems, although changing within certain limits, are certainly more static than their chemical control-methods, which are currently undergoing great and rapid changes.

Control methods have frequently been taken from standard sources, or from lists of susceptible or non-susceptible plants. Documentation of these methods has not been given after every species—instead, references to the biology of the weed in question have generally been given preference, as chemical methods will change greatly over the years, whereas the biological aspects will change to a much smaller degree.

Not too much attention has been given to the problem of weed-control methods and techniques for specific crops. The emphasis has been rather on the biology and the control, when known, of the weeds of various regions, as well as on their specific relations to associated crops. The problem of specificity and selective spraying with each crop is a highly specialized subject, and varies with environmental conditions to such an extent that it was deemed wiser to exclude suggestions or recommend-ations on this topic, although many literature references are listed. Some general aspects of weed-control methods are presented later in this volume, and a number of the tables provide exemplary methods for many crops. Useful guides to the field application of herbicides include the *GLF Chemical Weed Control Guide* (Ithaca, New York, 1963–4 [cf. Ch. XIV]); the *Weed Control Handbook* issued by the British Weed Control Council (London, 1958, and the new edition of 1963 [cf. Woodford & Evans 1963, Ch. XIV]); the *Suggested Guide for the Chemical Control of Weeds*, issued by the Agricultural Research Service of the U.S.D.A. (Washington, 1961 [cf. Danielson *et al*, 1961, Ch. XIV]); and E. A. Helgeson's *Methods of Weed Control*, issued by F.A.O. (Rome, 1957).

As various forms of '2,4-D' (2,4-dichlorophenoxyacetic acid) have been the most widely tested of the newer organic herbicides, the reference to sensitivity throughout all of the check-lists refers to the responses following application of this chemical—generally the water-soluble 'amine' formulation, unless otherwise stated. 'Ester' formulations refer to the butoxyethanol ester or other 'low-volatile' type esters of '2,4,5-T' (2,4,5-trichlorophenoxy acetic acid), and they are generally used alone or

xxi

in combination with the comparable low-volatile esters of 2,4-D. In the check-lists, 'S' indicates that the plant is highly sensitive (and, therefore, readily killed by a 2,4-D (or possibly a 2,4,5-T) product; 'R' indicates the exact opposite, i.e. that the plant is highly resistant, and therefore not killed at the usual rates of field application; while a small 's' or 'r' refers to moderate sensitivity or resistance, respectively. The designation 'r-s' indicates a range of response, and questionable responses are always marked with a question mark.

One of the most complete guides to the chemistry and uses of the great range of pesticides (including herbicides) now on the market is H. Martin's *Guide to the Chemicals Used in Crop Protection* (fourth edn. 1961), Canada Department of Agriculture, Ottawa. D. E. H. Frear's *Pesticide Handbook* (15th edn. 1963) lists all such products by their trade name together with the name of the manufacturer; moreover the composition is stated where known. A comparable list for insecticides is *Entoma* (fourteenth edn. 1961–62), where, in addition, many formulating agents, manufacturers, and equipment, are also listed. A European work noted, *Memorandum Antiparasitaire Européen* (Centre International des Anti-parasitaires, Zurich, 1954), contains a list of products and their composition and manufacturers, and also a list of experimental stations.

The discussion on the use of herbicides in the present volume, and the many suggestions scattered throughout the check-lists, are merely to serve as examples of the manner in which these various herbicides have been successfully used. While these examples are accurate to the best of our knowledge, they should be employed only at the full risk of the user. Local authorities should always be consulted on any problem concerning which there is doubt, or on which insufficient information is at hand.

The Bibliographies

In general, selection of the literature cited has been based on an attempt to include significant articles presenting information resulting from commonly-accepted research procedures. Articles of a more or less popular and abbreviated nature, appearing in farm papers and related types of publication, generally have not been included, because the information they contain is usually adapted from detailed research reports, or is readily available elsewhere.

The bibliographies listed under the respective countries are reasonably complete—at least for the years following 1900. However, references considered to be more clearly associated with weed biology and weed ecology will often be found at the ends of the respective chapters in volume I, instead of being listed in the more extensive bibliography under the country of origin in the later volumes. Often a full reference has been listed only once, in one chapter of this work, as the Author Index will always assist in locating a particular citation.

It should be emphasized that this entire work does not, and of course could not, represent first-hand knowledge of the subject for the many regions concerned—save, perhaps, North America to a limited extent—and so, as far as the weed check-lists and bibliographies are concerned, is of necessity a compilation. While this also holds true in large measure for much of volume I, it is hoped that here more of a contribution has been achieved.

Many of the bibliographies are quite extensive, and it has not been possible in a work of this size to refer in the text to every reference listed. Rather is it hoped that the bibliographies may serve upon close inspection to indicate the range, variety, and special approaches of weed problems in each of the respective regions or countries covered. The bibliographies should also serve as a guide to further enquiry in the various scientific aspects involved.

Many publications listed in the bibliographies are obscure and difficult to locate. Abstracts of most of these may be found in the principal abstracting journals, particularly in the *Experiment Station Record*, the *Botanisches Zentralblatt*, *Biological Abstracts*, *Field Crop Abstracts*, and *Horticultural Abstracts*. The Library of the United States Department of Agriculture in Washington, D.C., as well as the Library of the International Institute of Agriculture (now F.A.O.) in Rome, Italy, and the Biologische Zentralanstalt für Land- und Forstwirtschaft in Berlin-Dahlem, contain the majority of the literature items referred to in this work. Arrangements for microfilming and the preparation of photoprints of particular articles can generally be made with little difficulty (cf. directions for such in any recent issue of the *Bibliography* of *Agriculture*). The *Union List of Serials*, New York, 1943 and supplements, and the *World List of Scientific Periodicals* (1900–1950), London, 1952*—all should facilitate locating full journal title readings and library holdings.

The ready availability of a large number of bibliographic aids has materially shortened the labour expended and, at the same time, has ensured a more comprehensive coverage. Outstanding among these may be listed the following: *Experiment Station Record*, United States Department of Agriculture, Washington, D.C. (1880–1946); *Bibliographie der Pflanzenschutz Literatur* (Berlin-Dahlem) (1914–38, 1940–45, 1950–51); *Plant Science Literature*, United States Department of Agriculture Library, Washington, D.C. (1935–42), and the continued *Bibliography of Agriculture* (1942 to date); *Biological Abstracts* (1920 to date); *Horticultural Abstracts* (1931 to date); *Field Crop Abstracts* (1948 to date); *Bibliography of Tropical Agriculture* (1931–42) and the *International Bulletin of Plant Protection* (1927 to date), both from the International Institute of Agriculture in Rome. The *Bibliography of Weed Investigations*

---

* *See* new edition, P. Brown and G. B. Stratton (eds.), *World List of Scientific Periodicals Published in the Years 1900–1960*. Butterworths, London. Vols. I–III (1963–65).

of the United States Department of Agriculture, published in the journal, *Weeds* (1951 to 1961), has been most helpful, as has *Weed Abstracts* (1950 to date) of the Unit of Experimental Agronomy, Oxford University. Also useful have been certain general indexes such as the *Agricultural Index* (1910 to date); *Bibliographie der deutschen Zeitschriftenliteratur* (1896 to date), and the associated *Fremdsprachigen Auflage* (1911 to date); *Botanisches Zentralblatt* (1880 to 1945); *Bibliography of Soil Science, Fertilizers and General Agronomy* (1931 to date), as well as abstracts and titles in *Zeitschrift für Pflanzenkrankheiten* (1891 to date); *l'Agronomie Tropicale* (1946 to date); and individual indexes of many agricultural and botanical journals. A recent and excellent guide to the literature of agricultural and botanical research is that of Blanchard & Ostvold (1958).

It was the great privilege of the writer to have access to the splendid library of the Boyce Thompson Institute for Plant Research, while individual study in the following libraries has greatly improved coverage of the subject: the United States Department of Agriculture Library and the Library of Congress, Washington, D.C.; Yale University, New Haven, Connecticut; the Widener Library, the Gray Herbarium Library, the Harvard-Yenching Library, and the Economic Botany Library, all at Harvard University, Cambridge, Massachusetts; the John Crerar Library, the University of Chicago Library, and the Chicago Natural History Museum, all in Chicago, Illinois; the Lloyd Library, Cincinnati, Ohio; the Michigan State University Library, East Lansing, Michigan; and the Mann Agricultural Library, Cornell University, Ithaca, New York. The New York Botanical Garden has been particularly helpful in providing ready access to its fine library, and gratitude is expressed to the Librarian, Elizabeth C. Hall, and to the successive Directors of the Garden. The Science Service Library in Ottawa was most helpful for Canadian material. Generous assistance has also been provided by Elizabeth W. Johnson, Librarian of the Philadelphia College of Pharmacy and Science, and by Elizabeth Thorp, Librarian of the Biology Library, University of Pennsylvania.

Particular courtesies were also extended to me in England during visits to the libraries of the Rothamsted Experimental Station, the Royal Botanic Gardens, Kew, the British Museum of Natural History, and the Science Museum in South Kensington, London. Studies at the Bibliothèque National de l'Institut Agronomique and the Bibliothèque de la Musée Nationale d'Histoire Naturelle—both in Paris—were also highly profitable. The libraries at the Landwirtschaftlichen Hochschule at Stuttgart-Hohenheim, Germany, and at the Technische Hochschule, Zürich, Switzerland, were helpful. Particular mention should also be made of the Library of the International Institute of Agriculture in Rome (now the F.A.O. library), for special courtesies extended during a brief study period.

The present volume was initiated largely through the great need for a survey of the major weeds and their literature, as conceived jointly by the author and Prof. Nicholas Polunin when the latter was at Yale and Harvard Universities in the Middle 1950's. This survey is reasonably complete to 1957. Owing to the subsequent fantastic increase in the number of publications on weeds, only books and certain other important research contributions have been noted since that date. However, most of the important new contributions on chemical weed control have been incorporated in volume I—practically up to the date of publication.

For more detailed information the reader is referred to the annual indexes issued with the final number to each volume of *Weed Abstracts* (*see* p. 31). These indexes include a weed species index, a subject index, and an author index. A very useful list of the common names and abbreviations used for herbicides is also to be found on the back cover of each issue.

Weed Abstracts, although available as a weekly news-sheet for restricted circulation from 1950, in 1956 became available to the public on a subscription basis. All earlier issues were mimeographed, but from the beginning of volume 11 (1962) it was properly printed and became available from the Commonwealth Agricultural Bureaux, Farnham Royal, Bucks, England. Since 1960 it has been prepared by the Agricultural Research Council Weed Research Organization at Kidlington near Oxford.

It may be of interest to note the approximate number of titles listed or abstracted in *Weed Abstracts* for the following years: 1957 (2,128), 1958 (2,376), 1959 (2,181), 1960 (2,104), 1961 (1,806), 1962 (2,022), 1963 (1,908), and 1964 (1,935). A total of 101 patents for herbicides and related items was noted or abstracted in the volume for 1961.

The selection of illustrations for the chapters covering regional weed problems in the present volumes has presented considerable difficulty. Except in a few cases, maps of climate and vegetation, which should provide a basis from which to visualize the weed vegetation in its entirety, as well as illustrations of problems engendered by the growth of weeds, have been used, rather than pictures of specific weeds which are already available in the weed manuals and the floras. The author is grateful to all who have sent material for the illustrations, or permitted reproduction —and credit is given whenever these outside sources have been used.

The writer would appreciate having called to his attention any research studies on weeds, particularly from some of the lesser-known areas of the world, as undoubtedly many important studies have been missed or not yet translated. The author would therefore welcome copies of, or references to, studies on weeds and their control and allied subjects —from any part of the world.

ACKNOWLEDGEMENTS

The transmission of the scientific heritage is impressively symbolized in a documentary emblem of the Royal Swedish Academy of Sciences which depicts an elderly man planting a tree. To those, likewise, who have brought this heritage and enthusiasm to the classroom, field, and laboratory, a great indebtedness is due: to Dr. Millard S. Markle and Dr. Murvel R. Garner of Earlham College; to my former associates and teachers in the Botany Department of the University of Chicago, including the late Dr. S. V. Eaton, the late Dr. E. J. Kraus, Dr. C. E. Olmsted, Dr. Karl C. Hamner, the late Dr. C. A. Shull, Dr. P. D. Voth, and the late Dr. J. M. Beal.

The Boyce Thompson Institute, together with its fine library, has provided much of the inspiration and resources for the inception and partial completion of this project. Without the vision, the enterprise, and the financial investment of Colonel William Boyce Thompson (1869–1930), there would be no Institute. Colonel Thompson was a mining engineer and an astute business man with a keen and inquisitive mind. He wished to probe the fundamental nature of living matter. As an adviser in this undertaking he engaged the services of one of the most distinguished botanists of the time, Dr. John Merle Coulter (1851–1928), who, for nearly thirty years, was Chairman of the Botany Department of the University of Chicago. Dr. Coulter served as an adviser from 1920, through the dedication of the Institute in 1924, until his death in 1928. Mrs. William Boyce Thompson (1877–1950) likewise was interested in the Institute and her benefactions also have contributed to its advancement (cf. Hagedorn 1935).

The contributions of Dr. Percy W. Zimmerman (1884–1958) to the development of the growth regulator herbicides are discussed in Chapter XIII. Dr. Zimmerman was a member of the Boyce Thompson Institute staff for thirty-two years, and it was the author's valued experience to have known him for more than a decade. Dr. G. L. McNew has related how, early in the planning sessions, Dr. Zimmerman was to have been designated honorary chairman of the Fourth International Conference on Plant Growth Regulation, 1959, but fate intervened. A most fitting tribute, however, has been made in the dedication of the volume of the proceedings of this conference to Dr. Zimmerman. The biographical notice by his long-time associate Dr. A. E. Hitchcock (1959), and the dedicatory account by Dr. G. L. McNew (1961), are further tributes.

The first director of the Institute, Dr. William Crocker (1877–1950), states (Crocker, 1948, p. 5—see below and also Bibliography to Chapter VI) that another specialist, Eugene Davenport, former Dean of Agriculture of the University of Illinois, in his advice on areas of study remarked, '. . . agricultural extension is well organized and well cared for in the United States, but if we do not have more fundamental knowledge, we may soon have nothing to extend'. Thus Dr. Crocker, in surveying the aims and scope of the Institute, noted that these should involve basic research in all its relations, 'including its meaning in nature, in agriculture, and in the industries' (Crocker, 1948, p. 7).

Thus was founded a world-renowned institution, the only private plant research institute of its type in the world. The early accomplishments of the Institute are reviewed by Dr. Crocker in his book, *Growth of Plants: Twenty Years' Research at Boyce Thompson Institute* (1948), while the steady stream of research has been published largely in the *Contributions from Boyce Thompson Institute* (1925 to date).

Many of the staff of the Boyce Thompson Institute were helpful in the early phases of the production of this work: Dr. George L. McNew, the Managing Director; Dr. A. E. Hitchcock, Dr. Lela V. Barton, Dr. S. E. A. McCallan, Dr. L. P. Miller, and the successive Librarians, Mary Ruth Bateman and Joan De Fato. Among the many jewels in the crown of the Boyce Thompson Institute, one, the library, has already been mentioned. Another is the illustration division, directed by William G. Smith, jr. It is largely through his keen judgement and technical skill that the illustrations in these volumes have been reproduced so successfully.

From 1946 to 1959 the present author was a Senior Research Fellow (affiliated with the former Union Carbide Chemicals Company Fellowship) at the Boyce Thompson Institute. This agricultural fellowship had its origin in 1939, when Dr. Richard H. Wellman, the first Fellow, became associated with Dr. S. E. A. McCallan of the Institute staff in a research programme on fungicides. Owing to the success of these early efforts, the research of the Fellowship grew to encompass investigations into most aspects of the pesticide field, resulting in an impressive array of marketable products (e.g. the fungicide Crag Glyodin, the herbicide Crag Sesone, and the insecticide Crag Sevin). Many of the writer's associates were helpful in some of the earlier phases of this work: Dr. Richard H. Wellman, head of the Fellowship until 1954 and currently head of the Crag Agricultural Chemicals Division of the Union Carbide Chemicals Company, as well as Dr. H. C. Chitwood, Dr. J. B. Harry, Dr. E. R. Marshall, Dr. A. J. Vlitos, Dr. D. M. Yoder, and Robert J. Zedler.

Valuable assistance with language problems has been rendered by a number of present and former staff members of the Boyce Thompson Institute, including Friedrick Arndt, Alvaro Goenaga, Horst Börner, Joseph Gwirtsman, Marissa Bianchi, Vladamir Zakartchenko, and Simone Mavrodineanu, and also by Dr. and Mrs. Askell Löve of the University of Montreal. It is to two of my close associates in the herbicide research programme that a special tribute is due. Horace G. Cutler*, formerly a student at the University of Dublin, in remembering well his Latin,

---

* Currently, Botany Department, University of Maryland, College Park, Maryland.

recalled the 'woad' reference of Caesar and noted the seeming similarity of 'weod' and 'woad'. He likewise assisted with a number of the almost thankless yet certainly arduous tasks necessary in the preparation of these volumes. Herbert Hatfield, jr., also kindly assisted with a great many details that were necessary to bring these volumes to a greater degree of usefulness.

The major portion of the burdensome typing—interpreting a none-too-legible handwriting and an alien Latin nomenclature for the regional weed check-lists—has been admirably accomplished by my sister, Louise King Niewoehner. For careful rendering and typing of the bibliography, and particularly so for the non-English sections, gratitude is expressed to Kathryn Weiss Torgeson. Much other assistance with typing and organization has been ably given by Mary B. Fetherston and associates: May Coyle, Catherine McCabe, Nancy Nicholas; and likewise by Dorothy Pardini and Bettie M. Brooks. Furthermore Mrs. Brooks gave most generously of her time and long editorial experience in checking the page proofs of this entire volume, and its accuracy and readability have been vastly improved by her efforts.

Without the early encouragement and planning of the editor, Prof. Nicholas Polunin, this work might never have reached beyond the talking stage; and much of its final form and appearance are due to his tireless and exacting efforts.

Finally, an acknowledgement of a general and cosmopolitan nature is extended to the countless individual research efforts which essentially give these volumes their structure and form, to those who contributed to the development of the organic herbicides which has resulted in the elevation of this area of study to a scientific discipline, and to the host of botanists and explorers whose insatiable curiosity concerning plant life not only provided the actual specimens upon which the structure of modern plant taxonomy rests, but developed and expanded the system of nomenclature—despite its painful complexities—whereby the noxious and all other forms of plants are individually catalogued for ready recognition by plant scientists throughout the world.

SPECIAL ACKNOWLEDGEMENTS

Special credit must be given to the monumental study of W. S. Woytinsky & Emma S. Woytinsky, *World Population and Production Trends and Outlook* (The Twentieth Century Fund, New York, 1953), as a source of numerous facts and figures used throughout these present volumes.

Some illustrations from the herbal of Dioscorides (*De Re Materia Medica*) have been reproduced in this work. They have been made from the photographic copy of the original Vienna manuscript (512 A.D.), *Codex Aniciae Julianae picturis illustratis, nunc Vindobonensis Med. gr. I, photographice editus* (A. W. Sijthoff, Leyden, 1906). The English translations used in the legends to the herbal illustrations have been taken from *The Greek Herbal of Dioscorides* (translated by John Goodyer A.D. 1665, and edited by R. T. Gunther A.D. 1933), Oxford University Press, 1934).

Likewise, illustrations of plants from the Aztec herbal, *Libellus de medicinalibus Indorum herbis*, by Martinus de la Cruz & Juannes Badianus, Santa Cruz, Mexico, 1552 (reproduced in colour facsimile in *The Badianus Manuscript*, by Emily Emmart, The Johns Hopkins Press, Baltimore, 1940), are included in these volumes. Permission to reproduce these illustrations has kindly been granted by The Johns Hopkins Press.

A few illustrations have been copied from the Chinese herbal of Shih Chen Li, *Pen Ts'ao Kang Mu*, published about 1590. These artist's copies of the original illustrations have been prepared from Chang's edition of this work, through the courtesy of Dr. Shiu-ying Hu of the Arnold Arboretum, Harvard University.

The following publishers have permitted reproduction of certain illustrations: G. Bell & Sons Ltd., *The Reproductive Capacity of Plants*, by E. J. Salisbury (1942); Allen & Unwin, *Chromosome Botany*, by C. D. Darlington (1956); MacMillan Co., New York, *Chromosome Atlas of Flowering Plants*, by C. D. Darlington and A. P. Wylie (1956); Longmans Green, London, *The Geography of the Flowering Plants*, second edn., by R. Good (1953); W. Junk, Leyden, *Manual of Phytogeography*, by L. Croizat (1952); LT's Forlag, Stockholm [*Studies on the Genus* Taraxacum *Wigg., with Special Reference to the Group* Vulgaria Dt. *in Scandinavia*], by C. G. von Hofsten (1954); Simon & Schuster, and Scientific American, *Plant Life* (1957); Oregon State College, *Weeds of the Pacific Northwest*, by Helen M. Gilkey (1957); and the University of Pennsylvania Press, *Weeds of Lawn and Garden: A Handbook for Eastern Temperate North America*, by John M. Fogg, jr. (1945).

Two works published by the United Nations Educational, Scientific, and Cultural Organization (UNESCO) have been most useful, and a number of illustrations from them have been used: *Arid Zone Research— VI, Plant Ecology, Reviews of Research* (Strasbourg, 1955); *Humid Tropics Research, Study of Tropical Vegetation, Proceedings of the Kandy Symposium* (Ceylon, 1956; Paris, 1958).

Publishers of a number of scientific and technical journals have kindly permitted certain reproductions: University of Chicago Press, *The Botanical Gazette*; American Association for the Advancement of Science, *Science*; American Chemical Society, *Journal of Agricultural and Food Chemistry*; Weed Society of America, *Weeds*; American Society of Agronomy, its *Journal*; United Nations, FAO, *Unasylva*; and Grampian Press Ltd., *World Crops*.

INDIVIDUAL ACKNOWLEDGEMENTS

In addition to the many acknowledgements listed throughout these volumes, it is a pleasure to record here the names of persons who have been especially helpful, through correspondence or otherwise, in making these volumes ever more complete and useful:

Åberg, E., Uppsala, Sweden
Alcala, R. P., La Paz, Bolivia
Anderson, E., St. Louis, Missouri
Andrews, F. M., Maidstone, Kent, England
Arndt, F., Stuttgart-Hohenheim, Germany
Bercaw, Louise O., Washington, D.C.
Blackman, G. E., Oxford, England
Boalch, D. H., Rothamsted, England
Bourgin, R., Paris, France
Bruhn, W. C., Ithaca, New York
Buchholtz, K. P., Madison, Wisconsin
Chabrolin, C., Paris, France
Cifferri, R., Milan, Italy
Chouard, P., Paris, France
Crafts, A. S., Davis, California
Croizat, L., Caracas, Venezuela
Crovetto, R. M., Buenos Aires, Argentina
Dansereau, P., formerly of Montreal, Canada
Darrow, R. A., College Station, Texas
Demiriz, H., Istanbul, Turkey
Dodd, A. P., Brisbane, Australia
Edwards, Phyllis, London, England
Ennis, W. B., Beltsville, Maryland
Everist, S. L., Brisbane, Australia
Ferri, M. G., São Paulo, Brazil
Finn, T. P., White Plains, New York
Frankton, C., Ottawa, Canada
Gäumann, E., Zürich, Switzerland
Gill, L. S., Fort Collins, Colorado
Green, K. R., Sydney, Australia
Hanf, M., Limbergerhof, Germany
Harper, R. L., Bangor, Wales
Healy, A. J., Christchurch, New Zealand
Heslot, M., Paris, France
Hinds, T. E., Fort Collins, Colorado
Hofsten, G. von, Uppsala, Sweden
Hu, Shiu-ying, Cambridge, Massachusetts
Kasahara, Y., Kurashiki, Japan

Kasasian, L., Oxford, England
Kenoyer, L. A., San Antonio, Texas
Kern, H., Zürich, Switzerland
Kilsheimer, J. A., Metuchen, New Jersey
Klingman, G. L., Raleigh, North Carolina
Longchamp, P., Versailles, France
Loomis, W. E., Ames, Iowa
Mathews, L. J., Wellington, New Zealand
Meadly, G. R., Perth, Australia
Melo Carvalho, J. C. de, Buenos Aires, Argentina
Mulligan, G. A., Ottawa, Canada
Naib, F., Baghdad, Iraq
Niering, W. A., New London, Connecticut
Overbeek, J. van, Modesto, California
Owen, P. C., Suffolk, England
Pekoldt, K., Stuttgart-Hohenheim, Germany
Pignatti, S., Milan, Italy
Poignant, P., Lyon-Vaise, France
Rademacher, B., Stuttgart-Hohenheim, Germany
Ramirez, Adríana, Santiago, Chile
Robinson, D. W., Loughgall, Northern Ireland
Rollins, R. C., Cambridge, Massachusetts
Row, V., Yonkers, New York
Salisbury, E. J., formerly of Kew, Surrey, England
Shaw, W. C., Beltsville, Maryland
Sikka, S. M., New Delhi, India
Southwick, L., Midland, Michigan
Staniforth, D. W., Ames, Iowa
Stearn, W. T., London, England
Sweet, R. W., Ithaca, New York
Thornton, N. C., La Lima, Honduras
Thurston, Joan M., Rothamsted, England
Timmons, F. L., Denver, Colorado
Trueblood, H. M., jr., Dobbs Ferry, New York
Turrill, W. B., the late, Kew, Surrey, England
Tutin, T. G., Leicester, England
Uppal, B. N., New Delhi, India
Valdes Barry, F., Santiago de las Vegas, Cuba
Velez, I., Rio Piedras, Puerto Rico
Walter, H., Stuttgart-Hohenheim, Germany
Wilson, J. A., Chicago, Illinois
Woodford, E. K., Oxford, England
Yue, Zunvair, Cambridge, Massachusetts

The author is indebted to Dr. George L. McNew, to Dr. S. E. A. McCallan, and to Dr. Lawrence P. Miller, for critically reading this entire work in the initial manuscript form; to Dr. Lela V. Barton for reading Chapter VI of Volume I; to Dr. Charles El Olmsted of the University of Chicago for reviewing portions of Chapters I–XIII of Volume I; and to Dr. Edgar Anderson of the Missouri Botanical Garden for reading Chapter IX, 'Genetic Aspects of the Origin and Development of Weeds'; and to Dr. Johannes Van Overbeek and associates for critically reading Chs. XII–XIV and the Appendices.

Grateful acknowledgement is given to the late Dr. Martin S. Dunn (1898–1964),* formerly chairman of the Biology Department of the Philadelphia College of Pharmacy and Science. Dr. Dunn's patient understanding and wise counsel will always be remembered. He encouraged research, and particularly so in the areas of his specialization, medicinal plants and pharmacognosy. His interests here were largely in the *Labiatae*, and those studies dealing with the various genera (*Mentha, Salvia, Lavandula,* etc.) have been published in the *American Journal of Pharmacy*. The author's long-time friend and associate, Professor M. White, was helpful in many aspects pertaining to the final phases of this work. Gratitude is also expressed to President Arthur Osol, Dean Linwood F. Tice and Registrar John E. Kramer—all of the college—for many kindnesses.

It is a pleasure to acknowledge the expert assistance of both Dr. W. H. Gentner of the Agricultural Research Service, United States Dept. of Agriculture, and Mr. G. Hulings Darby of the college for their meticulous checking of the names and structures of the herbicides presented in the Appendices.

To my wife Joyce I am eternally grateful for encouragement and help during the protracted final stages of this work and for masterly contributions on the Indexes.

See Amer. J. Pharm., 136, 140–1, 1964.

I

AN INTRODUCTION TO WEEDS

In the examination of what precisely is meant by the term 'weed', we shall consider several aspects: firstly, the origin of the word 'weed' in the English language, as well as some of the equivalents in other languages, together with the development of the weed concept; secondly, an examination of the several definitions following present-day usage; and, thirdly, what the contemporary sciences of ecology, cytogenetics, and taxonomy, offer in the explanation and study of the kinds of plants that are classified as 'weeds'.

As a general introductory statement, we may say that weeds comprise the more aggressive, troublesome, and undesirable, elements of the world's vegetation. In the terms 'troublesome' and 'undesirable' resides the real core of our definition problem, as they are inherently or essentially anthropic. The elucidation, then, of the role of man—and, to a very much smaller extent, other animals—in the manipulations of both plants and their associated environments throughout the ages, will provide much of the basic understanding of current weed problems.

History of the Term 'Weed'

Although weeds were perhaps recognized individually in the ancient near-Eastern civilizations, there is little evidence that a word or words existed for the collective term 'weed'. Furthermore, most plants were considered useful. Dr. John A. Wilson (*in litt.*, 1956) has stated that, in the ancient Egyptian language, *kaka*, commonly identified as the castor oil plant (*Ricinus communis*), was used in figures of speech for a plant which grows rankly and may be used as fuel, and also that *senmit*, a word occurring only once in some such context as: 'How unguarded speech grows like a *senmit* plant!', may well mean 'weed'.

Ebbell's detailed study (1937) of the *Papyrus Ebers* (c. 1550 B.C.) identified large numbers of plants used principally as remedies, including mustard, pond-weeds, and the castor bean. Hieroglyphics have been isolated and identified for rush, rush with shoots, herb, reed, reeds side by side, etc. (Gardiner, 1950). A recent study of a Sumerian tablet on agriculture, from Nippur in Iraq (1700 B.C.), does, at least in a free translation, refer to clearing the field of weeds and stubble before crop planting (Kramer, 1956). However, R. C. Thompson's (1949) Assyrian botanical study reveals no equivalents for weeds.

The last stage of Egyptian, Coptic, has a word *entêg* (NTHσ) for the Greek ζιζάνια, *tares*: for example, Matthew xiii, 25, in the Bible (Wilson, 1956). 'Tares' in some translations of the Bible has been freely translated as 'weeds'. However, the latest authorities, Moldenke & Moldenke (1952), identify this with darnel (*Lolium temulentum* L.)—a poisonous weed of cereals known even to Theophrastus.

In Greek, the word βοτανη (botáne) means pasture, fodder, herb, and then noxious herb and thus 'weed', and it was used by Theophrastus. The verb form here is βοτανίζω (botanizo), 'I weed'; while the nouns, βοτάνι and ἀγειοβότανον, are used in modern Greek (G. Smith, *in litt.*, 1957).

Attempts to trace our modern term back to any recognizable equivalents in the Latin language have been unsuccessful. Rather, as a goddess of weeding, *Runcina*, was worshipped during the Augustinian period, variations such as *runco*, *erunco*, and *runciatio*, acquired the meaning of weeding. Early Roman writers employed several forms for the weed concept— such as *herba* (Pliny), '*officiant laetis ne frugibus herbae*' (Virgil), and *erunco herbas* (Columella). The descriptive term for some leaf-margins, runcinate—as applied to the dandelion leaf, for example—appears to be our only current derivative (Yancey, 1945; King, 1957).

According to White & Riddle (1872, p. 1711), both Columella and Pliny employed *runcatio -onis* (*runco*) in the sense of 'a weeding' or 'weeding out'; and they claim that this same root, *runco*, through metonymy (i.e. the use of one word for another that it suggests) also came to be used for 'weeds', as in the following quotation from Columella: '(*faba*) secernatur a cetera runcatione.' A reference to *Runcina* ('the weeding one or weeder') occurs in St. Augustine's *De Civitas Dei* (cf. White & Riddle, 1872, p. 1711).

The Oxford English Dictionary (1933) traces the earliest usage of the word in the English language back to the Anglo-Saxon 'weod', as used by Aelfred (*c.* 888), and indicates it to be of unknown origin. The Saxon name for the month of August was 'Woed-monath'—the month of weeds! However, further search has revealed that 'weed' might be derived from earlier forms of the German *weyt* (*c.* 1150), the Dutch *weet* (*c.* 1597) and *weeda*, the Belgian *weedt* (*c.* 1576), etc., for woad or dyeweed (*Isatis tinctoria* L.) (Hurry, 1930).

A comparative study of the equivalents used for 'weed' in several of the Germanic and Romance languages has shown how descriptive many of these terms are. Some examples here would be the French *mauvaise herbe*, the Italian *malerba*, and the German *Unkraut*. In the Spanish language, 'hierbas malas', 'malezas', 'yerbas nocivas', and 'plantas dañinas', are equivalents for our term.

The cruciferous genus *Isatis* consists of some thirty species. *I. tinctoria* is apparently native in southeastern Russia, where it is recorded as growing on exposed hillsides and in brushy places. It is one of the most widely-distributed species of the genus, and occurs almost throughout Europe, North Africa, and Asia as far as China and Japan. This woad, or 'devil's weed', is also common in western Tibet, Afghanistan, etc., occurring both wild and in cultivation. It is also grown in certain regions of China and yields the indigo of that country; the seeds were used as a source of oil (Schulz, 1936) (Fig. 1).

By courtesy of Oregon State University, from Helen M. Gilkey,
'Weeds of the Pacific' North-west, 1957

FIG. 1.—Dyer's woad (*Isatis tinctoria*, Cruciferae), a widely grown dye-plant in medieval times. *a* = winged seed-case. The name 'woad' (also *weedt*, *weeda*, etc.) is believed to be involved in some manner in the history of the term 'weed'. Oddly enough, it is not a very important weed in the scattered places in which it is now found: these include Idaho, northwestern California, southwestern Oregon, a small area in Virginia, Chile, and perhaps a few places in continental Europe, though apparently not so (as a weed) in England.

Woad is a biennial or perennial herb with many of the characteristics of a plant belonging to the temperate zone. The active period in England extends from about February to November, the resting period from December to January. The rosette is formed in the first season, and the flowers and fruits in the second season. The foliage leaves live throughout the winter. The plant flowers in July and sets seed in September. Cultivation of woad from the earliest times has led to its occasional, apparently spontaneous, appearance in many parts of Europe, including England. It is one of those species which occasionally appears in plenty when ground is newly turned, doubtless on the site of former woad-crops, from which stragglers have persisted and seeded from time to time. In England it is often found in old lime-pits and chalk quarries—thus indicating an alkaline soil requirement. It thrives in rich soil, and soon exhausts it to such an extent that, in former times, the woad crop had frequently to be shifted to new land (Dunn, 1905).

Knowledge of this plant extends far back into antiquity. It is briefly described by Dioscorides and illustrated under the Greek name 'Isatis' (Gunther, 1934). In the ancient Latin language it was referred to as *vitrum*, and a reference occurs in Caesar's *De bello gallico* (V, cap. *xiii*): '*omnes vero se britanni vitro inficiunt, quod coeruleum efficit colorem atque hoc horridiores sunt in pugna aspectu.*' It was thought to be owing to this custom of painting the body blue with woad that the tribe of the Picts were thus named by the Romans. The ancient Romans also called the plant *glastum*, which name is said to be derived from the Celtic word *glas*, meaning blue.

Of interest, perhaps, is the fact that an impression of the characteristic fruit of woad has been found in an earthenware vessel from Somersham, Huntingdon, belonging to the Anglo-Saxon Period (Jessen & Helbaek, 1944).

Dr. J. B. Hurry in 1930 published an extensive study of the woad plant and its culture. This plant had been cultivated since ancient times for its blue pigment, the name *wad* being applied to it in England as far back as the thirteenth century, although it has been nearly extinct there as a crop since 1900. Hurry, in examining the comparative philology of 'woad', refers to the study of M. Heyne who suggested that this problem involves a root which takes two forms. The first is *wis-*, as met with in the Greek *isatis* (or variations in spelling thereof) and in the Gothic *wiz-dila*. The second form is *wi-*, passing into the Latin *vi-trum*, the Old German *wai-d*, the Middle German *waidso*, the Early German *wad*, and finally into the English *woad*.

It is interesting to note that the two most ancient forms appearing in print, *wad* for woad, and *weod* for weed, maintained separate and distinct meanings although they sounded much alike and, following our present analysis, were probably derived from some common root. Just how 'weod' or 'weed' arose from the early Germanic forms listed earlier is not clear.

4

Some speculation may, however, be in order, as neither the proto-Germanic forms nor their modern counterparts above given as common names for the woad plant ever acquired the current meaning of our term 'weed'. In the German language, for example, *weyt* or *waidt* having been given to the crop plant *Isatis*, another word, *Unkraut*, came to be the modern equivalent of 'weed'. In this connection it is interesting to observe that the verb *wieden*, 'to weed', is retained in the Dutch language, although the noun here is *onkruid*—a variant of '*Unkraut*'. In all fairness it should be stated that A. A. Lawrence (*in litt.*, 1958), of the editorial staff of the *Oxford English Dictionary*, does not agree with this theory of the origin of 'weed' as presented in the article in *Nature* (King, 1957); but then, perhaps the evidence is more convincing botanically than etymologically.

From the title page of the weed book by M. Hanzawa, 1910

FIG. 2.—The Chinese and Japanese ideographs for (reading from the top downwards) 'tza ts'ao' or 'weed' (i.e. literally, 'miscellaneous herb'). The usage of 'ts'ao' (the lower ideograph) extends back to the Han Dynasty (200 B.C.) in China, while the combined forms were used in a Japanese work in the early centuries A.D. The derivation of the lower character, 'ts'ao', involves the literal meaning of three components at the levels marked *a*, *b*, and *c*, where *a* (the two dagger-like strokes) is a reduced picturization of two small plants or seedlings; *b* (the rectangle with the horizontal centre stroke) represents the early rising sun; *c* (the long horizontal stroke) indicates the earth; *b* and *c* together constitute the ideograph ts'ao (early). So the entire character can be interpreted as herbs that grow and mature early, earlier than the crop. (*By courtesy of Dr. Shiu-ying Hu.*)

Perhaps 'weed' is another example of language as an accident of usage. It alone, of all the equivalents for 'weed' in both the Germanic and Romance languages, has no intrinsic meaning or self-description that would appear appropriate. Then, again, perhaps a simple and direct analysis would indicate that any plant (or thus, weed) which germinated rapidly, and suddenly appeared in profusion, was likened to 'woad' for its well-known habit in former times of sudden appearance in newly-turned ground. The suggestions proposed for origin are certainly only tentative. One last question arises, 'Has *Isatis tinctoria* ever been classed as a weed'? The answer is generally in the negative for the majority of the countries examined, the few exceptions including Chile, Oregon, and a localized area in western Virginia. Why should this be so? The answer probably resides in two aspects of the life of the plant—the fact that it is dicyclic, requiring two seasons for maturity, which would largely rule it out as a weed of annually cultivated ground; and, secondly, its great dependence upon seeding and proper care for its survival.

Woad is one of the relatively few members of the Cruciferae having winged fruits (cf. Fig. 1). Accordingly its seeds would likely be more widely dispersed through wind action than the seeds of most cultivated plants. The rapid germination and thick appearance of seedlings, and their rapid growth, are also characteristic of plants of the Cruciferae.

Hanzawa (1910) has observed that the single Chinese ideograph for weed, *ts'ao* (herb), was adopted from a poem of Y. Kiang (Han Dynasty, 200 B.C.), while the later modified form *tza ts'ao* (miscellaneous herb), employing two characters, first occurred in a Japanese work of early date (*see* Fig. 2).

Thus in the ancient languages, as might logically be expected, the word for a highly typical and outstanding example—in one case a poisonous weed of grain—also came to mean 'weed', while in the later Greek and Latin the rather nondescript *herba*, or its equivalent, also came to mean weed. This was followed later by a refinement or a descriptive phrase generally including some form of *herba*, or its equivalent, and has continued on into the modern forms in most of the Romance languages. The Germanic and its derivatives have evolved and retained the single noun—with the modern German word, at least, implying inedibility.

DEFINITIONS OF 'WEED'*

Perhaps no shorter definition of a weed has appeared than that attributed to Professor Beal, formerly weed specialist at Michigan State College, who defined a weed as 'a plant out of place.' Many and diverse are the definitions available, other than this much-abbreviated one, and, from a detailed study of more than thirty such definitions, the following appear to be the ten most commonly accepted characteristics, discussed in the order of their importance, of what constitutes a weed:

1. *A concept of growing in an undesired location*:—This is essentially the chief characteristic in the weed definition given in the report of the Terminology Committee of the Weed Society of America (Shaw, 1956), namely 'A plant growing where it is not desired'.

2. *Competitive and aggressive habits*:—This aspect is brought out in one part of Campbell's (1923) definition, when he says that a weed is an honest, independent competitor for food materials in the struggle for existence. Brenchley (1920) defines a weed as, in part, 'A plant that grows so luxuriantly or plentifully that it chokes out all other plants that possess more valuable nutritive properties'.

* Further definitions are given by Harlan and de Wet (1965, *see* their Table I; ref. p. 48). They note that there are two traditions with respect to weed definitions: 'one based on ecological behaviour and one on man's response to the species in question', and this is evident in their definition 'a generally unwanted organism that thrives in habitats disturbed by man'. A. L. Bunting's definition is cited: 'weeds are pioneers of secondary succession, of which the weedy arable field is a special class.'

3. *Of wild and rank growth*:—Brenchley's (1920) partial definition quoted above also applies here.

4. *Persistence and resistance to control or eradication*:—This is inherent in the title of Asa Gray's publication of 1879, 'The predominance and pertinacity of weeds'.

5. *Consisting often of large populations, with abundant, rank, and extensive growths*:—Rarely is an isolated plant alone considered weedy— except in so far as it means that, with seeding, large populations might ensue. Perhaps this is the one real difference between natural or native vegetation and weed infestations—the latter consist of massive growths often of a single species, or at most of only a few species.

6. *Useless, unwanted, and undesirable*:—These characteristics are implied in the definition of L. H. Bailey & E. Z. Bailey (1941), '. . . a plant not wanted and therefore to be destroyed', and of Emerson's classic, 'a plant whose virtues have not yet been discovered'.

7. *Harmful to man, animals, and crops*:—Implicit in the Italian equivalent for weed, malerba, and the Spanish hierbas malas.

8. *Spontaneous growth, appearing without being sown or cultivated*:— Indicated by one portion of Brenchley's (1920) definition, 'any plant other than the crop sown', and by Harper (1944), 'a plant that grows spontaneously in a habitat that has been greatly modified by human action . . .'.

9. *Of high reproductive capacity*:—Weeds, in contrast to non-weeds, generally produce vast numbers of propagules in proportion to plant size; they may also possess highly effective methods of vegetative reproduction.

10. *Unsightly, with disfigurement of the landscape*:—This is indicated by a number of definitions, such as 'A plant which grows wild, or is intrusive in cultivated ground, and is not valued for its usefulness or its beauty' (*Dictionary of American English*, 1944); or, by Thomas (1956), 'a useless, undesirable, and often very unsightly plant of wild growth, usually found in land which has been cultivated, or in areas developed by man for specific purposes other than cultivation . . .'.

Not all weeds qualify in all of these characteristics, but large numbers come close to fulfilling all of the requirements involved. McCall (1945) has stated that there are at least thirty weeds (in the United States) which are truly noxious in every sense of the word—and bindweed (*Convolvulus arvensis*) is one of them. These ten characteristics have been listed in Table I, together with their morphological, physiological, and ecological expression and control measures.

An anthropic aspect is inherent in almost every one of the above characteristics. Campbell (1923) indicated just how vague the usage of

TABLE I

BIOLOGICAL CHARACTERISTICS OF WEEDS, THEIR EXPRESSION, AND SUGGESTED CONTROL MEASURES

Principal characteristic	Morphological expression	Physiological expression	Ecological expression	Control measures*
Undesirable location	Objectionable size	Ability to thrive almost anywhere	Transient phytocoenoses	Selective measures if in a crop; otherwise non-selective
Competitive; aggressive	Diverse forms of reproduction	Rapid establishment; growth under adverse conditions	Phytocoenoses that exclude desirable plants	All types of control measures may need to be considered for serious infestations
Wild; rank growth	Sizeable plants covering large areas	Rapid growth; highly efficient use of habitat; nitrophious	Deep rooting	Apply herbicides in early growth-stages; withhold water if irrigated
Persistence; resistance	Diverse forms of propagules; structural protection from herbicides	Survival of plant fragments; biochemical resistance	Annual and perennial habit; dormancy	Attack vulnerable point in life-cycle
High reproductive capacity	Structures aiding dispersal; heteromorphy; apomixis	Varying levels of seed dormancy; food attractants	Seed abundance in proportion to plant size	Prevent reproduction

Large populations	High seed numbers; dispersal near mother plants	Growing thickly; not antagonistic; no teletoxicity	Adaptations to excessive crowding	Aerial herbicidal treatments on large populations, or biological measures
Useless and undesirable	Thorns; trichomes	No known contemporary value	Yet may be of value as plant cover	Mechanical; fire; animal grazing
Harmful to man, animals, crops	Thorns; indigestible fibres	Contains poisons; secretes teletoxins; parasitic habit	Non-edibility; dominance; teletoxins and aggression; host dependence	All types of control; high selectivity needed for parasites
Not sown; spontaneous growth	Propagules small, obscure, buried in soil	Dormancy;; sensitive to tillage	Adaptations to crop cycles, to tillage, and to high fertility levels	Soil fumigation; tillage; competitive cropping
Unsightly	Flowers and foliage not attractive	Rank growth and establishment; replacing desirable forms	Dominant, agressive in man-created areas	Bare soil should have desirable plant cover; ecological control

* The suggested control measures are extremely generalized, of course, and are proposed (when applicable) for each of the 'principal characteristic' categories when that particular category is the *predominating* aspect or feature of any specific weed problem.

the term 'weed' is at times, saying that 'a plant is a weed—not according to specific qualities—nor by a definite concept in the mind of man, but by human caprice'. Following this line of thought we have the older comment of L. H. Bailey (1895), 'nature . . . knows no plants as weeds'.

W. T. Stearn (1956), in a review of W. C. Muenscher's *Weeds* (1955), epitomizes one contemporary view by saying, 'Taken as a whole, weeds are not so much a botanical as a human psychological category within the plant kingdom, for a weed is simply a plant which in a particular place at a particular time arouses human dislike and attempts are made at its eradication or control, usually because it competes with more desirable plants, sometimes because it serves as a host to their pests and diseases or is unpalatable or dangerous to domestic beasts'.

The definition of a weed as it appears in the *Oxford English Dictionary* (1933) reads, 'a herbaceous plant not valued for use or beauty, growing wild and rank, and regarded as cumbering the ground or hindering the growth of superior vegetation'. This is reasonably comprehensive except that recent usage would probably include noxious woody plants as well.

Moore (1954) has defined a weed as 'a plant which interferes with man's utilization of land for a specific purpose'. The term weed is thus associated with land use—but also occasionally with plant use in the case of epiphytes and parasites. Few species are inherently weeds in all circumstances—although a number approach this status. Moore (1954) cites *Paspalum dilatatum* as one of the most useful grasses for coastal dairying districts in Australia, while it is also a weed of major importance in irrigated areas. The counterpart of this example in the southern United States is Bermuda grass (*Cynodon dactylon*). Other examples are afforded by useful plants, such as castor beans (*Ricinus communis*) and *Zinnia* sp., as well as *Zoysia* and *Dichondra*—which in some parts of the world are considered as weeds.

ANCIENT WEED RECORDS

Man altered the earth's vegetal cover in ancient times, and fossil evidence for such alteration is found in pollen records obtained from certain areas in northern Europe and America. Iversen (1941), in studies of this nature, has made certain interpretations of changes in the pollen spectra of particular dwelling-sites in Denmark. He has noted that elm and mixed oak forest generally fell to a minimum (which was temporary), while birch and hazel rose in abundance. There was also a concentration of charcoal, and pollens of herbaceous plants increased in frequency. Among these were pollens of cereal grasses and of plantains (*Plantago major* and *P. minor*). Iversen holds that these changes indicate the arrival of farmers, the phase of the 'Landman' or land occupation, that the charcoal comes from clearance fires, while the herbaceous pollen shows the opening up of the land; the cereals indicate fields, the plantains represent weeds, and the birch and hazel show regeneration of the forests which followed the exhaustion of the plot. Other neolithic weed records include those obtained from the remains of the Swiss lake dwellings (Heer, 8166), as exemplified in Fig. 3.

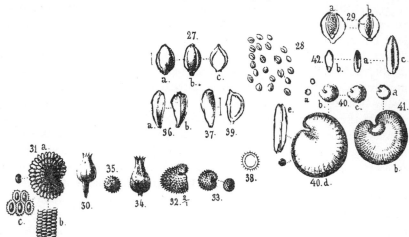

From Heer 1866

FIG. 3.—Seeds and fruits principally of weeds, largely from remains found in the Swiss lake dwellings at Robenhausen (*c.* 2,000 B.C.). Drawings reproduced with the same numbers from the original plate: 27, *Panicum miliaceum* (*a, b, c*)—single enlarged grains; 28, seeds of *Setaria italica*; 29 (*a, b*), enlarged seeds of *S. italica*; 30, capsule of Cretan flaxweed, *Silene cretica*; 31 (*a, b, c*), enlarged seed of *S. cretica* with surface details; 32, seed of corn cockle, *Agrostemma githago*; 33, seed of *Lychnis vespertina*, enlarged; 34, enlarged capsule of sandwort, *Arenaria serpyllifolia*; 35, fruit of bedstraw, *Galium aparine*; 36, fruit of *Lappa major*; 37, enlarged fruit of *Centaurea cyanus*; 38, enlarged seed of *Spergula pentandra*; 39, achene of *Ranunculus repens*, enlarged ; 40, seed of *Chenopodium album*—(*a*) natural size, (*b* and *c*) enlarged, (*d*) greatly enlarged, (*e*) side view; 41, probably seed of *Chenopodium glaucum*—(*a*) enlarged, (*b*) greatly enlarged; 42, fruit of darnel, *Lolium temulentum*—(*a* and *b*) natural size, (*c*) enlarged.

The discovery in the last several decades of remarkably well-preserved human bodies in the peat bogs of northwestern Europe, particularly in Denmark, northwestern Germany, and Holland, has provided—through a study of the well-preserved stomach contents—a detailed account of the food habits of this period. The two best-known accounts are those of Tollund Man and of Grauballe Man of the Iron Age, dating from the third to the fifth centuries A.D. The last meal of Tollund Man and of Grauballe Man was studied in some detail botanically by Helbaek (1950, 1958). The latter study summarizes and compares the contents of the stomachs of the two individuals. The combined list of finds contains sixty-six distinct plant taxa. Thousands of intact fruits of *Polygonum lapathifolium* agg. were found, indicating that the grinding of the material in food preparation was not very thorough. Also included were seeds of such familiar weedy plants as *Holcus lanatus, Bromus mollis, Rumex acetosella, Chenopodium album, Stellaria media, Spergula arvensis, Plantago major*, and *P. lanceolata*. Helbaek notes that in the poorer districts of

Jutland the land had to lie fallow for long periods, and, the arable being thus restricted, the peasants could not afford to disregard the food value of the wild plants which sprang up on otherwise unproductive land.

Tutin (1955), in a study of sediments from Lake Windermere in England, observed two well-marked horizons in the pollen diagrams corresponding with dates of about 1000 B.C. and 1000 A.D. At both of these horizons the grass pollen increased relatively to tree pollen, and at the lower horizon the pollen of some common weeds of cultivation appeared for the first time since an advanced stage of the glacial period. This is interpreted as representing 'the first extensive human settlement, which was by Neolithic (megalithic) peoples between 1800 and 1000 B.C., and secondly the first extensive forest clearance by a farming people, which began with the Norse invasions of the tenth century A.D., and was continued by extensive sheep-farming practised by the Cistercian monasteries founded on the margin of the Lake District in the twelfth century'.

The number of plants definitely known and recorded by the ancients has been summarized by Kanngiesser (1912). Most of these were useful plants, of course, but a few in later times have come to be considered as noxious (cf. the illustrations from the herbal of Dioscorides included in these volumes). Known to the ancient Egyptians were some 55 species. Bible plants included some 83 species, of which about 70 fall within the Pentateuch (1500 B.C.). In the writings of Homer (900 B.C.), some 60 plants are mentioned. Hesiod (800 B.C.) mentioned 15, Herodotus (484–424 B.C.) 63, and in the Anabasis of Xenophon (400 B.C.) 20 species were included. In the Hippocratic writings (c. 400 B.C.) 236 plants were named, in the writings of Theophrastus (300 B.C.) 450, and in the work of Dioscorides (c. 50 A.D.) 500.

The grand total of all the species of plants known to the Greeks and Romans would not include more than 1,200. Around the middle of the eighteenth century Linnaeus recognized some 6,000 flowering plants, in contrast to some 250,000 species known today—of which the orchids (Orchidaceae) alone involve over 15,000 species, and the Compositae many more.

As a group of cultivated plants, the grain amaranths are inextricably involved in any history of the non-cultivated or weedy amaranths or 'pigweeds'. J. D. Sauer (1950a) has examined at length the ethnological and botanical aspects of the grain amaranths, which are cultivated for the preparation of flour, for dye, and for certain ceremonial uses in various parts of the world. He concludes that they are all of New World origin, though from which wild species they were derived is less clear. 'The grain species are all cultigens unknown in the wild except as infrequent escapes. *Amaranthus leucocarpus* is morphologically fairly close to two non-cultivated species, *A. hybridus* and *A. powellii*, both widespread in North and Central America. *A. cruentus* is more like *A. dubius* of Central America and the West Indies, while *A. caudatus* and *A. edulis* are closer to a South American wild species, *A. quitensis.*' There has been an almost universal practice of selecting pale seeds for planting, a colour feature in contrast with the black seeds of the wild forms. In the several collections of charred amaranth seeds obtained from ancient camp sites, this distinction is not possible. One such collection from an ancient Indian camp site near Albuquerque, New Mexico, found by G. A. Agogino (1957), was subjected to the radiocarbon dating-technique and found to be 6,800 years old. These pigweed seeds are at least 2,400 years older than samples of maize found on the 4,000-year-old sites. Likewise, species of *Chenopodium* have been cultivated in Mexico and elsewhere for their grain (Hunziker, 1943). Except in certain remote areas, the culture of these forms has practically vanished. Did their abandonment lead to their extension over the adjacent countryside, and even into the newly-cultivated areas of other crops at that early time and since?

Another source of information on weed introductions is the finding of weed seeds in the adobe bricks used in the building of dwellings in the southwestern United States (Hendry, 1931). Hendry was able to date three periods with some species selected as examples from the total list of 34 species. These were (i) the pre-mission period, before 1769 (*Rumex crispus, Erodium cicutarium, Sonchus asper*); (ii) the mission period, 1769–1824 (*Poa annua, Chenopodium album* and *C. murale, Amaranthus retroflexus*); and (iii) the post-mission period, after 1824 (*Lolium temulentum, Brassica campestris* and *B. arvensis, Cirsium lanceolatum*).

Similar in nature are the studies of Chowdhury & Ghosh (1955) in India. From the evidence of rice husks used as soil binders in plastering the walls of ancient houses, they concluded that rice had been used as a food in this area more than 3,000 years ago. No reports are available on a weed-seed analysis of the soil, but this would certainly seem possible here also. Designs on ancient coins (cf. Plate 6*a*), wall paintings, and sculptures of tombs, monuments, and the like, provide additional illustrative sources of ancient plant forms. The study of Greiss (1957) is concerned with the anatomical identification of some ancient plant materials found in Egyptian tombs, and that of Bernhard (1924) with plant design on ancient coins.

A number of other works are available which are helpful in studies of this nature: Wittmack's (1903) accounts of plant remains from the ruins of Pompeii; Neuweiler's (1905) studies of prehistoric plant remains from Central Europe; Werth's (1937) studies on prehistoric cultivated plants; and the general work of Zeuner (third edn. 1951) on geochronology. The many standard works on paleobotany are, of course, useful for the more ancient fossil records—the record and literature citations for many species being given in the Engler & Prantl series, *Die NatürlichenPflanzen-amilien.*

From the standpoint of the introduction of weeds into eastern North America, little in the way of prehistoric data seem to be available. As colonization and settlement occurred there within historic times, a number of very early accounts are available which shed some light on the earliest weed introductions. John Josselyn (1672), in an early account, noted the large number of weeds introduced into New England, and associated their presence with the introduction of cattle by the English.

However, a little light is shed on this problem from the many ethno-botanical studies of American Indian tribes (cf. Palmer, 1871; H. H. Smith, 1923 *et seq.*, as cited in Chapter IV). There is no doubt that the many uses of plants by these early tribes resulted in increases in the numbers and distribution of certain plants. Harper (1944), in Alabama, has remarked on the wide distribution of the Chickasaw plum (*Prunus angustifolia*), and has noted that it is still generally associated with ancient Indian camp-sites and other habitations; likewise he has commented that the Maypop (*Passiflora incarnata*) may have been cultivated by the Indians.

Many have noted the similarity of the weeds of northeastern America, particularly, to those of northern Europe; these have been referred to by some authors (Good, 1953) as the 'Scandinavian element'. Both Claypole (1877) and Asa Gray (1879) noted the particularly aggressive nature of this group. Additional aspects of this subject are considered in the later section on North American weeds.

From a consideration of the environmental aspects of the origin and introduction of weeds, it is obvious that the new environment is generally as favourable as—and often more favourable than—the original environment. Asa Gray (1879), in discussing this problem, noted that most of the American weeds came from Europe—as the native herbs could not flourish on cleared ground—especially with emigrants from the Old World. European weeds, here 'prepotent', had survived and adapted themselves to the change from forest to cleared land in Europe. This change was far more sudden in America than it had been in Europe. Most of the European herbaceous weeds were never indigenous to the originally forest-covered regions of the Old World, but as western and northern Europe became agricultural and pastoral, those plants came with the husbandman and the flocks, or followed them, from the woodless or sparsely wooded regions farther east, where they had originated.

Marie-Victorin (1938), in surveying the phytogeographical problems of eastern Canada, noted that many of the forms of *Crataegus* arose as a result of deforestation and human settlement. They were therefore to be regarded as very young species; and it was concluded that, in certain circumstances, forms of this kind may have been produced in two or three hundred years.

THE ORIGINS OF WEEDS

GENERAL ASPECTS

How and where did our weeds originate? The genetic aspects of these questions will be presented at some length in Chapter IX, only the more historical aspects being considered here. Weeds are essentially components of the native and naturalized flora. As such, the elucidation of their origin requires knowledge of the phylogeny and distribution of the particular plant groups in question. However, at this point it may be stated that weeds belonging to the native flora have been termed 'apophytes', as contrasted with those of the introduced or naturalized group (in which several classes have been recognized).

Not only is a knowledge of the group origin helpful, but of at least equal importance is a knowledge of the respective environments—the original one and the one of the new naturalization—and of how these two environments differ. This does not imply that the environmental requirements of a specific weed are fixed or static, for we know that 'physiological races' or ecotypes may arise as one stage of plant evolution. These new forms are taxonomically very close to, or often morphologically identical with, the parent species. They may differ, for example, in height of flowering stalk, time of flowering, change in low-temperature requirements for dormancy breaking, etc.—all indicating so-called 'micro' changes in relation to differing environments. Perhaps it is a characteristic of certain weedy genera that they possess this capacity to produce forms that are adaptable to new environments more readily than some of the 'non-weedy' taxa.

The anthropic factors are intricately involved, and inter-related to both the innate characters of the plants concerned and to their environments. Important here are man's activities, such as the gathering, use, and disposal, of extraneous or unused portions of plants; the mechanical or fire-clearing of land; the nitrophilous habitats created by habitations of man and animals, the disposal of refuse, and the cultivation of soil resulting in increased nitrification; the domestication of plants (and of animals, with food and waste-disposal problems as well); the wider dispersal following tribal movements, immigration, military operations and movement, shipping, road and railroad building; and the scarcely-assessed role of aircraft transportation. The unassessed, though unlikely, possibilities of dispersal by missiles and interplanetary vehicles may be a problem for the future. Hence, the appellation of anthropophyte to the kinds of plants associated with man (both cultivars and weeds) is certainly appropriate. To distinguish these two kinds of anthropophytes, perhaps 'philanthropophyte' (for cultivars) and 'malanthropophyte' (for weeds) are suitably descriptive terms.

ANTHROPIC FACTORS AND WEED ORIGINS WITH PARTICULAR REFERENCE TO THE BALKAN PENINSULA

The Balkan Peninsula includes within its boundaries the homes of very ancient human civilizations; so here, as Turrill (1929) has commented, there has been both time and opportunity for man to impress changes of considerable magnitude upon the natural vegetation. Locally, man's greatest destructive effort has been deforestation with consequent soil erosion. Associated with man in this destruction are the sheep and goats whose unrestricted grazing has been inimical to forest rejuvenation. So denuded are some areas that Turrill, upon his first visit there, compared the physiognomy mentally with that of the sub-arctic vegetation of Iceland.

Transhumance has been widespread for centuries in the Balkans—migrating shepherds and their flocks shifting with seasonal change to fresh grazing areas—as have other forms of nomadic movements. Zoochory is important here in dispersal, giant specimens of *Artemisia*, *Chenopodium*, and *Urtica* having been observed growing on dung around cattle pens. Other influences have been the drainage of lakes and marshes, and in more recent times the flooding of areas for rice culture.

Turrill states that it is sometimes difficult to determine whether the weeds originated from the native flora or were introduced by man's activities. As 41 species of weeds and 16 ruderals were endemic to this region, additional evidence is provided for the local origin of part of the arable-land and waste-ground floras. *Centaurea cyanus* occurs as a weed in cereal and other fields and as a component of the indigenous vegetation. The species number in the genera *Plantago* (26 spp.) and *Galium* (70 spp.) appears unusually high, and this area may likewise be the centre of origin of these genera.

Commerce in grain was well developed here in ancient times, and as the grain could scarcely have been 'clean' by modern standards, it doubtless provided facilities for weed dispersal. The Balkan Peninsula exported grain as well as hides to ancient Greece and to many other parts of the Roman world. It is possible that the spread of some species of southern weeds to Central Europe and even to the British Isles (and hence to North America) was direct from the Balkan Peninsula. It thus seems probable that the Peninsula has contributed its share to the weed flora of Europe. Commerce, foreign invasions, and movements of armies, have introduced and spread native as well as alien plants. Turrill (1929) notes that the common chicory, *Cichorium intybus* var. *glabratum*, found in old chicken runs and similar places in the British Isles, is the same variety that is common in the Balkans. Furthermore, the vast majority of the arable-land weeds found in the British flora occur also as weeds in the Balkans. Turrill commented also that the Mediterranean is given as the most important single geographical source of the weed-aliens of Montpellier (Thellung, 1912) and Tweedside (Hayward & Druce, 1919), 416 species in the former and 113 in the latter having this origin.

Plants associated with camps—whether military, nomadic, or otherwise—have been termed 'synanthropes', i.e. 'camp-followers'. They are well represented in the Balkans, the centre of strife and of movements of peoples for many millennia. Turrill (1929) has noted the species introduced from North Africa and elsewhere in bales of hay used for army fodder.

He cites the work of Heldreich (1878) in which it is recorded that a single synanthrope was found on the Isle of Lero—*Urtica pilulifera* near a disused lime-kiln—whereas on the Acropolis of Athens 106 Phanerogams were collected, of which 24 (23·5 per cent) were synanthropic plants. Anderson (1955), in the United States, has noted that a *Viola* sp., the 'Confederate violet', appears to be associated with old Civil War camp-sites. Notice was previously made of the association of certain plants with American Indian camp-sites. It is not unlikely that many synanthropic plants later became further 'domesticated' and thus, in effect, true weeds.

The conception of a Mediterranean Region with two divisions, the Mediterranean Basin and the Orient, is well established botanically, the animal route for the 'Oriental migration' consisting of both Oriental and Siberian routes. The former route was in use during Tertiary times and followed over the Old Aegean continent and through the Balkan peninsula, persisting until the formation of the Aegean Sea in post-glacial times. Knowledge of these routes provides significant additional information for tracing plant migration routes (Turrill, 1929).

As many of our important weeds apparently have had their origin in the Eastern Mediterranean region, the comments of Turrill (1929) on the flora of one portion of this area are of interest here. Of the 6,530 species of flowering plants in the entire flora, some 16 per cent are monocotyledons and some 84 per cent are dicotyledons. By their weedy members alone, the four families most plentifully represented are: Compositae (100 spp.), Gramineae (99), Umbelliferae (82), and Cruciferae (65).

The weed flora consists of 407 annuals, 39 biennials, and 121 perennials —a total of 567 species, or 8·7 per cent of the total flora. The ruderal flora consisted of 172 annuals, 39 biennials, and 77 perennials. The 61 species of the 17 genera of the Chenopodiaceae are of interest because of the representative halophytes which they include. The main halophytic invasion has been one of central Asian species via South Russia into the Dobruja. In the entire flora, the Compositae form 13·9 per cent of the total number of flowering plant species, with *Centaurea* the largest genus (171 spp.). They are perennial, with a distinctly xeromorphic structure; the majority are summer-flowering (July) plants of stony, grassy, or rocky habitats. Among plants of the more highly organized families, maximum flowering occurs in many cases as the monthly precipitation decreases in late summer, and both the flowers and fruits are better protected against extremes of temperature and drought than are those of the more simply organized families. Turrill (1929) has indicated that there has been an extended distribution in species of the Compositae, and an increase in their number, as a consequence of forest destruction within the human period. This deforestation has reduced the obstacles to wind dispersal and has been especially favourable to spreading by blowing along or slightly above the ground.

Turrill (1929) does not consider that the horticultural uses of plants are an important contributory factor in the origin and dispersal of weeds. This may have been the case within recent times; but a period of several millennia, wherein plants were used for medicine, in mystical rites, and for food, clothing, ornamentation, and shelter, would indicate that such usage might have been a more important factor in the origin and dispersal of weeds. Many plants, singled out then from the native flora for any one of these uses although later abandoned, will have stood a fair chance of survival as ruderals, synanthropes, or weeds: for example, orna-mentals surviving from the time of the Roman occupation of southern France, rather recently received recognition (Gidon, 1940).

Much the same basic pattern as that developed in the previous section applies also to the northern regions. One of the oldest weeds of antiquity, the darnel (*Lolium temulentum*, Gramineae), was known in biblical times. It spread throughout the temperate regions of the world wherever cereals were grown—a true satellite weed of cereals. As man moved northwards into the forested regions and cleared the land for crops and habitation, plants that could thrive in this open habitat also invaded. As we have seen, many of these came from the Balkan area. Both grain and hides (sheep) were shipped from these early centres of human culture to many parts of the Roman empire, and in later years commerce with Australia and the western world was instrumental in both the introduction and world-wide dissemination of weeds. Of interest in this connection is the summary of many years' work on the European wool-adventive flora published by Probst (1949—*see* Ch. VIII).*

Italian botanists (Negri, 1948; and others) have also in recent years investigated farm-land weeds and ruderal plants as anthropic com-munities of vegetation. Negri states that these plants are of great ecological and phytogeographical interest in those communities which are directly conditioned by man. These peculiar anthropic stations may be viewed as a widespread experiment in soil occupation by plants, and in the 'settling down' process of mature plant cover. This natural experiment is in progress continually and may lead towards characteristic ecological settlements of plants, biological competition, and (possibly) specific mutations. Linkola (1916, 1921), in Finland, and Tüxen (1931), in Central Europe, have also examined the anthropic factors in relation to vegetation.

THE EVOLUTION OF DOMESTICATION

This subject has recently been examined in detail by Dr. Edgar Anderson (1960), and the following material is abstracted from his study. One aspect of the origin of domestication lies not in a history of the more specialized system of European clean-crop agriculture but in a history of the more primitive types of garden plots adjacent to dwellings. In such

* Citations of this kind are to references in the Bibliographies at the ends of the chapters indicated.—Ed.

plots the plants would not be cultivated in straight rows; also included would be weeds actively discouraged (very few of these), permitted weeds, encouraged weeds, and cultivated plants (fruits, vegetables, fibre plants, utensil-producers, drug and condiment plants, and certain ritual, seed, and root staples).

Special significance is attached to crops with widespread multiple uses—such crops are thus believed to have been longer in cultivation than others. Hemp (*Cannabis*) is an example, as there are specialized varieties for fibre, for drugs (marijuana and hashish), and for oil seeds, as well as rampant weedy forms.

Anderson raises the question of what non-food plants must have been domesticated as early as, or earlier than, food plants. Non-food plants include those used for body paint, for living stockades, as poisons, for chewing, for fatigue drugs, and for purposes of ritual—all character- istic of very early man. Fatigue-relieving plants most certainly have been used in some ways by prehominids. Thus in Ethiopia, monkeys, which eat the berries, are one of the most difficult plagues to deal with in coffee forests. As the Ethiopian coffees are somewhat weedy, monkeys may well be one of the agents which help in their dispersal. An examination of the uses of plants for construction, as well as for food, by some of the early primates in their native habitats, might provide some further useful information in this connection (cf. Voss, 1955; Kots, 1959).

The study of weed population dynamics—i.e. the determination of the various intermediate stages between an out-and-out weed and an out-and-out crop plant—involves another important phase in the history of domestication. As noted above, noxious weeds, permitted weeds, and encouraged weeds, can be found in areas of ancient agriculture.

Anderson explores the possibility that there was a very early trans- mission of domesticated plants from Africa to India. It apparently occurred prior to the Aryan invasion, as the plants involved bear Sanskrit names: Guar or cluster bean (*Cyanopsis* sp.); Galla potatoes (*Coleus* sp.); pearl millet (*Setaria* sp.); Ragee millet (*Eleusine corocana*); Aframomum or grains of paradise (*Amomum* sp.). Such botanical evidence suggests where one should look for the beginnings of proto-agriculture.

The problem of domestication also involves an examination of the human emotional attitudes towards plants—especially ornamental plants. Anderson has noted that a world look at floral versus non-floral agricultures reveals that they are concentrically arranged around separate poles. The pole of non-floral seed-crop agriculture is in central Africa. The pole of floral agriculture is in Indonesia, radiating outwards to Oceania and the flowery kingdoms of China and Japan, and to India and even dry and rocky Afghanistan. The question is thus raised as to whether the 'fertile crescent' of the 'Near East' became so through being at an early date the area in which were cross-fertilized at least two quite different early agricultures? One was characterized, among other things, by a devotion to seed crops and a complete lack of interest in flowers and ornamental plants; it would have spread out from the hominid centre in Africa. The other, flower conscious, including many root crops, spread out from the ancient centre in Indonesia. Other work has provided evidence, likewise, of an African proto-agricultural complex involving perennial grasses (possibly the ryes, *Secale* spp.) functioning at least in part as cereals.

Multiple origins are known for some crop plants, and such reticulate relationships with a crop's precursors and the weeds derived from it are known. Many documented cases exist of weeds which arose from cultivated species, and vice versa. Anderson notes, for example, the present-day use of weed lettuce (*Lactuca* sp.) in breeding new cultivated varieties, as well as the frequent introgression from cultivated varieties into weed lettuce which greatly increases the variability of the latter.

Thus an elucidation of the many facets cited will lead to a more thorough understanding of the origins of domestication. Perhaps what is even more important will be a thorough understanding of what happens to a plant when it is domesticated, i.e. in terms of germ-plasm structure and population dynamics. It is also hoped that a similar understanding will eventually materialize concerning the nature of our aggressive and pernicious weeds. Problems of domestication and the origin of cultivated plants are comprehensively surveyed in the recent book of Wilsie (1962).

CONCLUSION

Returning to the general subject of the origin of weeds, the nomad species that are commonly thought of in this connection are well-defined components of the floras of regions occurring practically the world over. They are the plants adapted to unstable and ever-changing environments. Such would include plants of eroding stream-banks, of shifting sand-dunes, of recent lava-flows, of flood-plains of rivers (*Ambrosia, Xanthium,* etc.), of flooded and seasonally inundated margins of rivers, of wind-throws in the forest, and of areas opened up by fire, by landslides, or by other extensive land disturbances.

Plants adapted to these habitats, long before the advent of man, have thus, in later times, provided the reservoir from which many weeds now characteristic of man-disrupted areas have developed.

A diagrammatic presentation of the origins of weeds is shown in Fig. 4. It can be seen that weeds principally arise from two major arbitrarily-defined groups:

(1) Anthropophytes (those consciously used and cultured by man).

(2) Spontaneous apophytes (not consciously associated with man's activities, but invading man-created habitats, etc.).

Essentially, weeds arise from forms that were originally intricate components of the native flora of one region or another. Thus the characteristics of certain groups of weeds are certainly close to the characteristics

20

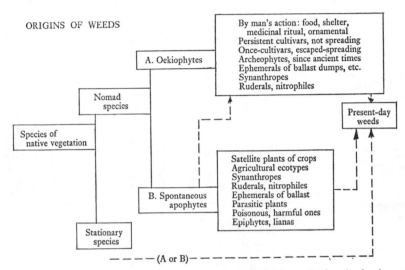

FIG. 4.—Diagram showing the many and diverse paths which may lead to the development of present-day weeds. The term 'anthropophytes', as explained in the text, is preferable to the older term 'oekiophytes' (cf. A, above), and is a more inclusive term than the definition of 'oekiophytes' proposed originally by Thelling (1912). For explanation of the diagram, *see* the text pp. 20 and 24.

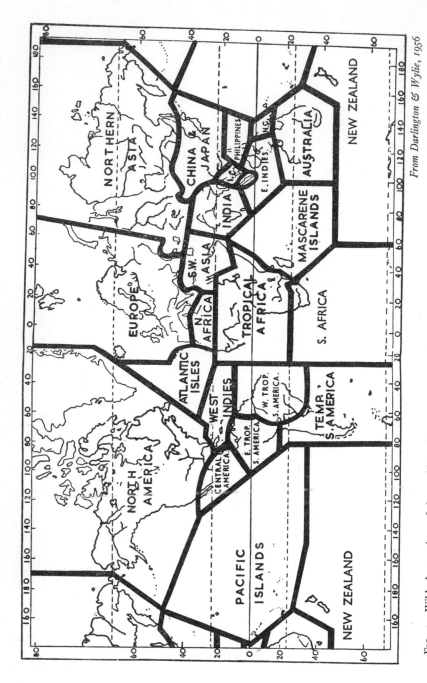

From Darlington & Wylie, 1956

Fig. 5.—Wild plant regions of the world as delimited by the authors cited. The twelve regional weed catalogues contained in the present volumes each represent, in large measure, these wild plant regions. Some of the 'smaller' divisions e.g. in Central America, in South America, and in the Indo–Malayan region, have, however, been combined in the present work.

22

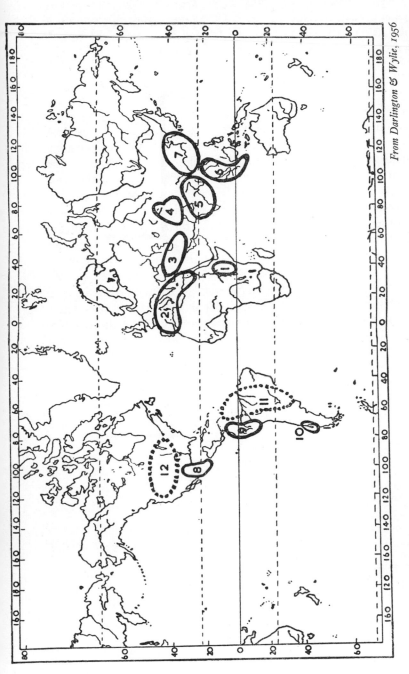

From Darlington & Wylie, 1956

FIG. 6.—Cultivated plant regions of the world as recognized by Vavilov (1935, 1949–50). These mapped areas are actually centres of diversity of crop plants. A few key types for each of these regions is here selected from Darlington (1956): 1, Abyssinia (castor-oil bean, coffee, okra); 2, Mediterranean (lettuce, parsnip, hop); 3, Persia (bread wheat, oats, rape); 4, Afghanistan (cotton, spinach, mungo bean); 5, Indo-Burma (rice, hemp, amaranth); 6, Siam-Malaya-Java (yam, ginger, banana); 7, China (millet, buckwheat, radish); 8, Mexico (maize, sweet potato, guava); 9, Peru (tomato, tobacco, potato); 10, Chile (mango grain, Chilean tarweed); 11, Brazil-Paraguay (tapioca, peanut (ground nut), passion fruit); 12, United States (sunflower, Jerusalem artichoke). Many of these plants are from genera that contain common weeds, and some have themselves escaped and become noxious; in all cases the culture of these plants opened up areas which encouraged weed growth and, often, the development of satellite weeds.

23

of the wild plants in the region where they were originally evolved. The wild plant regions defined by Darlington & Wylie (cf. Fig. 5) each have, to some extent, characteristic weeds. On the other hand, this picture is modified by man's activities in the manipulation of plants in the various agricultural centres, or more specifically in the twelve centres of diversity of crop plants recognized by Vavilov (1935, 1949–50) and mapped in Fig. 6. These centres correspond, in part, to the anthropophytes in the diagram, while the wild plant regions in Fig. 5 correspond in part to the apophytes referred to in Fig. 4.

Thus we may conclude that the weed class as generally defined has its origins extending back to indigenous species of some specific region. These indigenous species, through the development of some special adaptive features, entered into and persisted in essentially artificial areas created largely by man's activities or, to a lesser extent, by his domesticated and ancillary animals. These environments have appeared to be especially suitable for the growth of weedy plants and for their further evolutionary development. It is thus through both man's conscious and non-conscious manipulation and use of specific plants throughout his long pre-historic period and in historic times, as well as in relation to the specific genetic character of the germ-plasm of certain plant taxa—particularly in dispersal and adaptability through diverse and highly effective reproductive methods and ecotype formation—that a group of aggressive and trouble-some plants, aptly termed anthropophytes for the most part, have appeared on the scene.

In terms of the Darwinian concept of the struggle for existence, weeds as a class probably well represent the most successful plant forms that have evolved simultaneously with the destruction or disruption by man of the indigenous vegetation and its habitats.

BIBLIOGRAPHY

(An Introduction to Weeds)

AGOGINO, G. A. (1957). Pigweed seeds dated oldest U.S. food grain. *Sci. News Lett.*, *Wash.*, **72**, 345.

Agricultural Index (1910–). H. W. Wilson Co., New York.

AGRICULTURAL RESEARCH SERVICE (1956). *Suggested Guide for the Chemical Control of Weeds*. U.S. Dept. Agriculture.

L'Agronomie Tropicale (1946–). Institut de Reserches Agronomiques Tropicales et des Cultures Vivrières, Paris.

ANDERSON, E. (1952). *Plants, Man and Life*. Little, Brown, Boston, 245 pp.

—— (1955). Confederate violets. *Landscape*, 1955, pp. 7–11.

—— (1957). Man as a maker of new plants and new plant communities. *Annu. Rep. Smithson. Instn.* (Washington, D.C.) for 1956, pp. 461–79.

—— (1960). *The Evolution of Domestication*. Preprint, 30 pp., from the Darwin Centennial volumes, ed. S. Tax, University of Chicago Press.

ANON. (1954). *Memorandum Antiparasitaire Européen*. Centre International des Anti-parasitaires, Zurich, 125 pp.

BAILEY, L. H. (1895). Some reflections upon weeds. *Bull. Cornell Agric. Exp. Sta.*, 102, 522–6.

—— & BAILEY, E. Z. (1941). *Hortus the Second*. Macmillan, New York, 778 pp.

BAILEY, W. W. (1878). About weeds. *Amer. Nat.*, 12, 740–3.

BEDEVIAN, A. K. (1936). *Illustrated Polyglot Dictionary of Plant Names*. Botanical Section, Ministry of Agriculture, Giza, Cairo, Egypt.

BERNHARD, M. O. (1924 [1925]). Pflanzenbilder auf Griechischen und Romischen Münzen. *Schweiz. Gesell. f. Gesch. Med. u. Naturwiss.*, 3, pp. 1–47. (Also as a separate, O. Füssli, Zurich, 1925, 47 pp. Tafel V.)

Bibliographie der Deutschen Zeitschriftenliteratur (1896–). Leipzig.

Bibliographie der fremdsprachigen Zeitschriftenliteratur (1911–14/20, 1925–26—). Leipzig.

Bibliographie der Pflanzenschutz Literatur (1914–38, 1940–45, 1950–51). Paul Parey, Berlin.

Bibliography of Agriculture (1942–). National Agricultural Library, U.S. Dept. Agriculture, Washington.

Bibliography of Soil Science, Fertilizers and General Agronomy (1931–). Harpenden, England.

Bibliography of Tropical Agriculture (1931–42). International Institute of Agriculture, Rome.

Biological Abstracts (1920–). University of Pennsylvania, Philadelphia.

BLAKE, S. F. (1961). *Geographical Guide to Floras of the World. Part II: Western Europe*. U.S. Dept. Agriculture, Miscellaneous Publications, 797, Washington, D.C., 742 pp.

—— & ATWOOD, A. C. (1942). *Geographical Guide to Floras of the World. Part I: Africa, Australia, North America, South America, and Islands of the Atlantic, Pacific, and Indian Oceans*. Miscellaneous Publications, 401, 336 pp. U.S. Dept. Agriculture, Washington.

BLANCHARD, J. R. & OSTVOLD, H. (1958). *Literature of Agricultural Research*. University of California Press, Berkeley & Los Angeles, 231 pp.

BLOM, C. (1938). Woher kommt das Unkraut? *Geisenheim Mitt. Obst– u. Gartenb.*, 53, 106–8.

BOAS, F. (1953). Unkraut oder biologisch unbekannte Pflanzen. *Z. PflBau*, 4, 182–8.

BONAVIA, E. (1894). *Flora of the Assyrian Monuments and its Outcomes*. Westminster, 215 pp.

Botanisches Zentralblatt (1880–1945). Gustav Fischer, Jena.

BRENCHLEY, W. E. (1920). *Weeds of Farm Land*. Longmans, Green, London, 239 pp.

BRENDEL, F. (1870). Distribution of immigrant plants. *Amer. Ent. and Bot.*, 2, 378.

BRODIE, D. A. (1931). What is a weed? *Hoard's Dairym.*, 76, 425.

BROUWER, W. & STÄHLIN, A. (1955). *Handbuch der Samenkunde*. DLG Verlag-GmbH, Frankfurt-am-Main.

CACCIATO, A. (1952). La vegetazione antropocora dello scalo ferrorviario Ostiense di Roma. *Nuovo G. Bot. Ital.*, n. s. 59, 119–43.

CAMPBELL, E. M. (1923). What is a weed? *Science*, 58, 50.

CHEEL, E. (1922). The weeds of civilization. *Aust. Nat.*, 5, 25–28.

CHEVALIER, A. (1943). Laitues, chicorées et pissenlits, l'origine des formes cultivées. *Rev. Bot. Appl.*, 23, 273–81.

CHILDE, V. G. (1951). *Prehistoric Migrations in Europe*. Routledge & Kegan Paul, London, 250 pp.

CHOWDHURY, K. A. & Ghosh, S.S. (1955). The study of archaeological plant remains and its significance. *Trans. Bose Res. Inst.*, Calcutta, 20, 79–85.

CLAYPOLE, E. W. (1877). On the migration of plants from Europe to America, with an attempt to explain certain phenomena connected therewith. *Montreal Hort. Soc. and Fruit Growers Assoc. of the Province of Quebec Rep.*, 3, 70–91.

CLINCH, F. A. (1950). Many ancient flowers have turned into weeds. Farm and Garden Section, *Watertown (N.Y.) Daily Times*.

COBAN, R. (1928). Le piante adventizie esotiche orservata del Vicentino. *Arch. Bot., Forli* 4, 20–35; 97–114.

Contributions from Boyce Thompson Institute (1925–). Boyce Thompson Institute for Plant Research, Inc., Yonkers, New York.

CROCKER, W. (1948). *Growth of Plants. Twenty Years' Research at the Boyce Thompson Institute.* Reinhold, New York, 459 pp.

DANNFELT, H. JULIEN-. *See* JULIEN-DANNFELT, H.

DARLINGTON, C. D. (1956). *Chromosome Botany.* Allen & Unwin, London, 186 pp.

—— & WYLIE, A. P. (1956). *Chromosome Atlas of Flowering Plants.* Macmillan, New York, 519 pp.

DAYTON, W. A. (1936). The term 'range weed' as used by western stockmen and the U.S. Forest Service. *J. Amer. Soc. Agron.*, 28, 327–8.

DEWEY, L. H. (1897). The eastward migration of certain weeds in America. *Asa Gray Bull.*, 5, 31–34.

Dictionary of American English on Historical Principles (1944). University of Chicago Press, Chicago, vol. 4, 2,460 pp.

DREESEN, J. (1954). *Herbicide Law Manual. A Guide to the Laws Affecting Distribution, Sale, and Use of Pesticides, with Special Attention to Herbicide Laws.* National Agricultural Chemicals Association, Washington.

DUCHESNE, E. A. (1836). *Répertoire des plantes utiles et des plantes vénéneuses du globe.* Jules Renouard, Paris, 572 pp.

DUNN, S. T. (1905). *Alien Flora of Britain.* West, Newman, London, 208 pp.

DUPERREX, A. (1946). Origine et histoire de quelque mauvaises herbes. *Rev. Hort. Suisse*, 19e. ann., p. 229.

EBBELL, B. (1937). *The Papyrus Ebers. The greatest Egyptian Medical Document.* Levin and Munksgaard, Copenhagen, 135 pp.

ENGLER, A. & PRANTL, K. (1897–1915, 1924–). *Die natürlichen Pflanzenfamilien.* Vols. 1–20, 2nd edn. 1924—incomplete. Gebrüder Borntraeger, Berlin.

Entoma (E. H. Fisher, ed.) 14th edn., 1961–62. Entomological Society of America, Madison, Wis. 325 pp. The 15th edn. is now combined with *Pesticide Handbook* (D. H. Frear, ed.), 1965 edn.

Experiment Station Record (1880–1946). U.S. Dept. Agriculture, Washington.

Field Crop Abstracts (1948–). Commonwealth Bureau of Pasture and Field Crops, Farnham Royal, England.

FISCHER, H. (1929). *Mittelalterliche Pflanzenkunde.* Munich, 326 pp.

FISKE, J. G. (1951). Plants called weeds. *J. N.Y. Bot. Gdn.*, 52, 108–10.

FLAHAULT, C. (1899). La naturalisation et les plantes naturalisées en France. *Bull. Soc. Bot. Fr.*, 46, 91–108. (XCLI-CVIII, Suppl.)

FREAR, D. E. H. (1961). *Pesticide Index.* College Science Publications, State College, Pennsylvania, 193 pp.

—— (1963). *Pesticide Handbook.* 15th edn. College Science Publications, State College, Pennsylvania, 311 pp.

Fremdsprachigen Auflage (1911–). Leipzig.

GARDINER, SIR A. (1950). *Egyptian Grammar*, 2nd edn. Oxford Univ. Press, London.

GEORGIA, A. E. (1914). *A Manual of Weeds.* Macmillan, New York, 593 pp.

GERTH VAN WIJK, H. L. (1911–16). *A Dictionary of Plant Names.* Nijhoff, The Hague, Vol. I, 1,444 pp., Vol. II, 1,696 pp.

GIDON, F. (1940). Survivance comme rudérales d'espèces horticoles gallo-romaines et medievales dans la Campagne de Caen. *C.R. Soc. de Biogéogr.*, No. 147.

GILLOT, X. (1900). Étude des flores adventices, adventicité et naturalisation. *Actes du 1er Congrés International de Botanique*, pp. 370–85.

GLEASON, H. A. (1952). *Illustrated Flora of the Northeastern United States and Adjacent Canada*. Botanical Gardens, New York, Vols. 1–3.

GOLITSYN, S. V. (1945). [L'influence de l'homme sur la répartition des vegetaux—in Russian.] *Sovetsk. Bot.*, 13, 19–29.

GOOD, R. (1953). *The Geography of The Flowering Plants*. Longmans, Green, London; John Wiley & Sons, New York, 452 pp.

GRAY, A. (1879). The predominance and pertinacity of weeds. *Amer. J. Sci.*, 118. 161–7.

GREGORY, WINIFRED, ed. (1943). *Union List of Serials*, 1st edn. H. W. Wilson Co., New York.

GREISS, E. A. M. (1957). Anatomical identification of some ancient Egyptian plant materials. *Mem. Inst. d'Egypte*, 55, 1–165 and 138 figs.

GUNTHER, R. T. (1934). *The Greek Herbal of Dioscorides* (Illustrated by a Byzantine A.D. 512; English edn. by John Goodyer A.D. 1655; Edited and first printed A.D. 1933 by R. T. Gunther). Oxford University Press, Oxford, 701 pp.

HAGEDORN, H. (1935). *The Magnate: William Boyce Thompson and His Time* (1869–1930). John Day, New York, 343 pp.

HALLER, H. L. (1958). The impact of public law 518 on Herbicide Research and Recommendations. *Weeds*, 6(3), pp. 251–6.

HANZAWA, M. (1910). *Zasso-gaku* (Weeds). [In Japanese.] Tokyo. (Copy in National Agricultural Library, Washington.)

HARPER, R. M. (1908). Some native weeds and their probable origin. *Bull. Torrey Bot. Cl.*, 35, 347–60.

—— (1944). Preliminary report on the weeds of Alabama. *Bull. Geol. Surv. Ala. Univ.*, *Ala.*, No. 53, 275 pp.

HAYWARD, J. M. & DRUCE, G. C. (1919). *The Adventive Flora of Tweedside*. Buncle, Arbroath, 296 pp.

HEER, O. (1866). Die Pflanzen der Pfahlbauten. *68 Neuj. Zurich. Naturf. Ges. auf das Jahr.*, 1866.

HELBAEK, H. (1950). Tollund-Mandens sidste Måltid. [With English summary.] *Årboger f. nordisk Oldkyndighed og Historie*, 1950.

—— (1958). Graaballemandens Sidste Måltid. [With English summary.] *Kuml*, *Årbog for Jysk arkaelogisk Selskab* (Arhus, Denmark), 1958, pp. 83–116.

—— (1959). Domestication of food plants in the old world. *Science*, 130, 365–72 [40 references].

HELDREICH, T. (1878). L'Attique au point de vue des caractères de la végétation. *Bot. Congr., Paris, 1878*, p. 106.

HELGESON, E. A. (1957). *Methods of Weed Control*. F.A.O., Rome, 189 pp.

HELLWIG, F. (1886). Über den Ursprung der Ackerunkrauter und der Ruderalflora Deutschlands. *Bot. Jb.*, 6, 383–434.

HENDRY, G. W. (1931). The adobe brick as a historical source. Reporting further studies in adobe brick analysis. *Agric. Hist.*, 5, 110–27.

HITCHCOCK, A. E. (1959). Percy W. Zimmerman (23 February 1884-14 August 1958). *Contr. Boyce Thompson Inst.*, 20, 1–5 *and portrait*.

HOCKING, G. M. (1947). Henbane—healing herb of Hercules and of Apollo. *Econ. Bot.*, 1, 306–16.

Horticultural Abstracts (1931–). Imperial Bureau of Fruit Production, East Malling, England.

HOWES, F. N. (1946). Fence and barrier plants in warm climates. *Kew Bull.*, No. 2, pp. 51–87.

HUNZIKER, A. T. (1943). Las especies alimenticias de *Amaranthus* y *Chenopodium* cultivadas por los indios de America. *Rev. Argent. Agron.*, 10, 297–354.

HURRY, J. B. (1930). *The Woad Plant and its Dye*. Oxford University Press, London, 328 pp.

ILTIS, H. (1949). An immigrant conquers a continent: the story of the wild garlic. *Sci. Monthly*, 68, 122–8.

Index Kewensis (1895–1959). Clarendon Press, Oxford. Vols. 1, 2, Supp. I–XII.

International Bulletin of Plant Protection (1927–46). International Institute of Agriculture, Rome.

IVERSEN, J. (1941). [Land occupation in Denmark's stone age—in Danish.] *Danm. Geol. Unders.*, 66(2), 68 pp. and 9 pl.

JESSEN, K. & HELBAEK, H. (1944). Cereals in Great Britain and Ireland in prehistoric and early historic times. *K. Danske Vidensk. Selsk. Biol. Skr.*, 3(2), 1–68.

JONES, G. N. (1951). On the number of species of plants. *Sci. Monthly*, 72(5), 289–94.

JOSSELYN, J. (1672). *New Englands Rarities*. London, 114 pp. (Facsimile-edn.; by W. Junk, No. 25, 1926.)

JULIEN-DANNFELT, H. (1919). [Review of weed laws of different countries.] *K. Landtbr-Akad. Handl.*, *Stockh.*, 58, 166–74.

KANNGIESSER, F. (1912). Die Flora des Herodot. *Arch. Gesch. Naturw. Tech.*, 3, 81–102.

KENNEDY, P. B. & FREDERICK, A. (1927). Old world weed introductions. *J. Amer. Soc. Agron.*, 19, 569–73.

KING, L. J. (1957). Some early forms of the weed concept. *Nature, Lond.*, 179, 1366.
—— (1958). On the origin of the term 'weed'. *Proc. Ind. Acad. Sci.*, 67, 287–9.

KOMAROV, V. L. ed. (1934). *Flora U.R.S.S.* Editio Academiae Scientiarum, Leningrad.

KORSMO, E. (1935). *Weed Seeds*. Stechert, New York; Williams & Norgate, London.

KOTS, N. N. L. (1959). [Constructive and implement-using activity of the higher apes (Chimpanzee)—in Russian.] Moscow, 399 pp.

KRAMER, S. N. (1956). *From the Tablets of Sumer*. Falcon's Wing Press, Indian Hills, Colorado, 293 pp.

KUCKUCK, H. (1934). *Von der Wildpflanze zur Kulturpflanze*. Berlin, 70 pp.

KRZYMOWSKI, R. (1905). Kulturpflanzen, Unkräuter, und Haustiere als Intensitätsindikatoren. *Fühlings Landw. Ztg.*, 54.

LANGE, K. & HIRMER, M. (1955). *Aegypten*. . . . Hirmer, München, 95 pp. [Fig. 77 for *Equisetum* sp.].

LAPI, G. (1767). *Discorso sull' esterminio del loglio e di altre pianti nocive*. Stecchi e Pagani, Firenze.

LAUS, H. (1908). *Mährens Ackerunkräuter und Ruderalpflanzen. Zugleich ein Beitrag zur Phytogeographie des Landes*. Rohrer, Brun, 269 pp.

LAVIOSA ZAMBOTTI, P. (1943). *Le Più antiche culturi agricole europeò*. Casa Editrice Guiseppe Principato, Milano, 614 pp. [Neolithic agriculture].

LAWRENCE, A. A. (1958). Letter to L. J. King, dated 2 August 1958.

LEHMANN, E. (1931). Erinnerungen an den Waid. *Naturforscher*, 7, 11.

LINKOLA, L. (1916, 1921). Studien über den Einfluss der Kultur auf die Flora in den Gegenden nördlich vom Ladogasee. I: Allgemeiner Teil. *Acta Soc. Fauna Flora Fenn.*, 25(1), 1–430, with 6 figs., 6 tables, and 20 maps. II: Spezieller Teil. *ibid.* 25(2), 1–492, with 4 tables. (Cf. *Bot. Jb.*, 58, lit., 76–77, 1923.)

LONG, H. C. (1910). *Common Weeds of Farm and Garden*. John Murray, London, 451 pp.

LORET, V. (1887). *La flore pharaonique d'après les documents hiéroglyphiques et les spécimens découverts dans les tombes*. J. B. Baillière et fils, Paris, 64 pp.

McCALL, M. A. (1945). A general look at the weed problem. *J. Amer. Soc. Agron.*, 37, 378–86.

McNEW, G. L. (1961). Dedication of volume to Percy W. Zimmerman. Pp. vi-vii, in *Plant Growth Regulation, Fourth International Conference on Plant Growth Regulation*. Ames, Iowa, Iowa State University Press, 1961. 850 pp.

MARIE-VICTORIN, FRÈRE (1938). Phytogeographical problems of eastern Canada. *Amer. Midl. Nat.*, 19, 489–558.

MARTIN, H. (1961). *Guide to the Chemicals Used in Crop Protection*. 4th edn. Canada Dept. Agriculture, Ottawa.

MOLDENKE, H. N. (1951). *Poisonous Plants of the World*. Yonkers, New York, 25 pp. Published by author.

—— & MOLDENKE, ALMA (1952). *Plants of the Bible*. Chronica Botanica Co., Waltham, Mass. 328 pp.

MOORE, R. M. (1954). The nature of weeds. *Pastoral Rev.*, 64, 497, 499.

MUENSCHER, W. C. (1955). *Weeds*. 2nd edn. Macmillan, New York, 560 pp.

MURR, J. (1914). Weiteres zur Adventivflora von Gross Britannien. *Allg. Bot. Z.*, 2, 25-26.

NEGRI, G. (1948). [The plant cover of anthropic stations in Italy—in Italian.] *Nuovo G. Bot. Ital.*, 55, 519-26.

NELSON, J. G. (1917). Introduction of foreign weeds in ballast as illustrated at Linnton, Ore. *Torreya*, 17, 151-60.

NETOLITZSKY, F. (1914). Die Hirse aus antiken Funde. *S.B. Kgl. Akad. Wiss. Wien*, 123 (6, Abt. 1), 725-59, with 10 figs. and 1 map. (Cf. *Bot. Zbl.*, 129, 310-12, 1915.)

NEUWEILER, E. (1905). Die prähistorischen Pflanzenreste Mitteleuropas, mit besonderer Berücksichtigung der schweizerischen Funde. ('Botanische Excursionen und pflanzengeographische Studien in der Schweiz', herausgegeben von Professor Dr. C. Schröter, Zürich. Verlag von A. Raustein, Heft 6, 110 pp.) Also in *Vschr. Naturf. Ges. Zürich, Jahrg*, 50, 23-132, 1905. (Cf. *Bot. Zbl.*, 99, 605-6, 1905.)

ORTMAN, R. (1914). Unkräuter Deutschlands in prähistorischer Zeit I. *Z. Naturw.*, 85, 329.

OTTO, J. J. (1794). *Ganz neue Entdeckung der in Deutschland noch unbekannten wahren, achten, zahmen, Waidtpflanze*. Frankfurt am Main, 72 pp.

Oxford English Dictionary (1933). Clarendon Press, Oxford, England, vol. xii.

PALMER, E. (1871). Food productions of the North American Indians. *Annu. Rep. U.S. Dep. Agric.*, 1870, pp. 404-28, with 10 pls.

PALMÉR, I. (1917). Baldersbra (*Anthemis cotula*). *Arkiv. för Nordisk Filologi*, 34, 232-5.

PAMMEL, L. H. (1911). *A Manual of Poisonous Plants*. The Torch Press, Cedar Rapids, Iowa, 977 pp.

PIETERS, A. J. (1935). What is a weed? *J. Amer. Soc. Agron.*, 27, 781-3.

Plant Science Literature (1935-42). Library, U. S. Dept. Agriculture, Washington.

POLUNIN, N. (1948). Botany of the Canadian Eastern Arctic. Part III, Vegetation and Ecology. *Bull. Nat. Mus. Can.*, No. 104, 304 pp.

RADEMACHER, B. (1948). Gedanken über Begriff und Wesen des 'Unkrauts'. *Zeit. für Pflanzenkr. und Pflanzenschutz*, 55, 3-10.

RATZEBURG, I. T. E. (1859). *Die Standortsgewächse und Unkräuter Deutschlands*. Nicolaische Verlagsbuchhandlung, Berlin.

RIEDLE, A. (1932). Daseinkampf zwischen Unkraut und Kulturpflanzen. *Mitt. Dtsch. Landw. Ges.*, 47, 562.

SAUER, C. O. (1952). *Agricultural Origins and Dispersals* (Bowman Memorial Lectures). American Geographical Society. New York, 110 pp.

SAUER, J. D. (1950). Amaranths as dye plants among the Pueblo peoples. *Sthwest. J. Anthrop.*, 6, 412-15. (See Rev. in *Amer. Antiq.*, 19, 90-92, 1953.)

—— (1950a). Grain amaranths: survey of their history and classification. *Ann. Mo. Bot. Gdn*, 37, 561-632.

SCHIEMANN, E. (1932). Entstehung der Kulturpflanzen. *Handb. d. Vererbungswissenschaft*, Baur & Hartmann, Berlin, Bd. III, pp. 1-377.

—— (1943). Entstehung der Kulturpflanzen. *Ergebn. Biol.*, 19, 409-552. [566 references.]

SCHULZ, O. E. (1936). Isatis. In A. Engler, *Die Natürlichen Pflanzenfamilien*. Zweite Auflage, Band 17b, W. Engelmann, Leipzig, pp. 420-2.

SCHWANITZ, F. (1957). *Die Entstehung der Kulturpflanzen*. Springer, 151 pp.

SCHWEINFURTH, C. (1919). Pflanzenbilder im Tempel von Karnak (Theben). *Bot. Jb.*, 55, 464-80.

SEARS, P. B. (1959). The ecology of man. *Annu. Rep. Smithson. Instn.* (Washington, D.C.) for 1958, pp. 375–98.

Seed Trade Buyers' Guide (1965). Seed World Publications, Chicago, Ill. 48th edn. 234 pp. (cf. pp. 111–212).

SHAW, W. (1956). Terminology Committee Report, Weed Society of America. *Weeds*, 4, 278.

STEARN, W. T. (1956). Book review of *Weeds* by W. C. Muenscher. *J. R. Hort. Soc.*, 81, 285–6.

SWEDERSKI, W. (1925). [Les mauvaises herbes trouvées dans les fouilles archéologiques en Samogitie et Petite Pologne—in Polish, French summary.] *Acta Soc. Bot. Polon.*, 3(2), 242–52.

TEIRLINCK, I. (1924). *Flora Diabolica. De plant in de Demonologie.* 'De Sikkel', Antwerpen, 322 pp.

—— (1930). *Flora Magica; de Plant in de Tooverwereld.* 'De Sikkel', Antwerpen, 388 pp.

THELLUNG, A. (1908). Neuheiten aus der Adventivflora von Montpellier. *Fedde Repert.*, 5, 85–90, pp. 61–63.

—— (1912). La flore adventice de Montpellier. *Mém. Soc. Nat. Sci. Cherbourg, 1911–1912*, 38, 57–728. (Cf. *Bot. Zbl.*, 120, 444–6, 1912, French summary.)

—— (1915). Pflanzenwanderungen unter dem Einfluss der Menschen. *Bot. Jb.*, 53, Beibl. No. 116, pp. 37–66.

—— (1918–19). Zur Terminologie der Adventiv- und Ruderalfloristik. *Allg. Bot. Z.*, 14/15, 36–42 [1922].

—— (1925). Kulturpflanzeneigenschaften bei Unkräutern. Festschr. Schröter. *Veröff. Geobot. Inst. Rübel*, Heft 3, pp. 745–61.

—— (1930). Die Entstehung der Kulturpflanzen. *Naturw. u. Landw.*, Freising, München, Heft 16, 89 pp.

THOMAS, W. L., Jr. (ed.) (1956). *Man's role in changing the face of the earth.* An international symposium under the co-chairmanship of C. Sauer, M. Bates, and L. Mumford. Sponsored by the Wenner-Gren Foundation for Anthropological Research. University of Chicago Press, Chicago, 1,193 pp.

THOMPSON, Mrs. William Boyce. See *New York Times*, 28 August 1950, p. 17, col. 5.

THOMPSON, R. C. (1924). *The Assyrian Herbal.* Luzac, 294 pp.

—— (1949). *A Dictionary of Assyrian Botany.* The British Academy, Burlington Gardens, London, 405 pp.

TUTIN, WINIFRED (1955). Preliminary observations on a year's cycle of sedimentation in Windermere, England. *Mem. Ist. Ital. Idrobiol.* (suppl.), 8, 467–84. (*Colloque I.U.B.S.*, N. 19.)

TURRILL, W. B. (1929). *The Plant-life of the Balkan Peninsula. A Phytogeographical Study.* Clarendon Press, Oxford, 490 pp.

TÜXEN, R. (1931). Die Grundlagen der Urlandschafts-forschung. Ein Beitrag zur Erforschung der Geschichte der anthropogenen Beeinflussung der Vegetation Mitteleuropas. *Nachr. Niedersachs. Urgesch.*, 5, 59–105.

VAN WIJK, H. L. GERTH. See GERTH VAN WIJK, H.

VAVILOV, N.I. (1920). [On the origin of the cultivated rye—in Russian, English summary.] *Bull. Appl. Bot.*, 10, 561–90.

—— (1926). [Studies on the origin of cultivated plants—in Russian, English summary.] *Bull. Appl. Bot.*, 16(2), 3–248.

—— (1935). [*Theoretical bases of plant breeding*—in Russian.] Moscow.

—— (1950). The origin, variation, immunity and breeding of cultivated plants. *Chron. Bot.*, 13, 1–366.

VICTORIN, FRÈRE MARIE. See MARIE-VICTORIN FRÈRE.

VOSS, H. (1955). Bibliographie der Menschenaffen (Schimpanse, Orang, Gorilla). . . . Gustav Fischer, Jena, 163 pp.

WAUGH, F. A. (1897). Some phases of weed evolution. *Science*, 5, 789.

Weed Abstracts (1950–). Commonwealth Agricultural Bureau, Farnham Royal, England.

Weeds (1951–). Weed Society of America, Geneva, New York. (Including *Bibliography of Weed Investigations*.)

WEIN, K. (1912). Die synanthropen Pflanzen des Harzes im 16. Jahrhundert nach der 'Sylva Hercynia' von Johann Thal. *Beih. Bot. Zbl.*, 29(2), 279–305.

WERTH, E. (1937). Weitere Untersuchungen an prähistorischen Kulturpflanzen *Ber. Dsch. Bot. Ges.*, 55, 622–30.

—— (1944). Der Hafer, eine unordische Getreideart. *Z. Pflanzenz.*, 26, 92–102.

WHITAKER, T. W. (1947). American origin of the cultivated cucurbits. I: Evidence from the herbals. II: Survey of old and recent botanical evidence.*Ann. Mo. Bot. Gdn.*, 24, 101–11.

WHITE, J. T. & RIDDLE, J. E. (1872). *A Latin-English Dictionary*. Longmans, Green, London, Vol. II.

WIJK, H. L. GERTH VAN. *See* GERTH VAN WIJK, H. L.

WILSIE, C. P. (1962). *Crop Adaptation and Distribution*. W. H. Freeman, San Francisco, 448 pp.

WILSON, J. A. (1956). Letter to L. J. King, dated 21 November 1956.

WITTMACK, L. (1903). Die in Pompeji gefundenen pflanzlichen Reste. *Bot. Jb.*, 33(3), 38–66.

WOENIG, F. (1897). *Die Pflanzen im alten Aegypten*. Leipzig, 426 pp.

World List of Scientific Periodicals (1952). Butterworths Scientific Publications, London. 3rd. edn., 1,085 pp.

WOYTINSKY, W. S. & WOYTINSKY, E. S. (1953). *World Population and Production Trends and Outlook*. Twentieth Century Fund, New York. 1,268 pp.

YANCEY, P. J. (1945). Origins from mythology of biological names and terms. *Bios Classroom Series*, No. 5, 47 pp. (from *Bios* 16).

ZAMBOTTI, P. LAVIOSA. *See* LAVIOSA ZAMBOTTI, P.

Zeitschrift fur Pflanzenkrankheiten (1891–), Eugen Ulmer, Stuttgart.

ZEUNER, F. E. (1951). *Dating the Past. An Introduction to Geochronology*. 3rd edn. Methuen, London, 516 pp.

ZIMMERMAN, F. (1907). *Die Adventiv- und Ruderalflora von Mannheim, Ludwigshafen und der Pfalz nebst den seltenerne einheimischen Blütenpflanzen und den Gefässkryptogamen*. Haas'sche Buchdr., Mannheim, 171 pp.

ZINGER, N. (1913). Über Anpassung von Unkräutern. *Festschr. f. Kusnezow*, pp. 179–90.

ADDENDA

HELBAEK, H. (1953). Early crops in Southern England. *Proc. Prehist. Soc.*, 18, 194.

—— (1954). Prehistoric food plants and weeds in Denmark. *Danm. Geologiske Undersøgelse*, II R, 80.

—— (1955). Ancient Egyptian wheats. *Proc. Prehist. Soc.*, 21, 93.

—— (1960). Comment on *Chenopodium* as a food plant in prehistory. *Ber. d. Geobot. Inst. Rubel*, Zurich, 31, 16.

—— (1960a). Palaeoethnobotany of the Near East and Europe. *Prehistoric Investigations in Iraqi Kurdistan*, by R. J. Braidwood & B. Howe (No. 31 in series, *Studies in Ancient Oriental Civilization*), pp. 99–118. Univ. Chicago Press.

HUTCHINSON, SIR J. (1965). *Essays on Crop Plant Evolution*. Univ. Press, Cambridge. 204 pp. (*See* H. Godwin, *The Beginnings of Agriculture in North West Europe*, Ch. I, pp. 1–22.)

31

II

THE CLASSIFICATION OF WEEDS

THE VARIOUS SYSTEMS

WEEDS as a unique biological group—apart from the traditional systematic classification—have been classified in several ways. The one employed in this work has been used by many authors, and actually draws upon the units of several systems—producing a generally usable and workable system. Briefly it draws upon life-form, life-span, habitat, and whether the weed is independent or parasitic in growth-habit. Meanwhile it may be of interest to examine a number of other proposed classifications, as they bring out certain aspects of the origin and growth of weeds.

The system of Korsmo. The distinguished Norwegian weed biologist, Emil Korsmo, has stated (Korsmo, 1930) that weeds constitute a biological group characterized by certain adaptations to life. He proceeds to classify weeds with specific reference to their reproductive habits. Three classes are recognized by him: weeds that reproduce by seeds only; perennials that reproduce by seeds but which may form shoots that assist in reproduction; and perennials reproducing principally by creeping shoots.

The system of Anderson. Anderson (1939), in his classification of weedy plants, designates two classes associated with man's activities, namely weeds —which are plants unintentionally grown by man in fields, gardens, pastures, lawns, etc.—and ruderals, which are plants spreading into man-created habitats (barnyards, roadways, dumps, etc.) though not actually cultivated. His two remaining classes are cultivated plants and nomads.

The scheme of Thellung. Of the many classifications proposed for weeds, the outline as first described in A. Thellung's classical study *La flore adventice de Montpellier* (1912), and further described and elaborated in later publications (Thellung, 1915, 1918–19, 1925—*see* Ch. I *), provides a realistic and usable one. The scheme is all-inclusive, as all the vascular flora is considered—the basis of classification resting upon the past history of the species in question, so far as it can be determined. Thellung's region of study, the Mediterranean seaport area of Montpellier, provided a particularly good area for critical review, as alien plants had entered

---

* The frequent citations of this nature are to references in the Bibliographies at the ends of the chapters indicated.—Ed.

this region throughout many millennia, following the activities of men in both pre-historic and historic times.

The flora of any region may be grouped into the indigenous or native species of the area on one hand, and, on the other, into two specific groups that represent the adventive and the more aggressive or troublesome elements: the *apophytes* and the *anthropochores* (or, preferably, *anthropophytes*). It has been noted in Chapter I (cf. Fig. 4) that these two major groups are the principal ones from which the majority of our weeds are derived. The apophytes are the emigrants or deserters, i.e. those indigenous plants that leave the natural environment to enter the artificial and man-disturbed areas. The anthropophytes include all species of a given region which are not originally indigenous, whether introduced by man intentionally or not. These embrace plants which are propagated and/or spread by man—including cultivated plants as well as weeds of foreign origin (*see* Addendum, p. 48).

The latter two broad groups are further divided by Thellung into seven classes for the anthropophytes and two classes for the apophytes:

1. *Ergasiophytes*:—These comprise the exotic species which are cultivated for food, forage, medicinal, and ornamental uses. They occupy their habitats through the conscious action of man; examples include rye, wheat, opium poppy, geranium, etc.

2. *Ergasiolipophytes*:—These comprise those species that persist after a period of cultivation, but which do not spread.

3. *Ergasiophygophytes*:—These comprise once-cultivated plants that have escaped from cultivated areas and have spread into both natural and artificial habitats and persist in them. Examples are *Anthriscus*, *Robinia pseudo-acacia*, and *Ailanthus altissima*.

4. *Archeophytes*:—These comprise the weeds of fields and other cultivated places which have been encountered since prehistoric times, but which probably did not exist there before man. Examples include *Centaurea cyanus*, *Agrostemma githago*, and *Lolium temulentum*—remains of these having been found in the ancient lake-dwelling areas of Switzerland.

5. *Neophytes*:—These comprise plants which newly enter an area through the often unintentional activities of man. They appear to be components of the native vegetation, reproducing and spreading much as do the indigenous members. Their future existence is independent of man. Examples include *Heliotropium curassavicum* and *Paspalum distichum* var. *paspaloides*.

6. *Epoekophytes*:—These comprise plants that are found in the region concerned for a long time (since ancient times), that are well established and have a high level of reproduction, but that are restricted to artificial habitats. Examples include *Anemone coronaria*, *Xanthium orientale*, *Tulipa oculis*, and *Tulipa praecox*.

7. *Ephemerophytes*:—These have variously been termed ephemerals, travellers, nomads, waifs, etc. They generally occur only in small numbers and in artificial habitats. Many plants of ballast dumps, railroad rights-of-way, the environs of wool mills, etc., would be included here. Examples include *Melilotus infestus, Linum nodiflorum*, and *Daucus aureus*.

8. *Oekiophytes*:—These comprise indigenous or apophytic species that are cultivated for food, ornament, etc. Examples include *Fragaria vesca* and *Narcissus poeticus*.

9. *Spontaneous apophytes*:—These comprise indigenous or apophytic species that emigrate or spontaneously move into artificial habitats such as cultivated areas. Examples are *Medicago lupulina* and many other species of this genus, and *Melilotus indicus*.

It can thus be seen that this classification of Thellung is of particular merit in revealing the many possible origins of the heterogeneous groups of plants that are referred to as weeds.

The system of Raunkaier. This system, involving the life-form of plants, is based on the degree of protection afforded to the perennating buds during the dormant season. It is generally related to temperature, but not entirely so. All vegetation is included here, not just weeds alone. However, the latter group is certainly best represented by the therophytes. The five principal categories in this system are:

    I. Phanerophytes—trees and tall shrubs.
    II. Chamaephytes—low shrubs.
    III. Hemicryptophytes—with buds at the soil surface, so that they are generally protected by snow or organic debris.
    IV. Cryptophytes (Geophytes)—with buds buried in the soil.
    V. Therophytes—annuals with the embryonic bud protected by a seed-coat.

Gates (1940), in his 'Flora' of Kansas, provides the life-form classification for each of the species included, as does the extensive work of Hegi (1909–31), *Illustrierte Flora von Mittel-Europa*.*

THE TYPES OF WEEDS

The recognized groups of weeds generally follow along the principal lines of botanical classification. Thus, in accordance with the two great angiospermous groups, monocotyledonous and dicotyledonous weeds are commonly recognized, with further subdivisions that are based generally on habitat and the life-form or some specialized or unique aspect such as

* Other classifications include the places in which they grow (cultivated fields, waste places, pastures etc.), the degree of unwantedness (tolerable, noxious, damnable, etc.) according to the "weedy" adaptations (*see*, e.g. pp. 8–9 for biological characteristics) as well as obligate weeds (highly adapted to the haunts of men) and facultative weeds (still native species but increasing under man's activities) (*see* Harlan and de Wet, 1965, ref. p. 48).

parasitism. Naturally, these are not always entirely clear-cut, and over-lapping often occurs; but the groups are well recognized, and are helpful in the understanding of the various types encountered among the more obnoxious vegetal forms throughout the world. Other, more precise but less well-known groupings, include the following:

Narrow-leafed weeds. In recent years the usage of narrow-leafed weeds, or occasionally merely 'grass weeds', has generally been employed to include chiefly members of the Gramineae, the Cyperaceae, and the Juncaceae—as well as other monocotyledonous plants whose leaves are not always 'narrow'. This is in contrast to the usage of 'broad-leafed weeds', which would include principally the dicotyledonous plants.

The Gramineae include some 4,500 species that together inhabit all terrestrial regions of the globe. They represent ancient forms, and as a group are generally low-growing and anemophilous. Their morphological feature involving the protection of the apical meristem by the sheathing leaf-bases is a general protective one, as well as an effective barrier in herbicidal control measures; it is also a protective feature in the treading action of animals.

Annual forms, while abundant, are perhaps not as troublesome as the perennial grasses. One has only to mention quack grass (*Agropyron repens*), Johnson grass, Bermuda grass, Lalang or Cogon grass (*Imperata cylindrica*), and *Saccharum spontaneum*, to bring to mind the immense acreages covered by these pests. The annual grasses are particularly troublesome in annual crops—for example, crab grasses (*Digitaria* spp.), giant foxtail (*Setaria feberii*), and wild oats (*Avena fatua*); whereas the perennial forms may be involved here too, they are often more pernicious in peren-nial crops or on land that is only occasionally, if ever, cultivated.

Broad-leafed weeds. The extremely short life-cycle exhibited by some annual weeds and other plants is apparently an adaptation to the environ-ment in general and to available moisture in particular. Many authors have observed that the annual habit is best exemplified among species in the Mediterranean area—here again in response to the very short and favourable growing-periods. The annual habit is also evident in species that live along the edges of bodies of water—the littoral zone or adjacent areas that are occasionally inundated, where perennial vegetation has little opportunity to develop. These seasonal growth-periods for certain selected regions in the world are given in the later volumes. While not generally classed as weeds, the so-called 'belly plants', and other more visible desert annuals, represent some of the shortest lived forms known—there may be as few as thirty days between their germination and seed-ing, after which they die. Many weeds, if germinating late in the season, will, under a favourable photoperiod, produce flowering and fruiting forms only a few inches in height—often called depauperate forms, for example in *Erigeron canadensis*, *Cyperus esculentus*, *Digitaria ischaemum*, *Setaria* spp., and others. Sometimes seeding occurs before the cotyledons have dropped.

Annuals. Such forms, which originated largely in response to seasonal moisture, later became adapted to the seasonal cultivation of land that also afforded a favourable habitat—as regards both moisture and space. The annual regularity of cropping, from the very earliest days of man's agricultural efforts, was timed with regard to seasonal moisture for early growth—followed often by drier periods during harvest. In Egypt, this was determined by the annual flooding of the Nile, with resultant silt deposition on the new planting areas. Thus short, favourable growth-periods, even in the warmer regions of the world—the Near East, for example—where the growing of upland cereals developed, resulted also in a selective process operating on certain annuals of the native flora. These factors contributed to the eventual establishment of a flora associated with the particular crop and cropping practices—a truly distinctive weed flora.

Annuals, by their very definition, are quick growers, and complete their life-cycle within a single season. They produce large quantities of seed in a relatively short time-span. In a low-rainfall year, for example, they set some seed, although their normal growth period may be shortened by the unfavourable season. With some quick growers seed will be set by plants which may be only a few inches high. While the seed of most annuals remain dormant in the soil from one growing season to the next growing season, one group, termed *winter annuals*, are capable of germinating before the close of the growing season in which they are matured. Members of this group generally form rosettes that survive the winter season, and are thus ready to resume active growth in the next growing season. Examples of this latter group include shepherd's purse (*Capsella bursa-pastoris*), peppergrass (*Lepidium virginicum*), henbit (*Lamium amplexicaule*), corn cockle (*Agrostemma githago*), and mayweed (*Anthemis cotula*).

Perennials. Broad-leafed weeds include those aggressive members of the flora that have renewed growth, year after year, from the same root system. While many are associated with annually cropped land, by far the larger number are found on non-cultivated areas or on land that is only occasionally cultivated—including roadsides, pastures, and waste land. Although also propagated by seeds, they are highly effective in vegetative reproduction—especially on land that is frequently cultivated. Here the root or stem portions, cut and disseminated by modern agricultural implements, ensure the continuation of the species in an area. Canada thistle (*Cirsium arvense*), bindweed (*Convolvulus arvensis*), and others, are examples. In former days, a farmer cultivating with a mule learned to avoid local infestations. The spread of nutgrass (*Cyperus* spp.) was, to a degree, avoided in this manner.

36

Biennials. These require two years from germination to flower and seed production. During the first year, the seedling develops with a sturdy root system—generally into a 'mat plant' or rosette, in which growth-form it usually over-winters. Apparently a low temperature is needed here for flower initiation and seeding, and so this group of plants is more characteristic of the temperate than warmer regions. Naturally such plants are not generally associated with annually-tilled land—unless, as in a few cases, pieces of root or stem serve also as a means of reproduction. Members of this group include the dandelion (*Taraxacum* spp.), wild carrot (*Daucus carota*), and *Plantago* spp.

Woody Plants. These constitute a very special and distinct group, and by some authors would not be included among weeds—but perhaps rather under the heading of 'noxious plants'. They include those plants whose stems develop secondary thickening, generally involving an annular growth increment. However, in certain highly specialized—as well as diversified—agricultural regions, such as occur in North America, South Africa, and perhaps Australia, many woody plants are aggressive and competitive with regard to certain forms of agriculture and forestry.

The woody plants which compete with the more desirable range grasses on the vast grazing lands of the western United States, Argentina, parts of Australia, Hawaii, and other countries, are very important members of this group. Some are semi-woody or near-woody types—for example the blackberries (*Rubus* spp.), the palmettos (*Sabal* spp.), and the Cactaceae. Large numbers of the truly woody forms, however, are frequently members of the native flora of these grazing regions, or of peripheral areas that are less suitable for grazing. Outstanding in importance are, perhaps, the mesquites (*Prosopis* spp.), salt-cedar (*Tamarix pentandra*), and others. Species of *Acacia* (Leguminosae), for example, occur widely throughout the tropics and subtropics and the flat-topped trees of this genus are characteristic features of the drier wooded grassland or savanna country of Africa—particularly East Africa. In the more humid areas of North America, several members of the genus *Rhus*—including poison-ivy and poison-sumac—are poisonous and irritating to large numbers of people.

In modern forestry practice the term 'weed tree' is commonly used, and with the introduction of the newer chemical control techniques an entirely new phase of handling this problem has been initiated. These woody forms are aggressive and noxious primarily because they have highly efficient methods of seed production and dissemination, as well as vegetative forms of reproduction. Many thrive in the more arid regions—having a xeric growth adaptation with deep rooting—and are capable of rapid spread by certain crown buds and spreading roots. They frequently attain a considerable size, and shade out (or compete for both space and moisture with) the more desirable range or forage grasses. These

37

moisture-thieving plants when occurring along watercourses in arid regions have been termed phreatophytes.

Aquatic weeds. These are a very loosely defined and difficult group to delineate—except for the one common aspect, the aquatic habitat. The group is generally considered to include the emerged and floating forms. as well as the fully submerged ones, and accordingly to involve a vast number of species, many of which can readily qualify as weeds. Aquatic plant manuals exist for many countries, and so only the more noxious types need be treated in these volumes. Naturally, those associated with one of man's oldest crops and one involving approximately half the people of the globe—namely, rice or paddy—are given pride of place in this work. Those associated with irrigation or other types of agricultural land also receive attention, as do species interfering with navigation, with fish culture, and with public health and the recreational use of bodies of water. The wide dispersal of numerous aquatic species has been noted throughout the world.

Mirashi (1957), in his study of the hydrophytes of Umred, at Nagpur in India, has provided a classification into six life-forms based on their contacts with soil, water, and air:

(i) *Floating hydrophytes:*—These are in contact with water and air only. They include species of *Trapa, Hygrorhiza,* and *Ipomoea,* as well as the *Azolla-Spirodela-Lemna* community, the *Eichhornia-Pistia** community, and the *Neptunia oleracea-Jussiaea repens* community.

(ii) *Suspended hydrophytes:*—These are rootless, submerged hydrophytes that are in contact with water only, for example *Ceratophyllum demersum,* which grows in shallow waters often to the complete exclusion of other plants. Species of *Utricularia* have their vegetative organs suspended in water, but their inflorescences are aerial.

(iii) *Anchored submerged hydrophytes:*—These are entirely, or for the most part, in contact with soil and water only. These include species of *Najas, Hydrilla, Vallisneria,* and *Blyxa.*

(iv) *Anchored hydrophytes with floating leaves:*—These are in contact with the soil and with water as well as air. Included here are species of *Aponogeton, Nymphaea, Limnanthemum, Sagittaria,* and *Ottelia.*

(v) *Emergent amphibious hydrophytes:*—The root, the lower part of the stem and, in some cases, even the lower leaves, of these hydrophytes are usually submerged under water. These include species of *Aeschynomene, Sesbania, Hygrophila,* and *Limnophyton.*

(vi) *Wetland hydrophytes:*—These are rooted in soil that is usually saturated with water, at least in the early part of their life. Included here are species of *Malachra, Ammania, Veronica, Polygonum, Sphaeranthus,*

---

* *Index Kewensis,* Pt. II (1893), p. 824, lists *Eichhornia* (named after J. A. F. Eichhorn), often *Eichornia* in American publications.

and *Commelina*. Some of them continue to thrive even after the substratum has dried up considerably.

In a consideration of the various types of aquatic plants in Florida, West (1948–49) places these plants in three categories, namely *floaters*, *bankers*, and *sinkers*. The 'floaters' live on the surface of the water and grow without the necessity of any attachment to the soil. Genera here include *Eichhornia*, *Pistia*, *Limnobium*, *Ceratopteris*, and *Lemna*. The 'bankers' are so named because they must have their roots in the soil of the banks or margins of the body of water invaded. Their stems are usually hollow or inflated, so that they float on or near the surface of the water and may extend out 10 or more feet from the bank where the root system is embedded. They often extend out from both banks and completely cover canals or small streams. Examples here include species of *Panicum* (especially *P. purpurascens*, Para grass—the worst one), *Hydrochloa*, *Paspalum*, *Hydrocotyle*, *Achryanthes*, *Polygonum*, *Brasenia*, and *Myriophyllum*. The 'sinkers', strictly speaking, do not sink but have their roots in the bottom of the body of water. They are perhaps the most insidious, as they are submerged and hence inconspicuous, but yet greatly impede water flow and slow down navigation. Genera here include *Ceratophyllum*, *Najas*, *Potamogeton*, *Utricularia*, *Cabomba*, and *Elodea*.

Special techniques are required to control or eradicate these aerial or submerged forms. Control is further complicated by the fact that no contamination of adjacent crops is permissible, nor is action that would be inimical or products that would be toxic to fish or other wildlife. Whether the treatment is applied in a still body of water, or in a rapidly moving stream, or irrigation ditch, also involves different application methods—all to be considered later (cf. Pl. 18).

Vines, climbers, and stranglers. These involve a diverse group of plant species whose one common feature involves vine-like growth. This is not to imply that they lack importance as noxious plants—quite the contrary. In the north-temperate regions, species of *Vitis*, *Smilax*, *Lonicera*, *Rhus*, *Celastrus*, and *Campsis*, are aggressive and present considerable control problems. In many tropical regions the strangling figs, *Ficus* spp., are destructive to ornamental, fruit, and otherwise useful trees. The lianas that are so typical of tropical rain forests present a problem in lumbering operations.

Richards (1952) defines a strangler as a plant which begins its life as an epiphyte and later sends down roots to the soil, becoming an independent plant and often killing the tree by which it was originally supported. Hemi-epiphytes are similar, except that they never become mechanically self-supporting. Species of *Ficus* are not so abundant in the South American rain forest as, often, elsewhere, a more important genus being *Clusia*—especially in Guiana and the West Indies. *Clusias* seldom kill their hosts, although they often greatly stunt and deform their crowns.

39

Most members of this group belong to the genera *Ficus* (Moraceae), *Schefflera* (Araliaceae), and *Clusia* (Guttiferae). A similar habit is shown by South American species of *Coussapoa* (Moraceae) and *Posoqueria* (Rubiaceae), and by some species of *Mebrosideros* (Myrtaceae).

In the rain forests of Africa, Indo-Malaya, and Australia, the strangling figs (*Ficus* spp.) are abundant in both species and individuals. The seeds germinate on tall trees, forming a stout bush which develops descending roots. Many of these roots remain close to the trunk of the host tree, and eventually reach the ground and ramify in the soil. With new root-growth and extensive anastomosing, the host is encased in a network of woody meshes. After a time the 'host' tree usually dies and rots away, leaving the fig as a hollow but independent tree.

These strangler vines have been examined by Dobzhansky & Murça-Pires (1954) as an illustration of a central problem in the theory of evolution: how did the haphazard process of chance mutation and natural selection produce such complicated adaptations? These stranglers represent a variety of adaptations for life under the exacting conditions of the tropical forest. Such adaptations arise from the competition for sunlight, and for the survival value of accomplishing growth upwards by clinging to other trees and then breaking through the dense forest canopy to open sunlight. Different genera represent different stages from non-stranglers to facultative stranglers, and then on to obligatory stranglers. Three members of the family (Moraceae) to which *Ficus* belongs illustrate this: *Coussapoa* acts as a strangler frequently; *Pouroma* less often; and *Cecropia* only occasionally. The widespread genus *Clusia* provides climbers and epiphytes; but rarely, if ever, do they kill their support. They stop short of killing the host tree and taking its place, and when the host dies, so presumably does the *Clusia*. These illustrate the selection in nature of useful hereditary modifications. The authors believe that these selective responses of the organism to opportunities in the environment are the primary driving force in the evolutionary process.

Although lianas are generally considered independent plants, Herbert (1928), in studying the matchbox-bean liana, *Entada scandens*, growing on species of *Eucalyptus* in the rain forest of Dunk Island off North Queensland, Australia, found close contact of the liana with the parenchyma of the host tree. His work implied nutritional exchange, but was based on a study of these dried liana attachments to the supporting tree rather than of living plants. These attachment points, after the disappearance of the liana, appeared as woody buttons—similar to a date-stone in shape—in the limbs of the host tree.

In North America, poison-ivies, principally represented by *Rhus radicans* in the eastern areas of the United States and by *R. diversiloba* (poison-oak) in the western regions, are perhaps the most noxious of vines. Besides being widely distributed in farm and recreational areas, they are a particular menace in various orchard sites. Poison-ivies thrive under the sod system of soil management practised in many kinds of orchards. If not controlled, they develop into a solid mat in the tree-row, making it difficult for persons to work around the trees. Continuous cultivation will control these pests, but in hilly regions the sod system is necessary to prevent soil erosion. Sprays of 2,4,5-T as well as of ammonium sulphamate have given satisfactory control. Applications in orchards should be made early in the summer, before the bending down of the branches (McNair, 1923; Hewetson, 1951).

Wild grape-vines (*Vitis* spp.) present a problem of considerable magnitude in certain areas. In young forest stands and open areas in West Virginia, dense impenetrable tangles often cover the ground to a depth of 10 or more feet, completely smothering valuable tree seedlings. Such grape tangles may be killed by spraying with mixtures of 1 per cent 2,4,5-T and water in the spring, at any time after the foliage has become fully developed. In older stands, large vines climb into the tree-tops—often reaching a height of 80 or 100 ft.—and shade the crowns with their thick foliage. In time, their weight deforms and breaks even the sturdiest trees. Almost complete eradication of these larger vines has been obtained by basal chemical treatment. A band of bark, 1 ft. in height and encircling the base of the vine, is thoroughly saturated with a 4 per cent solution of 2,4,5-T in an organic carrier (Carvell & Tryon, 1955).

The eradication of a species of wild grape (*Vitis girdiana*) in California was desired, so that a barrier to the outward migration, from the centre of infestation, of the western grape skeletonizer (*Harrisina brillans*) might be formed. This insect first arrived in San Diego County vineyards in 1947, and its larvae feed on leaves and fruit of both cultivated and wild grape-vines. Here, sprays of 2,4-D were effective in the control of the *Vitis* (Stewart & Gammon, 1947).

Japanese honeysuckle (*Lonicera japonica*) has become oppressively established in many parts of the United States; having been introduced as an ornamental from eastern Asia, it is now fully naturalized. As it becomes so easily established in poor soil and forms an extensive root system in a very short time, it is one of the best plants for protection of railroad embankments, road cuts, and the like. The extensive spread of this weed along the entire eastern section of the United States has been attributed to its use by the railroads for this purpose (Hurt, 1926).

This species has, for example, become a serious pest in Virginia apple orchards, especially flourishing in the Piedmont fruit-belt. It handicaps the cultivation of fruit trees, drains the soil of moisture during the dry summer, and affords habitations for mice. It spreads when bits of the root system are dispersed during cultivation, etc., and by seeds. The seeds are borne in small black berries which mature in autumn, and they may be washed about or carried by birds (Hurt, 1926).

In the forests of the eastern United States, bittersweet (*Celastrus scandens*), as well as *Vitis* spp., cause considerable damage to young trees through constriction and deformation of young branches. Lutz (1943) has observed such injuries, as well as the concomitant development of very abnormal wood structures, in *Sassafras albidum*, *Acer rubrum*, *A. saccharum*, *Liriodendron tulipifera*, *Pinus strobus*, and *Hamamelis virginiana*. Such injuries may facilitate the entry of wood borers and start decay, which may render the affected trees worthless. Lutz noted similar injury by honeysuckle to young ash stems (*Fraxinus* sp.) in Switzerland. He concluded that, during cultural operations in the forest, it is good practice to sever the stems of all vines which are climbing trees—except where the vines are needed as sources of food for wildlife.

Trumpet creeper (*Campsis radicans*) is a deep-rooted, drought-resistant, woody perennial vine found in woods, thickets, river bottoms, swamps, fields, and pastures—being especially abundant and troublesome in the southern United States. It is native to the southern regions, and this species, together with the asiatic *C. chinensis*, are the only two known members of the genus. Both have been cultivated as ornamentals in the United States, the former being the more cold-tolerant. Sprouts persisting in fields seriously interfere with the harvesting of crops. The pods, 5 to 7 in. long, split open and permit wind dispersal of the seeds. The plants persist through the sprouting of old individuals and of intact or mutilated roots. Many other noxious 'vines' in the genera *Cuscuta*, *Cassytha*, *Mikania*, etc., have been noted in the check-lists.

Epiphytes. In the north-temperate regions the predominant components of epiphytic growth are generally the lichens and mosses. The vascular members—save perhaps the ferns—are much less prominent and are rarely destructive. For an excellent bibliography of studies on the ruderals and adventive plants (many of them epiphytic) of the walls, ruins, etc., of Italian cities, cf. Anzalone (1951).

Studies of vascular epiphytic communities in Europe, particularly in Finland and Sweden, have disclosed the presence of a sizeable number of vascular species growing in this type of habitat. Many, of course, may be considered accidental epiphytes: thus *Stellaria media* is frequently listed on *Alnus glutinosa* and other lower growing plants (Holmboe, 1904; Häyren, 1942). In Germany, coppiced willows have provided habitats for some 20 species distributed largely by wind and birds (Geysenheyner, 1894); while near Turin, Italy, 17 species were observed (Beyer, 1894). In these lists, weed species in the genera *Solanum*, *Taraxacum*, *Polygonum*, *Galium*, *Plantago*, *Rubus*, *Poa*, *Oxalis*, and others, are noted. Similar studies have also been made in Zürich, Switzerland (Vareschi, 1936), and elsewhere in Italy (Cozzi, 1908). The last-named found 78 phanerogams on *Salix alba* in the Lombardy region, with *Stellaria media* and *Lamium album* very common. Just how harmful these epiphytes are has not been fully assessed, but it is evident that, if flowering and fruiting occur, they may serve as seed sources for new field infestations.*

Spanish moss, *Tillandsia usneoides* (Bromeliaceae), is perhaps the commonest and best known of the vascular epiphytes in subtropical regions—particularly in the southern humid regions of the United States (Garth, 1955). It has found a number of uses and hence has not generally been classed as a weed. However, there are times when it is considered unsightly on fine specimen trees in parks and other public gardens, where it may be removed by hand. It also occurs occasionally on public utility lines (Velez, 1953) but perhaps only temporarily so. It is much less common on coniferous than broad-leaf tree species.

In Texas, Spanish moss infests the valuable pecan trees. Control was achieved with the use of lead arsenate (6 lb. per 100 gallons). Ball moss (*Tillandsia recurvata*), growing in a rosette-shaped ball composed of from 20 to 60 individual plants, is also a problem in parts of Texas. It is generally found attached to deciduous trees with rough bark, attachment being by several short holdfasts for each rosette. It is believed that the ball moss is responsible for the death of shade trees. Such injury apparently results from the smothering of the buds of the host tree by the dense growth of the 'moss'. Many workers have attempted to remove the 'moss' by scraping the trees; but tests have shown that one thorough spraying with the mixture noted above is sufficient to kill all of the 'moss' on the tree.

The luxuriance of epiphytic growth is nowhere more prominent and conspicuous than in the humid tropical regions the world around. In the American tropics, members of the Bromeliaceae are particularly common (Schimper, 1888). Epiphytic growths have generally become a problem only on tropical tree crops of various types, and on ornamentals. The 'air plants' on buildings and other structures, however, often hasten or lead to deterioration. Epiphytic plants also occur on the exposed wood and pilings of docks and wharves, and have been reported on public utility lines.

Sands (1926) investigated the nature and effects of epiphytes on cultivated trees in Malaya. Here, too, epiphytes or 'air plants' belong to widely dissimilar classes—lichens, mosses, ferns, orchids and other flowering plants—but, from a planter's standpoint, the most noteworthy are several species of ferns and flowering plants. They occur on various situations on trees: in forks of branches, in old wounds, at the bases of the leaves of palms—especially those remaining attached to the stem for long periods (e.g. the African oil palm, *Elaeis guineensis*). The seeds of this group of plants are particularly adapted to dispersal by wind or birds.

Sands recognized three classes: (1) True epiphytes—those species thriving epiphytically; many, such as the ferns, thrive also on the ground.

---

* Large numbers of phanerogamic epiphytes, often forming a considerable tangle and sometimes including sizeable saplings, have been observed growing on pollarded willows in England, for example around Oxford and Cambridge.—Ed.

(2) Half-epiphytes—air plants that pass their earlier stages of development on trees but subsequently become connected with the ground—particularly species of *Ficus*, such as *F. bengalensis, F. benjamina, F. indica, F. elastica*, and others. (3) Nest epiphytes—those which collect humus in pockets or funnels in specialized leaves arranged in a particularly effective manner.

In Malaya the true epiphytes can be damaging to useful trees if allowed to overrun them. One such epiphyte is the creeping fern, *Drymoglossum heterophyllum* ('Sakat ribu-ribu'), which is commonly found on rubber, coconut, and fruit and shade trees, and which spreads by means of a long, creeping rhizome. It often completely covers the stems of palms such as the coconut (*Cocos nucifera*) and the Pinang (*Areca catechu*), as well as the trunks, branches, and twigs of forest trees. Often associated with it is the rather similar *Cyclophorus adnascens*, and the asclepiad *Dischidia gandichandi* ('Petis'). *Drymoglossum heterophyllum* has a slender climbing stem which, rooting at the nodes, grows rapidly. It quickly covers stems, twigs, and leaves of fruit and other trees, and damages them severely if allowed to remain.

The half-epiphytes include the species of *Ficus* noted above, the 'Ara' trees as they are called in Malaya, which are capable of destroying useful trees by means of their strangling aerial roots and the overhead shade of their leaves. *Ficus* is an entomophilous genus, but the flowering habit is an example of flagelliflory combined with cauliflory. The fruits are sought by birds and especially bats. In *Ficus ribes* the fruits are dispersed by *Chironax melanocephalus*, a bat that roosts underneath nest-ferns in the mountain forest. Some of these species also grow on towers and roofs of lofty buildings.

The nest epiphytes include several species of ferns: the oak-leafed fern (*Drynaria quercifolia*), the bird's-nest fern (*Asplenium nidus*), and the stag's-horn fern (*Platycerium* sp.). These are not as damaging as members of the other two classes, but, if present near damaged or wounded areas, they may hasten the decay of the stem or branch by retaining debris and moisture.

It was also noted by Sands that the ferns *Nephrolepis exaltata, N. acutifolia*, and other species, get into the inflorescences and among the fruits of the African oil palm. Careful and early removal is advocated.

Ruinen (1953, 1956) and others (Anstead, 1925; Lebrun, 1937; Went, 1940; Eggeling, 1948; and Hosokawa, 1954) have reviewed the information on these forms, and Gessner (1956) has dealt with their water-relations. Ruinen studied the components of the epiphytic vegetation in Indonesia—especially a small epiphytic fern, *Drymoglossum piloselloides*. It grows on the trunks, branches, and leaves of trees, attaching itself by spreading roots and root-hairs. Trees overgrown by this epiphyte decline, with loss of green colour and an inhibition and death of lateral buds. Fungi living in the rhizosphere of the fern sometimes infest the tree-support and cause die-back of the branches. In this work the free-living nitrogen-fixing bacterium *Beijerinchia* was found on a very high percentage of the leaves studied from various habitats—indicating one ultimate cause of the luxuriance of the vegetation.

In Puerto Rico the orchid, *Oncidium variegatum*, is epiphytic on trunks of coffee trees, and when abundant becomes noxious, as the growth raises the humidity around the trunk.*

In Trinidad and Tobago, in the British West Indies, bromeliad epiphytes and 'moss' have invaded grapefruit trees. Attempts to remove them with sprays of 2,4-D acid at 25 parts per million resulted in large numbers dropping off after three weeks; but quite as many remained firmly attached on the treated trees. There was little dropping of the 'wild pines' from untreated trees.

Bromeliads and Malaria. There are about 1,600 species of Bromeliaceae, all but one being natives of the New World. In the more advanced epiphytic types, the broad leaves overlap in a watertight spiral, forming a tank that, according to the species, may hold from a thimbleful to well over a gallon of water—thus serving as ideal breeding places for malaria-carrying mosquitoes. Terrestrial types also store water in this manner. The importance in spread of the disease depends upon the frequency of the bromeliad species, and whether or not the tanks have broad openings (Smith, 1953).

There have been only three instances of serious malaria infestation attributed to bromeliad-breeding mosquitoes, although the disease is world-wide in tropical and warm-temperate regions. The first case was in the coastal rain forest of São Paulo, Brazil, the second in the British island of Trinidad, and the third, and worst, in Santa Catarina, again in the Brazilian coastal forest. According to Smith (1953), bromeliads which store their water in open tanks are particularly concentrated in the eastern areas of Brazil, while those storing water in the leaf tissues predominate in the interior. Species of bromeliads that are proved habitats of malaria mosquitoes are recorded for practically the entire length of the Brazilian coast.

In Trinidad the presence of malaria-carrying mosquitoes was associated with bromeliads that had invaded immortelle trees (*Erythrina* spp.) which had been grown alternately with cacao trees to provide the latter with the necessary shade. The epiphytes were at first removed by hand, and later controlled by sprays of 2 per cent copper sulphate solution. In other instances it has been necessary to deforest a belt around the cities. Herbicides could not always be used, because there were not enough roads to carry wheeled pumps within striking distance of the forest area;

* Parasitic Loranthaceae, 'When combined with epiphytic growths, such as mosses, the tree-inhabiting ferns, the bromeliads, and the orchids, . . . can cause serious . . . injury' to coffee trees in tropical countries (F. L. Wellman, 'Coffee: Botany, Cultivation, and Utilization'; *Leonard Hill*, London, and *Interscience*, New York, p. 271, 1961).—Ed.

moreover, spraying into the tops of the highest trees has not been effective, nor has spraying from aircraft. The foremost authority on the Bromeliaceae, Dr. L. B. Smith of the United States National Museum, has published extensively on this group (Smith, 1953, 1955), while Veloso (1952, 1953) has examined in detail the ecological aspects of the subject.

Just what relationship, if any, water-holding epiphytes of the Old World tropics may have to the spread of malaria, has not been noted.

BIBLIOGRAPHY

(The Classification of Weeds)

ANDERSON, E. (1939). A classification of weeds and weed-like plants. *Science*, 89, 364–5.

ANSTEAD, R. D. (1925). Epiphytic growths on rubber trees. *The Planter*, 6(3).

ANZALONE, B. (1951). Flora e vegetazione dei muri di Roma. *Ann. Bot., Roma*, 23, 393–497.

ARBER A. (1920). *Water plants, a study of aquatic angiosperms*. Cambridge University Press, Cambridge, England, 436 pp. (Reprinted 1962.)

AV SEGERSTAD, F. HÅRD. *See* HÅRD AV SEGERSTAD, F.

BEYER, R. (1894). Weitere Beobachtungen von Ueberpflanzen auf Weiden. *Verh.Brand.*, 35, 37–41.

CARVELL, R. L. & TRYON, E. H. (1955). Wild grape vines—they can be controlled. *Bull. W. Va. Agric. Exp. Sta.*, 369, part 3, p. 3.

COZZI, C. (1908). Le arboricole del Salcio nell'agro Abbiatense. *Atti Soc. Ital. Sci. Nat.*, 47(1–2), 158–72.

CROOKS, D. M. & KEPHART, L. W. (1958). Poison-ivy, poison-oak, and poison-sumac: identification, precautions, eradication. *Fmrs' Bull. U.S. Dept. Agric.*, No. 1972, 30 pp., 34 photographs, 4 figs.

DOBZHANSKY, T. & MURÇA-PIRES, J. (1954). Strangler trees. *Sci. Amer.*, 190(1), 78–80. (Also in *Plant Life*, Simon & Schuster, New York, pp. 131–6, 1957.)

DUDGEON, W. (1923). Succession of epiphytes in the *Quercus incana* forest at Landour, Western Himalaya. *J. Ind. Bot.*, 3, 270–2.

EGGELING, W. J. (1948). Epiphytes in the Bundong Forest. *Uganda J.*, 12(1), 106–7.

FASSETT, N. C. (1940). *A manual of aquatic plants*. McGraw-Hill, New York, 382 pp.

GAMS, H. (1950). The importance of growth forms for taxonomical and ecological systematics. *Proc. Seventh Int. Bot. Congress*, Stockholm, pp. 654–5 (published 1953).

GARTH, R. E. (1955). An ecological study of Spanish moss (*Tillandsia usneoides* L.) with special reference to growth and distribution. Ph.D. Thesis, Emory University.

GATES, F. C. (1940). Annotated list of the plants of Kansas. . . . W. C. Austin, State Printer, Topeka, Kansas, 266 pp.

GESSNER, F. (1956). Der Wasserhaushalt der Epiphyten und Lianen. *In* W. Ruhland, *Handbuch der Pflanzenphysiologie*, Springer-Verlag, Berlin, Band III, pp. 915–50.

GEYSENHEYNER, L. (1894). Zur epiphytischen Kopfweidenflora. *Verh. Brand.*, 36, 57–60.

GLASS, E. H. (1956). An entomologist visits Europe. *Farm Res.*, 22(3), 8–9.

GROH, H. (1925). Wintering over of weeds. *Dominion Exp. Farm. Seasonable Hints*, No. 33, Ottawa, Canada.

HANSEN, H. M. (1956). *Life forms as age indicators*. A. Rasmussens, Rungkjobing, 48 pp.

HÅRD AV SEGERSTAD, F. (1944–46). [Les épiphytes des blocs erratiques dans les forêts de conifères du Värmland—in Swedish.] *Acta Hort. Gothoburg.*, 16, 113–23.

HARPER, R. M. (1937). Mimicry in two southern weeds. *Torreya*, 37, 104–8.

HAUDRICOURT, A. G. et HEDIN, L. (1943). *L'homme et les plantes cultivées*. Gallimard, Paris, 233 pp.

HÄYREN, E. (1942). Vascular plants as accidental epiphytes in Finland. *Acta Soc. Fauna Flora Fenn.*, **63** (paper No. 2), 1–28.

HEGI, G. (1907–31). *Illustrierte Flora von Mittel-Europa* . . . Munich, J. F. Lehman, 7 vols. in 14.

HERBERT, D. A. (1928). Nutritional exchange between lianas and trees. *Proc. Roy. Soc. Qd.*, **39**, 115–18.

HEWETSON, F. N. (1951). New herbicides for controlling poison ivy in apple orchards. *Proc. Amer. Soc. Hort. Sci.*, **58**, 125–30.

HOLMBOE, J. (1904). Hoiere epifytisk planteliv i Norge. *Forh. VidenskSelsk. Krist.*, No. 6, 39 pp.

HOSOKAWA, T. (1954). On the vascular-epiphyte communities in tropical rain forests of Micronesia. VIII, *Congrès International de Botanique Paris*, Sect. 7, pp. 190–1; see also pp. 11–16.

—— (1954*a*). On *Campnosperma* forests of Kusaie in Micronesia, with special reference to the community units of epiphytes. *Vegetatio*, **1**, 351–63.

HOTCHKISS, N. (1942). *Check-list of marsh and aquatic plants of the United States.* U.S. Dept. Interior, Fish and Wildlife Service, Wildlife Leaflet No. 210.

HURT, R. H. (1926). Honeysuckle eradication in Virginia apple orchards. *Bull. Va. Agric. Exp. Sta.*, **244**, 1–8.

KORSMO, E. (1930). (Ed. H. W. Wollenweber.) *Unkräuter im Ackerbau der Neuzeit. Biologische und praktische Untersuchungen.* J. Springer, Berlin, 580 pp.

LEBRUN, J. (1937). Observations sur les épiphytes de la forêt équatoriale congolaise. *Ann. Soc. Sci., Brux.*, **57**, 13–38.

LUTZ, H. J. (1943). Injuries to trees caused by *Celastrus* and *Vitis. Bull. Torrey Bot. Cl.*, **70**, 436–9.

McNAIR, J. B. (1923). *Rhus dermatitis from Rhus toxicodendron, radicans and diversiloba (poison ivy) its Pathology and Chemotherapy.* University of Chicago, Chicago, Ill., 293 pp.

MALSUMURA, Y., & HARRINGTON, H. D. (1955). The true aquatic vascular plants of Colorado. *Tech. Bull. Colo. Agric. Exp. Sta.*, **57**, 130 pp.

MIRASHI, M. V. (1954). Studies in the hydrophytes of Nagpur. *J. Indian Bot. Soc.*, **33**, 299–308.

——(1957). Studies in the hydrophytes of Umred. *J. Indian Bot. Soc.*, **36**, 396–407.

MUENSCHER, W. C. (1944). *Aquatic plants of the United States.* Comstock, Ithaca, N.Y., 374 pp.

PHILLIPS, N. E. (1929). The influence of *Usnea* sp. (near *barbata* Fr.) upon the supporting tree. *Trans. Roy. Soc. S. Afr.*, **17**, 101–7.

PORSILD, M. P. (1932). Alien plants and apophytes of Greenland. *Medd. Grønland*, **92**, 1–85.

RAUNKIAER, C. (1934). *The life forms of plants and statistical plant geography.* Trans. by H. Gilbert Carter *et al.*, Clarendon Press, Oxford, England 632 pp.

RICHARDS, P. W. (1952). *The tropical rain forest, an ecological study.* Cambridge Universty Press, Cambridge, England, 450 pp.

RUINEN, J. (1953). Epiphytosis. A second view on epiphytism. *Ann. Bogorienses*, **1**(2), 101–57.

—— (1956). Occurrence of *Beijerinchia* species in the 'phyllosphere'. *Nature, Lond.*, **177**, 220–1.

SAMUELSSON, G. (1934). Die Verbreitung der hoheren Wasserpflanzen in Nordeuropa. *Acta Phytogeogr. Suec.*, **6**, 1–211.

SANDS, W. N. (1926). Epiphytes on cultivated trees. *Malay. Agric. J.*, **14**, 13–17.

SCHENCK, H. (1892). Beiträge zur Biologie und Anatomie der Lianen, im Besonderen der in Brasilien einheimischen Arten. 1. Teil: Beiträge zur Biologie der Lianen. G. Fischer, Jena, 253 pp. (Review in *Bot. Jb.*, **15**, Heft 1 (Nr. 33), litt. pp. 50–54, 1893, by Taubert.)

SCHIMPER, A. F. W. (1888). *Die epiphytische Vegetation Amerikas*. Botan. Mittl. aus den Tropen, Heft II, Jena, 162 pp. (Cf. *Bot. Zbl.*, 37, 180–2, 1888; *Bot. Jb.*, 11, 1–4, 1890.)

SMITH, L. B. (1953). Bromeliad malaria. *Rep. Smithson. Instn. for 1952*, 385–98.

—— (1955). *The Bromeliaceae of Brazil*. Smithson. Misc. Coll., No. 126, pp. 1–290.

SPRING, F. G. (1926). Effect of fern and other growth on the health and growth of the rubber tree. *Malay. Agric. J.*, 14, 119–24.

STEWART, W. S. & GAMMON, C. (1947). Fog application of 2,4-D to wild grape and other plants. *Amer. J. Bot.*, 34, 492–6.

VARESCHI, V. (1936). Die Epiphytenvegetation von Zürich. *Ber. Schweiz. Bot. Ges.*, 46, 445–87.

VELEZ, I. (1953). Does Spanish moss (*Tillandsia*) grow on telephone lines? *Turtox News*, 31, 92–93.

VELOSO, H. P. (1952). O problema ecológico: vegetaçãobromeliáceas-anofelinos. I. *An. Herb. Barbosa Rodrigues*, 4, 187–270.

—— (1953). O problema ecológico: vegetaçãobromeliáceas-anofelinos. II. *An. Herb. Barbosa Rodrigues*, 5, 1–37, and pls. 1–39.

WARBACH, O. (1953). Control of Japanese honeysuckle (*Lonicera japonica*) in wildlife borders. *J. Wildlife Mgmt.*, 17, 301–4.

WENT, F. W. (1940). Soziologie der Epiphyten eines tropischen Urwaldes. *Ann. Jard. Bot. Buitenz.*, 50, 1–98.

WEST, E. (1948–49). Symposium I. The control of water plants from the standpoint of water management and navigation in the lakes, rivers and canals of the South. The general characteristics of the principal plants involved. *Proc. Soil Sci. Soc. Florida*, 9, 15–20.

ZIMMERMAN, P. W. (1952). Water weeds. *Plants & Gdns.*, 8(1), 56–57.

ADDENDUM

J. R. Harlan and J. M. J. de Wet in their recent study, 'Some thoughts about weeds' (*Econ. Bot.*, 19, 16–24, 1965) comment on origins. They conclude that weeds have come from (1) wild species that have long been adapted to sites of natural disturbance, and (2) new species or varieties that have evolved since agriculture was developed. They emphasize that the chief temperate weeds are Eurasian or North American species developed in or near areas of disturbance caused by Pleistocene glaciation—'where whole floras have been uprooted and replaced by imported floras and where great masses of plants separated for great periods of time are suddenly brought together under under conditions promoting mass hybridization'. Further, weeds have come from a larger number of plant families than cultivated crops, and in different proportions—thus weedy adaptations have evolved many times independently, but only a relatively few species were found suitable for domestication. The wide distribution of weeds throughout the Angiosperms suggests that the adaptiveness and specializations required for weediness are under relatively simple genetic control. Our current weed problems are essentially related to a dilemma: 'that both domesticated plants and weeds are adapted to the same habitat and thus practices that tend to favour domesticates also tend to favour weeds.'

For a 'weedy' animal (*Engystomops* sp.), O. J. Sexton has defined as a weed 'any species which (1) invades a niche not available to it previously, or (2) in whose niche some limiting factor is made less restrictive'. For a discussion of the concept of plant and animal weeds *see* pp. 193–5 in R. L. Rudd's *Pesticides and the Living Landscape* (1964). (A Conservation Foundation Study). Univ. Wisconsin Press, Madison. 330 pp.

III

THE PARASITIC WEEDS

THE phanerogamic, or flowering, parasites are distributed among some 10 families, about 6 of which contain the more troublesome species. MacDougal & Cannon (1910) stated that one genus in every 200 includes parasites, with a grand total of (then) about 2,500 species of parasitic seed plants—about 2 per cent of the total seed-plant species then recognized. However, only those that are regarded as troublesome or injurious to the culture of plants will be considered in the present work. Physiologically, autotrophic and heterotrophic groups have been recognized; that is, respectively, plants with a degree of independent growth, and plants which exhibit complete parasitism. As pests, the two general groups of stem parasites and root parasites have been recognized. For systematic review here, the important forms are examined according to their respective plant families.

CUSCUTACEAE

In the temperate regions the most easily recognized and the most widely distributed parasitic weeds belong to the genus *Cuscuta*, the dodders. The taxonomy of this genus and its many species (some 150) have been the subject of considerable study by Yuncker (1921, 1922–23, 1932), a *Cuscuta* bibliography of an extensive nature having been published (cf. Dean, 1937). In southern zones the counterpart of *Cuscuta* is the genus *Cassytha*, a considerably less known genus. *Cassytha* (Lauraceae) is often mistaken for *Cuscuta*, but as noted below differs principally in that the stems are green in the former.

Stitt's study (1939) of the Lespedeza dodder (*Cuscuta pentagona*) in North Carolina reveals certain typical life-history details. There, this species germinated from March to September; in laboratory tests, germination occurred over a period of 101 days. Seedlings in the field, out of reach of the host plant, lived from four to nine days following germination. Flowering occurred in twenty-one days, and seed was mature thirty-eight days after germination. Flowering was continuous over a period of two to three months. The screening of Lespedeza seed with a $\frac{1}{16}$ in. screen removed 54·8 per cent of the Lespedeza and left 170 dodder seeds per pound of cleaned sample.

Dodder is considered a noxious weed in 47 states of the contiguous United States. One particular characteristic of the dodder seed has been of some importance in its separation from the more desirable crop seed—the rough or sticky character of its surface. By the use of a 'dodder mill', consisting of rollers covered with felt cloth to which the seeds readily adhere, much cleaner seed has resulted than from the conventional screening techniques.

The destructiveness of dodder resides in its capacity to parasitize rapidly a specific crop host—Lespedeza, for example. Not only do the pests draw heavily on the host for sustenance, but they also provide a dense and shady barrier or canopy which drastically reduces the growth and vigour of the host plant. Dodder reproduces by means of very small seeds (in the size-range of white clover seed and alfalfa seed) and also vegetatively by detached stem-pieces. Moreover the climbing and sprawling 'vine' character can lead to a rapid covering of extensive areas, while a tendency towards perennial growth has been observed by several investigators (Stewart & French, 1909; N. L. Rao, 1938; Krassulin, 1941; Baker, 1950; Truscott, 1955) in the over-wintering of stem-pieces or haustoria in host tissue. A good survey of the dodders is provided by Heald (1933).

Dean (1942) experimentally planted *Cuscuta polygonum* near Iowa City, Iowa. It developed on *Salix* and on *Polygonum virginianum*, and its growth from the time of seeding on 30 April to 26 August 1938 was 6 ft. 9 in. for the longest single piece. The total length of the stems of this plant was 2,406 ft., due to its repeated branching. It is probable that under ideal growing conditions a single dodder seedling would develop a mile or more of stems.

Control of dodder is chiefly effected by the use of dodder-clean crop seed, and by employing certain chemical sprays on the vegetative growths. Stitt (1939) stated that local infestations can be controlled by burning with a blow-torch, by cutting out by hand, or by spraying with any of the following: 2·5 per cent by weight of sulphuric acid, 1 lb. of ammonium thiocyanate in 2 gallons of water, or $1\frac{1}{2}$ lb. of 'Atlacide' per gallon of water—all of which, however, when thoroughly applied, resulted in the killing of both the dodder and the Lespedeza crop. Naturally, pre-emergence or early post-emergence sprays would be preferable—particulary if selective to the crop. Later studies (W. O. Lee & Timmons, 1954) indicated that the herbicide chloroisopropyl phenyl carbamate (Chloro-IPC) may be used.

The non-specific character of dodder—the fact that many species of the genus will parasitize large numbers of quite diverse plants—has led to its widespread and destructive nature. In studies on *Cuscuta hyalina* in India, Narayana (1956) observed that this species especially parasitized weeds and other small annual or perennial herbs—in all, 42 species in 35 genera belonging to 16 families. Apart from a group of five primary hosts (species in the genera *Tribulus*, *Bachhaavia*, *Trianthera*, and *Gieseckia*), secondary and tertiary hosts were also listed. One advantage of this diffuse parasitism was brought out in Narayana's study. He observed that *Cuscuta hyalina* also attacked members of the Cyperaceae and Gramineae; these plants serve as minor hosts and assist the parasite by acting as bridges which enable it to travel small distances to reach principal or secondary hosts. In Gorki Province, Russia, Aleksandrov (1947) observed that *C. lupuliformis* parasitized 131 species of plants. In Ceylon, *Cuscuta* parasitization serves as a natural check to the rampant growth of the vine *Mikania scandens* (Compositae).

The question of the presence of chlorophyll and whether photosynthesis occurs is frequently presented. Two species, *C. campestris* and *C. reflexa* parasitic on *Impatiens sultani* and leaves of *Bulbine* sp., were examined in this relationship by MacLeod (1962). The presence of small quantities of chlorophylls *a* and *b* in the same ratio as in autotrophic plants was established. Relatively high quantities of carotenoid pigment are presented and these completely mask any green colour in *C. campestris*. It was shown that CO_2 fixation (photosynthesis) occurs in both species. In studies on the fixation of CO_2 by *C. epithymum*, Cifferri and Poma (1963) concluded that the photosynthate production involved carboxylating enzymes other than ribulose-1,5-diphosphate carboxylase—the enzyme most commonly found in similar studies of wholly autotrophic plants.

Dodder has few if any real uses, though pathologists in recent years have employed species of *Cuscuta* in the experimental transmission of certain plant viruses to a desirable host plant. At the same time, passage of virus preparations through certain species of *Cuscuta* often results in the survival or successful transmission of only one type of virus—rather than a mixture of a poorly defined combination of several viruses. Just how *Cuscuta* is related to virus transmission under natural environmental conditions has not been noted. (*See* Fritsché, 1958; Tronchet, 1961.)

LAURACEAE

This principally woody plant family is represented by one parasitic genus, *Cassytha*, containing some 18 species. *C. filiformis* ('woevine') is perhaps the most common species of the genus in tropical and subtropical regions throughout the world. It is a slender, thread-like cylindrical herbaceous vine, with leaves wanting or reduced to mere scales, and which covers other vegetation like a mantle. In some respects it resembles dodder (*Cuscuta* spp.), but it has somewhat more chlorophyll than does dodder and it has a spicy fragrance that is characteristic of some other members of the Lauraceae (cinnamon, camphor, sassafras, etc.).

Cassytha occurs apparently naturally on almost all tropical coasts, and thrives on both herbaceous and woody hosts. It is quite destructive on the evergreen shrub, rosemary (*Ceratiola ericoides*, Empetraceae), in peninsular Florida and the Keys. It is troublesome on other ornamentals in

Hawaii, the East Indies and elsewhere; it has been declared Public Enemy No. 1 by the authorities in Puerto Rico. *C. filiformis* occasionally attacks orange trees in India (the Northern Circars), and it is reported to occur in almost all parts of the Indian sub-continent. The fruit of this species is a globose drupe, 1–2 in. in diameter, and is covered by a fleshy receptacle. Dispersal methods have not been noted, but perhaps the seeds are distributed by birds eating these fleshy fruits.

LORANTHACEAE

This family of 36 genera and about 1,300 species contains some of the most destructive parasites known, principally in the following genera: *Phoradendron* and *Viscum* (the mistletoes), *Arceuthobium* (dwarf-mistletoes), and the very large and heterogeneous genus *Loranthus*, found chiefly in the far-eastern and tropical regions. The members of these genera are typically stem parasites on trees.

The one important species in the United States is *Phoradendron flavescens*, which occurs on various deciduous trees, chiefly at low altitudes. It is difficult to think of this plant as a pest, as it is widely used for decorative purposes in winter, chiefly at Christmas time. Moreover, instances of this mistletoe completely killing trees are not frequent, though pear and pecan trees in Florida have been so badly infested that they have lost more than 50 per cent of their leaf surface through branches being killed, and have ceased to bear fruit (Weber, 1938). Species of this genus have also been found growing on persimmon (*Diospyros*) in California (Condit, 1940).

A case of infestation of *P. libocedri* on a 448-year-old incense cedar, described by Wagener (1925), indicates what harm may be done. In this case the original infection in the lower bowl was ancient, dating back some 400 years—but while little harm had occurred to the rest of the tree, the market value of the timber was seriously reduced.

The species of *Phoradendron* are large-leafed forms, eventually developing on the host tree into globose masses of considerable size (1 to 2 ft. across). They live on an average for about ten years, usually being killed because of excessive shade or mechanical breakage. Some species have frequently been reported to attain an age of twenty years, and records have indicated sixty- to seventy-year-old plants (Weber, 1938).

Members of this genus are semi-parasites, as their foliage and stems contain chlorophyll and they are therefore able to manufacture carbohydrates; but their water, mineral salts, and other soluble materials— and perhaps sometimes even soluble carbohydrates—are withdrawn from the host plant. The seeds of mistletoes are produced in white berries that are surrounded by a persistent and very adhesive pulp. The berries are eaten by certain birds and are largely disseminated by them, as the adhesive pulp sticks to their feet and beak, and thus the berries are carried about and lodged on the twigs and branches of trees. The seed are also spread in the excrement of birds. When mature, the berries may fall to lower branches; where—under favourable conditions—germination takes place, the young radicle growing into the cortex of the host tree, where it enlarges and forms an attachment disc. A peculiar root-like structure, the haustorium, develops from the undersurface of this disc and grows through the cortex to the cambium. From here, further root-like growths known as sinkers penetrate into the water-carrying tissue of the host during the first year, and it is not until the second year that a sprout develops from buds on the attachment disc and produces the first pair of green leaves (Weber, 1938).

If it is desired to remove large growths of mistletoe from desirable trees, infected branches may be cut out. The cuts should be made at least a foot below the point of attachment of the mistletoe, to ensure the removal of the penetrating cortical haustoria that extend up and down the branch. If complete removal in this fashion is not feasible, the large branches of the parasite may be broken off close to the point of attachment. This will not prevent the development of new sprouts, but it will reduce the demands of the parasite on the host for some time. The process should be repeated annually.

A monograph of the genus has been prepared by Trelease (1916), and the anatomy of several species was studied by Cannon (1901) and York (1909). Physiological studies, including those of chlorophyll production and photosynthesis, were undertaken by Freeland (1943), and the water relations (Harris *et al.*, 1930) have been investigated, as have the germination phases (Cannon, 1904) and the effects of the parasitic fungus *Protocoronospora* (Darling, 1940); there have also been floristic studies (Eaton & Dow, 1940; Rhoads, 1943). Little (1927) has prepared a brochure on this plant as the State flower of Oklahoma.

The European mistletoe (*Viscum album*) has been considered by K. F. von Tubeuf (*see* Boodle, 1921) to consist of three physiological races, two occurring on conifers, and one on various dicotyledonous plants. This last race, in Switzerland, occurs on thirty-seven different hosts, among which apple, linden, and poplar, are the most common. This pest has been particularly troublesome in European pear orchards, and has received special attention there (Heinricher, 1920; Zöpfig, 1933; Paine, 1950; Scholl, 1956). The forests of southern Europe have also been damaged by *Viscum album* ('le gui') (Anon., 1934; Peter-Contesse, 1937; Plagnat, 1950). *V. cruciatum* has been reported on olive trees in Israel (Glimcher, 1938; Harenbeni, 1938).

It is believed that, probably, the European and American custom of including mistletoe in the decoration of the home at Christmas was connected with its supposed protection against evil.

Kingdon Ward (1912) observed the widespread distribution of *V. album* and related species in Shenshi Province in western China— especially on the poplars and willows planted along the stream banks.

Most viciously attacked, however, were the cultivated trees—walnuts, pears, and persimmons. The foliage of the persimmon was completely hidden by the parasite.

Sanzen-Baker (1938), of the Imperial Forestry Institute, Oxford, has reviewed the literature on mistletoes; the mystical and ceremonial uses have been considered by B. Barnes (1953), and the origin of the word 'mistel' by Lüstner (1936). Oddly enough, because of certain ceremonial uses, attempts have been made to cultivate a mistletoe, at least in England (Nicholson, 1932).

The classical monograph of the genus is that of K. F. von Tubeuf et al (1923). Danser (1941) has studied the Indian species of *Viscum* and compared them with those of southeastern Asia and Australia. A survey of the species in Norway has been made by Hanssen (1933), while the haustorial system has been studied by Thoday (1951), and the nutritional aspects by Winkler (1913).

An extensive study of the Indo-Malayan species of *Viscum* has been prepared by R. S. Rao (1957). He lists 15 species for this region, and states that the genus is mainly distributed in the tropics. Africa has the largest number of species, in all about 50, while Madagascar has about 40 species. From the available data, it appears that the line of distribution may have proceeded from Africa through Madagascar to India, whence it gradually extended farther East—to Japan in the north and to tropical Australia in the south.

Perhaps more destructive, and certainly more insidious by reason of their near-microscopic size, are the dwarf-mistletoes, *Arceuthobium* spp., which are serious pests of the coniferous forests of the western United States. From an investigation that continued for thirty years, it was concluded that dwarf-mistletoe was the greatest single cause of loss in ponderosa pine in the southwestern United States. A number of studies in the western States indicated that dwarf-mistletoe may reduce the lumber production of a tree by from 30 to 50 per cent. Five species are recognized in North America: *A. pusillum*, mainly occurring on spruce in the Great Lakes region and to the east, and 4 western species. Of these, *A. americanum* is restricted to the ranges of lodgepole pine and jackpine; *A. douglasii* to the range of Douglas-fir; *A. vaginatum* is confined to three-needled pines, particularly *Pinus ponderosa* var. *scopulorum* in the southwestern United States and Mexico; while *A. campylopodum* attacks pine, spruce, fir, hemlock, and larch, from Alaska to Arizona and, probably, Mexico. The Himalayan species *A. minutissimum*, occurring on *Pinus excelsa*, has the distinction of being the smallest known dicotyledonous plant—its entire length being from 2 to 5 mm. (Datta, 1951).

A United States forestry report (Anon., 1933) states that in the West there are few conifers free from the attack of dwarf-mistletoes, and valuable stands of ponderosa pine suffer severely. Over extensive areas throughout the range of this pine, many trees are so deformed that they are worthless, some being killed, while many others are so infected that the rate of their growth is considerably reduced. A normally-stocked stand of forty- to fifty-year-old ponderosa pine in northern California, moderately infected with dwarf-mistletoe, was found to have one-third of the trees infected and 14 per cent ruined by stem infections. On another area, where the attack was heavier, every tree was infected and over 80 per cent were ruined by stem infections. In northern Arizona the average volume-increment over a five-year period was found to be 4·53 cu. ft. for healthy trees and 2·23 cu. ft. for heavily infected trees. Over limited areas, stands of ponderosa pine are so severely attacked that they are worthless for lumber (Pl. 2).

One species of *Arceuthobium* has been troublesome in California walnut groves—especially in those located near creek or river bottoms, or in other places where cottonwood and other host trees abound. In such places during the dormant season, Graser (1954) used a spray consisting of two tablespoonfuls of 2,4-D (35 per cent triethanolamine salt) plus two tablespoonfuls of dormant emulsion oil, all in one quart of water. If the 2,4-D isopropyl ester is used (44 per cent ester), then only one tablespoonful is needed in the above preparation. No damage was observed to either English or black walnuts, but it is necessary to wait at least one year for the control results. In these trials, kills of the parasite ranged from 50 to 85 per cent.

Some field observations by Dowding (1929), of *A. americanum* growing on *Pinus banksiana* in Alberta, Canada, are illustrative. The seeds are projected edastically with such considerable force that they could reach a cotton sheet hung 11 yd. away from the point of explosion (cf. Fig. 7). In this study, no infection was observed on pines less than fifteen years old—although the larch dwarf-mistletoe had been reported on trees as young as five years of age. The parasite produces definite host-responses: it causes the branches to be negatively geotropic, the bark to change from black to pale brown, and the leaves (normally lost in the third year) to be retained for several years longer. The parasite penetrates every tissue of the stem, for several feet from the source of the infection. In *A. oxycedri* the aerial stems and flowers appear three years after germination of the seed.

There has been some question as to the length of life of the *Arceuthobium* shoot after it has fruited; in *A. oxycedri* the shoots survive from year to year and produce several crops of flowers. The flowers produced in one summer do not ripen fruit until the following summer—in fact about fourteen months elapse between flowering and seed dispersal. A few flower-buds were observed in May. Flowers from the previous year explode their fruits around September 10–20th. Seeds may germinate during the same autumn, but penetration of the pine bark does not occur until late June in the following summer. The flowers are pollinated by wind or by insects in May, and the fruits so formed remain on the plant for two summers, exploding in September of the second summer. The seeds then germinate on the pine bark during June of the third summer (Dowding, 1929). A review by Kuijt (1955) covers to that date the extensive literature on this genus.*

A description of the expulsion of the seed, and of the ballistics of the seed flight, of the dwarf-mistletoe (*Arceuthobium vaginatum* f. *cryptopodum*) which is so destructive to ponderosa pine in the southwestern United States, has been given by Hawksworth (1959). Each fruit contains a single fusiform seed, and when it is ripe the pedicel is elongated and recurved so that the perianth-end points downwards. An abscission zone develops between the tip of the pedicel and the base of the fruit. A layer of viscin cells lying between the seed and the exocarp creates considerable internal pressure, which shears the fruit from the pedicel and, as the exocarp contracts rapidly, the seed is hurled for some distance (cf. Fig. 7).

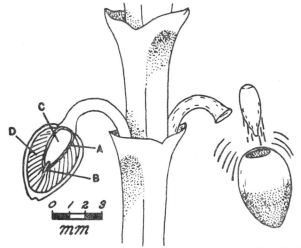

From Hawksworth, 1959

FIG. 7.—Semi-diagrammatic drawing of a portion of a dwarf-mistletoe (*Arceuthobium vaginatum* f. *cryptopodum*) shoot bearing mature fruits. Left, a longitudinal section through a fruit showing a seed (A), embryo (B), endosperm (C), and viscin cells (D). Right, a fruit immediately after the expulsion of the seed. These projectile-shaped seeds are 'shot' for an average horizontal distance of about 530 cm., with a maximum of about 1,280 cm. The author cited calculated that these seeds have an initial velocity of about 2,400 cm./sec.

In a study of the geographic distribution and ecology of *A. oxycedri*, Palhinha (1942) observed that this species is chiefly Mediterranean, but that it extends eastwards to Persia and the Caucasus. The genus contains about 50 species, all but 5 of which occur in boreal America, and all of which are parasitic on conifers. *A. oxycedri* occurs also in the Central Azores, where the annual rainfall is 1,400 mm. and a high relative humidity prevails. The small seeds are projected forcibly for a distance of about 5 metres, and are very adhesive, sticking readily to birds and to tree bark.

* *See also* Hawksworth, F. G. (1961). Dwarf-mistletoe of ponderosa pine in the south-west. *U.S. Dept. of Agric. Tech. Bull. 1246*, 112 pp. For further data on seed discharge *see Science*, 140, 1236–8, 1963.

One species of *Arceuthobium*, *A. occidentale*, which is parasitic on the digger pine (*Pinus sabiniana*), is used by the Yuki Indians of northern California, mixed with tea, to make a decoction for the relief of digestive distress. Their name for this decoction is 'Shâ-lē-kō-em' (Chestnut, 1902 cf. Ch. IV).

Parasites may themselves be parasitized (hyperparasitism), and *Wallrothiella* (Dowding, 1931), *Fusarium* (Ellis, 1939), and *Septogloeum* (Ellis, 1946), have been observed on species of *Arceuthobium*. Dowding (1929) felt definitely that *Wallrothiella* had checked the spread of *Arceuthobium* in the areas studied in Alberta. Likewise the *Septogloeum* was noted by Ellis (1946) as occurring on stems and fruits, and particularly on pistillate plants, while in some localities this disease greatly reduced the reproduction and local spread of *Arceuthobium*—surely indicating possibilities for biological control.

The number of *Loranthus* species has been listed as several hundreds; however, following revisions of this group, particularly by Danser (1929–37), the number remaining in the genus is considerably reduced. In fact, according to the latest revision, there are no species of the true *Loranthus* in India! In the present work the older names are used, but full synonymy may be found, at least for India, in Kanjilal *et al. Flora of Assam* (1934–40); cf. Danser (1933) for complete synonymy of the Old World Loranthaceae. *Loranthus* reaches its greatest development in tropical regions, where it parasitizes valuable forest trees, the tea bush, and most of the species of tropical fruit trees.

The destructiveness of species of this genus (*sensu lato*) has been appreciable in India. Fisher (1926), in a study of this group in southern India, found 28 species on 275 hosts, including 185 trees, 63 shrubs, 17 climbers, 7 *Loranthus* parasites (hyperparasitism), and 2 herbs—all lending credence to that author's conclusion that attachment was simply a matter of opportunity. He did, however, observe that bark shedding provides some degree of immunity from attack.

Loranthus has been a particular problem in Indian forest plantations—especially of teak and *Casuarina* (Koppikar, 1948). In the late 1940's it was reported to be spreading fast on 5,000 acres planted to teak in the Honavar range, North Kanara district, of which about 2,400 acres consisted of older plantings (1919–28). Also involved are the *Casuarina* plantations consisting of 450 acres along the Arabian seaboard which are worked on a twenty-year rotation. Out of these two areas, about 950 acres of teak and over 250 acres of *Casuarina* are infested with *Loranthus* to a greater or lesser extent. The younger plantations are not infected so far. The affected areas are on abandoned sites that were formerly cultivated. *Casuarina* is grown for firewood, and hence infestations of it are not so critical as are those of teak, which is used for timber.

Koppikar suggests maintaining an insular belt of minor forest between the cultivated areas and the plantations, to attract the birds and other wildlife and thus keep back the means of spreading. It would also be necessary to insist on eradication of *Loranthus* from all cultivated areas, including gardens, orchards, and villages. He suggests the slogan, 'Kill *Loranthus* and save the trees!'

The eminent botanist, Sir Joseph Hooker, accorded some 60 species of *Loranthus* to India. *L. longiflorus* and its var. *falcatus* are stated to parasitize 110 kinds of trees, including teak and *Acacia* (Kadambi, 1954). *Loranthus* also attacks the rosewood and sandalwood trees. The wattle plantations in Nilgiris, South India, and the *Gmelina arborea* plantations of West Bengal, are notorious examples of the destructive propensities of this parasite. In natural forests the valuable timber tree, 'Sissoo' (*Dalbergia sissoo*), is often attacked.

Kadambi (1954) reviews some chemical treatments that have been successful: copper sulphate ($CuSO_4$) was effective, but its action is slow, and combinations with Fernoxone (a 2,4-D product) were found to be more promising. Kadambi's method was to bore, with a carpenter's auger, two rows of holes down the tree; the holes were 6 in. apart and projected down and inwards to the sapwood at a 45-degree angle. Into each hole was placed $\frac{1}{4}$ oz. of $CuSO_4$ and $\frac{1}{32}$ oz. of Fernoxone. The treatment was most effective during March and April. Once killed, the parasite does not reappear for at least four years. A workman can treat between 20 and 30 medium-sized trees in a forenoon.

In Assam, *Loranthus* is found on the tea plant, its foliage being so similar to that of the host that the leaves of the parasite are often picked with the tea leaves, and their presence is detected only through the bitter flavour imparted to the drink.

Sarma (1952), in India, notes that 90 per cent of the *Loranthus* species have green leaves, and that the small berries which they produce are attractive to birds. However, the berries contain a gummy substance which is unattractive to birds, and which they try to remove from their beaks—in doing so, helping in the dispersal of the seeds present in the gum. The fact that many of the host trees produce fruits that are valued by man and bird alike, also assists in the bird-distribution of the parasite. *L. longiflorus* has been found on 29 different kinds of trees, of which 13 were important fruit-bearing trees, including custard apple, jack fruit, Seville orange, citron, fig, mango, mulberry, guava, pomegranate, tamarind, and jujube. The same species damages mango trees (*Mangifera indica*) all over India. The spread to citrus is from the natural abode in the nearby forests. The mandarin orange (*Citrus reticulata*) is a host for 4 species: *L. longiflorus*, *L. involucratus*, *L. ampullaceus*, and *L. scurrulus*.

In the Philippines, Sulit (1930), in surveying the Loranthaceae, noted 8 genera comprising 102 species, *Loranthus* alone contributing 79 of these. The two commonest and most damaging species were *L. philippensis* and *Viscum orientale*—the former on the lukban (*Citrus maxima*). In 1911, *Loranthus secundiflorum* was found on *Citrus decumana*, of which many plants were dying, on Mindanao Island. Approximately 80 per cent of the lansones (or langsat, *Lansium domesticum* [Meliaceae], an important and widely cultivated Malayan fruit tree) in the Province of Laguna were affected by one or both of these parasites. The lansone when infested with *Loranthus*, lives for only five or six years—depending upon the severity of the infestation. When a native forest tree is infected, it lives for seven or eight years. *Loranthus* is said to be medicinal when attached to 'Lagundi' (*Vitex negundo*), both the host and parasite being gathered and boiled and then used as a cough remedy.

Sands (1924) has studied the damage done by Loranthaceae to cultivated trees in Malaya. He found that some 45 species of the family occur in Malaya but only a few—belonging to the genera *Loranthus*, *Elytranthe*, and *Viscum*—attack rubber trees. He notes the type of growth in *L. grandifrons*, which has leaves up to 10 in. long and $5\frac{1}{2}$ in. wide, and rosy-pink flowers 3 in. in length. *L. ferrugineus* and other species are pollinated by the beautiful little sun-birds (of the group Nectariniidae) that insert their beaks into the flowers in search of food. The common honey-sucker bird of Ceylon is a member of this same group and visits *Loranthus* flowers in the early morning. Sands observes that, apart from having sticking or adhering properties, the gelatinous seed-coat is able to absorb water from rain, mist, or dew, and thus prevent the seed from perishing. The natural fall of berries, from higher to lower levels of the same host tree, ensures a continuous infestation. In the older specimens of *Loranthus*, the original hold-fast may become as large as a tennis ball, completely surrounding the branch. Sands noted an unusual case of hyperparasitism on a durian (*Durio zibethinus*) tree attacked by *Elytranthe barnesii*. For on this latter species was growing *Viscum articulatum*, and on the *V. articulatum* was growing *Loranthus ferrugineus* (Sands, 1924, Pl. III, Fig. 6).

Among the species of Loranthaceae described, Sands lists 5 as being the most important: *Loranthus ferrugineus* has been found on 20 species of fruit and other useful trees, and on tapioca, but rarely on rubber trees, though it is present in all districts; *L. pentandrus* is found on 25 species of useful plants, including teak and silk-cotton tree, occurring in all districts, being common on rubber (*Hevea brasiliensis*), and in some districts often damaging rubber trees severely; *L. grandifrons* is widely distributed on fruit trees but not on rubber; *L. pentapetalus* is widely distributed but found on only two cultivated trees; and *Elytranthe globosa* is a common species, frequently found on rubber as well as on 14 other species of trees—including the cashew (*Anacardium occidentale*).

In the Kapok plantations of Java, Haan (1928) observed that the damage caused by *Loranthus pentandrus* and *Viscum articulatum* was principally through the withholding of water and nutrient salts from the affected branch. This destroyed great quantities of fruiting branches, and led to deteriorating production and very often the death of the tree.

Seeds are distributed by the bird *Dicaeum flammeum*. The control measures advised were: cutting out the parasitized branches and shooting the birds that were known to disseminate the seeds. Losses of 20 to 30 per cent of the harvest were reported to result from the attacks of these parasites.

The role that birds play in the life-histories of some Javanese Loranthaceae has been examined by Leeuwen (1954), who observed that the Loranthoideae have bird-pollinated flowers, while the Viscoideae have insect-pollinated flowers. The flower-picker birds (Dicaeidae) disseminate seeds of the Loranthaceae, eating the fruit, swallowing the pulp and seed, and discarding the skin. The birds consume a number of seeds, sitting quietly while digestion takes place—rapidly, in some twelve to twenty-two minutes. The seeds are defecated and adhere to the branches, in due course sprouting and growing into the host tissue.

The Loranthaceae of Kwangsi, China, have been studied by Tso-chie Hwang (1955). The genera here included *Loranthus*, *Elytranthe*, and *Viscum*, which were parasitic on 57 genera and 67 species of plants representing 36 families.

McLuckie (1923) studied the physiology of the Loranthaceae of New South Wales, noting 12 species of *Loranthus* and observing their effects on *Casuarina* and *Eucalyptus*. These trees were almost enveloped with *Loranthus*, and the tops of every branch died—the attacks having a disastrous effect on the trees, as very few new leaves could be formed each year.

Garmendia (1936) writes concerning a governmental decree for the eradication of the 'Quintral' pest (*Loranthus tetrandrus*) from fruit and forest trees in Chile. He also noted that it had invaded olive trees in the Department of Serena. In 1916, *Loranthus* species had become very troublesome in lime plantations in certain districts in St. Lucia and Dominica, British West Indies. It was also observed that the fruit of the mistletoe was attacked by the larva of a certain insect. *Phoradendron flavescens* had been observed in the native brush, but as yet had not appeared on cultivated plants.

In Panama, the woody parasitic vine *Psittacanthus schiedeanus* (Loranthaceae) grows throughout the crowns of *Quercus baruensis* at altitudes of around 6,000 ft. near Cerro Punta. *Struthanthus marginatus* (Loranthaceae), also a woody parasitic vine, occurs in similar situations.

SANTALACEAE

In this family the following genera are parasitic: *Santalum, Commandra, Thesium, Arjona, Osyris, Exocarpus, Choretum,* and *Scleropyrum* (N. L. Rao, 1942). *Santalum* includes the well-known cultivated sandalwoods. *Thesium* and *Osyris* are the only troublesome members of this family, and they are largely restricted to the Mediterranean region. *Thesium* has received detailed study in North Africa by Chabrolin (1934, 1935), and in Spain by Mendizabel (1945). *Thesium humile* in the poorer soils can be quite destructive to the culture of cereals. *Osyris alba* ('Harnstrauch') has been reported on the roots of the grape vine, and of fruit and forest trees, in Yugoslavia (Anić, 1941). It has also been reported on the grape vine in southern France.

One of the most important and most injurious of the stem- or blister-rusts occurring on pines is *Peridermium pyriforme*, a heteroecious rust, the summer stage of which occurrs on species of *Commandra*. Eradication of the rust is closely associated with the eradication of *Commandra*—the several species of which are semi-parasitic upon the roots of some 46 species of plants (Hedgecock, 1915). *Arjona tuberosa* is common in Patagonia (Argentina). It is found on *Stipa humilis* (Gramineae) around Santa Cruz, and could become dangerous on cultivated cereals.

OROBANCHACEAE

This family consists entirely of parasitic genera, with *Aeginetia*, *Christisonia* and *Orobanche* the most important and troublesome (Beck von Mannagetta 1930). These genera are root parasites and occur on many important crops, chiefly in the subtropical and tropical regions of the world.

The sugar-cane root parasite, *Aeginetia indica* 'Bunga', is chiefly restricted to the Philippines, Formosa (Taiwan), Japan, India, and certain adjacent areas. The morphology and anatomy have been studied by Kusano (1908*a*), while the observations of Lee & Goseco (1932) in Formosa, where this species occurs on rice and maize as well as on sugar-cane, are very useful. The destructiveness of *A. indica* resides in its ability to produce an enzyme that is capable of reducing, to glucose and other reducing sugars, the highly desirable sucrose in the cane plant. In fact, the loss in sucrose from the affected plants appears to be greater than the dry-weight of the parasite itself. The following juice analyses tell the story:

	Per cent Sucrose	Per cent Reducing Sugars
Healthy	13·98	0·521
Infected	5·05	1·563

Lee & Goseco also explored the possibilities of biological control of this pest through the use of a pterophorid moth (*Platyptilia* sp.) and a pyralid moth (*Daulia*, near *D. afralis* Walker). They observed that the larvae of these insects fed on about eight species of very common weeds; but the results at the time of their publication were inconclusive.

Roxas (1931) stated that *A. indica* was widely spread in the Philippines, especially in Balaga and Laguna, and had appeared in Pampanga and Negros. It was steadily gaining ground, with a few sugar-cane fields 100 per cent infected—generally in drainage areas and along watercourses. Spot treatment with Atlacide was practicable, whereas overall treatment was prohibitive in cost. Agati & Tan (1931) studied various methods of using Atlacide for control of this pest.

In Formosa there are thirty parasitic diseases of sugar-cane, but *A. indica* is the only flowering one (Ling, 1955). It is fairly widely distributed in cultivated areas of sugar-cane in Formosa—particularly in the southern and eastern parts of the island—and causes considerable losses every year. The parasite is an annual plant, 15 to 30 cm. high, with seeds 0·2 to 0·3 mm. in diameter which are viable for less than two years even when left in a dry condition. The seed has a very high fat-content, and has a thick-walled seed-coat which prevents water absorption until it reaches the proper host. The flowers are solitary, on pedicels 2 to 6 cm. long. *A. indica* flowers over about a four-month period, from autumn until the middle of winter. The capsule contains from 40,000 to 70,000 seeds, which are disseminated by wind and by irrigation water. Suggested control measures include eradication of the flower-stalk before flowering, and withholding irrigation water at a critical time. Lo (1955) states that this disease, the 'Bunga', occurs on more than 20 monocotyledonous species in Formosa, and that more than 1,000 hectares have been attacked. As a result of a breeding programme, he describes two new varieties of cane-sugar that are resistant to this disease.

A closely-related parasite, *Christisonia wrightii*, has also been found to be destructive to sugar-cane in the Philippines (Quisumbing, 1940).

The genus *Orobanche*, according to the most recent generic monograph (Mannagetta, 1930), contains about 130 species, mostly of the north-temperate regions, of which 5 species are found in the United States, where they are said to be troublesome on tobacco (Garman, 1903), and, in California, on tomatoes. Most of the reports have been sporadic, and damage appears not to be too severe, although recent reports from California indicate that some of the earlier-reported infestations have spread into neighbouring areas.

From a survey of the literature, it appears that the most serious damage from *Orobanche* occurs in southern Europe—especially on beans in Italy—and to tobacco and other solanaceous plants in India. Scattered reports in the Near East, particularly Egypt where the parasite's stalks were some 4 ft. high (Henslow, 1898), indicate heavy infestations in bean plantings. The studies of Marudarjan (1950), on the Indian *O. cernua* var. *desertorum*, are illustrative. This is a common root-parasite of tobacco, causing a 'near-wilt' appearance of the crop plants in the field, and affecting the yield and quality of the leaves.

O. cernua var. *desertorum* also parasitizes large numbers of wild solanaceous plants, including *Datura fastuosa* var. *alba* which is parasitized heavily—in one host plant the formation of nearly 500 nodules (places of infection) was noted. Some hosts have the capacity to stimulate the germination of *Orobanche* seeds without being parasitized themselves; these include *Capsicum annuum*, *Tridax procumbens*, and *Bidens pilosa*, close to the roots of which from 13 to 15 per cent of the seeds of the parasite germinated, but without developing any haustorial connections. The *Capsicum* crop can be grown in rotation with tobacco, and tends to reduce the infestation in the soil. While Garman (1903), earlier, had claimed that seeds of *Capsicum annuum* remained viable for thirteen years in soil, Marudarjan's studies (1950) indicate that the seeds of this species do not remain viable for more than two-and-one-half years either in soil or in special containers in the laboratory.

Cattle and goats feed freely on *Orobanche* shoots. Their faeces were collected and tested on tobacco plants, whereupon the development of *Orobanche* shoots indicated that seeds of the latter had passed unharmed through the alimentary tracts. The indiscriminate grazing of such animals in the field is thus a source of dissemination of this parasite. A long rotation, with tobacco grown once in three years and preceded by a chilli (*Capsicum*) crop, will save high losses due to this parasite—especially in Virginia tobacco.

Shaw (1917), and M. K. Rao (1919), have studied this parasite in detail on Indian tobacco—Rao observing that the seeds of *Orobanche* are so minute that they readily mix with tobacco seed, and indeed look like tobacco seed. A bad attack will destroy one-quarter of the crop. One bad practice at that time was to leave the tobacco stumps after harvest in the field, where the parasite continued to mature.

Giliarov (1941) has reported *O. ramosa* on *Taraxacum kok-saghyz* in Russia, where, during August, 48 per cent of the plants were attacked. As many as five individuals were observed on one host-plant—even on lateral roots 4 to 5 cm. away from the main root. The rubber content of diseased plants was reduced by two-thirds.

The germination of seeds of *O. crenata* on *Vicia faba* (broad bean) in Egypt has been described by Kadry & Tewfic (1956). This parasite causes very serious damage to the crop, which is one of the main economic crops of Egypt. Each plant of the parasite produces about 40,000 seeds (0.35 mm. long and 0.26 mm. wide), which remain viable for more than ten years. The seeds of *O. crenata* germinate about one week before the flowering of the host plant—taking about one week of stimulation to start germination. A substance which encourages germination is produced by the roots of mature host plants. As a result of this, seeds germinate at a distance of less than 1 cm. from the host plant, while only those at a distance of 2–3 mm. actually cause infection.

O. ramosa has been reported to have been present in tomato fields in California in 1929, 1934, and again in 1951–52. It had been spread by seed-infested soil that had been retained on farm implements. The hosts include *Amaranthus retroflexus*, *Capsella bursa-pastoris*, *Solanum* sp., and *Xanthium spinosum* (Pl. 5(a)). Survival may to some small extent be effected on the weeds themselves—a method of survival which, if it occurs, would be of importance in California, where *O. ramosa* grows in

63

considerable abundance on weeds in harvested fields of cucumber and along dirt roads separating old sugar-beet fields (two non-host crops). Many people have indicated the possibilities of biological control of *Orobanche* through certain natural insect pests, such as *Phytomachia orobanchia*, etc., and through the fungus pathogens *Thielavia basicola* (Aspergillaceae) and *Fusarium*.

In Italy, treatment with monochloroacetic acid of infected soils in bean fields was unsuccessful, whereas pre-emergence treatments of soils in Indian tobacco fields with herbicide 'Sesone' (Na 2,4-dichlorophenoxy-ethyl sulphate) have been highly successful (Prasad, 1954). Cultural methods have generally involved the use of a susceptible species (often termed a 'trap crop'), alternating in rotation with the desirable crop species.

SCROPHULARIACEAE

The other great family containing noxious root parasites is the figwort family, which is cosmopolitan and comprises some 175 genera and 4,000 species. Among the more important parasitic genera are *Rhinanthus*, *Pedicularis* (Volkart, 1899), *Sopubia*, *Centranthera*, *Rhamphicarpa*, *Euphrasia*, two less well-known indigenous genera of Japan (*Monochasma* and *Siphonostegia*) (Kusano, 1908), and finally two very important and destructive genera, *Melasma* (*Alectra*) and *Striga*.

Rhinanthus crista-galli (yellow rattle), an annual that is common throughout Europe, is largely parasitic on meadow grasses (Carre, 1895; Anon., 1931; Stryckers, 1951). Similar in range and character is *Pedicularis palustris*, 'lousewort'. *Centranthera humifusa*, of India, parasitizes grasses and sedges (e.g. *Fimbristylis* spp.), and is found attached to the nitrifying nodules of *Desmodium triflorum* (E. Barnes, 1941).

Species of *Rhamphicarpa* parasitize rice in Madagascar, and sorghum in East Africa (Fuggles-Couchman, 1935); they also apparently parasitize maize and cowpeas. Species of *Melasma* (*Alectra*) are destructive parasites of leguminous plants, being found on cowpeas, French beans, peanuts (groundnuts), sugar-beans, and soybeans—principally in Rhodesia and South Africa (Anon., 1924; Rattray, 1932; Brain, 1934; Saunders, 1934; Botha, 1948). *Melasma brasiliensis* has been reported as destructive in the West Indies on badly cultivated sugar-cane lands.

The most prominent and destructive members of this family occur in the genus *Striga*, and have been called 'witchweeds'. Some 23 species have been recognized in this genus, and they are largely restricted to the more tropical regions of the world—extending to about 30 degrees north and south of the Equator. Nine species are reported from the Sudan, and 4 from India. *S. asiatica* (*S. lutea*) has been particularly troublesome in South Africa, which probably sustains greater loss every year through the prevalence of this pest than through all of the fungus diseases combined. It is consequently not surprising that much of our information on this pest comes from work done in South Africa, e.g. by Hattingh (1954). Here the plant, also known as 'rooiblom' or 'vuurbossie', causes considerable crop losses in maize and kaffir-corn each year. It also parasitizes other members of the grass family, such as Sudan grass, cane sorghums, Columbus grass, rice, teff, manna, and even winter cereals when they are grown during the summer. It occurs mainly on sandy soils and light sandy loams in the outlying districts of the western, northern, and southeastern Transvaal, northwestern Orange Free State, and almost the whole of Natal.

Striga asiatica is classed as a root parasite, as, from early germination, attachment occurs on the roots of a susceptible host plant. The seeds of witchweed only germinate after some 18 months. When maize is planted and its germination occurs, secretions from the maize roots induce the germination of witchweed seeds. The witchweed roots have no root-hairs, and therefore cannot independently absorb water or soluble nutrients from the soil. The greatest damage is done by the parasite before it emerges from the ground, i.e. during the first six to eight weeks of its growth. Upon emergence, the aerial portions become green, with the consequent production of carbohydrates. About a month after emergence, when a height of from 7 to 9 in. is attained by the pest, the first, generally bright red, flowers are formed basally. Within a month of the opening of the first flowers, the seed-capsules burst open, dispersing the seeds—in all some three to four months after the germination of the seed. *S. orobanchoides* is capable of flowering and seeding entirely beneath the soil surface.

It has been known for some time that root secretions from susceptible host plants stimulated the germination of *Striga* seeds in the soil. Worsham & Klingman (1962) examined 41 coumarin derivatives, and found just 2 (scopoletin and 4-hydroxycoumarin) that would stimulate the germination of *Striga* seeds in the absence of roots of a susceptible host or of their secretions. These authors note that H. Börner (1960) (*see* Ch. X, and also Pl. 12*b*) had reported scopoletin from plant roots, and thus suggest the possibility that the naturally occurring germination stimulant may be a coumarin-type substance. They note, too, that earlier work had demonstrated that kinetin and certain other 6-(substituted) purines also stimulated the germination of *Striga* seeds (*see* Pl. 5(*b*)).

Each seed capsule of *Striga asiatica* contains an average of 1,350 seeds, and a plant may produce anything from 50,000 to 500,000 seeds. They are microscopic—about one-twentieth the size of tobacco seeds—and are dispersed by wind or water, or sometimes by means of millet or certain hay crops, implements, or animals. In a distribution study of witchweed seeds in certain North Carolina soils, Robinson & Kust (1962) found seeds in undisturbed Lakeland sand in all layers down to 60 in.

Maize, kaffir-corn, and other plants attacked by witchweed always show signs of wilting, are stunted, and in most cases yellowish in colour.

D

This sickly appearance is due to the fact that the parasite robs the plants of nutrients and water. There are also strong indications that it secretes certain substances into their roots, which not only hamper growth and development of the plants, but also have a detrimental effect upon their transpiration. As an example, maize on infested land often shows signs of wilting even though the soil is wet (Hattingh, 1954).

Control can be effected by planting either catch, or trap, crops. A crop employed as a true host of witchweed, such as Sudan grass, is termed a *catch crop*. Planting and ploughing under such a host crop before the witchweed produces seeds will reduce the weed seeds of the parasite in infested fields. Crops that will cause witchweed seeds to germinate but are not true hosts, such as cowpeas or soybeans, are termed *trap crops*. Such crops will not support the parasite's growth, but again serve to reduce the number of witchweed seeds in infested areas.

Trap plants should be planted alone or in rotation for at least four years, to allow the witchweed seeds to germinate and be rendered harmless. Spraying with 2,4-D prevents seed formation, while ¾ to 1 lb. of 2,4-D-acid in 20 gallons of water, sprayed per 'morgen' (2·1 acres) just before the weed begins to flower, will kill witchweed plants reaching the soil surface even as late as a month after spraying (Hattingh, 1954).

Striga has recently increased in importance as the result of finding *S. asiatica* on more than 100 farms in North and South Carolina—the first time this genus has been found in the Western Hemisphere. In the Carolinas it has been found on crabgrass (*Digitaria* spp.) in fields of tobacco, peanuts, beans, peas, and sweet potatoes. It is believed by some investigators that graminaceous plants are first required for stimulation of germination, after which the young seedlings may attach themselves to non-graminaceous hosts (Pl. 5(*b*)).

A bulletin from the United States Department of Agriculture (Anon. 1957) has provided some of the above information, and suggests also a rotation by planting wheat, oats, barley, or rye in autumn, and following this the next year with either catch or trap crops. Crabgrass should be kept out of infested fields, and sprays of 2,4-D (1 lb./acre) will kill the parasite. Other measures involve prohibiting the transfer of farm machinery and packing or storage containers (unless thoroughly cleaned), from infested to uninfested areas. This also applies to harvested crops and to plants used for propagation. (*see* Ch. XIV).

Agarwala & Naguvi (1952) have reported that natural biological control of *Striga euphrasioides* occurs in India from the feeding of the caterpillars of the lepidopterous *Precis orithya* ('blue pansy'). The caterpillars were more effective against the first flush of *Striga* (September to October) and less effective against the second flush (November to December). They were also found on the local weed, *Justicia quinqueangularis*. In Rhodesia, *Rhizoctonia solani* is recorded as causing a root-root of *S. asiatica*. With a view towards biological control, perhaps, Davidson (1963) investigated the insect damage to *Striga hermonthica* in Kenya. The most common pest was a small agromyzid fly (*Ophiomyia strigialis*), a previously unknown species. This species produced some root injury, but it appears to offer little in the way of control possibilities.

The extensive literature (some 298 citations) of this genus has been well reviewed, with extensive abstracts, in a publication by McGrawth *et al.* (1957), and so only certain major contributions need here be listed in the bibliography.* A summary of the more important species is presented in Table II.

TABLE II

DETAILS OF THE MORE IMPORTANT *Striga* SPECIES

Name	Distribution †	Cultivated hosts	Wild hosts
Striga asiatica (L.) Kuntze (*S. lutea* Lour.)	India, South Africa, Burma, Mozambique, Sumatra, Mauritius, United States	Sorghum, maize, millet, sugar-cane, rice, *Nicotiana tabacum*	*Panicum, Cyanotis cucullata* (India) *Paspalum dilatatum, Digitaria sanguinalis, Echinochloa crusgalli, Chloris* sp., *Dactylis glomerata*
Striga densiflora Benth.	India	Sorghum, sugar-cane, millet	?
Striga curvifolia Benth.	Queensland	Sugar-cane	?
Striga euphrasioides Benth.	India, Burma	Sugar-cane, rice, sorghum	*Fimbristylis miliacea*
Striga hermonthica Benth.	Egypt, Sudan, Rhodesia, West and Central Africa	Sorghum, maize, *Setaria italica, Arachis hypogaea, Vigna unguiculata, Dolichos lablab,* sugar-cane, cucurbits	*Cynodon dactylon, Panicum, Pennisetum*
Striga orobanchoides Benth. (*S. gesnerioides* Vatke)	Central Africa, Rhodesia, South Africa, India, Australia	*Nicotiana, Arachis hypogaea, Nicotiana rustica, Ipomoea batatas*	*Cleome, Indigofera, Tephrosia, Ipomoea, Euphorbia, Sanseveria, Cissus, Rhynchosia, Panicum maximum, Echinochloa colona*
Striga parviflora Benth.	Australia	Sugar-cane	?
Striga senegalensis Benth.	Nigeria	Sorghum	?

*Two good reviews of the phanerogamic parasites are those of Schmucker (1959) and Subramanian & Srinivasan (1960).

† A map showing the world-wide distribution of four important species of *Striga* is included in 'Advances in witchweed control' by W. C. Shaw *et al.*, *Weeds*, 10, 182–91, 1962.

Species of *Striga* parasitize sugar-cane in Australia, Madagascar, etc. In the latter country, it has been noted that heavy shading by the cane is a protective feature against serious infestations. This is in contrast with infestations in maize.

B. A. Razi (1957), of the Central College, Bangalore, India, has recently published an annotated list of the phanerogamic parasites of India and Pakistan—as represented by specimens in ten American herbaria. While this is not of course a complete list for India and Pakistan, it provides an indication of the number and variety of such plants occurring in the area concerned. In all there are listed 40 genera representing some 198 different taxa. The two largest families are the Loranthaceae (with 13 genera and 56 taxa), and the Scrophulariaceae (with 4 genera and 88 taxa, of which *Pedicularis* provides 66 and *Striga* 5). The Orobanchaceae are represented by 6 genera and 18 taxa, of which *Orobanche* provides 9.

The more destructive forms are, however, centred in a few genera: *Loranthus* (*sensu lat.*), *Viscum*, *Phoradendron*, *Arceuthobium*, *Striga*, *Orobanche*, and *Cuscuta*. These genera parasitize either the aerial portions of plants, or the roots (but not both), and herein resides the basis for their destructiveness. Most species are aerial or stem parasites (generally photosynthetic, i.e. hemi-parasites), and these would appear to be relatively advanced phylogenetically. They have been relatively more widely dispersed naturally, because of their habitat and often wide host-ranges. On the other hand many of the root parasites, as might be expected from their lack of a photosynthetic system (and occurrence in much reduced light), are very limited in size, and often are reduced to the reproductive structures alone (e.g. *Rafflesia*). They have in this respect been likened to some of the subterranean fungi.

Addendum

B. Singh (1962) has studied extensively the loranthaceous parasite *Dendrophthoe falcata* (L.f.) Ettingsh. (*Loranthus falcatus* L. of this chapter) (*Bull. Nat. Bot. Gardens*, Lucknow, India, No. 1, 1–75). Particularly valuable are the extensive bibliography and the discussion of control measures. Excellent control was achieved without damage to a wide range of hosts by the use of a 40 per cent emulsion in water of the refined diesel oil 'powerine', aided by about 0·005 per cent of bar washing-soap as the emulsifying agent. Sprays are applied during the summer (April to June), but the percentage must be raised to 50 during the winter. (For discussions of other control measures *see* pp. 381–2.)

BIBLIOGRAPHY

(The Parasitic Weeds)

ACHEY, D. M. (1933). A revision of the Section *Gymnocaulis* of the Genus *Orobanche*. *Bull. Torrey Bot. Cl.*, **60**, 441–51.

ADDY, S. K. (1956). Preliminary experiments on control of *Orobanche* on Brinjal (eggplant) by Crag Herbicide 1. *Sci. & Cult.*, **22**, 231–2.

AGARWALA, S. B. D. & NAGUVI, S. Z. HAIDER (1952). *Precis orithya* Swinhoe L. (The Blue Pansy) as a controlling agent for *Striga euphrasioides*: a root parasitic weed on sugar cane. *Proc. Bihar Acad. Agric. Sci.*, **2**(3), 120–5.

AGATI, J. A. & TAN, J. P. (1931). The effect of Atlacide on *Aeginetia indica*. (Also in Spanish.) *Sug. News*, **12**, 82–89.

—— & —— (1931*a*). Controlling the *Aeginetia indica* in cane fields. *Sug. News*, **12**(12), 852.

ALEKSANDROV, F. (1947). [On the biology of *Cuscuta lupuliformis* Krock—in Russian.] *Sovetsk. Bot.*, **15**, 218–19.

ANDREWS, F. W. (1945). The parasitism of *Striga hermonthica* Benth. on *Sorghum* spp. under irrigation. I: Prelimary results and the effect of heavy and light irrigation on *Striga* attack. *Ann. Appl. Biol.*, **32**, 193–200.

—— (1946). Parasitism of *Striga* spp., on *Dolichos Lablab* Linn. *Nature, Lond.*, **57**, 515.

—— (1947). The parasitism of *Striga hermonthica* Benth. on leguminous plants. *Ann. Appl. Biol.*, **34**, 267–75.

ANDREWS, S. R. (1957). Dwarf-mistletoe of ponderosa pine in the southwest. *Forest Pest Leaflet, Forest Serv., U.S. Dept. Agric.*, No. 19, 4 pp.

ANIĆ, M. (1941). [Harnstrauch (*Osyris alba* L.) als Schmarotzerpflanze auf Wurzeln von Weinrebe, Obst- und Waldbäumen im Mittelmeergebiet—in Yugoslav.] *Rev. Sci. Agric. (Zagreb)*, **4**, 75–82.

ANON, (1919). The eradication of yellow rattle. *University College of Wales, Aberystwith*, 8 pp.

—— (1924) *Melasma*: a root parasite on peanuts. *J. Dept. Agric., S. African Transvaal*, 3 pp.

—— (1931). Yellow rattle. *Min. Agric. & Fish. Adv. Leaflet* No. 48, London, 4 pp.

—— (1933). *A National Plan for American Forestry*. A national letter from the Secretary of Agriculture transmitting in response to *S. Res.* 175 (72nd Congr.), the report of the Forest Service of the Agriculture Dept. on the forest problems of the U.S. 73rd Congr. 1st Sess. Senate Doc. 12, 2 vols. U.S. Govt. Ptg. Office, Washington. (Mistletoe, pp. 700, 1,420).

—— (1934). Les dommages causés par le gui, *Viscum album* L. *Ann. Ec. Eaux For.*, Nancy, **5**, 231–3.

—— (1945). Trapcropping to control witchweed (*Striga asiatica*). *Rhod. Agric. J.*, **42**, 278–87.

—— (1957). Watch out for witchweed. *U.S. Dept. Agric.*, Pamphlet No. 331, 4 pp.

BAKER, K. F. (1950). Perennation in relation to control of dodders on native shrubs in southern California. *Phytopathology*, **40**, 213–14.

BAKER, R. G. SANZEN-. *See* SANZEN-BAKER, R. G.

BALDRATI, I. (1941). Una fanerogama parassita dei cereali (*Striga lutea* o erba strega). *Agricoltura Colon.*, **35**, 14–21.

BARNES, B. (1953). Mistletoe: its life and legends. *Discovery*, **14**, 374.

BARNES, E. (1941). A note on the root-parasitism of *Centranthera humifusa* Wall. *J. Bombay Nat. Hist. Soc.*, **42**, 668–9.

BASINSKI, J. J. (1955). Witchweed and soil fertility. *Nature, Lond.*, **175**, 431.

BECK VON MANNAGETTA, G. (1890). *Monographie der Gattung* Orobanche. Theodor Fischer, Kassel, 275 pp.

—— (1927). *Orobanche. Pflanzenareale*, 1, 73–81 (maps).

—— (1930). *Orobanchaceae.* In *Das Pflanzenreich*, Bd. 96, IV, 261, ed. A. Engler, 348 pp.

BELL, A. F. & COTTRELL-DORMER, W. (1931). Cane-killing weed. *Qd. Agric. J.*, 36, 463–73.

—— & —— (1932). The cane-killing weed. *Qd. Bur. Sugar Expt. Sta.*, No. 3, 13–24.

BLANCHARD, M. (1951). Contribution a l'étude de la biologie de l'orobanche et à sa destruction. *C.R. Acad. Agric.*, Fr., pp. 582–4.

—— (1952). Contribution a l'étude de la biologie de l'orobanche et à sa destruction. *Ann. Inst. Agric. Algér.*, 6(9), 1–49.

BLIN, H. (1925). Les treflières et l'orobanche. *J. Agric Prat.*, 44, 380.

BOESHORE, I. (1920). The morphological continuity of Scrophulariaceae and Orobanchaceae. *Thesis, University of Pennsylvania*, 38 pp.

BOEWIG, H. (1904). The histology and development of *Cassytha filiformis* L. *Trans. Bot. Soc. Pa.*, 1, 399–416, pls. 33, 34.

BOODLE, L. A. (1921). Mistletoe on (lime) trees. *Kew Bull.*, pp. 212–5.

BOTHA, P. J. (1948). The parasitism of *Alectra Vogelii* Benth. with specific reference to the germination of its seeds. *S. Afr. J. Sci.*, 44, 119.

BOURIQUET, G. (1933). Une Scrophulariacée parasite du riz à Madagascar. *Rev. Path. Vég.*, 20(3), 149–51.

BRAIN, C. K. (1934). The weeds and poisonous plants of Southern Rhodesia. I. *Rhod. Agric. J.*, 31, 779–91.

BRESALOA, M. (1919). [Devitalization of the seed of *Cuscuta*—in Italian.] *Staz. Sper. Agr. Ital.*, 52, 193–207.

BROOKS, F. T. (1914). Parasitic flowering plants on rubber trees. *Malay. Agric. J.*, 2, 165–6.

—— (1914a). Species of *Loranthus* on rubber trees. *Malay. Agric. J.*, 3, 7–9.

BROWN, K. & EDWARDS, M. (1944). The germination of the seed of *Striga lutea*. I. Histological influences and progress of germination. *Ann. Bot.*, 8, 131–48.

BUCKLAND, D. C. & MARPLES, E. G. (1952). Management of western hemlock (*Tsuga heterophylla*) infested with dwarf mistletoe (*Arceuthobium campylopodum*). *B.C. Lumberm.*, 36(5), 50–51, 136, 138, 140.

CANNON, W. A. (1901). The anatomy of *Phoradendron villosum*. *Bull. Torrey Bot. Cl.*, 28, 374–90.

—— (1904). The germination of mistletoes. *Bull. Torrey Bot. Cl.*, 31, 435.

CARRE, A. (1895). Destruction de la rhinanthe. *Progr. Agric. Vitic.*, 23, 609–10.

CHABROLIN, C. (1934). La germination des graines de *Thesium humile* exige l'intervention de champignon saprophytes. *C.R. Acad. Sci.*, Fr., 199, 225–6.

—— (1935). Monographie d'une Santalacée: le *Thesium humile*. *Thesis, University of Paris*, Sér. A, No. 157, 130 pp.

CHATIN, A. (1856–92). *Anatomie comparée des végéteaux, Plantes parasites*. J. B. Baillière et fils, Paris, Livr. III, xv + 560 pp., atlas 113 pls. (Cf. rev. in *Bot. Zbl.*, 51, 211–12, 1892.)

CHEMIN, E. (1920). Observations anatomiques et biologiques sur le genre 'Lathraea'. *Thesis, University of Paris*.

CHEVALIER, A. (1930). Le *Striga hermontica* parasite des céréales en Afrique tropicale. *Rev. Bot. Appl.*, 10(103), 175–7.

—— (1939). Sur un Scrophulariée (*Striga harmontica*) parasite des céréales en Afrique tropicale. *C.R. Acad. Sci.*, Fr., 189, 1308–10.

CIFFERRI, O. & POMA, G. (1963). Fixation of carbon dioxide by *Cuscuta epithymum*. *Life Sci.* 3, 158–62.

COERT, J. H. (1924). *Aeginetia* species; a root parasite of sugar cane. *Meded. Proefst. Java-Suikerind.*, No. 13, 437–47.

CONDIT, I. J. (1940). Mistletoe on persimmon. *Madroño*, 5, 272.

CONTESSE, J. PETER-. See PETER-CONTESSE, J.

COUCHMAN, N. R. FUGGLES-. See FUGGLES-COUCHMAN, N. R.

DANGER, L. (1887). *Unkräuter und pflanzliche Schmarotzer. Ein Beitrage zur Erkenntnis und Bekämpfung derselben für Landwirte und Gartenfreunde.* Carl Moyer, Hanover, 166 pp.

DANSER, B. H. (1929–37). Loranthaceae. *Bull. Jard. Bot. Buitenz.*, 10, 14, and 15.

—— (1931). On the harmony and nomenclature of the Loranthaceae of Asia and Australia. *Bull. Jard. Bot. Buitenz.*, Ser. 3, 10, 291.

—— (1931a). The Loranthaceae of the Netherlands Indies. *Bull. Jard. Bot. Buitenz.*, Ser. 3, 11, 233–519.

—— (1933). A new system for the genera of Loranthaceae Loranthoideae, with a nomenclator for the Old World species of this sub-family. *Verh. Akad. Wet. Amst., Naturk.*, 29(6), 1–128.

—— (1935). A revision of the Philippine Loranthaceae. *Philipp. J. Sci.*, 58, 1–151.

—— (1941). The British-Indian species of *Viscum* revised and compared with those of Southeastern Asia, Malaysia and Australia. *Blumea*, 4, 261–319.

DARLING, L. (1940). *Protocoronospora* on *Phoradendron flavescens* in California. *Madroño*, 5, 241–6.

DATTA, R. M. (1951). Occurrence of a hermaphrodite flower in *Arceuthobium minutissimum* Hook., *Nature, Lond.*, 167, 203–4.

DAVIDSON, A. (1963). Insects attacking *Striga* in Kenya. *Nature, Lond.*, 197, 923.

DEAN, H. L. (1937). An addition to the bibliographies of the genus *Cuscuta. Stud. Nat. Hist. Ia. Univ.*, 17, 191–7.

—— (1942). Total length of stem developed from a single seedling of *Cuscuta. Proc. Iowa Acad. Sci.*, 49, 127–8.

DE HAAN, J. T. See HAAN, J. T. DE

DEL GINDICE, E. See GINDICE, E. DEL

DOWDING, E. S. (1929). The vegetation of Alberta. IV: The sandhill areas of central Alberta with particular reference to the ecology of *Arceuthobium americanum* Nutt. *J. Ecol.*, 17, 82–105.

—— (1931). *Wallrothiella arceuthobii*, a parasite of the Jack-pine mistletoe. *Canad. J. Res.*, 5, 219–30.

DURHAM, E. (1933). Zelkova as a mistletoe host. *Gdnrs' Chron.*, 93, 32.

EATON, R. J. & Dow, R. (1940). New England mistletoe. *New Engl. Nat.*, 9, 1–5.

ELLIS, D. E. (1939). A fungus disease of *Arceuthobium. Phytopathology*, 29, 995–6.

—— (1946). Anthracnose of dwarf mistletoe caused by a new species of *Septogloeum gillii. J. Elisha Mitchell Sci. Soc.*, 62, 25–50.

ESPINO, R. B. (1947). Eleven years study on ' bungang tubo', a resumé. *Philipp. Agric.*, 31, 151–3.

—— & PANTALEON, F. T. (1935). Effects of heat upon the viability of bunga (*Aeginetia indica* L.) seeds. *Philipp. Agric.*, 24, 439–50.

FARQUHAR, H. H. (1937). Witchweed. New light on the means by which it is spread. *Rhod. Agric. J.*, 34, 563–9.

FISHER, C. E. C. (1926). Loranthaceae of southern India and their host plants. *Rec. Botan. J. India*, 11, 159–95.

FREELAND, R. O. (1943). American mistletoe with respect to chlorophyll and photosynthesis. *Plant Physiol.*, 18, 299–302.

FRITSCHÉ, EMMA et al. (1958). Quelques observations sur la biologie de *Cuscuta europa* L. *Acad. Roy. Belg., Bull. Cl. Sci.*, 5e ser. 44, 163–87.

FUGGLES-COUCHMAN, N. R. (1935). A parasitic weed of Sorghums (*Ramphicarpa veronicaefolia* Vatke). *E. Afr. Agric. J.*, 1(12), 145–7.

GAERTNER, E. E. (1956). Studies of seed germination, seed identification, and host relationship in dodders. *Mem. Cornell Agric. Exp. Sta.*, 294, 1–56.

—— (1952). Observations of *Cuscuta europaea* among the Compositae. *Canad. J. Bot.* 30, 682–4.

GARMAN, H. (1903). Broomrapes. *Bull. Ky. Agric. Exp. Sta.*, 105, 1–32.

GARMENDIA, J. ORTIZ. See ORTIZ GARMENDIA, J.

GHIKALOV, S. (1935). Hemp resistance to *Orobanche ramosa* in relation with varietal peculiarities, photoperiodicity, and races of the parasite. *Pl. Prot. Leningr.*, 1(7), 99–118.

GILIAROV, M. S. (1941). *Orobanche ramosa* on kok-saghyz—in Russian. *Proc. Lenin Acad. Sci., U.S.S.R.*, 11, 30–31. (*Biol. Abst.*, 17, 3021, 1943.)

*GILL, L. S. (1957). Dwarf mistletoe on Lodgepole Pine. *U.S. Dept. Agric. For. Service Forest Pest Leaflet*, No. 18.

—— & HAWKSWORTH, F. S. (1954). Dwarf mistletoe control in southwestern ponderosa pine forest under management. *J. For.*, 52(5), 347–53.

GINDICE, E. DEL (1935). Ricerche sull'oro-banca della fava. I: Sulla germinazione del seme. *Staz. Sper. Granicolt. 'Benito Mussolini'* (Sicily), Publ. 7, 5–27.

GLIMCHER, J. (1938). The germination of *Viscuum cruciatum* Sieb. *Pol. J. Bot. Jer. Ser. Jerusalem*, 1, 103–5.

GOIKO, A. (1930). *Orobanche ramosa* auf *Abutilon avicennae*. *Z. Angew Bot., Charkiw.*, No. 5–6, 109–11.

GRASER, H. I. (1954). Methods for control of mistletoe; spot spraying in winter proves effective. *Diamond Walnut News*, 36(1), 10.

GROF, B. (1928). *Orobanche ramosa* und ihre Vertilgung. *Koztelek (Budapest)*, 38, 1220–1, 1275–6.

HAAN, J. T. DE (1928). De *Loranthus*–plaag in Kapokaan plantingen. *Arch. Cacao Algem. Landbouw-Sundie (Batavia)*, 2, 53–57.

HAMBLER, D. J. (1956). Further chromosome counts in Orobanchaceae. *Nature, Lond.*, 177, 438–9.

HANSSEN, J. (1933). [Mistletoe in Norway—in Norwegian, German summary.] *Nyt Mag. Naturvid.*, 72, 283–340.

HARENBENI, A. (1938). [*Viscum cruciatum* Sieb. on olive trees—in Hebrew.] *Hatteva Vehaaretz (Tel Aviv)*, 5, 169–74.

HARRIS, J. A., HARRISON, C. J. & PASCOE, T. A. (1930). Osmotic concentration and water relations in the mistletoes, with special reference to the occurrence of *Phoradendron californicum* on *Covillea tridentata*. *Ecology*, 11, 687–702.

HÄRTEL, O. (1941). Über die Okologie einiger Halbparasiten und ihrer Wirtspflanzen. *Ber. Dtsch. Bot. Ges.*, 59, 136–48.

—— (1956). Der Wasserhaushalt der Parasiten. In *Handbuch der Pflanzenphysiologie* (W. Ruhland, Ed.), 3, 951–60.

HATTINGH, I. D. (1954). Control of witchweed—*Striga lutea*. *Fmg. in S. Afr.*, 29, 316–18.

HAUMAN-MERCK, L. (1928). La modification de la flore Argentine sous l'action de la civilization (essai geobotanique humaine). *Mém. Acad. R. Belg. Cl. Sci.*, 9(3), 1–99.

HEALD, F. D. (1933). *Manual of plant diseases*. McGraw-Hill, New York, 2nd edn., 953 pp.

HEDGECOCK, G. G. (1915). Notes on some diseases of trees in our national forests. V. *Phytopathology*, 5, 175–81.

HEFER, S. R. (1950). The control of witchweed—*Striga lutea*. *Fmg in S. Afr.*, 25, 263–5.

* *See* related studies of this author: *J. Forestry*, 54, 384–90, 1956, 57, 919–22, 1959, 61, 587–91, 1963, 62, 27–32, 1964; *Phytopath.*, 46, 561–2, 1956; *Brittonia*, 16, 54–7, 1964; *Southw. Nat.*, 8, 204–9, 1964.

HEINRICHER, E. (1920). [Relations between mistletoe and pear trees—in German.] *Z. PflKrankh.*, **30**, 41–51.

—— (1924). Methoden der Aufzucht und Kultur der parasitischen Samenpflanzen. In *Handbuch der biologischen Arbeitsmethoden* (E. Abderhalden, Ed.), Abt. XI, Methoden . . . t. 2, 1 Hefte, pp. 237–50.

HENSLOW, G. (1898). *Orobanche speciosa. Gdnrs' Chron.*, ser. 3, **24**, 89.

HERBERT, D. A. (1924–25). The root parasitism of Western Australian Santalaceae. *J. Roy. Soc. W. Austr.*, **11**, 127–49.

HOLMBERG, O. (1917). *Orobanche carophyllacea* Sm. tagen i Sverige. *Bot. Notiser*, pp. 193–5.

HWANG, TSO-CHIE (1955). [The Loranthaceae of Kwangsi (China)—in Chinese, English summary.] *Acta Phytopathol. Sinica*, **1**, 217–30.

JONES, K. W. (1953). Relation of witchweed (*Striga*) to fertility in tropical soils. *Nature, Lond.*, **172**, 128.

—— (1953). The witchweeds (*Striga*) of Africa. *World Crops*, **5**(7), 263–6.

—— (1953). Further experiments on witchweed control. I: The effect of hormone weed-killer application at different rates and times on irrigated dura. *Emp. J. Exp. Agric. (Lond.)*, **21**, 331–9.

—— (1955). Further experiments on witchweed control. II. The existence of physiological strains of *Striga hermontheca. Emp. J. Exp. Agric. (Lond.)* **23**, 206–13.

JULIANO, J. B.(1935). Preliminary experiments on the inoculation of potted plants with bunga seeds. *Philipp. Agric.*, **24**, 262–82.

—— (1935). Anatomy and morphology of the bunga, *Aeginetia indica* Linnaeus. *Philipp. J. Sci.*, **56**, 405–51.

KADAMBI, K. (1954). On *Loranthus* control. *Indian For.*, **80**, 493–5.

KADRY, A. E. R. & TEWFIC, H. (1956). Seed germination in *Orobanche crenata* Forssk. *Svensk Bot. Tidsk.*, **50**, 270–86.

KANJILAL, U., KANJILAL, P. C., & DAS, A. (1934–40). *Flora of Assam*, Vols. 1–5, pp. 184 (Pt. I), 409, 578, 377, 480. M. D. Das, Calcutta.

KHARITONOV, V. N. & SUK, A. V. (1955). [Control of *Orobanche* on the tobacco and makhorka plantations—in Russian.] *Tabak, Mosk.*, **16**, 15–16.

KHREBTOV, A. A. (1931). [On the appearance of *Cuscuta epilinum* Weihe in the Ural region—in Russian, English summary.] *Bull. Appl. Bot. Gen. & Plant Breed (U.S.S.R.)*, **25**, 285–8.

KINGDON WARD, F. (1912). Mistletoe in Shenshi. *Gdnrs' Chron.*, **52**, 147–8.

KOCH, L. (1887). *Die Entwicklungsgeschichte der Orobanchen, mit besonderer Berücksichtigung ihrer Beziehungen.* C. Winter, Heidelberg, 389 pp.

KÖHLER, E. (1923). Phanerogame Parasiten. In *Handbuch der Pflanzenkrankheiten* (P. Sorauer, Ed.), P. Parey, Berlin, Band III, 4te Auflage, pp. 199–228.

KOPPIKAR, H. T. (1948). Control of *Loranthus* pest in forest plantations. *Indian For.*, **74**, 207.

KORSTAIN, C. F. (1922). Western yellow pine mistletoe. *Bull. U.S. Dept. Agric.*, No. 1112, 35 pp.

KRASSULIN, V. P. (1941). [Wintering stems of *Cuscuta epithymum* var. *vulgaris*—in Russian.] *Proc. Lenin Acad. Agric. Sci. U.S.S.R.*, **4**, 34–36.

KUIJT, J. (1955). Dwarf mistletoe. *Bot. Rev.*, **21**, 569–626.

KUMAR, L. S. S. (1944). Flowering plants which attack economic crops. III: *Loranthus. Indian Fmg.*, **5**, 460–2.

—— & SOLOMON, S. (1941). A list of hosts of some phanerogamic root parasites attacking economic crops in India. *Proc. Ind. Acad. Sci.*, **13**, 151–6.

—— —— & RAO, V. V. (1951). Synthetic hormones as weed-killers. *The Farmer*, **2**(5), 1–6.

KUSANO, S. (1903). Notes on *Aeginetia indica* Roxb. *Bot. Mag., Tokyo*, **17**, 1.

KUSANO, S. (1908). On the parasitism of *Siphonostegia* (Rhinantheae). *Bull. Coll. Agric. Tokyo* 8, 51–57.

—— (1908a). Further studies on *Aeginetia indica*. *Bull. Coll. Agric. Tokyo*, 8, 59–78.

LAUBACH, H. VON SOLMS-. *See* SOLMS-LAUBACH, H. VON

LAVERGNE, J. (1893). *Contribution à l'histoire des Orobanches: Etude des éspèces vivantes sur les plantes cultivées.* Bordeaux, Montpellier, 71 pp.

LEE, A. & GOSECO, F. (1932). Studies of the sugar-cane root parasite, *Aeginetia indica*. *Internat. Soc. Sugar Cane Technol. Congr. (San Juan) Proc. 4*, 1–12.

LEE, W. O. & TIMMONS, F. L. (1954). CIPC gives promise of controlling dodder in alfalfa. *Fm. Home Sci.*, 15 (Mar.), 3, 20.

LEEUWEN, W. M. D. VAN. *See* VAN LEEUWEN, W. M. D.

LING, K. C. (1955). Bunga. *Taiwan Sugar*, 2(1), 21.

LITTLE, B. E. (1927). Mistletoe (ethereal plant). Oklahoma State Flower, 45 pp.

LO, T. T. (1955). N : Co 310 highly resistant to the root parasite bunga (*Aeginetia indica*). *Taiwan Sugar*, 2(4), 18–20.

LÜSTNER, G. (1936). Ueber die Bedeutung des Wortes 'Mistel.' *Z. PflKrankh.*, 46, 270–1.

MACDOUGAL, D. T. & CANNON, W. A. (1910). *The conditions of parasitism in plants.* Carnegie Institute of Washington, Publ. No. 129, 60 pp.

MCGRAWTH, H., SHAW, W. C., JANSEN, L. L., LIPSCOMB, B. R., MILLER, P. R., & ENNIS, W. B. Jr. (1957). *Witcheed (Striga asiatica) a new parasitic plant in the United States.* U. S. Dept. Agric., Pl. Dis., Epid. & Ident. Sect. Spec. Publ. 10, 142 pp. (298 refs. annotated).

MACLEOD, D. G. (1962). Some anatomical and physiological observations on two species of *Cuscuta*. *Trans. Bot. Soc. Edinb.* 39, 302–15.

MCLUCKIE, J. (1923). Studies in parasitism. A contribution to the physiology of the Loranthaceae of New South Wales. *Bot. Gaz.*, 75, 333–69.

MCWHORTER, F. P. (1922). Concerning the sugar-cane parasite, *Aeginetia indica*. *Philipp. Agric.*, 11(3), 89–90.

MANNAGETTA, G. BECK VON. *See* BECK VON MANNAGETTA, G.

MARUDARJAN, D. (1950). Note on *Orobanche cernua* Loefl. *Current Sci.*, 19(2), 64–65.

MATHUR, A. K. (1949). Angiospermic parasites of our forests. *Indian For.*, 75(11), 449–56.

MELCHIOR, H. (1940). Beitrag zur Kenntnis der Gattung *Melasma*. *Notizbl. Bot. Gart. u. Mus. Bln.-Dahlem*, 15, 119–27.

MENDIZABEL, M. (1945). *Thesium humile* Vahl, santalacea parasita de los cultivos y toxica para el ganado. (Nota previa.) *Bol. Pat. Veg. Ent. Agric. Madr.*, 14, 309–14.

MILLER, P. M. (1956). Discovery of *Striga*, a parasitic flowering plant, in Western Hemisphere. *Plant Prot. Bull.*, 5, 47–49.

MUNERATI, O. (1929). Sul problema della canopa di fronte allo orobanche. *Ital. Agric.*, 66, 177–84.

MUNZ, P. A. (1931). The North American species of *Orobanche*, section *Mycorrhiza*. *Bull. Torrey Bot. Cl.*, 57, 611–24.

NARASIMHAN, M. J. (1920). Parasitic plants as enemies to crops. *J. Mysore Agr. Exp. Union*, 2(1), 18–20.

NARAYANA, H. S. (1956). Diffuse type of parasitism in *Cuscuta hyalina*. *Sci. & Cult.*, 21(8), 447–50.

NELSON, R. T. (1957). Preliminary studies on the *Striga* parasitic weed of corn. *Plant Dis. Reptr.*, 41, 377–83.

NICHOLSON, C. (1932). The mistletoe and its hosts. *Gdnrs' Chron., Lond.*, 91, 102–4, 145–6, 259.

ORTIZ GARMENDIA, J. (1936). Es obligatoria la destruccion del 'Quintral' *Phrygilanthus (Loranthus) tetrandrus*. *Bol. Soc. Agric. Norte*, 24, 87.

OSMAN, A. (1928). L'Orobanche rameuse (*Phelipaea ramosa* C. A. Mey). *Rev. Tech. Monop. Tabacs Turq.*, **1**, 127–31.

OSTAPETZ, M. L. (1925). [L'Orobanche sur tournesol dans le gouvernement de Voronezh, d'apres les observations en 1924—in Russian.] *Pl. Prot.*, *Leningr.*, **2**, 334–41.

PAINE, R. A. (1950). The susceptibility of pear trees to penetration and toxic damage by mistletoe. *Phytopathol. Z.*, **17**, 305–7.

PALHINHA, R. T. (1942). [The geographic distribution and the ecology of *Arceuthobium oxycedri* (DC.) M.-Bieb—in Spanish.] *Bol. Soc. Broteria.*, **16**, 137–43.

PATWARDHAN, G. B. (1925). Some hosts of lucerne dodder (*Cuscuta chinensis*). *Poona Agric. Coll. Mag.*, **17**, 152–3.

PETER-CONTESSE, J. (1937). Influence du gui sur la production du bois. *J. For. Suisse*, **7**, 145–3.

PETERS, L. & SCHWARTZ, M. (1912). *Krankheiten und Beschädigungen des Tabaks.* Mitt. Kais. Biol. Anstalt Landwirtsch. u. Forstw., Berlin, Heft 13, pp. 7–76.

PIERCE, G. J. (1905). The dissemination and germination of *Arceuthobium occidentale*, Eng. *Ann. Bot.*, *Lond.*, **19**, 99–113.

PIERCE, W. D. (1939). The dodder and its insects. *Bull. S. Calif. Acad. Sci.*, **38**, 43–53.

PIJL, L. VAN DER (1936). Fledermäuse und Blumen. *Flora*, **131**, 1–40.

PIJL, P. A. VAN DER (1920). A list of host-plants of some of the Loranthaceae occurring near Durban, Natal. *S. Afr. J. Sci.*, **16**, 354–9.

PINEWICH, L. M. (1933). On the physiology of *Orobanche ramosa* L. *Acta Inst. Bot. Acad. Sci. URSS*, Ser. 4, Fasc. 1, 189–203.

PLAGNAT, F. (1950). Le gui du sapin. *Ann. Ec. Eaux For. Nancy*, **12**, 156–231.

POETEREN, N. VAN (1917). Der Hanfwürger, *Orobanche ramosa* L. *Tijdschr. PlZiekt.*, **23**, 1–16.

PRASAD, N. (1954). Control of *Orobanche* in tobacco by Crag Herbicide 1. *Indian Tobacco*, **4**(3), 139.

QUISUMBING, E. (1940). On *Christisonia wrightii* Elmer, a parasite of sugar cane. *Philipp. J. Agric.*, **11**, 397–401.

RAO, M. K. (1919). *Orobanche* on tobacco. *J. Mysore Agric. Exp. Un.*, **1**(3), 18–20.

RAO, N. L. (1938). Perennation in *Cuscuta reflexa* Roxb. *New Phytol.*, **37**, 474–7.

—— (1942). Parasitism in the Santalaceae. *Ann. Bot.*, **6**, 131–50.

RAO, P. G. (1955). A rapid method for studying the germination of the seeds of the root parasite *Orobanche cernua* Loefl. var. *desertorum* (Beck.). *Sci. & Cult.*, **21**, 258–62.

RAO, R. SASHAGIRI (1957). A revision of the Indo-Malayan species of *Viscum* Linn. *J. Indian Bot. Soc.*, **36**, 113–68.

RATTRAY, J. M. (1932). A parasite on cowpeas (*Alectra vogelii* Benth.). *Rhod. Agric. J.*, **29**, 791–4.

RAZI, B. A. (1957). An annotated list of phanerogamic parasites from India and Pakistan. *Lloydia*, **20**, 238–54.

REED, C. F. & REED, P. G. (1951). Host distribution of mistletoe (*Phoradendron flavescens*) in Kentucky. *Castanea*, **16** (Mar.), 7–15.

RHOADS, A. S. (1943). Observations on the occurrence of mistletoe in Florida. *Plant Dis. Reptr.*, **27** (23).

RICHTER, A. A. (1926). [The physiology of *Orobanche cumana*—in Russian, German summary.] *J. Exp. Landw. S.-O. Europ. Russ.*, **3**(1), 32–9.

ROBERTS, W. E. and NELSON, R. R. (1962). Penetration and nutrition of *Striga asiatica*. *Phytopath.*, **52**, 1064–70.

ROBINSON, E. L., & KUST, C. A. (1962). Distribution of witchweed seeds in the soil. *Weeds* **10**, 335.

ROXAS, M. L. (1931). *Aeginetia indica* in sugar cane. *Sug. News*, **12**(2), 89.

SANDS, W. N. (1924). Mistletoes attacking cultivated trees in Malaya. *Malay. Agric. J.*, 12, 64–76.

SANZEN-BAKER, R. G. (1938). Literature on the mistletoes. *Imperial Forestry Inst.*, *Oxford*, Paper No. 12.

SARMA, K. (1952). The *Loranthus* parasite as a pest of citrus trees in Assam. *Indian J. Hort.*, 9(2), 18–21.

SAUNDERS, A. R. (1933). Studies in phanerogamic parasitism with particular reference to *Striga lutea* Lour. *S. African Dept. Agric. Sci.*, *Bull.* No. 128, 56 pp.

—— (1934). *Melasma*—a dangerous parasite on legumes. *Fmg. in S. Afr.*, 9, 342.

SAWYER, A. M. (1921). Result of investigations made by the Department of Agriculture, Burma, into the extent of the damage caused by *Striga lutea*. *Bull. Dept. Agric.*, *Burma*, No. 18, 7 pp.

SCHMUCKER, T. (1959). Höhere Parasiten. In *Handbuch der Pflanzenphysiologie* (W. Ruhland, Ed.). Springer-Verlag, Berlin, Band 11, pp. 480–529.

SCHOLL, R. (1956). Weitere Untersuchungen über Veründerungen der Reaktionslage des Birnbaumes (*Pyrus communis* L.) gegenüber der Mistel (*Viscum album* L.). *Phytopath. Z.*, 28, 237–58.

SCHREDL, H. (1937). Beiträge zur Physiologie von *Cuscuta*. *Diss. Würzburg* (1938), 47 pp.

SESHAGIRI RAO, R. *See* RAO, R. SESHAGIRI.

SHARMA, S. L., RAO, D. & TRIVEDI, K. N. (1956). Taxonomy of three species of *Striga* parasitic on sugar cane. *Proc. Ind. Acad. Sci.*, Sect., 43, 67–71.

SHAW, F. J. F. (1917). *Orobanche* as a parasite in Bihar. *Mem. Dep. Agric. India, Bot.*, 9, 107–30.

SMITH, B. E. (1934). A taxonomic and morphological study of the genus *Cuscuta*, dodders, in North Carolina. *J. Elisha Mitchell Sci. Soc.*, 50, 283–302.

SOLMS-LAUBACH, H. VON (1867). Über den Bau und die Entwicklung parasiticher Phanerogamen. *Jb. Wiss. Bot.*, 6, 509–638.

SOLOMON, S. (1952). Studies on the physiology of phanerogamic parasites with special reference to *Striga lutea* Lour. and *S. densiflora* Benth. on *Sorghum vulgare*. I: The osmotic pressure of the host and parasite in relation to the nutrition of the host. *Proc. Ind. Acad. Sci.*, Sect. B, 35, 122–31.

—— (1952a). Studies on the physiology of phanerogamic parasites with special reference to Strigas on Sorghums. II: Influence of temperature on germination. *Proc. Ind. Acad. Sci.*, Sect. B, 36, 198–214.

SPERLICH, A. (1925). *Die Absorptionsorgane der parasitischen Samenpflanzen*. Handbuch der Pflanzenanatomie, Berlin, Gebrüder Borntraeger II, Abt. 2, Bd. IX/2, 55 pp.

STAHEVITCH, B. Y. & KOULECHOFF, N. N. (1929). Observations biologiques sur la développement de la cuscute dans les champs. *Mitt. Intern. Vereinigung Samenkontrolle*, 105, 350.

STEVENS, O. A. (1952). Dodder (*Cuscuta*) on cultivated plants. *Bull. N. Dak. Agric. Exp. Sta.*, 15 (Nov./Dec.), 80–81.

STEWART, F. C. & FRENCH, G. T. (1909). The perennation of clover dodder, *C. epithymum*. *Torreya*, 9, 28–30.

STITT, R. E. (1939). Dodder control in annual Lespedezas. *J. Amer. Soc. Agron.*, 31, 338–43.

—— (1940). Yields of Korean Lespedeza as affected by dodder. *J. Amer. Soc. Agron.*, 32, 969–71.

STOUT, G. L. (1936). A rare case of dodder (*Cuscuta indecora* Choisy) attacking olive in California. *Bull. Calif. Dept. Agric.*, 25, 213–15.

—— (1940). A case of dodder (*Cuscuta subinclusa* Durand and Hilgard) on Valencia orange (*Citrus sinensis* Osbeck) in southern California. *Bull. Calif. Dept. Agric.* 29, 121–4.

STRYCKERS, J. (1951). [The control of *Rhinanthus major* Ehrh—in Flemish.] *Meded. Land-boogesch. Gent.*, 16, 81–94.

SUBRAMANIAN, C. L. & SRINIVASAN, A. R. (1960). A review of the literature on the phanerogamous parasites. *Ind. Counc. Agr. Res. Monogr.* 10.24, *New Delhi*, 96 pp. (incl. bibliogr. of 15 pp.)

SUBRAMANIAN, T. V. & SUBRAMANIAN, C. L. (1954). *Fimbristylis miliacea* Vahl—a new host for *Striga euphrasioides* (Vahl) Benth. (Res. note.) *Madras Agric. J.*, 41(1), 18.

SULIT, M. D. (1930). Some tree destroyers belonging to the mistletoe family (Loranthaceae). *Philipp. Agric.*, 19, 665–73.

TATE, P. (1925). On the anatomy of *Orobanche hederae* Dubu., and its attachment to the host. *New Phytol.*, 24, 284–93.

THODAY, D. (1951). The haustorial system of *Viscum album. J. Exp. Bot.*, 2(4), 1–19.

—— (1963). Mode of union and interaction between parasite and host in the Loranthaceae. VII. Some Australian Loranthoideae with exceptional features *Proc. Roy. Soc. Lond.* Ser. B. 157, 507–516.

THOMPSON, J. C. (1954). [Witchweed seed commits 'suicide'—in Afrikaans.] *Landbouweekblad*, 36(1840), 3,537.

TIKHOVIDOVA, V. K. (1952). [Combating dodder (*Cuscuta europaea*) on grapevine—in Russian.] *Vitic & Wine-Mak.*, *Moscow*, 2 (Feb.), 46–47.

TIMSON, S. D. (1929). Witch-weed: *Striga lutea*, methods of control. *Bull. Dept. Agric. S. Rhod.*, No. 759, 12 pp.

—— (1945). Trap-cropping to control witchweed. *Rhod. Agric. J.*, 42, 278–87.

—— (1945a). Witchweed demonstration farm. *Rhod. Agric. J.*, 42, 404–9.

TOOHEY, C. L. (1953). Cane-killing weed in the Mackay district. *Cane Gr. Quart. Bull.*, 17(1), 7–10.

TRABUT, M. (1907). Les cuscutes du nord de l'Afrique. *Bull. Soc. Bot. Fr.*, 54, 34–43.

TRELEASE, W. (1916). *The genus* Phoradendron; *a monographic revision.* University of Illinois Press, Urbana, Ill., 224 pp.

TRONCHET, JOSETTE (1961). Contribution à l'étude de la croissance et des mouvements de la plantule de *Cuscuta Gronovii* Willd. *Ann. Sci. Univ. Besançon*, 2e ser. Bot., fasc. 16, 206 pp. (84 figs., 802 refs.)

TRUSCOTT, F. H. (1955). On the regeneration of new shoots from isolated dodder haustoria. *Ph.D. Thesis*, Rutgers University.

TSO-CHIE HWANG. *See* HWANG, TSO-CHIE.

TUBEUF, K. F. VON (1919). Überblick über die Arten der Gattung *Arceuthobium* (*Razoumowskia*) mit besonderer Berücksüchtigung ihrer Biologie und praktischen Bedeutung. *Naturw. Z. Forst- u. Landw.*, 17, 167–271.

—— (1928). Die Mistel *Viscum album* auf dem Ölbaume *Olea eureopaea. Z. PflKrankh.*, 38, 139–40.

——, NECKEL, G. & MARZELL, H. (1923). *Monographie der Mistel.* R. Oldenburg, München, 832 pp.

URTON, N. R. (1945). Dodders and lucerne in South Africa. *S. Afr. J. Sci.*, 41, 231–7.

UTTAMAN, P. (1949). An introduction to the study of *Striga lutea* Lour. as a root parasite on rice in Malabar. *Madras Agric. J.*, 36(7), 303–7.

—— (1950). Parasitism of *Striga lutea* Lour. on rice and methods to protect rice plants against *Striga. Madras Agric. J.*, 37(3), 99–118.

—— (1950a). A study of the germination of *Striga* seed and on the mechanism and nature of parasitism of *Striga lutea* on rice. *Proc. Ind. Acad. Sci.*, Ser. B, 32, 133–42.

VALDÉS, B. F. (1958). 'Striga' planta parásita de las raíces. Una nueva amenaza para la Caña de Azúcar. *Comn. de Defensa del Azucar y de la Caña Fomento.*, 1(11), 11–12.

VALLANCE, K. B. (1950). Studies on the germination of the seeds of *Striga hermonthica*. I: *Ann. Bot.*, 14, 347–63.

VALLANCE, K. B. (1951). Studies on the germination of the seeds of *Striga hermonthica*. II: *J. Exp. Bot.*, 2(4), 31–40.

—— (1951*a*). Studies on the germination of the seeds of *Striga hermonthica*. III: *Ann. Bot.*, 15, 109–28.

VAN DER PIJL, P. A. *See* PIJL, P. A., VAN DER.

VAN DER PIJL, L. *See* PIJL, L. VAN DER.

VAN LEEUWEN, W. M. D. (1954). On the biology of some Javanese Loranthaceae and the role birds play in their life-history. *Beaufarha Ser. Misc. Publ.* No. 41, 4, 105–207.

VAN POETEREN, N. *See* POETEREN, N. VAN.

VASQUEZ, A. (1927). El jopo de las habas y su destruccion (*Orobanche crenata*). *Rev. Vinic.*, 45, 24–25.

VERDOORN, I. C. (1923). The flowering parasitic plants found in South Africa. *S. Afr. J. Nat. Hist.*, 4, 221–8.

VOGEL, F. (1954). Der Tabakwürger und seine Bekämpfung. *Deutsche Tabakbau*, pp. 145–6.

VOLKART, A. (1899). *Untersuchungen über den Parasitismus der Pedicularisarten*. Zürich.

VON MANNAGETTA, G. BECK. *See* BECK VON MANNAGETTA, G.

VON SOLMS-LAUBACH, H. *See* SOLMS-LAUBACH, H. VON.

VON TUBEUF, K. F. *See* TUBEUF, K. F. VON.

WAGENER, W. W. (1925). Mistletoe in the lower bole of incense cedar. *Phytopathology*, 15, 614–6.

WARNER, H. H. (1930). The mistletoe and its hosts. *Gdnrs' Chron.*, 88, 512.

WEBER, G. F. (1938). Mistletoe in crop and shade trees. *Pr. Bull. Fla. Agric. Expt. Sta.*, No. 523, 2 pp.

WEERARATNA, W. G. (1960). The ecology and biology of parasitism of the Loranthaceae of Ceylon. Pp. 189–202 in *The Biology of Weeds* (ed. J. L. Harper), Blackwell, Oxford. 256 pp.

WILD, H. (1948). A suggestion for the control of tobacco witchweed (*Striga gesneriodes* (Willd.) Vatke) by leguminous crops. *Rhod. Agric. J.*, 45, 208–15.

WILSON JONES, K. *See* JONES, K. W.

WINKLER, H. (1913). Versuche über die Ernährung der Mistel. *Naturw. Z. Forst- u. Landw.* No. 1.

WORSHAM, A. D., & KLINGMAN, G. C. (1962). Promotion of germination of *Striga asiatica* seed by coumarin derivatives and effects on seedling development. *Nature, Lond.*, 195, 199–201.

YORK, H. H. (1909). The anatomy and some of the biological aspects of the 'American mistletoe', *Phoradendron flavescens* (Pursh) Nutt. *Bull. Univ. Tex. Sci. Ser.* No. 13, No. 120, 31 pp.

YUNCKER, T. G. (1921). A revision of the North American and West Indian species of *Cuscuta*. *Illinois Biol. Monogr.*, 6, 95–231 (includes 287 refs.).

—— (1922–23). Revision of the South American species of *Cuscuta*. I: *Amer. J. Bot.*, 9, 557–75; II: *ibid.*, 10, 1–17.

—— (1927). Additions to a bibliography of the genus *Cuscuta*. *Proc. Indiana Acad. Sci.*, 36, 259–62 (includes 77 refs.).

—— (1932). The genus *Cuscuta*. *Mem. Torrey Bot. Cl.*, 18, 109–331.

ZAHLOUL, M. A. (1944). Investigation in combating *Orobanche*. *Agric. J. Egypt*, 1, 21–36.

ZEIGLER, H. (1955). *Lathraea*, ein Blutungssaftschmarotzer. *Ber. Dtsch. Bot. Ges.*, 68, 311–18.

ZÖPFIG, F. (1933). Die Mistel (*Viscum album* L.), Pflanzenschadling. *Kranke Pflanze*, 10, 59–62.

IV

THE USES OF WEEDS

MANY kinds of weeds have found certain limited uses. However, this is rather an anomalous situation; for if a plant has a reputed use, strictly by definition it should cease to be classed as a weed. Yet it is the thesis of this work that a large proportion of the autotrophic land weeds at one time or another were used by man, and that, because of this removal from the natural environment, they became incorporated into the weed class (cf. Pl. 6). Be that as it may, one does frequently encounter references to the *uses* of weeds and many of these have been cited in the check-lists for the various regions throughout the world. It is also true, of course, that a plant classed as a weed in one region where it has few if any uses, may, when growing in another region, possess some very valuable uses, or in a few cases may actually be cultivated.

Prehistoric man was dependent upon herbaceous plants for his elemental needs, and later used them for ceremonial, medicinal, and ornamental purposes; in fact weeds and wild plants are still used quite largely by primitive peoples in medicine and as emergency food supplies.

UTILIZATION AS FOOD FOR ANIMALS

The grazing animal, as well as much of our wildlife, is dependent on vegetation which quite frequently contains a high proportion of weeds. The usage of such plants by American wildlife is summarized in the work of Martin *et al.* (1951), and in the study of McAtee (1939). In Colorado, cattle grazing on pastures of native grama and buffalo grass consistently made better gains where weeds and shrubs constituted from 10 to 20 per cent of the total forage than where the grass stands were nearly pure. The prevalence of different kinds of weeds was indicative of the degree of grazing. These 'range weeds' are generally broad-leafed forbs that are ordinarily considered to have little grazing value, and are quite often indigenous species (Costello, 1942). However, a study in England (Tribe *et al.*, 1952) of young cattle on temporary pasture of mixed character, provided no evidence to support the opinion that it benefits grazing animals to have access to browse in addition to good forage.

A large number of studies that have been made in Europe, and parti-cularly in Germany, have sought to determine the nutritive value of weeds—especially as emergency rations, as they were used in several war-periods. Investigations have been carried out by Hiltner (1917–18), Kling (1918), Naumann (1918), König (1954), and others. The use for animal feed of weed seeds from grain screenings has been examined by Weiser (1924), in some Canadian work (Anon., 1915), and by Kling (1917). Kling analysed the seeds of nineteen weed species for their value for feeding poultry. The ensiling of weeds in Vermont was examined by Washburn (1912). Species of *Digitaria* have long been used for forage in pastures, and also offer some soil protection. Sagebrush (*Artemisia tridentata*) provides winter feed for deer (A. D. Smith, 1950), while the prickly-pear cactus (*Opuntia* sp.) is used for cattle feed during periods of drought.

THE VALUE OF WEEDS AS FOOD FOR HUMANS

Fukai (1940), in Japan, has examined the nutritive value of some 40 species of weeds—particularly with regard to their content of Vitamin C, Carotene, and Vitamin B_1 and B_2. Brewer & Blinn (1924), in a study from Delaware, have reported on the nutritive value of wild 'greens'; while both Fox (1942) and Palmer (1949) cover the general uses of weeds as a source of food. There are, of course, a large number of ethnobotanical studies of plant utilization which cover particularly the food and medicinal uses (Train *et al.*, 1957).

Contributions to the study of the value of weeds as food for humans have been made by Chestnut (1902), and Densmore (1928). Specific weeds have also been studied, e.g. the dandelion (Bennet, 1934), and *Chenopodium* (by R. U. Virchow). Claassen (1919) has reviewed the uses of *Typha*, which is employed by the American Indian to make sweet flour, derived from the dried and pulverized rhizome. In New Zealand the pollen is used to make bread. The rhizomes of *Typha* form a network lying 3 to 4 in. underground, and may be $\frac{3}{4}$–1 in. in diameter. The yield of flour can be as high as 5,500 lb. per acre.

The uses of bulrushes have been reviewed by Beetle (1950). Innes (1908) notes that a list of the jungle products used by the natives of Balrampur Estate, India, during the famine of 1896–97, includes many common weeds.

A series of Canadian studies on the utilization of oils prepared from monthly samples of cleaned weed-seed screenings, and of screenings oil (commercially solvent-extracted), examined over a six-month period (November 1948 to April 1949), indicated that whereas the composition of the screenings varied widely, that of the oil was remarkably constant. The seeds were obtained at the Fort William factory, and represented the accumulated screenings from cereals crops of the Prairies (including *Brassica arvensis*, *B. juncea*, *B. nigra*, and *B. campestris*, as well as some 34 other weed species in smaller quantities). The composition of the screenings was: wild mustard (mostly *Brassica arvensis*), average 68 per cent;

mixed weed seeds, average 23 per cent; crop seeds, average 6·0 per cent; and broken and unidentified seeds, average 3 per cent. The appearance of the oil and its response to processing were similar to those of rape and mustard-seed oils. Small-scale taste panel tests indicated that processed screenings oil was not generally as palatable as corn or cottonseed salad oils, but that screenings shortening was generally as acceptable as the control (commercial vegetable shortenings) (Grace, 1948).

MEDICAL USES OF WILD PLANTS

The native medicine men, the herbalists and their herb gardens, and the herb shops and apothecaries, have all played an important role in the collection, dispersal, and population increase, of many plants that at one time or another have had medical uses. Some of these plants in later ages have come to be regarded as weeds (cf. Pl. 6).

Henkel (1904) has reviewed the medicinal uses by the American Indian of a large number of weeds. Practically all of the ethnobotanical studies cited in this chapter and elsewhere throughout these volumes, devote a considerable amount of space to the uses of plants for medical purposes. Professor Charles Welch (1961) of the Philadelphia College of Pharmacy and Science has surveyed the medicinal plants utilized by the American Indians and checked their present-day value and utilization with the documentation found in the *United States Dispensatory* (Osol & Farrar, 1960).

One of the more striking medical uses of a wild plant has been that of *Lithospermum ruderale*, by one settlement of the Shoshone Indians of Nevada, for control of conception (Train *et al.*, 1941). This is in addition to its wider use among the Shoshone as a treatment for diarrhoea. A cold-water infusion from the roots, taken daily as a drink for a period of six months, was believed to ensure sterility thereafter. This activity has been experimentally verified in laboratory animals, and extracts were found to interfere with the production or function of sex hormones and hence with ovulation and conception (cf. E. M. Cranston, cited in Drasher & Zahl, 1946). These findings have led to further work in this area of pharmacological regulation of conception, to the identification of a steroid in *Lithospermum* roots, and to the experimental use of these substances in cancer therapy (Davis & Ross, 1955).

Of interest in this relationship, perhaps, is the list of plant materials reportedly used by primitive peoples to affect fertility which has been published by de Laszlo and Henshaw (1954). These authors point out that information of this nature from the literature of folklore, popular medicine, and from older works on *materia medica* has often been questioned by modern investigators—and rightly so—in a great many of their reports. They further comment, however, that confidence in such sources of information may be strengthened when a number of valuable drugs of present-day usage are examined with respect to sources and original usage: the use of soils for treatment (a mould source for antibiotics); an antithrombic agent (rutin, from *Ruta graveolens*); a muscle relaxant, tubocurare, from an arrow poison of the Guiana Indians; the heart-regulating agents (cratioaegolic acid, etc.) from *Crataegus oxycantha*; the sedative and hypertensive *Rauwolfia* alkaloids from *R. serpentina* of India; a cardiac stimulant (foliandrin) from *Oleander* sp.; the coronary stimulant, khellin, from *Ammi visnaga*; and the antimalarial, febrifugine, from *Hydrangea* roots, originally of Chinese origin.

There are 60 species in the list just referred to (de Laszlo & Henshaw, 1954) that in some manner affect human fertility (*though mostly of an unscientific character*). Among the many genera so involved are such weedy ones as *Achillea*, *Apocynum*, *Asclepias*, *Asparagus*, *Capsella*, *Chenopodium*, *Cicuta*, *Cordia*, *Eupatorium*, *Geranium*, *Lithospermum*, *Phoradendron*, *Plantago*, and *Polygonum*.

The literature concerning medicinal plants is extensive, and hence only a few works with comprehensive bibliographies will here be listed. The bibliography of de Laszlo (1958) lists some 1,500 books and pamphlets from all parts of the world. The publication of Quisumbing (1951) on the medicinal plants of the Philippines is most useful, for the data are obtained from local sources as well as from publications from other tropical areas throughout the world. The study of Martinez (1944) on Mexican medicinal plants, and the volume of Chopra & Chopra (1955) on Indian medicinal plants are also useful. There are at least three scientific journals dealing with this subject, and their files may be profitably consulted: *Lloydia* (1938 to date); *Economic Botany* (1947 to date); and *Planta Medica* (1953 to date).

SOME GENERAL USES

Many agriculturists have recognized that weeds, despite their nuisance value, do at times serve some useful purpose. This has been examined at length in a book, *Weeds—Guardians of the Soil* (Cocannouer, 1950). Campbell (1924) has noted that deeply-leached nitrates can, in part, be returned to the upper soil layers by the growth and decay of weed species. Early, late, and winter annuals, appear to conserve nitrogen at times when no cultivated plants are present on the land. Studies conducted in 1894 revealed that 17·3 lb. of N per acre were found in *Stellaria media*, which had grown during the winter in sugar-cane fields. This was about one-half of the N in fertilizers employed each year at that time, and was saved from being washed away by permitting the ground to be covered with the weed. Even the water-hyacinth (*Eichhornia*) has been proposed for use in Natal to trap a source of fertility which would otherwise be lost. It has been suggested that water-hyacinth could be dragged on to river banks and composted there for its fertility value.

Weeds often provide a protective cover against erosive action of raindrops as well as guarding against surface washing and run-off. Moreover, weeds are frequently used in the form of a mulch around cultivated plants. Some antibiotics, as well as insecticides, have been extracted from weeds. Other weeds have at one time or another been considered ornamentals (e.g. species of *Rudbeckia*, *Helianthus*, *Daucus*, *Melilotus*, etc.).

EXAMPLES OF PLANT USAGE BY THE INDIAN TRIBES OF NORTHERN CALIFORNIA

The use of plants by the Indians of Mendocino County, Northern California, has been investigated in some detail by Chestnut (1902). The uses of some 200 species of plants are described, the Indian names for most of them being also given. Particularly helpful is the classified list of the economic plants, arranged according to the specific category of their usage. A few of these economic plants are treated below, and exemplify the importance of the treatment of the unused portion of the plant, and how it can frequently aid in the dispersal and population increase of the plant in question. It is interesting to note that the Indians ignore the very common weeds, and use only those that were employed by their ancestors, which could be much more difficult to obtain.

SEEDS AND FRUITS USED FOR FOOD

The 'seed' of the wild oat (*Avena fatua*), a pernicious weed in many northern cereal-growing regions, is consumed by the Indians in large quantities. The 'seeds' are gathered almost exclusively by an old squaw, who, providing herself with a V-shaped basket that is capable of holding more than a bushel, goes out into the fields at the proper season, and, by means of a piece of basketwork made into the form of a tennis racket, beats off the ripe 'seed' into the basket and then carries it home. The hair and the sharp points are singed off the 'seeds', which at the same time are parched, by skilfully tossing them about with live coals in a shallow basket. The parched seed is then ground in a mortar until the flour is as fine as desired. Common salt, or the ash from certain plants, is added, and the flour is generally eaten in the dry condition.

The Spanish word *pinole* has come to be almost universally applied, both by the Indians and non-Indians, to any meal that is made from parched seeds. Only one kind of *pinole* seed is usually collected at any one time, and each collection is generally kept separate until after the chaff has been removed (either by winnowing or by basket-sieving) and the seeds can be ground into meal. Blends with the different kinds of seeds (e.g. certain aromatic seeds) are often made, depending upon individual preference. The more important pinole seeds used include *Calandrinia elegans* (Portulacaceae), *Ranunculus eisenii* (Ranunculaceae), *Ceanothus integerrima* (Rhamnaceae), *Trifolium virescens* (Leguminosae), *Madia dissitiflora* (Compositae), *Hemizonia luzulaefolia*, 'tarweed' (Compositae), *Wyethia longicaulis* (Compositae) a perennial short-stemmed sunflower, and

83

Boisduvalia densiflora (Onagraceae). The smaller seeds, of such plants as the following, are also gathered in small quantities for this purpose: *Polygonum aviculare* (Polygonaceae), *Rumex crispus* (seeds ground for mush, also Polygonaceae), *Amaranthus retroflexus* (Amaranthaceae), *Capsella bursa-pastoris* (Cruciferae), *Plagiobothrys campestris* (Boraginaceae), *Salvia columbariae* (Labiatae)—the seeds of this species are mucilaginous, and are highly valued for making soup—and *Achyrachaena mollis* (Compositae).

The acorns of the white oak (*Quercus lobata*) are gathered when ripe in the autumn by beating them off the tree, or obtained from small branches that are cut and thrown to the ground. Some 400 to 500 lb. may thus be gathered by one family for a year's supply. They are then dried, ground into flour, percolated with water in a sand-pit to remove the tannins, and used in mush or bread-making.

FISH POISONS

Second in importance to the use of the bulb of *Chlorogalum pomeridianum* (Liliaceae) as a substitute for soap, is its use as a means of stupefying fish and thus procuring them for food. After the last June freshet, when the water was running very low, the village inhabitants gathered at a convenient place on the river and constructed a weir. A quantity of the fleshy bulbs were mashed up on the nearby rocks. Bushel after bushel of the crushed pulp was thrown into the water and thoroughly stirred in—the finer pieces passing through the weir, while the larger pieces were taken out and again crushed and thrown into the water. The Indians, stationed all along the stream for 3 miles or so, added fresh bulbs here and there, and kept the water in a state of thorough agitation. After a very short time all of the fish (and also the eels, but not the frogs) were so stupefied by the poison that they floated to the surface and were captured. As much as 100 bushels were caught in this way at one time and divided equally among the participants. Used in a similar manner are the bruised leaves of turkey-mullein, the fish soapwort or *yerba del pescado* (*Croton setigerus*, Euphorbiaceae).

USES FOR AMUSEMENT

A number of plants are described that have some association with gambling. The root of *Delphinium nudicaule* (Ranunculaceae), 'sleeproot', has very marked narcotic properties, which are made use of in causing an opponent to become stupid while gambling. A number of plants are valued as a talisman in gambling. The root of *Angelica* sp. (Umbelliferae) is found in nearly every household, and is frequently carried about the person for good luck in gambling or hunting, while *Daucus pusillus* (Umbelliferae) is also used as a talisman in gambling, as is the root of *Sanicula menziesii* (Umbelliferae), which is supposed to bring good luck in gambling if chewed or rubbed on the body. A small bunch of the roots of *Vicia americana* (Leguminosae), is said sometimes to be kept in the pocket for good luck while gambling.

CEREMONIAL AND RELIGIOUS USES

The first appearance or the maturation of certain plants that were highly valued for their food, was the occasion of ceremonial dances—e.g. the nut season, the harvest of the fruits of the digger pine (*Pinus sabiniana*), and the clover (*Trifolium* spp.) season. *Trifolium* has also entered into the games of certain tribes.

The flowers of *Dodecatheon hendersoni* (Primulaceae) are used by women to ornament themselves at dances. A dancing enclosure in one locality had been made by planting the recently-cut poles of a willow (*Salix lasiolepis*) within an inch or two of each other, and arranging them in the form of a circle around a small tree, leaving a wide opening for the entrance. The leaves, which soon sprouted all along the poles, together with the dead leafy branches arranged on top, afforded ample protection from the sun and wind.

MISCELLANEOUS USES

Several plants are used as insect repellants. Many of the Indians place the culled plants of *Pogogyne parviflora* (Labiatae) in or about their houses, to drive away fleas. The leaves of a laurel, *Umbellularia californica*, were likewise used for driving away fleas, being said to be effective in this manner if strewn about the yard.

Indian hemp (*Apocynum cannabinum*) was at one time the sole source of the fibre (from the inner bark) used for making ropes, nets, garments, and thread. Root baskets are among the strongest and costliest of baskets, and are made from the underground portions of *Carex* spp. (Cyperaceae). The rootstocks are often traced through the sand for a distance of from 2 to 5 ft. in order to obtain strands of sufficient length. Species of *Juncus* (Juncaceae) and *Scirpus* (Cyperaceae) are also used in basketmaking.

As mentioned above, the bulb of *Chlorogalum pomeridianum* is used as a substitute for soap, as are parts of various other plants—including some that are apt to be classed as weeds.

THE CONTRIBUTIONS OF ETHNOBOTANICAL STUDIES

What appears to be the first specific work on ethnobotany has recently been published by P. J. Faulks (1958), of the University of Aberdeen, and raises the interesting question as to whether man would have evolved at all if it had not been for the advent of arborescent Dicotyledons. This recalls the statement of Takhtajian (1959), that, if it had not been for the seed plants, man might not have evolved and spread over the earth. Ames (1939) has likewise appraised the important role of the seed plants in man's history and evolution.

Faulks (1958) states that the subject of ethnobotany is concerned with the relationships between man and vegetation—involving man's dependence upon vegetation, as well as the tremendous influence man has had on vegetation. His book comprises four sections: (1) the ways in which vegetation is useful to man (goods and services); (2) troubles caused by vegetation to man, both physically and psychologically; (3) what man does to vegetation by way of destruction, conservation, culture, and conversion to his own ends; and (4) aspects of the relationship between vegetation and mankind collectively—for the history of civilization is the history of the inter-relationships between man and vegetation.

The folklore of plants is a vast subject and has been touched upon briefly above. Sir James Frazer (1854–1941) in his monumental study of magic and religion, *The Golden Bough* (1911), devotes two chapters of one volume to the worship of the oak and other trees. Thiselton Dyer (1889) has written on this subject; while the Dutch botanist, Teirlinck (1924, 1930, *see* Ch. I), has covered the subject of plants in magic lore, and in demonology. A more recent work by Lehner & Lehner (1960) covers the symbolic aspects of plants throughout man's long history. Dr. R. E. Shultes of Harvard University has more recently (1960) called attention to the need for tapping our heritage of ethnobotanical lore.

Oakes Ames, in his now classical *Economic Annuals and Human Cultures* (1939), reviewed the importance of the origin of Angiosperms and of the resulting land flora capable of sustaining mankind and his institutions. Of particular importance in the evolutionary development of the successful seed habit was the retention, until after fertilization had been effected, of the megaspore within the tissues of the parent Angiosperm plant. This ensured the continuous nutrition of the embryo by the parent plant up to an advanced age, as well as food storage for future growth during the early stages of germination. The embryo was thus able to pass through a more or less prolonged dormant period, and to withstand a considerable degree of desiccation, without losing its vitality. In these two features, truly, the destiny of man has resided: the factor of dormancy, which permitted not only use for food but also for carrying over from season to season for planting purposes; and desiccation, which provided safe food storage and in addition permitted carry-over for planting the following season. Ames states that, to the Angiosperm seed perhaps more than to any other structure, the economic evolution of the human race is due.

Weeding Operations in Primitive Agriculture

Reference has been made earlier (cf. Ch. I) to the Roman goddess of weeding, Runcina, of the Augustinian period, and the derivation of terms for 'weeds' and 'weeding' from 'Runcina'. This material, as well as the survey of 'weod' and 'woad' provides some examples from early western agriculture. Since the following material is primarily ethnobotany it is discussed here rather than in the final chapter (Ch. XV).

The distinguished anthropologist, Bronislaw Malinowski (1884–1942), has provided in his treatise, *Coral Gardens and their Magic* (1935), an account of the methods of tilling the soil and of agricultural rites in the Trobriand Islands. The natives of these islands (a coral archipelago off New Guinea in the south-east Pacific) are considered typical representatives of the South Sea natives in general. Of particular interest are magical rites for the weeding operations. Their mixed-crop gardens, divided off into squares, each contain one or two banana seedlings, a couple of taro tops, two or three sticks of sugar-cane, and a few tubers of the larger yam, *kuvi*. The women weed these gardens. Weeds are either simply torn out with the hands or, when they have grown too rank through neglect, uprooted with a small digging stick.

The magical rites of the garden sorcery are quite extensive. Aside from the inaugural rite of weeding there are five rites of the magic of growth (of the unripe crop); another is the growth magic cycle of the ripening crops—the purpose being to stimulate the growth and formation of tubers (taro). The weeding ceremony is performed by the garden magician of the community—an office of hereditary origin, and often this power is possessed by the Chief or head-man. For example, in the taro gardens of Omarkanana such a weeding ceremony with its short spell and simple rite is performed in every garden plot. The weeding or 'sweeping clean' is inaugurated by a very simple magical rite—consisting of a conventionalized mimic weeding act; with a symbolic digging stick the magician scratches the ground, uprooting perhaps a few weeds and uttering an incantation.

The magic of weeding in the village of Teyava is done in two instalments—first, the magician medicates the point of his digging stick. This medication is prepared from a mixture of seven herbs and material from a bush-hen's nest tied up in a banana leaf and stored for one day prior to the rite. He then goes to the plots and inaugurates the removal of the big weeds (the *pwakova* proper). A few days later he chants another spell over the point of his digging stick and gives the magical blessing to the *sapi* (literally, 'to scratch'), the cleaning or brushing away of small weeds.

The term for 'weeding' is *pwakova* (used as both a noun and a verb), which is a specific term for uprooting a weed. While only indicated by Malinowski, this term may have some relationship to *ka'i*, or *kay* (a general term for any plant, or for a long stick of wood). These natives employ, however, the word *munumunu* for 'weeds'. This term refers to nameless plants, those of no known use, and those that *cannot be burned in preparing a fire* (apparently largely herbaceous plants). Thus in this remote and primitive culture we find here, too, a word that has been developed to describe that group of plants which merit no particular use—being in this case even useless for preparing a fire.

87

BIBLIOGRAPHY

(The Uses of Weeds)

AMES, O. (1939). *Economic annuals and human cultures.* Botanical Museum of Harvard University, Cambridge, Mass., 153 pp. (reprinted, 1953).

ANON. (1915). Grain screenings with results of feeding experiments. *Canada Dep. Agric.*, p. 44.

—— (1950). Fly killer found in weed (ox-eye daisy). *Fm. J.*, p. 26.

BEETLE, A. A. (1950). Bulrushes (*Scirpus* spp.) and their multiple uses. *Econ. Bot.*, **4**, 132–8.

BENNETT, E. (1934). Why dandelions? *Science*, **80**, 142.

BESSEY, C. E. (1904). Weeds used in medicine. *Science*, **19**, 868.

BIANCHI, D. E., SCHWEMIN, D. J., & WAGNER, W. H., JR. (1959). Pollen release in the common ragweed (*Ambrosia artemisiifolia*). *Bot. Gaz.*, **120**, 235–43.

BLAKESLEE, A. F. (1947). Glorification of a native weed, *Rudbeckia hirta. Horticulture*, **25**, 369.

BRENCHLEY, W. E. (1919). The uses of weeds and wild plants. *Sci. Progr. Twent. Cent.*, **14**, 121–3.

BREWER, L. & BLINN, A. (1924). Wild greens that are good to eat. *Bull. Del. Agric. Exp. Sta.*, **104**, 50.

CADY E. R. (1944). Winter quail foods on abandoned farm lands in the Norris Reservoir area. *J. Tenn., Acad. Sci.* **19**, 10–15.

CAMPBELL, E. G. (1924). Weed value. *J. Amer. Soc. Agron.*, **16**, 91–96.

CHESTNUT, V. K. (1902). Plants used by the Indians of Mendocino County, California. *Contr. U.S. Nat. Herb.*, **7**, 295–408.

CHOPRA, R. N. & CHOPRA, I. C. (1955). *A Review of Work on Indian Medicinal Plants, including Indigenous Drugs, and Poisonous Plants.* Indian Coun. Med. Res., Spec. Rep. Ser., No. 30, New Delhi.

CLAASSEN, P. W. (1919). A possible new source of food supply. *Sci. Mon.*, **9**, 179–85.

COCANNOUER, J. A. (1950). *Weeds—guardians of the soil.* Devin-Adair, New York, 179 pp.

COSTELLO, D. F. (1942). Weight gains of cattle strongly influenced by weeds and shrubs as well as by grasses. *Colo. Fm. Bull.*, **4**(1), 14–15.

DAVIS, W. & ROSS, W. C. J. (1955). The isolation of beta-sito-sterol from *Lithospermum officinale. Chem. & Ind.*, pp. 1739–40.

DE LASZLO, H. & HENSHAW, P. S. *See* LASZLO, H. DE & HENSHAW, P. S.

DENSMORE, F. (1928). Uses of plants by the Chippewa Indians. *44th Ann. Rep. Bur. of Amer. Ethnology*, pp. 275–397.

DRASHER, M. L. & ZAHL, P. A. (1946). The effect of *Lithospermum* on the mouse estrous cycle. *Proc. Soc. Exp. Biol., N.Y.*, **63**, 66–70.

ECONOMIC BOTANY (1947–). Published for the Society for Economic Botany by the New York Botanical Garden, New York, N.Y. Vol. 1.

ERISMAN, A. (1952). Weeds for hangman's rope, wart cures, and Sunday dinner. *N.Y. State Conserv.*, **6**(4), 12–13.

FAULKS, P. J. (1958). *An introduction to ethnobotany.* Moredale Publications, London, 152 pp.

Fox, H. M. (1942). Edible weeds of wayside and woods. *J. N.Y. Bot. Gdn.*, 43, 108–111. (Also in *Nat. Hort. Mag.*, 21, 9–14.)

Frazer, Sir J. G. (1911). *The Golden Bough, a Study in Magic and Religion.* Macmillan, London, 3rd edn. Vol. 2. (cf. 'Worship of Trees', Ch. IX; 'The Worship of the Oak', Ch. XX).

Fukai, G. (1940). Studies on the nutritive value of weeds. *J. Agric. Chem. Soc. Japan*, 16, 519–27.

Grace, N. H. (1948). Canadian erucic acid oils. I: Refining and bleaching. *Canad. J. Res. (Sec. F)*, 26, 349–59; II: Edible use of rape and mustard seed oils. *Ibid.* 26, 360–5.

Harris, B. C. (1955). *Eat the weeds.* Publ. by the author, Worcester, Mass., 147 pp.

Henkel, A. (1904). Weeds used in medicine. *Fmrs' Bull. U.S. Dep. Agric.*, 188, 47 pp.

Hiltner, L. (1917–18). *Vermehrte Fullergewinnung aus der heimischen Pflanzenwelt.* Stuttgart, I Teil, II Teil, 84 pp.

Innes, T. E. D. (1908). List of jungle products used by the poor during the famine, 1896–7. *Indian For.*, 34(2), Appendix, 20 pp.

Kennedy, P. B. (1927). An alkali forage weed—*Bassia hyssopifolia. J. Amer. Soc. Agron.*, 19, 750–3.

Kling, M. (1917). [On the use of mill wastes, particularly weed seeds as war-time feeding stuffs—in German.] *Landw. Jb. Bayern*, 7(9), 718–38.

—— (1918). *Die Kriegsfuttermittel.* (Wartime feeding stuffs.) Eugen Ulmer, Stuttgart, 214 pp.

König, F. (1954). Der Futterwert der Grünlandunkräuter. *Mitt. Dtsch. LandwGes.* 69, *Jahrg.*, Hefte 20–22, pp. 480–2, 497–8.

Laszlo, H. G. de (1958). *Library of Medicinal Plants Collected by Henry G. de Laszlo.* W. Heffer & Sons, Cambridge. 56 pp.

—— & Henshaw, P. S. (1954). Plant materials used by primitive peoples to affect fertility. *Science*, 119, 626–31.

Lehner, E. & Lehner, Johanna (1960). *Folklore and Symbolism of Flowers, Plants and Trees.* Tudor Publishing Co., New York. 128 pp.

Little, J. E., Foote, M. W., & Johnstone, D. B. (1950). Xanthatin: an antimicrobial agent from *Xanthium pennsylvanicum. Arch. Biochem.*, 27, 247–54.

Lloydia (1938–). Lloyd Library and Museum and American Society of Pharmacognosy, Cincinnati, Ohio.

McAtee, W. L. (1939). *Wild fowl food plants.* New value, propagation and management. Collegiate Press, Ames, Iowa, 141 pp.

Malinowski, B. (1935). *Coral Gardens and their Magic.* Vol. 1 ('The Description of Gardening'), 500 pp.; Vol. 2 ('The Language of Gardening'), 350 pp. American Book Co., New York; Allen & Unwin, London.

Malthern, R. O. (1962). Research in the development of unconventional foods. *U.S. Quartermaster Food & Container Inst. Armed Forces Activ. Report*, 14, 170–6. (Bacteria, algae, yeast, weeds, etc.)

Martin, A. C., Zim, H. S. & Nelson, A. L. (1951). *American wildlife and plants; a guide to wildlife food habits: the use of trees, shrubs, weeds and herbs by birds and mammals of the United States.* McGraw-Hill, New York, 500 pp.

Martinez, M. (1944). *Las Plantas Medicinales de México.* Ediciones Botas, Mexico. 3rd edn. 630 pp.

Meyer, J. E. (1934). *The herbalist.* Hammond, Indiana, 399 pp.

Moldenke, H. N. & Moldenke, Alma L. (1951). The mysterious silphium. *Gdn. J.*, 1, 140–2. (Cf. *Zur Silphionfrage*, by Elsa Strantz, p. 90).

Morris, P. F. (1943). Some vegetable foods of the Wimmera and Mallee. *Vict. Nat.*, *Melb.*, 59, 167–70.

Naumann, A. (1918). [Field weeds and their relation to forage: Determination of their fruit and seed—in German.] *Arch. Wiss. Prakt. Tierheilk.* 44, Suppl. pp. 310–56.

OSOL, A. & FARRAR, G. E. (Eds.). (1955, 1960). *The Dispensatory of the United States of America*. J. B. Lippincott, Philadelphia. 25th edn. Vol. 1, 2139 pp.; Vol. 2, 240 pp.

PALMER, E. (1870). Food products of the American Indians. *Annu. Rep. U.S. Dep. Agric.*, Washington, D.C.

PALMER, E. L. (1949). Edible weeds. *Nature Mag.*, 42, 178.

PLANTA MEDICA (1953–). Organ der Deutschen Gesellschaft für Arzneipflanzungen. Hippokrates Verlag, Stuttgart.

QUISUMBING, E. (1951). Medical Plants of the Philippines. *Philipp. Dep. Agric. & Nat. Resources Tech. Bull.* No. 16, 1–1234 pp. Manila, Bureau of Printing.

ROYS, R. L. (1931). *Ethnobotany of the Maya*. Tulane Univ., Middle American Res. Ser. Public. No. 2. Univ. Louisiana, New Orleans, 359 pp.

SHULTES, R. E. (1960). Tapping our heritage of ethnobotanical lore. *Econ. Bot.*, 14, 257–62.

SIEVERS, E. (1952). Prickly pears. *Farm Quart.*, 7, 50–51, 120–2.

SKINNER, A. (1921). Material culture of the Menomini. *Ind. Notes and Monog.*, Mus. Amer. Indian, Heye Found. (Story of wild rice, *Zizania aquatica*, pp. 142–52).

SKINNER, C. M. (1911). *Myths and Legends of Flowers, Trees, Fruits and Plants in all Climes*. J. B. Lippincott, Philadelphia, 301 pp.

SMITH, A. D. (1950). Sagebrush as a winter feed for deer. *J. Wildlife Mgmt.*, 14, 285–9.

SMITH, H. H. (1923). Ethnobotany of the Menomini Indians. *Bull. Publ. Mus. Milwaukee*, 4, 1–174, 36 pls.

—— (1928). Ethnobotany of the Meskwaki Indians. *Bull. Publ. Mus. Milwaukee*, 4, 175–326, 9 pls.

—— (1932). Ethnobotany of the Ojibwe Indians. *Bull. Publ. Mus. Milwaukee*, 4, 327–525, 33 pls.

—— (1933). Ethnobotany of the forest Potawatomi Indians. *Bull. Publ. Mus. Milwaukee*, 7, 1–230, 38 figs.

SNIJDERS, J. H. (1950). [Aspects of the research on the positive value of weeds—in Dutch.] *Bergcultures (Buitenzorg)*, 19, 391, 393, 395, 397, 399.

STRANTZ, ELSA (1909). *Zur Silphionfrage, kulturgeschichte und botanische Untersuchungen über die Silphionpflanze*. Berlin, Friedlander, 263 pp. (cf. *Just's Bot. Jahresb.*, 37(2), 1055, 1909; *Bot. Zbl.*, 113, 475, 1910).

STRATTON, R. (1943). Edible wild greens and salads of Oklahoma. *Bull. Okla. Agric. Mechan. College*, 40(2), 1–29.

TAKHTAJIAN, A. L. (1959 [1954]). *Origins of Angiospermous plants*. Ed. G. L. Stebbins, trans. from the Russian by Olga H. Gankin. Amer. Inst. Biol. Sci., Washington, D.C., 63 pp.

THISELTON DYER, T. F. (1889). *The Folk Lore of Plants*. D. Appleton & Co., New York, 328 pp.

THONE, F. (1941). Wealth from weeds. *Sci. News Lett., Wash.*, 40, 166–7.

TRAIN, P., HENDRICKS, J. R., & ARCHER, W. A. (1941, 1957). *Medicinal uses of plants by Indian tribes of Nevada*. Part II. Flora of Nevada Project. Issued by the Division of Plant Exploration and Introduction, Bureau of Plant Industry, U.S. Dep. Agric., Washington, D.C. (Revised edn. 1957, 139 pp.)

TRIBE, D. E., GORDON, J. G. & GIMINGHAM, C. H. (1952). The nutritive value of weeds and coarse herbage (browse) for young cattle grazing on temporary pasture. *Emp. J. Exp. Agric.*, 20(79), 240–8.

WASHBURN, R. M. (1912). The ensiling of weeds. *Bull. Vt. Agric. Exp. Sta.*, 170, 131–4.

WEISER, I. (1924). The nutrient value of some weed seeds. *Rep. Hung. Agric. Exp. Sta.*, 27(1–2), 1–15.

WELCH, C. E., Jr. (1961). Drugs of the North American Indians then and now. Unpublished, 25 pp. Philadelphia, Pa.

V

HARMFUL ASPECTS OF WEEDS

AMONG the definitions of weeds examined earlier, the words troublesome and even harmful occur. The harmful or injurious aspects to both man and animals may be quite direct and immediate in nature—such as those involving contact- or systemic-poisonous plants. Or they may take the form of some human malady or maladies, such as allergies. Perhaps the most insidious are those involving harmful aspects of an indirect nature, i.e. serving as hosts for a multitude of plant diseases and other pests that are detrimental to the growth of more desirable plants. The most widespread and direct influences are those of competition with crop plants for space, moisture, and nutrients—aspects of which will be examined at length in Chapter X.

POISONOUS PLANTS

This group of plants includes those that are directly poisonous to man and animals when ingested or by direct contact, as well as those plants that taint foods. Perhaps the most widespread of poisonous plants are those associated with man's oldest cultivated crops, the cereals. The best known are perhaps darnel (*Lolium temulentum*), corn-cockle (*Agrostemma githago*), and the fungus disease, ergot (caused by *Claviceps* spp.). Each of these was a more serious problem in former times, when the seed for sowing was not as well cleaned as it is at present.

Darnel is a widespread weed in all cereal-growing regions of the world —particularly in fields of small cereals, such as wheat. It is a weed of great antiquity, having been known to the Ancients as 'tares' (King, 1957). It is also a member of the grass family, and its 'seeds' contain an endophytic fungus that is believed to be responsible for the poisonous nature of this weed (Muir, 1931; Willmot & Silberbauer, 1931). An ancient illustration of darnel is reproduced in Plate 1. Corn-cockle has much the same distribution as darnel. It, too, is an ancient weed, having been known for perhaps as long as darnel. Likewise, because of its abundance and association with grain, the name 'cockle' or 'cockles' finds application to a number of weeds in India, Australia, and elsewhere. It has in certain regions become almost a group or class name, similar in meaning to 'tares'. The seeds of corn-cockle are poisonous, and the presence of one-half of 1 per cent in the grain proves toxic in bread flour.

Ergot, besides being commonly found infesting the seeds and inflorescences of many kinds of grasses, occurs on numerous other types of
weeds as well (Barger, 1931).

In the southwestern Cape Province of South Africa, apart from darnel
(which is there referred to as 'Drabok'), the seeds of several species of
Senecio (*S. burchellii* and *S. ilicifolius*) are also poisonous when present in
flour or baked bread made from poorly cleaned wheat seed. These two
species grow abundantly as weeds on cultivated land in this region, and
many persons have lost their lives from such poisoning. Here, also, seeds
of *Datura stramonium* and *Vicia sativa* (the latter containing a cyanogenic glucoside) cause poisoning when they contaminate bread flour
(Steyn, 1934). A comprehensive work on the medicinal and poisonous
plants of southern and eastern Africa has recently been prepared by
Watt and Breyer-Brandwijk (1962).

In grazing regions, there grow large numbers of plants that are
dangerous and frequently fatal to the grazing livestock. It has been
estimated that, in the State of Colorado, poisonous plants kill 8 per cent
of the grazing cattle. In the State of Texas, 69 species of plants have been
identified as poisonous or harmful. In the ranges of the western United
States, the annual *Halogeton glomeratus* is poisonous to sheep, due to
high concentrations of oxalate. Equally poisonous are some other plants
that accumulate selenium, including the genera *Stanleya*, *Xylorrhiza*,
Oonopsis, and some species of *Astragalus*.

Halogeton glomeratus (Chenopodiaceae) is a poisonous weed of the
western range-lands of the United States. This species was probably
introduced there from Russia as a contaminant in agricultural seed. It
has since spread over two million acres in Nevada, Utah, Idaho, Montana,
and Wyoming, with reported occurrences in California and Oregon. It is
found on disturbed areas of alkaline soils with 3 to 20 in. of annual rainfall,
at altitudes ranging from 3,000 to 7,000 ft. Soluble oxalate is the poisonous
principle, and amounts ranging from 8.7 to 17 per cent have been reported
for 'dry Halogeton.' When Halogeton contains 17 per cent soluble oxalate
a hungry sheep weighing about 110 lb., would require about 0.37 lb. of
dry Halogeton *eaten at one time* to cause its death. The intake of dry
Halogeton at the rate given would be about 12 per cent of the food capacity of the sheep. When mixed with other forage, or when eaten over an
extended period of time, larger amounts (perhaps up to 1.51 lb. of dry
Halogeton, or 47 per cent of the diet) may be safely tolerated (Stoddart
et al, 1951, Erickson *et al.*, 1951).

One of the more important poisonous weeds of the northeastern
United States, horse-nettle (*Solanum carolinense*), has recently been studied
in considerable detail by Tisdell (1961); the result is a fine representative
of the newer comprehensive studies of weed biology.

One puzzling aspect of the application of certain hormonal weed-
sprays to some species has been the observation that plants so sprayed

are often more palatable to cattle than unsprayed plants of the same species—presumably because of the production of soluble and sweet-tasting sugars from stored carbohydrate. Trouble has ensued with a few species—notably *Prunus serotina, Conium maculatum,* etc.—where the foliage has become more palatable, but the poisonous properties (e.g. hydrocyanic acid in *Prunus*) of the plant have not been appreciably altered by the sprays. Nitrate levels may also be elevated. As a control measure, stock should be kept away from poisonous plants for three to four days after they are sprayed (Stahler & Whitehead, 1950; Frank & Grigsby, 1957).

A rather serious problem, recently disclosed in Tasmania and Australia, is the role of plant thioglycosides that are present in the milk from certain areas, in the incidence of endemic goitre. Bachelard & Trikojus (1960), reviewing earlier work done in Tasmania, suggested that an appreciable amount of endemic goitre may be due to a goitrogen present in the milk of cows which have been fed 'chou moellier' (*Brassica* spp.); they moreover report that samples of milk from the goitrous area of Warwick in Queensland, where in spring and early summer the pastures are heavily contaminated with turnip weed (*Rapistrum rugosum*), were also shown to be goitrogenic. By implication, certain other cruciferous weeds might also be suspect in this respect. Bachelard & Trikojus isolated an aglycone, cheiroline (*gamma*-methylsulphonyl-propyl-*iso*-thiocyanate), from the fruits and leaves of *Rapistrum rugosum*; it was present in the extracts of fresh leaves to the extent of 0·4 gm. of crystalline aglycone per kg. of wet-weight. This indicates a potentially high intake by a cow grazing on heavily contaminated pastures; and cheiroline was shown to be goitrogenic in experimental animals. The action of such substances in the rumen, and their passage into, and effect upon, the milk, are further problems.

In addition to the several works on poisonous plants referred to in the Preface the following studies are of interest: *The Edible and Poisonous Plants of the Caribbean Region* (Dahlgren & Standley, 1944), *The Edible and Poisonous Plants of Brazil* (Dahlgren & Standley, 1939), *Poisonous Plants of Venezuela* (Blohm, 1962), *The Toxic Plants of Western Australia* (Gardner & Bennetts, 1956) and *Poisonous Plants of the United States and Canada* (Kingsbury, 1964; *see* p. 392).

FOOD-TAINTING WEEDS

A particularly important problem in dairy regions is created by weeds that occur in the grazing areas and impart a flavour to the finished dairy produce. These food-tainting plants are diverse; but some, for example *Allium* spp. (onions and their allies), are well known and widespread. The stage of development of the weed is sometimes related to its tainting qualities. A flavour, e.g. of onion, will appear in milk four to five minutes after feeding, and will require five to six hours of grazing for the flavour

93

to disappear—the flavour and odour of frenchweed (*Thlaspi arvense*), however, do not disappear until seven to eight hours after the weeds are eaten. Most cows will eat frenchweed that is growing with pasture grass, or when pastures are short. The onion flavour is associated with the butterfat, and is not related to the volume of weed eaten. To prevent flavours derived from weeds from occurring in the milk, cows must be kept off weedy pastures for a period that varies between three and eight hours, before milking.

There is some indication that the difficulties of off-flavour may be overcome by using one of the several types of vacuum pasteurizers. Bitterweed (*Actinea odorata*) is another important weed of this class; it occurs throughout the southern United States. In the middle-west, a common pasture weed (*Eupatorium rugosum*) was, in pioneer times, the cause of 'milk sickness' of the early settlers. A pink yolk-colour in eggs has been noted in poultry feeding on *Malva rotundifolia* (Fenton & Robertson, 1931; Hanson & Dice, 1936; Dice, 1944; Bohmont & Slater, 1954, Wolf, *et al* 1918).

POISONOUS AND FETISH PLANTS USED BY PRIMITIVE PEOPLES

As some primitive peoples have used native plants for strange and diverse purposes, these plants sometimes became more widespread because of their removal from their native environment and the discarding of used or useless portions. If the environmental requirements are not too limiting, the plants may become effectively dispersed as a result of such uses.

Chevalier (1951) has examined some of the fetish and ceremonial uses of poisonous plants by the Oubangui peoples of the Congo, in tropical Africa. Some of the plants were used in poisonous concoctions, being in a few cases actually cultivated. Briefly, the plants included the genera *Strophanthus*, *Periploca* (an asclepiad liana), and *Rauwolfia*; plants of *Dioscorea anthropophagorum* were cultivated for their toxic bulbils; *Euphorbia cactiformis* was cultivated in all villages as a fetish plant for the caustic latex (actually, 5 or 6 species were used for this, some of them being imported, and others spontaneous in the country), while *E. hermentiana* was often planted in the villages, as the natives were assured that this plant served as a lightning-bolt arrester and protector.

Perhaps better known are the uses of species of curare (*Strychnos*) as arrow poisons, and of species of *Dahlstedtia*, *Camptosema*, *Serjania*, and *Derris*, as fish and insect poisons in Brazil (Santos, 1951).

A survey of some uses of squill, or sea onion (*Urginea maritima*, Liliaceae), and allied species, particularly in Africa, has disclosed some primitive beliefs concerning this group of plants. Some species are very poisonous, and a few of these (*U. macrocentra*, *U. burkei*, *U. altissima*, and *U. capitata*) are highly toxic to grazing animals in the Republic of

South Africa. The Basuto natives of the Laribe plateau of South Africa ascribe magical powers to species of this genus. They believe that the use of it may avert evil influences, may break spells cast on certain individuals, and, further, that it may protect the treated one from the evil influences of persons living at some distance. Such species are the plants of the area most esteemed by the native 'doctors', and Basuto chiefs are vaccinated with a preparation from these plants. *U. maritima* has had medicinal uses since ancient times, and as a result of its long association with the wanderings of man has at times been cultivated. In some areas in North Africa it is so prolific as to be considered a weed. *Urginea* spp. have been used in shrines over doorways as protection against evil in West tropical Africa, and they have had certain symbolic uses both in ancient Egypt and in the ancient Greek culture (King, 1963).

Weeds as Hosts for Fungal and Bacterial Diseases

One alarming aspect of researches into the origin of this group of plant diseases, so detrimental to full crop production, has been the realization that a considerable reservoir of inoculum is to be found in the native vegetation, and in the weed species growing in or around the crop lands. The more closely the botanical affiliation of the crop species approaches that of the weeds or native plants, the greater is the likelihood that many of the diseases of the weeds, etc., will find the crop plant a suitable host as well. An exception here would be the heteroecious rusts.

Soil-borne diseases include a complex of different bacterial and higher fungus species. Many root-rots and diseases associated with the germination and seedling establishment of crop plants are believed to be associated also with certain weed species. A number of cruciferous weeds are believed to be hosts of the club-root disease (*Plasmodiophora brassicae*) of cabbage and related vegetable crop plants—as well as of the widespread European grass *Holcus lanatus*, which has been found to be a host for the zoosporangia of this pest (Webb, 1949).

Padwick's studies in Canada reveal the importance of weed hosts in the foot-rot problem of wheat, where species of *Ophiobolus* and *Helminthosporium*, that are associated with this disease, were found on the roots of quack-grass (*Agropyron repens*) and western rye-grass (*Agropyron tenerum*) (Padwick & Henry, 1933; Padwick, 1935). Cooley (1938) has examined the susceptibility of crop plants and weeds to *Sclerotium rolfsii*. *Synchytrium* has been found in *Stellaria media*, the widespread chickweed, in Louisiana (Clendenin, 1894). A. G. Walker (1945) has studied the relationships between rhizomatous grass weeds and *Ophiobolus graminis*. A survey in Texas of the *Phymatotrichum* root-rot on winter and spring weeds was conducted by Taubenhaus (1936).

In the southern regions of the United States, a number of surveys have been made that demonstrate the relationship of weeds to plant

95

diseases. T. E. Smith & Godfrey (1938) examined weed species in relation to the control of Granville-wilt of cotton. Rogers (1936), in Texas, examined weeds occurring in the native hay meadows for cotton root-rot. *Physalis subglabrata* was found to be a natural host for *Bacterium angulatum* infecting tobacco (Valleau & Johnson, 1936), while *Solanum sarachoides* has been reported to be an important weed host of *Verticillium alboatrum* (Wilhelm & Thomas, 1952).

The cause of smutty wheat, *Ustilago utriculosa*, has been found on dock-leafed persicary in Canada (Aamodt & Malloch, 1932). In England, the grey mould of fruit and hops (*Botrytis cinerea*) was commonly found on the flower-heads of certain Compositae—especially *Sonchus* spp. (Wormald, 1941). In North Carolina, Crossan (1954) observed that the *Cercosporella* leaf-spot (*Cylindrospermum brassicae*) that infests turnips, was found on two common cruciferous weeds of the area, *Draba verna* and *Sisymbrium thalianum*. The ubiquitous *Portulaca oleracea* (common purslane) is a host for *Dichotomophthora portulaceeae* (Mehrlich & Fitzpatrick, 1935).

Studies at Colorado State University have shown that purslane (*P. oleracea*) can be systematically infected with the root-rot fungus, *Rhizoctonia* sp., but without apparent disease symptoms. The pigweed (*Amaranthus retroflexus*), as well as many other common weeds that grow in potato fields, may be heavily infected with *Rhizoctonia* and have symptoms typical of this disease which is often economically important on the potato.

Better known, of course, are the rusts—especially cereal rusts—which are heteroecious, i.e. besides infesting e.g. a crop plant, have another plant serving as an alternative host—generally for another reproductive stage. This alternative host is often a weed. In North America the stem-rust of wheat (*Puccinia graminis* var. *tritici*), with its alternate stage on the common barberry (*Berberis vulgaris*), is all too well known.

The stem-rust fungus of wheat (*Puccinia graminis* var. *tritici*) is a complex of over 250 physiological races and biotypes. It is estimated that losses from rusts on wheat throughout the world may reach an average of 10 per cent, or approximately 600,000,000 bushels per year. The alternative hosts for this fungus are species of *Berberis* and *Mahonia* which are closely-related genera of the Berberidaceae. It was early recognized in the United States that eradication of the common barberry and related species would reduce the incidence of rust epidemics. Ultimately eighteen states, together with the federal government, entered into an eradication programme in which nearly half-a-billion barberry bushes were destroyed. This campaign resulted in estimated annual savings to farmers of well over thirty million dollars (Stakman & Harrar, 1957). Johnson & Green (1951) have studied the different varieties of this rust occurring on barberry in eastern Canada. The problem as it exists in the State of Illinois has been examined by Bills (1935), and in Germany it has been reported on by Hinke (1955).

An extensive study of the cereal rusts of India (Mehta, 1952) includes lists of alternative hosts.

In a similar manner, the rust of oats has an alternate stage on the common buckthorn (*Rhamnus catharticus*) (Chambers *et al.*, 1955). White pine blister-rust (*Cronartium ribicola*) occurs on the alternative host *Ribes* (gooseberries, etc.). A concerted effort has resulted in the eradication of a billion and a half *Ribes* bushes from the vicinity of susceptible pine forests. It was once thought that white pine plantings would eventually decline, but, following the eradication effort, they are flourishing once again (Offord, 1950; Stakman & Harrar, 1957).

WEEDS AS HOSTS OF VIRUS DISEASES

One of the best known and also most widely distributed of virus diseases, aster yellows, was examined by Frazier & Severin (1945) in California with regard to possible weed hosts. They found four insect vectors (leafhoppers) on 67 weed species. In all, 41 species of weeds belonging to 31 genera in 14 families were demonstrated to be spontaneously infected with the aster yellows virus. These weeds included 28 annuals, 5 annuals or biennials, 4 biennials, and 4 perennials. In the western areas of the United States, the curly-top virus of sugar beets causes considerable damage; the overwintering weed hosts of this virus have been studied by Piemeisel (1932) and by Severin (1937). Weeds have also been examined by Dykstra (1933) as possible carriers of the leaf-roll virus and the rugose mosaic of potato. Younkin (1942), in surveying the weed suspects of the potato yellow dwarf virus, found that the ox-eye daisy (*Chrysanthemum leucanthemum* var. *pinnatifidum*) may be a more important source of the virus in the field than the medium red clover. He was able to demonstrate the presence of the virus in the ox-eye daisy, in *Rudbeckia hirta*, in *Barbarea vulgaris*, and in red clover. In Sierra Leone, the alternative hosts of the leaf-curl disease of tobacco (and of cotton) were the common weeds *Sida carpinifolia*, *S. cordifolia*, and *S. veronicaefolia*. This virus was intertransmissible, by means of the white fly (*Bemisia* sp.), between solanaceous and malvaceous plants.

An examination of the weed hosts of tomato mosaic in Indiana revealed that horse-nettle (*Solanum carolinense*) and several species of groundcherry (*Physalis heterophylla*, *P. subglabris*, and *P. virginiana*) were sources of the virus. The ubiquitous crabgrass (*Digitaria sanguinalis*) was found in Cuba to be the source of the sugar-cane mosaic disease, and was transmitted by the corn aphid (*Aphis maidis*) (Brandes, 1919; M. N. Walker & Stahl, 1926). In Germany the 'browning' virus (cucumber virus I) that infects greenhouse-grown lupins was found in common chickweed (*Stellaria media*), *Capsella bursa-pastoris*, *Galinsoga parviflora*, spinach, and tomato.

As a result of his studies of the southern celery mosaic virus, Wellman (1935, 1937) recommended its control by removing weeds that served as a source of infection—especially the most important one, *Commelina nudiflora*. The vector was the cotton aphis (*Aphis gossypii*). Hein in Germany (1953, 1956, 1957) has extensively examined the role of weeds in the epidemiology of virus diseases. Likewise, Noordam (1955) in Holland has examined the role of weeds as hosts of vector-transmissible and soil-borne viruses. Kassanis (1944) has studied a virus attacking both lettuce and dandelion, while Sylvester (1953) has examined the virus relationships of the common black mustard (*Brassica nigra*).

Weeds as Hosts for Nematodes

Nematodes or eelworms are recognized as a group of pests that are becoming increasingly serious with intensified crop production. There are free-living forms in the soil, those that are closely associated with plant tissue (especially in root-galls), and the ecto-parasitic forms found in any portion of the above-ground parts (including the dried and dispersed seed). The soil forms are the most numerous in the top 2 in., and also horizontally in the region of roots (especially of grasses). Probably some 10,000 species of nematodes—half of them free-living—have been described to date, with the possibility that there may be some 500,000 species in the world. They may occur in soil in densities of up to 20 million per cubic metre (Peters, 1955).

In the United States, attention has focused upon some four outstanding problems associated with nematodes: the golden nematode of potato (*Heterodera rostochiensis*), the species associated with spreading decline of citrus trees, the meadow nematode causing root-rot in tobacco, and the soybean cyst nematode which was recently found in some of the southern soybean-producing states.

The golden nematode of potato became such a serious threat in the producing areas of Long Island, New York, that infested areas were quarantined against further potato culture. Potato yield reductions of 84 per cent were recorded. Species allied to the potato—especially certain weeds—may also serve as hosts. These include *Solanum dulcamara*, *S. rostratum*, *S. triflorum*, *S. xanthii*, and others. Apart from survival in weed hosts, nematodes produce cysts, which in the case of the golden nematode have been observed in England to remain alive (in the absence of host plants) for seventeen years (Mai & Spears, 1954).

The chief nematode associated with the spreading decline of citrus is *Tylenchus semipenetrans*, which in recent years has become a serious pest in the Florida citrus-growing regions. Other hosts for this pest are a number of ornamental tropical plants grown in nurseries in the same area; indeed it is believed that the infestation originated from these ornamentals.

The soybean cyst nematode (*Heterodera glycines*) was previously known only in the Orient, a heavy infestation being first observed in the

United States in southeastern North Carolina in 1954. As nearly twenty million acres of soybeans are grown in the United States, there is just cause for concern. Since 1954, *H. glycines* has been reported in the mid-south and in the Delta region. In North Carolina, tests indicate that this pest could develop three or four generations during the growing-season (mid-May to late September). Apart from soybeans, other susceptible hosts are snap beans, annual lespedeza, and vetches (*Vicia* spp.). Vetches yield important cover-crops in some areas, and with allied species are found abundantly as weeds in many regions.

There are, of course, many more kinds of nematode infestations of crop plants and ornamentals. A South Carolina study of the sting nema-tode (*Belonolaimus gracilis*) revealed that it was commonly found on all vegetable crops except members of the Cruciferae and the Compositae. Two grasses, crab-grass (*Digitaria sanguinalis*) and Bermuda grass (*Cynodon dactylon*), were important hosts in the maintenance of the sting nematode in infested fields. Again in South Carolina, an investigation of the nema-tode causing root-rot of tobacco—i.e. the meadow nematode (*Praty-lenchus*)—disclosed that this pest was also found in the roots of weeds and other plants belonging to the following genera: *Andropogon, Diodea, Eremochloa, Fragaria, Lespedeza, Lupinus, Cynodon, Crotalaria, Dacty-loctenium, Vigna*, and *Digitaria sanguinalis*. The nematodes over-wintered in the roots of *D. sanguinalis* even though the plants were killed by frosts, the roots remaining in good condition.

The tobacco cyst nematode (*Heterodera tabaccum*), very closely related to the golden nematode, has been reported in Connecticut on the roots of regular shade tobacco. Other susceptible plants are the Marglobe tomato, and *Solanum integrifolium, S. dulcamara*, and *S. rostratum*—almost the same as for the golden nematode—as well as the preferred hosts, *S. nigrum* and *S. burbankii*.

POLLINOSIS AND RELATED ALLERGIES

Certain plants produce light pollen in large quantities which, when airborne, may produce allergic responses, including 'hay fever', in susceptible individuals. A recent survey conducted in New York State (Ogden, 1957) provides some very useful information here.

Ogden's survey of airborne pollen at thirty-five localities throughout the State indicated that such pollen came chiefly from three groups of plants: from trees (from 25 different genera, with birches (*Betula*), elms (*Ulmus*), hickories (*Carya*), and oaks (*Quercus*), all quite important); from grasses (from 20 to 25 different species, the principal ones producing pollen in large quantities, and including *Anthoxanthum odoratum, Phleum pratense, Agrostis alba, Poa pratensis*, and *Dactylis glomerata*); and from weeds (all were of minor importance, except the ragweeds, *Ambrosia* spp., which were of great importance). The total count for one year from rag-weeds exceeded that over a similar period from all other groups, with the exception of the total grass pollen, which was slightly more. Most of this pollen was from short or common ragweed (*A. artemisiifolia*) (Fig. 8), but in some areas giant ragweed (*A. trifida*) supplied large amounts. Other weeds that produced sufficient buoyant pollen to be recorded on at least some of the graphs were, in order of their appearance: docks (*Rumex*), plantains (*Plantago*), pigweeds (*Chenopodium* and *Amaranthus*), wormwoods (*Artemisia*), marsh-elders (*Iva*), and goldenrods (*Solidago*). Fungus spores (especially of *Cladosporium* and *Alternaria*) usually closely approached (and often surpassed) the total number of pollen grains. Plant hairs were also found on all of the approximately 15,000 samples examined. The pollen record for 1953 as recorded at Utica, New York (Ogden, 1957), which is just about centrally located in the State, is given in Fig. 9. Airborne pollen and fungus spores have been found even in the vicinity of the North Pole (Polunin, 1951; Polunin & Kelly, 1952) and other remote regions (cf. Gregory, 1961).

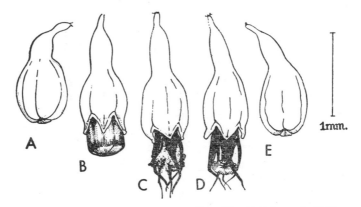

From Bianchi, Schwemmin & Wagner, 1959

FIG. 8.—Stages in pollen release of the common ragweed, *Ambrosia artemisiifolia*: A, mature flower; B, extension of anther sacs; C, dehiscence of anthers; D, extension of pistillodium; E, closure of flower. Closed pollen sacs are partly stippled; opened sacs are black. Actual pollen release is accomplished mainly by enlargement of the filaments of the stamens, which extends the pollen sacs and pushes open the corolla lobes, by dehiscence of the sacs by pleating and separation of their walls, and by extension of the anther appendages. The pistillodium may function as a 'sweeper' of any pollen grains that still remain in the anthers. Field studies at Ann Arbor, Michigan, disclosed that extension and opening of the anthers occurs between 6.30 and 8.00 a.m. (normal flowering of *A. artemisiifolia* is around 15 August in this area), and is correlated with rise in temperature and a reduction of relative humidity. (cf. addendum, p. 114).

The two principal works by Wodehouse (1935 and 1945) provide a splendid survey of this subject, the latter work including a section systematically reviewing the ten recognized hay-fever regions of the United States.

A summer hay-fever plant survey of an interior city of the United States (Manhattan, Kansas) has been described by Horn (1953). The survey showed that 571·8 acres within the city limits—or 22 per cent of its area—were in weeds. The check-list included 43 species of grasses,

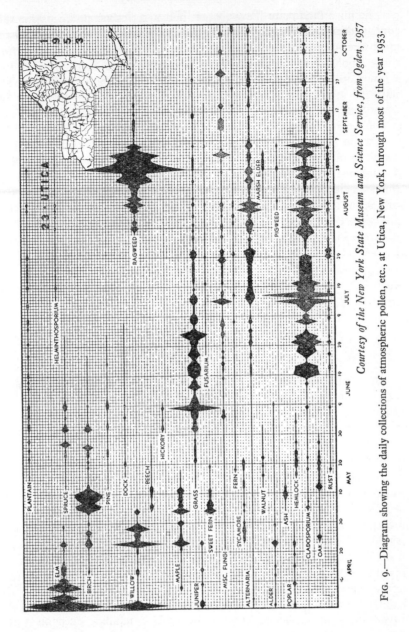

FIG. 9.—Diagram showing the daily collections of atmospheric pollen, etc., at Utica, New York, through most of the year 1953.

Courtesy of the New York State Museum and Science Service, from Ogden, 1957

24 species of hay-fever weeds, and 75 species of other wild herbaceous plants. In the city, 67·8 acres were overrun by ragweeds, pigweeds, goosefoot, and hemp. Of the ragweed pollen alone, this acreage would emit annually 2 tons into the air at a 'rate' of 60 lb. per acre. The annual estimate for the entire United States is a production of 1 million tons of ragweed pollen (Pl. 7).

Shelmire (1939), in Texas, examined a series of 56 weeds for their contact dermatitis by patch-testing their oleo-resins. He concluded that most weed-sensitive persons, like victims of pollen hay fever and asthma, show a polyvalent sensitivity. Most hay-fever plants were found to have a low skin-sensitizing index. In tests where poison ivy was used as a standard in the patch tests, the top seven plants (including poison ivy) were *Helenium tenuifolium, Iva angustifolia, Parthenium hysterophorus, Xanthium speciosum, Helenium microcephalum,* and *Ambrosia elatior.**

Of the many species of plants causing a contact-dermatitis in man, none are more familiar than certain genera of the Anacardiaceae (*Rhus, Semecarpus* [*Anacardium*], etc.), and *R. toxicodendron* (poison ivy) and allied species in particular (McNair, 1923). Urushiol is the principal constituent of the irritant oil of poison ivy and of other species of *Rhus*. This substance contains derivatives of catechol having unsaturated side-chains of 15 carbon atoms, which upon hydrogenation yield the same 3-pentadecylcatechol. Other irritant species include the 'itchwood tree' (*Semecarpus vitensis*), as well as *S. atra*, both from the Pacific islands. The Australian 'tar tree' (*S. australiensis*) sap produces a severe dermatitis upon contact (Sulit, 1940).

Problems of Malaria Control

In an earlier section (pp. 42 *et seq*) devoted to epiphytes in the tropical regions, and to the 'tank' bromeliads in particular, it was shown how this group of plants could harbour malaria-carrying mosquitoes. Likewise, the broken hollow stems of bamboo (*Bambusa* and perhaps other genera) have been observed in Hawaii to provide reservoirs for breeding mosquitoes.

In the southern United States, some floating water-plants, such as water-lettuces (*Pistia* spp.), harbour mosquitoes. Here the vast stretches of water, artificial impoundments etc., and especially water-level management, all create noxious plant problems associated with malaria. Studies conducted in the Tennessee Valley (Hall *et al.*, 1946) have indicated that water-level management is effective in controlling the larvae of the malaria vector (*Anopheles quadrimaculatus*); but it is also very important in the management of the marginal vegetation, which creates a favourable habitat for the aquatic stages of the mosquito. These authors found that a constant pool phase should be maintained as long as is feasible during the first part of the growing-season, and seasonal recession should be kept to the minimum necessary for adequate larval control. A 2 ft. seasonal recession and an over-all fluctuation zone of 3 ft. has proved adequate. This programme promoted the growth of the desirable, wetland, flexuous species at the expense of undesirable, stiff-stemmed plants.

* *See* Addendum p. 114.

VEGETATION CONTROL AND THE TSETSE FLY

In East and Central Africa, particularly, the destruction or alteration of the breeding areas of tsetse flies (*Glossinia* spp.) is essential for control of trypanosomiasis. Morris (1946) records that the control of *Glossinia palpalis* and *G. tachinoides* in the northern territory of the Gold Coast (now renamed Ghana) requires 'eradicative clearing' of all vegetation throughout a considerable area (in excess of 5 miles). Between 1940 and 1945 this type of clearing became effective in an area of 1,050 square miles, with a fall in incidence of sleeping sickness cases amounting to 92 per cent. Controlled grass fires in certain localities were helpful in reducing the numbers of *G. morsitans*.

Periodic clearing of the bush around villages, fords, and boat landings, as well as along the sides of roads, is advisable for *G. palpalis*, but not so practicable for *G. morsitans*. Lewis (1941) recommends, for *G. palpalis*: (1), clearing the riparian bush, in which flies reside, for a width of 1,000 yards; (2), thinning the thickets surrounding protective barriers; (3), trapping flies; and (4), patrolling infested zones.

With the advent of the newer organic herbicides and defoliants, new approaches to the tsetse fly problem have been reported by Ivens (1954). As earlier work had shown that tsetse flies are dependent on the shade provided by the trees among which they live and breed, an experiment was carried out in 1930, wherein a square mile of bush was defoliated by applying arsenic pentoxide solution to the bases of the trees. In 1952, 2,4,5-T acid was applied to an infested area in East Africa. Although this spraying did not result in the eradication of the fly, a considerable degree of defoliation was brought about by it, and as this largely removed the canopy, grasses and other vegetation entered, so that the area could later be burned. It appeared that burning plus defoliation might constitute a control measure.

Further experiments, in an evergreen sub-riverine forest in Kenya (where the dominant trees were *Olea chrysophylla* and *Euclea divinorum*), using aerial applications of 2,4,5-T butyl ester in diesel oil at rates ranging from 0·5 to 3 lb. per acre, resulted in approximately 70 per cent of the larger trees and a similar proportion of the smaller trees and shrubs being defoliated by the spray. With a single spraying, the effect persisted for about four months; while a second spraying, three months after the first, considerably delayed regeneration—so that after six months there was still a large degree of defoliation. In this experiment, dry weather interfered with new grass growth in the area, so that burning experiments here were not successful. Other experiments in the defoliation of *Commiphora-Combretum* savanna in Tanganyika were also reported by Ivens (1957).

MISCELLANEOUS HARMFUL PLANTS

There are numerous reports in the literature of bacterial and protozoan parasites in the latex of a large number of plant species, many of which belong to the Euphorbiaceae. Franchini (1922, 1931) describes *Herpetomonas* (*Leptomonas*) *ganorae* from the latex of a specimen of fig, *Ficus hochstetteri*, from Sicily, and *Spirochaeta roubaudi* from *Euphorbia* spp. in Italy. He suggests that the *Spirochaeta*, at least, was presumably deposited there in dejecta of flies. In a survey of Queensland plants, Bancroft (1927 [1928]) found species of *Phytomonas* in the genera *Sarcostemma*, *Hoya*, *Secomone*, and *Ficus*. The insect, *Oncopeltas quadriguttatus*, sucks the milky juice of some of these plants and harbours flagellates in its intestines. In a survey conducted in the Philippine Islands (Hegner & Chu, 1930) flagellates were found in only one of many species of latex-bearing plants examined—about 60 per cent of the plants of *Euphorbia hirta* were infected. In 489 specimens of three species examined in Mexico by Hewitt (1940) (*Asclepias curassavica*, *A. neglecta*, and *A. glaucescens*) a total of only 18 flagellate infections (3.7 per cent) were found. Harvey & Lee (1943) in the United States reported 12 species of plants as hosts of flagellates. All examined species of *Chamaescyce* (Euphorbiaceae) were infected.

Insects undoubtedly are involved as vectors of these latex-inhabiting organisms. Franca (1927) describes the protozoan, *Leptomonas davidi*, as occurring in the salivary glands of *Stenocephalis agilis*, and indicates that the latter was capable of infecting *Euphorbia* plants. The question arises as to whether these are only transient infections, or whether they may persist for a length of time in a single plant without reinfection. No experimental studies of this nature have been noted.

The above survey was prompted by the statement of the noted American botanist, Paul C. Standley (1884–1963), in his *Flora of the Panama Canal Zone* (1928), that *Euphorbia hirta* harbours certain micro-organisms in the plant latex which is reported to cause tropical ulcers. No study has been located which demonstrates, or even suggests, such an etiological relationship for tropical ulcers. Furthermore, it is surprising that most of the standard works on microbiology and on plant pathogens, as well as the more specialized works on protozoology, have almost completely ignored the above published material. The fact that the latex of one member of the Euphorbiaceae, *Hippomane mancinella*, (the manchineal tree) is poisonous and causes blister formation and edema when placed in contact with the skin suggests other complications in any attempts at clarifying the above suggested etiology of tropical skin ulcers (Phalen, 1930).

It is of interest to note that De Siqueira-Jaccoud (1956) found a species of *Phytomonas* in the latex of *Euphorbia brasiliensis*—a species investigated because of folklore assigning medicinal properties to this plant, particularly for the eyes. Isakova (1935) examined some 60 species of plants in the U.S.S.R. for latex-containing micro-organisms; while a number of reports list several genera of bacteria (*Bacillus*, *Achromobacter*, and *Erwinia*) in the latex of the cultivated rubber-tree (*Hevea brasiliensis*) (Corbet, 1930; Simonart, 1952).

Other harmful plants include such examples as nettles (*Urtica* spp.) and hemp or marijuana (*Cannabis sativa*). The latter frequently occurs along ditches, fences, roadsides, and on wastelands with moist, fertile soil—often covering extensive areas. The culture or tolerance of this plant is prohibited by law in some localities in the United States since it is the source of the powerful narcotic, marijuana or hashish.

WEEDS AND ASSOCIATED INSECTS

Reference has already been made to the role of insects, associated with weeds and other wild plants, as vectors in the transmission of virus, bacterial, and other plant diseases (Carter, 1940). Perhaps one of the more remarkable examples of the intimate relationship between a weed host and an insect that is destructive to an important food crop in North America, is that of the Colorado potato beetle (*Leptinotarsa decemlineata*, Coleoptera).

This beetle is a very well-known and destructive enemy of the potato (*Solanum tuberosum*). Brues (1947) states that there is good evidence that this is a Neotropical insect of Mexican or Central American origin, which extended its range within historic times into the middle-western United States as far as Colorado, following the probably northward migration of its original food plant, *Solanum rostratum*, which is a common roadside weed. Up until the middle of the nineteenth century, the potato beetle was apparently a rather harmless insect living on wild *Solanum* spp. in the Colorado mountains. But when the gold-miner brought in potatoes to Colorado (in the 1860's or earlier), the beetle changed to this new food, and by the late 'sixties had made considerable inroads into the crop. Within twenty-five years, it had encompassed the entire United States east of the Rocky Mountains, breeding upon potato plants everywhere, and had even invaded Europe—where, however, most of its incipient colonies were wiped out. Apparently the potato beetle now feeds on *Solanum rostratum* far less commonly than on the potato, practically never occurs on the tomato, and rarely on egg plant, although it occasionally affects tobacco; all of these belong to the Solanaceae.

Perhaps the close association of certain insects with weeds and other wild plants will be better understood from an examination of the classification of the host plants of insects as outlined by Thorsteinson (1953):

1. Plants which are either not attractive to the ovipositing females or not acceptable to the larvae, due either to their lack of chemical constituents which positively stimulate the chemoreceptors of the insect, or to the presence in their tissues of repellent constituents which stimulate negatively the chemical senses of the adults and/or larvae.

2. Attractive plants. Plants that contain chemicals which attract, probably by olfaction, gravid females of the insect species, and stimulate them to lay eggs on them.

3. Acceptable plants. Plants that contain chemical constituents which by olfaction or gustation stimulate the feeding stages, only, of the insect to chew and ingest them. This group may be further classified as follows:

(*a*) Plants that contain constituents which inhibit feeding—either by repellent action or by masking the stimulus of attractant substances (e.g. *Solanum demissum* with respect to the Colorado potato beetle).

(*b*) Plants on which insects will feed but which contain toxic chemical constituents that hinder vigorous development, so resulting in low fecundity or actually causing death of the insect (e.g. *Petunia hybrida* with respect to the Colorado potato beetle).

(*c*) Plants which possess morphological characteristics such as hairiness or toughness of cuticle which deters feeding.

(*d*) Plants which contain trophic stimulants and are free from chemical constituents and physical characteristics that inhibit feeding, but which do not contain a complete complement of the nutrients, vitamins, and minerals, required by the insect.

(*e*) Plants which have phenological characteristics that are out of phase with the requirements of the insect.

(*f*) Plants which do not occur in the geographical range of the insect. Thus the host range of an insect infesting a great botanical garden may be far greater than is afforded by the surrounding countryside.

A survey of the insects inhabiting the roots of weeds growing near Ames, Iowa, has been prepared by Sweetman (1928). Some 42 species of weeds were examined during the summer months. On the roots of these weeds the author found about seventy-five different insects belonging to seven orders (Collembola, Corrodentia, Homoptera, Coleoptera, Lepidoptera, Hymenoptera, and Diptera). Among the weed species having a large number of insect species were: *Amaranthus retroflexus*, with 18 species in 16 genera; *Oenothera biennis*, with 9 species in 6 genera; *Erigeron canadensis*, with 10 species in 10 genera; *Xanthium canadense*, with 20 species in 17 genera; and *Taraxacum officinale*, with 9 species in 8 genera.

A knowledge of the kinds of insects that are particularly destructive to wild plants, and especially to weeds, is very valuable for considering their possible use in a programme of biological control of the plant in question. This subject is dealt with later in the present volume—*see*, especially, pp. 411–16.

In the delicately-balanced system of nature, it is not surprising to learn that the control, or eradication, of certain weeds or wild plant hosts of certain insects may have disastrous effects on the agriculture of a region. Wolcott (1928) has described just such a situation in Haiti, in the West Indies. The aphid vector of the mosaic disease of sugar-cane, *Aphis maidis*, in cane fields ordinarily lives on small grasses; but when these are destroyed by cultivation, the aphids are forced on to the cane. Yet if these graminaceous hosts could be eliminated, the vector might also disappear. Wolcott cites another example of the undesirable effects of such an upset balance—the destruction of weeds at a time when they are being devoured by caterpillars. These caterpillars are then forced to attack the crop to obtain sufficient food to complete their growth. The instance noted is of cutworms (*Prodenia* sp. and *Xylomiges* sp.), feeding on *Boerhaavia erecta*, being forced to eat the leaves of cotton and even of sisal.

BIBLIOGRAPHY

(Harmful Aspects of Weeds)

AAMODT, O. S. & MALLOCH, J. G. (1932). Smutty wheat caused by *Ustilago utriculosa* on dock-leaved persicary. *Canad. J. Res., Sect. C., Bot. Sci.*, 7, 578–82.

ALTSTATT, G. E. (1944). Disease reported on weeds and miscellaneous plants in Texas. *Plant Dis. Reptr.*, 28, 275–6.

ANON. (1931). *The root-infesting eelworms of the genus Heterodera; a bibliography and host list.* Imperial Bureau of Agricultural Parasitology, St. Albans, England, 99 pp.

—— (1947). Hay fever weeds bloom. *Sci. News Lett., Wash.*, 52(8), 115–16.

BACHELARD, H. S. & TRIKOJUS, V. M. (1960). Plant thioglycosides and the problem of endemic goitre in Australia. *Nature, Lond.*, 185, 80–81.

BAILEY, V. (1903). Sleepy grass and its effects on horses. *Science*, 17, 392–3.

BANCROFT, L. (1927 [1928]). Flagellates in certain Queensland plants. Preliminary notes. *Proc. Roy. Soc. Queensland*, 39, 22.

BARGER, G. (1931). *Ergot and ergotism.* Gurney & Jackson, London & Edinburgh. 296 pp.

BEATH, O. A. (1919–21). [On larkspur, arrow grass, woody aster, silvery lupine, and poisonous plants of Wyoming—various publications.] *Wyoming Bulletins*, 120, 123, 125, 126, and 144; *Wyoming Ann. Rep.*, 30 and 31.

—— (1937). Seleniferous vegetation in Wyoming. *Bull. Wyo. Agric. Exp. Sta.*, 221. 64 pp. 14 fig.

BERNARD-SMITH, A. (1923). *Poisonous plants of all countries.* Baillière, Tindall & Cox, London, 2nd edn., 112 pp.

BIANCHI, D. E., SCHWEMMIN, D. J. & WAGNER, W. H. JR. (1959). Pollen release in the common ragweed (*Ambrosia artemisiifolia*). *Bot. Gaz.*, 120, 235–43.

BILLS, R. W. (1935). Barberry eradication in Illinois. *Ill. State Acad. Sci.*, 27, 59.

BLACK, W. L. & PARKER, K. W. (1936). Toxicity tests on African rue (*Peganum harmala* L.) *Bull. N. Mex. Agric. Exp. Sta.*, 240. 14 pp.

BLOHM, H. (1962). *Poisonous Plants of Venezuela.* Harvard University Press, Cambridge, Mass., 136 pp.

BOHMONT, D. W. & SLATER, I. W. (1954). Weeds flavor milk and destroy quality. *Wyoming Agric. Coll. Ext. Circ.*, No. 135, 8 pp.

BOUGHTON, I. B. (1937). Toxicity of bitterweed, *Actinea odorata*, for sheep. *Bull. Tex. Agric. Expt. Sta.*, No. 552. 15 pp.

—— & HARDY, W. T. (1935). Mescal bean, *Sophora secundiflora*, poisonous for livestock. *Bull. Tex. Agric. Expt. Sta.*, No. 519. 18 pp.

BRANDES, E. W. (1919). The mosaic disease of sugar cane and other grasses. *Bull. U.S. Dep. Agric.*, No. 829. 26 pp.

BRATLEY, H. E. (1949). Weed host plants of the nematode found in the three year tobacco rotation. *Proc. Soil Sci. Soc. Fla.*, 4B (1942), 118–20.

BRUES, C. T. (1947). *Insects and human welfare; an account of the more important relations of insects to the health of man, to agriculture, and to forestry.* Rev. edn., Harvard University Press, Cambridge, Mass., xiii, 154 pp.

BULLOCK, A. A. (1952). South African poisonous plants. *Kew Bull.*, No. 1, 117–29.

BUXTON, P. A. (1955). *Natural history of tsetse flies.* London Sch. Hyg. Trop. Med. Mem., No. 10, 800 pp.

CAMPBELL, H. W. (1931). Poisoning of chickens with whorled milkweed. *Ann. Vet. Med. Assoc.*, 79, 102.

CARTER, W. (1940). Insects and the spread of plant diseases. *Smithson. Rep.*, 1940, 329–42.

CHEVALIER, A. (1951). Les plantes-poisons de l'Oubangui et du Moyen Congo. *Rev. Int. Bot. Appl.*, 31, 249–57.

CHOPRA, R. N., BADWAR, B. L. & GHOSH, S. (1900). *Poisonous plants of India.* Indian Council of Agricultural Research, New Delhi.

CLENDENIN, I. (1894). *Synchytrium* on *Stellaria media. Botan. Gaz.*, 19, 296–7.

COBB, G. S., STEINER, G. & BLUNTON, F. S. (1934). Observation on the significance of weeds as carriers of the bulb or stem nematode (*Anguillulina dipsaci*) in narcissus plantings. *Plant Dis. Reptr.*, 18, 127–9.

COOK, M. T. (1945). Species of *Synchytrium* in Louisiana. I: Description of species found in the vicinity of Baton Rouge. *Mycologia*, 37, 284–94.

COOLEY, J. S. (1938). Susceptibility of crop plants and weeds to *Sclerotium rolfsii. Phytopathology*, 28, 594–5.

COOPER, W. E. SHEWELL-. *See* SHEWELL-COOPER, W. E.

CORBET, A. S. (1930). An organism (*Bacillus pandora*) found in the latex of *Hevea brasiliensis. J. Bact.*, 19, 321–6.

COSTA, A. S. & BENNET, C. W. (1950). White fly transmitted mosaic of *Euphorbia prunifolia. Phytopathology*, 40, 266–84.

CROSSAN, D. F. (1954). *Cercosporella* leafspot of conifers. *N. Carolina Tech. Bull.*, 109, 23 pp.

CROSSMAN, L. & CHRISTIE, J. K. (1937). Lists of plants attacked by miscellaneous plant infesting nematodes. *Plant Dis. Reptr.*, 121, 144–67.

CURTIS, J. T. & GRANT, C. (1950). Antibiotics and autotoxic effects in prairie sunflower. *Bull. Torrey Bot. Cl.*, 77(3), 187–91.

DAHLGREN, B. E. & STANDLEY, P. C. (1944). *Edible and Poisonous Plants of the Caribbean Region.* Issued by the Navy Dept., Bureau of Medicine and Surgery. U.S. Government Printing Office, Washington, D.C., 102 pp.

DASKEVIC, B. N. (1935). [*The chemistry of vegetable poisons*—in Russian.] Institut Zascity Rastenii, Leningrad, 156 pp.

DE SIQUEIRA-JACCOUD, R. J. (1956). [Contribution to the study of *Euphorbia brasiliensis* —in Spanish]. *Mem. Inst. Oswaldo Cruz*, 54, 103–13.

DICE, J. R. (1944). Weed flavours in dairy products. *N. Dakota Sta. Bimonthly Bull.*, 6(4), 6–9.

DOOLITLE, S. P. (1950). Weeds often carry serious diseases of our cultivated crops. *What's New Crops Soils*, 2(6), 28.

DURRELL, L. C. & NEWSON, I. E. (1936). Poisonous and injurious plants of Colorado. *Bull. Color. Agric. Exp. Sta.*, No. 429, 75 pp.

DYKSTRA, T. P. (1933). Weeds as possible carriers of leaf roll and rugose mosaic of potato. *J. Agric. Res.*, 47, 17–32.

ERICKSON, L. C., TISDALE, E. W., MORTON, H. L. & ZAPPETTINI, G. (1951). *Halogeton*, intermediate range menace. *Idaho Agric. Exp. Sta. Circ.* No. 117, 10 pp.

ES, L. VAN. *See* VAN ES, L.

FENTON, E. W. & ROBERTSON, E. D. S. (1931). Poisonous and milk tainting plants. *Edinburgh & E. Scotland Coll. Agric.*, n.s. 4.

FILIPIEV, I. N. & STEKHOVEN, J. H. S. (1941). *A manual of agricultural helminthology.* Brill, Leiden, 878 pp.

FRANCA, C. (1927). Notes sur la biologie de 'Stenocephalis agilis (Scop.)'. *J. Scien. Mat. Fris. e. Nat., Lisboa*, 24, 25–27.

FRANCHINI, G. (1922). Amibes et autres protozoaires des plantes à latex du Muséum de Paris. *Bull. Soc. Path. Exot., Paris*, 15, 197–203.

—— (1931). Encore au sujet des spirochètes des euphorbes. *Bull. Soc. Path. Exot., Paris*, 24, 809–11.

—— (1931a). Étude sur une flagelle spécial du latex d'un figuier de l'Erythrée (*Ficus hochstetteri* (Mg.) A. Rich.). *Bull. Soc. Path. Exot. Paris*, 24, 843–8.

FRANK, P. A. & GRIGSBY, B. H. (1957). Effect of herbicidal sprays on nitrate accumulation in certain weed species. *Weeds*, 5, 206–17.

FRAZIER, N. W. & SEVERIN, H. H. P. (1945). Weed-host range of California aster yellows. *Hilgardia*, 16, 619–50.

FREEMAN, E. M. (1903). The seed-fungus of *Lolium temulentum* L., the darnel. *Phil. Trans. B.*, 196, 1–27.

GARDNER, C. A. & BENNETTS, H. W. (1956). *The Toxic Plants of Western Australia.* West Australian Newspapers Ltd., Perth, 253 pp. (52 col. pls.; refs., 241–4).

GOODEY, T. (1933). *Plant parasitic nematodes and the disease they cause.* Methuen, London, 306 pp.

—— (1940). *The nematode parasites of plants catalogued under their hosts.* Imp. Bur. Agric. Parasit., St. Albans, England, 80 pp.

—— (1944). On the stem eelworm (*Anguillulina dipsaci*), attacking oats, onions, field beans, parsnips, rhubarb, and certain weeds. *J. Helminth.*, 22, 1–12.

—— (Rev. by J. B. Goodey & M. T. Franklin) (1956). *The nematode parasites of plants catalogued under their hosts.* Comm. Agric. Bur., Farnham Royal, England, 140 pp.

GRAHAM, T. W. (1951). Nematode root rot of tobacco and other plants. *S. Carolina Agric. Bull.*, No. 390, 25 pp.

GREGORY, P. H. (1961). *The microbiology of the atmosphere.* (Ed. N. Polunin.) Leonard Hill, London, 251 pp.

GRIGSBY, B. H. & BALL, C. D. (1952). Some effects of herbicidal sprays on the hydrocyanic acid content of leaves of wild black cherry (*Prunus serotina* Ehrh.). *North Cent. Weed Cont. Conf. Proc.*, 6, 327–30.

HALL, T. F., PENFOUND, W. T., & HESS, A. D. (1946). Water level relationships of plants in the Tennessee Valley with particular reference to malaria control. *J. Tenn. Acad., Sci.*, 21(1), 18–59.

HANSON, H. C. & DICE, J. R. (1936). Milk-tainting weeds and their control. *Bull. Agric. Ext., N. Dak.*, No. 143, 4 pp.

HARRIS, M. R. (1933). Weeds as a factor in the spread of plant diseases in California. *Mon. Bull. Calif. Dep. Agric.*, 22, 273–7.

HARVEY, R. B. & LEE, S. B. (1943). Flagellates of laticiferous plants. *Plant Physiol.*, 18, 633–5.

HEGNER, R. & CHU, H. J. (1930). A survey of protozoan parasites in plants and animals of the Philippine Islands. *Philipp. J. Sci.*, 43, 451–2.

HEIN, A. (1953). Die Bedeutung der Unkräuter für die Epidemeologie pflanzlicher Virosen. *Deutsch. Landwirtsch. Jahrb.*, 4(19), 521–5.

—— (1956). Beiträge zur Kenntnis der Viruskrankheiten an Unkräutern. I: Das *Malva* virus. *Phytopathol. Z.*, 28(2), 205–34.

—— (1957). Das Luzernemosaik und das Lamium-Gelbmosaik virus. *Ibid.* 29, 79–116.

—— (1957a). Das Gurkenmosaikvirus. *Ibid.* 29, 204–29.

HESS, A. D. & HALL, T. F. (1945). The relation of plants to malaria control on impounded waters with a suggested classification. *J. Nat. Malar. Soc.*, 4(1), pp. 20–46.

HESSLER, R. (1911). Plants and man; weeds and diseases. *Proc. Ind. Acad. Sci. for* 1910, 49–69.

HEWITT, R. (1940). [Flagellates from Mexican latex plants—in Spanish]. *Rev. Inst. Salubriad y Enferm. Trop. Mexico*, 1,(2), 179–80.

HINKE, F. (1955). Bekampfungsmassnahmen gegen die Berberitze zur Verhütung von Schwarzrostschäden an Getreide. *Pflanzenschutz*, 7, 171–4.

HODGDON, A. R. (1951). Is *Onoclea sensibilis* poisonous to horses? *Amer. Fern J.*, 41, 61–62.

HOEHNE, F. C. (1939). *Plantas e Substâncias Vegetais Tóxicas e Medicais*. 'Graphicars', São Paulo & Rio de Janeiro, 335 pp. (26 col. pls.).

HOLMGREN, A. H. (1943). New poisonous weed invades western ranges. *Fm. Home Sci. (Utah Sta.)*, 4, 3, 11.

HONARD, C. (1908–9). *Les zoocecidies des plantes à Europe et du basin de la Méditerranée*. Hermann & Fils, Paris, 2 vol., 1450 pp.

HORN, E. E. (1953). A summer hay fever plant survey of Manhattan, Kansas. *Trans. Kans. Acad. Sci.*, 36, 91–97.

ISAKOVA, A. A. (1935). [The relationship between higher plants and lower organisms. I. On the association of plants containing latex with micro-organisms—in Russian, Engl. summ.]. *Bull. Acad. Sci. URSS Cl. Sci. et Nat.*, 1933(3), 383–95.

IVENS, G. W. (1960). Species of *Acacia* as weeds. In *The Biology of Weeds* (ed. J. L. Harper), Blackwell, Oxford, pp. 167–75.

JOHNSON, L. R. (1936). A note on the occurrence of *Anguillulina dipsaci* (Kühn, 1858) on certain weeds, including a new host record. *J. Helminth.*, 14, 233–5.

JOHNSON, T. & GREEN, G. J. (1951). The varieties of stem rust, *Puccinia graminis* Pers., occurring on barberry in eastern Canada. *Canad. J. Bot.*, 29(1), 1–9.

JONES, M. D. (1952). Time of day of pollen shedding of some hay fever plants. *J. Allergy*, 23, 247–58.

KASSANIS, B. (1944). A virus attacking lettuce and dandelion, *Nature, Lond.*, 154, 16.

KING, L. J. (1957). Book Review, *Weeds*, by W. C. Muenscher. *Science*, 123, 334.

—— (1963). The Ethnobotany of the Squills (*Urginea*, Liliaceae) in Africa, Europe, and Asia. Unpublished MS., Philadelphia, 26 pp.

KLOTS, A. B. (1951). Ecological study of insects on *Alnus incana*, with their predators and symbionts. *Biol. Rev.*, 13, 14–17.

KROCHMAL, A. & LAVENTIADES, G. (1955). Poisonous plants of Greece. *Econ. Bot.*, 9, 175–89.

LEWIS, A. N. (1941). Interim report on experiments to control *Glossinia pallidipes* in the Lambine Valley. *Kabete, Kenya*, 11 pp.

LI, L. V. & LI, T. C. (1938). Notes on *Heterodera marioni* as root parasites in some Kwangtung economic plants and weeds. *Lingnan Sci. J.*, 17, 533–7.

LOCKWOOD, S. (1933). The relation of weeds to insect pests. *Mon. Bull. Calif., Dep. Agric.*, 22, 279–82.

LONG, H. C. (1917). *Plants poisonous to livestock*. University Press, Cambridge, England, 119 pp.

MCNAIR, J. B. (1923). *Rhus dermatitis from Rhus toxicodendron, radicans, and diversiloba (poison ivy). Its pathology and chemotherapy*. University of Chicago Press, Chicago, 298 pp.

MAI, W. F. & SPEARS, J. F. (1954). The golden nematode in the United States. *Amer. Potato J.*, 31, 387–96.

MARTIN, G. E. (1950). Combined eelworm and weed control. *Rhodesian Farmer*, 4(8), 29.

MASSEY, A. B. (1954). Poisonous plants in Virginia. *Virginia Agric. Ext. Serv. Bull.*, No. 222, 47 pp.

MATHEWS, F. P. (1933). The toxicity of *Drymaria pachyphylla* for cattle, sheep, and goats, *J. Amer. Vet. Med. Assoc.*, 83, 255.

MATHEWS F. P. (1933a). The toxicity of *Baileya multiradiata* for sheep and goats. *J. Amer. Vet. Med. Assoc.*, 83, 673.

—— (1936). The toxicity of broomweed, *Gutierrezia microcephala*, for sheep, cattle, and goats. *J. Amer. Vet. Med. Assoc.*, 88, 55.

MAY, W. L. & LEACH, J. G. (1920). Notes on weeds and plant diseases. *Colorado Agric. Sta. Ext. Circ.*, No. 28, 40–46.

MEHRLICH, F. P. & FITZPATRICK, H. M. (1935). *Dichotomophthora portulacae*, a pathogene of *Portulaca oleracea*. *Mycologia*, 27, 543–50.

MEHTA, K. C. (1952). Further studies on cereal rusts in India. IV: *Indian Council of Agric. Res., Delhi, Sci. Monograph* No. 18, 368 pp.

MILDNER, T. (1951). *Giftpflanzen in Wald und Flur*. Geest & Portig, Leipzig, 49 pp.

MORRIS, K. R. S. (1946). The control of trypanosomiasis by entomological means. *Bull. Ent. Res.*, 37, 201–50.

MUIR, J. (1931). Drabok (*Lolium temulentum*) poisoning. *J. Med. Ass. S. Afr.*, pp. 485–6.

MURPHY, E. V. A. (1947). *Stock poisoning plants; a stockman's pocket book*. O.S.C. Coop. Assoc., Corvallis, Oregon.

NOORDAM, D. (1955). [The role of weeds as hosts of vector-transmissible and soil-borne viruses—in Dutch, English summary.] *Meded. Dir. Tuinb.*, 18, 639–45.

OFFORD, H. R. (1950). Operation gooseberry. For the first time a helicopter has been used to spray from the air in an attempt to control white pine blister rust. *Amer. Forests*, 56(1), 21, 36, 37.

OGDEN, E. C. (1957). Survey of airborne pollen and fungus spores of New York State. *N.Y. State Mus. and Sci. Serv., Bull.* 356, 62 pp.

ORCHARD, H. E. (1946). Weeds which taint food. *J. Dep. Agric. S. Aust.*, 50, 173–80.

ORLANDO, A. & SILBERSCHMIDT, K. (1946). Studies of the natural dissemination of the virus of the 'infection chlorosis' of Malvaceae (Abutilon Virus I Baur) and its relation to the insect vector *Bemisia tabaci* (Genn.). *Arch. Inst. Biol. S. Paulo*, 17, 1–36.

PADWICK, G. W. (1935). Influence of wild and cultivated plants on the multiplication, survival and spread of cereal foot-rotting fungi in the soil. *Canad. J. Res.*, 12, 575–89.

—— & HENRY, A. W. (1933). The relation of species of *Agropyron* and certain other grasses to the foot-rot problem of wheat in Alberta. *Canad. J. Res.*, 8, 349–63.

PAMMEL, L. H. (1914). Poisonous and medical plants of Missouri. *Bull. Mo. Bd. Hort.*, No. 14.

PENFOUND, W. T. (1942). The relation of plants to malaria control. *Publ. Health Repts.*, 57(8), 261–8.

PETERS, B. G. (1955). Soil-inhabiting nematodes. In *Soil Zoology*, Butterworth Sci. Publ., London, pp. 44–54.

PHALEN, J. M. (1930). The manchineal tree (*Hippomane mancinella*). *Mil. Surgeon*, 66, 225–7.

PIEMEISEL, R. L. (1932). Weedy abandoned land and the weed hosts of the beet leaf hopper. *United States Dep. Agric. Circ.* No. 229, 24 pp.

POLUNIN, N. (1951). Seeking airborne botanical particles about the North Poles. *Svensk. Bot. Tidskr.*, 45, 320–54.

—— & KELLY, C. D. (1952). Arctic aeropalynology. Fungi and Bacteria, etc., caught in the air during flights over the geographical North Pole. *Nature, Lond.*, 170, 314–16.

RAGONESE, A. E. (1956). Plantas toxicas para el ganado en la région central Argentina. *Rev. Facul. de Agronomia de la Plata*, 31(3), 1–336.

REEVES, R. S. (1950). Ragweed control and pollen studies in the Philadelphia area. *Proc. Northeast. States Weed Contr. Conf.*, 4, 288–90.

ROGERS, C. H. (1936). Cotton root-rot and weeds in native hay meadow of Central Texas. *J. Amer. Soc. Agron.*, 28, 820–3.

SALLANS, B. J. (1940). The relationship of weeds to losses caused by common root rot in wheat. *Sci. Agric.*, **20**, 632–7.

SANTOS, E. (1951). [Plants which kill fish and insects—in Portuguese.] *Fauna (São Paulo)*, **10**(7), 57–59.

SCHMELZER, K. (1957). Die Passage durch *Stellaria media* in ihrer Bedeutung für die Mechanische Ubertragung von Viren un Nelken. *Phytopathol. Z.*, **28**, 457–60.

SEVERIN, H. H. (1937). Weed host range and over-wintering of curly-top virus. *Hilgardia*, **8**, 263–77.

SHEFFIELD, F. M. L. (1957). Virus diseases of sweet potatoes in East Africa. II: Transmission to alternative hosts. *Phytopathology*, **48**, 1–6.

SHELMIRE, B. (1939). Contact dermatitis from weeds: patch testing with their oleoresins. *J. Amer. Med. Ass.*, **113**, 1085–90.

SHEWELL-COOPER, W. E. (1950). Preparing for phlox; eelworm is the enemy and infected weeds must be eradicated. *Field*, **196**, 751.

SIMONART, P. (1952). Bactéries et latex. *Bull. Agric. Congo Belge*, **43**, 63–70.

SIMPSON, G. W., SHANDE, W. A., & WYMAN, O. L. (1945). Weeds and the aphid leaf roll problem in potatoes. *Bull. Me. Agric. Exp. Sta.*, **333**, 1–20.

SMITH, A. BERNARD-. *See* BERNARD-SMITH, A.

SMITH, K. M. (1931). *A textbook of agricultural entomology.* University Press, Cambridge, England, 285 pp.

SMITH, T. E. & GODFREY, R. K. (1938). Field survey of the relation of susceptible weeds to Granville-wilt control. (Abst.) *Phytopathology*, **29**, 22.

SOUTHEY, J. F. & STANILAND, L. N. (1950). Observations and experiments on stem eelworm, *Ditylenchus dipsaci*, with special reference to weed hosts. *J. Helminth.*, **24**, 145–54.

SPAIN, W. C. (1953). The importance of weeds in allergic maladies. *Northeast Weed Control Conf. Proc.*, **7**, 313–19.

—— (1953*a*). Review of pollenosis and the role of weeds. *Publ. Hth. Rept., Wash.*, **68**, 885–9.

SPERRY, O. E. (1951). Experimental control of poisonous range plants in Texas. *Texas Agric. Exp. Sta. Prog. Rep.*, No. 1334, 4 pp.

—— (1951). Experimental control of poisonous range plants. *Cattleman*, **37**(12), 100–2.

STAEHELIN, M. (1931). Les vers nématodes, Anguillules, parasites des plantes horticoles et maraîchères. *Annu. Agric. Suisse*, 41 pp.

STAHLER, L. M. & WHITEHEAD, E. J. (1950). The effect of 2,4-D on potassium nitrate levels in leaves of sugar beets. *Science*, **112**, 749–51.

STAKMAN, E. C., KEMPTON, F. E. & HUTTON, L. D. (1927). The common barberry and black stem rust. *U. S. Dep. Agric. Farm. Bull.* No. 1544, 28 pp.

—— & HARRAR, G. J. (1957). *Principles of plant pathology.* Ronald Press, New York, 581 pp.

STANDLEY, P. C. (1928). Flora of the Panama Canal Zone. *Contrib. U.S. Nat. Herbarium.* **27**, 1–416.

STANILAND, L. N. (1945). The occurrence of *Anguillulina dipsaci* (Kühn.) on weed hosts, including new host records in fields of oats affected by 'tulip-rot'. *Ann. Appl. Biol.*, **32**, 171–3.

STEINBAUER, G. P. & STEINMETZ, F. H. (1945). Eradication of certain Maine weeds, an important step in control of potato diseases spread by aphids. *Misc. Publ. Me. Agric. Exp. Sta.*, No. 602, 22 pp.

STEYN, D. G. (1933). Poisoning of human beings by weeds contained in cereals (bread poisoning). *Onderstepoort J. Vet. Sci.*, **1**, 219–66.

—— (1934). The poisoning of human beings by weeds contained in wheat (bread poisoning). *Fmg. in S. Afr.*, **9**, 45–46.

STODDART, L. A., BAIRD, G., STEWART, G. S., MACKHAM, B. S. & CLEGG, H. (1951). The *Halogeton* problem in Utah. *Utah Agric. Exten. Bull.* 250, 12 pp.

SULIT, M. D. (1940). Plants to be avoided or handled with care in the forest. *Philipp. J. Forestry*, 3, 177–89.

SWANSON, C. R. & SHAW, W. C. (1954). The effect of 2,4-D on formation of hydrogen cyanide in Sudan grass. (Abst.) *Southern Weed Conf. Proc.*, 7, 226.

SWEETMAN, H. L. (1928). Notes on insects inhabiting the roots of weeds. *Ann. Ent. Soc. Amer.*, 21, 594–600.

SYLVESTER, S. E. (1953). *Brassica nigra* virus transmission; some vector-host-plant relationships. *Phytopathology*, 43, 209–14.

TAUBENHAUS, J. J. (1936). *Phymatotrichum* root rot on winter and spring weeds of South Central types. *Amer. J. Bot.*, 23, 167–8.

THORSTEINSON, A. J. (1953). The chemotactic responses that determine host specificity in an oligophagous insect (*Plutella maculipennis* (Curt.) Lepidoptera). *Canad. J. Zool.*, 31(1), 52–72.

TISDELL, T. F. (1961). A life cycle study of horse nettle (*Solanum carolinense*). (Ph.D. Thesis, Rutgers University, 1961.) *Dissert. Abstr.*, 22, 1344.

VALLEAU, W. D. & JOHNSON, E. M. (1936). *Physalis subglabrata :* a natural host of *Bacterium angulatum*. *Phytopathology*, 26, 388–90.

VAN ES, L., CANTWELL, L. R., MARTIN, H. M. & KRAMER, J. (1929). On the nature and cause of 'Walking Disease' of northwestern Nebraska. *Nebraska Res. Bull.*, No. 43, 47 pp.

VERALL, A. F. (1943). Ambrosia beetles. *J. Agric. Res.*, 66, 135–44.

WAGNER, J. S. (1952). Marijuana eradication by the New York City Department of Sanitation. *North Cent. Weed Cont. Conf. Proc.*, 6 (suppl.), 119–21.

WALKER, A. G. (1945). Rhizomatous grass weeds and *Ophiobolus graminis* Sacc. *Ann. Appl. Biol.*, 32, 177–9.

WALKER, M. N. & STAHL, C. F. (1926). Certain grass hosts of the sugar cane mosaic disease and of the corn aphid considered in relation to their occurrence in Cuba. *Bull. Trop. Pl. Res. Fdn.*, No. 5, 14 pp.

WALLACH, A. (1952). Ragweed control in Yonkers, New York. *North Cent. Weed Cont. Conf. Proc.*, 6 (suppl.), 101–9.

WATT, J. M. & BREYER-BRANDWIJK, M. G. (1962). *The Medicinal and Poisonous Plants of Southern and Eastern Africa*. E. & S. Livingston, Edinburgh.

WEBB, P. C. R. (1949). Zoosporangia, believed to be those of *Plasmodiophora brassicae*, in the root hairs of non-cruciferous plants. *Nature, Lond.*, 163, 608.

WEINSTEIN, I. & FLETCHER, A. H. (1948). Essentials for the control of ragweed. *Amer. J. Publ. Hlth.*, 38, 664–9.

WELLMAN, F. L. (1935). Dissemination of southern celery mosaic virus on vegetable crops in Florida. *Phytopathology*, 25, 289–308.

—— (1937). Control of southern celery mosaic in Florida by removing weeds that serve as sources of infection. *Tech. Bull. U.S. Dep. Agric.*, No. 548. 16 pp.

WILHELM, S. & THOMAS, H. E. (1952). *Solanum sarachoides*, an important weed host to *Verticillium alboatrum*. (Abst.) *Phytopathology*, 42, 519–20.

WILLMOT, F. C. & SILBERBAUER, S. F. (1931). Darnel (*Lolium temulentum*) or drabok poisoning. *J. Med. Ass. S. Afr.*, *1931*, p. 381.

WODEHOUSE, R. P. (1935). *Pollen Grains : Their Structure, Identification and Significance in Science and Medicine*. McGraw-Hill, New York, 574 pp.

—— (1939). Weeds, waste and hayfever. . . . *Natural History*, 43(3), 150–63.

—— (1945). *Hayfever Plants*. Chronica Botanica Co., Waltham, Mass., 245 pp.

WOLF, F. A., CURTIS, R. S. & KAUPP, B. F. (1918). A monograph on trembles or milk sickness and White Snakeroot (*Eupatorium urticaefolium*). *N. C. Agric. Exp. Sta. Tech. Bull.* 15, 74 pp. (12 pls.).

WOLCOTT, G. N. (1928). Increase of insect transmitted plant disease and recent damage through weed destruction in tropical agriculture. *Ecology*, 9, 461–6.

WOODSIDE, A. M. (1947). Some weed hosts of bugs that cause cat-facing of peaches. *Virginia Fruit*, **35**, 12.

WORMALD, H. (1941). The grey mould of fruit and hops: weeds as possible sources of infection. *Annu. Rep. E. Malling Res. Sta.*, **29**, 44–47.

YAMASAKI, M., & NAKAUSA, M. (1953). Physiological studies on the poisonous action of 2,4-D on plants. II: On the change of chemical constituents of Kikuimo (Jerusalem Artichoke) sprayed with 2,4-D. *Proc. Crop Sci. Soc. Japan*, **21**, 295–7.

YOUNKIN, S. G. (1942). Weed suspects of the potato yellow dwarf virus. *Amer. Potato J.*, **19**, 6–11.

ADDENDUM

Additional studies from the University of Michigan project include: A. N. Dingle *et al.* (1959), The emission, dispersion and deposition of ragweed pollen, *Advances in Geophysics*, 6, 367–87; W. W. Payne (1963), The morphology of the inflorescence of ragweeds (*Ambrosia-Franseria*: Compositae), *Amer. J. Bot.*, 50, 872–80; W. W. Payne (1964), A re-evaluation of the genus *Ambrosia* (Compositae), *J. Arnold Arbor.*, 45, 401–30, 8 pls.; W. H. Wagner, Jr. (1959), An annotated bibliography of ragweed (*Ambrosia*), *Rev. Allergy & Appl. Immunol.*, 13, 353–403; Anon. (1964–65), Aeroallergens, an interdisciplinary study, *Res. News* (Univ. Mich.), 15(6–7), 1–16.

VI

THE ESTABLISHMENT OF WEEDS: SEED STRUCTURE, GERMINATION, AND SEEDLING ECESIS

WHEN new weed infestations first make their appearance, often the first control measure employed is to chop them down, or exterminate them with an appropriate chemical weed-killer—generally so effectively as to prevent seed formation and dispersal. More thorough measures are needed for perennials when once they have attained ecesis (i.e. become success-fully established); but the checking of seed production is an important first step where annual weeds and perennials too are concerned.

THE ANGIOSPERM SEED

As the majority of weeds belong to the predominant group of seed plants, the Angiosperms, some consideration will be given to their type of seed. The angiosperm seed differs primarily from the gymnosperm seed in that it is enclosed in an ovary; this also distinguishes it from the spore of the Pteridophytes. In general, the weed seed does not differ in any marked way from the non-weedy members of the native flora. How-ever, the condition of dormancy of many weed seeds distinguishes them, as will be seen hereafter. Moreover, there are some notable features of the structure and over-all appearance of weed seeds that are commonly associated with this group of plants—although not exclusively so.

SEED SIZE AND WEIGHT

The studies of Stevens (1932), Salisbury (1942), and King (1952), indicate the range in weight at least for many of our temperate weeds. The data for some representative species, together with the number of seeds per plant (taken from the last work mentioned), are given in Table IV (p. 139). These data show that large numbers of weeds have seed weights ranging from about 0·10 gm. per thousand seeds to about 3·00 gm. per thousand seeds, as in the Cruciferae (cf. Stevens, 1932), and naturally in dissemination it is considered that the lighter seeds have a decided advantage—particularly the anemochores. Some of the parasitic weeds, such as species of *Orobanche* and *Striga*, bear seeds of near-microscopic size in prodigious numbers; for example, seeds of *O. minor* are 0·2–0·3 mm. long, 0·2 mm. wide, and 0·1 mm. thick. These minute seeds are dissemin-ated in unusual ways—in *Striga*, which is often parasitic on grasses, apparently by sifting into the spaces between the glumes. Seeds of some *Striga* species are so similar to seeds of tobacco that they are inseparable and undetectable from these crop seeds. They, too, can parasitize this crop (Salisbury, 1942).

THE SHAPE OF WEED SEEDS AND THE VOILURE CONCEPT

Many investigators have noted the similarity in appearance of certain weed seeds with those of the crop with which the weeds are customarily associated, and some weeds are frequently so much an integral part of a cultivated crop that they have been termed satellite weeds—e.g. *Lolium temulentum* of wheat; *Agrostemma githago* of wheat; *Avena fatua* of oats; *Camelina sativa* of flax. The shape and weight of the seeds in question determine this association (Fig. 10).

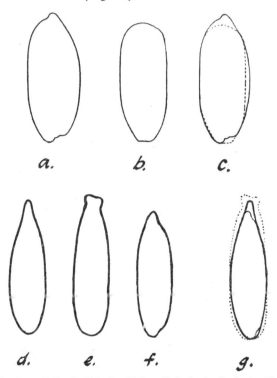

From Keller, Lubimenko, Malzev, Fedtschenko, Roshevitz & Kamensky, 1934

FIG. 10.—Outline drawings of crop seed or fruit and of similarly-shaped weed seeds or fruits associated with these crops—illustrating the voilure principle. *Above :* outlines of wheat grain (*a*) in side view, and of grain of darnel (*Lolium temulentum* var. *muticum*) (*b*) in dorsal view, separately, and then placed one on the other (*c*). *Below :* outlines of flax seed (*d*), of *Chaerophyllum bulbosum* fruit (*e*), and of *Lallemantia iberica* nutlet (*f*), separately, and all placed on one another (*g*).

As weed seeds contaminate the seeds saved for sowing, methods have been devised to rid the desirable crop seed of such contaminants, and two general procedures of winnowing and screening have been used. Winnowing the seed is perhaps the most ancient form of seed cleaning. By this method the treaded or thrashed grain is forked into the air, where the air-currents carry away the chaff and lighter material, leaving the heavier crop seeds to fall back to earth. The more similar a weed seed is to the crop seed, the more likely it would be to fall back to earth with the crop seeds and be planted again. Thus man, through winnowing, exerted a selective action, favouring weeds whose seeds simulated crop seeds; accordingly he has been a breeder of weeds as well as of crops!

N. Zinger (1909), in his early studies on *Camelina sativa* as a satellite weed of flax, introduced the voilure concept. This concept, in the studies

TABLE III

VOILURE COEFFICIENTS (K)* FOR THE SEEDS OF A NUMBER OF COMMON WEEDS (*from Hitrovo*, 1912)

Note that small size together with an irregular surface provides a higher K value. Thus lighter 'seeds' with elaborate appendages (as in many Compositae) may be widely dispersed.

Class No.	Name	K	Class No.	Name	K
I (0–4)	*Vicia angustifolia*	3·5	V (40–79)	*Bromus arvensis*	40
				Capsella bursa-pastoris	67
II (5–9)	*Agrostemma githago*	6		*Juncus bufonius*	70
	Convolvulus arvensis	6		*Pastinaca sativa*	61
	Polygonum hydropiper	9		*Sonchus arvensis*	63
				Veronica arvensis	52
III (10–19)	*Allium oleraceum*	12	VI (80–159)	*Plantago major*	83
	Centaurea cyanus	19·5		*Rumex acetosella*	84
	Cirsium arvense	11·4		*Sagina procumbens*	85
	Echinochloa crusgalli	19	VII (160–319)	*Leontodon autumnalis*	178
	Lolium temulentum	11		*Sisymbrium thalianum*	257
	Polygonum aviculare	13	VIII (320–639)	*Crepis tectorum*	438
	Setaria viridis	15	IX (> 640)	*Erigeron canadensis*	670
	Thlaspi arvense	17·5		*Taraxacum officinale*	667
IV (20–39)	*Bromus secalinus*	23·5			
	Chenopodium album	22			
	Poa annua	30			
	Rumex crispus	39			
	Sinapis arvensis	23·5			
	Stellaria media	20			

*$K = \dfrac{S}{M} = \left(\dfrac{cm.^2}{gm.}\right)$, i.e. the surface area of the seed as determined by microscopical measurements divided by the weight in grams.

of Hitrovo (1912), has been extended to include the 'voilure coefficient'. Such coefficients are given in Table III for a number of common weeds.

Sinskaia & Beztuzheva (1931), in their studies of *Camelina sativa* in connection with climate, flax, and man, emphasize that the evolution of different ecotypes of the weed *Camelina* is closely connected with the processes of morphological and geographical differentiation of flax. Thus just as there are short forms of flax, there are short forms of *Camelina*; and even as there are shattering forms of flax, there are also shattering forms of *Camelina*, etc. These aspects will be considered in further detail in the section devoted to genetics (pp. 226–39).

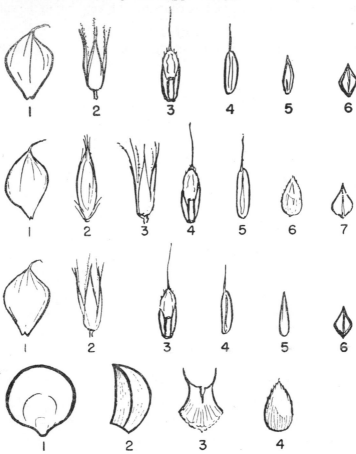

From Welch, 1954

FIG. 11.—Drawings of crop seeds or fruits, together with the asssociated weed ones that are generally found with them and require separation. *Top row*—Fescue and weeds commonly associated: 1, Wild Onion; 2, Wild Barley; 3, Darnel; 4, Cheat; 5, Fescue; 6, Dock. *Second row*—Oats and weeds commonly associated: 1, Wild Onion; 2, Oat; 3, Wild Barley; 4, Darnel; 5, Cheat; 6, Johnson Grass; 7. Dock. *Third row*—Ryegrass and weeds commonly associated: 1, Wild Onion; 2, Wild Barley; 3, Darnel; 4, Cheat; 5, Ryegrass; 6, Dock. *Bottom row*—Sorghum and weeds commonly associated: 1, Sorghum; 2, Morning Glory; 3, Prickly Sida; 4, Johnson Grass. (Mississippi Agricultural Experiment Station.)

Winnowing has largely been replaced in the more advanced types of agriculture by mechanical screening devices—although air drafts are generally incorporated in modern equipment for certain gross or early-stage separations. The bulletin prepared by G. B. Welch (1954), of the Mississippi Agricultural Experiment Station, provides a detailed account of modern seed-processing equipment. The weed seeds, etc., that are commonly found in the crop seed from the State of Mississippi, have been illustrated in this study and are reproduced in Figs. 11, 12, and 13.

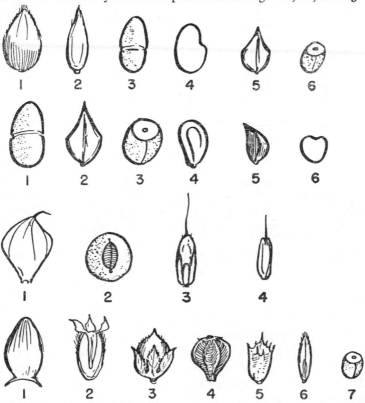

From Welch, 1954

FIG. 12.—Drawings of crop seeds or fruits, together with the associated weed ones that are generally found with them and require separation. *Top row*—Red Clover and weeds commonly associated: 1, Johnson Grass; 2, Canary Grass; 3, Plantain; 4, Red Clover; 5, Dock; 6, Dodder. *Second row*—White Dutch Clover and weeds commonly associated: 1, Plantain; 2, Dock; 3, Dodder; 4, Peppergrass; 5, Evening Primrose; 6, White Dutch Clover. *Third row*—Wild Winter Pea and weeds commonly associated: 1, Wild Onion; 2, Wild Winter Pea; 3, Darnel; 4 Cheat. *Bottom row*—Lespedeza and weeds commonly associated: 1, Beggar Tick; 2, Buttonweed; 3, Lespedeza; 4, Sump Weed; 5, Ragweed; 6, Crabgrass; 7, Dodder. (Mississippi Agricultural Experiment Station.)

THE TYPES OF DORMANCY OF WEED SEEDS

The prolonged dormancy of weed seeds, and the associated periodicity of germination throughout extended periods of time, constitute one of the more pernicious aspects of our annual weed problem. Delayed germination

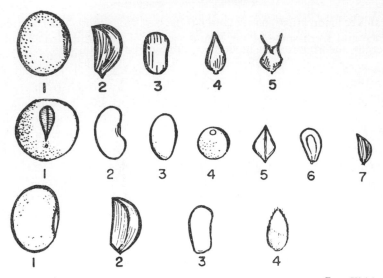

From Welch, 1954

Fig. 13.—Drawings of crop seeds or fruits, together with the associated weed ones that are generally found with them and require separation. *Top row*—Soybean (large) and weeds commonly associated: 1, Soybean (large); 2, Morning Glory; 3, Coffee Weed; 4, Johnson Grass; 5, Prickly Sida. *Second row*—Crimson Clover and weeds commonly associated: 1, Narrow-leaf Vetch; 2, Crimson Clover; 3, Wild Geranium; 4, Wild Mustard; 5, Dock; 6, Peppergrass; 7, Primrose. *Bottom row*—Soybean (small) and weeds commonly associated: 1, Soybean (small); 2, Morning Glory; 3, Coffee Weed; 4, Johnson Grass. (Mississippi Agricultural Experiment Station.)

has survival value. In the temperate zones, survival of plants in an arrested condition—as whole leafless plants, perennial root systems, specialized structures (such as the over-wintering buds of *Elodea*), and seeds—occurs regularly through freezing winter temperatures, or through other adverse environmental conditions such as drought or fire.

In the tropical regions many seeds have no dormancy, but generally germinate soon after reaching the ground. *Galinsoga parviflora*, a tropical composite weed venturing into the temperate regions of several continents, still retains this capacity of immediate germination; but some of its fruits are also capable of surviving the winter in soil. Several truly temperate weeds, such as *Taraxacum* and perhaps other early-maturing types, behave in a similar fashion; but fortunately most of our crop seeds have only short periods of dormancy. Oats, however, consists of several forms—the true crop species with little or no seed dormancy, false wild oats consisting of aberrant forms with no appreciable seed dormancy, and the pernicious wild oats (*Avena fatua* and *A. ludoviciana*), whose seeds shatter badly at maturity and possess prolonged dormancy of many years' duration.

THE ONSET OF DORMANCY

Several recent studies have helped in the elucidation of some aspects of this problem of dormancy—particularly those involving climate. Von

Abrams & Hand (1956) have examined the bases for reports from southern France and from some of the inland valleys of California that claimed successful germination of hybrid rose 'seed' without resorting to low-temperature treatment. These authors observed that the dormancy of hybrid rose 'seed' of a given genetic origin may vary widely from year to year, and from one region to another. Their controlled experiments on the formation, maturation, and germination of hybrid rose 'seed' led them to conclude that the dormancy of these 'seeds', and their consequent germination pattern in time, may vary widely between years; and low-temperature treatment is not invariably a prerequisite of extensive germination. Von Abrams & Hand also observed that there was good correlation between germination and pre-harvest climate—particularly with the mean daily temperatures for the thirty-day period during the formation and maturation of the 'seed'.

The dormancy that develops or is present at the apparent maturity of the seeds is termed 'primary dormancy'. One of the most common causes of primary dormancy in seeds is the need for certain complex physiological and chemical changes to occur within the seed; these are known as 'after-ripening'.

The prolonged dormant condition of seeds has developed during the evolution of the species in question, and may frequently be a direct reflection of the composite pattern of the microclimate and macroclimate where this particular species developed. When plants become dispersed into new environments, aspects of the basic dormancy are often retained, but also the plants may frequently be altered or adjusted to the new environment through the development of physiological races or ecotypes. When a question of prolonged seed dormancy, or any other growth problem for that matter, arises with regard to any particular non-crop plant, it is useful to investigate the region of origin of the species in question, and also the associated environmental conditions.

Prolonged dormancy of seeds has survival value, of course—affording protection from the adverse conditions or responses of the natural environment, such as unseasonable growth, drought, fire, flood, soil erosion, and, in the case of weeds, from the man-made modifications of these aforementioned disruptive forces, such as repeated cultivation of the soil. The various tissues and specific structures within the seed have responded differently, during the evolution of the various plant families, to these disruptive forces. We shall now examine some of these 'barriers' to the immediate germination of viable seeds in an environment that otherwise appears conducive to normal germination.

IMPERMEABLE SEED–COATS

Seeds of many members of the Malvaceae and Leguminosae have seed-coats that are impermeable to water even when embedded in moist soil. These seeds are frequently referred to as 'hard seeds', and in nature germinate after being in the soil for long periods of time which result in the softening and wearing down of the seed-coat. The softening and wearing down of the seed-coat occurs through the leaching action of soil water, and is due to the growth of soil micro-organisms on and about the seed-coat, and perhaps to fracture of the seed-coat through abrasive action of the soil or through soil animal activity. Undoubtedly, biochemical changes occurring within the seed-coat during ageing, together with the influence of environmental factors, all contribute to increasing the permeability to water and thus lead to germination. Weed seeds with such impermeable seed-coats, when consumed by animals as food, still retain their viability; but they are so affected by their sojourn in the digestive tract that impermeability and the normal dormant period are drastically altered.

Various methods have been devised in the laboratory to shorten the dormant period and stimulate seeds to germinate: for example, the seed-coat may be filed; the seeds may be rolled with an abrasive substance such as sand; or they may be treated with concentrated sulphuric acid.

OXYGEN-IMPERMEABLE SEED-COATS

Much that has been said about the impermeability of the seed-coat to water applies equally to oxygen. The classic demonstration of the importance of oxygen is the common cocklebur (*Xanthium canadense*). In each bur or fruiting structure there is a pair of seeds;* commonly the lower of the pair shows prompt germination, whereas the upper may show no germination under ordinary conditions until after many months or even years have elapsed. Many weed species in the Compositae and Chenopodiaceae produce several different kinds of seeds on the same plant (often in the same capitulum); these are termed heteromorphic seeds, and differ not only in appearance but in their dormancy states (Fig. 14).

Crocker (1906), Shull (1914), and others have studied this problem from a physiological point of view, and have observed that both seeds germinate promptly if the seed-coats are removed. The difference in the time of germination of the two seeds is principally due to structural differences in their seed-coats, which in one of the two seeds shows low permeability to oxygen. Not all burs contain 'upper' and 'lower' seeds (Fig. 14, *right*), as some appear only to be paired (Fig. 14, *left*). In the latter condition, structural differences in the seed-coats still occur, however.

LOW-TEMPERATURE REQUIREMENT

Seeds of weeds growing in the temperate zones generally fail to give a very high percentage of germination unless they have been exposed in a moist medium to temperatures between 0° and about 6°C. for a few

* It is proposed henceforth in this volume to dispense with technical distinctions between seeds and fruits.—Ed.

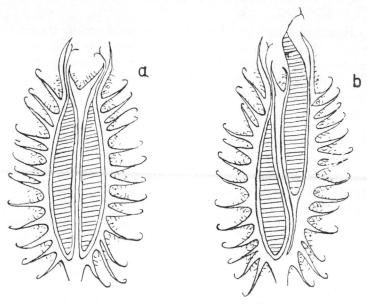

From Löve & Dansereau, 1959

FIG. 14.—*Xanthium* fruits showing positions of: (*a*) normal seeds, and (*b*) 'upper' and 'lower' seeds in the bur.

weeks or up to several months. This specific treatment represents, in part, what the temperate weed seed would have received in its natural environment had it remained in the soil over the winter season. Studies on hazel seeds (*Corylus avellana*) at a low temperature of 5 °C. on a moist medium, have demonstrated that part of the mechanism of low-temperature after-ripening may involve a stimulation of nucleotide synthesis in both embryonic axis and cotyledons (as there is an increase in the phosphorus). This results in the accumulation of nucleotides and nucleic acids in the embryonic axis (Bradbeer *et al.*, 1964).

ALTERNATING TEMPERATURES

Another phase of the low-temperature requirement of temperate weed seeds is the more specific aspect of a definite alternation, or cycle, of a higher temperature followed by a period of lower temperature. This, too, represents a condition that is found in the natural environment, and again indicates how closely adjusted some weed seeds are to the major as well as minor fluctuations in environmental conditions. Examples of plants having such requirements are orchard grass (*Dactylis glomerata*), Kentucky bluegrass (*Poa pratensis*), barberry (*Berberis vulgaris*), and others. Kolk (1947) found that varying temperatures (between 5° and 22°C.) favoured the germination of most of the species studied (e.g. *Sinapis arvensis*), as compared with constant temperatures (20° to 22°C.).

123

LIGHT REQUIREMENT

It is not unexpected that seeds of many weed species should have a light (or darkness) requirement for germination—especially as so many weeds associated with crop-lands germinate at extremely shallow soil depths in the open environment that is exposed to the highest light-intensities. Kinzel (1920) examined this subject in some detail. He found that, of 964 species examined, germination of 672 was favoured by light, whereas that of 258 was inhibited by light. Many species of the Gramineae are light-sensitive, the northern species of *Poa* providing an example. Many seeds of parasitic and epiphytic plants that frequently germinate on fully exposed tree branches, or in light shade in the higher levels of the forest canopy, are also light-sensitive—especially those of species of *Loranthus, Viscum, Arceuthobium,* etc.

The discovery, by Flint & McAllister (1954), of the reversible photo-reaction in the germination of lettuce seed, is of great significance to field germination problems. Reversible photoreaction refers to the fact that certain pigments controlling seed germination (and other aspects of plant growth and development such as photoperiodic flowering) may exist in two physiologically active states—an oxidized state initiated by irradiation in the red portion of the spectrum, and a reduced state inhibited by the infrared. Since a change from either of these states to the alternate one may be induced, it is said to be reversible. Toole *et al.* (1955, 1955*a*) found the reversible photoreaction in seeds of many of the higher plants, but it is not always necessary for germination. This photoreaction can be altered by temperature. As Billings (1957) points out, this new information indicates the complexity of seed germination—particularly in regard to patterns and combinations of light of various wave-lengths, temperature, and water conditions. The effect of light on germination is examined in some detail in a later section (pp. 141–2).

OTHER ASPECTS OF AFTER-RIPENING

Conditions to which the seeds of plants are subjected following maturation on the plant, or after collection, or even after falling to the soil surface, have been referred to as 'after-ripening' conditions. For example, many freshly-collected weed seeds will not germinate when cultured under conditions ordinarily conducive to germination. However, if they are stored in a dry condition in the laboratory—without subjection to low temperature in a moist medium—a fair percentage of germination is usually obtained. This is the case with giant foxtail grass (*Setaria faberii*), for example (King, 1952). While this condition is not generally experienced in the natural environment, there still are certain circumstances in which it exists and has a bearing on weed problems. The inadvertent collection, storage, and later dissemination, of weed seeds present as contaminants in agronomic and horticultural seeds, and in hay and other stored plant products, are examples of this. Davis (1930) has shown that the embryos of the fruits of the giant ragweed (*Ambrosia trifida*) also after-ripen in dry storage; but the process is very slow, and unequal in different embryos—some germinating readily after a few months of dry storage, while others may still remain dormant after one or more years.

The presence of germination inhibitors in seeds has been demonstrated by a number of investigators (Stout & Tolman, 1941; Evenari, 1949). In germination studies of the giant foxtail (*Setaria faberii*), some experimental data obtained were interpreted as indicating the presence within the seed of substances inhibitory to germination. These substances were withdrawn experimentally from germinating seeds by special alternate wetting and drying. It also was postulated that, under field conditions, alternate wetting and drying of soil (found to stimulate the germination of this grass) results in a withdrawal of, or some other action upon, these inhibitory substances; with their reduction in concentration or other reaction, germination could then proceed (King, 1952).

In the germination studies of the desert species of *Atriplex*, Beadle (1952) and Koller (1957) report that germination was inhibited by the presence of the surrounding bracts. In five Australian species studied, this inhibition was due to the presence of chloride-ion in the bracts, although Koller (1957) reports that, in *A. dimorphostegia* from the Negev Desert, the chloride-ion is not directly responsible for inhibition.

SPECIAL CONDITIONS OF THE EMBRYO

Justice (1941) found that the dormancy of seeds of climbing buckwheat (*Polygonum scandens*) was localized in the embryo. Less than 10 per cent of the excised embryos from mature untreated seeds germinated when placed on nutrient agar, while 76 per cent of those which had been isolated from stratified* seeds germinated. The excised embryos also gave high germination values when subjected to low-temperature treatment, or if they were cultured in an oxygenated nutrient solution, or after exposure to oxygen concentrations of 50–80 per cent for six days at 21°C.

In the early seedling stages, after some root development has occurred, a condition known as 'epicotyl dormancy' has been observed in both the tree paeony and the herbaceous paeony. This can be overcome by moist storage at from 1°–10°C. for two to three months after the seed has germinated to form a root (Crocker & Barton, 1953). Some species possess a combination of root and epicotyl dormancy, to remedy which low-temperature treatments in a moist medium at two separate periods are required; examples include certain spring-flowering temperate species in the genera *Trillium*, *Convallaria*, *Sanguinaria*, and *Smilacina*. This

---

* According to Barton (1961, p. 95), ' "Stratification" is a term derived from the practice of nurserymen to spread layers of seeds alternating with layers of moist soil or sand for over-winter or other low-temperature treatment of seeds. The same term is now generally used to denote any low-temperature treatment of seeds in a moist medium'.—Ed.

phenomenon has been referred to as 'double dormancy' (Crocker & Barton, 1953). Examples of these more specialized types of dormancy have not been noted among weedy plants.

There is considerable variability in the development of the embryo at the time of apparent seed maturity and dispersal. The presence of immature embryos may occasionally account for the dormant condition. This arrested development does not change until the germination or after-ripening processes begin, at which time growth is resumed. For example, at the time when the berries of the American holly (*Ilex opaca*) fall from the tree, they contain only rudimentary cotyledons and no hypocotyl or plumule (Crocker & Barton, 1953).

SECONDARY DORMANCY

Dormancy induced in seeds by unfavourable germination conditions has been termed 'secondary dormancy' (Crocker, 1916). Several investigators have noted that seeds which have become after-ripened or which, on reaching maturity, show no dormancy, may be forced into dormancy if placed under warm, moist conditions with deficient oxygen or, in some cases, with an excess of carbon dioxide.

It has also been observed that light-inhibited seeds will, if placed in a lighted germinator, soon change so that they will not germinate later in darkness; and conversely, light-favoured seeds may be so altered by dark exposure in the germinator that they will not germinate when later transferred to light. Thus the after-ripening process is reversible. Davis (1930) found that *Xanthium* seeds could be caused to pass alternately through two dormant and two after-ripening periods without apparent injury. Crocker & Barton (1953) note that many of these unfavourable conditions prevail in the soil and may account for the existence there of viable, non-germinated seeds.

SUMMARY ON DORMANCY

Kott (1947), in the U.S.S.R., has examined some aspects of the germination of weed seeds, which he has come to consider as physiologically defective—presumably, that is, when compared with most crop seeds, which germinate readily. The germination of weed seeds depends on the weather conditions that obtained during their formation on the mother plant. Seeds that are formed in a hot, dry year emerge from their dormant condition in a much shorter time than those whose development has taken place under wet and cold weather conditions. Weed seeds which have ripened in dry and hot years germinate well in the autumn if sufficient moisture is available in the soil, and in that case the percentage germinating in the spring after over-wintering is lower than normal; in wet and cold years, germination of weed seeds in the autumn is very low, whereas in the spring after over-wintering in the soil it is markedly higher, though greatly protracted. In the spring after over-wintering in the soil, germination of seeds of annual weed plants is better, and that of seeds of biennial and perennial weed plants is markedly poorer, than in the autumn—which is the reverse of the germination of weed seeds in the autumn after their ripening. This peculiarity of seeds of wild plants is adapted to their life-cycle. In an experiment conducted in the winter period, after a dry and hot year, the total germination of weed seeds was 52 per cent, autumn-germinated seeds constituting approximately 40 per cent and spring-germinated seeds 12 per cent. In addition, a considerable proportion of the seeds died during the winter, and some were found to be physiologically defective.

In an examination of dormancy and its relationship to weed control, Harper (1957) recognizes three types of dormancy: those seeds that are 'born' dormant (innate); those seeds that 'achieve' dormancy (induced); and those seeds that have dormancy 'thrust' upon them (enforced). He notes that in the past the acts of ploughing and surface cultivations have been largely directed towards the control of weeds, but that the development of selective herbicides makes cultivations largely unnecessary for this purpose and even undesirable where annual weeds are concerned. Thus weed seeds left on the soil surface will not be buried but will be left there to be killed by spraying when they do germinate; while those seeds which have been buried by past ploughing can then be forgotten, for there will be no operation returning them to the surface (except, perhaps, weathering and erosive forces!).

Thurston (1960) has commented upon the complexities involved in the various dormancy-classification schemes that have been proposed. She notes, for example, that the groups, *environmental* and *inherent* dormancy of one investigator are the equivalents, respectively, of the terms, *induced* and *natural* dormancy, of another investigator. She notes, too, Crocker's (cf. Crocker & Barton, 1953) use of *primary* and *secondary* as subdivisions of inherent dormancy, and that it is difficult to distinguish between *secondary* dormancy of Crocker and some examples of *environmental* dormancy. Thus Joan Thurston (1960) believes that the classification of Harper (1957) noted above is more convenient and comprehensive than the older schemes. Perhaps this is more related to *basic mechanisms*, and less to the classification of *processes* that respective investigators have discovered.

In a recent review, Amen (1963) concludes that the exact mechanisms and causes of seed dormancy are somewhat obscure, but that the patterns of dormancy suggest a very positive correlation between the termination of the dormant state and predictable environmental conditions—and, as such, dormancy is a time-measuring device. Dormant seeds represent a most interesting biological adaptation, and 'that such mechanisms are present timing devices is indicative of numerous other biological processes notwithstanding the phenomenon of senescence. As an endogenous rhythm or "biological clock", seed dormancy stands at the forefront of such processes' (cf. also, Bünning, 1956). In concluding statements, Amen (1963) notes that 'variable rates of change characterize living systems . . ., and that the breaking of dormancy and effecting germination restore or reconstitute the continuum of changing living processes.' 'A unifying biological systems theory remains to be constructed . . . in which a study of seed dormancy will undoubtedly play a significant role.'

THE WEED SEED POPULATIONS OF SOIL

The vast reservoirs of dormant and viable weed seed contained in the upper cultivated layers of the soil present a problem in control that projects far into the future. The matter of buried viable weed seeds in agricultural soils has received considerable study. In a series of samplings from twenty-one pastures in New Hampshire, Prince & Hodgon (1946) were able to identify 73 genera of weeds after inducing the seeds to germinate. The floristic spectrum obtained did not always reflect the current plant composition of the pastures. In all of the samples there was a great abundance of seeds of *Chenopodium*, *Ambrosia*, and *Amaranthus*—indicating that these pastures were probably under cultivation many years earlier. The presence, in the current composition of the pastures, of such vegetatively reproducing weeds as *Antennaria*, *Fragaria*, *Aster*, *Chrysanthemum*, *Daucus*, *Leontodon*, and *Taraxacum*, was not reflected in the germination data.

A soil seed-population study by Hofsten (1947) of *Sinapis arvensis* in Sweden, revealed an average of 267 living seeds for each 16·8 litres of soil (0 to 30 cm. in depth), or 4,445 seeds per square metre down to that depth, for nine different samples, the highest concentration of seeds occurring in the depth-range of 15 to 25 cm.

Seeds have been found at considerable depths in soil (i.e. 10 to 14 in.). As Chippendale & Milton (1932) and others have pointed out, this results from earthworm activity and, to a smaller extent, from rain washing the seeds down through fissures in the soil. The latter procedure is more likely to occur following periods of drought. Chippendale & Milton found viable weed seeds in earthworm casts. These casts appear on the surface of the ground in considerable numbers in autumn (in Wales), and to a lesser extent in spring, but at other times of the year the worms void them beneath the surface—where they are employed to line the burrows.

Weed-seed population studies in the semi-arid regions of south-western Saskatchewan (Budd *et al.*, 1954) have shown values as high as 2,131 viable weed seeds per square foot down to a 6-in. depth in wheat fields. The principal weeds with high values were *Thlaspi arvense* (1,638), *Salsola pestifer* (162), *Amaranthus retroflexus* (94), and *Sisymbrium altissimum* (234). Brenchley and co-workers, in England, have examined the problem of buried weed seeds in some detail (1917, 1918, 1944). They found that the seed content at different soil levels varied with the past history of the land, and that crop, soil type, and method of cultivation, may influence the species and abundance of buried weed seeds. Champness & Morris (1948), also in England, in studying the viable weed-seed populations down to a 7–in. depth in pastures and in arable areas, found for *Stellaria media* 5·07 millions of viable seeds per acre (5·7 lb./acre) in pastures, compared with 10·78 millions in arable areas. For *Poa annua* there were 12·27 millions (5·4 lb./acre) in grassland, and 25·42 millions in arable areas.

CONDITION AND LONGEVITY OF WEED SEEDS IN THE SOIL

The fact that large numbers of seeds, buried in the soil, have remained dormant for a great many years, has been demonstrated by the classical experiments of Beal (1905), whose results are reported by H. T. Darlington (1931, 1941, 1951). In these experiments starting in 1879, seeds of 20 common Michigan weeds were chosen and 20 lots of 50 of each were prepared. Each lot was mixed with subsoil sand (which was presumably weed-free), placed in a pint glass bottle, and the bottles were buried with the necks pointing downwards, at a depth of 20 in. In 1919 the tests of viability showed that seeds of 10 of the species were still viable, a total of 82 seeds out of the 1,000 germinating (i.e. 8·2 per cent). In 1929, tests again showed 8·2 per cent germination; those in 1940 showed 5·6 per cent germination; while those made in 1950—seventy years after the original burial—disclosed 4·8 per cent germination. This last value was comprised of 3 species (the same 3 as the sixty-year period): *Oenothera biennis*, *Rumex crispus*, and *Verbascum blattaria*. *Brassica nigra* and *Polygonum hydropiper* survived the fifty-year period, while *Amaranthus retroflexus*, *Ambrosia elatior*, *Lepidium virginicum*, *Plantago major*, and *Portulaca oleracea* survived only as long as the forty-year period.

The recent report of H. T. Darlington & Steinbauer (1961) provides data for the eighty-year period of Dr. Beal's seed viability experiment. The same 3 species that survived the seventy-year period are still viable after eighty years: curled dock (*Rumex crispus*) (2 per cent survival), evening primrose (*Oenothera biennis*) (10 per cent survival), and moth mullein (*Verbascum blattaria*) (70 per cent survival). The authors conclude that it is highly probable that the longevity of buried seeds of the last-named species would extend over a century.

A somewhat similar experiment, started by J. W. T. Duvel in 1902 (reported by Goss, 1924), and employing 107 species (including weeds as well as cultivated plants), disclosed that the seeds of weeds and wild plants survived better than those of cultivated plants. After twenty years' burial, some seeds of 51 of the 107 species were still alive—including species of *Poa*, *Cyperus*, *Polygonum*, *Rumex*, *Chenopodium*, *Portulaca*, *Brassica*, *Convolvulus*, *Cuscuta*, *Solanum*, *Plantago*, *Ambrosia*, *Carduus*, etc.

F   129

The probable longevity record for seeds buried in the soil goes to the sacred lotus (*Nelumbo nucifera*). The Japanese botanist, Ichiro Ohga, found seeds of this species in the peat of a long-dried-up Manchurian lake (Ohga, 1923, 1926). The sequence of events as outlined by Ohga, and by Chaney (1951), seems to have been as follows: on the floor of a lake, which was about a mile across, situated in the Pulantien Basin of southern Manchuria, a thick layer of plant fragments accumulated— among them the durable fruits of the lotus, a species which grows in shallow water. This process may have taken several centuries. Later the lake drained, and dust from the Gobi Desert covered the peat with several feet of loess. The species nowadays does not grow wild within a thousand miles of the one-time lake, and these Pulantien fruits differ in size and shape from those of the modern Indian form of the species with which they have been compared. Ohga had earlier concluded that these fruits must be from 300 to 400 years old. However, a preliminary investigation by Dr. W. F. Libby (1951), of the residual carbon-14 isotope of a few fruits that were available, puts their age at 1,040 years (plus or minus 210 years).

Nelumbo fruits are nut-like and commonly regarded as seeds, the apparent fruit being a large obconical receptacle; they have a very hard coat that is impervious to air and water, and will not germinate until this coat has been broken or softened—for example, by filing or by the use of concentrated sulphuric acid. This form of covering protects the embryo and its food-reserves against molecular change. Another record, which is not as well-founded as that of the lotus seeds, is the one concerning some seeds found in a buried canoe near Tokyo. These seeds were viable, and the wood of the canoe was found to be 3,075 ($\pm$ 180) years old. The life-span of seeds has been reviewed by Crocker (1938, 1948), Crocker & Barton (1953), and Barton (1961).*

Thus the seeds of weeds and other wild plants may survive in the soil for very many years. As many records exist of the chromosome changes and mutations of plants that are caused by ageing, heating, chemical treatment, and irradiation, Crocker (1948) points out that, likewise for the buried seed, changes which may occur in molecular arrangements in the delicate structures of the nuclei may be among the means by which new forms of plants are produced and evolution is carried forward.

GERMINATION

Germination, naturally, is a major factor in the establishment of plant communities, as Went (1954) has investigated in some detail. Most

* For a note on the record length of time that seeds are known to have been kept in a viable condition in dry storage in a herbarium, which appears to be about 250 years, *see* the editorial footnote on page 3 of Barton (1961). Meanwhile it is necessary to preach extreme caution regarding any acceptance of ancient records which it is impossible to authenticate fully.—Ed.

work in plant ecology has dealt with the plant communities of non-agricultural land, but in recent years increasing attention has been given to the existing, though often transient, weed communities in agricultural land (Hanf, 1937–38 (*see* Ch. XI*); Ellenberg, 1950). Went (1954) states that only those plants which can germinate under the conditions that crop plants are sown or planted in, can establish themselves as weeds. Thus winter crops such as cabbage have, as weeds, *Stellaria*, *Poa*, and other low-temperature germinators, whereas summer crops such as tomatoes and maize have, as weeds, high-temperature germinators such as *Amaranthus*. From a study of germination under desert conditions, in saline and other areas, Went concludes that evolution is effective largely in the germination stages of these plants, which explains the great variation in germination mechanisms.

Among weed seeds, too, there exists a variety of germination mechanisms. The most striking of these are the ones associated with the tillage of the soil—which involves the altering of environmental factors, often only minutely, so that the germination process is initiated. Among the parasitic weeds—as already described in Chapter III—a number of highly specialized germination mechanisms also exist.

Heydecker (1956) has recognized four stages in this process of germination in the wide sense. Hanf (1943, 1943a) has also included stages in his sequence of events. The following four stages may be distinguished:

Germination. The germination process involves 'the inception of rapid metabolic activity within the seed, resulting in perceptible growth of the embryo, first the radicle and then the aerial parts appearing from inside the testa'. For many investigators, radicle emergence has been one of the best visible criteria for identifying the initial stage of germination.

Underground elongation. At this stage there is considerable underground elongation of the seedling, which relies on its food reserves. As will be noted later, the survival of young seedlings depends upon the rapidity of growth of the primary root, so that moisture at lower levels becomes available to them. Several of the illustrations of weed seedlings which follow, show the extent to which these young roots may grow.

Emergence. At this stage the aerial parts emerge from the soil. Heydecker (1956) notes that emergence is occasionally used in botanical terminology to describe the final stages of the first stage given above; however, agronomically the present usage is generally employed.

Various ways in which weed seedlings emerge from the soil are shown in Figs. 15 and 16. Two principal types have been recognized: 'hypogeal', in which the cotyledons remain below the soil after seedling emergence (as in *Vicia cracca*, Fig. 15, no. 1); and 'epigeal', in which the cotyledons are carried above ground with the emerging seedling (as in *Cymanchum*

---

* The frequent citations of this nature in the present volume are to references in the Bibliographies at the ends of the chapters indicated—cf. footnote on p. 18.—Ed.

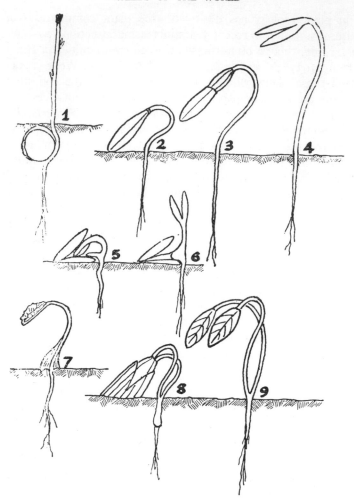

From Keller, Lubimenko, Malzev, Fedtschenko, Roshevitz, & Kamensky, 1934

FIG. 15.—Germination and emergence from the soil of some dicotyledonous plants: 1, *Vicia cracca* (Leguminosae); 2, 3, 4, *Cymanchum acutum* (Asclepiadaceae); 5, 6, *Citrullus* (Cucurbitaceae); 7, *Tribulus* (Zygophyllaceae); 8, 9, *Smyrnium* (Umbelliferae).

and *Smyrnium*: Fig. 15, nos. 2 3, 4, 8, 9, as well as in *Ricinus communis*, etc.). The various ways in which the seedling escapes from the seed-coat are also illustrated by several different examples in Fig. 15. Particularly striking is the 'peg' structure, on the hypocotyl of members of the Cucurbitaceae, by which the halves of the seed-coat are literally prized apart (Fig. 15, nos. 5 and 6). In the grasses there is only one cotyledon, the scutellum, which functions in absorbing the digested food from the endosperm and transferring it to the growing parts. The plumule of the grass is enclosed within a sheathing structure, the coleoptile—which is the first structure noted above ground in the emergence of grass seedlings from the soil. For a time these two structures grow at about the same

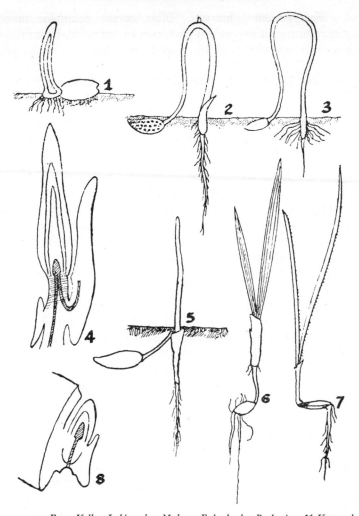

From Keller, Lubimenko, Malzev, Fedtschenko, Roshevitz, & Kamensky. 1934

FIG. 16.—Germination and emergence from the soil of some monocotyledonous plants: 1, Type germination of a sedge (*Carex* sp.); 2, *Allium* (Liliaceae); 3, a water-plant; 4, in field crops, *Avena fatua* (Gramineae) showing a section through the mesocotyl; 5, *Iris* (Iridaceae); 6, another grass, *Andropogon halepensis*, with mesocotyl; 7, *Bromus squarrosus* (Gramineae) without mesocotyl; 8, growing-point of *Bromus squarrosus* (without mesocotyl).

rate, but later the plumule breaks through the coleoptile—*see* Fig. 22 (p. 147) for a diagram of a grass seedling.

Some weed seeds, by germinating in multiple fashion at the same spot, exert a greater force in emerging through hard or crusty soil than they would do if they had been growing separately, and thus ensure emergence. This is also one aspect of the advantage in planting 'hill-dropped' cotton or other seed. Such events probably occur naturally when seeds are scattered thickly in the vicinity of the parent plant, or when seedlings develop from multiple fruits or aggregate structures.

Independent growth. This stage includes the beginning of photo-synthesis, resulting in dry-weight increases in the plant. From this stage on, normally functioning seedlings may be considered as established.

FACTORS INVOLVED IN THE GERMINATION OF WEED SEEDS UNDER FIELD CONDITIONS

As the weeds occurring in crop lands are among the most troublesome and costly of all, it is pertinent to review here some of the factors involved in their first appearance.

Temperature Requirements. The optimum temperature at which the non-dormant seed of various weeds will germinate is generally quite specific. The role of temperature in the breaking of dormancy has been discussed in a previous section (pp. 122–3). As indicated there, varying temperatures favoured the breaking of dormancy. Such temperature alterations also favour germination and emergence. Kolk (1947) observed, in the range of weed species studied (which were largely north-temperate), that variations between 5° and 22°C. appeared to be more effective than variations between 10° and 22°C. Varying temperatures were especially effective in stimulating the germination of *Sinapis arvensis*, but had very little effect upon *Centaurea cyanus*, *Stellaria media*, and *Galium mollugo*. Seeds of *Agrostemma githago* germinated as readily when exposed to constant temperatures (20°–22°C.) as when exposed to varying temperatures. Figs. 17 and 18 illustrate some of the above points.

Many factors are related to the optimum temperature requirements—such as the type of crop the weed is usually associated with, the geographic origin of the weed, and whether ecotypes have developed. In the largely north-temperate group of weeds studied by Kolk (1947) in Sweden, nearly all were consistently retarded by the higher temperature of 30°C. However, *Cirsium arvense*, a weed of possibly Mediterranean origin, germinated better at 30°C. than at 20°–22°C. At the lower end of the scale, *Apera spica-venti* germinated better at 11°C. (51·8°F.) than at higher temperatures, while seeds of *Agrostemma githago* behaved in the same way at 11°C. as they did at 20°–22°C. *Stellaria media*, a weed of world-wide distribution, has developed, as might be expected, a number of geographical races or ecotypes with different temperature optima for germination. It is quite likely that *Poa annua*, another of the most wide-spread of weeds, has likewise developed a considerable range of ecotypes.

Although little work has been done in this field, it seems likely that, if sufficient records of soil and air temperatures were available, together with the emergence dates of specific weeds over a period of years, a correlation would be found between the number of 'heat units' accumulated in the soil and the date of emergence of any species of weed. A number of studies have utilized air temperatures, but soil temperatures are more pertinent. This field of study belongs to phenology, and has

more often taken the form of predicting the flowering dates of ornamentals (*see* Lindsey & Newman, 1956). An indication of these effects
and how they may be graphically presented are shown in Fig. 17, taken
from Hofsten (1947).

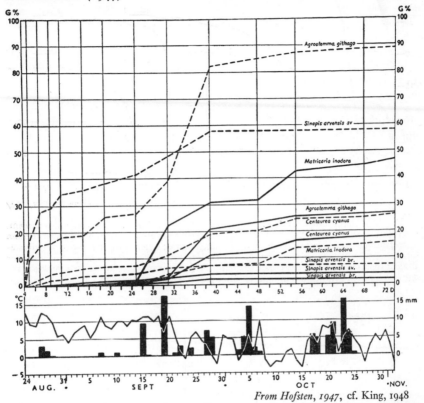

From Hofsten, 1947, cf. King, 1948

FIG. 17.—Germination curves, lowest soil temperature (curve at the bottom), and rainfall
(black columns), in a stubble cultivation experiment in the autumn of 1943. Unbroken lines,
not cultivated; broken lines, cultivated; G, germinated seeds; D, days after seeding. Tests
conducted at Uppsala, Sweden. [sv. = light-brown seeds; br. = brown seeds; *see also* fig. 18, p.
136.]

Soil temperature is related *inter alia* to the intensity of the solar
radiation and to the length of day. Kolk (1947), in his studies on germination, kept a record of the intensity of solar radiation, and germinated
his seeds under this natural radiation—with varying amounts of shading
to provide a range of intensities. Studies have been made of the relationship of day-length to the germination of weed seeds, as indicated in
Fig. 19 (cf. Isikawa, 1954). While not enough evidence is yet at hand for
any conclusive data, it would appear likely that day-length is a factor in
seed germination.

Soil Moisture. An adequate amount of available soil moisture in the
germination zone is essential for weed-seed germination, although with
some species, at least, this amount varies rather widely under different

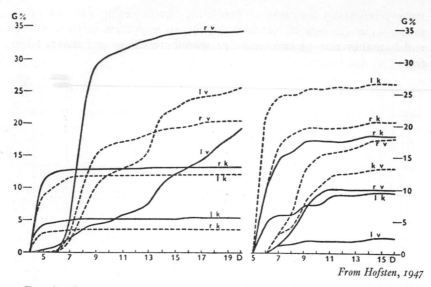

From Hofsten, 1947

FIG. 18.—Germination curves of *Sinapis arvensis* seeds of different character and treatment. Unbroken lines, dark-brown seeds; broken lines, light-brown seeds; *r*, stored indoors at room temperature; *l*, stored in soil outdoors at low temperature; *k*, germination at constant temperature; *v*, germination at varying temperature. The ordinate represents per cent germination; the abscissa represents time in days. The graph to the left: germination in darkness in sand; the one to the right: germination in light on filter paper. Tests conducted at Uppsala, Sweden.

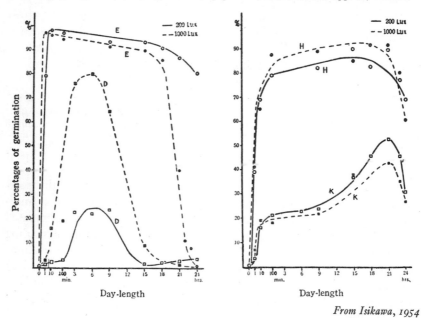

From Isikawa, 1954

FIG. 19.—The effect of day length on the percentage of germination of various seeds under different light-intensities (200 lux and 1,000 lux). D, *Lepidium virginicum*; E, *Rumex* sp.; H, *Epilobium cephalostigma*; K, *Eragrostis ferruginea*. Seeds were collected in the vicinity of Tokyo, Japan, and the experiments conducted at the Botanical Institute, University of Tokyo.

136

conditions. In general, plants of xeric or halophytic character may germinate at lower moisture levels than plants from more mesic habitats. *Taraxacum* is a member of the latter group, and the data of Hofsten (1954) for this genus show that germination of four apomicts was highest in the range of 60 to 80 per cent of the maximum water capacity of the soil. The value of 90 per cent was too high and caused reduced germination (from 20 to 60 per cent), while moisture ranges of 30 to 40 per cent were much too low for this species (under 27 per cent germination for three apomicts, though another apomict, *T. fasciatum*, gave 63 per cent germination after nine days at 40 per cent soil moisture).

Few data are available on the minimal amount of soil moisture at which non-dormant weed seeds will germinate. Members of the family Chenopodiaceae are good examples here; thus in the northeastern United States, *Chenopodium* has been observed to germinate during the hot, droughty periods of late summer when few other species were able to do so.

Some very precise physical measurements of moisture absorption and germination of wheat grains have been made by Owen (1952, 1952*a*, 1952*b*), at Rothamsted, England. He observed that the critical level of water potential that was necessary to inhibit germination of wheat seeds completely was much lower than had been expected. 'After 15 days, 20 per cent of the seeds germinated at a potential of — 320 mm. of water or a pF* of 4·5, well below the Permanent Wilting Point which is generally accepted to be at pF 4·2, or a potential of — 160 mm. of water. Under very extreme conditions, air drying can produce a soil pF of 6, equivalent to a relative humidity of 50 per cent, but this would not normally occur in the field in a temperate climate except at the surface of the soil. Recent Danish work has shown that the relative humidity in the soil rarely falls as low as 98 per cent, therefore the moisture conditions corresponding to a pF of 4·5 or a relative humidity of 97·7 per cent can be considered extremely dry.'

While germination with radicle emergence may occur under quite dry conditions, seedling establishment and growth are another matter. Death of the young seedling may occur through an inability to withstand low water potentials, or through the attack of pathogenic organisms. The data on absorption indicate two phases: the first phase, representing the purely physical process of imbibition by starch, occurs both in living and dead seeds, while the second phase, occurring only in the living seed, is presumably associated with growth and water absorption by the embryo—involving in the beginning the initiation and progress of starch hydrolysis.

Alternate Wetting and Drying of the Soil Surface. The amount of moisture present, its duration, and especially the alternation with periods

* The pF is the logarithm of the capillary potential or the free energy when the latter is expressed in centimetres of water.

of dryness, are all important. Variation is also closely associated with diurnal temperature—as a wet soil, through evaporation, etc., may be cooler than a dry soil. It is believed that extremes of wetting and drying, even in an undisturbed soil such as that in a lawn, result in increased germination of such types as crab-grass (*Digitaria* spp.). Experiments with giant foxtail grass (*Setaria faberii*) disclosed that germination could be stimulated by allowing the soil to dry out, followed by a period of ideal cultural conditions. It was postulated that this alternate wetting and drying may assist in the removal of inhibitory substances from the seeds (King, 1952).

Depth of Seed Burial and Germination. The emergence of weed seeds from various depths, and under various soil conditions, has been studied in considerable detail by Hanf (1941, 1943, 1943*a*, 1944). He observed that the greater the seed's weight, the greater was its ability to grow through the soil. In loose, sandy soil, emergence was possible with seeds planted at a greater depth than in heavy, clay soil. Weeds which normally emerge from a depth of only a few millimetres, can germinate successfully in deeper layers of soil providing the temperature is optimal at these levels and the soil is not too compact. Hanf also observed that soil pressure seemed to have little influence on the normal retardation of germination, although lack of air resulting from soil pressure is important.

In a soil-depth germination study of *Galium aparine*, Hanf (1941) observed that, in very solid soils, the germinated seeds at a depth of 4 cm. could not break through the soil layer. In other soils, with seeds sown at a depth of 10 cm., seedlings emerge seven to twelve days later than seeds sown in the upper layers, and flowers and fruit are formed much later. Hanf also noted that, on plants which were sown in the deeper layers of the soil, the main root system was supplemented by the formation of roots from the hypocotyl. The number and size of the adventive roots at first were very small, and the differences between the root system of the shallow- and the deep-germinated seedlings were equalized only after some weeks of growth. In a later study, Hanf (1943) observed the effect of soil pressure obtained by weights (1, 5, and 10 gm.) on the emergence and character of several dicotyledonous species. In studies of *Poa* and other grasses, he observed the elongation of the mesocotyl and the growth of nodal or coronal roots with deeper planting (*see* Figs. 22, 23 and 24).

In depth-germination studies of the giant foxtail grass (*Setaria faberii*), considerable variation in the maximum depth of germination was observed, depending upon the nature of the container used. This work (King, 1952) indicated the need for standardization of experiments of this nature, and showed that the best and most useful experiments would be those that were conducted out-of-doors under normal field conditions during the regular germination of the weed in question. Under green-house conditions, *S. faberii* germinated at a maximum depth of 12 cm., the optimum depth appearing to be 0·5 to 1·5 cm. Here, too, considerable elongation of the mesocotyl was noted with greater depths of planting.

Kirk & Pavlychenko (1932) found that seedlings of the wild oat (*Avena fatua*) reached the surface of the soil from depths down to 17·5 cm., but that the length of the mesocotyl varied with the depth of sowing, the coleoptile node being always within 2·5 cm. of the soil surface. Waldron (1904) observed that, in the first year after planting *Setaria viridis* under field conditions in North Dakota, the optimum depth for emergence was 2·5 cm., with the maximum depth 7·5 cm. Seeds planted at depths of 17·5 and 25 cm. did not emerge at any time during the five years of observation; but seeds removed from these levels after this period of time were found upon testing to be viable.

TABLE IV

COMPILED DATA ON THE 1000–SEED WEIGHT, THE OPTIMUM AND MAXIMUM DEPTHS OF EMERGENCE FROM SOIL, AND THE NUMBER OF SEEDS PER PLANT, FOR VARIOUS COMMON WEEDS.* (*Adapted from King*, 1952.)

Species	1000–Seed wt. in gm.	Optimum depth for emergence in cm.	Max. depth for emergence in cm.	No. of seeds per plant
Agrostemma githago	9·845‖	0·5	10·0†	
Ambrosia artemisiifolia	3·950	—	—	
A. trifida	17·400	5·0	12·5	
Anthemis cotula	0·240	—	—	
A. tinctoria	—	1·0	2·0†	
Avena fatua	17·520	2·5	17·5	
Avena fatua	—	—	12·5	
Capsella bursa-pastoris	0·096	0·5	2·0†	
Centaurea cyanus	4·800‡	0·5	8·0†	
Chenopodium album	0.650	0·5–1·0	5·0†	27,940
Cirsium arvense	1·575	1·0	6·0†	
Cuscuta epithymum	0·274	—	—	—
Digitaria sanguinalis	0·270	1·0‡	4·0†	8,246
Galium boreale	0·600	—	—	—
G. mollugo	—	1·5	4·0†	
Matricaria inodora	—	0·5	2·0†	
M. matricarioides	0·130	—	—	
Orobanche elatior	0·0049	—	—	270,000
O. picridis	0·0029	—	—	94,000 to 116,000
Portulaca oleracea	0·130	—	—	
Setaria faberii	1·727	0·5–1·5	3·0	
Setaria faberii	—	—	12·0	
S. glauca	4·200	—	—	12,618
S. glauca	1·280	—	—	
S. italica	1·830	—	—	
S. viridis	1·475	2·5	7·5	3,375
Sinapis (Brassica) arvensis	1·900	1·0	6·0	
Sinapis (Brassica) arvensis	—	2·5	7·5	
Stellaria media	0·505	1·0	2·0†	
Thlaspi arvense	0·785	0·5	2·0†	
Thlaspi arvense	—	—	5·0	

* Unless otherwise noted, the seed weights given are from Stevens (1932) and the depths of emergence from Kolk (1947).
† Maximum depths tested.
‡ Determined by L. J. King.
‖ Data from D. Isleib.

In Table IV are presented some data on seed weights and optimum and maximum depths for germination. They were largely compiled from the literature (King, 1952), but include a few new additions. From the data presented, there appears to be corroboration of Hanf's suggested correlation of seed-weight and depth of germination. It might be observed here that, although stated in far less technical terms, the rule-of-thumb method of planting seeds no more deeply than four times their diameter, has long been the practice.

Disturbance of the Soil Surface. While some weeds may make their appearance in undisturbed soils, most species are stimulated to germinate by mechanical soil disturbance. Movement or shifting of the soil surface may be occasioned following heavy rains, with consequent sheet erosion; by all types of tillage; by earthworm or other animal activity; by wind erosion; and by shifting and cracking of the soil during alternate wetting and drying of the soil surface. The relationship of this disturbance to the stimulation of germination is not clearly understood. However, mechanical or abrasive action on the seed-coat appears to be one aspect; and it is recorded that, if dormant 'imbibed' *Amaranthus* seeds are rubbed gently in the palm of the hand, they may be stimulated to germinate (Crocker & Barton, 1953).

There are many factors associated with soil disturbance, such as better aeration, stimulation of nitrate production by the soil micro-organisms, and changes in moisture levels—generally to a drier condition. Seeds that are light-sensitive, including those of many of the grasses, are brought up from lower zones to higher light-levels by turning the soil. Fig. 17 indicates some effects of cultivation as well as of some other environmental factors on the germination of weed seeds.

The alteration of pH levels by lime and fertilizer applications un-doubtedly plays a part in the stimulation of germination, and affects periodicity of germination as well. It is now recognized that application of both mineral and organic fertilizer stimulates weed-seed germination, and also alters the weed flora present—particularly through favouring nitrophilous species.

Aeration. Even in its most quiescent state, the buried weed seed carries on respiration—though usually so feebly that it is hardly detectable. In many seeds, the seed-coats must imbibe water before they permit oxygen to diffuse through them readily, and a few seeds are known which can germinate in the total absence of oxygen. However, the buried seed is considered to be fully 'imbibed', and in fact probably has the capacity to withdraw water from the soil with a force equivalent to some 965 atmospheres, as is indicated by the experiments of Shull (1916) with *Xanthium* seeds. One reason for the increased germination following tillage is improved aeration. In poorly aerated soils, as in peat and water-logged soils, the absence of viable seeds at any great depth below the surface has been noted by a number of investigators. Although no data appear to be available in this connection, it is conceivable that deep burial of weed seeds in certain kinds of soils, at least, would result in decreased viability through reduced aeration and other associated factors.

Light. Kolk (1947), in his studies in Sweden, has considered the effects of light on the germination of weed seeds. He noted that these effects are modified by the age of the seeds. Four groups were recognized: (1) species in which young seeds germinate well in bright daylight and old seeds do likewise in weak daylight (e.g. *Cirsium arvense*); (2) species, the seeds of which germinate well in weak daylight (e.g. *Capsella bursa-pastoris*); (3) species, the seeds of which germinate well in weak daylight or darkness (e.g. *Stellaria media*); and (4) species, the young seeds of which are unaffected by light, while older seeds germinate well in weak daylight (e.g. *Agrostemma githago*).

A recent study of the germination of the common field weed, henbit (*Lamium amplexicaule*), by Jones & Bailey (1956), revealed that this process in non-dormant seeds is inhibited by light. For example, light from an incandescent source of an intensity of 1 foot-candle reduced germination from 70 to 14 per cent, while higher intensities prevented the germination of all seeds. The seeds are most sensitive to light after twelve hours of imbibition of water; shorter or longer periods of soaking reduce the light-sensitivity, and dry seeds are unaffected by light. Jones & Bailey also found that germination of these seeds is prevented by far-red radiation (7,300 to 8,700 Ångstroms), and that this inhibition is overcome by subsequent treatment with red light (5,800 to 7,000 Ångstroms). The effect of an alternating sequence of the two types was determined entirely by the final light-treatment.

There are, of course, many seeds which require light for germination, and one of these is Grand Rapids lettuce. This seed was the one originally used when the stimulation of germination by red light, and its inhibition or reversal by the far-red, was discovered by Flint & McAlister (1954), and confirmed by other work (Borthwick *et al.*, 1952, 1954). Such observations have also been extended to other genera, such as *Lepidium* (Toole *et al.*, 1955).

Extending these findings back to conditions as they actually occur during the germination process in the field can only be speculative. However, in the case of henbit, it is known that seed of this species germinates in the autumn and constitutes a nuisance in over-wintered spinach plantings in the northeastern United States. The factor of reduced sunlight in the autumn and winter seasons, probably combined with a depth requirement in the soil for germination, would largely explain the above findings. On the other hand, small seeds of hot-weather weeds germinate under the high light-intensities of this period, and probably germinate at very shallow depths in the soil as well (e.g. *Digitaria, Amaranthus*, etc.).

It is quite likely that, under field conditions, there exists a direct correlation between the high light-requirement for germination and the relatively high temperature optima for the germination process—with, conversely, the seeds whose germination is inhibited by light having also a relatively low temperature requirement for germination. There is a definite need for germination studies of this nature, conducted under field conditions throughout the year, and with all environmental factors examined and recorded by modern meteorological and other appropriate equipment (cf. Figs. 17 and 18).

The Effects of pH. Some weeds are reasonably reliable indicators of soil reaction. Thus the germination, as well as the establishment, of weeds is related within certain limits to pH ranges of the soil. If a generalization were to be made, however, it would be that a good percentage of the common weeds of cultivated land will germinate and develop in soils having a considerable range of pH. Often certain species of the native flora are better indicators than weeds, or are more reliable for the narrower ranges of soil reaction—for example *Calluna*, *Pteridium*, etc. Ellenberg (1950), in his extensive study of weed communities, recognized several groups: R_1 comprises species of strongly acid soils, R_5 those of neutral to alkaline soils, and R_0 the species that are indifferent to the pH of the soil. Other environmental factors are similarly grouped by Ellenberg (1950).

Soil Nitrate Levels and Germination. A number of observations have indicated that, when nitrate levels in the soil are high, the germination of weed seeds may be benefited thereby. This is more understandable, too, when it is realized that a large number of weeds of cultivated ground are nitrophilous species. The present writer observed, some years ago, that turnip seed would not germinate in a quartz sand medium to which a nutrient solution, adequate in all respects except for nitrate, had been applied; on the other hand, abundant germination occurred when the full nutrient solution with nitrate was applied—both series being maintained under otherwise identical conditions. Thus it is quite understandable that increased weed germination may result from soil cultivation (which increases the nitrate level), and from the application of fertilizers containing some form of available nitrogen.

It has also been observed by a number of investigators that, for example, potassium nitrate and urea will stimulate or improve the germination of seeds that are difficult to germinate under laboratory conditions.

Seed Structures Facilitating Germination. It has long been recognized that the presence of bent or twisted awns, and the position occupied by the hairs, all assist in burying grass 'seed' in the soil. The role of the awn in establishing seed of the cultivated grass *Danthonia penicillata* provides an interesting example. These seeds actually consisted of the florets, which included the lemmas, a central awn 8–12 mm. long, and a tuft of hairs attached principally at the base of the pedicel. The awn is flattened and spirally twisted at the base with, usually, three spiral twists. Experiments with awned and de-awned seeds, lined up in rows on moist paper, disclosed that after ten days the awned seeds had made at least one complete turn, while the de-awned seeds had exhibited little movement. It was also observed that, when the top of the awn comes in contact with soil surface, the action of unscrewing causes the seed to arch, so that the lower part of the lemma is inclined to the soil surface at a sharp angle, the pedicel end being then in a position to be forced into any depression or crevice. With an irregular soil surface, this assists the burying of the seed. The upwardly-directed hairs then prevent the withdrawal of the seed, and subsequent windings and unwindings of the awn only cause further burial. In outdoor planting experiments of de-awned and awned seed on rough soil, it was noted that, after six months, there were twelve times as many seedlings from the awned seeds as from the de-awned ones.

At this point it is of interest to note Hofsten's (1954) observation on the seeds of *Taraxacum*. He found that the pappus not only functions in the wind-dispersal of the seed, but that its hygroscopic movements, together with the spinuli present on the achenes, all assist in the accumulation, piling, and penetration of the seeds into cracks in the surface of the ground.

Periodicity of Germination. One of the most pernicious aspects of the weed problem, particularly in cultivated soils, is the ability of seeds in the soil—even of the same age-lot—to germinate at periodic or seasonal intervals throughout a period of many years. Thus the cultivation of the soil to destroy the seedlings produced from one of these 'flushes' or seasonal peaks of germination, really does not destroy the infestation, as there remain in the same area many seeds of the species from the same age-lot. These may not germinate until several years later, although turning the soil does frequently provide a stimulus to further germinations.

A good example of this periodicity is provided in the data of Barton (1945), and of Crocker & Barton (1953), on the germination behaviour of *Amaranthus retroflexus* seeds. These data show peaks of germination at approximately ten, twenty-two, forty-four, and seventy months after continuous culture at 20°C. Bünning has examined these 'endogenous rhythms' with special reference to the germination of seeds (1949), and has presented a general review of the problem (1956).

N. G. Lewis (1949) commenting upon the problem of irregular germination of weeds, has suggested that the similar responses of numerous species of weeds to simple changes in the environment suggest the action of some common controlling mechanism, such as oxygen relations. He outlines a respiratory mechanism which requires oxygen at a rate that is proportional to the temperature, but which can enter the anaerobic or activated state if the rate of supply of oxygen is too slow at a given temperature. Here too, it can presumably recover in the presence of oxygen, but at a conditioned rate. Lewis also notes that a barrier or control mechanism, acting in the vicinity of the seed-coat membranes, limits the rate of oxygen supply to the embryo, but may lose this power with after-ripening He further reports that micro-organisms in the soil can reduce the oxygen in soil water to zero. All of these interactions could account for many of the common responses or irregular germination of weed seeds that may be observed throughout the year.

In commenting on the waxing and waning of weed-seed populations in the soil, Lewis (1949) stated that from 60 or 70 to virtually 100 per cent of these populations are lost annually by death or germination. Unfortunately, the dormant remainder, whether large or small, always appeared to constitute a significant number in the surveys conducted in Canada. A detailed survey of recent studies on the germination of weed seeds has been prepared by Dr. Lela V. Barton (1962) of the Boyce Thompson Institute.

FACTORS IN SEEDLING ESTABLISHMENT

In cultivated soils the dominant weed problem may consist of one or two principal species, or the populations may be quite heterogeneous, consisting of a dozen or more species. The basis for these two extremes may reside in how long the land has been in agricultural use, in the nature of the more widely-dispersed weeds of the region in question, in the dominance and effectiveness of one or more methods of reproduction, or in the details of land tillage and use—including the frequency and depth of cultivation, the liming and fertilizer practices, the nature of the crop and its place in the rotation, the harvesting methods, and finally the post-harvest care of the land. Of course, the nature and density of the weed seeds per unit area or volume of the soil ultimately determine the magnitude of the weed-seedling problem. In the seedling stages, assuming environmental factors are ideal, the most important problem of seedling establishment is competition. In dense stands of a single species, this would essentially be competition between individuals of the same species; in mixed populations it would be largely between different species; and with crops germinating at about the same time, competition would involve one or more weed species in addition to the crop species.

GENERAL ASPECTS

While there are great differences in the rate of seedling growth— and indeed in that of older plants too—among the various weed species, it is not an incorrect generalization to say that weed seedlings do make rapid growth, with early and extensive root development (particularly of the primary root). In the several illustrations of seedlings, it can be seen how prominent is the primary root in very small seedlings of many cruciferous species (Fig. 20), and also of *Taraxacum* and other Compositae (cf. Fig. 21). For example, there can scarcely be a greater contrast than exists between the extremely slowly germinating and dwarfed seedlings of certain *Nicotiana* species and the rapidly developing and maturing seedlings of many cruciferous species. Naturally, few weeds occur in the former genus; while the latter family has a plethora of them.

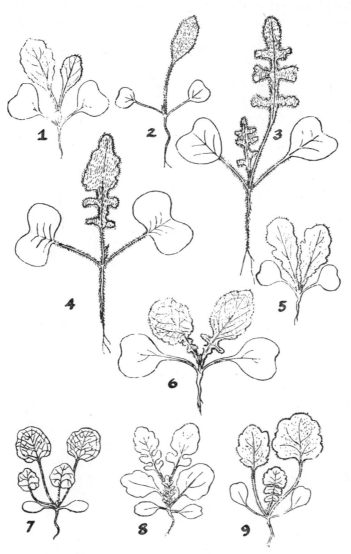

From Keller, Lubimenko, Malzev, Fedtschenko, Roshevitz & Kamensky, 1934

FIG. 20.—Seedlings of some weedy members of the Cruciferae. Note the large leaf-areas of these small seedlings. 1, *Brassica campestris*; 2, *B. elongata*; 3, *Sinapis dissecta*; 4, *Brassica juncea*; 5, *Sinapis arvensis*; 6, *Raphanus raphanistrum*; 7, *Barbarea vulgaris*; 8, *Rorippa palustris*; 9, *Sisymbrium officinale*.

145

Certain weed seedlings have large and expansive foliar-type cotyledons that, through early photosynthetic function, enable the young seedling to become established quickly. This is true of many Compositae (*Xanthium*), Cruciferae (*Raphanus*), and Euphorbiaceae (*Ricinus*). The rate of new leaf production in the young seedling is likewise important, as on it depends the total surface area of the young leaves that are available for photosynthate production—cf. Figs. 20 and 21 which illustrate the foliate portions of the seedlings. The root systems of most of these

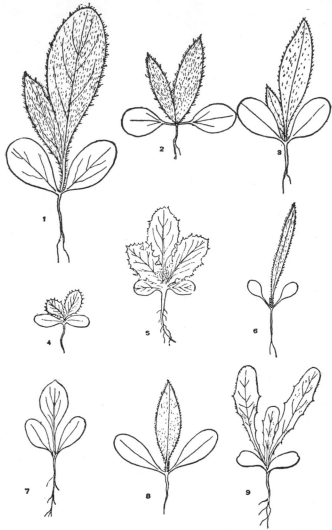

From Keller, Lubimenko, Malzev, Fedtschenko, Roshevitz, & Kamensky, 1934

FIG. 21.—Seedlings of some weedy members of the Compositae. Note the large leaf-areas of these small seedlings. 1, *Cirsium ciliatum*; 2, *C. setosum*; 3, *Carduus acanthoides*; 4, *Cirsium palustre*; 5, *Silybum marianum*; 6, *Centaurea diffusa*; 7, *C. jacea*; 8, *C. scabiosa*; 9, *Cichorium intybus*.

species are more accurately depicted in the work of Dr. Anna P. Kummer, *Weed Seedlings* (1951).

In the Gramineae another feature is manifested—multiple shoot development. These auxiliary shoots arise early in the seedling stage.

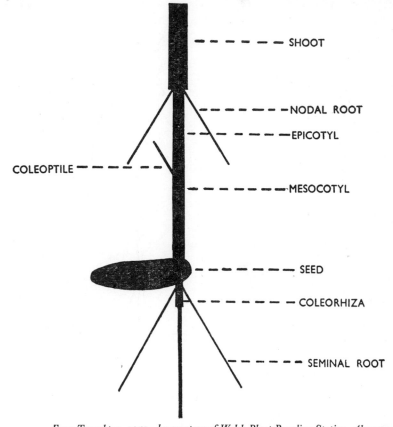

SHOOT

NODAL ROOT

EPICOTYL

COLEOPTILE

MESOCOTYL

SEED

COLEORHIZA

SEMINAL ROOT

From Troughton, 1957—by courtesy of Welsh Plant Breeding Station, Aberystwyth

FIG. 22.—Schematic drawing of a young grass seedling. Mesocotyl and epicotyl are shown elongated to approximately equal lengths. The primary root is shown emerging from the coleorhiza.

Quadri (1956) has observed, in *Lolium*, that both tiller buds and tillers may be found at the fifth-leaf stage. Seminal roots are a common and useful feature of the developing grass seedling (*see* Figs. 22, 23, and 24). As these are the first roots to develop and function, it had been thought that, after the crown (or nodal) roots developed, the seminal roots would tend to disappear. Pavlychenko (1940—*see* Ch. VII) states that the seminal roots of spring and winter annual cereal crops do not die off but, at least in a dry climate, persist and function throughout the life of the plant, constituting in most years its main support from emergence to maturity. Crown roots develop more extensively only in wet years. Thus the presence of several seminal roots is important in the struggle

147

for survival with other plants. Pavlychenko found three such roots in wild oats (*Avena fatua*), one being 63 in. long, while the length of the individual seminal roots averaged 4·4 in. in Marquis wheat and 6·3 in. in Hannchen barley.

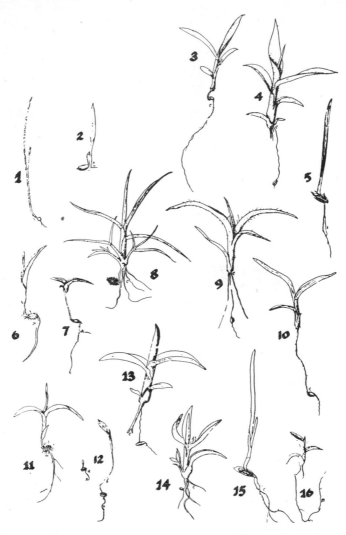

From Hitchcock & Norton, 1895

FIG. 23.—Seedlings of members of the Gramineae, and of a species of *Yucca* (Liliaceae). Note the elongation of the mesocotyl, and the general prominence of the nodal roots as compared with the seminal roots. 1, Panic Grass (*Panicum depauperatum*). 2, Spanish Bayonet (*Yucca angustifolia*). 3, Green Foxtail (*Setaria viridis*). 4, Witch-grass (*Panicum capillare*). 5, Wild Barley (*Hordeum pratense*). 6, Barnyard Grass (*Echinochloa crusgalli*). 7, Switch Grass (*Panicum virgatum*). 8, Sandbur (*Cenchrus tribuloides*). 9, Paspalum (*Paspulum setaceum*). 10, Yellow Foxtail (*Setaria glauca*). 11, Sandbur (*Cenchrus pauciflorus*). 12, Foxtail (*Setaria* sp.) 13, Crabgrass (*Digitaria sanguinalis*). 14, Stink-grass (*Eragrostis major*). 15, Chess (*Bromus secalinus*). 16, Drop-seed Grass (*Sporobolus cryptandrus*).

Seedlings may early develop protective means of surviving aridity. In *Jatropha* sp., water storage begins in seedlings that are only a few days old. Seedlings of *Caesalpinia pyramidalis*—as well as those of some members of the Portulacaceae—develop their leaves and leaflets in the best way to expose their surfaces to light in wet conditions; in dry conditions the leaflets incline upwards, so that the surface exposed to the sun's rays is greatly reduced (Went, 1954). Another survival factor is the ability of many species in the seedling stage to cease growing and to remain in a more or less arrested state of development until more favourable conditions return—crabgrass (*Digitaria* spp.) affords an example of this.

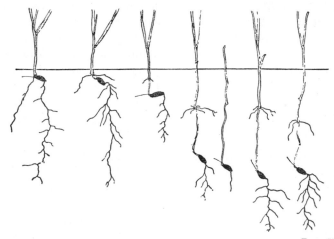

From Hanf, 1944

FIG. 24.—Underground growth of *Alopecurus myosuroides* thirty days after germination. Seeds planted at depths of from near the surface to 5 cm. Note the elongation of the mesocoty to regulate the depth of planting and to provide for the crown of roots at the coleoptile node nearer the surface of the soil. Seeds have been blackened to show up better.

Studies of the establishment of *Eragrostis* seedlings are perhaps illustrative here. Germination occurred from three to four days after planting, and one week after planting the seminal or primary root appeared; the first coronal (or crown) roots appeared in the third week, just before the beginning of tiller formation. With the appearance of the coronal roots, the plants commenced to grow at a much faster rate. The seminal roots died off after the seventh week, and at eight weeks the root-crown appeared as small tufts. In *Eragrostis* this crown is elevated slightly above ground-level, which makes it more prone to damage by trampling than in the case of *Themeda*, where the crown is just about at ground-level.

Few studies are available that analyse in any detail the competition factors existing among weed seedlings under field conditions. Our best examples are those drawn from the studies of competition problems encountered in compounding forage-seed mixtures, where the principles involved are essentially the same. Many of these same factors of competition are important in the mature weed, and will be discussed later in the section concerned with weeds and crop competition (*see* Ch. X).

COMPETITION AT THE SEEDLING STAGES

The study, in Virginia, of Blaser *et al.* (1956), is illustrative of the mechanics of competition in the establishment of a forage crop consisting of two legumes (alfalfa and red clover) and orchard grass (*Dactylis glomerata*). The six principal categories of factors that were studied are discussed below. Some reference to a publication earlier in 1956 by these same authors is also made (cf. Blaser *et al.*, 1956*a*).

(i) *Differential responses of the different species to the environment:*—The time of year that the crop is planted can be important, as red clover seriously suppressed alfalfa in spring plantings—but not in summer ones. This is due to the rapid seedling development of red clover. It grows faster than alfalfa during the low-temperature periods in the spring. The spring moisture appears to favour the red clover seedlings. Thus a differential response between the two legume species exists, and this initiates competition. The seedling stands of alfalfa and of orchard grass were the same for the two planting dates.

(ii) *Growth-habit of the seedlings:*—The erect growth of red clover shades the alfalfa seedlings. The earliness of growth (rate of emergence), and the profuse and rapid tillering of orchard grass, are factors in its quick establishment. Red clover seriously suppressed alfalfa stands, as indicated by root weights per square foot and by botanical composition, for the spring seedings but not for the summer ones. In the earlier study of a larger number of forage species (Blaser *et al.*, 1956*a*) it was observed that, once certain grasses emerged, their rate of seedling development was apparently faster than that of legumes.

(iii) *Soil factors:*—Low concentrations of soil nitrogen in the spring retarded the seedling growth of orchard grass, but did not affect the growth of the legume seedlings. The spring moisture favoured the growth of the red clover seedlings. Alfalfa seedlings are more tolerant of high soil and air temperatures, and of low levels of available soil moisture, than are red clover seedlings. As other studies have shown (Blackman & Templeman, 1938), the competition for nitrogen is one of the two most critical aspects of such competition—the other being competition for light.

(iv) *Botanical composition:*—The differential responses of seedlings among species from spring and summer seedings is associated with the botanical composition. Each species has its own range of responses, and these may often interact or conflict with the other species of a forage mixture . The larger the number of species in the mixture, the greater are the interactions. In natural environments, where weed seedlings are involved—

and with long usage of the land—rather complex weed community patterns have developed. This involves a sequence of germinations throughout the season, with each species appearing in response to some specific environmental requirements, or to adaptations to land tillage or unseasonable factors.

(v) *Stand:*—Competition is directly related to stand or density of population. DePeralta noted in 1935 (*see* our Ch. X) that competition is purely a physical process, and is essentially a decrease in the amount of water, nutrient, or light, that is available for each individual; consequently it increases in intensity with the density of the plant population.

(vi) *Shading:*—The final, harmful effect of the differential response to temperature of the two legume species in spring plantings appears to be the low light-intensity at the growth level of the alfalfa plants. It was too low for seedlings. A dense canopy is formed, which raises the humidity —with a consequent increase in disease problems. These concurrent alfalfa diseases may reduce the alfalfa stands in summer, although the disease problem is then less serious.

The nature of competition between plants in the early phases of their development has also been examined by Varma (1938), employing species of *Papaver, Hypericum, Brassica,* and *Silene.* It has been held by Charles Darwin and others that the severity of competition between plants belonging to the same species, because of the similarity of their demands, is more severe than that between individuals of two distinct species or varieties. Varma's experimental results did not show this hypothesis to be generally true. It was found that in a number of instances, the severity of competition was greater when two different, but ecologically allied, species were competing, than when the competition was between individuals of the same species.

Varma (1938) observed that there was no evident competition between closely-aggregated seeds in the soil, but that signs of competition began just after germination. The severity of competition increases with the growth and increasing differentiation of the seedlings, up to a certain stage when the death-rate reaches a maximum—after which the competition gradually decreases. When the plants reach maturity, competition may again be severe, though perhaps much less selective in character. The high seedling mortality was due to production of albino seedlings, to the premature drying up of the cotyledonary leaves, to the inability to stand erect, and to other unknown physiological causes.

The role of possible toxic substances from roots was also examined by Varma (1938), in his search for an explanation of the high seedling mortality. His results indicated that, when two species are growing in mixed culture, the toxic substances produced by one of them may be more harmful to the individuals of the other species than to the individuals of the same species. Thus each competing species may produce these

151

toxic substances, from either living or dead roots, which depress the vigour of its competitors, thus exerting a profound influence upon the outcome of the competition. However, in contrast, Varma (1938) found that in some cases (*Silene pendula* var. *compacta* and *S. noctiflora*) the substances produced appear to stimulate, rather than depress, the growth of the competing species. Salisbury (1929) also considered many of these factors in his extensive survey of the biological equipment of species in competition. This entire subject, involving the role of excretory or secretory substances in plant competition, or 'teletoxicity' as it has been termed (Wildeman, 1946), is a highly controversial one. It will be considered further in some detail in a later section (pp. 248–54).

Genetic factors are important here also and Haskell (1955), in his study of blackberry (*Rubus* spp.) populations, has observed that hybrid seeds tend to germinate somewhat earlier than selfed seeds from the same mother plant, and that earliness of germination is at least partly a manifestation of heterosis. Accordingly the more heterotic seedlings of *Rubus* may have a better chance than the selfed ones of establishing themselves in nature (*see* Addendum, p. 225).

JUVENILE PHASES AND SEASONAL DIMORPHISM

One aspect of plant juvenility which has been recognized for a long time is that of the morphological differences in the first leaves and in the mature leaves. These early leaves, apart from the cotyledons ('cotyledonary leaves', when leaf-like), have been termed 'seed-leaves'. They, together with the cotyledons and other portions of the plant, are helpful in the identification of weeds and other plants during the seedling stages. A number of publications have been issued depicting weed seedlings, so that they might readily be identified in the early stages of development. Among the best and earliest of these publications is the little-known one of Hitchcock & Norton on Kansas weed seedlings (1895). Other useful contributions include the work of Kummer (1951), and those for Minnesota and for Canada. Many of the manuals for the various countries include abundant illustrations of weed seedlings (Keller *et al.*, 1934, etc.).

The physiological aspects that are unique to this juvenile stage are less clearly understood. Some seedlings, such as those of crabgrasses (*Digitaria* spp.), can become arrested in growth and remain so for a period of time. Growth may then be resumed under more favourable conditions. It is known that, if the seedlings for some reason become established somewhat out of season for the species in question, they may develop the aspect of an older and more mature plant—but only in miniature. These dwarf or depauperate forms have been discussed in an earlier section (*see* p. 35). In a few species of plants (*Panicum* sp., *Ruellia strepens*, etc.), the late-season or autumnal appearance of the species is so different from the early-season growth that these so-called autumnal forms had earlier been named as separate species. This growth phenomenon has been termed 'seasonal dimorphism'.

Much work has been done in recent years on pre- and post- (i.e. soon after) emergence weed control. It has been recognized that, in the later stages of post-emergence, the young seedlings are quite susceptible to chemical sprays, regardless of whether these are selective or non-selective. The cuticle is generally not so well developed at these younger stages, and so thorough wetting is more likely to be obtained. Further aspects of this problem will be considered in the later chapters of this volume, which deal with weed control.

SEEDLING SURVIVAL AND MORTALITY

The success of the newly-established weed community on cultivated land or in other areas depends largely upon the survival of sufficient individuals of the same and/or different species to assure growth and eventual seed production. A number of factors in seedling survival have been reviewed, particularly with reference to annuals. With biennials and perennials, other and often more severe environmental factors are involved. Seedlings of these forms germinate in one year, but undertake more extensive growth and flower production generally in the second year. In the northern latitudes and comparable areas, survival of these first-year plants through the winter period presents a further hazard to the establishment and reproduction of the species in the region concerned. Similar problems are encountered in other regions of the world where periods of abundant rainfall may be followed by periods of extreme aridity.

Hofsten (1954) observed that, in Sweden, *Taraxacum* seeds are disseminated at a density of approximately 10,000 to 20,000 per sq. metre in some places. However, the maximum number of plants ever recorded by this author were 50–125 per sq. metre in ley, and 100–500 per sq. metre in perennial grassland. Thus a large gap exists between the maximum seeding potential and the actual number of seedlings developing. Germination biology as well as overwintering factors are certainly important here.

Lucy Moore (cf. Moore, 1950 etc.), in her studies of *Rumex acetosella* communities in New Zealand, examined at length the overwintering aspects. She observed that, with many of the young seedlings, the breakage of the root system which resulted from the soil heaving following the periods of freezing and thawing, were often so severe that the plants did not survive.* With some plants, however, re-rooting occurred, while in others the tensile strength of the root was such that it could withstand the heaving process within certain limits.

* Such 'congeliturbation' is well known to be an important factor in the establishment and survival of seedlings in arctic and high-alpine regions, where it may also jeopardize the life of all manner of mature plants.—Ed.

One striking difference between crop seedlings and weed seedlings is the resistance of the latter to the adversities of the environment, particularly with respect to seedling diseases and other pathogenic factors. This, of course, is not difficult to understand, as resistance, to the various pathogenic factors present, of the many types of weed seedlings in the soil, is almost essential for their survival. Natural selection has been operative here, whereas it has not been operative for the most part with crop seedlings.

BIBLIOGRAPHY
(The Establishment of Weeds)

AAMODT, O. S. (1935). Germination of Russian pigweed seeds in ice and in frozen soil. *Sci. Agric.*, 15(7), 507–8.

ABRAMS, G. J. VON. *See* VON ABRAMS, G. J.

AGOGINO, G. A. (1957). Pigweed seeds dated, oldest U.S. food grain. *Sci. News Lett.*, *Wash.*, 72, 345.

—— & FEINHANDLER, S. (1957). Amaranth seeds from a San Jose site in New Mexico. *Texas. J. Sci.*, 9, 154–6.

AMEN, R. D. (1963). The concept of seed dormacy. *Amer. Sci.*, 51, 408–24.

ANON. (1929). The 1000 kernel weight in some economics of plants and weeds. *Assoc. Offic. Seed Anal. N. Amer. News Lett.*, 3, 6.

ATKESON, F. W., HULBERT, H. W. & WARREN, T. R. (1934). Effect of bovine digestion and of manure storage on the viability of weed seeds. *J. Amer. Soc. Agron.*, 26, 390–7.

BARTON, L. V. (1945). Respiration and germination studies of seeds in moist storage. *Ann. N.Y. Acad. Sci.*, 46, 185–206.

—— (1961). *Seed Preservation and Longevity.* (Ed. N. Polunin.) Leonard Hill, London.

—— (1962). The germination of weed seeds. *Weeds*, 10, 174–82.

—— & CROCKER, W. (1948). *Twenty Years of Seed Research.* Faber & Faber, London, 148 pp.

—— & SOLT, M. L. (1952). Growth inhibitors in seeds. *Contr. Boyce Thompson Inst.*, 15, 259–78.

BEADLE, N. C. W. (1952). Studies on halophytes. I: The germination of the seedlings of five species of *Atriplex* in Australia. *Ecology*, 33, 49–62.

BEAL, W. J. (1905). The vitality of seeds. *Bot. Gaz.*, 40, 140–3.

BIBBEY, R. O. (1935). The influence of environment upon the germination of weed seeds. *Sci. Agric.*, 16, 141–50.

—— (1948). Physiological studies of weed seed germination. *Plant Physiol.*, 23, 467–84.

BILLINGS, W. D. (1957). Physiological ecology. *Annu. Rev. Pl. Physiol.*, 8, 375–92.

BLACKMAN, G. E. & TEMPLEMAN, W. G. (1938). The nature of the competition between cereal crops and annual weeds. *J. Agric. Sci.*, 28, 247–71.

BLAKE, A. K. (1935). Viability and germination of seeds and early life history of prairie plants. *Ecol. Monogr.*, 5, 407–60.

BLASER, R. E., GRIFFETH, W. & TAYLOR, T. H. (1956). Seedling competition in establishing forage plants. *Agron. J.*, 48, 118–23.

——, TAYLOR, T., GRIFFETH, W. & SKRDLA, W. (1956a). Seedling competition in establishing forage plants. *Agron. J.*, 48, 1–6.

BORISS, H. (1940). Über die inneren Vorgänge bei der Samenkeimung und ihre Beeinflussung durch Aussenfaktoren. (Untersuchungen an Caryophyllarensamen.) *Jb. Wiss. Bot.*, 89, 254–339.

BORTHWICK, H. A., HENDRICKS, S. B., & TOOLE, V. K. (1952). A reversible photo-reaction controlled seed germination. *Proc. Nat. Acad. Sci., Wash.*, 38, 662–6.

—— —— & TOOLE, E. H. (1954). Action of light on lettuce-seed germination. *Bot. Gaz.*, 115(3), 205–25.

BRADBEER, J. W. & FLOYD, V. M. (1964). Nucleotide synthesis in Hazel seeds during after-ripening. *Nature, London*, 201, 99–100.

BRENCHLEY, W. E. (1917). Buried weed seeds. *J. Bd. Agric., Lond.*, 24, 299–306.

—— (1918). Buried weed seeds. *J. Agric. Sci.*, 9, 1–31.

—— (1938–39). The vitality of weed seeds. *Proc. Linnean Soc., Sess.*, 151, 145–52.

—— (1940). Weed seeds in the soil. *Rothmill Quart. Mag.*, 11, 177–81.

—— (1944). Weed control and the dormancy of weed seeds. *J. Minist. Agric. Lond.*, 50, 452–5.

—— & WARINGTON, K. (1930). The weed seed population of arable soil. I: Numerical estimation of viable seeds and observations on their natural dormancy. *J. Ecol.*, 18, 235–72.

BROWN, E. O. & PORTER, R. H. (1942). The viability and germination of seeds of *Convolvulus arvensis* L. and other perennial weeds. *Res. Bull. Ia. Agric. Exp. Sta.*, No. 294, 32 pp.

BRUNS, V. F. & RASMUSSEN, L. W. (1953). The effects of fresh water storage on the germination of certain weed seeds. I: *Weeds*, 2, 138–47.

—— & —— (1957). The effects of fresh water storage on the germination of certain weed seeds. II: White top (*Cardaria draba*), Russian knapweed (*Centaurea repens*), Canada thistle (*Cirsium arvense*), morning glory (*Convolvulus arvensis*), and poverty weed (*Iva axillaria*). *Weeds*, 5 (1), 20–24.

BUDD, A. C., CHEPIL, W. S. & DOUGHTY, J. L. (1954). Germination of weed seeds. III: The influence of crops and fallow on the weed seed population of the soil. *Canad. J. Agric. Sci.*, 3(1), 18–27.

BÜNNING, E. (1948). *Entwicklungs- und Bewegungsphysiologie der Pflanze.*

—— (1949). Zur Physiologie der endogenen Jahresrhythmik in Pflanzen, speziell in Samen. *Z. Naturf.*, 4B, 167–76.

—— (1956). Endogenous rhythms in plants. *Ann. Rev. Pl. Physiol.*, 7, 71–87.

—— (1959). Tagesperiodische Bewegungen. In *Handbuch der Pflanzenphysiologie.* (Ed. W. Ruhland.) Springer, Berlin, Bd. 17, t. 1, pp. 579–656 (lit., pp. 653–6).

—— (1963). *The Physiological Clock.* Academic Press, New York, 145 pp.

BUSSARD, A. (1935). Longévité et faculté germinative des semences. *Ann. Agric., Paris*, 5, 249–77.

BUSSE, W. F. & BURNHAM, C. R. (1930). Some effects of low temperatures on seeds. *Bot. Gaz.*, 90, 399–411.

CHAMPNESS, S. S. & MORRIS, K. (1948). The population of buried viable seeds in relation to contrasting pasture and soil types. *J. Ecol.*, 36, 149–73.

CHANEY, R. W. (1951). Fossils which truly live. *Bull. Gdn. Cl. Amer.*, 39, 12–14.

CHEPIL, W. S. (1946). Germination of weed seeds. I: Longevity, periodicity of germination and vitality of seeds in cultivated soil. *Sci. Agric.*, 26, 307–46.

—— (1946a). Germination of weed seeds. II: The influence of tillage treatment on germination. *Sci. Agric.*, 26, 347–57.

CHIPPENDALE, H. G. & MILTON, W. E. J. (1932). Notes on the occurrence of buried seeds in the soil. *J. Agric. Sci.*, 22, 451–2.

—— & —— (1934). On the viable seeds present in the soil beneath pastures. *J. Ecol.*, 22(2), 508.

CHURCHILL, B. R. (1940). The weed problem of the Upper Peninsula. *Mich. Agric. Exp. Sta. Quart. Bull.*, 22, 255–8.

CROCKER, W. (1906). Role of seed-coats in delayed germination. *Bot. Gaz.*, 42, 265–91.

—— (1916). Mechanics of dormancy in seeds. *Amer. J. Bot.*, 3, 99–120.

—— (1938). Life-span of seeds. *Bot. Rev.*, 4, 235–74.

CROCKER (1948). *Growth of Plants. Twenty Years' Research at Boyce Thompson Institute.* Reinhold, New York, 459 pp.

—— & BARTON, L. V. (1953). *Physiology of seeds.* Chronica Botanica, Waltham, Mass., 267 pp.

DARLINGTON, H. T. (1931). Dr. W. J. Beal's seed-viability experiment. *Amer. J. Bot.*, 18, 262–5.

—— (1941). Dr. W. J. Beal's seed-viability experiment. *Amer. J. Bot.*, 28, 271–3.

—— (1951). The seventy-year period of Dr. Beal's seed viability experiment. *Amer. J. Bot.*, 38, 379–81.

—— & STEINBAUER, G. P. (1961). The eighty-year period for Dr. Beal's seed viability experiment. *Amer. J. Bot.*, 48, 321–5.

DAVIS, W. E. (1930). Primary dormancy, after-ripening and development of secondary dormancy in embryos of *Ambrosia trifida. Amer. J. Bot.*, 17, 58–76.

DELOUCHE, J. C. (1955). Dormancy in seeds of *Agropyron smithii, Digitaria sanguinalis,* and *Poa pratensis.* Thesis, Iowa State College.

—— (1956). Dormancy in seeds of *Agropyron smithii, Digitaria sanguinalis,* and *Poa pratensis. Iowa Sta. Coll. J. Sci.*, 39, 348–9.

DE WILDEMAN, É. *See* WILDEMAN, É. DE.

DORE, W. G. & RAYMOND, L. C. (1942). Pasture studies. XXIV: Viable seeds in pasture soil and manure. *Sci. Agric.*, 23, 69–79.

DORPH-PETERSON, K. (1925). Examination of the occurrence and vitality of various weed seed species under different conditions, made at the Danish State Seed Testing Station during the years 1896–1923. *Fourth Internat. Seed Testing Congress, Rep.*, 4, 124–38.

EHRENBERG, P. (1935). [The question of weed seeds in farming and manure.—in German.] *Z. PflErnähr. Düng.*, 39, 85–94.

EKLUND, O. (1929). On the resistability of some seeds against salt. *Mem. Soc. p. F. Fennica*, 5, 6–11.

ELLENBERG, H. (1950). *Landwirtschaftliche Pflanzensoziologie.* Bd. 1, *Unkrautgemeinschaften als Zeiger für Klima und Boden.* Verlag E. Ulmer, Stuttgart z. Z. Ludwigsburg. 144 pp. (cf. review by B. Rademacher, *Z. Pflanzenkr.*, 58, 71–72, 1951).

EVANARI, M. (1949). Germination inhibitors. *Bot. Rev.*, 15, 153–94.

EVERSON, L. E. (1950). Further studies on the effect of 2,4-D on seeds. *Proc. Assoc. Offic. Seed Analysts*, 40, 84–87.

—— (1952). The germination of mature and immature seeds of buckthorn plantain (*Plantago lanceolata*). *Proc. Assoc. Offic. Seed Analysts*, 42, 83–84.

FAWCETT, H. S. (1908). The vitality of various weed seeds with different methods of treatment and investigations of their rest period. *Proc. Iowa Acad. Sci.*, 15, 25–45.

FLINT, L. H. & McALISTER, E. D. (1954). Wave lengths of radiation in the visible spectrum inhibiting the germination of light-sensitive lettuce seed. *Smithson. Misc. Coll.*, 94(5), 1–11.

FRYER, J. R. (1915). Weed seeds in farm lands. *Agric. Gaz. Canada*, 2, 21–23.

GARRARD, A. (1955). The germination and longevity of seeds in an equatorial climate. *Gdns' Bull.*, 14, 534–45.

GIANFAGNA, A. J. & PRIDHAM, A. M. S. (1951). Some aspects of dormancy and germination of crabgrass seed. *Digitaria sanguinalis* Scop. *Proc. Amer. Soc. Hort. Sci.*, 58, 291–7.

GILL, N. T. (1938). The viability of weed seeds at various stages of maturity. *Ann. Appl. Biol.* 25, 447–56.

GOSS, W. L. (1924). The vitality of buried seeds. *J. Agric. Res.* 29, 349–62.

—— (1933). Buried seed experiments. *Bull. Calif. Dep. Agric.* 22, 302–4.

HALPERN, K. (1894). Die Bestandtheile des Samens der Ackermelde, *Chenopodium album. Landwirts. Inst. Halle*, 21 pp.

HANF, M. (1941). Keimung und Entwicklung des Klettenlabkrautes (*Galium aparine* L.) in verschiedener Aussaattiefe. *Angew. Bot.* 23, 152–63.

—— (1943). Keimung von Unkräutern unter verschiedenen Bedingungen im Boden. *Landw. Jb.* 93, 169–259.

—— (1943*a*). Bewurzelung und Wuchs von Unkrautkeimlingen in verschiedenen Böden. *J. Landw.*, 90, 125–46.

—— (1944). Der Einfluss des Bodens auf Keimen und Auflaufen von Unkräutern. *Beih. z. Bot. Zentralbl.* 57, *Abt. A*, 405–25.

—— (1958). Bekämpfung des Klettenlaubkrautes. *Mitt. Dtsch. Landwirts.*, 73, 509–10.

HARMON, G. W. & KEIM F. D. (1934). The percentage and viability of weed seeds recovered in the feces of farm animals and their longevity when buried in manure. *J. Amer. Soc. Agron.* 26, 762–7.

HARPER, J. L. (1957 [1959]). The ecological significance of dormacy and its importance in weed control. *Proc. Fourth Intern. Congr. Crop Protection*, Hamburg (1957), vol. 1. 415–20. (Publ. Braunschweig, 1959.)

HASKELL, G. (1955). Heterosis in seedling plants. *Proc. Roy. Soc., Lond., B.* 144, 221.

HELGESON, E. A. (1958). A weed seed problem in irrigation. *Bi-m. Bull., N. Dak. Agric. Exp. Sta.* 20(3) 24–25.

HEYDECKER, W. (1956). Establishment of seedlings in the field. I: Influence of sowing depth on seedling emergence. *J. Hort. Sci.* 31, 76–88.

HITCHCOCK, A. S. & NORTON, J. B. S. (1895). First report on Kansas weeds—The seedlings. *Kansas Agric. Exp. Sta. Bull.*, No. 50, 54 pp.

HITROVO, V. (1912). [Sur la voilure des organes de propagation des plantes messicoles de niveaux différents—in Russian, French summary.] *Bull. Angew. Bot.*, 5, 103–38.

HJELMQVIST, H., (1950). The flax weeds and the origin of cultivated flax. *Bot. Not.* (*Lund*), No. 2, 257–98.

HOFSTEN, C. G. VON (1947). [Investigations of germination biology in some weed species—in Swedish, English Summary.] *Publ. Inst. Plant Husbandry, Royal Agr. College Sweden*, 2, 91–107.

—— (1954). [*Studies on the Genus* Taraxacum *Wigg. with Special Reference to the Group* Vulgaria *DT. in Scandinavia*—in Swedish, English Summary.] LT's Förlag, Stockholm, 432 pp.

HOHENDORF, E. (1953). [The influence of electric short waves on the germination of seeds and the development of certain plants after application of rays—in Polish.] *Rocz. Nauk. Roln. Ser. A, Roslinna*, 66(3), 147–8.

HOPKINS, C. Y. (1936). Thermal death point of certain weed seeds. *Canad. J. Res.*, (C), 14, 178–83.

HOPPER, W. C. (1931). The longevity of weed seeds. *J. Agric. Hort., Quebec*, 34, 179.

ISHIKAWA, E., TAKEUCHI, S. & SHIRAISHI, K. (1955). [On the germination and growth of weeds sown to a field monthly throughout the year—in Japanese.] *Shikoku Agric. Exp. Sta. Bull.*, 2, 103–12.

ISIKAWA, S. B. (1954). [On photoperiodism in weed seeds—in Japanese.] *Bot. Mag., Tokyo*, 67, 51–56.

JONES, M. B. & BAILEY, L. F. (1956). Light effects on the germination of seeds of henbit (*Lamium amplexicaule* L.). *Plant Physiol.*, 31, 347–9.

JULIANO, J. B. (1940). Viability of some Philippine weed seeds. *Philipp. Agric.* (*Laguna*), 29, 313–26.

JUSTICE, O. L. (1941). A study of dormancy in seeds of *Polygonum. Mem. Cornell Agric. Exp. Sta.*, 235, 43 pp.

—— (1956). Germination behavior in seeds of nutgrass (*Cyperus rotundus* L.). *Proc. Assoc. Offic. Seed Analysts*, 46, 67–71.

—— & WHITEHEAD, M. D. (1946). Seed production, viability, and dormancy in the nutgrasses, *Cyperus rotundus* and *C. esculentus. J. Agric. Res.*, 73, 303–18.

KAUTER, A. (1939). Der Einfluss der Nutzungsart auf die Keimung und die Entwicklung einiger Wiesenunkräuter. *Pflanzenbau*, 15, 289–98.

KELLER, B. A., LUBIMENKO, V. N., MALZEV, A. I., FEDTSCHENKO, B. A., ROSHEVITZ, R. J. & KAMENSKY, K. V. (1934). [*The Weeds of USSR : A Guide to the Determination of the Weeds of USSR*—in Russian.] Botanical Institute of the USSR, Academy of Sciences and Institute of Plant Industry of the Lenin Academy of Agriculture, Leningrad, vols. 1–4.

KINCH, D. M. (1953). *Physical factors affecting the germination vitality of weed seeds.* Thesis, Michigan State College, East Lansing, Mich., 123 pp.

KING, L. J. (1948). Book Review (*Weed Control Experiments*, ed. H. Osvald. Almquist & Wiksells, Uppsala, 318 pp., 1947.) *Science*, 107, 524–5.

—— (1952). Germination and chemical control of the giant foxtail grass. *Contr. Boyce Thompson Inst.*, 16, 469–87.

KINZEL, W. (1920). *Frost und Licht als beeinflussende bei der Samenkeimung.* 2nd edn. Stuttgart.

KIRK, L. E. & PAVLYCHENKO, T. K. (1932). Vegetative propagation of wild oats, *Avena fatua*, and other economically important species of Aveneae and Hordeae. *Canad. J. Res.*, 7, 204–20.

KJAER, A. (1941). Germination of seeds buried in soil and under dry storage. I: 1934–1939. *Tidsskr. Planteavl.*, 45(3), 486–507.

KLING, M. (1931). Ein Beitrag zur Keimfähigkeit der Unkrautsamen. *Fortschr. Landw.*, 6, 577–9.

KOLK, H. (1947). [Studies on germination biology of weeds—in Swedish, English Summary.] *Publ. Inst. Plant Husbandry, R. Agric. College of Sweden*, 2, 108–67.

KOLLER, D. (1957). Germination-regulating mechanisms in some desert seeds. *Ecology*, 38, 1–13.

KONDO, M. & KASAHARA, Y. (1935, 1938, 1941, 1942). Untersuchungen über Unkrautsamen Japans, I-VIII. *Ber. Ōhara Inst.*, 6, 525; 8, 147, 163, 231, 371, 389, 409; 9, 1.

KORSTIAN, C. F. (1927). Factors controlling germination and early survival in oaks. *Yale Univ. Sch. For. Bull.*, 19, 1–115.

KOTT, S. A. (1947). [Germination of weed seeds—in Russian.] *Soviet Agron.*, No. 4, 86–88. (Abstr. in *Field Crop Abstr.*, 1, 140, 1948.)

—— (1953). [*Quarantined Weeds and their Control*—in Russian.] Gos. Izdvo Selkhoz Litry, Moscow, 2nd edn., rev. and enlarged, 223 pp.

KREFTING, L. W. & ROE, E. I. (1949). The role of some birds and mammals in seed germination. *Ecol. Monog.*, 19, 270–86.

KRUG, H. (1929). Beiträge zur Keimungsphysiologie und Bekämpfung von Samenunkräutern. *Bot. Arch.*, 27, 419–518.

KUMMER, A. P. (1951). *Weed seedlings.* University of Chicago Press, Chicago, 435 pp.

LAMBERT, D. W., WORZELLA, W. W., KINCH, R. C., & CHEADLE, J. N. (1950). Devitalization of cereal and weed seeds by high frequency. *Agron. J.*, 42(5), 304–5.

LAUDE, H. M. (1949). Delayed germination of California catgrass, *Danthonia californica*. *Agron J.*, 41(9), 404–8.

LAUER, E. (1953). Über die Keimtemperatur von Ackerunkräutern und deren Einfluss auf die Zusammensetzung von Unkrautgesellschaften. *Flora*, 140, 551–95.

LEHMANN, E. (1909). Zur Keimphysiologie und Biologie von *Ranunculus sceleratus* und einiger anderer Samen. *Ber. Deutsch. Landwirts.-Ges.*, 27, 476.

LEWIS, N. G. (1949). Problem of irregular germination of weed seeds. *W. Canad. Weed Control Conf. Proc.*, 3, 163–6.

LIBBY, W. F. (1951). Radiocarbon dates II. *Science*, 144, 291–6.

LINDSEY, A. A. & NEWMAN, J. E. (1956). Use of official weather data in spring time-temperature analysis of an Indiana phenological record. *Ecology*, 37, 812–23.

158

LIPPERT, R. D. & HOPKINS, H. H. (1950). Study of viable seeds in various habitats in mixed prairie. *Trans. Kansas Acad. Sci.*, 53, 355–64.

LÖVE, DORIS & DANSEREAU, P. (1959). Biosystematic studies on *Xanthium*: Taxonomic appraisal and ecological status. *Canad. J. Bot.*, 37, 173–208.

McGUGAN, J. M. (1948). Seeds and seedlings of the genus *Brassica*. *Canad. J. Res. (C)*, 26, 520–87 (67 figs., 66 refs).

MALLERY, T. D. (1939). Germination and seedling development of certain desert perennials. *Amer. J. Bot.*, 26(8), 672 (Abstract).

MARTIN, A. C. (1946). The comparative internal morphology of seeds. *Amer. Midl. Nat.*, 36, 513–660.

MARTIN, J. N. (1943). Germination studies of the seeds of some common weeds. *Proc. Iowa Acad. Sci.*, 50, 221–8.

MARTIN, S. C. (1948). Mesquite seeds remain viable after 44 years. *Ecology*, 29(3), 393.

MAXWELL, H. (1915). The longevity of seeds. *Nature, Lond.*, 94, 562.

MILTON, W. E. J. (1930–35). Investigations on the improvement of hill grazings. III: The buried viable seeds of enclosed and unenclosed hill land. *Welsh Plant Breeding Station, Ser. H*, No. 14, 58–84.

—— (1943). The buried viable seed content of a Midland calcareous clay soil. *Emp. J. Exp. Agric.*, 11, 43–44.

MOORE, LUCY B. (1950, pub. 1953). Mat plants of the genus *Raoulia* as weeds in pastoral land. *7th Internat. Bot. Congr. Proc.*, 1, 677–8.

MOORE, R. P. (1943). Seedling emergence of small-seeded legumes and grasses. *J. Amer. Soc. Agron.*, 35, 370–81.

MÜLLER-OLSEN, C. & SIMAK, M. (1955). X-ray photography employed in germination analysis of Scots Pine (*Pinus sylvestris* L.). *Reps. Forest Res. Inst. of Sweden*, 44(6), 1–19.

MUNERATI, O. (1913). Inefficiency of cultivation for destroying weed seeds. *Atti R. Accad. Lincei, Rend. Cl. Sci. Fis. Nat.* 5 Ser., 22, 120–6.

MUSIL, A. F. (1950). Identification of Brassicas by seedling growth or later vegetative stages. *Circ. U.S. Dep. Agric.* No. 857, 26 pp.

MYERS, A. (1940). Longevity of seed of native grasses. *Agric. Gaz. N. S. W.*, 51(7), 405.

NAPP-ZINN, K. (1954). Zusammensetzung der Unkrautgesellschaften in Abhängigkeit von der Keimungstemperatur. *Kosmos, Stuttgart*, 50 (8), 416.

NETOLITZKY, F. (1926). Anatomie der Angiospermensamen. In *Handbuch der Pflanzenanatomie*, Bornträger, Berlin, Bd. X, 364 pp.

OHGA, I. (1923). On the longevity of the fruit of *Nelumbo nucifera*. *Bot. Mag., Tokyo*, 37, 87–95.

—— (1926). The germination of century-old and recently harvested Indian lotus fruits, with special reference to the effect of oxygen supply. *Amer. J. Bot.*, 13, 754–9.

—— (1926a). On the structure of some ancient, but still viable fruits of Indian lotus with special reference to their prolonged dormancy. *Jap. J. Bot.*, 3, 1–10.

OLSEN, C. MÜLLER-. *See* MÜLLER-OLSEN, C.

OOSTING, H. J. & HUMPHREYS, M. E. (1940). Buried viable seeds in a successional series of old fields and forest soils. *Bull. Torrey Bot. Cl.*, 67, 253–73.

OWEN P. C. (1952). Effect of water potential on germination and water uptake of wheat seeds. *Rothamsted Expt. Sta., Harpenden*, Rept. for 1951, 65–67.

—— (1952a). The relation of germination of wheat to water potential. *J. Exp. Bot.*, 3, 188–203.

—— (1952b). The relation of water absorption by wheat seeds to water potential. *J. Exp. Bot.*, 3, 276–90.

PAMMEL, L. H. (1910). Delayed germination. *Proc. Iowa Acad. Sci.*, 17, 20–33.

PEARSALL, W. H. (1953). Growth inhibition and stimulation. *Sci. Progr.*, 41(163), 491–5.

PETERSON, K. DORPH-. *See* DORPH-PETERSON, K.

PRINCE, F. S. & HODGON, A. R. (1946). Viable seeds in old pasture soils. *Tech. Bull. N. H. Agric. Exp. Sta.* No. 89, 15 pp.

QUADRI, S. W. S. (1956). Recognition of ryegrass species and strains in the seedling stages. *Emp. J. Exp. Agric.* **24,** 27–36.

ROSENFELS, R. S. (1940). Spread of white-top seed in the droppings of grazing cattle. *Bull. Nev. Agric. Exp. Sta.* No. 152.

SALISBURY, E. J. (1929). The biological equipment of species in relation to competition. *J. Ecol,* **17,** 197–222.

—— (1942). *The Reproductive Capacity of Plants.* G. Bell & Sons, Ltd., London, 244 pp.

SAROSPATAKY, G. (1957). [Verbreitung und Keimfähigkeit von *Cenchrus tribuloides*—in Hungarian.] *Novenyvedelem Időszerü Kérdisei,* 1957(1), 8–12.

SHISHINY, E. E. & THODAY, D. (1953). Inhibition of germination in *Kochia indica. J. Exp. Bot.,* **4**(10), 10–22.

SHULL, C. A. (1914). The role of oxygen in germination. *Bot. Gaz.,* **57,** 64–69.

—— (1916). Measurement of surface forces in soils. *Bot. Gaz.,* **62,** 1–31.

SIFTON, H. B. (1959). The germination of light-sensitive seeds of *Typha latifolia* L. *Canad. J. Bot.,* **37,** 19–39.

SINSKAIA, E. N. & BEZTUZHEVA, A. A. (1931). [The forms of *Camelina sativa* in connection with climate, flax, and man—in Russian.] *Bull. Appl. Bot. Pl. Breed.,* **25** (Pt. I), No. 2, 98–200.

SNELL, K. (1912). Über das Vorkommen von keimfähigen Unkrautsamen im Boden. *Landw. Jb.,* **43,** 323–47.

SONAVNE, K. M. (1942). Longevity of seeds of weeds of cultivation. *Poona Agric. Coll. Mag.,* **34,** 33–37.

SOUGY, M. P. (1938). Structure et déhiscence de la graine des *Oxalis. Rev. Gén. Bot.,* **50,** 245–60.

SPERRY, O. E. & MORROW, J. (1953). Germination and growth of bitterweed (*Actinea odorata*) from seed matured on plants killed with herbicides. *Texas Agric. Exp. Sta. Prog. Rep.* No. 1580, 3 pp.

STEVENS, O. A. (1932). The number and weight of seeds produced by weeds. *Amer. J. Bot.,* **19,** 784–94.

STOKER, G. L., TINGEY, D. C. & Evans, R. J. (1934). The effect of different methods of storing chicken manure on the viability of certain weed seeds. *J. Amer. Soc. Agron.,* **26,** 600–9.

STOUT, M. & TOLMAN, B. (1941). Factors affecting the germination of sugar beet and other seeds with special reference to the toxic effects of ammonia. *J. Agric. Res.,* **50,** 429–34.

THURSTON, JOAN M. (1960). Dormacy in weed seeds. In *The Biology of Weeds. A Symposium of the British Ecological Society.* (Ed. J. L. Harper.) Blackwell, Oxford, pp. 69–82.

TILDESLEY, W. T. (1937). A study of some ingredients found in ensilage juice and its effect on the vitality of certain weed seeds. *Sci. Agric.,* **17,** 492–501.

TOOLE, E. H. (1939). Physiological problems involved in seed dormancy. Mimeographed Public., 9 pp. (slightly revised from *Internat. Seed Testing Assoc. Proc.* 8, 33–34, 1936).

—— & COFFMAN, F. A. (1940). Variations in dormancy. *J. Amer. Soc. Agron.,* **32,** 631–8.

—— & HENDRICKS, S. B. (1956). Physiology of seed germination. *Ann. Rev. Plant Physiol.,* **7,** 299–324.

——, TOOLE, V. K., BORTHWICK, H. A. & HENDRICKS, S. B. (1955). Photocontrol of *Lepidium* seed germination. *Plant Physiol.,* **30,** 15–21.

——, ——, —— & —— (1955a). Interaction of temperature and light in germination of seeds. *Plant Physiol.,* **30,** 473–8.

TOOLE, V. K. & TOOLE, E. H. (1954). Seed dormancy in relation to seed longevity. *Internat. Seed Testing Assoc. Proc.*, 18, 325–8.

TROUGHTON, A. (1957). *The Underground Organs of Herbage Grasses*, Commonweath Agricultural Bureaux: Farnham Royal, Buckinghamshire, England, No. 44, 63 pp.

TRZCIŃSKI, W. (1933). [Vitality of weed seeds kept in ordinary manure and in Krantz-manure—in Polish, English Summary.] *Polish Agric. Forestry Ann.*, 30, 213–32.

TURNER, J. H. (1933). The viability of seeds. *Kew Bull. Misc. Inform.*, No. 6, 257–69.

VARMA, S. C. (1938). On the nature of the competition between plants in the early phases of their development. *Ann. Bot.*, n.s. 2, 203–25.

VENGRIS, J. (1956). Weeds—robbers of our farms. *Bett. Crops*, 40, 7–12; 46–47.

VISSER, T. (1956). The role of seed coats and temperature in after-ripening, germination and respiration of apple seeds. *Verh. Akad. Wet. Amst.* Ser. C, 59, 211–22.

VON ABRAMS, G. J. & HAND, M. E. (1956). Seed dormancy in *Rosa* as a function of climate. *Amer. J. Bot.*, 43, 7–12.

VON HOFSTEN, C. G. *See* HOFSTEN, C. G. VON.

WALDRON, L. R. (1904). Vitality and growth of buried weed seed. *Bull. N. Dak. Agric. Expt. Sta.*, 62, 439–46.

WARINGTON, K. (1936). The effect of constant and fluctuating temperature on the germination of the weed seeds in arable soil. *J. Ecol.*, 24, 185–204.

WEAVER, J. E. & MUELLER, I. M. (1942). Role of seedlings in recovery of Midwestern ranges from drought. *Ecology*, 23, 275–94.

WEISER, S. (1927). Zusammensetzung und Nährwert einiger Unkrautsamen. *Fortschr. Landw.*, 2, 6–9.

WELCH, G. B. (1954). Seed processing equipment. *Bull. Miss. Agric. Exp. Sta.*, 520, 23 pp.

WELTON, F. A. (1942). Killing weed seeds. *Annu. Rep. Ia. Hort. Soc. (Trans.)*, 76, 214–17.

WENT, F. W. (1939). Ecology of desert plants. II: The effect of rain and temperature on germination and growth. *Ecology*, 30, 1–13.

—— (1954). Germination as a major factor in the establishment of communities. *8th Internat. Botan. Congr.*, Sect. 7, 228–9.

—— JUHREN, G. & JUHREN, M. C. (1952). Fire and biotic factors affecting germination. *Ecology*, 33, 351–64.

WEST, D. W. (1952). The distinguishing characteristics of Johnson grass and Sudan grass seed. *Proc. Assoc. Offic. Seed Analysts*, 42, 72–75.

WILDEMAN, É. DE (1946 [1947]). Allélopathie ou télétopie en particulier dans le règne végétal. *Bull. Acad. Belg. Cl. Sci. V.*, 32, 117–26.

ZAHNLEY, J. W. & FITCH, J. B. (1941). Effect of ensiling on the viability of weed seeds. *Amer. Soc. Agron. J.*, 33(9), 816–22.

ZINGER, N. *See* SINSKAIA & BEZTUZHEVA, 1931.

ZINN, K. NAPP-. *See* NAPP-ZINN, K.

VII

THE GROWTH AND DEVELOPMENT OF WEEDS

AMONG the many definitions of 'weed' examined in Chapter I, the word 'aggressive' constantly recurs. Just what is meant by this term, and how does it specifically apply to the growth of weeds? These questions are perhaps best answered by examining the several aspects of the growth and development of weeds. The germination of weeds and the rapidity of seedling establishment have already been described in some detail.

GENERAL GROWTH ASPECTS

In the definitions, the words 'rank' and 'unsightly' also appear. Thus another important feature of weed growth—particularly in competition with crops—is the rapidity of growth and the early maturity, complete with flowering and seed production.

Another aspect of competition occurs in the older plant as well, and that is competition for space, involving the factors of light, moisture, and nutrients. One notable feature of weed growth that is quite characteristic of this group of plants when growing in cultivated soils, is the high plant density or carpet-like effect which these plants present *en masse*. *Galinsoga*, *Abutilon*, *Digitaria*, and many others, present examples in point. This manner of growth is often sufficient to choke out a slower-growing crop if the weeds are not removed.

In the case of the broad-leafed weeds, this rank growth often involves a high growth-rate not only in terms of production of new leaves but also of their general size and total surface area. Pavlychenko (1940) notes that, in a wheat field for example at the blooming stage, *Sinapis arvensis* has a total leaf surface of 7,300 sq. cm. per plant, and *Amaranthus retroflexus* an area of 1,400 sq. cm., as opposed to an area of 140 sq. cm. for Marquis wheat at the same growth stage.

ROOT SYSTEMS

Many of the most pernicious aspects of weeds can ultimately be traced to the nature of their root systems. In the perennial weeds at least, the mechanisms by which the root grows and extends are many and diverse, and the plant sometimes provides the basis for various types of vegetative reproduction either from the intact root or from isolated or fragmented portions of the root.

162

The Growth and Development of Weeds

There has been no satisfactory general classification of root systems with a brief and concise terminology. However, the tentative one proposed by W. A. Cannon (1949) is here examined and its ten component types are listed. A new feature is the attempt to develop a descriptive term for each type. These ten types are illustrated in Fig. 25, and are taken from

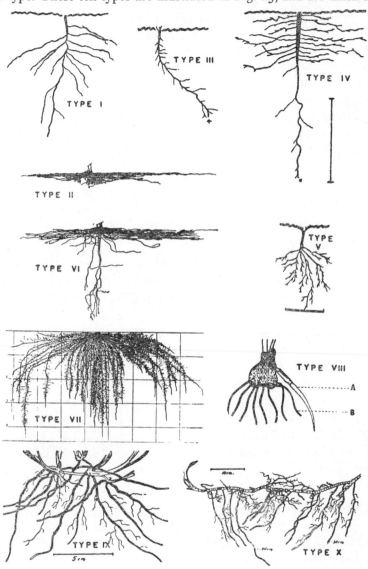

From Cannon, 1949

FIG. 25.—The ten types of root systems recognized by Cannon. Explanations are in the text. For each of the primary root systems the scale is: I, nat. size; II, 1 cm. = 4 metres; III, 1 cm. = 2.5 cm.; IV, scale line = 1 ft.; V, scale line = 10 cm.; VI, 1 cm. = 4 metres. For each of the adventitious root systems the scale is: VII, squares = 1 ft.; VIII, A, contractile root, B, absorbing-anchoring roots, scale, ⅓ nat. size; IX, scale line = 5 cm.; X, scale line = 10 cm.

the work of Cannon (1949); but the nomenclature is the present author's, taken in part from Cannon's descriptions. The first six types are based upon the primary root systems, whereas the last four types are based upon the adventitious root system—which may or may not be present at the same time as the primary root system.

Type I. Longi-monaxial:—The primary root is fibrous or fleshy; it is relatively long. First-order roots arc acropetalous, and thus the oldest are near the surface of the ground. It is a mesophytic type. Examples are many annual and biennial weeds such as species of *Brassica, Sinapis, Amaranthus*, etc.

Type II. Plano-monaxial:—The primary root is relatively short and fibrous. The first-order lateral roots are fibrous, relatively long, and close to the surface (in a plane parallel with the surface of the ground). They are well branched in a dry habitat, but branch little in a wet one. *Echino-cactus* is an example.

Type III. Brevi-monaxial:—The primary root is usually long and fibrous. The first-order lateral roots are short, often well-branched, and rather evenly distributed along the primary root. This is a xerophytic type. *Dyssodia papposa* is an example.

Type IV. Divari-monaxial:—The primary root is usually long and slender. The first-order lateral roots closest to the ground are relatively long and well branched. This is a xerophytic and mesophytic type. *Solanum rostratum* is an example.

Type V. Bifurco-monaxial:—The primary root is divided, forked, or branched, and fibrous—with few first-order lateral roots, or, in age, apparently with none. This is a xerophytic type that is not common. *Lithospermum linearifolium* is an example.

Type VI. Pileo-monaxial:—Named after *pileus*, i.e. cap-like. The primary root is usually as in Type V, i.e. branched at the lower levels. The first-order lateral roots are mostly on the upper portion of the primary root, spreading radially and 'cap-like', and, as in Type IV, they are the longest. Frequently a xerophytic type. *Artemisia filifolia* and *Erigeron microthecum* are examples.

The remaining four types of Cannon (1949) are based on adventitious root systems which are polyaxial and composed of distinct units. Adventitious roots by definition arise from the axis—often from the aerial stem and occasionally from the leaves—but are mostly formed on bulbs, corms, rhizomes, and stolons. An adventitious root may or may not form first-order laterals; on the other hand, laterals may be formed to the fifth order in some root systems. If only one kind of adventitious root is present, the root system is *uniformal*; if more than one kind is present, it is *multiformal*. When the adventitious roots form one group, the root system is *centralized*; when they are in more than one group, the root system is *decentralized*.

Type VII. Centro-uniformal :—The adventitious roots are of one kind, in one group, and arise on a short horizontal, or vertical, axis of the shoot. First-order lateral roots, even in one and the same root system, may or may not be formed. This is a mesophytic and hydrophytic type. It has usually a centralized-uniformal root system. *Zea mays*, and many other annual grasses, would be included here; also *Carex capillaris* and *Sium latifolium*.

Type VIII. Centro-multiformal :—The adventitious roots are of more than one kind (fibrous and fleshy, or fibrous and thick), but are in one group. The fibrous-adventitious roots are absorbing-anchoring roots and usually bear laterals to the second order. The fleshy adventitious roots are anchoring, as well as food-accumulation, roots; the thick roots are contractile and change the position of the organ to which they are attached. The type is mesophytic. The root system is centralized-multiformal. Examples are *Oxalis* spp. and *Brodiaea lactea*.

Type IX. Decentro-uniformal :—The adventitious roots are of one kind and are in more than one group. These adventitious roots may arise on the aerial stems and branches of some herbaceous species and of shrubs and treees, as well as on creepers, vines, and runners, and on subterranean rhizomes and stolons. They may also be formed on parts of the shoot which lie on the ground (layering). The roots that are formed on the aerial portions of the shoot are fibrous, as also are those that are developed on fibrous rhizomes; but the adventitious roots of fleshy rhizomes are also fleshy, or mostly so. They are variously, but consistently, distributed, either singly or in groups (a basic feature). Frequently the shoot and the roots spring from the same node. First-order laterals are usually present in the xerophytes and mesophytes, but are mostly wanting in the hydrophytes. The largest number of species with adventitious root systems are of this type, which is decentralized-uniformal. Examples are *Agropyron repens*, *Ficus bengalensis*, *Phragmites communis*, *Carex irrigua*, and *Trifolium parryi*.

Type X. Decentro-multiformal :—The adventitious roots are of more than one kind (fibrous, fleshy, or thick), and are in more than one group. Fibrous and fleshy roots, or fibrous and aerating roots, occur in each root system. The adventitious roots are mostly formed singly on the nodes of the rhizomes, which may be relatively extensive. The root system is decentralized-multiformal. Examples are *Carex vesicaria* and *Jussiaea repens*.

Cannon (1949) notes that, if both a primary root system and an adventitious root system are present at the same time, whether this situation is temporary or enduring, each kind of root system is considered by itself. Where permanent, such a condition would be a basic feature in the root classification. He uses the wild or cultivated carrot (*Daucus carota*) as an example here: its primary root system is Type IV, while its adventitious root system is Type VII. The crown of the 'carrot', for about 2·5 cm. down, is the enlarged and succulent portion of the hypocotyl—and therefore stem tissue. Roots arising here are by definition adventitious, and are unbranched and relatively short. The 'carrot' is about 15 cm. long and merges into the slender portion of the primary root, which reaches a depth of 60 or more cm.

One disadvantage of this classification is the overlapping that may occur, as in the case of *Daucus* cited above. Contrary to Cannon's suggestion, it is possible that this conflict might be avoided by placing the root system in the type to which the major portion of it belongs; for in many cases a knowledge of the ontogenetic anatomy of the root system in question would not be available. Nevertheless, it is hoped this classification may be further improved. Boterenbrood *et al.* (1955—*see* Ch. XI) have examined in some detail the root systems of dune plants of the Mediterranean coast of France, and have provided a detailed classification. The study of Kutschera (1960) on the root systems of both weeds and crop plants of central Europe is a valuable contribution.

Depth and Extent of Root Development

Weeds vary widely in the depth to which their roots may penetrate. As a group, annual weeds are more shallow-rooted than are perennial herbaceous plants, with woody plants tending to be the most deeply rooted. The rainfall pattern is also important: in general, the less rainfall there is, the less deeply do the roots penetrate, and the greater is their lateral spread. For example, annual plants in desert regions seldom penetrate to a depth of more than 8 in., the greatest development being in the upper 2 or 3 in. Some Spanish bayonet plants (*Yucca* spp.) in the semi-arid regions of the western plains of the United States have been found to have roots only 18 in. deep but with a lateral spread of 30 or more ft.

There are a number of species of plants that develop exceedingly long tap-roots extending down to the water-table. Alfalfa (*Medicago sativa*) is such a plant; records show that its roots may penetrate from 10 to 20 ft.* (Weaver, 1926). Paczosky (1914) has recorded the root-penetration depths of the following weeds in Russia: *Cirsium arvense* (20 ft.), *Euphorbia virgata* (9·8 ft.), *E. gloriosa* (8·5 ft.), *Centaurea scabiosa* and *Salvia nemorosa* (7·2 ft.), *Reseda lutea* (9·2 ft.), and *Melandrium album* (6·9 ft.).

The roots of trees and other woody plants may reach considerable depths. This has been confirmed in the recent study of indicator

* According to Bolton (1962), root penetration of alfalfa to depths of '10 to 15 ft. is not uncommon, and 30 to 40 ft. has been recorded'.—Ed.

plants used in the botanical prospecting for uranium ores in Colorado (H. L. Cannon, 1957). It is stated that ore beds which lie there at no greater depth than 70 ft. may be detected by sampling branch tips of such trees as *Pinus ponderosa*, *Abies concolor*, and others. Such plants which tap the ground-water supplies or the water in arid-zone rivers have been termed 'phreatophytes'. Their growth often results in considerable losses of valuable water in such arid or semi-arid regions (*see* Robinson, 1957).

The extents of the ramifications of the roots of the wild oat (*Avena fatua*) have been measured by Pavlychenko (1940). He found that one seminal root 63 in. long, together with its branches of the first and second orders, measured 256,678 linear inches, and possessed 146,176 absorbing root-tips. A two-year-old plant of *Agropyron cristatum* was found to have a root system whose total linear length measured 319·5 miles, while root systems of *Bromus inermis* measured 147·4 miles and of *Agropyron pauciflorum* 183·8 miles (Pavlychenko, 1940).

Crested wheat-grass (*Agropyron cristatum*), a forage grass, can, through its extensive growth, clear the land of volunteer vegetation. This can occur largely through the extensive root system which it produces, and which frequently penetrates to a depth of 7 or more feet. Approximately 75 per cent of the total root material is located in the first foot of soil (Pavlychenko, 1940). This same author has determined the weight per acre of the roots of several grass species: *Agropyron cristatum* (2426·5 kg.), *Bromus inermis* (2248·5 kg.), and *Triticum vulgare* (564·1 kg.)—all illustrating the extent of root production in the soil.

A feature that is common to a number of weed species and wild plants is the presence of some very specialized roots known as 'contractile roots'. In these plants it is generally the tap-root which continues to contract for a long time and thus keeps the growing-point at or near the surface of the ground. Schaffner (1903) has examined some of these plants, which include *Plantago major*, *Taraxacum* spp., and others (Figs. 25 and 26). Contractile roots have been studied in some detail by Rimbach (1895), and recently by Galil (1958).

PHYSIOLOGY OF ROOT GROWTH

Few studies appear to be available on the physiology of the root growth of weeds. Doi (1952), in Japan, has examined some of the inter-relationships of the roots of crop plants and those of wild plants, including wild grasses. Under paddy-field conditions he found the highest respiration rate ('oxidizing power') in species of the Gramineae and Compositae; the figures were somewhat lower in the Leguminosae, and lowest in the Cruciferae, Cucurbitaceae, Solanaceae, and vegetable crops. He also attempted the planting of soybeans (*Glycine max*) under paddy-field conditions as well as together with paddy rice under these same conditions. In the former case the roots were severely injured, and the plants generally

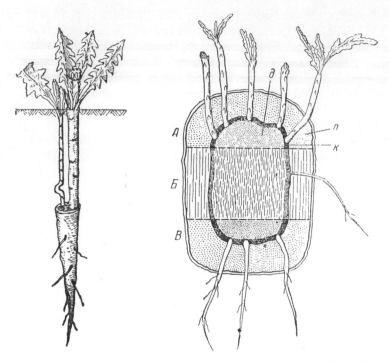

From Kott, 1953

FIG. 26.—Diagrams of the root system and vegetative reproduction of cut sections of a dandelion (*Taraxacum* sp.). Contractile root shown on left of left-hand figure.

did not survive; but when the two were planted together, the root injury was slight, indicating that the soybean roots benefited from the high oxidizing power of the paddy rice root. It is also possible that the aerenchyma tissue in the rice root system provided a source of additional oxygen for the respiration of soybean roots in the submerged and generally anaerobic environment.

These studies show why the flooding of rice is a good weed-control measure, and also indicate that some of the weeds which do persist under these flooded conditions are often closely related botanically to rice and are generally members of the Gramineae (e.g. *Echinochloa crusgalli*, one of the worst pests), Juncaceae, or Cyperaceae. For a long time, too, horticulturists have known of the high sensitivity of certain members of the Solanaceae (e.g. the potato) to a decreased oxygen supply to the roots resulting from flooded field conditions.

Some observations have been made by C. F. Rogers (1929) on the winter activity of the roots of perennial weeds. These studies were made in Iowa on Canada thistle (*Cirsium arvense*), principally when the soil was frozen to a depth of about 50 cm. (from about the middle of December to 15 March). Before this freezing, buds upon the horizontal roots continued to develop new shoots; but these were killed back to the roots with the freezing of the soil. Rogers noted, however, that in early January the latent buds on the larger roots of this weed were noticeably larger than they had been three weeks previously. By the middle of January these buds had developed thick, vigorous shoots, 15 to 20 mm. long, with free, sharp growing-points. By February the shoots were from 4 to 7 cm. long, and young roots had appeared, 10 to 20 cm. long, upon the old roots. After the thawing around 15 March, root growth became more rapid, and green shoots were observed above the soil surface on 12 April. Rogers (1929) also noted that the cycle of bud and root formation in wild morning-glory (*Convolvulus arvensis*) and poverty weed (*Franseria tomentosa*) was similar in almost every respect to that described for *Cirsium arvense*.

One aspect of the growth of roots in relation to competition is the controversial subject of root excretions or secretions that may have a deleterious effect on different species developing in the area of these roots. This will be considered at some length under the section devoted to harmful aspects (pp. 248–54).

General Soil Factors and the Growth of Weeds

The Influence of Soil pH

Judging from the available literature, this topic has been one of the most widely investigated of all those comprising weed biology—particularly with respect to studies under actual field conditions. This is understandable, as successful crop production is dependent upon an understanding and a proper regulation of soil reaction. However, as we noted earlier when discussing soil reaction and weed seed germination, individual weed species are not entirely reliable as indicators of narrow ranges of soil pH values.

This variation in pH range is particularly evident in the study of Artist (1931), who surveyed the soil reaction of the habitats of that classic 'acid-soil-type' *Rumex acetosella*, in twenty-three different field locations in three counties of central and southern Indiana, U.S.A. In this study, somewhere in the vicinity of 80 per cent of the surface samplings fell between the ranges of pH 5·0 and 6·0; somewhat less than 10 per cent each fell between pH 4·5 to 5·0 and pH 6·0 to 6·5, respectively; while only a negligible number were in the pH range of 6·5 to 7·0 and higher. These data certainly support the long-held belief that this plant grows in 'acid' soils, although the pH range is considerable.

The widespread European weed *Scleranthus annuus*, has been noted by several authors (Steyer & Eberle, 1928; Schmalfuss, 1935) to be another plant growing in acid soils—ranging from pH 5·1 to 5·6. Schmalfuss also observed in his studies in Germany that *Chenopodium album* grew in soil, ranging from pH 4·5 to 7·01, with the peak of populations at the latter value. The extensive studies of Buchli in Switzerland (1936) and of Ellenberg (1950) in Germany, provide a most excellent listing of the major European weed species with regard to their range of soil reaction. The recent study of Lefevre (1956), of the agronomy station at Amiens, France, reviews the soil reaction ranges of 60 common weeds. Some of these are grouped into three different categories as shown below.

Basophile	Acidophile	Neutrophile
Brachypodium pinnatum (at both pH 6·1 and 8·1)	*Chrysanthemum segetum* (pH 5·9 to 6·2)	*Stellaria media* (pH 7·6 to 8·2; pH 5 to 7·9)
Sonchus sp. (pH 6·2 to 8·0)	*Pteridium latiusculum* (pH 4·35 to 5·0; others 5·4 to 6·1 and 5·0 to 7·5)	*Polygonum aviculare* (pH 5·6 to 8·4)
Rumex acetosa (pH 6·0 to 7·2 and 7·95)	*Rumex acetosella* (pH 5 to 7·3, with most at at 5·5 to 6·0)	*Capsella bursa-pastoris* (pH 7·1 to 8·5)
Agropyron repens (pH 6·2 to 8·0)		
Taraxacum officinale (pH 6·5 to 7·9)		

Lefevre (1956) includes also in his study the analyses for soil calcium, which is associated with the growth of a large number of weeds. He concludes that observations of this nature on adventive plants are principally useful for establishing the homogeneity of the soil in a particular field, or on a farm, as well as in delimiting the zones of characteristic differences.

In their studies of soil pH and the growth of *Halogeton glomeratus*, Bohmont & Legg (1953) found that this toxic weed would thrive and accumulate toxic amounts of oxalate on acid rangeland (pH 4) under moist conditions.

While a number of weeds—as we have seen—have a rather narrow range of soil reaction, it is unwise to attempt any generalizations about species, or groups of species, based on only one soil factor among the large number of complicated actions and interactions that go on within the soil environment. The problem of the development of ecotypes in a number of common weed species further complicates the matter. The restricted value of the pH determination has been realized, too, by Goedewaagen (1938), who noted that, in addition to soil pH, such other factors as the soil type, the kind of crop, the cultural history of the land, and the water relations, were also important. He concluded that, in general, the weed vegetation must be considered a rough and not very reliable criterion for judging the reaction of the soil.

The observation that a number of species of lawn weeds cannot survive under conditions of high acidity has led to a theory that such injury is the result of aluminium toxicity (B. E. Gilbert & Pember, 1935).

In experiments with known amounts of aluminium added to the nutrient medium in which weeds and lawn grasses were cultured, the responses obtained led to the recognition of three groups based upon sensitivity to aluminium. The sensitive group (2 to 8 p.p.m. of aluminium) included *Cerastium vulgatum, Stellaria media, Taraxacum officinale, Setaria glauca, Prunella vulgaris,* and *Poa pratensis.* The medium-sensitive group (withstanding 16 to 32 p.p.m. of aluminium) included *Digitaria ischaemum* and *Leontodon autumnalis.* The resistant group (withstanding 32 to 80 p.p.m. of aluminium) included *Digitaria sanguinalis,* and the lawn grasses redtop (*Agrostis alba*) and colonial bent (*Agrostis tenuis*).

These results are in accordance with long-observed facts of the growth of the last two grasses as well as of crabgrass (*Digitaria sanguinalis*) on acid soils, and the sensitivity of bluegrass (*Poa pratensis*) to acid soils. Likewise, chickweed (*Stellaria media*) can be largely controlled by using aluminium sulphate, or by rendering the soil acid.

Weed Growth Under Saline Conditions

With the extension of agriculture into saline areas and the development of salt-tolerant crops—as well as the wider use of irrigation—the question of what weeds might also invade and become established in these new areas has become important.

Such weed populations and their salt-resistant behaviour on reclaimed tidal land in the Kojima Bay area of Japan have been examined by Kobayashi (1954). He studied 42 weeds belonging to 11 different families, and noted that weeds in the same family showed a similar degree of salt-resistance. He found that the maximum contents of sodium chloride in the soil which were tolerable for weed growth were as follows: Compositae and Polygonaceae, 1·2 to 1·5 per cent; Amaranthaceae, Gramineae, and Cyperaceae, 0·8 to 1·2 per cent; and Leguminosae, 0·5 to 0·8 per cent. The percentages of the total fresh-weight of weeds belonging to every family collected in the area were: Compositae, 71 per cent; Gramineae, 21 per cent; Cyperaceae, 4 per cent; and Chenopodiaceae, 1 per cent. It is noteworthy that the Chenopodiaceae, long considered to contain a very high percentage of halophytic species, is here of minor importance. Further aspects of the growth of halophytes have been reviewed by J. H. Chapman (1942) and by V. J. Chapman (1960).

Soil Aeration

The aeration of the soil and the water relationships are inextricably interrelated. In the section devoted to root growth (pp. 167–9) we considered the respiratory levels of the root systems of different species and their success or failure to grow under the flooded conditions of the paddy field. Poel (1951) in Scotland found that the advance of *Pteridium* was arrested by waterlogged soil. Romell (1923) has examined soil aeration as an ecological factor.

Soil Moisture

As moisture or rainfall is one of the most critical factors in determining the character and extent of the natural vegetation throughout the world, the weed growth also in large measure reflects the moisture availability.

That soil moisture determines the type of weed associations to be found on agricultural land has been recognized by a number of workers. Pignatti (1957—*see* Ch. XI), in his study of the weed associations of the grain-fields around Pavia, Italy, observed the strong influence of moisture on the character of the associations (*see* the illustrations in Chapter XI on weed phytosociology). Snog (1952), in Germany, and Talafantova & Zacha (1953), in Czechoslovakia, have also examined the growth of weeds in relation to soil moisture.

Hofsten's (1954—*see* Ch. VI) observations on the growth and occurrence of *Taraxacum* indicated how important water could be as a regulatory factor in the environment. He noted that the water factor is in its turn influenced by the texture and organic characteristics of the soil. He found that dandelions did not thrive on shallow and drought-sensitive soil such as occurred over and around underground stones, for example, in pastures. Drought conditions and a scarcity of dandelions were also noted near birch and oak trees. Hofsten observed the uneven drying of soil on naked ditch slopes and noted a zonation there, with the dandelions always occurring just below the so-called drought zone. He cites the long-held belief that dandelions are very resistant to drought. This is only the case for outgrown plants with 1·5 to 2 metres-deep root systems; for Hofsten concludes that the seedlings and young plants are very sensitive to drought, and that dandelions thus have limited possibilities of invading quickly-drying soils.

Soil Type and Structure

Extensive studies on the relationship of the weed flora to the nature of the soil structure have been made by Volkart (1936), of Switzerland. He concludes that, of the various direct and indirect effects of soil structure, the water-holding capacity and the nutrient level are frequently more important than is the soil type *per se* in determining the nature of the weed flora.

Sandy soils with a low absolute surface, have a low water-holding capacity, and water percolates readily through them, carrying much of the valuable nutrient material away and lowering the pH into the acid ranges. Clay soils have a much higher absolute surface, and a high water-holding capacity. Water does not percolate so readily through such soils, and their pH is more likely to be alkaline (or acid in the absence of calcium carbonate) than is the case with sandy soils. The weeds on clayey soils are basophilic and hygrophilic, and therefore need more nutrients than do those growing on sandy soils. As the absolute surface of the soil particles is larger in clayey than in sandy soils, more nutrients are retained in the former. The weeds of sandy areas, 'psammophiles', may occur in clay soils, and likewise weeds of clay soils, 'pelophiles', may occur in sandy soils—the latter case particularly occurs in humid regions where the water-table is high.

Volkart cites a group of plants that are based on the character of the root system—a flat and spreading type, which he terms 'hygrophiles'. Examples are *Centunculus*, *Juncus bufonius*, and *Polygonum hydropiper*. He further points out that, within this group which is based on habitat and root structure, not all are acidophilic. Individual species vary greatly in their response to the indirect effects of soil structure—such as aeration, water-holding capacity, and nutritive level—as well as to soil reaction. In classifying or grouping the weed flora with regard to soil type, one should utilize the entire weed flora in the area, and not base decisions upon one or two plants or species of weed.

Salzmann (1939), a student of Volkart, has done much more extensive work along this line. The studies of Buchli (1936) and of Ellenberg (1950), already cited, are also applicable. Hofsten (1954—*see* Ch. VI) likewise found in his population studies of *Taraxacum* that water-holding capacity and nutrient levels (especially of nitrate) were generally more important factors than was soil type.

NUTRIENT ABSORPTION AND WEED GROWTH

A great variation exists among weeds, as also among other kinds of plants, in the capacity to absorb the different elements from the soil. Singh & Singh (1939), at the Benares Hindu University in India, have examined this relative absorption in some detail. They found that maximum absorption occurred in the pre-flowering stage, and provide analyses for 49 species at this stage. A selection of species, showing the percentage composition on a dry-weight basis for the entire plant including the root, is given in Table V. They also recognized three groups: those weeds that were high in nitrogen (including eight members of the Leguminosae); those weeds that were high in calcium (especially members of the Euphorbiaceae and Compositae); and those weeds that were high in potassium (the genera *Amaranthus*, *Cleome*, *Chenopodium*, and *Portulaca*, rank well up in this group).

An interesting aspect of this 'relative' absorption is provided in the study of zinc absorption by weeds and volunteer grasses on the sandy soil areas of central Florida (L. H. Rogers *et al.*, 1939). These authors note that the 'land-resting' (alternating periods of arable cultivation with one or more years' rest of the soil) practised in this region has been considered for centuries to be good agricultural policy. However, the substitution of definite sown crops of selected grasses and clover (crop rotation), to be grown in the 'resting' year (or years), instead of the fortuitous development of an indefinite mixture of weeds and grasses, has been considered one of the greatest improvements in agriculture.

TABLE V

ABSORPTION OF NUTRIENTS BY WEEDS

(*From* Singh & Singh, 1939)

Weeds	Composition of weeds in percentage of dry-weight				
	N	CaO	K_2O	S	P_2O_3
Achyranthes aspera	2·21	2·12	1·32	0·60	1·63
Amaranthus blitum	2·10	3·19	3·23	0·52	1·46
A. spinosus	1·92	3·29	3·32	0·51	1·54
A. viridis	1·86	3·01	3·13	0·51	1·56
Argemone mexicana	1·01	1·89	1·33	0·53	1·36
Cassia occidentalis	3·08	5·65	2·31	0·54	1·56
Chenopodium album	3·99	3·99	9·99	0·51	1·51
Cleome viscosa	1·96	2·15	5·81	0·50	1·53
Commelina benghalensis	2·02	2·01	1·86	0·48	1·46
Convolvulus arvensis	2·02	2·11	2·00	0·51	1·01
Cynodon dactylon	2·08	1·58	1·22	0·50	1·01
Cyperus rotundus	1·61	1·32	1·13	0·54	1·52
Eclipta alba	1·61	1·62	1·52	0·53	1·49
Euphorbia hirta	1·98	1·99	1·22	0·49	1·53
Melilotus alba	2·45	2·12	1·96	0·53	1·53
Phyllanthus niruri	2·43	2·63	1·85	0·53	1·53
Portulaca oleracea	1·26	1·69	2·21	0·52	1·51
Solanum xanthocarpum	2·56	3·36	2·12	0·56	1·63

The local disease of maize in central Florida, named 'white bud', has been found to be due to zinc deficiency. It could be corrected by applying zinc sulphate, or by allowing the grass and weeds to develop in the resting year, though oddly enough the recommended cover crop, *Crotalaria*, did not result in any alleviation of this deficiency. Rogers *et al.* found that the dry matter of weeds and grasses collected from plots that had been 'rested' for two years averaged 140 p.p.m. of zinc, whereas *Crotalaria spectabilis*, planted annually, contained only 8 p.p.m. The dry matter of weeds and grasses collected from plots that had been 'rested' for one year averaged 70 p.p.m. of zinc, whereas that of 3 species of *Crotalaria* that had been planted in plots in a two-year rotation with maize and peanuts averaged only 21 p.p.m. As examples of two weeds, *Setaria lutescens* contained 585 p.p.m. of zinc, and *Diodia teres* averaged 373 p.p.m. These authors conclude that the data seem to indicate that the weeds and volunteer grasses are able to absorb much larger proportions of zinc than are planted land-covers, and that they apparently make available sufficient zinc to prevent the development of 'white bud'.

It has been shown that some species of plants will not grow in or invade areas that are deficient in some essential element. The studies of Billings (1950) revealed that lack of P and N (coupled with a low pH of 3·5 to 5·5) barred sagebrush (*Artemisia tridentata*) and its usual associates from soils that were formed from chemically altered volcanic rocks in the Virginia Mountains of western Nevada.

The responsiveness of weeds to both the absence of essential elements and to optimum levels of such elements, and also to the addition of these elements through fertilizer application, may at the same time offer some means of control; and yet in some cases it has led to increased weed problems. Such responsiveness to element deficiency has led Schipstra (1957), in Holland, to use weed responses as indicators of nutritional diseases. He associated potassium deficiency in rye with two weeds, *Chrysanthemum leucanthemum* and *Ranunculus repens*, whose leaves then had brown and dying leaf-margins; phosphorus deficiency with the dull, dark-green leaves of *Chenopodium album*; magnesium deficiency with yellowing of the leaves of *Solanum nigrum*, *Raphanus raphanistrum*, and *Euphorbia peplus*; manganese deficiency with the irregular leaf-blotches of *Chenopodium serotinum* and *Urtica urens*; molybdenum deficiency, and an excess of boron, with yellowing and drooping of the leaves of *Rorippa sylvestris*; and an acid condition with smallness and redness of plants of *Polygonum convolvulus* and *Rumex acetosella*.

A volunteer winter weed population occurring on fertilizer plots in a citrus grove in New South Wales, Australia, was analysed in some detail (Myers & Moore, 1952). The fertilizer experiment had been running for twenty-nine years. Capeweed (*Cryptostemma calendula*), a major component of all plots, was the only species to show a marked increase on the 'nitrogen alone' plots. Where nitrogen and phosphorus were applied together, grasses (species of *Hordeum*, *Bromus*, *Poa*, and *Avena*) afforded the principle species. Plots receiving phosphorus but no nitrogen, supported mainly burr medic (*Medicago denticulata*). Potassium had no significant effect upon the weed population. Although capeweed responded markedly to nitrogen, grasses competed successfully with it in the presence of nitrogen and phosphorus together. The burr medic possibly obtained sufficient nitrogen through the bacterial nodules on its root system.

Nitrogen Relationships

It is a well-known fact that the cultivation of soil during the ideal portion of the growing-season results in a marked increase in the level of nitrate nitrogen. This comes, in part, from the increased growth through better aeration etc. of the free-living bacteria, *Nitrosomonas* and *Nitrobacter*. The processes involved, known as nitrification and ammonification, are, under most conditions, associated with the tillage of the soil—at least, high levels of nitrate occur following such working of the soil. Thus it is not unexpected that certain groups of plants which are favoured in growth by these higher nitrate levels would, through the many centuries of primitive agriculture and land tillage, become especially adapted to, and closely associated with, these practices. Refuse heaps, areas for disposal of excrement, and the domestication of animals with their waste-disposal problems, were also influential in the development of this group of plants—the nitrophilous ruderals and weeds.

It is true that nitrate levels fluctuate widely in soils, and that large-scale sampling and replication throughout a season are necessary for adequate interpretation of such data. However, there are a number of studies which show that cultivation results in an increase in nitrate levels, that the type of crop which was growing in the area the previous year also has a bearing on these levels, and that the cover-crop turned under also affects the levels (Lyon & Bizzell, 1913). In 1916, J. Gourley & V. Shunk, from work in New Hampshire, reported that during the most active period of growth of the maize crop, concentrations of nitrates were frequently higher in the soil under maize than in cultivated soil bearing no crop.

That the type of mineral fertilizer, as well as the manure which is applied, have a bearing upon the character of the weed flora, has been pointed out by Warington (1924). In the fields at Rothamsted, annuals were generally more abundant upon the plots that were adequately fertilized, while plots that were deficient in one or more of the elements, as well as in nitrogen, seemed to have a preponderance of perennial weeds. Weed densities were higher on plots that were rich in nitrogen than on those which were poor in available sources of that element.

There are two species of plants that are almost cosmopolitan through-out the temperate regions of the world and that are also excellent examples of nitrophilous species: *Stellaria media*, the common chickweed, and *Urtica dioica*, the stinging nettle. The English name for the former is certainly appropriate, for in many countries of the world it is a weed commonly associated with poultry runs. Even the most ancient Chinese name for this plant carries the connotation of 'chicken'. Chickweed is related to these domestic birds in perhaps two ways. Firstly, the high nitrogen levels in the poultry pens, together with the usually adequate moisture and not-too-high temperature, certainly favour the growth of this species; and secondly, the poultry in turn feed upon the young buds, flower clusters, etc., as these are rich in the various elements—especially N and K. Thus a cycle is established and the seeds may be returned to the soil through the digestive tract. In agricultural soils that are heavily fertilized with nitrogen, this annual weed generally presents a problem—particularly for vegetable crops.

Urtica dioica, on the other hand, is a perennial, and grows in large compact communities most frequently without the intermingling of other species. Its gregarious, bed-forming habit is due to the spreading rhizomes of the plant, which occurs in open areas as well as in woodlands, and belongs in the class of ruderals—plants of man-created areas. According to Olsen (1921), it may thrive in light-intensities that are as low as 5 to 10 per cent of open daylight; but the best value for it lies between

10 and 20 per cent. Another requirement is that of active nitrification in the soil. Here Olsen (1921) reviews the opinions regarding the extent, if any, of nitrification in non-arable or non-agricultural soils (i.e. woodland soils, etc.). His studies, and those of others, have shown that there is, in non-tilled soils, adequate aeration to favour high rates of nitrification. Nutrient culture experiments confirmed the high N requirement of *Urtica*, as did the N analysis of the plant which contained 3.4 per cent N on a dry-weight basis. Ammonium nitrate as a nutrient source was toxic to the plant. Other areas commonly colonized by *Urtica* are dumps and refuse heaps, where, again, active nitrification occurs. Salisbury (1942) noted an ashes dump in England on which this species alone densely covered an acre or more.

Warming (1925) defined nitrophilous plants as those which thrive best in soils where compounds of ammonia and nitric acid are abundant, and which therefore tend to occur in the vicinity of human dwellings. They belong to special families such as Chenopodiaceae, Cruciferae, and Solanaceae; other species develop feebly on such soils, because there they take into their tissues more nitrates than they can endure.

Bauer (1938), at the University of Leipzig, studied the plants of the city dump of Leipzig-Moekern, and noted the high nitrate content of *Amaranthus retroflexus*, *Chenopodium album*, and *Atriplex nitens*. She graded plants according to their capacity to endure nitrates in high concentrations, and also graded them according to the quantity of nitrates which they stored in their tissues.

A formula for expressing the degree of nitrophily, 'N', has been developed by Bharucha & Dubash (1951). They formulated this as $N = A \times B \times C$, where A, B, and C are the frequency, the constancy of nitrates (i.e. the number of times a positive test was obtained for N, out of the total number of analyses), and the average content of nitrate nitrogen (in p.p.m.), respectively. Data are provided for the four following weeds:

For *Amaranthus spinosus*
$$N = 0.374 \times 0.858 \times 165 = 52.8 \tag{1}$$
For *Solanum xanthocarpum*
$$N = 0.1 \times 1.0 \times 311 = 31.1 \tag{2}$$
For *Portulaca oleracea*
$$N = 0.1 \times 1.0 \times 155 = 15.5 \tag{3}$$
For *Euphorbia pilulifera*
$$N = 0.075 \times 0.5 \times 56 = 2.1 \tag{4}$$

The numbers in parentheses refer to the ranking—in decreasing order of nitrophily.

Communities of nitrophilous species are particularly outstanding when observed in the far-northern latitudes. In these regions of low soil temperature, nitrification reaches a very low level, and nitrophilous plants are commonly restricted to manured habitats, where, however, they may flourish remarkably in contrast to the surrounding barrenness. Thus they have been observed by Holttum (1922) and Polunin (1943) around settlements in Greenland, and by Polunin around human abodes, birds-of-prey perches, whalers' middens, fox-earths, sea-bird 'rookeries', the nesting grounds of geese and ducks, and some other 'disturbed' habitats, in Spitsbergen, Lapland, Iceland, Greenland, Labrador, Ungava, the Canadian Northwest Territories, Alaska, and numerous islands of the Arctic Archipelago (Polunin, 1935, 1948, 1959, 1960, and numerous papers). In such situations a good deal of animal refuse is apt to accumulate, and some of the native vegetation responds in a remarkable manner— by far more luxuriant growth and density of certain plants than is found elsewhere, as in the case of the grass *Alopecurus alpinus*. The sites of old abandoned settlements are often still marked by the presence of thick growths of this species. In such areas, especially in West Greenland (with its long history of regular contact with Europe), introduced weeds have also been observed to be vigorous and flowering—including *Polygonum convolvulus*, *Stellaria media*, *Chenopodium album*, *Sinapis arvensis* and *Poa annua*. Certain nitrophilous communities were observed by Summerhayes & Elton (1928) and by Polunin (1945) in far-northern Spitsbergen, where they were particularly noticeable through the abundant growth of grass species and, in some cases, mosses and lichens as well. The increased nitrogen resulted from the manuring by birds and other animals, and from the deposition of refuse around settlements by man.

NITRATE CONTENT AND TOXICITY TO ANIMALS

One of the most detailed series of analyses of both nitrate nitrogen and total nitrogen in a series of weeds is that reported by Campbell (1924), who was primarily interested in investigating the claim, often made, that *Amaranthus* has the power to store nitrates. From the data obtained from *A. retroflexus* and twenty-five other species of weeds—taken at three stages, i.e. young, just before blooming, and mature, and analysed by the Kjeldahl-Gunning method for total nitrogen and by two methods for nitrate nitrogen—the author concluded that, in these species, the highest percentage of nitrate was found at the stage just before blooming; a high percentage also occurs at the young and immature stages, but disappears at full maturity. *A. retroflexus* and *Atriplex patula*, growing in areas of unusually high nitrate levels (manure piles), deviated from what appeared to be the normal course in nitrate absorption: at early maturity they showed considerable nitrate, and even at full maturity nitrate was still present.

Of all the weeds examined under average field conditions, none surpassed the nitrate level of *Amaranthus retroflexus*, whose values for root, stem, and leaves, just before blooming, were 0·92, 1·40, and 0·25 per cent, respectively, while the total nitrogen content for those organs was

3·12, 3·58, and 4·39 per cent, respectively all on a dry-weight basis. *Chenopodium album* and *Xanthium italicum* were perhaps next in rank, but here the nitrate levels were only from one-third to one-fifth of those of *Amaranthus*.

High nitrate levels in forage that may be cut for hay or silage, as well as in weeds and other plants that are grazed, are of concern to the stockman, as death of cattle through development of methemoglobinemia (a chemically altered state of the blood) may occur through feeding on such forage, or abortion may result. This condition is probably produced by nitrate which is formed from the nitrate in the gastro-intestinal tract. Methylene blue in doses of 2·0 g. per 500 lb. of animal, injected intravenously, immediately counteracts the effect of the ingested nitrate by converting the methemoglobin into normally functioning haemoglobin. In Wyoming, heavy losses of this nature occurred among cattle feeding on oat hay. This prompted an examination of the potassium nitrate levels—not only of oat hay, but also of many other plants that might be fed upon by cattle (Bradley *et al.*, 1940). Among eighty-three samples of oat hay that were sent in for analysis, the maximum level of potassium nitrate was 15·8 per cent of the sample; for barley, it was 5·5 per cent; for maize, it was 2·2 per cent, and for wheat, 4·8 per cent. It was interesting to note that oats grown on Morrison shale containing about 0·046 per cent of potassium nitrate contained 8·1 per cent of this salt, while on sandy loam containing 0·024 per cent of potassium nitrate the oats contained 14·4 per cent of this salt—in both cases calculated on a dry-weight basis.

On a ranch near Frankton, Colorado, eleven head of cattle died in 1937 from eating hay composed mostly of pigweed (*Amaranthus retroflexus*). A sample of this pigweed was analysed and found to contain 3·4 per cent of potassium nitrate. A survey of other weeds disclosed that nine of them contained over 4·2 per cent dry weight of potassium nitrate.

In this study, feeding experiments on calves using pure potassium nitrate established that the minimum lethal dose (M.L.D.) was 25 gm. per cwt. of animal. From the experiments of Bradley *et al.*, it would seem necessary for a 500-lb. animal to eat only about $5\frac{1}{2}$ lb. of hay containing 5 per cent of nitrate to be fatally poisoned. In advising as to whether a hay is safe to feed, the authors arbitrarily established 1·5 per cent potassium nitrate as the lower limit for hay to be toxic.

In a similar survey of the presence of nitrate in the expressed sap of a series of plants representing 53 different genera, values of from a trace to 10,000 p.p.m. were found. Only 11 determinations of the 122 that were made showed as little as 100 p.p.m., while 78 showed between 100 and 1,000, and 23 between 1,000 and 2,500. Only 10 determinations were above these amounts—red kidney-bean, broccoli, cucumber vine, pigweed (*Amaranthus retroflexus*) associated with millet (and other *Amaranthus* plants from oat stubble, from the end of a soybean row, and from test rows of the species), *Acnida tamariscina*, *Portulaca oleracea* from a garden, and watermelon vine. It was also noted that species of various genera of plants accumulated different amounts of nitrate when growing in together.

THE WATER RELATIONS OF WEEDS

Transpiration

Water is probably the most critical single factor of all the requirements for the growth of plants. One has only to study a map of the rainfall and moisture data for the world, to see how closely the character of the vegetation follows the rainfall pattern. From the standpoint of crop production, water is equally critical. Hence a great amount of work has been done on the water requirements of plants, and on the efficiency of their transpiration. Briggs & Shantz (1914) first introduced the concept of water requirement (i.e. transpiration coefficient, cf. Tab. VI) as the ratio of the water absorbed by the plant during its growth to the weight of dry matter produced, exclusive of the roots. The efficiency of transpiration was a concept introduced by Maximov (1929), and refers to the number of grams of dry matter produced per 1,000 gm. of water applied to the test unit (Dillman, 1931).

The water requirement for the growth of weeds is primarily of interest from the standpoint of competition with the crop plant for the available moisture, and to some extent from distributional and control aspects. In Table VI are given some of these values for water utilization by a number of weeds and crops—from the studies of Shantz et al. (1927) and Dillman (1931), conducted in the western area of the United States.

TABLE VI

THE COEFFICIENTS OF TRANSPIRATION AND EFFICIENCIES OF TRANSPIRATION OF IMPORTANT WEEDS AND CROP PLANTS, COMPILED FROM THE DATA OF SHANTZ ET AL. (1927) FROM AKRON, COLORADO, AND OF DILLMAN (1931) FOR THE NORTHERN GREAT PLAINS AREA OF THE UNITED STATES

Plant	Shantz et al. (1927)		Dillman (1931)	
	Trans. coeff.	Effi- ciency*	Trans. coeff.	Effi- ciency*
Amaranthus retroflexus	305	3·28	261	3·83
Chenopodium album	658	1·52	435	2·30
Panicum capillare	—	—	254	3·94
Portulaca oleracea	—	—	288	3·47
Salsola kali var. *tenuifolia*	314	3·18	224	4·46
Millet (Kursk) (*Setaria italica*)	274	3·65	251	3·98
Sorghum (var. Dakota Amber) (*Andropogon sorghum*)	285	3·51	268	3·73
Marquis wheat (*Triticum vulgare*)	550	1·82	403	2·48
Corn (Northwestern Dent) (*Zea mays*)	361	2·77	—	—
Soybeans (*Glycine max*= *G. soja*)	646	1·55	—	—

*i.e. the number of grams of dry matter produced per 1,000 gm. of water applied.—Ed.

These data show the range of water utilization, and indicate that the lowest value obtained for any *crop* was from the Kursk millet (*Setaria italica*), which showed a water requirement of 251. The lowest value of all was for Russian thistle (*Salsola kali* var. *tenuifolia*), with 224. This weed is remarkably efficient in the use of water, which helps to explain why it is such a serious weed pest in dry seasons. The millet, too, which has such a high water efficiency, is closely related to many weedy species of *Setaria*. Thus it appears that the millets, sorghums, and corn (maize), are the most efficient crop plants in the utilization of water. The small grains require almost twice as much water, while the legumes use nearly three times as much, as those most efficient crop plants.

Kiesselbach (1916) has stated that weeds, like sunflowers, use more than three times as much water per plant as maize. The water used by weeds per unit of dry-weight was more than twice that of maize. This is one of the reasons that favours the opinion that weeds make the 'cultivation' of maize necessary.

Bakke & Plagge (1925), in Iowa, provide some information on the rate of transpiration of the common mustard (*Brassica nigra*). Three plants, which were almost mature by 11 April, had a total of 57 leaves, with a total area of 5,369 sq. cm. The maximum water loss reached 68·4 gm. per sq. metre of leaf surface per hour on that date. In comparison, the value for oats in mustard at this date was 13·6 gm. per sq. metre of leaf surface per hour (the maximum was 42·8 gm. on 21 May), while for wheat in mustard the value was 18 gm. (the maximum was 47·6 gm., on 25 May). Thus it can be seen that on 11 April the rate of water loss from mustard leaves was nearly five times that from oats and nearly four times that from wheat.

There is a continuous search for methods of extending some type of agriculture into the semi-arid and even arid regions of the world. Apart from the use of irrigation, the chief effort has been expended in the search for plants of drought resistance and low water-economy. Much can be learned from some types of weedy plants.

Oppenheimer (1951), of the Agricultural Research Station, Rehovet, Israel, has reviewed the efforts in this direction in the Near East. Some plants, such as the dwarf bushes *Alhagi maurorum* and *Prosopis stephaniana*, have rhizomes penetrating to 15 metres—as was found in the Dead Sea Desert, for example. Some desert perennials (species of *Plumbago*, *Micromeria*, and *Thymus*) even grow a little during the dry season, drawing water from dying-off organs of their own body. Some sclerophyllous evergreens and conifers, such as olive, laurel, and others, were found to use water very economically, some of their organs even dehydrating—suggesting a condition of suspended animation (anabiosis). Some species of Mediterranean ferns (*Nothochlaena* and *Ceterach*) attain an air-dry condition, as do mosses and lichens, without permanent harm.

The water-supplying capacity of rocks is not well known, but some formations may store water in capillary or sub-capillary spaces, or in fissures. A chalk has been found to store up to 25·5 per cent of its volume of water. Roots of *Stachys palaestina* and other species have been found to penetrate soft limestone rock on Mt. Scopus. The relative preponderance of the root system over the top portion, together with a wide lateral root expansion, are characteristic features of many of these plants of arid regions, as are the deeply-penetrating roots of young seedlings. The reduction of the transpiring surface is widespread, and occurs through seasonal dimorphism, complete shedding of leaves, etc. In those plants which retain their foliage, the osmotic pressure in the root cells rarely exceeds 50 atmospheres, and structural adaptations, as well as highly efficient stomatal regulation—with a steep ultra-maximum in the early morning for the transpiration curve—are all characteristic features.

Oppenheimer (1951) reviews some of the transpiration values obtained for foliate trees in the hot moist periods—'spend-thrift types', as he termed them. On a day in May on Mt. Scopus, the olive was found to transpire 3,446 mg. of water per gram of fresh-weight per hour. This value is in the range reported earlier for *Salvia dumetorum* and other species in the black soil steppe of southern Russia, but does not come near to the highest ever reported—that by Vassiliev (1931) for groundwater plants of the sandy Karakum desert, which reached 4,890 mg. per hour. However, seasonal averages are more meaningful. Xeromorphic plants have relatively low transpiration rates (as succulents have long been known to have), especially if the total water-use per unit of soil surface penetrated by the roots is taken into account. Sclerophyllous maquis plants, such as the olive and carob, during the warm season rarely have values that rise above 300 mg. per gm. per hour. Genkel (1946) has similarly examined the drought resistance of plants in Russia. In the weed lists for North Africa and for the Near East, large numbers of xeric types—particularly thistles and related plants—predominate. Many others, of course, are short-lived annuals that thrive in the moist season or under conditions of irrigation.

As weeds and other forms of undesirable vegetation often compete for, as well as waste, valuable amounts of water, it may be profitable to review here some phases of the water economy of a mid-western farm region as represented by data taken at the Hydrological Research Station, Coshocton, Ohio (Anon., 1957). Of Ohio's average rainfall of 38 in., 13 in. were lost to the immediate area by surface run-off or by soil percolation into stream flow, while the remaining 25 in. passed into the atmosphere by evapo-transpiration from soil and plants.

A rather detailed analysis for the year 1941, when 41 in. of rainfall were available, indicated that, in grassland: one inch ran off the surface, 12 in. percolated below the root zone into the ground-water reservoir, while crops and evaporation consumed the remaining 28 in. of water. In maize land: 15 in. ran off the surface, 3 in. percolated through the root zone, while the remaining 23 in. were used by the crop and lost by evaporation (this 23 in. usage was 5 in. less than the 28 in. water requirement for an 80 bushels per acre yield of maize).

The water sources of the maize crop were further analysed: in early August, 75 per cent of the moisture came from the top 7 in. of soil, and 15 per cent from the next 7-in. layer—in all, 90 per cent from the uppermost 14 in. of soil—whereas in late August only about 72 per cent came from these top 14 in., about one-half of this percentage coming from each of the two 7-in. layers.

The role of dew (moisture condensed from the air) was also assessed; about $2\frac{1}{2}$ tons per acre may occur on an average summer evening—over 6 in. a year—and in August, 1951, dew supplied three times as much moisture as did rainfall, and was effective in reducing wilt. Many studies of water-vapour absorption by leaves and other plant tissues in recent years have indicated the importance of dew in arid and semi-arid regions, as well as elsewhere.

Waisel (1958) has studied the dew absorption by plants of certain arid zones in Israel—particularly in areas known for their heavy dews, and where the number of dew nights per annum exceeded 100. Surface condensation measurements for the upper leaf surface of *Ficus elastica* varied during a single night from $2 \cdot 8$ to $6 \cdot 7$ mg./cm^2, while for the surface of an iron cube the values were $5 \cdot 1$ to $11 \cdot 4$ mg./cm^2. His studies indicated that the following were pronounced dew-absorbers: *Lycium arabicum*, *Salsola inermis*, *S. vermiculata*, and *Zygophyllum dumosum*. *Kochia indica* was found to be a non-absorber, together with *Salsola autrani* and a number of species of *Anabasis*, *Artemisia*, *Haloxylon*, *Noaea*, *Peganum*, *Polygonum*, *Retama*, and *Thymelaea*. Waisel concluded that the recorded amounts of dew absorbed by the test plants appeared to be of little value in balancing their daily output of water; but the role of this dew in the life of the plants was left as an open question. Yet it would seem likely that certain weedy plants may owe their survival in arid regions to dew absorption, at least in part, and that these species may be sustained there and thence become dispersed into agricultural areas—particularly those that are irrigated during a portion of the year.

Phreatophytes

In evaluating the water economy of an area particularly in arid or semi-arid regions, the amount of water lost through transpiration by 'spendthrift types' or luxury consumers in the natural vegetation, or by other growth of waste areas, must be considered. The magnitude of this loss has not always been appreciated. Phreatophytes (the prefix comes from the Greek word for 'a well') comprise this group of plants which tap the ground-water in excessive fashion, or use water from streams and rivers that pass through arid zones.

These plants do not belong to any specific family. Their common characteristic is their heavy use of a large supply of water. Dense growths of willows, saltcedars, or cottonwoods, along stream channels, exemplify the types of vegetation that use a lot of water but give little benefit. Fletcher & Elmendorf (1955) state that phreatophytes occupy about 15 million acres of land in the western United States. A few dominant species are responsible for most of the heavy use of water—saltgrass (*Distichlis spicata*), greasewood (*Sarcobatus vermiculatus*), saltcedar (*Tamarix gallica*), cottonwoods (*Populus* spp.), baccharis (*Baccharis glutinosa*), willows (*Salix* ssp.), and mesquite (*Prosopis juliflora*). All occur in the valley bottoms and along streams. Fletcher & Elmendorf cite the seasonal discharge of ground-water in Utah, by plants surrounding the wells under study, as amounting to 27·2 in. of water for alfalfa, 22 in. for saltgrass, 3·1 in. for shadscale (*Atriplex confertifolia*), and 2·6 in. for greasewood. Studies of the Pecos River delta area which is covered by a dense growth of saltcedars, disclosed that the consumption of water by these plants was about 5 acre-ft.* annually—derived from ground-water, surface water, and precipitation.

Studies in southern California, cited by Fletcher & Elmendorf (1955), revealed that a saltgrass meadow lost 13 in. of water annually (by evapo-transpiration) when the water-table was 4 ft. below the soil surface, and 43 in. of water when the water-table was 1 ft. below the surface. When the water-table was at the surface, areas of tules (*Scirpus* spp.) and cattails (*Typha* spp.) lost 90 in. of water a year in central California, and 121 in. in the Mesilla Valley in New Mexico. Willows (*Salix* spp.) used between 30 and 53 in. of water in a year, and *Cyperus* and *Juncus* spp. about 77 in.

A related problem is the study of the use of water by vegetation along mountain streams. Studies are under way on the effect of timber cutting on streamflow. Some indication of the loss involved is found in studies in northern Utah, where evaporation losses from Farmington Creek amounted to one-third of the total streamflow from August to October.

Johnson & Kovner (1956) found that cutting a dense understorey of laurel and rhododendron in hardwood stands decreased evapo-transpiration and correspondingly increased streamflow in a perhumid climate in the southern Appalachian Mountains of the United States, where the understorey covered about 80 per cent of the area. On the basis of normal precipitation, cutting increased annual streamflow on the average by 2 in. of water-depth for the first six years after treatment. This means that the average annual evapo-transpiration correspondingly decreased 2 in. following cutting. The average annual increase in streamflow was 4 per cent, while the decrease in evapo-transpiration was 6 per cent.

All of these studies are of great importance, particularly in areas of the western United States where demands on water are so heavy for

* One acre-ft. is a unit of water volume equal to the volume of a prism 1 ft. high with a base 1 acre in area (43,560 cu. ft. or 12,335 cu. m.).

industrial, city-water supply, recreational, and agricultural use. Maintenance of maximum streamflow in the mountains that eventually feed into the reservoirs, is just as important as reducing water loss along the channels in arid regions. All of these studies indicate the economic feasibility of eliminating some of these losses by piping the water through some of the channels of highest use, or by controlling vegetation to a minimum on certain critical watersheds and along stream channels (Fletcher & Elmendorf, 1955).

Chemical control of some of these undesirable phreatophytes has been attempted. In the Gila River channel, near Phoenix, Arizona, six or seven applications of the amine salt of 2,4-D appear to be needed to kill saltcedar. Autumn and spring treatments, started in 1951, resulted in only a 63 per cent kill of the plants, with six sprayings. Esters of 2,4-D have resulted in a 100 per cent kill. Other efforts at controlling phreatophytes, such as by dredging, straightening out sections of the channels, etc., have been attempted—for example in portions of the Rio Grande River.

Weeds as Interceptors of Rainfall

Weeds and other forms of noxious vegetation do, at times, provide a usefully protective cover for the earth. In the absence of planted cover-crops in vulnerable agricultural land, such growth often provides for greater rainfall retention and reduces the amount of surface run-off and consequent soil erosion. Clark (1940), in Nebraska, examined some of these aspects. The grass *Andropogon gerardi* intercepted almost half (47 per cent) of an inch of rain falling during an hour; interception by common weeds varied from 34 per cent with $\frac{1}{2}$-in. rains to nearly 70 per cent with $\frac{1}{8}$-in. showers; and mat-forming weeds held upon their leaves and stems from 9 to 50 per cent of the water falling during applications of different intensities. It is evident that this interception by prairie grasses, weeds, and crop plants, results in an important loss of water to the soil. Light showers were ineffective in replenishing the soil water. In areas of minimal rainfall, and where 'dry-land' farming with alternate fallow years is practised, such vegetal cover on agricultural land is generally not permitted.

TEMPERATURE AND WEED GROWTH

The relationship of temperature to germination has been considered in an earlier section. The other matters of interest in connection with temperature, particularly from the weed control standpoint, are those involving the onset of the dormant or quiescent state in perennial or woody forms, and the survival of weeds at low temperatures.

In the north-temperate regions, weeds are able to survive from season to season regardless, for the most part, of the severity of the winter season. The life-cycle of the annual weed is completed with seed production, and even though the vegetative parts of the plant may continue to live for a while, they generally do not survive the winter season. The seeds, however, are able to survive the winter season and to grow the following year, or in some cases to remain dormant in the soil and germinate at some more favourable time in the future.

Many biennials, growing in the form of mat-plants during their first year, survive the winter, often retaining the foliage in the green condition and remaining photosynthetically active during this season. On the other hand there are a few weeds that retain the normal upright growth-form throughout the winter season, without injury by low temperatures. The most widespread and outstanding example of this group is the common chickweed, *Stellaria media*. This plant continues to grow throughout moderate winters at below-freezing temperatures presenting an erect appearance. During the winter, with its shorter days and lower light-intensities as well as lower temperatures, the plant continues to flower, i.e. flowers develop without petals and remaining tightly closed (cleisto-gamic). However, self-pollination occurs and fertile seeds are produced and scattered about throughout the winter. Investigations have shown that, with the onset of low temperatures, there is a shift in the storage physiology of the plant. Ordinarily, excess carbohydrate is stored in the form of starch; but with the approach of winter this mechanism shifts, so that winter food storage is in the form of soluble sugars. Thus the osmotic values of the cell-sap are high, and little if any free water exists in the cells to form otherwise damaging ice crystals. Doubtless there are other, less obvious, shifts in the physiology of the plant, that enable it to grow safely throughout the winter. Göppert (1881), in Germany, ob-served that, besides *Stellaria*, *Poa annua*, *Capsella bursa-pastoris*, *Lamium purpureum*, etc., could survive quite low temperatures—down to 10°–15°F.

Dexter (1937), in Michigan, examined, for their ability to withstand freezing conditions, excised portions of the roots of a number of perennials. In December, samples of roots and rhizomes were dug from the field, brought into the laboratory, and there subjected to low temperatures. At the end of five hours, the larger roots of Canada thistle (*Cirsium arvense*) and bindweed (*Convolvulus arvensis*) appeared to be unfrozen at −2° and even −3°C. Alfalfa crowns, however, did freeze promptly. After eight hours in various freezing baths, the samples were placed on blotters and put in a good seed-germinator. The Canada thistle was completely killed at −6°C. and −8°C., and was severely injured at −2°C. All quack-grass (*Agropyron repens*), which had frozen at −4°C. or below, was injured and made less growth than the unfrozen check. The quack-grass rhizomes from fertilized plots were all killed at −8°C., and many rhizomes were killed at −6°C. The rhizomes from unfertilized plots survived the −6°C. treatment fairly well, and about one-third of those exposed to the −8°C. treatment started to grow. The bindweed appeared hardier than the Canada thistle, but less hardy than the alfalfa or quack-grass in unfertili-zed plots. No bindweed roots survived −8°C., but about one-third of them survived −6°C.

Winter-annual weeds which commence growth in the autumn, after the usual tillage operations have been discontinued, and survive the freezing temperatures of the winter months, present a serious problem to the grower who wishes to sow his crop early in the spring. Wild oats (*Avena fatua*) often germinate in the autumn, and as the question had often been raised as to whether this weed was a winter annual, Aamodt & Platt (1934), in Alberta, Canada, sought to find out. Seedlings of wild oats, together with seedlings of standard varieties of rye, barley, oats, and wheat, were subjected to a pre-hardening period and then frozen at 15°C. (−5°F.) for four hours. The wild oat seedlings were all killed, but the crop seedlings all survived. Thus there exists little, if any, possibility of wild oats surviving the winter in central and northern Alberta when growth starts in the preceding year. The authors conclude that these findings lend support to the recommendation that stubble land should be disked in the autumn, in order to make conditions more favourable for the germination of wild oat seeds lying on the surface of the soil, and so to promote their destruction by winter killing.

Arthur & Harvill (1941), at the Boyce Thompson Institute, first proposed the use of the term 'thermoperiodism' for the flowering response brought about by periods of low-temperature exposure. For a number of years they grew many plants of *Digitalis purpurea* in the rosette stage, with night temperatures as low as 55° to 60°F. (13° to 16°C.), without having a single plant produce stems and flowers. However, low-temperature treatment at 41°F. (4°C.) caused the plants to flower within a month in a greenhouse with supplemental illumination to provide long-day conditions. This low-temperature requirement is typical of many biennial weeds (*Barbarea vulgaris*, species of *Verbascum*, etc.) in the northern latitudes. The low-temperature requirement for dormancy breaking in woody plants and seeds is all too well known for the north-temperate regions.

The term thermoperiodism was apparently proposed independently and differently by V. A. Tetjurev, who in 1940 applied it to an alternation of low and high temperatures in the process of vernalization of seed (*see* Whyte, 1946). Later, F. W. Went (1944) used the term 'thermoperiodicity' in describing the responses of the tomato plant to the daily cycle of temperature (*see* F. W. Went, 1957). Thus by priority in usage, 'thermoperiodism' involves low-temperature treatments or cycles in relation to the breaking of dormancy in plants or seeds.

THE RESPONSE TO DAY-LENGTH—PHOTOPERIODISM

The response of plants to different periods of illumination, that is, to different lengths of day or photoperiod, has been termed photoperiodism. Although photoperiodism is generally associated with the flowering processes, other aspects of plant growth, including apical stem growth, germination, and seasonal defoliation, are also responsive to day-length (Fig. 27).

Two species of *Ambrosia*, *A. trifida* (giant ragweed) and *A. artemisii-folia* (low ragweed), are good examples of important weeds that are respon-sive to day-length (Plate 10). The responses have been studied by Allard (1932, 1943, 1945), Jones (1936, 1936*a*), and Mann (1942). In this group the initiation of the flowering process, as well as the character of the inflorescence and sex expression are responsive to day-length. The comments given below are taken from the study of Allard (1945).

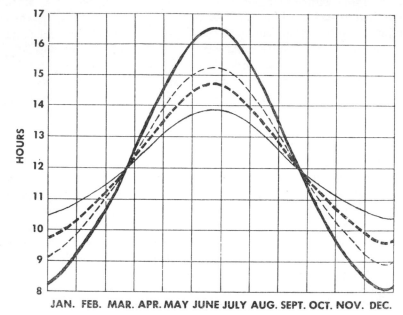

JAN. FEB. MAR. APR. MAY JUNE JULY AUG. SEPT. OCT. NOV. DEC.

From Went, 1957a by courtesy of Scientific American

FIG. 27.—Variation in day-length throughout the year at four latitudes in North America. The vertical co-ordinate in this figure is the length of day in hours and minutes; the horizontal co-ordinate represents the months of the year. The four curves depict the annual change in the length of day at four latitudes. Reading from the top downwards on the left, we have the curve of Miami (26 degrees North), that of San Francisco (37 degrees), that of Chicago (42 degrees), and that of Winnipeg (50 degrees).

About fifteen species of *Ambrosia* are known throughout the world, most of which are natives of the New World. *A. trifida* appears to flower in response to a slightly longer length of day than the low ragweed (*A. artemisiifolia*), so that the former is in anthesis somewhat earlier, and is usually the first to cease flowering. Consequently the giant ragweed extends somewhat farther north in range. Both species are near their northern limits at 50°N. latitude. North of this latitude these eastern ragweeds do not appear to be adapted to the prevailing cool climatic conditions; nor are they common in northern Europe, or in Asia. Super-ficially, the southern European or Mediteranean areas would appear favourable for ragweeds, except that the long, hot, dry summers do not favour their growth; nor are they prominent in the flora of humid subtropical and equatorial regions. This may be due to their low competitive ability when in contact with the indigenous rank tropical flora, to their limited stature, and to early seed production enforced by short days. Allard (1945) concludes that the eastern ragweeds, owing to inherent day-length requirements, are best adapted to flourish in middle latitudes, where long midsummer days, warm temperatures, and ample summer rainfall, prevail in both the southern and the northern hemispheres. The ragweeds are reported to be particularly abundant in portions of Argentina, where 'hay fever' is rife as a consequence of allergic reactions to their abundant and irritant pollens.

The normal period of flowering for the two eastern ragweeds here under discussion begins in early August, near the latitude of 39°–40° N., and extends until frost kills the plants or until they die from senility. The longer days at the initial stage of flowering favour a predominantly staminate condition; but shortening days favour the pistillate condition, so that late-flowering plants, and later-developing branches on early-flowering plants, may show a relatively great increase in the number of fertile flowers as compared with the initial flowering condition. Allard notes that in extreme instances this may amount to partial or even complete failure to develop a staminate inflorescence, resulting in apparent dioecism.

Schaffner (1928) examined a number of dioecious and monoecious plants for their behaviour under different photoperiods—including the common hemp, *Cannabis sativa*. In this species, as in the ragweeds, dioeciousness is very largely under environmental control. Mann (1942), working with *Ambrosia trifida*, found that lengths of day shorter than nine hours caused a reduction in the number of staminate involucres, in relation to the pistillate. With increasing numbers of photoinductive cycles and decreasing lengths of photoperiod, there was an increasing incidence of pistillate involucres. Mann also found reversions to vegetative conditions under photoperiods of less than nine hours.

Jones (1936a) found that low ragweed plants grown in December or January, when the natural day-length is very short, are dwarfed and produce few or no staminate flowers. When only lateral flowers develop, the plants are strictly pistillate. Jones stated that every staminate flower of this species has a vestigial pistil, so that these are always potentially dimorphic. Environment may thus accentuate femaleness by causing the vestigial pistil to differentiate into a sterile pistillate head. Allard's work (1945) indicates that, under long-day conditions, complete maleness may be induced in this species. Jones (1936) examined the flowering responses in *Ambrosia* from a genetic point of view. He found extreme variation in purely pistillate expression in progenies of open-pollinated plants of ragweed cultured in the field. This is to be expected, and, in the case of some well-defined ecotypes, different responses to day-length may well be found within a single recognized species. This appears to be the case in the various strains of a species of *Bouteloua* as described below.

Bouteloua curtipendula (side-oats grama) occurs over much of the eastern, central, and southwestern United States, extending northwards into Canada (southern Saskatchewan), southwards into Mexico, and, in South America, into Argentina. It is a valuable forage plant in the western part of the prairie region and at certain altitudes in the south-west. Olmsted (1943), at the University of Chicago, obtained 12 strains of this grass from localities between San Antonio, Texas, and Cannonball, North Dakota—a latitudinal range of about 17 degrees, representing effective photoperiods of near fifteen hours in the south and seventeen hours in the north. His study revealed that plants of this species from different latitudes prove to be morphologically and physiologically distinct when grown together under similar conditions.

The three strains from southern Texas and southern Arizona, in photoperiodism experiments, proved to be the ones nearest to normal (i.e. to actual responses under field conditions) in vegetative and flowering behaviour on a photoperiod (thirteen hours) close to that of their native growing-season. Most of them failed to flower, but grew luxuriantly, on photoperiods of longer than fourteen hours—thus failing to flower until the shorter autumn days, when frost injury in their vigorous condition is likely to occur. These strains were non-rhizomatous. In the absence of rhizomes, as well as of some other features, these southern strains were liable to winter injury. On the other hand, a northern strain from North Dakota exhibited normal vegetative and flowering behaviour only in photoperiods of fourteen hours or longer (long-day plants). In their natural growing-season, the southern strains are not subjected to light periods of much lower value. When grown in shorter photoperiods, most of the plants do not flower, nor do the internodes elongate, although the plants tiller abundantly and form rosettes. Rhizomes are formed in the shorter photoperiods, but not as abundantly as in the longer ones, and dry-weights are lower in the shorter photoperiods.

These experiments, and others, show that the habit of a strain in one environment is not predictable from its mode of growth in another. It is also unwise to attempt any generalizations at the species level until strains from a wide latitudinal range have been investigated. Olmsted considers that the species originated in the low latitudes, possibly the southwestern United States or Mexico, and that it has spread north and south to higher latitudes in southern Canada and Argentina. The plants were originally adapted to the short photoperiods, but within the strains that evolved were a few (possibly day-neutral) individuals which were able to flower on longer photoperiods—thus spreading northwards (Olmsted, 1943; Whyte, 1946).

While in no sense is this species of *Bouteloua* to be considered a weed, these responses of natural populations throughout a considerable latitudinal range do indicate how ecotypes may arise among weed species of wide climatic as well as latitudinal range. This certainly has happened in two weeds of cosmopolitan distribution, *Stellaria media* (Petersen, 1936) and *Poa annua* (Tutin, 1957). These authors have described the various known ecotypes and their growth-habits, including germination characteristics. The light requirements of a group of cultivated plants and weeds have been examined by Zillich (1926). Species of cocklebur (*Xanthium*), widely distributed weeds of the Compositae, are good examples of short-day plants, and have been extensively studied (Whyte, 1946). Photoperiodic ecotypes of *Betula* spp. have been described by Vaartaga (1954) and of *Populus* by Pauley & Perry (1954—*see* Ch. IX), while Olmsted (1951) has shown the relationship between leaf abscission in the sugar maple and natural (autumnal) photoperiod.

The 'weediness' of *Chenopodium* spp. may be positively correlated with the amount of phenotypic 'plasticity' which they exhibit, and with their lack of sensitivity in germination and photoperiodic response—postulations which appear to be supported by evidence obtained by Cumming (1959) at Ottawa. In the order of wideness of distribution as weeds in Canada, the species would be evaluated as:

$$C.\ album > C.\ glaucum > C.\ salinum > C.\ rubrum$$

When sensitivity, however, is evaluated by the amount of germination under different light qualities and energies, time sequences, and temperatures, the ranking of species is in the reverse order: thus the most exacting species, *C. rubrum*, as might be expected, has a more limited range in distribution, and, therefore, is relatively unimportant as a weed in Canada.

LIFE-FORMS AND GROWTH-FORMS

The subject of 'life-forms' of plants has been briefly touched upon in the introductory chapters relating to the various methods of classification. In his study of dune communities, Gimingham (1951), at the University of Aberdeen, notes that the introduction of the life-form of plants as the basis upon which community structure is analysed, has given a new ecological application to a long series of attempts to define this concept, and to establish an acceptable system of classification of the life-forms of plants. C. Raunkiaer defined life-form as 'all the adaptations of the plant to the climate', but in his classification he was forced to rely upon a single character ('the kind of protection which enables the growing points to survive the unfavourable season'). Gimingham (1951) believes that Raunkiaer's original definition can be used in full by combining his life-form classification with the 'growth-form' concept—the latter implying solely the architecture of the plant (i.e. referring in particular to the form, method of branching and arrangement of the shoot system, and, where possible, also of the underground system). These growth-forms might well be applied to weed growth and to weed communities; they include tussocks, tufted growths, large and small branched forms, large and small erect forms, large and small rosettes, and prostrate forms.

BIBLIOGRAPHY

(The Growth and Development of Weeds)

AAMODT, O. S. & PLATT, A. W. (1934). Resistance of wild oats and some common cereal varieties to freezing temperatures. *Sci. Agric.*, 14, 645–50.

AARNIO, B. (1931). [The dependence of weeds upon the reaction of soil—in Finnish.] *Maataloust. Aikakaust.*, 3, 117–21.

ALLARD, H. A. (1932). Length of day in relation to the natural and artificial distribution of plants. *Ecology*, 13, 221–34.

—— (1943). The North American ragweeds and their occurrence in other parts of the world. *Science*, 98, 292–4.

—— (1945). Flowering behavior and natural distribution of the eastern ragweeds (*Ambrosia*) as affected by length of day. *Ecology*, 26, 387–94.

—— (1948). Length of day in the past climates of geological eras and its possible effects upon the changes in plant life. *In* A. E. Murneek & R. O. Whyte, *Vernalization and Photoperiodism*, Chronica Botanica, Waltham, Mass., pp. 101–19.

ANON. (1957). What happens to water. *Agric. Res.*, 5(10), 6–7.

ARASHI, K. & KUNITAKE, M. (1951). [Studies on the distribution of weeds in the paddy field on which rice seeds were sown directly, with special reference to soil moisture —in Japanese.] *Kyushu Noji Shikinjo*, 8, 23–24.

ARNY, A. C. (1932). Variations in the organic reserves in underground parts of five perennial weeds from late April to November. *Minnesota State Tech. Bull.*, 84, 28 pp.

ARTHUR, J. M. & HARVILL, E. K. (1941). Flowering in *Digitalis purpurea* initiated by low temperature and light. *Contr. Boyce Thompson Inst.*, 12, 111–17.

ARTIST, R. C. (1931). Field sorrel: value of *Rumex acetosella* as an indicator. *Butler Univ. Bot. Stud.*, 2(7–8), 81.

ASLANDER, A. (1931). [A study of shoot formation by Canada Thistle.] *Medd. Cent. Anst. Forsöksv. Jordbr.*, No. 429, 36 pp.

ATKINS, W. R. G. & FENTON, E. W. (1930). The distribution of pasture plants in relation to soil acidity and other factors. *Sci. Proc. R. Dublin Soc.*, 19, 533–47.

BAILEY, E. H. S. & SAYRE, L. E. (1909–10). On the presence of barium in the ash and extract of certain Kansas weeds. *Trans. Kans. Acad. Sci.*, 23/24, 194–8.

BAKKE, A. L. & PLAGGE, H. N. (1925). The extent to which weeds modify the transpiration of cereals. *Res. Bull. Ia. Agric. Exp. Sta.*, 96, 211–39.

—— & GAESSLER, W. G. (1945). The effect of reduced light intensity on the aerial and subterranean parts of the European bindweed. *Plant Physiol.*, 20, 246–57.

BARNES, S. (1928). The effect of weeds on soil moisture. *Seas. Hints, Dom. Exp. Fms.*, 42, 8–9.

BARR, C. G. (1936). Preliminary studies on the carbohydrates in the roots of bindweed. *J. Amer. Soc. Agron.*, 28, 787–98.

BAUER, J. (1938). Beiträge zur Physiologie der Ruderalpflanzen. *Planta*, 28, 383–428.

BEAL, W. J. (1897). Syllabus for a short course on weeds. *Proc. Soc. Prom. Agric. Sci.*, 1897, pp. 41–52.

BEDSOLE, M. R. (1937). The effect of water-soluble and total nitrogen and of drying on the rate of nitrification of some common Florida weeds. *J. Amer. Soc. Agron.*, 29, 815–21.

BELGIUM (1955). [Weed research and improvement of grassland flora—in Flemish.] *Centre National de Recherches Herbagères et Fourragères, Ghent*, 18 pp.

BENNETT, E. (1953). Weeds contain valuable chemical compounds. *J. Agric. Food Chem.*, 1, 1223.

BHARUCHA, F. R. & DUBASH, P. J. (1951). Studies on nitrophily. Nitrophilous plants of Bombay. *J. Indian Bot. Soc.*, 30(1–4), 83–87.

BILLINGS, W. D. (1950). Vegetation and plant growth as affected by chemically altered rocks in the Western Great Basin. *Ecology*, 31, 62–74.

BLOMMAERT, K. L. J. (1955). The significance of auxins and growth-inhibiting substances in relation to winter dormancy of the peach tree. *Union of S. Afr. Dep. Agric. Sci. Bull.*, No. 368, 23 pp.

BÖCHER, T. W. (1950) [publ. 1953]. Cultivation experiments with *Geranium robertianum*, *Veronica officinalis*, and *Prunella vulgaris. Proc., 7th Internat., Bot. Congr.* 268–9.

BOHMONT, D. W. & LEGG, J. W. (1953). Effect of hydrogen-ion concentration upon growth and development of *Halogeton. Agron. J.*, 45, 450–1.

BOLTON, J. L. (1962). *Alfalfa: Botany, Cultivation and Utilization.* (World Crops Books, ed. N. Polunin.) Leonard Hill, London; John Wiley, New York, 473 pp.

BOOTH, W. E. (1941). Revegetation of abandoned fields in Kansas and Oklahoma. *Amer. J. Bot.*, 28, 415–22.

BOWMAN, I. (1937). Influence of vegetation on land-water relationships. *U.S. Dept. Agric. Soil. Conserv. & Forestry Service.* Miscell. Pub., pp. 76–105.

BRADLEY, W. B., EPPSON, H. F., & BEATH, O. A. (1940). Livestock poisoning by oat hay and other plants containing nitrates. *Wyo. Agric. Exp. Sta. Bull.*, 241, 1–20.

BRENCHLEY, W. E. (1911–12). The weeds of arable lands in relation to the soils on which they grow. *Ann. Bot.*, 25(97), 155; *Ann. Bot.*, 26(101), 95.

—— (1935). The weed flora in its relation to crop and agricultural treatment. *Proc., 6th Internat. Bot. Congr.* 2, 5–7.

BRIGGS, L. J. & SHANTZ, H. L. (1914). Relative water requirement of plants. *J. Agric. Res.*, 3, 1–64.

BROWN, D. (1944). *Imperata cylindrica.* VI. Grazing and fodder value. *Imp. Agric. Bur. Joint Publ., Great Britain*, No. 7, 27–37.

BUCHLI, M. (1936). *Ökologie der Ackerunkräuter der Nordostschweiz.* Verlag Hans Huber, Bern. 354 pp.

CALL, L. E. & SEWELL, M. C. (1918). The relation of weed growth to nitric nitrogen accumulation in the soil. *J. Amer. Soc. Agron.*, 10, 35–44.

CAMPBELL, E. G. (1924). Nitrogen content of weeds. *Bot. Gaz.*, 78, 103–15.

CANNON, HELEN L. (1952). The effect of uranium-vanadium deposits on the vegetation of the Colorado Plateau. *Amer. J. Sci.*, 250, 735–70.

—— (1957). Description of indicator plants and methods of botanical prospecting for uranium deposits on the Colorado Plateau. *Bull. U.S. Geol. Surv.*, 1030-M, 399–516.

CANNON, W. A. (1949). Tentative classification of root systems. *Ecology*, 30, 542–8.

CHAPMAN, J. H. (1942). Halophytes. *Quart. Rev. Biol.*, 17, 291–311.

CHAPMAN, V. J. (1960). *Salt Marshes and Salt Deserts of the World.* (Ed. N. Polunin.) Leonard Hill, London; Interscience, New York, xvi + 392 pp.

CHODAT, F. (1924). La concentration en ions hydrogène du sol et son importance pour la constitution des formations végétales. *Thèse no. 748 Univ. de. Genève, Inst. Bot. Ser.* 10, Fasc. 7.

CHOUARD, P. (1952). Photoperiodism, classification. *Rep., 13th Internat. Hort. Congr.* 2, 820.

CLARK, O. R. (1940). Interception of rainfall by prairie grasses, weeds, and certain crop plants. *Ecol. Monog.*, 10, 243–77.

COLE, H. E. & HOLCH, A. E. (1941). The root habits of certain weeds of southeastern Nebraska. *Ecology*, 22, 141–7.

COOK, H. H. (1937). Perennial weeds. *Gdnrs. Chron.*, **102**, 58.

COOPER, W. S. & STOESZ, H. D. (1931). The subterranean organs of *Helianthus scaber-rimus. Bull. Torrey Bot. Cl.* **58**, 67–72.

CUMMING, B. G. (1959). Extreme sensitivity of germination and photoperiodic reaction in the genus *Chenopodium* (Tourn.) L. *Nature, Lond.*, **184**, 1044–5.

CUNNINGHAM, J. C. (1913). Roots and rootstocks of weeds. *Bull. Iowa. Geol. Surv.*, **4**, 643–54.

CURÉ, P. (1941). Evaporation et transpiration. Action des alternances de sècheresse et d'humidité sur la structure des plantes. Toulouse.

CURTIS, R. W. (1949–50). Woody weeds. *Cornell Plantat.*, **5**, 29–30.

DAHLSTEDT, H. (1921). De svenska arterna av släktet *Taraxacum. Acta Flor. Suec.*, **1**, 1–160.

DANIEL, H. A. (1935). The total calcium, phosphorus, and nitrogen content of native and cultivated plants in the high plains of Oklahoma and a study of the mineral deficiencies that may develop in livestock when emergency feeds are fed. *Panhandle Bull.*, **56**, 18 pp.

DENFER, D. VON. *See* VON DENFER, D.

DERKEA, W. L. (1955). Frost damage. *Bull. Mo. Agric. Exp. Sta.*, No. 649. 15 pp.

DE SILVA, B. L. T. (1934). Calcicole and calcifuge. *J. Ecol.*, **22**, 532–53.

DE VAEL, W. B. (1943). The correlation of soil pH with destruction of woody plants in the Gainesville area. *Proc. Florida Acad. Sci.*, **6**, 9–24.

DE VRIES, D. A. (1955). Solar radiation at Wageningen. *Meded. Landb. Hoogesch., Wageningen*, **55**, 227–304.

DE VRIES, D. M. & ZANDSTRA, K. (1952). Field weeds in the course of the year. *Levende Nat.*, **55**(10), 184–8.

DE VRIES, O. (1934). [Weeds and lime status—in Dutch.] *Korte Meded. Rijkslandbouw. Pfroefstn. Groningen*, No. 26.

—— (1934*a*). [Weeds and degree of acidity—in German.] *Z. PflErnähr. Düng.*, **13B**, 356–60.

DEXTER, S. T. (1937). The winterhardiness of weeds. *J. Amer. Soc. Agron.*, **29**, 512–17.

DILLMAN, A. C. (1931). The water requirements of certain crop plants and weeds in the Northern Great Plains. *J. Agric. Res.*, **42**, 187–238.

DIRVEN, J. G. P., GALVIMANS, E. J. H. & HENDRIKS, J. A. H. (1955). [The weed flora on soils of the Old Coastal Plain—in Dutch.] *Surinaamse Landb.*, **3**, 199–208.

DITTMER, H. J. (1937). A quantitative study of the roots and root hairs of a winter rye plant. *Amer. J. Bot.*, **24**, 417–20.

DOI, Y. (1952). Studies on the oxidizing power of roots of crop plants. I: The difference with species of crop plants and weed grasses. *Proc. Crop. Sci. Soc. Japan*, **21**(1, 2), 12–13; 14–15.

DUNCAN, J. F. (1925). 'Pull roots' of *Oxalis esculenta. Trans. Bot. Soc. Edinb.*, **29**, 192–6.

DUNCAN, W. H. (1935). Root systems of woody plants of old fields of Indiana. *Ecology*, **16**, 554–67.

DUNFORD, E. G. & FLETCHER, P. W. (1947). Effect of streambank vegetation upon water yields. *Trans. Amer. Geophys. Un.*, **28**, 105–10.

EDELMANN, C. H. & EEUWENS, B. E. P. (1955). Bibliography of land and water use in Europe. *F.A.O. Publ.*, 347 pp.

EICHINGER, A. (1933). [Weed flora and the lime status of soils—in German.] *Z. PflErnähr. Düng.*, **12B**, 401–24.

—— (1939). [Weed flora and the lime status of soil—in German.] *Mitt. Landw.*, **54**, 605–6, 633–6.

ELLENBERG, H. (1950). *Landwirtschaftliche Pflanzensoziologie.* Bd. 1: *Unkraut gemein-schaften als Zeiger für Klima und Boden.* Verlag E. Ulmer, Stuttgart z. Z. Ludwigs-burg, 1950, 141 pp.

ESAU, KATHARINE (1960). *Anatomy of Seed Plants.* John Wiley, New York, 376 pp.

ESMARCH, F. (1928). Bodensäure und Unkraut. *Kranke Pflanze*, 5, 141–4.

EVANS, M. W., ALLARD, H. A. & McCONKEY, O. (1935). Time of heading and flowering of early, medium, and late timothy plants at different latitudes. *Sci. Agric.*, 15, 8.

FABIAN, I. (1938). Beiträge zum Lang- und Kurtztagsproblem. *Z. Bot.*, 33, 305–57.

FELFOLDY, L. J. M. (1940). Protein production of a weed plant society, a production-biological study. *Arch. Biol. Hung.*, 18, 384.

FERDINANDSEN, C. (1920). [Danish weed growth—in Danish.] *Nord. Jordsbr. Forskn.*, 1920(2), pp. 48–67.

FLETCHER, H. C. & ELMENDORF, H. B. (1955). Phreatophytes—a serious problem in the West. *Yearb. U.S. Dep. Agric.*, 1955, pp. 423–9.

FRAZIER, J. C. (1944). Nature and rate of development of root system of *Apocynum cannabinum. Bot. Gaz.*, 105, 463–70.

FRÖDIN, J. (1919). Über nitrophile Pflanzenformationen auf den Almen Jämtlands. *Bot. Notiser*, 1919, pp. 271–2.

FUELLEMAN, R. F. & GRABER, L. F. (1938). Renovation and its effect on the populations of weeds in pastures. *J. Amer. Soc. Agron.*, 30, 616–23.

FUNAIOLI, A. (1953). [Aspects of the problem of weeds in the region of the central Uebi Scebeli—in Italian.] *Riv. Agric. Subtrop.*, 47, 7–9, 319–40.

GALIL, J. (1958). Physiological studies on the development of contractile roots in geophytes. *Bull. Res. Counc. Israel, sect. D, Botany*, 6D, 221–36.

GENKEL, P. A. (1946). [Methods of developing drought resistance in plants—in Russian.] *Akad. Nauk SSSR. Inst. Fiziol. Rast. im K.A. Timiriazeva Trudy*, 5(1), 1–273.

GILBERT, B. E. & PEMBER, F. R. (1935). Tolerance of certain weeds and grasses to toxic aluminum. *Soil Sci.*, 39, 425–9.

GILBERT C. S. (1946). Nitrate accumulation in cultivated plants and weeds. *Bull. Wyo. Agric. Exp. Sta.* No. 277, 39 pp.

GIMINGHAM, C. H. (1951). The use of life form and growth form in the analysis of community structure, as illustrated by a comparison of two dune communities. *J. Ecol.*, 39, 396–406.

GLOCK, W. S. (1957). Tree growth and rainfall. *Trans. Amer. Geophys. Un.*, 36, 315–18.

GOEDEWAAGEN, M. A. J. (1938). A sociological study on the relation between the weed vegetation on arable land and the reaction of the soil. *Chron. Bot.*, 4, 21–23.

GÖPPERT, A. (1876). Der December 1875 und die Vegetation des Breslauer Gartens. *Jahrb. Schles. Ges. Vaterl. Cultur*, 54, 84–92.

—— A. G. (1881). Über Einwirkung niedriger Temperaturen auf die Vegetation. *Garten Flora*, 1881, pp. 10–13, 168–79.

GOURLEY, J. H. & SHUNK, V. D. (1916). Notes on the presence of nitrates in orchard soils. *N. H. Sta. Tech. Bull.*, 11, 3–31.

GUSTAFSON, F. G. (1938). Influence of the length of day on the dormancy of tree seedlings. *Plant Physiol.*, 13, 655–8.

HAAS, T. P. (1947). Observations on *Utricularia inflata* and *U. cleistogama*, a contribution to the biology of *Utricularia. Amer. J. Bot.*, 34, 583–4.

HAASIS, F. W. (1923). Frost heaving and pine seedlings. *Ecology*, 4, 378–90.

HALSTED, B. D. (1892). A century of American weeds. Their root systems tabulated. *Bull. Torrey Bot. Cl.*, 19, 141–7.

HANF, M. (1942). Ein Beitrag zur Frage der Beziehung zwischen Unkrautwuchs, Deckfrucht und Boden. *Pflanzenbau*, 19(6), 155–74.

—— (1943). Bewurzelung und Wuchs von Unkrautkeimlingen in verschiedenen Böden. *J. Landw.*, 90, 125–46.

—— (1944). Der Einfluss des Bodens auf Keimen und Auflaufen von Unkräutern. *Beih. Bot. Zbl.*, 62, 405–25.

HARDY, E. A. (1938). Tillage in relation to weed root systems. *Agric. Engng.*, 19, 435–8.

HARPER, H. J. (1924). The total nitrogen, phosphorus, and calcium content of common weeds and native grasses in Oklahoma. *Proc. Okla. Acad. Sci.*, 14, 36–44.

HARVEY, R. B. (1935). *An Annotated Bibliography of Low Temperature Relations of plants.* Rev. edn. Burgess Pub. Co., Minneapolis, 240 pp.

HOLTTUM, R. E. (1922). The vegetation of West Greenland. *J. Ecol.*, 10, 87–108.

HOOVER, M. D. (1944). Effect of removal of forest vegetation upon water yields. *Trans. Amer. Geophys. Un.*, Part VI, 967–77.

HOPKINS, E. S. (1926). Weeds and their effect on crop yields. *Canad. Exp. Farms. Div. Field Husb. Rep.*, 1926, 27.

ICHIKAWA, C. & SEO, Y. (1953). [Remarkable difference in manganese contents of ashes of weeds—in Japanese.] *J. Sci. Soil, Japan*, 23, 97–100.

INCE, J. W. (1915). Fertility and weeds. *N. Dakota Bull.*, 112, 233–47.

JOEL, A. H. (1929). Weed distribution and crop character in relation to soil type in Saskatchewan. *Sci. Agric.*, 9, 675–82.

JOHNSON, E. A. & KOVNER, J. A. (1956). Effect on streamflow of cutting a forest understory. *Forest Sci.*, 2, 82–91.

JOHNSTON, T. H. (1924). The relation of climate to the spread of prickly pear. *Trans., R. Soc. S. Austral.* 40, 268–96.

JONES, K. L. (1936). Studies on *Ambrosia* I. The inheritance of the floral types in the ragweed, *Ambrosia elatior* L. *Amer. Midl. Nat.*, 17, 673–99.

—— (1936a). Studies on *Ambrosia* II. Effect of certain environmental factors on floral development of *Ambrosia elatior*. *Bot. Gaz.*, 103, 780–7.

JUNGES, W. (1957). Beziehungen zwischen der photoperiodischen Angepasstheit der Pflanzen un der geographischen Breit ihrer Heimat. *Planta*, 49, 11–32.

KAMYSHEV, N. S. (1959). [A contribution to the classification of anthropochores—in Russian.] *Bot. J.*, 44, 1613–16.

KASERER, H. (1940). Uber die Beeinflussung des Bodens durch die Pflanzen in der Wurzelzone. *Godenk. u. PflErnähr.*, 21/22(66/67), 697–706.

KIESSELBACH, T. A. (1916). Transpiration as a factor in crop production. *Neb. Res. Bull.*, 6, 3–214.

KILTZ, B. F. (1930). Perennial weeds which spread vegetatively. *J. Amer. Soc. Agron.*, 22, 216–34.

KIVINEN, E. (1931). Uber die Reaktion der Standorte des Kleinen Ampfers (*Rumex acetosella*). *Maataloust. Aikakaust.*, 3(1).

KLAPP, E. & WAGENER, H. (1932).[Umbelliferae in permanent meadows, their nitrogen and ash contents—in German.] *Arch. PflBau*, 8, 755.

KLING, M. (1914). Uber die chemische Zusammensetzung einiger Unkräuter sowie deren Wert als Futter- und Düngemittel. *Landw. VersSta.*, 85, 433–70.

KLINKOWSKI, M. (1947). *Bodenanzeigende Pflanzen.* Erfurt, Germany.

KOBAYASHI, T. (1954). Studies on the salt resistance of cultivated plants. I. Classification of weeds in reclaimed tidal land with special reference to the salt-resistant behaviour. *Proc. Crop Sci. Soc. Japan*, 13, 34–35; 36–38.

KORSMO, E. (1954). *Anatomy of Weeds.* Oslo, Grondahl & Sons, 413 pp.

KREEB, K. (1956). Phänologisch-pflanzensoziologische Untersuchungen in einem Eichen-Hainbuchenwald im Neckargebiet. *Ber. Dtsch. Bot. Ges.*, 69, 361–74.

KUBIENA, W. L. (1955). *The Soils of Europe.* Thomas Murby, London.

KUTSCHERA, L. (1960). *Wurzelatlas mitteleuropäischer Ackerunkrauter und Kulturpflanzen.* DLG-Verlag, Frankfurt am Main, 574 pp. (250 figs).

LARMOUR, R. K. & MACEWAN, J. W. G. (1938). The chemical composition of Russian Thistle (*Salsola pestifer* A.Nels). *Sci. Agric.*, 18, 695–9.

LATYPOV, A. S. (1952). [The effect of depth of ploughing on the weediness of soil—in Russian.] *C.R. Acad. Sci. U.R.S.S.*, 11.

LAWALREE, A. (1947). Les *Ambrosia* adventices en Europe occidentale. *Bull. Jardin Bot. Etat Belg. Brux.*, 18, 305–15.

LEFEVRE, P. (1956). Influence du milieu et des conditions d'exploration sur le développement des plantes adventices. Effet particulier du pH et l'état calcique. *Ann. Agron. Paris*, **7**, 299–347.

LINDSAY, D. R. (1953). Climate as a factor influencing the mass ranges of weeds. *Ecology*, **34**, 308–21.

LINDSEY, A. A. & NEWMAN, J. E. (1956). Use of official weather data in springtime-temperature analysis of an Indiana phenological record. *Ecology*, **37**, 812–23.

LINKOLA, K. (1922). Zur Kenntnis der Überwinterung der Unkräuter und Ruderalpflanzen in der Gegend von Helsingfors. *Ann. Soc. Zoolog.-Bot. Fennicae Vanamo*, **1**(7), 90–228, 25 figs. (Cf. *Bot. Jb.*, **58**, lit., 96–97, 1923.)

—— (1936). Pflanzenphanologische Beobachtungen im Dienste der Autökologie der Pflanzen. *Ber. Schweiz. Bot. Ges.*, **46**, 80–84.

LINSTOW, O. VON (1929). Bodenanzeigende Pflanzen. *Abh. Preuss. Geol. Landesanst.* Neue Folge, **114**.

LLOYD, D. C. (1956). Remarks on a possible biological program with the weed *Acanthospermum hispidum* D.C. *Canad. Ent.*, **88**, 613–22.

LOHMEYER, W. (1954). Über die Herkunft einiger nitrophiler Unkräuter Mitteleuropas. *Vegetatio. Acta Geobot.*, **5/6**, 63–65.

LUNN, W. M., BROWN, D. E., McCARTNEY, J. E., & GARNER, W. W. (1939). Tobacco following bare and natural wood fallow and pure stands of certain weeds. *J. Agric. Res.*, **59**, 844–5.

LUTHER, H. (1951). Verbreitung und Ökologie der höheren Wasserpflanzen . . . II. *Acta Bot. Fenn.*, **50**, 1–370.

LYON, T. L. & BIZZELL, J. A. (1913). Some relations of certain higher plants to the formation of nitrates in soils. *Mem. N.Y. State Exp. Sta.*, No. 1, 111 pp.

LYRE, H. (1957). Beitrage zur Biologie und Ökologie der Vogelmiere *Stellaria media* (L.) Cyr. Diss. Stuttgart, Landw. Hoch., 68 pp.

McGINNIS, H. A. (1923). A comparison of the transpiration rate of corn and certain common weeds. *Trans. Ill. Acad. Sci.*, **16**, 82–88.

MAGROU, P. (1947). Adaptation du *Poa annua* L. aux hautes altitudes dans les Pyrénées centrales. *Bull. Soc. Bot. Fr.*, **94**, 317–19.

MALINGA, D. P. (1947). [Soils and plants as indices in the search for metals—in Russian.] *Priroda*, **36**(6), 13–17.

MANN, H. H. (1939). The weed herbage of a slightly acid arable soil. *J. Ecol.*, **27**, 89–113.

—— (1957). Weed herbage of slightly acid arable soils as affected by manuring. *J. Ecol.*, **45**, 149–56.

MANN, L. K. (1942). Effects of photoperiod on sex expression in *Ambrosia trifida*. *Bot. Gaz.*, **103**, 780–7.

MANTEUFFEL, K. (1928). Die Bestimmung der Kalkbedürftigkeit. *Fortschr. Landw.*, **3**(2), 68–69.

MARTHALER, H. (1937). Die Stikstoffernährung der Ruderalpflanzen. *Jb. Wiss. Bot.*, **85**, 76–106.

MATTSON, S. (1938). The constitution of the pedosphere. *Ann. R. Agric. Coll. Sweden*, **5**, 261–76.

MAXIMOV, N. A. (1929). *The Plant in Relation to Water*. Allen & Unwin, Ltd., London, 451 pp.

MEHL, S. (1936). Unkräuter als Anzeichen der Bodenreaktion. *Mitt. Landw.*, **51**, 341–2.

MEIKLEJOHN, J. (1955). Nitrogen problem in tropical soils. *Soils & Fertil.*, **18**(6), 459–63.

MEINZER, O. E. (1920). Plants as indication of ground water. *Geogr. J.*, **3**, 213.

—— (1927). Plants as indicators of ground water. *U.S. Geol. Surv., Water-Supply Paper No.* **577**.

MEULEN, H. TER (1932). Distribution of molybdenum. *Nature, Lond.*, **130**, 966.

MEYER, K. (1941). Über Begleitsamen verschiedener Leinsaatherkünfte. *Angew. Bot.*, **23**, 68–80.

MILÍC, M. (1952). [The effect of meteorological conditions on the character of weediness in crops—in Russian.] *Godish. Polopriv. Fak. Beograd*, 4, 387–403.

MOON, F. E. (1939). The carotene-contents of some grass and clover species, with a note on pasture weeds. *Emp. J. Exp. Agric.*, 7, 235–42.

MUELLER, I. M. (1941). An experimental study of rhizomes of certain prairie plants. *Ecol. Monogr.*, 11, 165–88.

MUKHERJI, S. K. (1936). The autecology of *Mercurialis perennis* L. IV. The effect of soil factors on distribution and growth. *J. Ecol.*, 24, 317–33.

MURPHY, A. H. (1954). Improving Klamath weed ranges. *Calif. Agric. Circ.* No. 437, 16 pp.

MYERS, L. F. & MOORE, R. M. (1952). The effect of fertilizers on a winter weed population. *J. Aust. Inst. Agric. Sci.*, 18(3), 152–5.

NATHANSON, A. (1913). Saisonformen von *Agrostemma githago* L. *Jb. Wiss. Bot.*, **53**, 125–56.

NIELSEN, N. C. (1926). [Weed occurrence and soil tests in determining lime deficiency in mineral soils—in Norwegian.] *Nord. Jordbrugforskning*, 1926(4–7), pp. 421–33.

NUTTONSON, M. Y. (1948). Some preliminary observations of phenological data as a tool in the study of photoperiodic and thermal requirements of various plant material. In A. E. Murneek & R. O. Whyte, *Vernalization and Photoperiodism*, Chronica Botanica, Waltham, Mass., pp. 145–7.

—— (1956). *Wheat-climate Relationships and the Use of Phenology in Ascertaining the Thermal and Photo-thermal Requirements of Wheat.* Amer. Inst. Crop. Ecology, Washington, D.C., 388 pp.

—— (1958). *Rye-climate relationships and the Use of Phenology in Ascertaining the Thermal and Photo-thermal Requirements of Rye.* Amer. Inst. Crop Ecology, Washington, D.C., 219 pp.

OLMSTED, C. E. (1943). Growth and development in range grasses. III. Photoperiodic responses in the genus *Bouteloua*. *Bot. Gaz.*, **105**, 165–81.

—— (1944). Growth and development in range grasses. IV. Photoperiodic responses in twelve geographic strains of side-oats Grama. *Bot. Gaz.*, **106**, 46–74.

—— (1951). Experiments on photoperiodism, dormancy, and leaf age and abscission in sugar maple. *Bot. Gaz.*, **112**, 365–93.

OLSEN, C. (1921). The ecology of *Urtica dioica*. *J. Ecol.*, **89**, 1–18.

—— (1923). Studies on the hydrogen ion concentration of the soil and its significance to the vegetation, especially to the natural distribution of plants. *C. R. Trav. Lab. Carlsberg*, **15**, 1–166.

OPPENHEIMER, H. R. (1951). Summer drought and water balance of plants growing in the Near East. *J. Ecol.*, **39**, 356–62.

PACZOSKY, I. (1914). [Investigations on roots—in Russian.] *Bull. Appl. Bot.* 8, 816–20.

PAVLYCHENKO, T. K. (1940). Investigations relating to weed control in western Canada. *In* R. O. Whyte, *The Control of Weeds*, Herbage Publ. Ser. Bull. **27**, 168 pp.

PENTON, A. (1953). Some plants steal water; watch out for phreatophytes, plants that take water and give nothing in return. *Org. Farmer*, 4(10), 22–23.

PETERSEN, D. (1936). *Stellaria*-Studien. Zur Zytologie, Genetik, Ökologie und Systematik der Gattung *Stellaria* insbesonders der Media-Gruppe. *Botan. Not.*, pp. 281–419.

PIEMEISEL, R. L. (1938). Changes in weedy plant cover on cleared sagebrush land and the probable causes. *U.S. Dep. Agric. Tech. Bull.* No. 654, 44 pp.

PLAGGE, H. H. (1919). The extent to which the weed factor will modify the transpiration of cereals. *Thesis, Iowa State College.*

POEL, L. W. (1951). Soil aeration in relation to *Pteridium aquilinum* (L.) Kuhn. *J. Ecol.*, **39**, 182–91.

POLUNIN, N. (1935). The vegetation of Akpatok Island, Part II. *J. Ecol.*, **23**, 161–209.

—— (1943). Contributions to the flora and phytogeography of south-western Greenland: an enumeration of the vascular plants, with critical notes. *J. Linn. Soc. London, Botany*, **52**, 349–406.

—— (1945). Plant life in Kongsfjord, West Spitsbergen, *J. Ecol.*, **33**, 82–108.

—— (1948). *Botany of the Canadian Eastern Arctic, Part III, Vegetation and Ecology.* Department of Mines and Resources, Ottawa, Canada, National Museum Bulletin No. 104, vii + 304 pp.

—— (1959). *Circumpolar Arctic Flora.* Clarendon Press, Oxford, England, xxviii + 514 pp.

—— (1960). *Introduction to Plant Geography and Some Related Sciences.* Longmans, Green, London, etc., and McGraw-Hill, New York, xix + 640 pp.

POOL, R. J. (1948). *Marching with the Grasses.* University of Nebraska Press, Lincoln, 210 pp.

POTTER, L. D., LONGWILL, J. & MODE, C. (1952). Shelterbelt snow drifts. *Bi-M. Bull. N. Dakota*, **14**, 176–9.

POTZGER, J. E. & VAN ENGEL, W. A. (1942). Study of the rooted aquatic vegetation of Weber Lake, Vitas Co., Wisconsin. *Trans. Wis. Acad. Sci. Arts Lett.*, **34**, 149–66.

PULLENG, H. (1918). Root habit and plant distribution in the far north. *Plant World*, **21**, 223–33.

RADEMACHER, B. (1938–39). Über den Lichteinfall bei Wintergetreide und Winterölfrüchten und seine Bedeutung für die Verunkrautung. *Pflanzenbau*, **15**, 241–65.

RIMBACH, A. (1895). Zur Biologie der Pflanzen mit unterirdischen Spross. *Ber. Dtsch. Bot. Ges.*, **13**, 141–55.

ROBINSON, T. W. (1952). Phreatophytes—water thieves. *Nat. Reclam. Assoc. Proc.*, **21**, 87–96.

—— (1957). Phreatophytes. *U.S. Geol. Surv. Water-Supply Paper* No. 577.

ROGERS, C. F. (1929). Winter activity of the roots of perennial weeds. *Science*, **69**, 299–300.

ROGERS, L. H., GAIL, O. E. & BARNETTE, R. M. (1939). The zinc content of weeds of volunteer grasses and planted land covers. *Soil Sci.*, **47**, 237–43.

ROMELL, L. G. (1923). L'aeration du sol. *Rev. Int. de Renseign. Agric.*, **1**(n.s.), 300–15.

RUSSELL, E. J. (1936). Critical review of the problems discussed, interactions between roots and between plants, weed flora as an indicator of soil conditions in agriculture. *Proc., 6th Internat. Bot. Congr.* **1**, 153–5.

SALISBURY, E. J. (1927). On the causes and ecological significance of stomatal frequency with special reference to woodland flora. *Phil. Trans., Roy. Soc.* B, **216**, 1–65.

—— (1942). *The Reproductive Capacity of Plants.* G. Bell, London, xi + 244 pp.

SALZMANN, R. (1939). *Die Antropochoren der schweizerischen Kleegraswirtschaft, die Abhängigkeit ihrer Verbreitung von der Wasserstoffionenkonzentration und der Dispersität des Bodens mit Beiträgen zu ihrer Keimungsbiologie.* Promotionsarbeit, Tech. Hoch. Zurich, Verbandsdruckerei AG., Bern, 82 pp.

—— (1954). Untersuchungen über die Lebensdauer von Unkrautsamen im Boden. *Mitt. Schweiz. Landw.*, **2**(10), 170–6.

SAMISH, R. M. (1954). Dormancy in woody plants. *Annu. Rev. Pl. Physiol.*, **5**, 183–204.

SAYRE, C. B. (1953). Forecasting maturity in peas. *Fm. Res. (New York,)* **19**(4), 12.

SCHAFFNER, J. H. (1903). Ohio plants with contractile roots. *Ohio Nat.*, **3**, 410.

—— (1904). Leaf expansions of trees and shrubs. *Ohio Nat.*, **5**, 210–13, 363.

—— (1928). Further experiments in repeated rejuvenations in hemp (*Cannabis sativa*) and their bearing on the general problems of sex. *Amer. J. Bot.*, **15**, 77–85.

SCHEER, W. (1934). Vergleichende Untersuchung über den Entwicklungsrhythmus verschiedener Unkrautarten in seiner Abhängigkeit von der Witterung und in seiner Beziehung zu dem der Deckfrüchte. *Arb. Biol. Abt. (Anst.-Reichsanst.)*, *Berl.*, 21, 153–200.

SCHIPSTRA, K. (1957). [Weeds as indicators of nutritional diseases—in Dutch.] *Tijdschr. PlZiekt.*, 63, 15–18.

SCHMALFUSS, K. (1935). Unkrautflora und Bodenreaktion. *Angew. Bot.*, 17, 191–9.

SCHMITT, L. (1941). Die Leistungen des deutschen Bodens im Verlauf der letzten 100 Jahre und sein Fruchtbarkeitszustand unter dem Einfluss der neuzeitlichen Düngungsmassnahmen. *Forschungsdienst*, 12, 1–36.

SCHMITZ, A. (1946). La répartition et la fréquence des plantes commensales des cultures en function du pH du sol en Belgique. *Bull. Inst. Agron. Gembloux*, 15, 18–78.

SCHNELLE, F. (1955). *Pflanzen-phänologie*. Geest & Portig, Leipzig, 299 pp.

SCHRAMM, G. (1954). Die Beziehungen der Ackerunkräuter und ihrer Gemeinschaften zum Reaktionszustand und zur Struktur des Ackerbodens. *Z. Acker- u. PflBau*, 97(4), 485–512.

SEARLE, S. A. (1953). *The Measurement of Plant Climate*. Chichester Press, Chichester, England, 36 pp.

SELLECK, G. W., COUPLAND, R. T. & FRANKTON, C. (1962). Leafy spurge (*Euphorbia esula* L.) in Saskatchewan. *Ecol. Monogr.*, 32, 1–29 (71 refs.).

SETCHELL, W. A. (1929). Morphological and phenological notes on *Zostera marina* L. *Univ. Calif. Publ. Bot.*, 14, 387–452.

SHANTZ, H. L., PIEMEISEL, R. L. & PIEMEISEL, LYDIA (1927). The water requirement of plants at Akron, Colorado. *J. Agric. Res.*, 34, 1093–1190.

SHAW, R. H. & THON, H. C. S. (1951). On the phenology of field corn, the vegetative period. *Agron. J.*, 43, 9–15.

SHULTZ, A. M., LAUNCHBAUGH, J. L. & BOSWELL, H. H. (1955). Relationships between grass density and brush seedling survival. *Ecology*, 36, 226–38.

SIDDINGS, L. A. (1914). Transpiration of *Silphium laciniatum*. *Plant World*, 17, 309–28.

SILVA, B. L. T. DE. See DE SILVA, B. L. T.

SIMPSON, J. F. H. (1937). Precise distribution of *Mercurialis perennis* according to soil hydrogen ion concentration. *Nature, Lond.*, 139, 632–3.

SINGH, B. N. & SINGH, L. B. (1939). Relative absorption of nutrients by weeds of arable land. *Soil Sci.*, 47, 227–35.

SINNOTT, E. W. & BAILEY, I. W. (1914). Investigations on the physiology of the angiosperms. 4. The origin and dispersal of herbaceous angiosperms. *Ann. Bot.*, 28, 547–600.

SMALL, J. (1946). *pH and Plants. Introduction for Beginners*. Van Nostrand Co., New York, 216 pp.

SMITH, L. P. (1956). A tale of two summers. *Gardeners' Chron. & Gard. Illus.*, 140, 598–9.

SNIDER, H. J. (1940). Probable effects of weeds on the fertility of soils. *Trans. Ill. Acad. Sci.*, 33, 34–35.

SNOG, M. (1952). Über Beziehungen von Unkrautarten und Unkrautgemeinschaften zum Wassergehalt des Bodens. *Diss. Hohenheim*.

SPARKES, C. H. & BUELL, M. F. (1955). Microclimatological features of an old field and an oak-hickory forest in New Jersey. *Ecology*, 36, 363–4.

SPILLMAN, W. J. & CATES, J. S. (1908). Agronomic habits of rootstock-producing weeds. *Proc. Soc. Prom. Agric. Sci., N.Y.*, 29, 57–66, 9 figs.

SPURWAY, C. H. (1941). Soil reaction (pH) preferences of plants. *Michigan Agric. Expt. Sta. Spec. Bull.* No. 306, 36 pp.

STEARNS, F. (1955). The influence of light and temperature on germination and flowering of five species of *Plantago*. *Proc., North Central Weed Control Conf.* 12, 8.

STEYER, K. & EBERLE, G. (1928). [Weeds and their value as indicators of soil reaction—in German.] *Arb. Biol. Abt. (Anst.-Reichanst.), Berl.*, 16, 325–422.

STONE, E. D. (1957). Dew as an ecological factor. I. Review of the literature. *Ecology*, 38, 407–13.

——, WENT, F. W., & YOUNG, C. L. (1950). Water absorption from the atmosphere by plants growing in dry soil. *Science*, 111, 546–8.

STOUT, D. V. P. (1934). Irrigation of weeds and other noncrop plants costly and unprofitable. *U.S. Dept. Agr. Yearbook*, 1934, pp. 250–3.

STUTZER, A. & SEIDLER, L. (1908). [The content of important plant food ingredients in some common weeds—in German]. *Fühlings Landw. Ztg.*, 57, 429–30.

SUMMERHAYES, V. S. & ELTON, C. S. (1928). Further contributions to the ecology of Spitzbergen. *J. Ecol.*, 16, 193–268.

SUND, J. M. & WRIGHT, M. J. (1957). Weeds containing nitrates cause abortion in cattle. *Agron. J.*, 49, 278–9.

TALAFANTOVA, A. & ZACHA, V. (1953). [Effect of weeds on the content of soil moisture and soil structure—in Czech.] *Sborn. Ceskoslov. Akad. Zemedel.*, 26, 387–94.

TER MEULEN, H. *See* MEULEN, H. TER.

TIMAR, L. (1954). [Field weeds on alkaline low soils in the region of Szeged—in Hungarian.] *Acta Bot. Acad. Sci. Hung.*, 1(2), 193–214.

TIMMONS, F. L. (1941–42). The rise and decline of cactus in Kansas. *Bienn. Rep. Kansas State Bd. Agric.*, 33, 37–46.

TRAUTMANN, W. (1954). Über den Einfluss von Bodenreaktion, Kali und Phosphorsäure auf die Verteilung der Ackerunkräuter im Göttinger Gebiet. *Z. PflErnähr. Düng.*, 66(3), 247–61.

TUTIN, T. G. (1957). A contribution to the experimental taxonomy of *Poa annua* L. *Watsonia*, 4, 1–10.

VAARTAGA, O. (1954). Photoperiodic ecotypes of trees. *Canad. J. Bot.*, 32, 392–9.

—— (1959). Evidence of photoperiodic ecotypes in trees. *Ecol. Monogr.*, 29, 91–111.

VAEL, W. B. DE. *See* DE VAEL, W. B.

VASSILIEV, I. M. (1931). Über den Wasserhaushalt von Pflanzen der Sandwüste in südöstlichen Kara-kum. *Planta*, 14, 225–309.

VEGIS, A. (1956). Formation of the resting condition in plants. *Experientia*, 12, 94–99.

VELEZ, I. (1950). Barbados, a tropical island without weeds. *Sci. Mon.*, 71(4), 276–7.

VENGRIS, J., DRAKE, M., COLBY, W. G. & BAIT, J. (1953). Chemical composition of weeds and accompanying crop plants. *Agron. J.*, 45(5), 213–18.

VINOGRADOV, A. P. (1943). Biogeochemical research in the U.S.S.R. *Nature, Lond.*, 151, 659–61.

VOLKART, A. (1933). Untersuchungen über den Ackerbau und die Ackerunkräuter im Gebirge. *Landw. Jb. Schweiz*, 47, 77–138.

—— (1935–36). The weed flora in its relation to the dispersion and reaction of arable soil. *Proc., 6th Internat. Bot. Congr.*, 1, 46; 7–8.

VON DENFER, D. (1939). Über das Zusammenwirken von Keimstimmung und täglicher Belichtungsdauer auf die Entwicklung von *Sinapis* und *Hordeum. Jb. Wiss. Bot.*, 88, 759–815.

VON LINSTOW, O. *See* LINSTOW, O. VON.

VRIES, D. A. DE. *See* DE VRIES, D. A.

WAGNER, H. (1948). *Die Lebensgemeinschaften der Pflanzen 'Bodenkultur'*. Fromme, Vienna.

WAISEL, Y. (1958). Dew absorption by plants of arid zones. *Bull. Res. Counc. Israel, Section D, Botany*, 6D, 180–6.

WARMING, E. (1925). *Oecology of Plants*. Oxford Universtiy Press, London, 2nd impr.

WARINGTON, K. (1924). The influence of manuring on the weed flora of arable land. *J. Ecol.*, 12, 111–26.

WEAVER, J. E. (1926). *Root Development of Field Crops.* McGraw-Hill, New York, 291 pp.

—— & FITZPATRICK, T. J. (1934). The prairie. *Ecol. Mon.*, 4, 109–295.

WEIGERT, J. & WEIZEL, H. (1936). Wirkung verschiedener Handelsdüngemittel auf das Auflaufen von Samenunkräutern. *Prakt. Bl. Pflbau*, 14, 129–39.

WELTON, F. A. (1932). Soil reaction not an efficient method of controlling some lawn weeds. *Ohio Agric. Exp. Sta. 50th Ann. Rep.*, 40–41.

WENT, F. W. (1944). Plant growth under controlled conditions, II. Thermoperiodicity in growth and fruiting of the tomato. *Amer. J. Bot.*, 31, 135–40.

—— (1950). The role of the environment in weed growth. *Proc. North Centr. Weed Control Conf. Ann. Meeting*, 7, 2–5.

—— (1957). *The Experimental Control of Plant Growth.* Chronica Botanica, Waltham, Mass., 343 pp.

—— (1957a). Climate and agriculture. Ch. II in *Plant Life.* Scientific American and Simon and Schuster, New York, 237 pp.

WHITE, J. W. (1914). Concerning the growth and composition of clover and sorrel (*Rumex acetosella*) as influenced by varied amounts of limestone. *Penna. Sta. Rep.*, 1914, pp. 46–64.

——, HOLBEN, F. J. & JEFFRIES, C. D. (1930). Growth of turf grasses and weeds in relation to soil acidity. *Penna. Sta. Bull.* No. 258, 18 pp.

WHITE, O. E. (1926). Geographical distribution and cold resisting characteristics of herbaceous perennials and woody plant groups. *Brooklyn Bot. Gdn. Rec.*, 15, 1–10.

WHITE, W. N. (1932). A method of estimating ground-water supplies based on discharge by plants and evaporation from soil. *U.S. Geol. Surv. Water-Supply Paper*, No. 659, 1–107.

WHYTE, R. O. (1946). *Crop Production and Environment.* Faber & Faber, London, 372 pp.

WILLIAMS, C. B. (1953). Graphical and statistical methods in the study of insect phenology. *9th Internat. Congr. Entomology*, 1951, 2 174–89.

WILLIS, S. J. (1953). *Cardaria draba*, a globe-trotting weed. *World Crops*, 1953, 310–12.

WITTMACK, L. (1919). Die Bonitierung des Bodens nach den Unkrautpflanzen. *Ill. Landw. Ztg.*, 39, 391–2.

WOO, M. L. (1919). Chemical constituents of *Amaranthus retroflexus. Bot. Gaz.*, 68, 314–44.

ZEDERBAUER, E. (1923). Versuche über Saisondimorphismus und verwandte Erscheinungen bei Ackerunkräutern. *Öst. Bot. Z.*, 72, 223–30.

ZILLICH, R. (1926). Über den Lichtgenuss einiger Unkräuter und Kulturpflanzen. *Fortschr. Landw.*, 1, 462–70.

ZURN, F. (1951). [The nutrient and mineral content of grasses, legumes and weeds in meadows—in German.] *Z. Acker. -u. PflBau*, 93, 444–63.

VIII

THE REPRODUCTION AND DISPERSAL OF WEEDS

FLOWERING AND SEED PRODUCTION OF WEEDS

THE flowering habits of weeds are of primary interest from the stand-point of knowing all phases of the life-cycle. With this knowledge, the vulnerable points may be attacked by the best control methods available. Weeds, of course, are not known for their showy flowers. On the contrary, the flowers of weeds are frequently small, often rather inconspicuous, and commonly quite unattractive. Here all methods of pollination exist, from almost exclusive wind-pollination among the grasses, to self- and insect-pollination among many other groups. The great Compositae family represents the culmination of floral development and complexity, with the condensation of the inflorescence to a capitulum (*see* Fig. 28). A large proportion of weeds belong to this family.

The several studies described below serve to show the range and details of anthesis among certain weeds. In Japan, Yamada & Adachi (1954) studied the flowering of Johnson grass (*Sorghum halepense*). They observed that the highest percentage of flowers (about 28 per cent of the total) opened at noon, while another peak (15 per cent) occurred between 2 p.m. and 3 p.m. The Johnson grass panicle contains about 700 flowers, of which about 50 per cent are hermaphroditic flowers and the remainder are staminate flowers. The largest percentage of hermaphroditic flowers open from three to nine days after the onset of flowering, the highest percentage of staminate flowers opening some seven to twelve days later. Almost all of the flowers were open at the end of 13 to 14 days from the onset of flowering in the panicle.

Kremer (1950), in Michigan, studied the flowering of the common dandelion (*Taraxacum officinale*) and its influence on bee behaviour during the blossoming period of a number of varieties of fruit trees. He was concerned with the possible preference of the bees for the dandelion flowers that were present in the orchards. Kremer concluded that temperature was the most important climatological factor controlling the dehiscence of pollen sacs and the secretion of nectar in dandelion and fruit bloom, these processes occurring at any hour of the day, from as early as 5.30 a.m., at temperatures of 65°F. or higher. On clear, cool mornings, the partial opening of the dandelion blossom (or capitulum) occurred when temperatures were approximately 50°–55°F. At 55°F. the anthers dehisced and small quantities of nectar were visible. At 55°–65°F., the

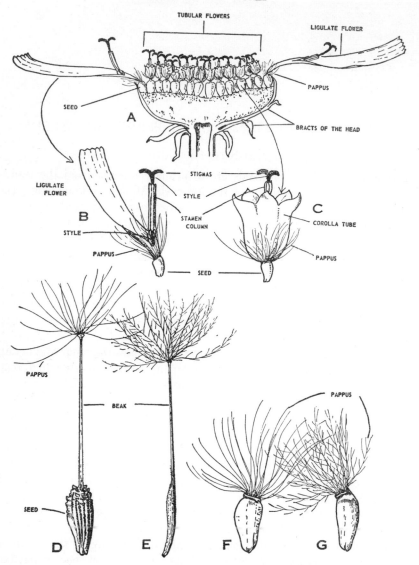

From Frankton, 1955; by courtesy of Canada Department of Agriculture

FIG. 28.—A, Cross-section of a flower head (capitulum) of a member of the Compositae with tubular and ligulate flowers (or florets); B, Ligulate flower; C, Tubular flower; D-G, Fruits of several species showing some different types of pappus; D, Simple pappus on a beaked fruit of dandelion (*Taraxacum officinale*); E, Plumose pappus on a beaked fruit of Cat's-ear (*Hypochaeris radicata*); F, Simple pappus on fruit of plumeless thistle (*Carduus acanthoides*); G, Plumose pappus on fruit of Canada thistle (*Cirsium arvense*).

full bloom or optimum stage was noted, and this appeared to be the most favourable temperature for good nectar secretion, pollen production, and bee activity. When temperatures remained at these latter levels throughout the day, no change occurred until late afternoon, when the normal closing period of the dandelion blossom led to a cessation of bee activity.

An increase in temperature above 70°F., however, effected the closure of the blossom soon after such temperatures were reached. This was usually between 10 a.m. and 2 p.m.

The dandelion retains its bloom over a long period—owing, in part, to the fact that the blossoms close during adverse weather. They can then remain in the closed state for several days, or more, and resume the open or full blooming state when climatic conditions are again favourable. Once closed, they were not observed to open again on the same day. Nectar was not necessarily present when the blossoms were open, unless the factors controlling nectar secretion were operative. Pollen may be present, however, or may have remained from a previous opening, as a feature attractive to insects. By contrast, fruit-tree blossoms, being stable when once the petals have unfolded, remain unaffected in structural appearance until petal-fall. Kremer concludes that the dandelion is a good honey plant, which is valuable as a source of food for bees in early spring, and that fruit growers would benefit by regarding its comparatively short competitive period as inconsequential.

The dandelion has also been the subject of considerable study by Hofsten (1954—*see* Ch. VI) in Sweden. In studying the flowering biology of a large number of apomicts, Hofsten found that certain apomicts flower during the germination year, whereas they only flower during their third or fourth year under unfavourable conditions. The greatest difference in the flowering period between two apomicts was thirteen days, and one apomict had four to five times as high a flowering intensity as had an apomict showing poor flowering. On certain favourable growing-sites, flowering was observed to occur from four to six weeks earlier than for the same apomict on other sites.

The seed production of the dandelion was also studied by Hofsten, and reference to some of these data has already been made (p. 153). He observed the number of flowering heads per plant to vary from 105 in the *picinum* apomict to a low of 18 in the *retroflexum* apomict—with an average of 51 for all of the apomicts (1943–4). The apomict *picinum* produced an average (on 10 plants in 1944) of 1,049 blossom heads, having a total number of 200 blossom days per plant in that year, and an average of 20·8 flowering heads per plant per day during the whole flowering period. The average flowering period for each flowering head was 4·4 days. The 'seed' production of certain apomicts during their third year was calculated and found to be from 3,700 to 20,800 seeds per solitary plant on fertile land. Hofsten also found that, in extreme cases, the number of seeds produced per hectare might exceed one million. He concluded that the apomicts of the *Vulgaria* group of *Taraxacum* seem rather well endowed for conquering suitable ground and producing new types, provided such activities are connected with seed production.

Sir E. J. Salisbury, in his book *The Reproductive Capacity of Plants* (1942), has examined some of these problems in considerable detail.

From a study of the seed and fruit weights of nearly 300 species taken from different types of habitat conditions, he concluded that the seed or fruit weight tends to increase with the degree of shading to which the seedling is normally subjected. Thus it would appear that the more advanced the phase of succession with which the species is naturally associated, the larger will be the amount of reserve food material provided in the seed. In brief, Salisbury states that the capacity to colonize in the face of competition appears to be associated with the amount of food reserve which the seed contains. He also notes the increased weight of the seeds of some polyploids, and calls attention to their possible ecological

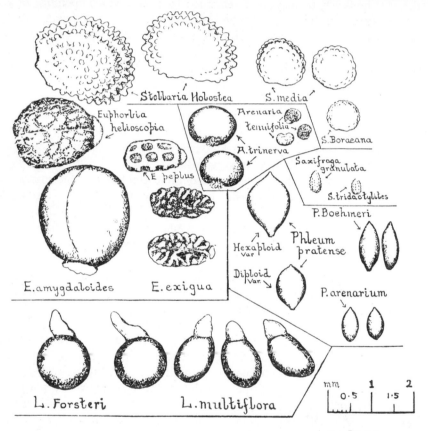

From Salisbury, 1942

FIG. 29.—Seed weight and habitat. Seeds of species characteristic of open and, contrastingly, more or less closed communities, but belonging to the same genus. Chickweeds: *Stellaria boraeana*, a species of sand dunes, *S. media*, of semi-open habitats, and *S. holostea*, a woodland plant. Sandworts: *Arenaria tenuifolia*, a species of open habitats, and *A. trinerva*, a woodland species. *Saxifraga tridactylites*, a dune species, and *S. granulata*, a species of meadows. Spurges: *Euphorbia exigua*, *E. peplus*, and *E. helioscopia*, all species of cultivated ground, and *E. amygdaloides*, a woodland species. Cat's-tail grasses: *Phleum arenarium*, a sand-dune species, *P. boehmeri*, a species of short turf, and *P. pratense*, a meadow species. Woodrushes: *Luzula multiflora*, a species of open patches and coppiced woodlands and *L. forsteri*, a species of partial shade. Note the smaller-sized seeds of the species of open habitats.

206

importance in advanced communities. He found that those species which demand particularly restricted environmental conditions have been shown to possess the more meagre reproductive equipment, whereas those species which have numerous niches or large areas that they can occupy (especially weeds), however infrequently—and which can thus most

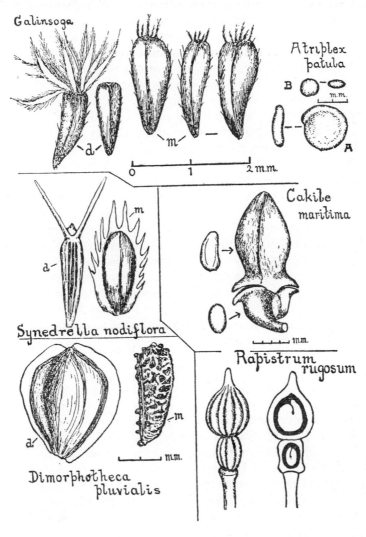

From Salisbury, 1942

FIG. 30.—Heteromorphic propagules: different types of seeds and fruits produced by the same plant. The upper figures are original. *Galinsoga parviflora : d*, disk fruits with and without the pappus; *m*, marginal fruits from the same capitulum (original). *Atriplex patula*: the two types of seed (A and B) in front view and side view (original). The lower figures are after Becker (1912). *Synedrella nodiflora* and *Dimorphotheca pluvialis*, two members of the Compositae showing the disk (*d*) and marginal (*m*) fruits. *Cakile maritima* and *Rapistrum rugosum*, two members of the Cruciferae, showing the fruits and the dimorphic seeds.

readily profit by a large output—have in fact the capacity for a high potential in their progeny (Fig. 29).

Salisbury commented that the seed output is to be regarded, not so much as an insurance against extinction, as an insurance against rarity, and that the effective premium which the organism can afford to pay doubtless bears a definite relation to the available niches in the natural habitats that the plant can occupy. Comparison of annual and perennial species demonstrated that the latter usually had the greater seed output, although the risks of failure in replacement were lower for the perennial than for the annual plants. He further noted that the largest seed productions were characteristic of species associated with habitats that were only intermittently available for colonization—such as woodland clearings, and the intermittently exposed mud of shallow lakes and ponds. Such 'opportunists' in the plant world constitute a biological category which has not hitherto been distinguished, but which it is of considerable ecological importance to recognize. The average output of 32 such species was about 227,000 seeds per plant. Salisbury also states that some of the most successful species are those which exhibit a large seed output and possess also a means of vegetative propagation. This latter method provides the equivalent of a large food supply in the seed—but over a much longer period—and thus permits tolerance of greater and more prolonged competition by the vegetatively produced offspring. Many pernicious perennial weeds exemplify this. Many plants have the capacity to flower and produce seed when in apparent seedling stages, these being termed 'depauperate forms' (Pl. 11). Fig. 30 shows some interesting examples of heteromorphic propagules—different types of seeds and fruits produced by the same plant.

PHENOLOGY

The study of organisms in relation to climate has been termed phenology. However, some of the more striking rhythmic or seasonal changes, such as flowering and fruiting periods, are more often associated with the definition of this area of study. One of the longest phenological records available is the series of observations made by the Marsham family of the village of Hevingham in Norfolk, England, being almost without a break from the year 1732 to the present time. The records show the date of the first-observed flowering of hawthorn (*Crataegus oxycantha*) annually for over 150 years. All records show that first flowering occurs between 15 April and 18 June, with a mean date of 12 May. When grouped by ten-year periods, the means for these periods vary from 3 to 18 of May. It is not known whether these plants were of one clonal group, or of diverse origin.

One of the most detailed studies of this nature is that of Lindsey & Newman (1956—*see* Ch. VII), who had available the earliest flowering dates (some for a thirty-year period) of 51 species of spring-flowering plants from the Charles C. Deam Arboretum at Bluffton, Indiana, U.S.A. This record was analysed in connection with an official temperature record. In this preliminary survey the 51 species were averaged also and grouped for each year, departures from normals in flowering date, daily mean temperature, and spring precipitation, being compared. The temperature data correlated strikingly with the flowering data.

These authors developed a new temperature summation method, based not on means but on the daily maximum and minimum, and on the assumption of a linear growth-curve that was designed to reflect the approximate duration of different temperature levels during the diurnal regime. This method improves on the mean in summation only for days when a rising or falling temperature crosses the threshold temperature level for the plant process or processes under consideration. Such days occur frequently in the spring months. For each of 24 species, heat sums obtained by the duration-summation formula for various presumptive thresholds and time periods were analysed by punch-card machines for standard deviation and coefficient of variation, and these values were plotted. The curves usually revealed clearly the threshold temperature for flowering (within 5°F.) and the time period of spring preflowering activity (within 10 days). From these values and the mean flowering date, the requisite heat sum for flowering was found for each species. For example, the lowest mean degree-hours sum was 2,034 for *Jeffersonia diphylla* (which flowered forty-eight days from 1 March), while the highest was 8,533 for *Aquilegia canadensis* (which flowered sixty-nine days from 1 March).

Much practical application has been made of such types of data. Sayre (1953—*see* Ch. VII), at Geneva, New York, describes a similar temperature summation method that assists in forecasting the maturity date of various pea varieties, and that (after a sufficient number of yearly records have been obtained) enables a farmer so to schedule his plantings as to facilitate orderly harvesting. This method uses 'effective heat units', which are defined as the amounts of daily temperature above 40°F., as only temperatures above 40°F. are counted as affecting the rate of *maturity* of peas. A close approximation to the effective daily heat units for peas can be obtained from the formula 'mean temperature minus 40°F.' In the vicinity of Geneva, New York, it requires a growing period of about 1,350 heat units to bring a crop of Thomas Laxton peas to the fancy table stage of maturity (indicated by a reading of 85 on the tenderometer scale).

Other applications of these data have been made by the larger commercial growers. It is important to know, for example, the optimum planting date for a certain variety of lima bean, or for predicting the first emergence of asparagus spears, or perhaps also the duration of harvest. For these latter applications, accumulative heat units of the soil have to be taken into consideration.

A detailed summary of the subject of heat units and crop growth, bringing the extensive literature up-to-date, is provided in the work of Holmes & Robertson (1959).

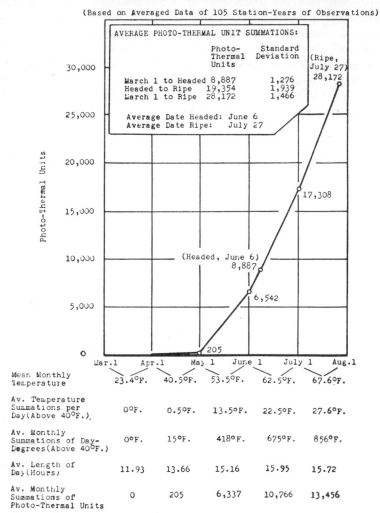

13 NORTH AMERICAN STATIONS

(Based on Averaged Data of 105 Station-Years of Observations)

AVERAGE PHOTO-THERMAL UNIT SUMMATIONS:

	Photo-Thermal Units	Standard Deviation
March 1 to Headed	8,887	1,276
Headed to Ripe	19,354	1,939
March 1 to Ripe	28,172	1,466

Average Date Headed: June 6
Average Date Ripe: July 27

(Ripe, July 27) 28,172

17,308

(Headed, June 6) 8,887

6,542

205

	Mar.1	Apr.1	May 1	June 1	July 1	Aug.1
Mean Monthly Temperature		23.4°F.	40.5°F.	53.5°F.	62.5°F.	67.6°F.
Av. Temperature Summations per Day(Above 40°F.)		0°F.	0.5°F.	13.5°F.	22.5°F.	27.6°F.
Av. Monthly Summations of Day-Degrees(Above 40°F.)		0°F.	15°F.	418°F.	675°F.	856°F.
Av. Length of Day(Hours)		11.93	13.66	15.16	15.95	15.72
Av. Monthly Summations of Photo-Thermal Units		0	205	6,337	10,766	13,456

From Nuttonson, 1958

Fig. 31.—Growth-development curve of Dakold winter rye in terms of photo-thermal units, based upon data from thirteen North American stations. This is illustrative of the practical applications of phenological data.

Some of the most exhaustive and far-reaching studies of this nature have been the several monographs dealing with photo- and thermal requirements for the growth and maturity of a number of important cereal crops. These monographs, as well as related ones covering ecological crop geography, have been prepared by the American Institute of

Crop Ecology, whose studies have been partly sponsored by the United States Weather Bureau. One that has recently become available is that of Nuttonson (1958—*see* Ch. VII), for the rye crop. Following a lengthy survey of phenological data for Dakold winter rye (*Secale cereale*) for the United States and for comparable growing areas in western Europe and Russia, combined with temperature and day-length data, Nuttonson (1958, p. 212) was enabled to construct a cumulative photo-thermal growth-development curve for this cereal crop. This curve is reproduced in Fig. 31. The principal base values used are the day-degree summations above 40°F. from 1 March, and the average day-lengths (at a specific latitude) for the months with mean temperatures above 40°F., and, finally, the cumulative photo-thermal units summation which is obtained by multiplying the monthly day-degree summations by the average day-lengths (for any one month) in hours. Totals are thus obtained, such as 28,172 photo-thermal units required for ripening (*see* Fig. 31).

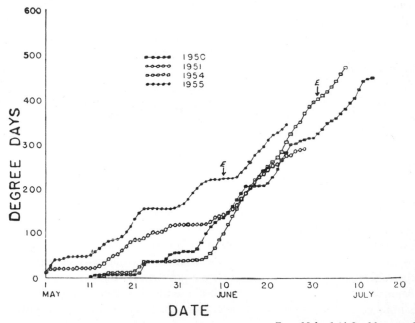

From Nylund & Stadtherr, 1956

FIG. 32.—Accumulated degree days (mean air temperature for the day, minus the basic air temperature of 60°F.) from 1 May to the date when crabgrass (*Digitaria* spp.) seedlings had from 2 to 4 leaves, for the four different growing-seasons involved. In 1954 and 1955, crabgrass emerged on the date indicated by '*E*'. Owing to the warmer May of 1955 (161 degree days), crabgrass emerged twenty-one days earlier than in 1954, when May was cooler (37 degree days). In the years 1951 and 1955, with warmer periods in May (118 and 161 degree days, respectively) crabgrass reached the 2- to 4-leaf seedling stage between 20 and 30 June . In contrast, in 1950 and 1954, in which May was relatively cool (56 and 37 degree days, respectively), crabgrass reached the 2- to -4-leaf seedling stage somewhat later, between 7 and 13 July. Knowledge of date of emergence and rate of early seeding development is essential for the most effective application of either pre- or post-emergence turf herbicides. (Tests conducted near St. Paul, Minnesota.)

But what does all this have to do with the growth and control of weeds, one may ask? Firstly, it might be noted that rye (*Secale cereale*) is one of our crops having a weed origin—it came from *S. anatolicum*, which is reported as a weed admixture in wheat fields of Asia Minor (*see* p. 237 on crop origins). However, from a more practical point of view, knowledge of weed phenology is important in control—and particularly so in using the pre-emergence methods of control. A good example of this is in the pre-emergence control of one of the most serious lawn pests of the central and northern latitudes of the United States—crabgrass (*Digitaria ischaemum* and *D. sanguinalis*) (Fig. 32). The chemical which is most effective in crabgrass control just before, or during the very early phases of, germination, i.e. Crag Sesone, must be applied at these stages. The question then arises: just when may crabgrass be expected *first* to germinate in the spring in any given locality? Of course, this may only be determined by a number of years' observations, which has in fact been done. To date, the first germination has been best correlated in the New York City area with the time-interval between the withering of the flowers of *Forsythia* spp. and the beginning of the flowering of dogwood (*Cornus florida*) (King, 1957). These, of course, are well-defined phenological events.

THE PROPAGATION OF WEEDS

This subject has been touched upon many times through the previous sections, and therefore need not be further elaborated upon but should be summarized. The mechanics of propagation are numerous, and a full understanding of their various aspects is essential if one is to cope with a specific weed problem, and to strike at one of the most vital aspects of weed growth—the spread into new habitats. The control of annual weeds might, on the surface, appear to be the most simple—particularly by destroying the vegetative growth before seed production. This can, of course, be done; but the vast reservoirs of seed already deposited in the cultivated layers of the soil present a problem for many years to come. Annuals also present another growth-phase that is sometimes overlooked: a number of weed species produce more than one generation a year— generally two—in the north-temperate regions (Fig. 33). Examples are *Stellaria media, Cardamine hirsuta, Veronica hederifolia, Mercurialis annua, Senecio vulgaris*, etc. *Stellaria media* may grow throughout the coldest winters, with the production at this period of cleistogamous flowers, and of fertile seeds that are dropped right through the winter. Fig. 33 illustrates some of these seasonal growth-phases.

The dispersal of weed seeds is an almost inexhaustible subject, and the one most frequently described and illustrated in weed texts. These seeds range from the near-microscopic seeds of parasitic *Striga* spp., that may be carried behind the glumes of grass 'seeds', to the most

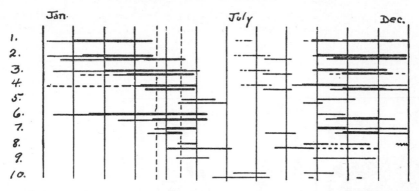

From Blum, 1925

FIG. 33.—Period of growth, throughout one year, of a series of annual weeds. The horizontal double bar indicates duplicate records for two years. The single thin line indicates light flowering; the heavy bar, the period of heavy bloom; and the broken line, a few plants flowering: 1, *Veronica agrestis*; 2, *Stellaria media*; 3, *Senecio vulgaris*; 4, *Capsella bursa-pastoris*; 5, *Thalspi arvense*; 6, *Lamium purpureum*; 7, *Lamium amplexicaule*; 8, *Fumaria officinalis*; 9, *Urtica urens*; 10, *Anagallis arvensis*. The various generations for a single year are shown. The space between two vertical lines represents one month, the whole year, from January to December, being covered. (Data taken at Frankfurt-am-Main, Germany.)

elaborate burred and plumed fruits of many Compositae. Illustrations of examples from these various types are given in Figs. 34 and 35. The seeds may be dispersed by such obvious methods as carriage in air currents, and through the droppings of birds and domestic animals—as well as through being carried on their fur or other body-covering, and in the mud on their feet. There are also many less obvious methods such as dispersal by ants (cf. Sernander, 1906), by earthworm activity, by irrigation ditches and water currents, and in and on aircraft and their occupants. The common dandelion (*Taraxacum*) is a good example of a plant that is widely dispersed, and its reproductive biology has been most exhaustively studied by Hofsten (1954—*see* Ch. VI) in Sweden, and has been referred to many times in this text.

Perhaps our most pernicious weeds, however, are those that not only reproduce by seed, but also by some vegetative method. These perennials differ from annuals in that they do not die after seed production, but live through the winter in some form of hibernating structure (usually a modified underground stem) and then flower and seed, extending underground for an indefinite number of years. Quack-grass (*Agropyron repens*), Canada or creeping thistle (*Cirsium arvense*), hoary cress (*Cardaria draba*), Johnson grass (*Sorghum halepense*), Bermuda grass (*Cynodon dactylon*), and the nutgrasses (*Cyperus rotundus* and *C. esculentus*) are examples (cf. Fig. 36 [for overground example]).

Formerly, when limited acreages and the most primitive and shallow methods of soil cultivation were prevalent, the perennial weeds were not so widely distributed. Today, with vast acreages cultivated, and through the use of modern implements of cultivation, many of these weed-roots

213

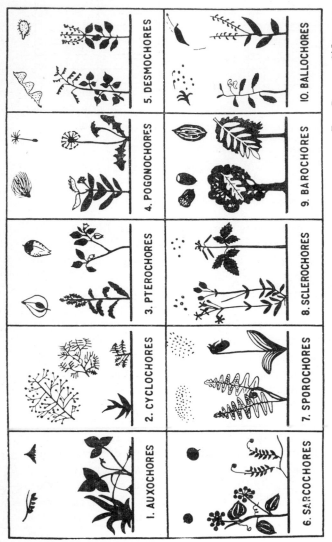

From Dansereau & Lems, 1957

FIG. 34.—Some major representative dispersal types based on adaptive morphology, recognized by Dansereau, & Lems (1957). 1, AUXOCHORES (no obvious adaptive morphology, no disarticulation, deposited by parent plant): *Carex plantaginea, Hepatica acutiloba*; 2, CYCLOCHORES (have accessory parts, forming a voluminous spherical frame): *Panicum capillare* and *Sisymbrium altissimum*; 3, PTEROCHORES (with scarious wing–like appendages): *Rumex crispus, Physalis heterophylla*; 4, POGONOCHORES (with plumose appendages, hairs, or aigrettes): *Asclepias syriaca, Taraxacum officinale*; 5, DESMOCHORES (appendages short, stiff, spiny, or glandular; adhering to rough surfaces): *Desmodium glutinosum, Circaea quadrisulcata*; 6, SARCOCHORES (with juicy or fleshy outer layers): *Smilax herbacea, Vaccinium oxycoccos*; 7, SPOROCHORES (small or light enough to be carried by a breeze): *Polypodium virginianum, Cypripedium acaule*; 8, SCLEROCHORES (light enough to be carried by wind): *Silene cucubalus, Dentaria diphylla*; 9, BAROCHORES (very heavy): *Quercus alba, Juglans cinerea*; 10, BALLOCHORES (parent plant has expulsion mechanism): *Impatiens capensis, Tovara virginiana*.

are finely chopped up and scattered widely throughout the land—a great 'improvement', in dispersal, over the slower methods of the natural processes. It is true, of course, that certain carefully controlled, and

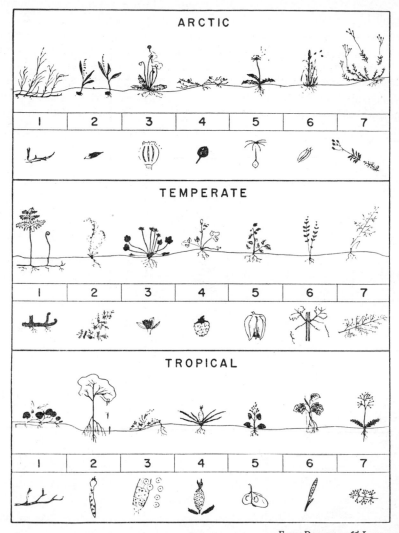

From Dansereau & Lems, 1957

FIG. 35.—Examples of the seven kinds of propagules (diaspores or disseminules) in three climatic regions as recognized by Dansereau & Lems (1957). The kinds are: 1, Rooting stem, leaf, or sprouting root; 2, Embryo, gemma, bulbil, or plantlet; 3, Single or clustered seeds or spores; 4, Part of fruit, entire fruit, or aggregate fruit; 5, Fruit plus floral parts or bracts; 6, Part of inflorescence or entire inflorescence; 7, Entire plant, or almost entire aerial part of plant. ARCTIC: 1, *Carex bigelowii*; 2, *Polygonum viviparum*; 3, *Papaver radicatum*; 4, *Empetrum nigrum*; 5, *Taraxacum lapponicum*; 6, *Elymus arenarius* subsp.; 7, *Saxifraga tricuspidata*. TEMPERATE: 1, *Pteridium aquilinum*; 2, *Cystopteris bulbifera*; 3, *Hepatica acutiloba*; 4, *Fragaria virginiana*; 5, *Physalis heterophylla*; 6, *Urtica procera*; 7, *Panicum capillare*. TROPICAL: 1, *Ipomoea pes-caprae*; 2, *Rhizophora mangle*; 3, *Pyrostegia venusta*; 4, *Bromelia fastuosa*; 5, *Begonia itatiaiensis*; 6, *Monstera deliciosa*; 7, *Eryngium fluminense*.

seasonally-timed, tillage methods can greatly reduce infestations of, for example, quack-grass. With some weeds, such as bindweed (*Convolvulus arvensis*), numerous cultivations throughout the growing year, such that no top-growth is permitted, and combined with several years' fallow, result in starvation and death of the underground portions. For valuable land this is, of course, an expensive procedure. Thus it was with great hope that the newer methods of chemical control by means of the growth-hormone chemicals was widely attempted. Some of the early-introduced chemicals have been disappointing (for example, on bindweed), but some of the later-introduced ones appear more promising in this respect. These methods will be examined in detail in Chapter XIV.

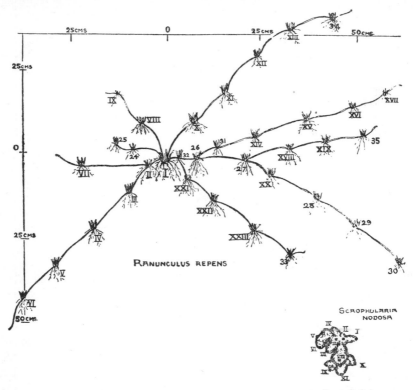

From Salisbury, 1942

FIG. 36.—Semi-diagrammatic representation of a plant of *Ranunculus repens*, showing vegetative spread, to illustrate open type of extension. Below, right, on the same scale, the closed type of extension of *Scrophularia nodosa*. In the former case the Roman numerals indicate vegetative, and the Arabic numerals indicate flowering, shoots. In the latter case the numerals indicate successive annual increments, all of which are fertile. (One-tenth natural size.)

DISPERSAL OF WEEDS

Stebbins (1951) has emphasized that seed dispersal is a critical phase in the life-cycle of the plant—one during which the forces of natural selection have a maximum opportunity to exert their influence. He further stressed the important consideration that selection operates on combinations of characters: the types (primitive or advanced) of vegetative and reproductive structures that will be found in successful association depend upon the habitat in which the plant lives, and on the various agents of pollination and seed dispersal which are available to it. Reference has been made earlier to Went's (1954—*see* Ch. VI) comment that evolution also is effective largely in the germination stages, this giving rise to the many kinds of germination mechanisms of seeds of weeds and other plants. In some respects the great distances to which weed seeds may sometimes travel has been over-emphasized, for, after all, the environment in which the parent plant reached maturity and succeeded in seed dissemination must already have been a satisfactory one.

Dispersal by Some of the Natural Forces

To many people, one of the outstanding features of weed seeds—in contrast to seeds of non-weeds—is the high percentage of them that possess some form of structure to provide extended buoyancy in the atmosphere. The parachute-like pappus of the dandelion (*Taraxacum*) is perhaps one of the most familiar. However, the smaller and lighter seeds do not always require such elaborate structures to provide movement by air—especially by dust-storms—as the following example illustrates. During the year 1936, Runyon (1936) observed that, in a severe dust-storm at Hays, Kansas, soil was deposited in one room to the extent of 4·3 tons per acre. The dust on pasture land had an average thickness of 0·75 in.—an equivalent of 86·2 tons per acre. Spring rains removed this from the slopes, but on the level areas it remained, forming part of the soil. Soil samples removed from the buildings apparently contained no viable seeds—at least as indicated by the methods of forcing that were used (no low-temperature treatment was employed); but surface soil that had been blown along for some distance was tested and found to contain weed seeds. Of these the four most numerous were: stink-grass (*Eragrostis cilianensis*), pigweed (*Amaranthus* sp.), foxtail grass (*Setaria viridis*), and *Panicum capillare*. These weeds, except for the *Setaria*, were all found in drifts in open sheds, in garages, and in the streets of Hays, Kansas—where there were also seeds of fireweed (*Kochia scoparia*).

Another group of familiar methods of transport are those involving water. In types ranging from the large water-buoyant coconut to some near-microscopic *Carex* 'seeds', structures have developed that assist in water transport. Stephens (1958) has examined the salt-water tolerance of seeds of *Gossypium* species, and notes that the seeds of coastal and insular forms usually have hard seed-coats and can remain viable after long periods of immersion in sea water—for example *G. hirsutum*, race *punctatum* (Florida wild cotton). As this latter form harbours, or may harbour, serious pests of cotton, efforts are made to eradicate it from cotton-growing areas. Vast numbers of species with smaller seeds have surfaces that are not readily wetted—thus they may be carried about when floating in or on water. This problem has become particularly acute in irrigated areas, where the water passing through irrigation ditches also disperses weeds (pp. 274–6).

A number of studies have been made in this sphere, including that of Egginton & Robbins (1920). In 156 wire traps that were placed in Colorado irrigation channels, seeds etc. of 81 species of weeds were found. Continued grazing in the area reduced weed growth, and it was also suggested that ditch banks be seeded to brome-grass. The weed problem in irrigated areas will be given some consideration under control measures in later chapters. A detailed discussion of the role of oceanic currents in the distribution of plants throughout the world may be found in the final section of Chapter XI (pp. 274–6).

Dispersal of Weeds by Animals

All too-well-known are the hooks and barbs that compose the surface covering of many seeds and fruits of wild plants. These have been particularly well developed in such families as the Compositae, Boraginaceae, and some Gramineae. Many of these 'armed' seeds and fruits readily attach themselves to the coats of animals and are dispersed far and wide by the living animals, or in the shipping of their hides.

A much less obvious, but generally well-known, method of animal dispersal, is that from incompletely digested remains passing through the digestive tract. This may be a more important method than the one just discussed, as birds are the major group of animals involved here, and they are found almost everywhere. Endozoochory is the technical term applied in this context. Man's domestic animals also disperse many seeds by this method. Numerous studies are available concerning the viability of seeds in manure (e.g. Salzmann, 1939), and how long it must be composted to reduce the content of viable seeds. There are also studies of seed viability in silage. There is no doubt that the seriousness of weeds on agricultural land is largely due to the application of their seeds through manure that is used as a fertilizer, as well as by the grazing animal.

A less important, yet intriguing, method is seed dispersal by ants. In fact, some seeds actually possess structures (elaiosomes), as well as secretions or natural substances within the seed, that stimulate the ants' feeding. The classical monograph on this subject is that of Sernander (1906), and a good modern review of the situation is available (Uphof, 1942). The detailed notes on the dispersal of the seed of *Pedicularis sylvatica,* published more recently by Berg (1954) in Norway, are illustrative. This plant is strongly myrmecochorous, as the appendage of the seed serves as an elaiosome. The ants under observation moved one seed a minute with twelve hours of work a day; while in thirty days on 300 square metres (seven *Formica* mounds), 604,800 seeds were transported in one season. They were moved over distances of only a few metres, the ants eating or sucking the elaiosomes. The hard seeds are not damaged, and they are later removed from the nest and placed in refuse heaps. This plant is a hygrophyte and the capsules open in damp weather, the seeds being washed away by the rain. Berg (1954) notes that myrmecochory is normally developed only in xerophytes and mesophytes, and that this species is the first hygrophyte recorded in this connection. The elaiosome consists of one gigantic cell in *Pedicularis*, and acts also as a lever or seed disjuncter. The seeds of many other plants, including often those growing around foundations of houses and in similar areas, such as *Veronica* spp. and *Stellaria media*, are transported by ants.

Dispersal of Weeds by Man

Most of the phases of seed movement by animals, including endozoochory, are also applicable to man. With his initiation and maintenance for a time of open habitats, and his conscious or unconscious uses of seeds, plant parts, and the like, man has, indeed, been perhaps even more closely associated with, and commonly responsible for, the dispersal of weeds than have other animals—hence the appellation 'malanthropophyte', discussed in Chapter I (p. 15).

The outstanding role of man in the dispersal of weeds is perhaps most clearly shown in their presence in the early cereal 'patches' and as seed admixtures in the harvested grain—both in the past and nowadays. As man selected and improved his cereals, so did he inadvertently encourage the associated weeds—thus, in a sense, becoming a breeder of weeds as well as of crops! And we have already described, in recounting the history of oats, how a weed present as an admixture in cereal grain may eventually serve man as a crop in a new and more suitable environment (cf. p. 212).

Sir E. J. Salisbury, until recently Director of the Royal Botanic Gardens at Kew, Surrey, England, has noted in a number of publications (1954 etc.), how weeds are dispersed, and particularly how man aids in their spread. Emphasis is give by Salisbury to the importance of knowing whether a single individual arising from a newly-dispersed seed can effectively reproduce its kind. Apomictic species such as *Taraxacum officinale*, or wholly self-fertile species such as *Capsella bursa-pastoris*, can effectively increase their numbers from a single individual. Weather conditions at the time of flowering are not important in these instances; for in the former case cited, seeds are set without pollination, while in the latter case, fertilization takes place before the flowers open. The range of potential spread is greater for a number of common weeds than for many other plants, because they are not dependent upon a particular photoperiodism for flower production. Salisbury speaks of 'primary spread', which is more or less continuous in character and is solely from the original infection centre; while dispersal from new infection centres lying at some distance from the original site is referred to as 'secondary spread'. Dispersal methods are largely responsible for this latter stage, against which the normal methods of farm hygiene are of little avail.

Reference is made by Salisbury to the study of weed populations appearing upon bombed sites in London. Of a total of nearly 140 species of flowering plants, wind-dispersal accounted for about 30 per cent, bird-dispersal for 25 per cent, man-dispersal for 15 per cent, while the remainder presumably grew from the seed present in the soil. A number of common weeds have seeds that become sticky when moistened, thus adhering to farm equipment, to birds' feathers and feet, and also to human footwear (e.g. *Capsella*, *Arabidopsis*, *Plantago*, *Juncus*, etc.). The presence of *Juncus tenuis* and other species of this genus along footpaths may well be due to their seed dispersal by walking people, together with their ability to withstand considerable treading. Salisbury (1954) was interested in seeds adhering in mud carried on footwear, and made a survey of sweepings from churches throughout a summer period. Most of the common weeds appeared upon germination tests of these sweepings being made in sterilized soil, and grasses showed the highest frequency.

From this study it was calculated that, as a conservative estimate, at least 6 seeds are carried in the mud on the footwear of a single person, while during the autumn the number may rise to 200 or more. Salisbury further assessed the weed populations of trouser turn-ups after walks in the country: one such sampling produced well over 300 seedlings.

Many studies of dispersal have been made, including the activity of the pocket gopher on the spread of Canada thistle in California (Cook, 1939); the role of aircraft in weed seed spread (Ryan, 1929); the River Thames in England as an agent in plant dispersal (Guppy, 1893); seed dispersal by human activity (Healy, 1943); and the extensive monograph of Probst (1949), listing all of the plants of central Europe that were introduced through the shipment, cleaning, and processing of wool

Small's (1919) comprehensive survey of many aspects of the biology of the great family Compositae (20,000 spp., 950 genera) notes that *Senecio* (1,300 spp., one of the largest genera of flowering plants) is the basal genus of the Compositae and that it originated from the Lobelioideae in the late Cretaceous or early Tertiary times in the Bolivian region of South America. The development of the capitulum is due to the abortion of the pedicels in a racemose umbel rather than the non-elongation of the main axis of a spike. The ordinary pappose fruit can be blown many hundreds of miles over land or sea. Other aspects considered, many experimentally, include; pollen-presentation mechanisms and irritability; fruit dispersal; experimental wind dispersal; hydrodynamics, and the latex systems.

BIBLIOGRAPHY

(The Reproduction and Dispersal of Weeds)

BAKKE, A. L. & SYLVESTER, E. P. (1953). Seed retention of some prairie plants. *Proc. Ia. Acad. Sci.*, **60**, 82–85.

BALLARD, L. A. T. (1956). Flowering of skeleton weed '*Chondrilla juncea*'. *J. Aust. Inst. Agric. Sci.*, **22**(Mar.), 57–61.

BATESON, A. (1887). The effect of cross-fertilization on inconspicuous flowers. *Ann. Bot.*, **1**, 255–61.

BEAL, W. J. (1898). *Seed Dispersal*. Ginn, New York, 90 pp.

—— (1909). The rapid extension of weeds in Michigan. *Michigan Acad. Sci., Arts & Letters, Ann. Rep.*, **11**, 33.

BECKER, H. (1912). Über die Keimung verschiedenartiger Fruchte und Samen bei derselben Species. *Beih. Bot. Zbl.*, **29**, 20–143.

BERG, R. Y. (1954). Development and dispersal of the seed of *Pedicularis silvatica*. *Nytt Mag. for Bot. (Oslo)*, **2**, 1–60.

BIRCH, W. R. (1957). Seeding and germination of some Kenya weeds. *J. Ecol.*, **45**, 85–91.

BLUM, A. (1925). Beiträge zur Kenntnis der annuellen Pflanzen. *Bot. Arch.*, **9**, 3–36.

BOLLEY, H. L. (1895). Weed seeds, distribution by wind. *N. Dakota Agric. Exp. Sta. Bull.*, **17**, 102.

BOTTUM, F. R. (1929). An analysis of the weeds of the Knapp Farm from the standpoint of plant invasion. *J. Tenn. Acad. Sci.*, **4**(1), 21.

BOYKO, H. (1953). Regeneration problems of the vegetation in arid zones. *Proc. 7th Internat. Bot. Congr.*, 678.

BOYNTON, M. F. (1895). Observations on the dissemination of seed. *Bot. Gaz.*, **20**, 502.

BRODIE, H. J. (1951). The splash-cup dispersal mechanism in plants. *Canad. J. Bot.*, **29**(3), 224–34.

CARN, K. G. (1937). Weed invasion. Its relationship to farming methods. *Agric. Gaz. N.S.W.*, **48**, 481–2, 492.

CLAYPOLE, A. (1877–78). On the migration of plants from Europe to America. *Montreal Hort. Soc., Third Rep.*, 70–91.

CLIFFORD, H. T. (1956). Seed dispersal on footwear. *Proc. Bot. Soc. British Isles*, **2**(2), 129–31.

CLUTE, W. N. (1945). Vegetation on the move. *Amer. Bot.*, **51**, 90–95.

COLLINGE, W. E. (1912). The food of the bullfinch (*Pyrrhus europaea*). *J. Econ. Biol.*, **7**, 50–57.

—— (1913). The destruction and dispersal of weed seeds by wild birds. *J. Bot. Agric.*, **20**, 15–26.

—— (1914). Some further observations on the dispersal of weed seeds by wild birds. *J. Econ. Biol.*, **9**(2), 69.

COOK, J. B. (1939). Pocket gophers spread Canada thistle. *Mon. Bull. Calif. Dep. Agric.*, **28**, 142–3.

COSTELLO, D. F. (1952). The tumbling throng. *Nature Mag.*, **45**, 301–3, 332.

COUPLAND, R. T., SELLECK, G. W. & ALEX, J. F. (1955). The reproductive capacity of vegetative buds on the underground parts of leafy spurge (*Euphorbia esula* L.). *Canad. J. Agric. Sci.*, **35**, 477–84.

CRESCINI, F., MARTINELLI, E. & BELLINI, P. (1956). [On the biology of weeds. II. Sensitivity to light and cold of the achenes of *Artemisia vulgaris* L.—in Italian.] *Ann. Sper. Agr.*, **10**, 2157–70.

DANSEREAU, P. & LEMS, K. (1957). The grading of dispersal types. *Contrib. Inst. Bot. Univ. Montréal*, No. **71**, 52 pp.

DARLINGTON, H. T. (1918). Weed immigration into Michigan. *Michigan Acad. Sci.*, *Ann. Rep.*, **20**, 261–7.

—— (1922). The introduced weed flora of Illinois. *Proc. Ill. Acad. Sci.*, **15**, 171–84.

DAVID, W. A. L. (1956). Air transport and insects of agricultural importance. *Commonwealth Inst. Entomol.*, *London*, 11 pp.

DEWEY, L. H. (1897). The eastward migration of certain weeds in America. *Asa Gray Bull.*, **5**, 54.

—— (1897a). Migration of weeds. *Yearbook U.S. Dep. Agric.* 1896, pp. 263–86.

DONY, J. G. & LOUSLEY, J. E. (1952). The travels of plants: wool imported from abroad is bringing with it the seeds of alien weeds. *Bedfordshire Mag.*, **3**, 155–9.

EGGINTON, G. E. & ROBBINS, W. W. (1920). Irrigation water as a factor in the dissemination of weed seed. *Bull. Color. Agric. Exp. Sta.* No. 253, 25 pp.

ELLENBERG, H. (1951). [Agricultural site mapping in a plant—in German.] *Z. Pflanzenernähr. Düng. Bodenk. Abt. A. u. B.*, **53**, 204–24.

ETTER, A. G. (1948). Seeds that ride livestock. *Mo. Bot. Gdn.*, *Bull.*, **36**, 170–2.

FELFÖLDY, L. (1947). Soziologisch-Cytogeographische Untersuchungen über die Pannonische Ruderalvegetation. *Arch. Biol. Hung.*, **17**, 104–30.

FERNALD, M. L. (1905). Some recently introduced weeds. *Trans. Mass. Hort. Soc.* 1905, pp. 11–22.

FINNERTY, D. W. (1953). Life-cycle and control studies of some annual bromegrasses. *Thesis, Nebraska University.*

FRANÇOIS, L. (1938). Dissémination des plantes adventices. *Ann. Agron.*, *Paris*, N.S. **8**, 699–706.

FRANKTON, C. (1955). Weeds of Canada. *Canad. Dep. Agric.*, *Publ.* 948, Ottawa, Ontario, 196 pp.

FRYER, M. A. & CHANCELLOR, R. J. (1956). Ragwort and its control. *Agriculture*, **63**, 65–69.

FRYZELL, P. A. (1957). Mode of reproduction of higher plants. *Bot. Rev.*, **23**, 135–233.

GATES, F. C. (1940). Recent migrational trends in the distribution of weeds in Kansas. *Trans. Kansas Acad. Sci.*, **43**, 99–117.

GLEASON, H. A. & McFARLAND, F. T. (1914). The introduced vegetation in the vicinity of Douglas Lake, Michigan. *Bull. Torrey Bot. Cl.*, **41**, 511–21.

GUPPY, H. B. (1893). The River Thames as an agent in plant dispersal. *J. Linn. Soc.* (*Bot.*), **29**, 333–46.

—— (1903–6). *Observations of a Naturalist in the Pacific between 1896 and 1899.* Macmillan, London, 2 vols., 627 pp.

—— (1912). *Studies in Seeds and Fruits.* Williams & Norgate, London, 528 pp.

—— (1917). *Plants, Seeds and Currents in the West Indies and the Azores.* Williams & Norgate, London, 531 pp.

—— (1917–1920). Plant distribution from the standpoint of an idealist. *J. Linn. Soc.* (*Bot.*), **44**, 439–71.

HALSTED, B. D. (1892). The migration of weeds. *Ann. Rep. N. J. Exp. Sta.*, **12**, 320–9.

—— (1892a). Eastern and Western weeds compared. *Ann. Rep. N.J. Exp. Sta.*, **12**, 329–33.

—— (1900). American and English weeds compared. *Plant World*, **3**, 171–3.

HARMON, G. W. & KEIM, F. D. (1934). The percentage and viability of weeds seeds recovered in the feces of farm animals and their longevity when buried in manure. *J. Amer. Soc. Agron.*, **26**, 762–7.

HARVEY, A. D. (1936). Rootsprouts as a means of vegetative reproduction in *Opuntia polycantha*. *J. Amer. Soc. Agron.*, **28**, 767–8.

HEALY, A. J. (1943). Seed dispersal by human activity. *Nature, Lond.*, **151**, 140.

HEIM, R. (1939). *Le réproduction chez les plantes.* A. Colin, Paris, 224 pp.

HEINZE, A. (1932). *Handbuch der Verbreitungsökologie der Pflanzen.* Stockholm, 134 pp.

HENSLOW, G. (1875). On the self-fertilization of plants. *Trans. Linn. Soc. Lond.*, II ser., 1, 317–98.

—— (1899). The fertilization of flowers by insects and other agencies. *J. Hort. Sci.*, 23, 102–5.

HILDEBRAND, F. (1873). *Die Verbreitungsmittel der Pflanzen.* Leipzig, 162 pp.

—— (1881). Die Lebensdauer und Vegetationsweise der Pflanzen, ihre Ursache und ihre Entwicklung. *Eng. Bot. Jb.*, 2(1/2), 51–135.

HILL, E. J. (1902). Notes on migrating plants. *Bull. Torrey Bot. Cl.*, 29, 564–70.

HITCHCOCK, A. S. & CLOTHIER, G. L. (1898). Vegetative propagations of perennial weeds. *Bull. Kans. Agric. Coll.* No. 76, 23 pp.

HITROVO, V. (1912). [Sur la voilure des organes de propagation des plantes messicoles de niveaux différents—in Russian, French summary.] *Bull. Exp. Bot.*, 5, 103–38.

HITZER, K. (1935). Die Bedingungen der Blütenbildung von *Stellaria media*. *Flora*, 29, 309–35.

HOFFMAN, J. V. (1917). Natural reproduction from seed stored in the forest floor. *J. Agric. Res.*, 11, 1–26.

HOLMBOE, J. (1900). Notizen über die endozoische Samenverbreitung der Vögel. *Nyt Mag. Naturv.*, 38, 305–20.

HOLMES, R. M. & ROBERTSON, G. W. (1959). Heat units and crop growth. *Canad. Dep. Agric.*, Ottawa, Publ. 1042, 31 pp. (incl. 59 refs.).

HURWITZ, S., LACHOVER, D. & HUBER, A. (1951–52). Farm manures, soils, and seeds of cultivated crops as sources of weed seed infestations of fields under subtropical conditions. *Proc. Int. Seed Test. Assoc.*, 17, 39–43.

HUTH, E. (1889). Die Verbeitung der Pflanzen durch die Exkremente der Tiere. *Sam. Naturwiss. Vorträge.*, 3, 1.

ILTIS, H. (1949). An immigrant conquers a continent: the story of the weed garlic. *Sci. Mon.*, 68, 122–8.

JACQUES, H. (1927). The prolificness of some common plants. *Proc. Ia. Acad. Sci.*, 33, 135–6.

JOHN, A. (1921). [Contributions to the knowledge of methods of fruit separation in the Compositae—in German.] *Bot. Centralbl. Beihefte Abt. A. Morph. u. Physiol. der Pflanz.*, 38, 182–203.

JOHNSON, D. S. (1921). Invasion of virgin soil in the tropics. *Bot. Gaz.*, 72, 305–12.

JONES, K. L. (1936). Studies on *Ambrosia*. I. The inheritance of floral types in the ragweed, *Ambrosia elatior* L. *Amer. Midl. Nat.*, 17, 673–99.

—— (1936a). Studies on *Ambrosia*. II. Effect of certain environmental factors on floral development of *Ambrosia elatior*. *Bot. Gaz.*, 98, 296–306.

—— (1951). Some nutritional aspects of the pistillate condition in ragweeds. *Pap. Mich. Acad. Sci.*, 35, 21–23.

KÁS, V. (1956). [Transfer of weeds by stable manure—in Czech.] *Za Socialist. Zemĕdĕl.*, 6, 204–8.

KEMPSKI, E. (1906). Über endozoische Samenverbreitung und speziell die Verbreitung von Unkräutern durch Tiere auf dem Wege des Darmkanals. *Diss. Universität Rostock*, 172 pp.

KENNEDY, P. B. & FREDERICK, A. (1927). Old world weed introductions. *Ann. Soc. Agric. J.*, 19, 569–73.

KING, L. J. (1957). When does crabgrass germinate? *Westchester Cty. Farm & Home News* (*White Plains, N.Y.*), 1957 (May).

KIRK, L. E. & PAVLYCHENKO, T. K. (1932). Vegetative propagation of wild oats, *Avena fatua*, and other economically important species of Aveneae and Hordeae. *Canad. J. Res.*, 7, 204–20.

KREMER, J. C. (1950). The dandelion and its influence on bee behaviour during the fruit blossoming period. *Proc. Amer. Soc. Hort. Sci.*, 55, 140–6.

LANGER, R. H. M. (1956). Growth and nutrition of timothy (*Phleum pratense*). I. The life history of individual tillers. *Ann. Appl. Biol.*, 44, 166–87.

LECLERC DU SABLON, M. (1884) Recherches sur la déhiscence des fruits à péricarpe sec. *Ann. Sci. Nat.* (Sèr. 6), 18, 5–104.

LINDBERG, H. (1935). Die Früchte der *Taraxacum*-Arten Finnlands. *Acta Bot. Fenn.*, 17, 1–60.

MCHARGUE, J. S. (1920). Mineral constituents of the paired seeds of cocklebur. *Science*, 52, 43.

MAURIZIO, A. (1927). *Die Geschichte unserer Pflanzennahrung von den Urzeiten bis zur Gegenwart.* Berlin.

METCALFE, C. R. (1939). The sexual reproduction of *Ranunculus ficaria*. *Ann. Bot.* n.s., 3, 91–103.

MEYER, K. (1938). Zur Kenntnis der aus Kleinasien nach Mitteleuropa mit türkischer Gerste und Hülsenfrüchten eingeschleppten Unkrautsamen. *Forschungsdienst*, 6, 332–41.

MOLINIER, R. & MULLER, P. (1938). La dissémination des espèces végétales. I. Les agents et les types de la dissémination. II. Classification des espèces d'après leur mode de dissémination. II*a*. La dissémination dans quelques groupements végétaux de la France méditérranéenne, II*b*. La garrigue a chêne kermès. II*c*. Les caractères de la dissémination dans la série du *Brachypodietum ramosi*. II*d*. Quercetum cocciferae rosmarinetosum. II*e*,*f*., Série du Querceto-Busetum. V. Les rapports entre les types de diaspores, les types de dissémination et les groupes de la systématique. *Rev. Gén. Bot.*, 50, 53–72, 152–69, 202–21; 277–93, 341–58, 397–414, 472–88, 533–46, 598–614; 649–70.

MUEGGLER, W. F. (1956). Is sagebrush seed residual in the soil of burns or is it windborne? *U.S. Forest Serv. Intermountain Forest & Range Exp. Sta.* Res. Note No. 35, 10 pp.

NELSON, C. T. (1951). *A Reproduction Study of Northern White Cedar.* Game Division, Dept. Conservation, Lansing, Michigan, 100 pp.

NYLUND, R. E. & STADTHERR, R. (1956). Studies on the control of crabgrass (*Digitaria* spp.) in bluegrass lawns. *Weeds*, 4, 264–74.

PAUZE, F. (1951). La propagation des mauvaises herbes. *Rev. d'Oka*, 25, 125–31.

—— (1951*a*). La propagation des mauvaises herbes. III. *Rev. d'Oka*, 25, 177–88.

PERTTULA, U. (1941). Untersuchungen über die generative und vegetative Vermehrung der Blütenpflanzen in der Wald-, Hain-, Wiesen- und Hainfelsenvegetation. *Ann. Acad. Sci. Fenn.* Ser. A, 63, 1–388.

PROBST, R. (1949). *Wolladventivflora Mitteleuropas.* Vogt-Schied, Solothurn, 192 pp.

QUADRI, S. W. S. (1956). Recognition of ryegrass species and strains in the seedling stage. *Emp. J. Exp. Agric.*, 24, 27–36.

RAVN, F. K. (1895). [On the buoyancy of the seeds of aquatic and marsh plants—in Swedish.] *Svensk Bot. Tidskr.*, 19, 178–88.

RESÜHR, B. (1939). Beiträge zur Lichtkeimung von *Amaranthus caudatus* L. und *Phacelia tanacetifolia* Benth. *Planta*, 30(3), 471–506.

RIEGEL, A. (1941). Some coactions of rabbits and rodents with cactus. *Trans. Kans. Acad. Sci.*, 44, 96–103.

—— (1942). Some observations on the food coactions of rabbits in western Kansas during periods of stress. *Trans. Kan. Acad. Sci.*, 45, 369–75.

ROSENFELS, R. S. (1940). Spread of white top seed in the droppings of cattle. *Bull. Nev. Agric. Exp. Sta.* No. 152, 5 pp.

RUNYON, H. E. (1936). Distribution of seeds by dust storms. *Trans. Kan. Acad. Sci.*, 39, 105–13.

RYAN, H. J. (1929). Airplanes a means for disseminating noxious weed seeds. *Mon. Bull. Calif. Dep. Agric.*, 18, 245.

Illustration of one of the most ancient weeds, darnel (*Lolium temulentum*), the 'tares' of the Bible. From the Herbal of Dioscorides (Vienna manuscript, illustrated by a Byzantine in A.D. 512), where it is termed 'Aira' and also 'Thyaron', and is noted as growing amongst wheat. The Romans called it 'Lolium'.

PLATE I

(a) Witches'-brooms in a ponderosa pine (*Pinus ponderosa*) in Colorado, caused by a dwarf-mistletoe (*Arceuthobium vaginatum*). The infestation has killed the tree.

(b) Lodgepole pine (*Pinus contorta*) killed by a dwarf-mistletoe (*Arceuthobium americanum*) in Colorado. Numerous witches'-brooms occur in the lower crown.

PLATE 2

(b) Features of the dwarf-mistletoe plant (*Arceuthobium vaginatum*). Part of stem bearing pollen-producing flowers in bloom.

(a) Features of the dwarf-mistletoe plant (*Arceuthobium vaginatum*). Cluster of leafless perennial shoots that have developed from a single infection close to the base of the living branch. While referred to as dwarf mistletoe, clusters of these shoots often reach sizable masses in the host tree—9 in. or more in diameter.

PLATE 3

(b) Features of the dwarf-mistletoe plant. Germinated seed showing radicle penetrating bark at the base of needle-bundle sheath. The seed is about 3·0 mm. in length.

(a) Features of the dwarf-mistletoe plant. Part of stem bearing immature fruits or berries approximately one year old, and two flowers of the current season. Each fruit is about 5·0 mm. in length.

PLATE 4

By courtesy of U.S. Dept of Agriculture

(b) Plants of witchweed (*Striga asiatica*). Removed from maize plants in North Carolina.

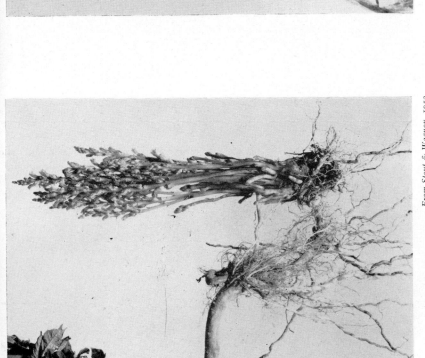

From Stout & Wagnon, 1953

(a) Four-branched broomrape (*Orobanche ramosa*) clusters showing attachment to the roots of a single tomato (*Lycopersicum esculentum*) plant. From a field infestation near Centerville, California. (See, *California Dept. Agric. B.*, **42**, 45–54, 1953).

PLATE 5

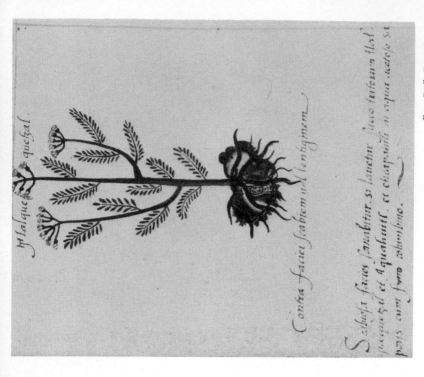

From Emily Emmart, 1940

(b) Illustration of *Tlalquequetzal* (i.e. 'earth plume', *Achillea millefolium*) from an Aztec herbal. This plant at one time had extensive medicinal use in Europe, Asia, and America—and apparently thereby greatly increased in abundance and distribution, so that in many areas it is now classed as a weed. The title immediately under the plant reads *Contra faciei scabiem lentiginem* (for scabies of the face or lentigo).

From Moldenke & Moldenke, 1951; see also Strantz, 1910 p. 90.

(a) Coins of the ancient city of Cyrene (Cyrenaica), dating from the fourteenth to the sixth centuries B.C., carried an embossed representation of a group of plants that were vital to the economy of the colony, namely, 'Silphium' (*Ferula* spp., Umbelliferae). A pungent resin was obtained from these plants, but extensive exploitation led to their eventual extermination and replacement by asafoetida (*Ferula asafoetida*). Here man's use led to extermination, not increased dispersal, although perhaps some *Ferula* spp. have been multiplied through man's activity in the North African-Mediterranean area where the Umbelliferae are so well represented in the native flora

(*a*) Top branches of low ragweed (*Ambrosia artemisiifolia*), *left*, and of giant ragweed (*Ambrosia trifida*), *right*, showing the abundance of pollen-producing flowers and the leaf characteristics of the two most common species of *Ambrosia* in Iowa and indeed much of North America.

By courtesy of Iowa Agricultural Experiment Station

(*b*) Giant ragweed growing along an Iowa, U.S.A., highway. The pollen-producing flowers add to the hay-fever hazard, while the tall (5 to 15 ft.) rank growth is unsightly and, through blocking vision, creates a traffic hazard.

PLATE 7

By courtesy of the National Geographic Society

Turkish women winnow grain thrashed by a farmer and his oxen at the foot of snowy Mount Ararat, traditional landing place of Noah's Ark. Winnowing of harvested grain or seed crops using the natural forces of air currents is an age-old practice not uncommon today in many countries of the world. By this method the lighter chaff and weed seeds are carried to peripheral areas, while the 'cleaned' grain (as well as weed seeds of the same general size and weight as the grain) returns to the earth. Man thus inadvertently disperses weeds in this manner, and at the same time exerts a selective action whereby new weed strains are developed.

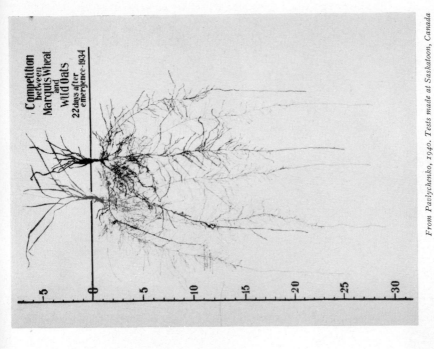

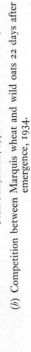

From Pavlychenko, 1940. Tests made at Saskatoon, Canada

(a) Competition between Marquis wheat and wild mustard 22 days after emergence, 1934. The wheat plant is on the left. Scale in inches.

(b) Competition between Marquis wheat and wild oats 22 days after emergence, 1934.

PLATE 9

By courtesy of the Journal of Agricultural Research

The effect of two different photoperiods upon the growth and flowering of *Ambrosia artemisiifolia* (low ragweed). This illustration is reproduced from the now classical pioneering paper on the subject, and is presumably the first photograph ever taken to show the effects of day-length upon the flowering of a weed. The plants on the left had been exposed to light from 9 a.m. to 4 p.m. daily (7 hours), and were shedding pollen freely from the staminate spikes when photographed on 9 July 1919. The plants on the right had been left out-of-doors as controls (about a 15-hour day), and showed no signs of flowering when photographed.

PLATE 10

SAXIFRAGA TRIDACTYLITES
(VERY LARGE PLANT WITH 313 CAPSULES
AVERAGE SEEDS PER CAPSULE about
177 or about 5500 seeds per plant)

SAXIFRAGA TRIDACTYLITES
(DEPAUPERATE PLANTS
BEARING A SINGLE CAPSULE
WITH about 42-104 SEEDS)

From Salisbury, 1942

Depauperate plants (*right*) of *Saxifraga tridactylites*, a species of open sand-dune communities and the tops of old walls (England), bearing a single capsule each and producing 42 and 104 seeds, and (*left*) an exceptionally large plant with 313 capsules and producing about 5,500 seeds. The scale on the right is in centimetres.

PLATE II

Unpublished research of L. J. King; by courtesy of Boyce Thompson Institute

(b) The brilliant fluorescence of five-day old seedling roots of cultivated oats (*Avena sativa*) grown in a Petri dish as revealed under ultra-violet radiation (3650 Å). This fluorescence is believed to be due to the coumarin-relative, scopoletin. This last, and its modified forms, belong to one class of substances which when released from living and decomposing roots, may modify the rhizosphere and affect the growth of plants in the immediate vicinity.

PLATE 12

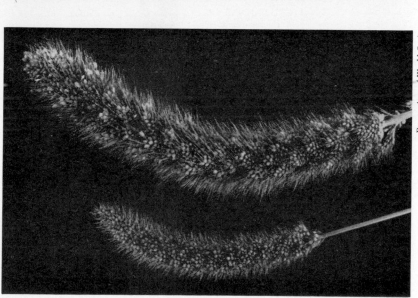

By courtesy of World Crops

(a) *Setaria viridis* (foxtail grass), a weed of extensive distribution (*left*), and the cultivated *S. italica* (common millet), which was probably derived from it (*right*).

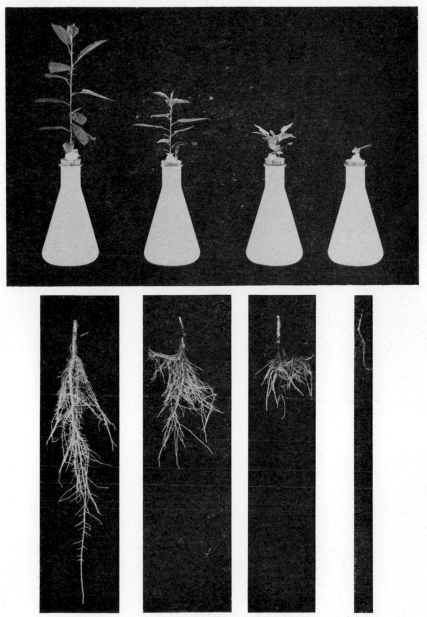

From Börner 1959: by courtesy of Boyce Thompson Institute

The influence of apple root-bark on the growth of apple seedlings in water culture. Concentration from left to right: control; 0.2; 1; and 10 gm. of root-bark per 500 ml. nutrient solution. Photographed after a culture duration of 32 days. *Above :* seedlings in culture. *Below :* corresponding excised roots.

PLATE 13

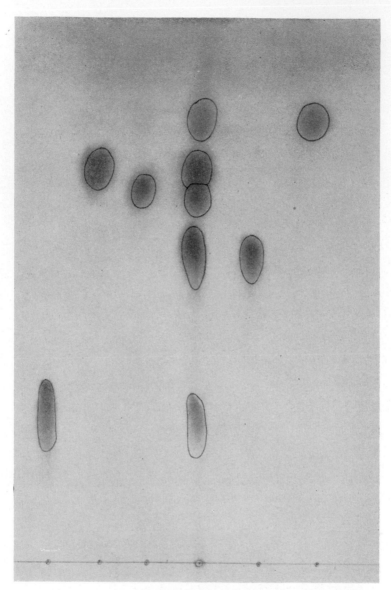

From Börner, 1959: by courtesy of Boyce Thompson Institute

Paper chromatographic separation of materials in a soil extract, 7 days after an addition of pure phlorizin. The materials (from 20–40 μl.), in the order named below, were placed at the spots indicated along the line at the bottom of the sheet of Whatman No. 1 chromatographic paper (size 28 × 44 cm.), and developed by the ascending method (i.e. diffusion upwards of the applied substances) in a special solvent preparation of acetone-H_2O (15:85 v/v), diazotized sulphanilic acid being added to the paper to obtain the colour reaction (i.e. the intensity of the large spots circled by pencil). From left to right: phloretin, *p*-hydroxybenzoic acid, phloroglucinol, soil extract, phlorizin, and *p*-hydroxyhydrocinnamic acid. The fourth row (soil extract) is the critical one, for by comparison with all of the other substances added in the pure form, they too are then seen to be present, and are, therefore, decomposition products of the originally-added phlorizin.

PLATE 14

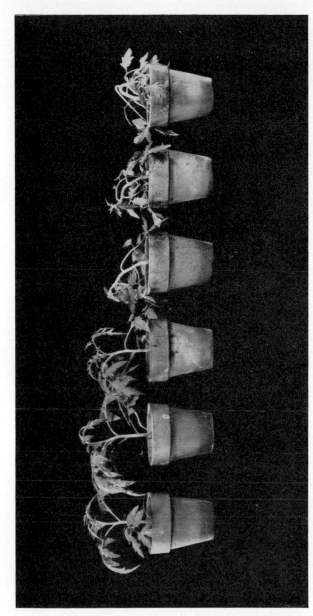

By courtesy of Boyce Thompson Institute

Reproduction of the first published photograph of 2,4-D activity from the now classic publication of Zimmerman & Hitchcock (1942, Fig. 1A, p. 326) in *Contributions from Boyce Thompson Institute*. Lanolin preparations of different concentrations of 2,4-D acid were applied to the stems of tomato plants. *Left to right*: (1) control; (2) 0·03 mg./g. of lanolin; (3) 0·06 mg./g.; (4) 0·125 mg./g.; (5) 0·25 mg./g.; (6) 10·0 mg./g. Photographed after 24 hours. The tomato plants were used as test plants because of their very high sensitivity to growth-regulating substances. Here strong epinastic responses are evident at these low dosages, and they were found to be more lasting than those resulting from the use of other hormone-like compounds.

PLATE 15

Infestations of Johnson grass (*Sorghum halepense*) at the right in test cotton plots at Greenville, Mississippi. The plot at the left which has been spot-sprayed with Dalapon has none of this grass; but where the spray hits the cotton plant, stunting may result—as is shown by the few cotton plants situated on the left of the standing figure.

PLATE 16

Pre-emergence weed control with the herbicide Sesone, in a strawberry planting in New Jersey. The rows on the left were cultivated but not sprayed with herbicide, while those on the right were cultivated and then sprayed three times with Sesone (sodium 2-(2,4-dichlorophenoxy)ethyl sulphate) at 3 lb. per acre. Sesone is more selective than 2,4-D, and sprays of it are not injurious to foliage, while soil is required for production of the active herbicidal component. The weeds controlled were principally crabgrasses (*Digitaria* spp.).

PLATE 17

By courtesy of Boyce Thompson Institute and Hitchcock et. al., 1950a

(*a*) Water-hyacinths (*Eichhornia crassipes*) in upper borrow-pit located on the Bonnet Carré Spillway Reservation, Louisiana, U.S.A., being sprayed with a 40 per cent preparation of 2,4-D from a Bell 47-D type helicopter on 19 July 1949. The plants completely cover the water's surface, from one bank to the other.

(*b*) Aerial view of the same area of the upper borrow-pit seven weeks later, showing 90 per cent of the area cleared, and only a narrow remaining fringe composed of water hyacinths which were not contacted by a lethal dose of the spray; also, dead plants which had not yet sunk.

PLATE 18

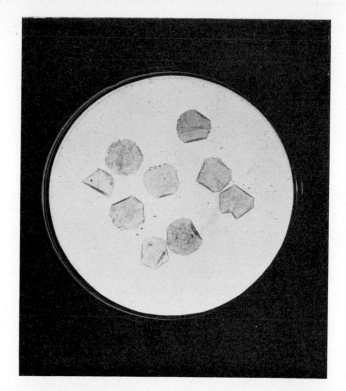

(*a*) Isolated disks of cuticle from the leaves of *Gardenia*. The cuticle
has been separated from the leaves by the pectic enzyme technique
of W. H. Orgell. The disks are 1·2 cm. in diameter, and are shown
in a standard Petri dish with a background of white filter paper.

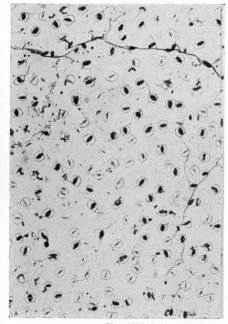 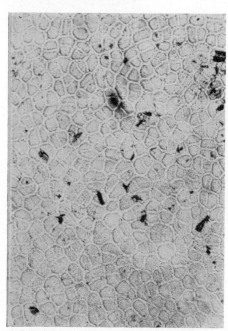

Unpublished research of L. G. King and H. G. Cutler: by courtesy of Boyce Thompson Institute

A   B

(*b*) Leaf cuticles isolated by the pectic enzyme technique of W. H. Orgell. (A) cuticle from the
upper surface of *Gardenia* leaf, showing the heavier character of the cuticle and the absence of
stomata; (B) cuticle from the lower surface of *Gardenia* leaf, showing the lighter character of the
cuticle and the abundance of stomata. Cuticles lightly stained with Sudan III. Photomicrographs × 100.

PLATE 19

By courtesy of the Iowa Agricultural Experiment Station

(b) Early post-emergence tillage in an Iowa soybean field with a weighted, penetrating rotary hoe travelling at 10 to 12 miles per hour. Note the 'curtain of soil' which, by covering the weeds, provides an age-old method of control. Useful for shallow cultivation when weeds have just appeared on the soil surface but have not elongated—commonly about 3 to 5 days after soybean emergence—and repeated as needed at 5-day intervals (two such hoeings are enough in most production fields). Between-the-row, sweep-type cultivators are used later to control surviving weeds and those occurring between the rows.

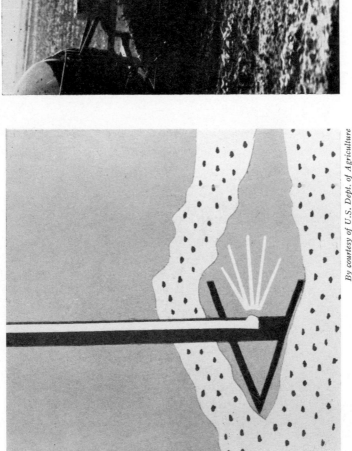

By courtesy of U.S. Dept. of Agriculture

(a) Diagram illustrating a sub-surface soil applicator for certain of the more volatile herbicides. Herbicide sprays back from the nozzles as a V-shaped cutting blade raises the soil layer 'umbrella fashion'. This device involves an experimental tractor-powered, two-row, rear-mounted cultivator-sprayer. It has been successful for application of EPTC (ethyl N, N-di-n-propylthiolcarbamate) herbicide in a thin band under the surface of seed-beds before cotton planting in Mississippi.

PLATE 20

By courtesy of E. A. Helgeson

Piles of weed seeds after their removal from wheat near a grain-cleaning station in North Dakota. Note the height of the piles with reference to the size of the truck at the right, and the utility poles showing above the piles.

PLATE 21

A utility or electric power-line right-of-way through a forested area cleared of brush and small plant growth by the use of 2,4-D and 2,4,5-T.

PLATE 22

By courtesy of Crag Agricultural Chemicals, Union Carbide Chemical Co.

Fumigant action of Mylone in soil (on *left*); on the *right* is the control. Entire area planted to turnips. Note the control of crabgrass, purslane, and low ragweed.

PLATE 23

SALISBURY, SIR E. J. (1942). *The Reproductive Capacity of Plants*. G. Bell, London, 244 pp.

—— (1942*a*). The weed problem. *Nature, Lond.*, 149, 594–7.

—— (1954). Weed dispersal and persistence. *J., Sports Turf Res. Inst.* 8, 378–86·

—— (1956). Fruit and seed production. *Nature, Lond.*, 177, 64–67.

—— (1962). *The Biology of Garden Weeds*. Royal Horticultural Society, London. 50 pp. (Reprinted from the *J. Roy. Hort. Soc.*, 87, parts 8–11, 1962.)

SALZMANN, R. (1939). [Farmyard manure as a source of viable seed—in German.] *Schweiz. Landw. Mh.*, 5, 172–6.

SCHAFFNER, J. H. (1938). Spreading of *Opuntia* in overgrazed pastures in Kansas. *Ecology*, 19, 348–50.

SCHALOW, E. (1922). Vom Einfluss der Kriege auf die Pflanzenverteilung. *Naturw. Wschr. Neue Folge*, 21, 499–502.

SERNANDER, R. (1906). Entwurf einer Monographie der europäischen Myrmekochoren. *K. Svenska Vetensk. Akad. Handl.*, 41(3), 1–410.

SINGH, H. N. (1952). Reproductive capacity of weeds of arable lands. *Allahabad Fmr.*, 26(1), 12–14.

SINNOTT, E. W. & BAILEY, I. W. (1915). Changes in the fruit type of angiosperms coincident with the development of the herbaceous habit. *Science*, 41, 179.

SMALL, J. (1919). *The Origin and Development of the Compositae*. New Phytologist Reprint, No. 11, 334 pp. London, W. Wesley and Son. (D.Sc. Thesis, Univ. London). (28 figs., 12 maps on 6 pls., 856 refs.).

STANTON, T. R., & BOERNER, E. G. (1936). An interesting seed combination. *J. Kansas Soc. Agron.*, 28, 329–40.

STEBBINS, G. L. (1951). Natural selection and the differentiation of angiosperm families. *Evolution*, 5, 299–324.

STEPHENS, S. G. (1958). Salt water tolerance of seeds of *Gossypium* species as a possible factor in seed dispersal. *Amer. Nat.*, 92, 83–92.

SZEMES, G. (1943). Zur Entwicklung der Elaiosoms von *Chelidonium majus*. *Öst. Bot. Z.*, 92, 215–19.

UPHOF, J. C. T. (1942). Ecological relations of plants with ants and termites. *Bot. Rev.*, 8, 563–98.

WEED, C. M. (1898). *Seed Travelers*. Ginn, Boston, 58 pp.

YAMADA, T. & ADACHI, A. (1954). Blooming habits of some forage plants and the artificial germination test of their pollen. *Proc. Crop. Sci. Soc. Japan*, 13, 55–59.

ZIMMERMANN, A. (1881). Uber mechanische Einrichtungen zur Verbreitung der Samen und Früchte. *Jb. Wiss. Bot.*, 12, 542–77.

ADDENDUM ON COMPETITION

This topic has been surveyed in 'Mechanisms in biological competition' (ed. F. L. Milthorpe), *Symposia Soc. Exptl. Biol.*, No. 15, 365 pp., 1961. In the introductory paper, Dr. J. L. Harper (p. 1 *et seq.*) suggests that the controversial term 'competition' be replaced by the word 'interference' to describe those hardships which are caused by the proximity of neighbours (usually other organisms feeding at the same trophic level). He further notes that the botanist has tended to understress mortality and its contribution to the dynamics of populations in appraisal of interference between plants; that he relates changes in the characteristic of a plant or one generation of plants to density and a time component may or may not be considered, and that the spacing of individuals is important since the higher plant normally remains rooted and fixed in position after establishment. He continues that increases in density of organisms may place a stress (measured in the mortality and plasticity of plants) on the development of individuals. There may be a differential between the stress on parts of a mixed population which results in some *selective advantage* of one component over others.

IX

GENETIC ASPECTS OF THE ORIGIN AND EVOLUTION OF WEEDS

'Where did our weeds come from?', is a question that is often asked. The general historical background of this subject was explored in the introductory chapters, and the role of man was particularly emphasized there. As Darlington (1956) has noted, 'Man's greatest biological experiment has been the invention of agriculture, a process of understanding and controlling and improving certain flowering plants' (and animals). As has already been stated, it appears that a sizeable proportion of the autotrophic land weeds exist in their present form today as a result of their use by man sometime during past ages. In most cases they were originally members of the native flora of the region concerned; but with removal from this environment, and their selection to some extent, as well as their dispersal into man-created habitats, certain genotypes among these populations persisted and thrived under these new conditions.

As will be noted below, the disturbed habitat—with its challenge to the invasion and establishment of new types, and its destruction of many of the barriers between populations—consistently forms one of the most important environmental causes for setting the intricate and diverse genetic mechanisms in operation. This results in more aggressive and successful forms—often weeds.

Interspecific Hybridization

In a detailed review of this subject, Baker (1951) states that many pairs of species are capable of forming relatively fertile hybrids in nature, and hybrid swarms may be expected to form where these species meet, followed by an interchange of genes. Such internal restrictive factors as physiological imbalance in hybrids—particularly in later generations—may be responsible for the elimination of many recombination types. As noted below (p. 227), back-crossing to the parents may reduce this imbalance. Other restrictive factors that prevent hybridization, and thus provide considerable stability among the species (as appears to occur among a large number of the commonest weeds), include habitual self-pollination (as in *Stellaria media*), facultative apomixis, and vigorous vegetative reproduction. There are also many internal factors, such as pollen-tube growth and the problem of compatibility in all the intricacies of the cytological phases, as well as differences in flower morphology and phenology, that may prevent the natural occurrence of hybrids.

Rollins (1954) has emphasized the importance of interspecific hybrids as 'agents of gene transmission, and that they are also important as a pool of recombinant genes to be screened by the forces of evolution'; further, that hybrid populations may arise and survive without back-crossing to either of the parental species, as is substantiated in a study of *Lesquerella* populations occurring near the upper part of the Harpeth River in Tennessee. *L. densipilia*, a cruciferous annual endemic to central Tennessee, grows along the flood-plain of the river and on the hill-slopes, while *L. lescurii* occurs abundantly in open glades and fields, and likewise is endemic. The closest together these populations have been observed is four miles, yet the nearest interspecific hybrids to these were found ten miles down the river, and the farthest at a distance of forty miles. These hybrids were thus not in the immediate vicinity of the parental populations, and hence no back-crossing had occurred. They were successfully established and were reproducing, being indeed so abundant in some fields as to be considered weeds. The original seeds of these hybrid populations were probably carried down the river by water; they then became established and were genetically isolated from the parental forms.

Another example of hybridization in weeds is provided by the study of Mulligan & Frankton (1954) of populations of the plumeless thistle (*Carduus acanthoides* var. *acanthoides*) and the nodding thistle (*C. nutans* var. *nutans*), growing together in rough pastures in Ontario, Canada. The plumeless thistle ($2n = 22$) grows towards the tops of the local knolls, while the nodding thistle ($2n = 16$) grows at or near the bases of the knolls. On these disturbed habitats, hybridization between the two parents, and back-crossing, have resulted in many isolated hybrid swarms. In these hybrid swarms all combinations, in many degrees, of certain morphological features of the inflorescence (for example, clustered and solitary heads) and other characters were observed. These hybrid populations consisted of individuals with chromosome numbers ranging from $2n = 16$ to $2n = 22$. These authors further note that, as there is a physiological difference between the two species involved, many combinations of these physiological differences can be expected in the hybrid swarms. After several back-crosses to the parents ('introgressive hybridization', *see* next section) 'perhaps a relatively uniform mongrel population will occur over the whole area. Then the gradual infiltration of new genes, into one of the parent populations, could result in plants which by natural hybridization would be physiologically, and possibly morphologically, better adapted to the habitats created by man.'

Mulligan & Frankton note that, in clearing and cultivating the land, man had unconsciously created conditions whereby closely-related entities, which were formerly well-isolated, could come together and hybridize—and, furthermore, these resultant hybrids depend upon the man-disturbed habitats for survival. 'Natural hybridization is commoner among weeds than any other group of plants. Man has carried them wherever he has travelled, breaking down geographical and ecological barriers between genetically compatible entities. Natural hybridization, infiltration of genes, and selection, have given rise to more vigorous weeds and will continue to give rise to still more vigorous weeds.'

Man's influence on hybridization in *Crataegus*, the genus of well-known, weedy, hawthorn shrubs, has been examined by Bradshaw (1954). He, too, notes that plant species differentiate when they are genetically isolated from each other, this isolation being achieved in different ways—the common one being where the incipient species have different ecological requirements that cause them to occupy different habitats. If the original vegetation is destroyed—as it has been very widely in Great Britain, Europe, and many other parts of the world with the rise of a farm economy—the natural habitats are upset and interspecific isolation may be broken down. In Great Britain the two native species of *Crataegus*—*C. monogyna* of open scrub areas and *C. oxycanthoides* of damp woodlands—hybridize freely and the hybrids are fertile. The amount of hybridization has been found to be related to the amount that the woodlands have been disturbed. As most of them have been disturbed, it is difficult to find pure populations of *C. oxycanthoides*. Bradshaw concludes that this process is likely to go on, and that *C. oxycanthoides* will ultimately be hybridized out of existence.

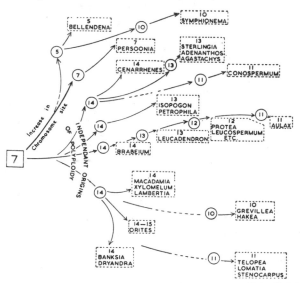

From Smith–White, *1959*

FIG. 37.—Chromosome evolution in the family Proteaceae, a very large family that is well represented throughout the tropics, including Australia. Several independent origins of polyploidy, and parallel series of numerical diminution, must be inferred. The numbers shown all refer to chromosome numbers for the genera listed. While this family is not noteworthy for noxious members, the chromosomal changes throughout illustrate in a concise manner the many new forms that may develop—in this example, from a basic chromosome number of 7.

On the other hand, the development of polyploid forms (i.e. forms possessing multiple sets of chromosomes) has increased the fertility of otherwise sterile hybrids, and has often enabled plants to invade and to survive in more adverse habitats than they were previously accustomed to (Fig. 37). This is well illustrated in Haskell's (1952) analysis of the relations between polyploidy and the British flora, the following comments being taken from his summary. The coefficient of polyploidy among types (CPT) was determined, being 0·65 for monocots and 0·46 for dicots. Thus in Britain the monocots have a much higher CPT than have the dicots, as has been found to be the case in all the other floras that have so far been examined. This is due to a number of factors, one being that the monocots and dicots have had separate environmental histories. There are more monocot species inhabiting low and wet places than there are dicots, and it has been noted that the CPT is higher in plants of low and wet habitats than of high and dry ones. Moreover, plants in low and wet habitats are more effectively dispersed by vegetative means than are those of high and dry habitats.

The hypothesis of polyploidy tending to increase with latitude is upheld, although some species which are polyploid in Britain are diploid in Greenland, for example. Higher polyploidy of monocots also favours the hypothesis that they returned to dry land following aquatic existence which promoted polyploidy. Both monocot and dicot perennial species have higher CPT's than annuals, but dicot trees and shrubs are intermediate. Polyploidy may change diploid annuals to perennials, but perennial diploids remain perennial on becoming polyploid. Plants in man-made habitats (weeds, etc.) commonly have lower CPT's than those of natural habitats. This is in contrast to Gustafsson's (1948) findings that man-made habitats induce polyploidy (*see* below). CPT's seem to be high for very wet habitats and also, in monocots, for alternating wet-dry situations; ordinary conditions are characterized by the lowest CPT's. Haskell concluded that polyploidy has not been an important factor influencing the ability of introduced species to spread in Britain, or increasing their general 'comital' frequency, or widening the distribution of diploid-polyploid pairs of species within genera. New autopolyploidy has aided some species in Britain to recolonize once-glaciated land, while old tetraploid relics may still remain confined to the unglaciated south, and some new polyploids have re-spread northwards.

Sakisaka (1950), in Japan, has also considered polyploidy in relation to plant habitat and to life-form. He has observed in herbaceous plants that, very commonly, those with small numbers of chromosomes have a short life (annual habit), while those with large numbers of chromosomes have a long life (perennial habit). These two groups differ in fertility, activity, adaptability, rate of growth, and hybridity. For example, the annual *Sonchus oleraceus* (16 chromosomes) and the perennial *S. arvensis* (64 chromosomes), *Helianthus annuus* (34 chromosomes) and the perennial

H. tuberosus (102 chromosomes), and the annual *Polygonum viscosum* (22 chromosomes) and the perennial *P. filiforme* (44 chromosomes) all bear this out.

Sakisaka has noted a gradual tendency to domination by vegetative propagation (by rhizomes, tubers, bulbs, bulbils, or runners) over seed propagation, in passing from diploid to polyploid plants in the same genus. This is exhibited by the series: *Polygonum orientale* (a diploid with no rhizome), *P. japonicum* (a tetraploid with some rhizomes), *P. amphibium* (a hexaploid with many rhizomes), and finally *P. reynoutria* [*P. cuspidatum*] (an octoploid with extreme rhizome development).

An all-too-successful example of an invading polyploid weed is provided in the giant foxtail grass (*Setaria faberii*). According to Kishimoto (1937), the common *S. viridis* is a diploid ($2n = 18$), *S. faberii* is a tetraploid ($2n = 36$) as likewise is *S. lutescens*, while only the octoploid *S. geniculata* ($2n = 72$) is perennial. Apparently, seed of *S. faberii* was introduced about 1925 into the United States from China, as a contaminant in a shipment of Chinese millet seed. Since that time it has spread over the Middle West, becoming a serious pest particularly in maize and soybean fields (King, 1952—*see* Ch. VI).

Dr. G. A. Mulligan, of the Plant Research Institute, Canada Department of Agriculture, has recently (1960) summarized a programme of study on polyploidy in weeds. The incidence of polyploidy in the common and widespread, native or introduced, weeds of Canada proved to be about the same as in the native flora of the same area. The creation of open habitats does not necessarily favour polyploid plants. Grain-field and row-crop weeds were mostly annual (up to 86 and 84 per cent, re-respectively). Hayfield weeds were all perennial, and 78 per cent of pasture weeds were perennial. The incidence of polyploidy was different in four specialized habitats: 37 per cent in weeds of grain-fields, 56 per cent in weeds of row-crops, 52 per cent in weeds of hay-fields, and 49 per cent in weeds of pastures. The relatively high incidence in the latter two habitats was attributed to the predominance of perennials. The low incidence of polyploidy among grain-field weeds was attributed to natural selection for the annual habit and for genetic stability, both of which are found to a greater degree among diploids. The high incidence of polyploidy in row-crop weeds, while partially due to the presence of a few rhizomatous perennials, was mostly attributed to selection through repeated cultivation for annual weeds with genetic variability—a characteristic which is commoner in polyploids than in diploids.

INTROGRESSIVE HYBRIDIZATION

This term denotes 'the gradual infiltration of the germplasm of one species into that of another as a consequence of hybridization and repeated back-crossing' (Anderson, 1949, 1952). Anderson's study of hybridization in plants has led him to conclude that 'one of the commonest, if not the commonest, results of hybridization is the enrichment of variation in the participating species, through successive back-crosses.' He further states (1952) that introgressive segments, once introduced through back-crossing, may spread through a population and on to other populations when they confer a selective advantage. As noted below, these new forms are most likely to arise and persist in disturbed habitats—frequently man-made ones, as in cleared areas about habitations, around dumps and refuse heaps, and in cultivated ground.

Thus, towards understanding the nature of these new forms and how they arise, one important approach is a detailed analysis of natural populations as they exist under field conditions. Many studies of this nature have now been made, one of the most illustrative being that of *Phlox bifida* populations in Tennessee by Anderson & Gage (1952). A careful mass collection was made from 30 clones growing in an area of an acre or more. They were growing on a cedar barren which was adjacent to both a school and a church, and which had been used partly as a picnic ground and partly as a dump-heap. Anderson (1948) earlier had shown that in just such disturbed habitats the immediate results of introgression are most clearly seen, as the 'hybridization of the habitat' provides unusual ecological niches in which some of the segregation products of introgression are at a selective advantage. The varying characters that could readily be measured from pressed herbarium material included pubescence, corolla shape, internode pattern, leaf-size and shape, pedicel length, flower number, and flower colour. This variation pattern of the population was carefully analysed, and the data all indicated introgression rather than the direct result of mutation. When these data were plotted as a pictorial diagram, it was evident that the variation of all of the selected characters of the population resolved into two complexes. The first complex represented the 'typical' taxonomic form of *P. bifida*: as the second complex departed from descriptions of the previous taxon, it was assumed that these plants represented the introgressants produced through back-crossing of hybrids with other species.

Other species involved in this hybridization probably resembled the second complex mentioned, but had many of their characters more extremely expressed. From the details thus gained in this study, Anderson & Gage were able to extrapolate the various characters from the *bifida* complex through the introgressed complex and to the supposed species, and to achieve a precise description of this latter taxon. They were unfamiliar with this hypothetical form as delineated, but by keying it out in a monograph of *Phlox* they found that it could indeed be assigned to *P. amoena*—a species which was known from that part of the country (clones existed about 20 miles away) but which belonged to another section of the genus. Subjecting known specimens of *P. amoena* to the same procedures resulted in their identical agreement with the postulated species. These authors theorized that the plants involved may have been

231

first or second back-crosses from an interspecific hybrid—all having arisen at least several decades ago, and possibly even in pre-Columbian times.

Anderson & Gage (1952) state that evidence is rapidly accumulating to show that, when introgression confers a strong selective advantage on some of the mongrel offspring, they and their descendants may spread well outside the immediate area in which the hybridization occurred, and Heiser's (1949) studies in California on *Helianthus* confirm this. Thus more aggressive, weedy forms may arise. In a subsequent review, Anderson (1952) stated that an analysis of population variability has produced 'no evidence for mutation as the immediate source of variability for natural selection. From Mendel's peas to Beadle's *Neurospora*, the plants used for genetic research have been weeds and cultivated plants. Their origin, where known, is a consequence of introgression, frequently multiple introgression.'

APOMIXIS

Reduction in chromosome number, brought about by meiosis and resulting in the formation of haploid gametes, is compensated for by the process of fertilization: this is the normal process of sexual reproduction. However, apomixis refers, as in parthenogenesis and apogamy, to reproduction without sexual union. This is the case when meiosis and fertilization fail together and in co-ordination, so that diploid may beget diploid, or triploid beget triploid (Darlington, 1956). According to that author it occurs very widely, and in some form or degree in most families, if not in most genera, of flowering plants. It may arise by mutation, by hybridization in either a first or a derived generation, or by triploidy. Sometimes an unreduced egg or a purely vegetative bud in the ovule can develop without fertilization, and the apomictic race proceeds. Frequently the suppression of sexual reproduction is not complete, nor is the apomictic replacement; thus a mixture of methods (including purely vegetative reproduction) occurs, and the reproduction is then versatile. Such forms are best known in *Rubus* and *Poa*. The highly polymorphic 'species' of *Taraxacum, Hieracium, Crepis*, and other genera, are additional examples. There is a great prevalence of polyploidy among apomictic forms, which apparently results from stronger gene-action—at least when the gene combinations are favourable.

Briefly, then, apomixis permits the continued propagation of both fertile and sterile forms of any strain that is ecologically adaptable. When sexual reproduction occurs occasionally, a means is provided for continued segregation and hybridization—leading to further polymorphic forms of possibly greater adaptability. The great range of these adaptations is evident in the various apomicts of *Taraxacum* studied by Hofsten (1954 –*see* Ch. VI), Darlington (1956), and Swanson (1957).

232

ECOTYPES

An ecotype has been defined as a category of variant individuals, based on genetical behaviour and ecological relationship (Whyte, 1946). In the preceding sections we have seen how the various genetic mechanisms, as well as combinations of them, function in the production of new forms—many of which have been identified and are recognizable as ecotypes.

Earnshaw (1950) has reviewed the nature of ecotypes, with the following further definition, 'an ecotype is defined as a plant population adapted by genetic specialization to the physiological conditions of a particular environment'. He lists three requisites for their formation: (a) the species population must possess an adequate potential range of genetic variability; (b) growing conditions in ecologically distinct habitats must be sufficiently different to provide adequate selection material; (c) isolation between populations in different habitats must be sufficient to permit genetic specialization.

Clausen et al. (1940) studied ecotype formation in Potentilla glandulosa along a 200-mile transect ranging from coastal to alpine conditions in California. Four main ecotypes were distinguished, and these were found to coincide with four taxonomic subspecies.

Hara (1954) has reviewed this problem in Eurasiatic species. In many species that are widely distributed from Europe to Japan, geographical races are observed, and characteristics (chromosome number or outer morphological characters) which separate these races are variable in kind and degree in the different species. The common weed Prunella vulgaris is divided by morphological characters into three major geographical races, i.e. European, East Asiatic, and north American—yet materials from Europe and Japan have the same chromosome number ($2n = 36$). However, in Glechoma (Nepeta) hederacea ($2n = 36$) the Japanese plant is always hexaploid, whereas triploid, tetraploid, and hexaploid races have been reported in Europe. Most of these races seem to have originated during the Ice Age. Some were at first isolated geographically and then differentiated into morphologically and ecologically distinct races, whereas, in other cases, polyploid and aneuploid races arise without much outer morphological differentiation and extend their distribution. A difficulty in nomenclature is thereby presented, and Hara suggests the use for them of new categories of taxa—for example, 'geovariety' and 'geosubspecies'.

Gregor (1956), in reviewing the concept of the ecotype unit, states that this has undergone some modification since so many intricate patterns of variation have been associated with discrete ecotypes. By definition, the ecotype is the product arising as a result of the genotypical response of an ecospecies to a particular habitat. Even the four early-recognized ecotypes of Potentilla glandulosa in California have since been found to be internally ecotypically fractionated. Gregor (1956) further states that

233

ecotypic differentiation of cross-fertilizing plant populations only becomes appreciable with the aid of at least a modicum of extrinsic isolation—except occasionally where strongly contrasting habitats happen to adjoin, or where a continuous population extends along an environmental gradient for a considerable distance.

In an earlier study, Gregor (1946) reviewed ecotypic differentiation with special reference to populations of *Plantago maritima*. The size and growth-habits were determined along an edaphic variant. At a low level of soil fertility, a decumbent habit was most common, and plant size was smaller than in forms of similar growth-habit which were a minor constituent of populations at higher levels of fertility. Erect forms were of larger size and more frequent occurrence on the more fertile soils.

Reference has already been made to Olmsted's studies of the various photoperiodic ecotypes in the range-grass *Bouteloua*. Pauley & Perry (1954) of Harvard University, have also discovered similar ecotypes among species of *Populus* (*P. deltoides* and *P. trichocarpa*). Samples from clones of the former species were collected throughout the northwestern parts of its area in North America. Analysis of the growth data of these clones, obtained in test areas near Boston, Massachussetts, disclosed that the time of height-growth cessation was inversely correlated with the latitude of origin of each clone. Among clones that were native of uniform day-length zones, the time at which height-growth ceased was directly correlated with the length of the frost-free season prevailing in the native habitat of each clone. The authors conclude that adaptation of *Populus* species to various habitats differing in length of frost-free season is effected by a genetic mechanism which controls the duration of their seasonal period of growth; as photoperiod is the only factor of the environment with a uniform seasonal variation that is constant from year to year, it functions as the timing device for this mechanism. Wilsie (1962—*see* Ch. I) in *Crop Adaptation and Distribution*, has reviewed the ecotype concept.*

AGRICULTURAL ECOTYPES

From an analysis of the effects of soil fertility on the structure of populations of *Plantago* as reviewed above by Gregor (1946), it is obvious that agricultural operations, when continued over a long period of time in the same general locality, might result in the differentiation of populations that would be better adapted to a certain agricultural habitat than were their ancestors. This does appear to have happened in the case of a species of *Ranunculus* described by Salisbury (1942—*see* Ch. VIII); the original

* J. Langridge (*Austral. J. Biol. Sci.*, 18, 311–21, 1965) has described temperature-sensitive, vitamin-requiring mutants of *Arabidopsis thaliana* (Cruciferae). Such conditioned mutants of thiamine- and biotin-requiring species are abnormal at one temperature and normal at another. A loss in biotin causes a complete but reversible cessation of growth. The heat inhibition of biotin synthesis may provide a means for plants to escape the deleterious sterilizing effects of heat-wave conditions. These mutants comprise naturally occurring ecotypes in Spain and Austria.

species, of tall form, grew on the borders of the grain-field, while within the field a lower-growing form, that flowered and set seed below the level of the cut of the reaping machine, had developed. Harper & Sagar's studies (1954) demonstrated how closely together three species of *Ranunculus* grew, each in a special 'micro' habitat within the field, thus generally avoiding competition. In British grasslands, a characteristic feature is the frequency of occurrence of ridge and furrow, which give a pattern of drainage conditions over the fields. Analysis of the distribution of the three buttercup species where they occur in the same field under moderate but not good drainage, showed *R. bulbosus* on the tops of the ridges, *R. acris* on the sides, and *R. repens* in the furrows.

This colonizing of new and disturbed habitats by polyploids, in-breeders, and apomicts, is explained by Smith-White (1959) (cf. Fig. 38): species occupying and adapted to habitat A gain access to a new and larger area. In I, on the left, the new area is reasonably uniform and rather similar to the original habitat A (below). Consequently the species in A are already adapted in all major respects to the new area. During expansion, old and tried genotypes will be favoured over new and experimental ones. In II, on the right, the new area comprises a great diversity of habitats. In the expansion of species from the original area, old genotypes (e.g. A) will not be highly adapted; but the new and experimental ones (e.g. B, C, D, E) are favoured by the diversified habitats.

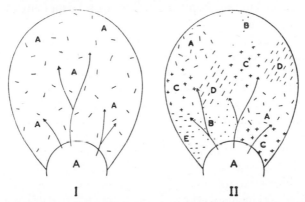

FIG. 38.—A diagram of geographical expansion of species under extreme circumstances. In I, on the left, a uniform new area similar to the older area, A, favours tried genotypes (i.e. A). In II, on the right, diverse new habitats (shown by different hatchings) provide evolutionary opportunity and favour new genotypes (i.e. B, C, D, E). *From Smith-White, 1959*

THE ORIGIN OF SOME CROP PLANTS FROM WEEDS

Prior to man's contact with plants, they were essentially all stable components of the regional flora. As early man discovered uses for some of them, they were gradually selected out of the natural environment and cultured in a primitive manner—perhaps along the lines of the dump-heap gardens, described by Anderson (1952), that are still prevalent in

Mexico and Central America. For the smaller grains, it was later found to be more expedient to grow them in somewhat larger areas than dump-heaps, in order to provide the necessary bulk. With cultivation on larger areas, foreign invaders—weeds—came in and occupied the same ground. In these grain patches, such weeds as simulated the grain plants were more likely to survive than those that differed greatly in appearance, time of bloom, seed-set, etc. Darnel (*Lolium temulentum*), in wheat, is an example. As we have noted earlier (p. 116), similarity in size and weight of the seed of the weed with that of the associated crop also developed as a result of primitive crop-seed cleaning methods—especially winnowing (Pl. 8).

This is apparently what happened in the origin of the oat crop (*Avena sativa*), which is the world's fourth most important cereal crop. Vavilov (1926) collected numerous samples of Emmer wheat, many of them containing admixtures of some *Avena* sp.; thus he came to speak of oats as the unfailing attendant of Emmer, and concluded that the history of oats was intimately connected with that of Emmer. He visualized Emmer spreading over the Old World, carrying with it an assortment of oats as weeds. When it reached the harsher climate of the north, oats, being the hardier plant, supplanted Emmer and became an independent crop. Werth (1945) stated that Emmer, with its attendant oats, was a widespread crop in northern Europe during the climatic optimum. When the climate began to deteriorate (from about 2000 B.C. onwards, according to Werth), the oats was better adapted to the changed conditions, and supplanted the Emmer (cf. Sampson, 1954).

The nature of the articulation of the floret and its inheritance is a critical factor in this history of the origin of oats. Sampson notes that any mutation in a wild weed-oat introducing non-articulate florets would have a selective value, as those grains which did not fall would be harvested with the main crop and planted the next year. Similar mutations arising in the wild oat would be fatal to such spreading. Undoubtedly the presence of intergrades with varying amounts of articulation, coupled with variation in harvest dates, still permitted some of the weed-oats to be carried over in the harvested grain in spite of heavy seed-fall. The rapid seed shattering of the weed oats (*Avena fatua* and *A. ludoviciana*) is one of their most pernicious features. Schiemann (1951) also has recognized this brittle axis (rachis) character and its adaptation to self-propagation; and further, that self-propagation and self-protection, once having been lost and being of no use in cultivation, the new cultivated type is fixed by conscious and unconscious selection. All cereals thus have a 'tough' axis.

In studies on the origin of the cultivated beet (*Beta vulgaris*), Zossi-movich (1939) has noted that, in the interior region of Asia, the local population uses as salad the leaves of the wild *B. vulgaris* when it is growing as a weed. The wild beet of the species *B. vulgaris* was introduced into cultivation in the valleys of the Tigris and Euphrates rivers from the weeds occurring on irrigated agricultural lands. Conditions of irrigation made it possible to select from populations of wild beet, good leaf-producers and later-maturing forms. This is the way the selection for leaves was started some 3,500 to 4,000 years ago. The large-rooted beet appeared later, in Babylonia or Iran—probably in the fifth or sixth centuries A.D. In the first century A.D., the leaf-beet spread to Western Europe, where it became later-maturing and possessed of a higher sugar-content. The process of its hybridization with the local wild beet of high sugar-content, *B. vulgaris* ssp. *maritima*, was in progress. The root forms of *Beta* were imported from the Near East in the thirteenth and fourteenth centuries. Thus the sugar beet is a product of selection among the products of re-combination of characters of two pre-existing forms of the cultivated beet. In an interesting *addendum*, Zossimovich notes that the name *Beta* is of Roman origin, and that it has been suggested that the Romans recog-nized the similarity of a young seedling of beet with the Greek letter β (beta).

Darlington (1956) has noted the statements (made independently by Engelbrecht, 1916, and by Vavilov, 1926) that many new crops began their lives by the following kind of selection: as the primary crop spread into territory that was less favourable for itself, it was replaced by one of its own weeds. Darlington (1956) has summarized the observations of these authors, and of Schiemann (1943), in Table VII. Anderson (1952),

TABLE VII

ORIGINS OF CROPS FROM WEEDS (*From Darlington, 1956**)

Primary crop	Secondary crop†	Origin as weed
Triticum vulgare	*Secale cereale*	S. W. Asia
Hordeum vulgare and *Triticum dicoccum*	*Avena sativa*	Europe and W. Asia
Linum usitatissimum	⎧ *Eruca sativa* ⎨ *Camelina sativa* ⎩ *Spergula linicola* *Brassica campestris*	C. Asia Trans-Caucasia Trans-Caucasia Trans-Caucasia
Fagopyrum esculentum	*F. tartaricum*	Altai
Cereals	⎧ *Vicia sativa*, etc. ⎨ *Pisum arvense* ⎩ *Coriandrum sativum* *Cephalaria syriaca*	S. W. Asia Trans-Caucasia Asia Minor
Various crops	*Cucumis trigonus* *Abutilon avicennae*	Turkestan Med. to China

* Derived from the observations of Engelbrecht (1916), Vavilov (1926), and cf. Schiemann (1943).
† Formerly weeds in the respective primary crop.

in reviewing the history of the wheats, notes that one of the wild or weed wheats eventually became the diploid Neolithic cereal which is now generally known by its German name, Einkorn; then some time later in the Neolithic, a polyploid hybrid of Einkorn and a weedy quack-grass (*Agropyron*) became Emmer wheat. In still later Neolithic times, probably by hybridization with weedy species of *Aegilops*, the tetraploid wheats such as the Persian and Lake Dweller wheats arose. Hexaploidy in combination with *Aegilops squarrosa* produced Spelt, perhaps in the Bronze Age; then still later hydridization with Lake Dweller wheats differentiated the first true bread wheats from Spelt (Anderson, 1952).

DEVELOPMENT OF RESISTANCE TO HERBICIDES

This is, as will be shown more clearly in Chapter XIV, a very critical aspect from the point of view of long-range chemical weed-control programmes. Little information is available on the development of resistance to chemicals by plants—although in the insect sphere it is well known. It has been reported that it takes fifteen generations for the common house-fly to develop resistance to DDT. As, however, the reproductive patterns differ in plants from those in insects (particularly in that plants have normally only one generation a year, and much smaller populations), such resistance has been much slower in developing in plants. Yet extrapolating from insect data such as the item just cited, weeds resistant to the herbicide 2,4-D might become evident in areas sprayed frequently with it for about fifteen years. As the earliest extensive use of 2,4-D herbicides was about 1945, resistant forms in some abundance could be expected during the decade, 1960–70.

Dr. J. L. Harper (1956), of Oxford University, reviewed this matter thoroughly. One of the earliest records of resistance in plants was that cited by Linser (1951: *see* Harper, 1956): in Louisiana in 1949, seed obtained from weeds that survived 2,4-D treatment were found to produce plants about twice as resistant to 2,4-D as the previous generation had been. Abel (1954: *see* Harper, 1956), in England, has noted that 'there is increasing evidence from field experience . . . that higher doses are now required to control certain weeds, e.g. creeping thistle (*Cirsium arvense*)'. In Hawaii, Hanson (1956: *see* Harper, 1956) has reported that *Erechtites hieracifolia*, which had previously been controlled in sugar-cane plantations by applications of 2,4-D, has developed resistant strains. Where these strains have appeared, strong doses of contact herbicides are now necessary to kill the weed. A number of investigators have also commented on the wide variation in 2,4-D resistance that occurs throughout a large number of crop varieties such as sweet corn. Harper (1956) further notes that changes in the phenology of weeds are perhaps the most likely ones to follow a continued and systematic programme of herbicide usage. Especially important are the timing mechanisms for weed emergence (which are under genetic control); thus such operations as the spraying of young weed seedlings are likely to select for strains of the weed which germinate slightly later and so avoid the spray damage. The vernal and/or autumnal germination periods might thus be altered for some species.

A similar problem arises when a weed changes in susceptibility with ageing—here, continued spraying at one stage of development could lead to the evolution of phenologically different plants. It was also pointed out that the trend towards reducing applications (lower concentrations and volumes) to sub-lethal levels where control but not kill is intended, provides ideal conditions for the evolution of resistant strains. In mixed populations of weeds, where the selected herbicide may kill the dominant species, it will also at the same time have an important selective action (genetically) on subsidiary, but slightly more resistant, species.

BIBLIOGRAPHY

(Genetic Aspects of the Origin and Evolution of Weeds)

ANDERSON, E. (1934). Origin of the angiosperms. *Nature, Lond.*, **133**, 462.
—— (1948). Hybridization of the habitat. *Evolution*, **2**, 1–9.
—— (1949). *Introgressive Hybridization.* John Wiley New York, 109 pp.
—— (1952). *Plants, Man and Life.* Little Brown, Boston, 245 pp.
—— & GAGE, A. (1952). Introgressive hybridization in *Phlox bifida. Amer. J. Bot.*, **39**, 399–404.
BABCOCK, E. B. & HALL, H. M. (1927). *Hemizonia congesta.* A genetic, ecologic, and taxonomic study of the hay-field tarnica. *Bot. Jb.*, **61**, Lit. 50.
BAKER, H. G. (1951). Hybridization and natural gene-flow between higher plants. *Biol. Rev.*, **26**, 302–37.
BATEN, W. D. (1934). A statistical study of *Daucus carota* L. *Biometrika*, **26**, 443.
BERNSTRÖM, P. (1953). Increased crossability in *Lamium* after chromosome doubling. *Hereditas*, **39**, 241–56.
BLAKESLEE, A. F. & BELLING, J. (1924). Mutations in the Jimson weed, *Datura Stramonium. J. Hered.*, **15**(5), 195–206.
BÖCHER, T. W. (1949). Racial divergencies in *Prunella vulgaris* in relation to habitat and climate. *New Phytol.*, **48**(3), 285–314.
BORRIEL, M. (1957). A morphologically distinct ecotype of *Dactylis glomerata* L. *Nature, Lond.*, **179**, 544–5.
BOSEMARK, N. O. (1956). On accessory chromosomes in *Festuca pratensis*. III. Frequency and geographical distribution of plants with accessory chromosomes. *Hereditas*, **42**, 198–210.
BOWDEN, W. M. (1940). Diploidy, polyploidy and winter hardiness relationships in the flowering plants. *Amer. J. Bot.*, **27**, 357–71.
—— (1959). The taxonomy and nomenclature of the wheats, barleys, and ryes and their wild relatives. *Canad. J. Botany*, **37**, 657–84.
BRADSHAW, A. D. (1954). Man's influence on hybridization in *Crataegus. Proc. 8th Internat. Bot. Congr.*, Sect. 9, p. 217.
CLAUSEN, J., KECK, D. D. & HIESEY, W. M. (1940, 1945, 1948). Experimental studies on the nature of species. I, II, and III. *Carnegie Inst. Washington*, Publ. Nos. 520, 564, 581, pp. 452, 174, 129, respectively.
DARLINGTON, C. D. (1956). *Chromosome Botany.* G. Allen & Unwin, London, 186 pp.
—— (1963). *Chromosome Botany and the Origins of Cultivated Plants.* G. Allen & Unwin, London. 2nd edn., 231 pp.
—— & CHATTERJEE, D. (1947). Wild and cultivated rice. *Nature, Lond.*, **160**, 234, 756–7.

DMITRIEV, V. A. (1952). [Problems in evolution of species and control of weeds—in Russian.] *Sov. Agron.*, 10(4), 17–27.

EARNSHAW, F. (1950). The nature of ecotypes. *Proc. 7th Internat. Bot. Congr., Stockholm*, pp. 269–70.

EDWARDS, D. C. (1937). Three ecotypes of *Pennisetum clandestinum* Hochst. *Emp. J. Exp. Agric.*, 5, 371–6.

ENGELBRECHT, H. (1916). Über die Entstehung einiger feldmässig angebauter Kulturpflanzen. *Geogr. Z.*, 22, 328–34.

FRÖST, S. (1954). The genetic effect of accessory chromosomes in *Centaurea scabiosa*. *Hereditas*, 40, 529–33.

GOOD, R. (1951). The evolutionary theories of Dr. J. C. Willis. *New Phytol.*, 50, 135–8.

—— (1956). *Features of Evolution in the Flowering Plants*. Longmans, Green, London, 405 pp.

GRANT, W. F. (1959). Cytogenetic studies in *Amaranthus*. I. Cytological aspects of sex determination in dioecious species. *Canad. J. Botany*, 37, 413–17; II. Natural interspecific hybridization between *Amaranthus dubius* and *A. spinosus*. *Ibid.*, 37, 1063–70.

GREGOR, J. W. (1944). The ecotype. *Biol. Rev.*, 19, 20–30.

—— (1946). Ecotype differentiation. *New Phtyol.*, 45, 254–70.

—— (1956). Adaptation and ecotypic components. *Proc. Roy. Soc. Lond.*, Ser. B, 145, 333–7.

GUSTAFSSON, Å. (1935). Studies on the mechanism of parthenogenesis. *Hereditas*, 21, 1–112.

—— (1935a). The importance of the apomicts for plant geography. *Bot. Not.*, 1935, pp. 325–30.

—— (1943). The genesis of the European blackberry flora. *Lunds Universitets Årsskrift, n.F., Avd.* 2, Bd. 39, No. 6, 1–199.

—— (1947). Apomixis in higher plants. II. The causal aspect of apomixis. *Lunds Universitets Årsskrift, n.F., Avd.* 2, Bd., 43, 1–109.

—— (1948). Polyploidy, life form and vegetative reproduction. *Hereditas*, 34, 1–22.

—— (1954). The species concept in apomictic groups *Proc. 8th Internat. Bot. Congr.*, Sect. 9, pp. 187–8.

HARA, H. (1954). Morphological and chromosome variations in widespread Eurasiatic species. *Proc. 8th Internat. Bot. Congr.*, Sect. 9, p. 217.

HARPER, J. L. (1956). The evolution of weeds in relation to the resistance to herbicides. *Proc. 3rd Brit. Weed Control Conf.* (Blackpool), 1, 179–88.

—— & SAGAR, G. R. (1954). Some aspects of the ecology of buttercups in permanent grassland. *Proc. 1st Brit. Weed Control Conf.* (Margate), 256–65.

HARTLEY, W. (1950). The global distribution of the tribes of Gramineae. *Austral. J. Agric. Res.*, 1, 355–73.

HASKELL, G. (1952). Polyploidy, ecology and the British Flora. *J. Ecol.*, 40, 265–82.

—— (1955). Analyses of sexual-apomictic blackberry-populations and their ecological consequences. *Cold Spring Harbor Symp. Quant. Biol.*, 20, 111–26.

—— (1955a). Heterosis in seedling plants. *Proc. Roy. Soc. Lond.*, Ser. B, 144, 221.

HEISER, C. B., JR. (1949). An evolutionary study of the sunflower species *Helianthus annuus* and *H. Bolanderi*. *Univ. Calif. Publ. Bot.*, 23, 157–208.

—— (1950). A comparison of the flora as a whole and the weed flora of Indiana as to polyploidy and growth habits. *Proc. Indiana Acad. Sci.*, 59, 64–70.

HERMANN, G. (1947). Über das Verhalten der polyploiden Arten höherer Pflanzen bei der Besiedlung von Brachland. *Planta*, 35, 177–87.

JONES, E. T. (1956). The origin, breeding and selection of oats. *Agr. Rev.*, 11, 20–8.

KISHIMOTO, E. (1937). Chromosomenzahlen in den Gattungen *Panicum* und *Setaria*. I. Chromosomenzahlen einiger *Setaria*-Arten. *Cytologia*, 9, 23–27.

KRISTOFFERSSON, K. B. (1923). Monohybrid segregation in *Malva* species. *Hereditas,* 4, 44–54.

—— (1926). Species crossings in *Malva. Hereditas,* 7, 233–354.

KUHN, J. (1932). Biologischer Daseinskampf zwischen Unkraut und Kulturpflanze *Mitt. Dtsch. Landw. Ges.,* 47, 7–8.

KUPFSOV, A. I. (1955). [Transition of wild plants and weeds into cultivated ones—in Russian.] *Priroda,* 44, 92–95.

LAURENCE, W. E. (1947). Chromosome numbers in *Achillea* in relation to geographic distribution. *Amer. J. Bot.,* 34, 538–45.

LÖVE, D. & DANSEREAU, P. (1959). Biosystematic studies on *Xanthium:* taxonomic appraisal and ecological status. *Canad. J. Bot.,* 37, 173–208.

MARGUEZ, V. MORENO. *See* MORENO MARGUEZ, V.

MITRA, S. K. & GANGULI, P. M. (1932). Some observations on the characters of weed rice hybrids. *Indian J. Agric. Sci. II,* Pt. III, 271–9.

MOORE, R. J. & LINDSAY, D. R. (1953). Fertilization and polyploidy of *Euphorbia cyparissias* in Canada. *Canad. J. Bot.,* 31, 152–63.

—— & FRANKTON, C. (1954). Cytotaxonomy of three species of *Centaurea* adventive in Canada. *Canad. J. Bot.,* 32, 182–6.

—— & MULLIGAN, G. A. (1956). Natural hybridization between *Carduus acanthoides* and *C. nutans* in Ontario. *Canad. J. Bot.,* 34, 71–85.

MORENO MARGUEZ, V. (1949). [Polyploidy as a possible means of obtaining bean varieties resistant to 'joko' (*Orobanche crenata*)—in Spanish.] *Bol. Pat. Veg. Ent. Agric., Madrid,* 16, 243–52.

MULLIGAN, G. A. (1957). Chromosome numbers of Canadian weeds. I. *Canad. J. Bot.,* 35, 779–89 (incl. 101 refs.).

—— (1958). Chromosome races in the *Chrysanthemum leucanthemum* complex. *Rhodora,* 60, 122–5.

—— (1959). Chromosome numbers of Canadian weeds. II. *Canad. J. Bot.,* 37, 81–92 (incl. 100 refs.).

—— (1960). Polyploidy in Canadian weeds. *Canad. J. Genetics and Cytol.,* 2, 150–61.

—— & BASSETT, I. J. (1959). *Achillea millefolium* complex in Canada and portions of the United States. *Canad. J. Bot.,* 37, 73–79.

—— & FRANKTON, C. (1954). The plumeless thistles (*Carduus* spp.) in Canada. *Canad. Fld. Nat.,* 68, 31–36.

MURBECK, S. V. (1904). Parthogenese bei den Gattungen *Taraxacum* und *Hieracium. Bot. Notiser, Lund,* 1904, pp. 285–96.

NIELSEN, E. L. (1947). Polyploidy and winter survival in *Panicum virgatum. J. Amer. Soc. Agron.,* 39, 822–7.

NORDENSKIÖLD, H. (1951). Cyto-taxonomic studies in the genus *Luzula. Hereditas,* 37, 325–55.

OSTENFELD, C. H. (1921). Some experiments on the origin of new forms in the genus *Hieracium* subgenus *Archieracium. J. Genetics,* 11, 117–22.

OWNBY, M. & AASE, H. C. (1955). Cytotaxonomic studies on *Allium.* I. The *Allium canadense* alliance. *State Coll. Washington, Res. Studies,* Monog. Suppl. No. 1, 106 pp.

PAULEY, S. S. & PERRY, T. O. (1954). Ecotypic variation of the photoperiodic response in *Populus. J. Arnold Arboretum,* 35, 167–88.

RICHENS, R. H. (1955). Studies on *Ulmus.* I. The range of variation of East Anglian Elms. *Watsonia,* 3, 138–53.

RILEY, H. P. (1936). The genetics and physiology of self sterility in the genus *Capsella. Genetics,* 21, 24–39.

ROLLINS, R. C. (1954). Interspecific hybridization and its role in plant evolution. *Proc. 8th Internat. Bot. Congr.* Sect. 9., pp. 173–80.

SAKAI, K. (1955). Competition in plants and its relation to selection. *Cold Spr. Harb. Symp. Quant. Biol.*, 20, 137–57.

—— & UTIYAMADA, H. (1956). Chromosome number hybridity and competitive ability in rice. *Nat. Inst. Genetics (Japan) Ann. Rep.* No. 6, 78–79.

SAKISAKA, M. (1950). Critical considerations of chromosome numbers in relation to plant habit (life forms). *Proc. 7th Internat. Bot. Congr., Stockholm*, pp. 286–7.

SAMPSON, D. R. (1954). On the origin of oats. *Harvard Univ. Bot. Mus. Leafl.*, 16(10), 265–303.

SCHIEMANN, E. (1943). Entstehung der Kulturpflanzen. *Ergebn. Biol.*, 19, 409–552.

—— (1951). New results on the history of cultivated cereals. *Heredity*, 5, 305–20.

SCHWANITZ, F. (1959). Selection and race formation in cultivated plants. *Cold Spr. Harb. Symp. Quant. Biol.*, 24, 107–14.

SHULL, C. A. (1934). Persistence of interspecific types of *Xanthium* under field conditions. *Bot. Gaz.*, 96, 175–9.

SMITH-WHITE, S. (1959). Cytological evolution in the Australian flora. *Cold Spr. Harb. Symp. Quant. Biol.*, 24, 273–89.

SÖLLNER, R. (1954). Recherches cytotaxomiques sur le genre *Cerastium. Ber. Schweiz. Bot. Ges.*, 64, 221–345.

SØRENSEN, T. & GUILJÓNSSON, G. (1946). Spontaneous chromosome-aberrants in apomictic Taraxaca. *K. Danske Vidensk. Selsk. Biol. Skr.*, IV(2), 1–48.

SPORNE, H. R. (1954). Statistics and the evolution of dicotyledons. *Evolution*, 8, 55–64.

SWANSON, C. P. (1957). *Cytology and Cytogenetics*. Prentice-Hall, Englewood Cliffs, New Jersey, 596 pp.

SYMON, D. E. (1955). A hybrid swarm in *Cassia. Austral. J. Bot.*, 3, 190–96.

TEDIN, O. (1925). [Vererbung, Variation und Systematik in der Gattung *Camelina*—in German, English summary.] *Hereditas*, 6, 275–386.

THELLUNG, A. (1930). Die Entstehung der Kulturpflanzen. *Naturwiss. Landwirtsch.*, Freising-München, 91 pp. (Festschrift für J. Braun-Blanquet).

TISCHLER, G. (1955). Der Grad der Polyploidie bei den Angiospermen in verschiedenen Grossarealen. *Cytologia*, 20, 101–18.

TURESSON, G. (1922). The genotypical response of the plant species to the habitat. *Hereditas*, 3, 211–350.

—— (1926). Habitat and genotypic changes—a reply. *Hereditas*, 8, 207–28.

TUTIN, T. G. (1957). A contribution to the experimental taxonomy of *Poa annua* L. *Watsonia*, 4, 1–10.

VAVILOV, N. I. (1926). Studies on the origin of cultivated plants. *Bull. Appl. Bot.*, 16(12), 138–248.

—— (1951). *The Origin, Variation, Immunity, and Breeding of Cultivated Plants*—trans. from Russian, K. Starr Chester, Chronica Botanica, Waltham, Mass., 304 pp.

WALTERS, M. S. (1957). *Studies of Spontaneous Chromosome Breakage in Interspecific hybrids of Bromus*. Univ. Calif. Press, Berkeley, 113 pp.

WERTH, E. (1945). Neues und Kritisches zur Kenntnis alter Kulturpflanzen. *Ber. Dtsch. Bot. Ges.*, 60, 232–58.

WHITE, S. SMITH-. *See* SMITH-WHITE, S.

WHYTE, R. O. (1946). *Crop Production and Environment*. Faber, London, 372 pp.

WIDDER, F. J. (1925). [Review of the species and hybrids of *Xanthium* in Europe—in Latin.] *Report. Nov. Spec. Regn. Veg.*, 21, 273–305.

WILLIS, J. C. (1922). *Age and Area*. A Study in Geographical Distribution and Origin of Species. Cambridge University Press, Cambridge, England, 259 pp.

—— (1949). *The Birth and Spread of Plants*. Chronica Botanica, Waltham, Mass., 561 pp.

WULF, H. D. (1936). Die Polysomatie der Chenopodiaceen. *Planta*, 26(2), 275–90.

ZOSSIMOVICH, V. P. (1939). Evolution of cultivated beet *Beta vulgaris* L. *C.R. Acad. Sci. U.R.S.S.*, 24(1), 73–76.

X

INJURIOUS INTERACTIONS OF WEEDS AND CROP PLANTS

INJURIOUS EFFECTS OF WEEDS ON CROPS

THESE effects are of prime importance, for they result in the reduction of crop yields and consequently cause an economic loss to the producer. It is at this point that the producer loses part of his investment, while the country suffers a reduction in agricultural products—chiefly food resources. These proportions of crops which are lost through the activities of all types of pests, have been aptly termed 'The Untaken Harvest' by Ordish (1952). In 1952, in the United States alone, the cost of controlling weeds, and the losses from not controlling them, represented an estimated national loss of 5 billion dollars (Ennis, 1958). A very conservative estimate places the annual weed cost to Canada at about 200 million dollars, while a more liberal interpretation places this loss at a value of over 500 million dollars (Frankton, 1955—*see* Ch. VIII). These figures may be more meaningful when it is realized that the 'cultivation' of crops costs about 16 per cent of the total value of the harvest, and, furthermore, about one-half of this 'cultivation' is made necessary by the presence of weeds. Some of the basic reasons for these losses will be discussed in the following sections.

COMPETITION FOR SPACE

The rate at which certain species of weeds grow in height as well as in leaf area, frequently enables them to surpass the growth of crop plants, and eventually to crowd them out altogether. Thus, competition for space involves occupying space around or very near to the crop plant. This may be achieved by one plant, or small numbers of plants, of great size and rapid growth-rate; or it may be achieved by very large numbers of plants possessing either moderate or rapid rates of growth. This competition is, of course, dependant upon such other limiting factors of the environment as moisture, nutrients, and light. These factors have already been considered in relation to the establishment of weeds, which was examined in Chapter VI.

In cultivated ground, especially, many species of weeds commonly appear in tremendous numbers, presenting a carpet-like effect *en masse*. Very often these 'carpets' are made up of only one species, for example, in the genera *Portulaca, Mollugo, Amaranthus, Chenopodium, Digitaria, Abutilon, Setaria, Echinochloa, Galinsoga*, etc. Thus, in many cases, the 'smothering-out' of crops by such masses of weed growth is literally what takes place, though the dwarfing and eventual disappearance of the crop plant in such situations is probably due to shading. Such abundant weed growths are particularly evident in vegetable-growing soils that are heavily fertilized year after year, and provided with irrigation as well. These are the areas that have required extensive and costly hand-weeding operations. With the advent of selective herbicides, many seeded crops may now be sprayed before their emergence, or in an early stage of post-emergence. It is in these early crop stages that emerging weeds are at their most vulnerable to chemical control, or to control by such mechanical methods as hoeing or burial in the soil.

With a knowledge of the specific weed problems in any given area, it is possible, by strict planting and cultivation schedules (and given favourable weather conditions), to minimize such weed problems. Sometimes a suitable crop must be chosen, and instead of being planted in rows it may have to be broadcast (e.g. soybeans). Infestations of perennial weeds present similar problems, and may involve *inter alia* the planting of fast-growing and shade-providing crops. Some of these procedures are examined in a later chapter under 'competitive cropping' (pp. 418–19).

COMPETITION FOR NUTRIENTS

A number of detailed studies of this subject have been prepared by Vengris (1953, 1955, 1956) at the Massachusetts Experiment Station, and are reviewed here. On arable land, and also often on grassland, weeds grow alongside cultivated plants and commonly constitute from 30 to 50 per cent of the total dry-matter production. Thus considerable competition exists between the weeds and crop plants (as indeed between any two species in the community) for nutrients, light, and moisture. It is pointed out that, in actual practice, there is virtually no such thing as completely weed-free land. In both grasslands and cultivated fields, weeds are major competitors with cultivated plants for nitrogen and especially for potassium. Certain weeds are often able to accumulate considerable amounts of these nutrients at the expense of cultivated plants, thereby reducing yields—particularly when the availability of these elements in the soil is low. Fig. 39 shows that weeds accumulate more N, P, K, Ca, and Mg (and especially of the last three elements) than do the crops. Thus the value of weeds as forage should not be underestimated.

Weeds with high rates of absorption and utilization of essential plant nutrients usually invade depleted, run-down land, thriving normally under poor fertility levels where cultural methods fail to produce normal yields of crops. Vengris notes that in one locality wormseed mustard (*Erysimum cheiranthoides*) exhibited high absorption for phosphorus when compared with companion crops of alfalfa and smooth bromegrass. Analysis of this weed from check plots showed a P content of 0·532 per cent of dry-weight, while the two crops on check plots contained 0·33 and 0·32 per cent, respectively. Some weeds are apparently able to use forms of soil phosphates that are relatively unavailable to many cultivated plants. The role of some species in releasing in the soil phosphorus that is not readily available to other plants has not been appreciated.

Further studies involved the competition of weeds with maize. When maize and weeds were growing together, competition for potassium was most noticeable, and competition for nitrogen also occurred—especially in the early stages of growth. The average potassium content in weed tissues was three times as high, and the nitrogen content twice as high, as in maize grown with these weeds. Average data for four years showed

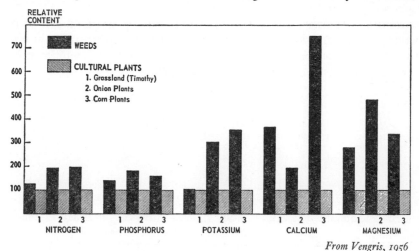

From Vengris, 1956

FIG. 39.—Weeds are represented as having a greater mineral content than their associated cultivated plants. The cultivated plants have been given the value 100. Average data of 1950–51. Samples collected from typical farms in the Connecticut Valley, Massachusetts, U.S.A.

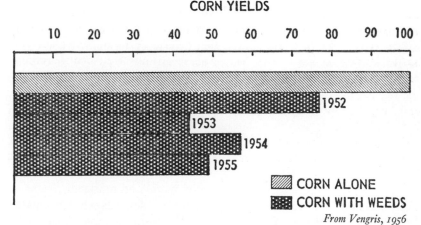

From Vengris, 1956

FIG. 40.—Yields of corn (maize) grown alone and grown with weeds, 1952–55. Relative values: corn alone = 100. Plots were fertilized with 200 lb./acre N, 200 lb./acre P_2O_5, and 200 lb./acre K_2O.

that maize, when grown with weeds, took up only 44 per cent as much potassium and 53 per cent as much nitrogen, and produced only 57 per cent as much dry matter, as did maize that had grown alone (Tab. IX).

In these maize experiments (Figs. 39, 40), competition was clearly expressed in the yield data; because of the weeds, maize yields for the dry growing-seasons of 1953 and 1955 were reduced by 51 and 56 per cent respectively, whereas under more normal weather conditions (1952 and 1954) the average reduction in maize yield as a result of weed competition was only 33 per cent (cf. Tables VIII and IX).

TABLE VIII

CHEMICAL COMPOSITION OF MAIZE GROWN ALONE, OF MAIZE GROWN WITH WEEDS, AND OF DIFFERENT WEEDS GROWN WITH MAIZE. DATA ARE AVERAGES FOR 1952–55 ON BASIS OF DRY-WEIGHT PLOTS RECEIVED 200 lb./ac.N, 200 lb./ac. P_2O_5, AND 200 lb./ac. K_2O. (Vengris et al., 1953).

Plant	Early maturity stage of growth				
	N%	P%	K%	Ca%	Mg%
Maize alone	1·46	0·20	1·04	0·17	0·27
Maize with weeds	1·38	0·19	0·76‡	0·20	0·36‡
Pigweed with maize (corn)	2·41	0·26	2·79	0·62	0·93
Lamb's-quarters with maize (corn)*	2·64	0·20	2·50	0·75	0·75
Crabgrass with maize (corn)†	2·09	0·20	1·80	0·38	0·96
Averages for weeds	2·38	0·22	2·36	0·58	0·88

* One year's data only.
† Two years' data only.
‡ Statistically significant in comparison with maize (corn) grown alone.

TABLE IX

COMPARISONS OF RELATIVE YIELDS AND OF PLANT NUTRIENT UPTAKE BY MAIZE ALONE, MAIZE WITH WEEDS, AND DIFFERENT WEEDS GROWN ALONE. MAIZE GROWN ALONE = 100. PLOTS RECEIVED 200 lb./ac. N, 200 lb./ac. P_2O_5, AND 200 lb./ac. K_2O. DATA ARE AVERAGE FOR 1952–55. (Vengris et al. 1953).

Plant	Relative nutrient uptake, Maize = 100					
	Yields	N	P	K	Ca	Mg
Maize alone	100	100	100	100	100	100
Maize with weeds	57	53	58	44	66	76
Pigweed alone	60	102	80	124	275	234
Lamb's-quarters alone*	69	120	74	121	281	216
Crabgrass alone†	67	100	64	157	131	228

* One year's data only.
† Two years' data only.

In tropical regions the conservation of available nitrate in the soils is particularly important. Owing to the higher temperatures, the oxidation rates of organic matter are higher than in temperate regions, and this, coupled with the leaching action of heavy rainfall, makes available nitrates quite transient. In a study of this problem, Meiklejohn (1955) notes that, after lack of water, lack of nitrogen is the greatest single cause of poor yields. He found that the average amount of available nitrogen in Indian soils was 0·05 per cent, while, as an example, the average from a European series of soils (not all of them fertile) was 0·15 per cent. In facing this problem we must certainly agree that weeds growing directly in the crop do compete for nitrates and other nutrients, while in non-crop land (or between croppings) the presence of weed growth could conceivably result in storing these nutrients within the weed tissue—to be released in the soil at a later time upon the decomposition of these tissues.

In addition to the studies cited here and in the earlier section on nutrient absorption (pp. 174–5), Vigorov (1955) has investigated the nitrogen removal by weeds in spring wheat plantings. The zinc content (Rogers et al., 1939), the manganese content (Ichikawa & Seo, 1953—see Ch. VII), and the N, P, and Ca contents (Harper H. J., 1924—see Ch. VII) of weeds have also been studied, as well as the carotene (Moon, 1939—see Ch. VII) contents of some forage species and pasture weeds. Moreover, several general studies (Kling, 1914—see Ch. VII; Ince, 1915—see Ch. VII) have been made, together with analytical studies of the local wild plants, in the search for metallic ores and other biogeochemical indications (Vinogradov, 1943—see Ch. VII; Malinga, 1947—see Ch. VII; H. L. Cannon, 1957—see Ch. VII).

SOME GENERAL CONSIDERATIONS OF COMPETITION

In a detailed analysis of the effects of weed competition on maize and oats, Li (1960), in New Jersey, found that allowing weeds to grow for longer than one week in oats and two weeks in maize, resulted in a loss of yield under some conditions. Oats when competing with weeds produced less grain-yield, less dry-matter, fewer tillers, and fewer seeds per panicle, and it had a lower content of nitrogen and of potassium, than oats that had been grown free from weed competition. Increase in the fertility level raised both yield and nitrogen content of the weedy oats to, or above, the level of the clean crop receiving no fertilizer. A 12-in. weed-free band along the maize row did not offset the effects of weed competition. The percentage of nitrogen in maize plants was lower when competition had continued for longer than three weeks after emergence. The results indicated that it is possible to counteract weed competition in maize by an increase in the level of fertilization under conditions where water is not limiting. Li further observed that weeds which were capable of making rapid growth during the early stages of crop development, depressed crop yields to a greater extent than those which developed later in the season. Weeds competed strongly with maize and oats for nutrients. In terms of percentage of dry-weight, the greatest concentration of N, P, K, and Ca, in weeds generally occurred during the first two to three weeks subsequent to the emergence of the crop. *See* the Addendum on Dr. J. L. Harper's work, p. 259.

The Influence of One Plant Upon Another

It has long been recognized that plants growing thickly together in an area are influenced in their growth by the presence of adjacent plants. This may result in such obvious responses as dwarfing in plant size, a chlorotic or nutrient-starved condition, wilting, and actual dying-out of the less successful plants. These responses are all various manifestations of competition. There are a number of more subtle types of response however, which are not so obvious as the ones mentioned, but may be related to a series of complex interactions between a specific plant (i.e. a crop plant) and adjacent competing plants (i.e. weeds growing around a crop plant). These less obvious interactions are primarily those involving the soil medium, the mesh-work of intertwining roots of the same or many different species, and the detritus of organic residues in all stages of decomposition. It is thus a highly complex medium and environment which biologists and others have for study and analysis.

No small wonder, then, that there has been considerable controversy over the precise nature of this influence of one plant upon another in the area of the root zone, or 'rhizosphere'. The multitude of organic substances which are secreted or excreted from living parts, as well as a comparably great number of substances from former living material in all stages of decomposition and molecular degradation—virtually down to the final product of respiration, CO_2—undoubtedly exert their effects in a fantastic array of actions and interactions. With advances in techniques for the separation of complex mixtures, such as paper chromatography, the identification of many of these substances is now being accomplished. Teletoxicity is the term applied to the action and interaction of these many substances upon the growth of higher plants, particularly in their adverse aspects.

TELETOXIC ACTION

This general area of study has been the subject of considerable controversy for over fifty years. The classical work in this field, by Molisch, *Über der Einfluss einer Pflanze auf die Andere, Allelopathie* (1937), is a rare one, and few copies have been available for study in the United States of America. This situation has been ameliorated somewhat by the appearance of Grümmer's *Die gegenseitige Beeinflussung höherer Pflanzen— Allelopathie* (1953). The subject has also been reviewed by Wildeman (1948), by Bonner (1946, 1950), by Russell (1961), by Martin (1957), by Rademacher (1959) Börner (1960) and Evenari (1961).

The early work which touched off the controversy goes back to the early part of the twentieth century—to the studies of Whitney (1904), of the United States Department of Agriculture. He believed that unproductiveness of cropped soils was due to the accumulation of toxic substances excreted by each crop plant, which proved injurious to that species of plant (truly an allelopathic action). This toxicity could be overcome by crop rotation and by the use of fertilizers, which served primarily as detoxifying agents. According to the account given by Bear (1956), this was heresy to Cyril G. Hopkins, of the University of Illinois, who had reduced the soil fertility problem to a bank-account system; and who held that nutrient depletion and reduction in crop yields would not occur if certain practices of rotating with leguminous crops, controlling the soil reaction with lime, and using fertilizers to replace the lost elements, were followed.

The issue was so sharply defined that it led to a Congressional investigation of the teachings of Whitney and his associates. Some writers of the period used Chinese agriculture as an example of one not employing mineral fertilizers. All of these matters, and others no doubt, prompted Professor F. H. King of the University of Wisconsin to go to China to investigate the matter. His findings were reported in *Farmers of Forty Centuries* (1927), written on his return. He concluded that by the Chinese system—a highly laborious and unsanitary one—fully as many pounds of plant nutrients were returned to the soil (in street sweepings, canal mud, and human and animal excreta, as well as crop rotations) as the harvested crops removed. This system was one of conservation. Our fertilizer system is far less laborious and much more sanitary. But the end results in terms of crop production are virtually identical. It is not clear how the problem of toxic residues in the soil, if there are any, was resolved (Bear, 1956).

Following the work in the United States, a number of investigators in England also came to believe that toxic substances were excreted, one case cited being of excretions from grass growing under fruit trees—to such an extent that the growth of the latter was seriously reduced (Pickering & Bedford, 1919). This work preceded that on penicillin and other antibiotics, as well as knowledge of 'auxins' and growth regulators. In the light of all of these later developments, the role of such postulated 'soil toxins' appears much more plausible, and indeed, re-investigations in this field are beginning to substantiate and extend the findings of these pioneer, but much maligned, investigators.

A renewal of research on this problem appears to have been made by Swedish workers (Osvald, 1947; Hofsten, 1954—*see* Ch. VI), as well as by the American, Bonner (1946). Osvald, too observed the dominating effects of grass populations, and in his study found that heavy growths of quack-grass (*Agropyron repens*) reduced the germination and growth of rape (*Brassica napus* and *B. rapa*). He prepared extracts from dried quack-grass stolons, and noted that more than twice as high a concentration of the extract was required for the total inhibition of a grass seed, such as oats, as was required for rape. Osvald noted too, that the effects of the extract on germination resembled those of the growth substances. These studies led him to hypothesize that, by such root secretions, many phenomena of plant growth and grouping in natural vegetation may be explained, such as 'the ability of many grasses to supersede clover, the detrimental effect of grasses on fruit trees, and the inability of many wild species in open vegetation (for instance, in mountains and along shores) to compete with grasses, even if these do not form a close stand' (Osvald, 1947; cf. King, 1948).

The chemical substances involved, and to which the various responses have been attributed, have been termed 'phytotoxins' (Osvald, 1947), and in part 'phytonicides' (cf. Tokin, 1956; Gramenitçaia, 1952—*see* Grümmer, 1953; Kretowitsch, 1965). Horticulturists in North America and Europe are involved, in part with this area of study in their apple and peach replant problems and the associated 'soil sickness' or 'Bodenmüdigkeit' (Börner, 1959). The chemical identification of such phytotoxins may well provide some useful clues to the synthesis of entirely new types of herbicides. The aggressiveness of members of the Gramineae both in the temperate and tropical regions (e.g. species of *Agropyron*, *Cynodon*, *Sorghum*, *Panicum*, *Imperata*, *Arundo*, *Saccharum*, *Paspalum*, and many others), may very well be due, in large part, to these phytotoxins released from living or dead plant members.

Hamilton & Buchholtz (1955) re-examined this problem with quack-grass, as well as the interaction with shading, under Wisconsin conditions. Their work has appeared to substantiate Osvald's findings, and is interpreted as indicating that each of the species observed has a characteristic response-curve to concentrations of the biologically active substance produced by quack-grass. They noted that maximum reduction of the germination of weed seedlings occurred on those plots in which both shade (from the 'canopy' of the grass) and living quack-grass roots were present. They also observed that the numbers of seedlings of the weeds *Veronica peregrina*, *Polygonum persicaria*, *Oxalis stricta*, *Setaria lutescens*, and *Trifolium repens*, were significantly greater on the plots with living quack-grass rhizomes than on the plots with no such rhizomes (presumably in the absence of shade). A delay of about one month in the period of maximum emergence of weedy species was noted on the plots that had living quack-grass rhizomes present—as compared with the controls which lacked such rhizomes.

Experiments at Rothamsted, however, have provided no support for the suggestion that the harmful effects of quack-grass (*Agropyron repens*) on crops is partly caused by toxic substances secreted by the living roots or rhizomes (Welbank, 1960, 1960a). Additional work has, however, explored the possibility that toxin production occurs during the decay of *Agropyron* residues in the soil. The author cited concludes that 'field observations suggest that the amounts of roots and rhizomes present in land heavily infested with *Agropyron* are enough to affect crop growth by toxin production when they decay in suitable conditions (in water-logged soil under poor aeration), but there is no reason to suppose that this effect is specific to *Agropyron*, for other workers have found that extracts of other plant residues incubated with soil inhibit germination and respiration of tobacco.'

An indication of the nature of some of these substances that may be released from grass roots (e.g. *Avena* spp.) is shown in the ultra-violet photograph where strong evidence for the probable presence of the lactone, scopoletin, is provided (Pl. 12(*b*) cf. Goodwin & Kavanagh, 1949).

Many other studies are available which indicate the existence of such types of root secretions (or by-products of dead or dying roots or rhizomes). Thus peach roots inhibit the growth of young peach trees (Proebsting & Gilmore, 1941); the presence of dead roots and 'stolons' of brome-grass inhibits the growth of young brome-grass plants (Benedict, 1941); a volatile substance (the alkaloid, absinthin) obtained from *Artemisia absinthium* was reported by Funke (1943) to prevent the encroachment of other plants; 3-aldehydo-4-methoxy-acetophenone was identified as the active material leaching into the soil from old leaves of the desert shrub *Encelia farinosa* and apparently responsible for the lack of seedling development within the area of leaf-fall (Bonner, 1950); Curtis & Cottam (1950) reported that the antibiotic and autotoxic effects of *Helianthus rigidus* appeared to be due to the presence of a substance derived from the decomposition of underground plant parts; Keever (1950) showed that *Erigeron canadensis* seedlings were stunted by decomposition products from roots of the same species; black-walnut trees (*Juglans nigra*) were found to exert a deterimental effect on certain other plants growing within the root zone of this tree (H. Bode, 1940); and Went *et al.* (1952) found that such species as *Chenopodium album* and *Amaranthus hybridus* varied in their ability to germinate and develop in the presence of seedling barley, tobacco, and sugar beets. The roots of flax (*Linum usitatissimum*) contain the cyanogenic glycoside, linamarin, and it is stated that its decomposition leads to the excretion of small amounts of HCN (hydrocyanic acid) which eliminate some pathogenic fungi from the rhizosphere flora.

Börner (1956) has also examined the activity of these toxic substances from three species of cereals, and many more studies of this general nature are cited by Grümmer (1953) and by Rademacher (1959; cf. Table X). Rivière (1959), at the Institut Agronomique (Paris), has provided a thorough examination of the rhizosphere of the wheat plant, including a detailed study of the wheat root secretions using paper chromatography —together with a useful survey of the literature.

Substances derived from roots and other underground portions of plants are also important in stimulating the germination of such parasitic weeds as witchweed (*Striga lutea*), and thereby a method of control termed 'trap cropping' has been successfully utilized (*see* Ch. III). Substances in this category from tomato roots have been found to stimulate the hatching of nematode cysts and to influence chemotoxically the movements of the nematode larvae (i.e. affect the larvae in such a way that they move towards the tomato roots). A lactone, ecleptic acid, was isolated which was active in this manner in dilutions of 1×10^{-7} and 1×10^{-8}. Of interest from a potential control standpoint is the observation that populations of certain nematode species (*Pratylenchus penetrans*) are reduced rather strongly in the soil, when *Tagetes* spp. (Compositae), and particularly *T. erecta*, are grown. This active substance has been found to be *alpha*terthienyl (cf. Aamisepp & Osvald, 1962).

Phytotoxic substances from decomposing plant residues (rye and timothy) have been shown to increase the susceptibility of tobacco to black root rot—indicating such toxins may be important in host-conditioning and thus favour disease development (*see* Patrick, Z. A. & Koch, L. W. (1963), *Can. J. Bot.*, 41, 747–58; *Phytopath.*, 53, 152–61, 1963, 53, 265–70, 1963).

TABLE X

SUBSTANCES FROM PLANT PARTS, CHIEFLY ROOTS, BELIEVED TO BE ASSOCIATED WITH TELETOXICITY[*]

Name	Structure	Plant Source	Reference
5-Hydroxynaphtho-quinone (juglone)	$HOC_{10}H_5O_2$	*Juglans nigra* (black walnut) roots	Davis, 1928
Absinthin (glucoside)	$C_{30}H_{40}O_8$	*Artemisia absinthium* leaves	Bode, 1940 Funke, 1943
trans-Cinnamic acid	$C_6H_5CH: CHCOOH$	*Taraxacum koksaghyz* leaves	Bonner & Galston, 1944
3-Acetyl-6-methoxy-benzaldehyde	$CH_3OC_6H_3CHOOCCH_3$	*Encelia farinosa* leaves	Gray & Bonner, 1948
Oxalic acid ?	$COOHCOOH . 2H_2O$	*Oxalis* spp., roots	Frey-Wyssling, 1930[†]
Scopoletin (7-oxy-6-methoxycoumarin)	$C_{10}H_8O_4$	*Avena sativa* roots	Eberhardt, 1954, 1955
Flavanone (3_1, 4_1-dihydroflavanone)	$C_{15}H_{10}O_2$	*Arachis hypogaea* roots	Petrů & Chrastil, 1955
Phlorizin, quercitrin	phloretin, $C_{15}H_{14}O_5$	*Malus sylvestris* roots	Börner, 1959

* Adapted, in part, from Rademacher (1959).
† Cf. Rademacher (1959).

The investigations of Dr. Horst Börner (1959), formerly visiting investigator at the Boyce Thompson Institute, and currently at the Institut für Pflanzenschutz, Technische Hochschule, Stuttgart-Hohenheim, Germany, may appropriately be described here. Although the problem has centred around the apple replant problem in Germany and its possible relationship to substances released from apple-root residues in the soil, the fundamentals involved are common to most plant-residue and root-secretion interactions with living plants, including those of weeds versus crops. A summary of these findings as reported by Börner follows.

Experiments were carried out to investigate the causes of the apple re-plant problem from the point of view of the possible action of substances released into the soil from residues. It was found that an addition of dried apple root-bark to water cultures produced a strong reduction in the growth of apple seedlings. As little as 1 gm. of root-bark per 500 ml. of nutrient solution caused a considerable effect (cf. Pl. 13). Paper chromatograms revealed five phenolic substances as obtainable from bark that had been held in nutrient solutions for 33 days. The same compounds are present in cold-water extracts from soils containing apple root residues.

Of the five phenolic substances that were present in nutrient solution and water extracts of soil, only phlorizin could be identified as a natural constituent of the bark and wood of apple roots, although quercitrin was also detected. The other four phenolic substances were detected in soils within two to ten days after pure phlorizin was added to different soils. It is obvious, therefore, that these substances were decomposition products of phlorizin. The detected compounds were identified as phloretin, p-hydroxyhydrocinnamic acid, phloroglucinol, and p-hydroxybenzoic acid (Plate 14). The breakdown of phlorizin in soils in all probability occurs as follows:

$$\text{phlorizin} \longrightarrow \text{phloretin} \begin{array}{l} \nearrow \text{phloroglucinol} \\ \\ \searrow \text{p-hydroxyhydrocinnamic acid} \\ \qquad\qquad\text{p-hydroxybenzoic acid.} \end{array}$$

The identified chemicals retarded the growth of apple seedlings in water culture at a concentration as low as $10^{-4}\ M$. The inhibitory effect on root development was very obvious, though the effectiveness of the compounds varied widely. The strongest inhibition was caused by phlorizin and phloretin, while phloroglucinol had only a slight influence.

To what extent the identified chemicals participate in the apple re-plant problem is not clear. Further investigations will be necessary to find out the amount of root residues left in the soil and the concentrations of the detected compounds under natural conditions.

As regards terminology, this type of antagonistic action has often been referred to as 'allelopathy', i.e. 'self-injury', but Wildeman (1948), in his review, indicates good grounds for the use of 'teletoxic action' or 'teletoxicity'. In the present author's opinion, one of the latter pair of terms is preferable, as the passage of toxicity from one plant or location to another (i.e. either back to the same plant and/or species, or to another) is indicated. Weiss (1949) touched upon this subject and stated that the teletoxic action of noxious weeds has not been appreciated. It would now appear that there are some grounds for believing in this type of activity, but more demonstrations *in situ* (i.e. under field conditions) are essential for assigning any important role here, either in aggressiveness of weeds or in the dominance of certain plant species.

BIBLIOGRAPHY

(*Injurious Interactions of Weeds and Crop Plants*)

AAMISEPP, A. & OSVALD, H. (1962). Influence of higher plants upon each other—Allelopathy. Some new results of research into allelopathy. *Nova Acta Soc. Sci. Upsal.* Ser. IV, 18(2), 1–19.

ANON. (1955). Weed losses. *Bull. Ont. Dep. Agric.*, No. 505, Feb.

ARMSTRONG, S. F. & PRATT, E. R. (1915). On the harmful effects of the growth of certain grasses and weeds around the roots of young forest trees. *Quart. J. For.*, 9(3), 225–30.

ARNOLD, H. C. (1930). Injurious effect of weeds on maize yields. *Rhod. Agric. J.*, 27, 1283.

BAKKE, A. L. & PAMMEL, L. H. (1923). The effect of weeds upon crop production. *Proc. Ia. Acad. Sci.*, 1922, 29, 271–9.

BALCOM, R. B. (1950). Weeds—water robbers. *J. Soil Wat. Conserv.*, 5(4), 165–8.

BARTON, L. V. & McNAB, J. (1954). Effect of antibiotics on plant growth. *Contrib., Boyce Thompson Inst.*, 17, 419–34.

BEAR, F. E. (1956). A look at the Orient. *Bett. Crops*, 40, 13, 16, 44, 46.

BENEDICT, H. M. (1941). The inhibiting effect of dead roots on the growth of brome-grass. *J. Amer. Soc. Agron.*, 33, 1108–9.

BHUVANESWARI, K. & SULOCHAVA, C. B. (1955). Assay of root exudates. *Curr. Sci.* (India), 24, 376–7.

BLACKMAN, G. E. & TEMPLEMAN, W. G. (1938). The nature of the competition between cereal crops and annual weeds. *J. Agric. Sci.*, 28, 247–71.

BLASER, R. E. & BRADY, N. C. (1950). Nutrient competition in plant associations. *Agron. J.*, 42, 128–35.

——, GRIFFITH, W. A. & TAYLOR, T. H. (1956). Seedling competition in establishing forage plants. *Agric. J.*, 48, 1–6.

——, —— & ——(1956a). Seedling competition in compounding forage seed mixtures. *Agric. J.*, 48, 118–23.

BLEASDALE, J. K. A. (1956). Interspecific competition in higher plants. *Nature, Lond.*, 278, 150–1.

BODE, H. R. (1940). Über die Blattausscheidungen des Wermuts und ihre Wirkungen auf andere Pflanzen. *Planta*, 30, 567–69.

BONNER, J. (1946). Further investigation of toxic substances which arise from guayule plants—relation of toxic substances to the growth of guayule in soil. *Bot. Gaz.*, 107, 343–51.

—— (1949). Chemical warfare among plants. *Sci. Amer.*, 180(3), 48–51.

—— (1950). The role of toxic substances in the interactions of higher plants. *Bot. Rev.*, 16, 51–65.

—— & GALSTON, A. W. (1944). Toxic substances from the culture media of guayule which may inhibit growth. *Bot. Gaz.*, 106, 185–98.

BÖRNER, H. (1956). Die Abgabe organischer Verbindungen aus den Karyospen, Wurzeln und Ernterückständen von Roggen (*Secale cereale* L.), Weizen (*Triticum aestivum* L.) und Gerste (*Hordeum vulgare* L.) und ihre Bedeutung bei der gegenseitigen. Beeinflussung der höheren Pflanzen. *Beitr. Biol. Pfl.*, 33, 33–83.

—— (1959). The apple replant problem. I. The excretion of phlorizin from apple root residues. *Contr. Boyce Thompson Inst.*, 20, 39–56.

—— (1960). Liberation of organic substances from higher plants and their role in the soil sickness problem. *Bot. Rev.*, 26, 393–424.

BOS, J. R. (1913). Interaction collaborations looking to control of pests and diseases of plants. *Tijdschr. PlfZiekt.*, 19(6), 153–235.

BOWEN-JONES, J. (1905). Influence of weeds on crops. *J. Roy. Agric. Soc.*, 66, 122.

BRADLEY, W. B. & EPPSON, H. F. (1940). Livestock poisoning by oat, hay and other plants containing nitrate. *Bull. Wyo. Agric. Exp. Sta.* No. 241, 20 pp.

BRENCHLEY, W. E. (1917). The effect of weeds upon cereal crops. *New Phytol.*, 16, 53–76.

—— (1940). The weed problems in non-rotational wheat-growing. *Emp. J. Exp. Agric.*, 8, 126–37.

CAMARGO, R. DE (1945). [The poisoning of its own environment by the coffee tree—in Portuguese.] *Pt. Biol. Sup. Serv. Café*, 20, 28–35.

COTTAM, G. & CURTIS, J. T. (1951). Antibiotics and plant competition. *Bull. Garden Club Amer.*, 39(2), 8–11. (*See also* next reference below.)

CURTIS, J. T. & COTTAM, G. (1950). Antibiotic and autotoxic effects in prairie sunflower. *Bull. Torrey Bot. Club*, 77(3), 187–91.

DAVIS, E. F. (1928). The toxic principle of *Juglans nigra* as identified with synthetic juglone, and its toxic effects on tomato and alfalfa plants. *Amer. J. Bot.*, 15, 620.

DE CAMARGO, R. *See* CAMARGO, R. DE.

DE PERALTA, F. *See* PERALTA, F. DE.

DE WILDEMAN, E. *See* WILDEMAN, E. DE.

DONALD, C. M. (1951). Competition among pasture plants. I. Intra-specific competition among annual pasture plants. *Austral. J. Agric. Res.*, 2, 355–76.

DUTOIT, R. (1937). Weeds and their control. Damage calculated in terms of money. *Farming in South Afr.*, 12, 353–5.

EBERHARDT, F. (1954). Ausscheidung einer organischen Verbindung aus den Wurzeln des Hafers (Avena sativa L.). *Naturwissenschaften*, 41, 259.

—— (1955). Über fluoreszierende Verbindungen in der Wurzel des Hafers. Ein Beitrag zum Problem der Wurzelausscheidungen. *Z. Bot.*, 43, 405–22.

ENNIS, W. B., JR. (1958). Weed control research pays dividends. *Nat. Agric. Chem. Assoc. News Pest. Rev.*, 16, 13, 18.

EVENARI, M. (1961). Chemical influences of other plants (alleopathy). In *Handbuch der Pflanzenphysiologie*. (Ed. W. Ruhland), Bd. 16, 691–736. Springer-Verlag, Berlin.

FLETCHER, F. (1912). Toxic excreta of plants. *J. Agric. Sci.*, 4, 245–6.

FUNKE, G. L. (1943). The influence of *Artemisia absinthium* on neighboring plants. *Blumea*, 5, 281–93.

GODEL, G. L. (1935). Relation between rate of seeding and yield of cereal crops in competition with weeds. *Sci. Agric. (Ottawa)*, 16, 165–8.

—— (1938). Cereal growing on weedy land in north-eastern Saskatchewan. Effect of heavy seeding with the use of fertilizer on the development of weeds and crops. *Sci. Agric. (Ottawa)*, 19, 21–32.

GOODWIN, R. H. & KAVANAGH, F. (1949). The isolation of scopoletin, a blue-fluorescing compound of oat roots. *Bull. Torrey Bot. Cl.*, 76, 255–65.

GRAY, A. P. (1944). *Imperata cylindrica*. V. The effect of *Imperata* on economic crops. *Imperial Agric. Bur. G.B. Joint Publica.* No. 7, 24–26.

GRAY, R. & BONNER, J. (1948). Structure determination and synthesis of a plant growth inhibitor, 3-acetyl-6-methoxy-benzaldehyde found in the leaves of *Encelia farinosa. J. Amer. Chem. Soc.*, **70**, 1249–53.

GRÜMMER, G. (1953). Die gegenseitige Beeinflussung höherer Pflanzen, Allelopathie. *Biol. Zbl.*, **72**, 494–518.

—— (1955). *Die gegenseitige Beeinflusssung höherer Pflanzen—Allelopathie.* Gustav Fischer, Jena, 162 pp.

GUYOT, L. (1951). Les excrétions racinaires toxiques chez les vegetaux. *Bull. Tech. Informat.*, **59**, 1–15.

HALSTED, B. D. (1892). The influence upon crops of neighbouring wild plants. *Proc. N.J. Hort. Soc.*, **17**, 110–22.

HAMILTON, K. C. & BUCHHOLTZ, K. P. (1955). Effect of rhizomes of quackgrass (*Agropyron repens*) and shading on the seedling development of weedy species. *Ecology*, **36**, 304–8.

HANSEN, A. A. (1922). The toll of weeds in Indiana. *Indiana Acad. Sci. Proc.*, 1921, pp. 105–9.

HELGESON, E. A. & KONZAK, R. (1950). Phytotoxic effects of aqueous extracts of field bindweed and Canada thistle. *N. Dak. Agric. Exp. Sta. Bi-Monthly Bull.*, **12**(3), 71–76.

HILLE, F. J. H. VAN (1952). Weed damage in potatoes in relation to their stage of growth. *Du Maandbl. Landb. Voore D.*, **9**, 20–27.

HOWARD, A. (1925). The effect of Grass on Trees. *Proc. Roy. Soc. Lond. Ser. B.* **97**, 284–321.

HUBBARD, R. L. (1956). The effects of plant competition upon the growth and survival of bitterbrush (*Purshia tridentata*) seedlings. *U.S. Forest Serv. Calif. Forest & Range Exp. Sta., Forest Res. Notes*, **109**, 9 pp.

KATZNELSON, H., ROUATT, J. W. & PAYNE, T. M. B. (1954). Liberation of amino-acids by plant roots in relation to desiccation. *Nature, Lond.*, **174**, 1110–11.

KAUL, R. N. (1951). Studies on weed crop competition. *Allahabad Farm.*, **25**(3), 103–15.

KEEVER, C. (1950). Causes of succession on old fields of Piedmont, North Carolina. *Ecol. Monogr.*, **20**, 229–50.

KILIAN, E. M. (1953). Certain reciprocal influence of oats and thistles. (Abs.) *Wyoming Univ. Public.*, **17**, 100–1.

KING, F. H. (1927). *Farmers of Forty Centuries.* Harcourt, Brace, New York.

KING, L. J. (1948). Book review of *Kampen mot Ogräset, 1935–1946.* (Weed Control Experiments), Ed. by H. Osvald. [Public. Inst. Plant Husbandry, Roy. Agric. Col., Sweden, No. 2 Almquist and Wiksells, Uppsala, 1947, 318 pp.] *Science*, **107**, 524–5.

KORSMO, E. (1932). Experiments from 1916 to 1923 on the harmful effects of weeds and their control on farm land. *Meld. Norg. LandbrHøisk.* **12**, 305–716.

KRETOWITSCH, W. L. (1965). *Grundzüge der Biochemie der Pflanzen.* G. Fischer, Jena. 473 pp. (*see* pp. 192 ff.)

LI, MING-YU, (1960). An evaluation of the critical period and the effects of weed competition on corn and oats. Ph.D. Dissertation, Rutgers Univ. *Dissert. Abstr.*, **20**(11), 4226.

LOEHWING, W. F. (1937). Root interactions of plants. *Bot. Rev.*, **3**, 195–239.

LONG, H. C. (1929). Weeds in the economy of agriculture. *Sci. Progr.*, **23**, 487–90.

MANN, H. H., & BARNES, T. W. (1949). The competition between barley and certain weeds under controlled conditions. III. Competition with *Agrostis gigantea. Ann. Appl. Biol.*, **36**(2), 273–81.

—— & —— (1950). The competition between barley and certain weeds under controlled conditions. IV. Competition with *Stellaria media. Ann. Appl. Biol.*, **37**(2), 139–48.

MANN, H. H., & BARNES, T. W. (1952). The competition between barley and certain weeds under controlled conditions. V. Competition with clover considered as a weed. *Ann. Appl. Biol.*, **39**, 111–19.

MARAIS, A. (1943). Weeds waste large percentage of valuable phosphates. *Farmer*, **32**(33), 8.

MARTIN, H. (1957). *Chemical Aspects of Ecology in Relation to Agriculture.* Sci. Serv. Dep. Agric., Ottawa, Canada, 96 pp.

MARTIN, P. & RADEMACHER, B. (1960). Studies on the mutual influence of weeds and crops. In *The Biology of Weeds. A Symposium of the British Ecological Society.* (Ed. J. L. Harper.) Blackwell, Oxford, pp. 143–52.

MEIKLEJOHN, J. (1955). Nitrogen problems in tropical soils. *Soils and Fert.*, **20**, 229–50.

MOLISCH, H. (1937). *Über der Einfluss einer Pflanze auf die Andere, Allelopathie.* Gustav Fischer, Jena, 106 pp., 15 figs.

MYERS, L. F. & LIPSETT, J. (1958). Competition between skeleton weeds (*Chondrilla juncea* L.) and cereals in relation to nitrogen supply. *Austral. J. Agric. Res.*, **9**, 1–12.

NEVENS, W. B. (1943). The relation of the kind of pasture crop to the weed content of the forage. *Illinois J. Dairy Sci.*, **26**, 877–82.

OKSBJERG, E. (1954). [Rejuvenation problems. 1. Root competition and root development—in Danish.] *Dansk Skovfor. Tidsskr.*, **60**, 39–92.

ORDISH, G. (1952). *The untaken harvest; man's loss of crops from weed, pest and disease— an introductory study.* Constable, London, 170 pp.

OSVALD, H. (1947). [Equipment of plants in the struggle for space—in Swedish, English summary.] *Växtodling*, **2**, 288–303.

—— (1953). On antagonism between plants. *Proc. 7th Internat. Bot. Congr., Stockholm,* pp. 167–71.

PANDE, H. K. (1953). Effect of weeding on the yield of wheat. *Emp. J. Exp. Agric.*, **31**, 297–304.

PANIKKAR, M. R. (1953). Crop-weed competition in farming. *Sci. & Cult.*, **19**, 293–6.

PAVLYCHENKO, T. K. (1937). Quantitative study of the entire root systems of weed and crop plants under field conditions. *Ecology*, **18**, 62–79.

—— (1942). Root systems of certain forage crops in relation to the management of agricultural soils. *Nat. Res. Counc. Canada & Domin. Dist. Agric.* No. 1088, Ottawa 1941, 46 pp.

—— (1950). Plant competition and weed control. *Agric. Inst. Rev.*, **4**, 142–5.

—— & HARRINGTON, J. B. (1934). Competitive efficiency of weeds and cereal crops. *Canad. J. Res.*, **10**, 77–94.

—— & —— (1935). Root development of weeds and crops in competition under dry farming conditions. *Sci. Agric.*, **16**, 151–60.

PERALTA, F. DE (1935). Some principles of competition as illustrated by sudan grass, *Holcus sorghum sudanensis* (Piper) Hitch. *Ecol. Monogr.*, **5**, 355–404.

PETRŮ, E. & CHRASTIL, J. (1955). The exosmosis of flavones from root exudations of *Arachis hypogaea* L. *Folia Biol.* (Kraków), **1**, 310–12.

PICKERING, S. (1903). The effect of grass on apple trees. *J. Roy. Agric. Soc.*, **64**, 365–76.

—— (1917). The effect of one plant on another. *Ann. Bot.* (London), **31**, 181–97.

—— & BEDFORD, DUKE OF (1919). *Science and Fruit Growing.* Macmillan & Co., London.

PIEMEISEL, R. L. (1951). Weeds, insects, plant diseases, and dust storms. *Sci. Agric.*, **73**(2), 124–8.

PROEBSTING, E. L. & GILMORE, A. E. (1941). The relation of peach root toxicity to the re-establishing of peach orchards. *Proc. Amer. Soc. Hort. Sci.*, **38**, 21–26.

RADEMACHER, B. (1940). Über den antagonistischen Einfluss von Roggen und Weizen auf Keimung und Entwicklung mancher Ünkrauter. *Pflanzenbau*, **17**, 131–43.

—— (1959). Gegenseitige Beeinflussung höherer Pflanzen. In *Handbuch der Pflanzenphysiologie.* (Ed. W. Ruhland). Springer, Berlin, Bd. **11**, pp. 655–706 (lit. pp. 696–706).

RIVIÈRE, J. (1959). Contribution a l'étude de la rhizosphère du blé. *Ann. Inst. Nat. Agron. (Paris)*, **45**, 93–337.

ROBINSON, R. G. (1949). Annual weeds, their viable seed population in the soil, and their effect on yields of oats, wheat and flax. *Agron. J.*, **41**, 513–18.

ROESKE, D. (1950). Antagonism between plants of the Cruciferae and Solanaceae families. *Pub. Pharm. Com. Pol. Acad. Sci.*, **2**, 207–64.

ROUX, E. R. (1953). The effect of antibiotics produced by *Trachypogon plumosus* on the germination of seeds of the Kakiebos (*Tagetes minuta*). *S. Afr. J. Sci.*, **49**, 334.

RUSSELL, E. J., Sir (1961). *Soil Conditions and Plant Growth.* 9th edn., rev. E. W. Russell. Longmans, Green, London; J. Wiley & Sons, New York, 688 pp.

SAUNDERS, A. N. (1942). Best way of minimizing effects of drought is weed control. *Farming in S. Africa*, **17**, 641–2.

SHADBOLT, C. A. (1955). Some quantitative studies of weed competition in vegetable crops. Ph.D. thesis, Univ. Wisconsin.

—— & Holm, L. G. (1953). A quantitative study of the competition of weeds with vegetable crops. (Abs.) *Proc. No. Cent. Weed Control Conf.*, pp. 10–12.

SHULL, A. E. (1932). Toxicity of root excretions. *Plant Physiol.*, **7**, 339–41.

STAHLER, L. M. (1949). Some biological aspects of competition between crop plants and field bindweed *Convolvulus arvensis*. *Univ. Minn. Sci. Ph.D. Theses*, **4**, 15–17.

STOA, T. E. (1955). Foxtail—how does it affect yields and nutritional needs of flax? *Bimo. Bull. (North Dakota)*, **17**, 163–6.

TEMPANY, H. T., Sir (1951). Imperata grass—a major menace in the wet tropics. *World Crops*, **3**, 143–6.

THOMPSON, H. C. (1927). Effect of weeds on crop yield. *Bull. Cornell Agric. Exp. Sta.*, **107**, 3–69.

TIMMONS, F. L. (1950). Competitive relationships of four different lawn grasses with field bindweed and dandelion under frequent close clipping. *Ecology*, **31**(1), 1–5.

TOKIN, B. P. (1956). *Phytonzide.* Berlin, VEB Verlag Volk und Gesundheit. 232 pp.

VENGRIS, J. (1955). Plant nutrient competition between weeds and corn. *Agron. J.*, **47**, 213–16.

—— (1956). Weeds—robbers of our farms. *Bett. Crops*, **40**(10), 9–12, 46–47.

——, DRAKE, M. & COLBY, W. G. (1953). Chemical composition of weeds and accompanying crop plants. *Agron. J.*, **45**, 213–18.

VIGOROV, L. I. (1955). [A removal of nitrogen by weeds in spring wheat plantings—in Russian.] *Bot. Zhur.*, Moscow, **40**, 703–5.

WEISS, F. (1949). Weeds fungi and the education of botanists. *Sci. Monthly*, **68**, 257–61.

WELBANK, P. J. (1960). Production of toxic substances by *Agropyron repens*. *Rep. Rothamsted Exp. Sta.* 1959, 85–86.

—— (1960a). Toxin production from *Agropyron repens*. In *The Biology of Weeds. A. Symposium of the British Ecological Society*. (Ed. J. L. Harper). Blackwell, Oxford, pp. 158–64.

WENT, F. W., JUHREN, G., & JUHREN, M. C. (1952). Fire and biotic factors affecting germination. *J. Ecol.*, **33**, 351–64.

WHITNEY, M. & CAMERON, F. K. (1904). The chemistry of the soil in relation to crop production. *Bull. U.S. Div. Soils*, **22**, 1–71.

WILDEMAN, É. DE (1948). [Bibliography of his writings, 486 papers.] *Bull. Jard. Bot. Brux.*, **19**, 1–35.

WILSON, J. K. (1943). Nitrate in plants: its relation to fertilizer injury, changes during silage making, and indirect toxicity to animals. *J. Amer. Soc. Agron.*, **36**, 279–90.

Woods, F. W. (1960). Biological antagonisms due to phytotoxic root exudates. *Bot. Rev.*, 26, 546–69.

Wright, J. M. (1951). Phytotoxic effects of some antibiotics. *Ann. Bot.*, N.S., 15, 493–9.

Addendum

The appearance of an increasing number of weed biology studies further supports our view that in order to control a weed one must know all about it. The following researches have been noted while this work was in press, and the citations are therefore necessarily abbreviated for space considerations.

Agnew, A. D. Q. (1961), (*Juncus effusus*), *J. Ecol.*, 49, 83–101; Bell, R. S. *et al.* (1962), (*Cyperus esculentus*), *R.I. Agric. Exp. Sta. Bull.*, 364, 33 pp.; Finnerty, D. W. & Klingman, D. L. (1962), (*Bromus* spp.), *Weeds*, 10, 40–47; Gay, P. A. (1960), (*Eichornia crassipes* in the Nile), *J. Ecol.*, 48, 183–91; Gressel, J. B. & Holm, L. G. (1964), (*Abutilon theophrasti* seeds and teletoxity), *Weed Res.*, 4, 44–53; Grümmer, G. (1963), (*Agropyron repens* rhizomes), *Weed Res.*, 3, 44–51; Håkansson, S. (1963), (*Allium vineale* in Sweden), Växtodling, 19, 1–208 (57 figs., 54 tables, 239 refs.); Hammerton, J. L. (1962, 1965), (*Polygonum*—competition, latitudinal ecotypes), *Weed Res.*, 2, 274–82, ibid., 5, 13–26; Hattingh, E. R. (1961), (The fern *Salvinia* in Kariba Lake, Africa), *Weed Res.*, 1, 303–6; Harper, J. L. & Gajic, A. (1961), (Mortality and plasticity of *Agrostemma githago*), *Weed Res.*, 1, 91–104; Hodgson, J. M. (1964), (Ecotypes of *Cirsium arvense*), *Weeds*, 12, 167–71; Ilnicki, R. D. *et al.* (1962), (*Solanum carolinense*), *R.I. Agric. Exp. Sta. Bull.*, 368, 54 pp.; Kacperska-Palacz, A. E. *et al.* (1963), (Developmental anatomy of *Echinochloa crusgalli*), *Weeds*, 11, 311–16; Kiewnick, L. (1963, 1964), (*Avena fatua* seed microflora), *Weed Res.*, 3, 322–32, ibid., 4, 31–43; Leuchs, F. (1961, 1962), (*Tussilago farfara*, I, II), *Weed Res.*, 1, 32–43, Ibid., 2, 283–305; McNaughton, I. H. (1960), (*Papaver* spp.), Ph.D. thesis, Oxford Univ.; McWhorter, C. G. (1961), (*Sorgum halepense*, morphology and development), *Weeds*, 9, 558–62; Moolani, M. K. *et al.* (1964), (*Amaranthus hybridus* competition with crops), *Weeds*, 12, 126–8; Peters, R. A. *et al.* (1963), (*Seteria lutescens, S. viridis S. faberii*), *R.I. Agric. Exp. Sta. Bull.*, 369, 18 pp.; Ramakrishnan, P. S. (1965), (Edaphic ecotypes of *Euphorbia thymifolia*), *J. Ecol.*, 53, 157–62; Rochecouste, E. (1962), (Studies on the biotypes of *Cynodon dactylon*), *Weed Res.*, 2, 1–23, 136–45; Rominger, J. M. (1963), (Taxonomy of *Seteria*), Univ. Ill. Press, Urbana, 130 pp.; Sagar, G. R. & Harper, J. L. (1961), (Competition in *Plantago* spp. populations), *Weed Res.*, 1, 163–76; Schreiber, M. W. (1962, 1965), (*Barbarea vulgaris*), *Weeds*, 10, 91–95; (*Seteria faberii*), ibid., 13, 40–43; Selleck, G. W. & Coupland, R. T., (*Artemisia absinthium*), *Weeds*, 9, 485–90; Thurston, Joan M. (1962, 1962a), (*Avena fatua* seeds and growth studies), *Weed Res.*, 2, 122–29, 192–207; Torell, P. J. *et al.* (1961), (*Elymus caput-medusae*), *Weeds*, 9, 124–31; Tumbelson, M. L. & Kommendahl, T. (1961), (*Cyperus esculentus*), *Weeds*, 9, 646–53; Welbank, P. J. (1963), (*Agropyron repens* teletoxicity, cites studies of Z. Lastuvka at Brno Univ.), *Weed Res.*, 3, 205–13; Williams, J. T. (1964), (*Chenopodium album* competition), *Weed Res.*, 4, 283–95.

XI

THE PHYTOSOCIOLOGY AND WORLD DISTRIBUTION OF WEEDS

INTRODUCTION AND PHYTOSOCIOLOGY

A NUMBER of investigators during recent decades have sought to describe the weed communities occurring on agricultural land. The majority of these studies have been carried out in Europe and have followed in general, the Zurich-Montpellier school of phytosociology. Becking (1957), in a detailed review of the methods of this study group, stated that the two key ideas of this school are: (*a*) distinction of associations and other vegetational units by means of their floristic composition only; and (*b*) the fidelity concept of species and its usefulness for floristic classification of vegetation units by means of character species, differentiating species, and characteristic species composition. The fundamental vegetation unit is the association, which is an abstraction (but at the same time occupying a definite and specific habitat) obtained by floristic comparison of a number of stands (phytocoenoses) in subjectively-selected

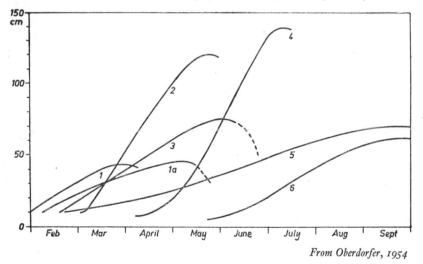

From Oberdorfer, 1954

FIG. 41.—Amount of average seasonal growth (in cm.), and initiation and duration (and decline) throughout the season, for the important ruderal associations of the southern area of the lower Balkans. These associations, with the conventional nomenclature after the dominant species, are: 1*a*, Hordeeto-Sisymbrietum orientalis; 1, Hordeeto-Sisymbrietum, Subass. with *Tortula* (Mauerkrone); 2, Geranieto-Silybetum; 3, Urticeto-Ecballietum; 4, Onopordetum illyrici; 5, Chenopodietum muralis; 6, Amarantheto-Atriplictum tartaricae and Heliotropeto-Chrozophoretum.

260

sites in the field, and defined by *diagnostic species groups* of differing character value.

These diagnostic species just referred to provide the nomenclature of the vegetation groups under study. For example, Oberdorfer (1954), in his graphical illustration of the ruderal associations in the lower Balkans (Fig. 41), refers to 'Hordeeto-Sisymbrietum orientalis'. This latter terminology means the [ruderal] association characterized by two species: *Hordeum* (in this case *leporinum*) and *Sisymbrium orientalis*, the ending, -etum, referring to the association. If a sub-association is recognized, then the ending is -etosum, and there are a number of other endings for various ranks in the hierarchy. Another example is a pond whose surface is covered with duckweed (*Lemna* sp.); by referring to this as a 'Lemnetum', one is informed of the name of the genus and that it is dominant in the area. Other examples are given in the brief references to the weed associations of cereal fields in Italy by Pignatti (*see* below), and to those of pioneer areas in bare city lots in Hungary by Ubrizsy, as described and illustrated below.

Pignatti (1957, 1957a) has studied the weed associations of cereal fields about Pavia, Italy, and particularly those of rice fields. The association most characteristic of the latter was found to be the 'Oryzeto-Cyperetum', named after the crop, *Oryza sativa*, and the dominating weed, *Cyperus* sp. Four dependent phanerogamic associations were found with it: 'Lemnetum', natant and moving; 'Najadetum', composed of submerged hydrophytes (e.g. *Najas* sp.); 'Drepanocladetum', composed of closely intermixed hydrophytes (c.g. the moss *Drepanocladus fluitans*); and the 'Heleocharetum', made up of ephemeral therophytes living on damp mud (e.g. [*H*]*Eleocharis* sp.). Purely or predominantly algal associations were also recognized, e.g. 'Spirogyretum' (Fig. 42 A & B).

Further, Pignatti has described the weed associations in upland cereals about Pavia—including maize, wheat, and oats. He found that the weed vegetation was similar in stands of maize and wheat, but different in oats. Floristic analysis showed the close relationship of the species with those of the Euro-Siberian, Mediterranean, and Mediterranean-Turanic floras. Five associations were recognized and are indicated on the Pavia-area map, Fig. 43. The dominant one, 'Alchemilletum Papaveretosum', occupied 50 per cent of the area. This is a shortened form of 'Alchemilleto-Matricarietum chamomillae Papaveretosum', which designates the sub-association of the *Alchemilla arvensis* and *Matricaria chamomilla* association, characterized by and named after the poppies (*Papaver*, four spp.).

Ubrizsy (1955) has examined in some detail the development of weed associations in relation to microclimate, as well as to soil and other environmental factors. An example is the study of a courtyard in Budapest, Hungary, with observation of the progressive ruderal successions that were exposed to trampling and other kinds of disturbances, which after four years of observation led largely to over-growth by grasses (Fig. 44).

This author states that nitrophily is not always a conclusive factor in the formation of ruderal associations, the site and vigour of growth being really determined by the joint effect of all the operative ecological factors. Yet, generally speaking, nitrophily is a characteristic of weed associations, although they often consist not of nitrophilous, but of nitrogen-tolerant,

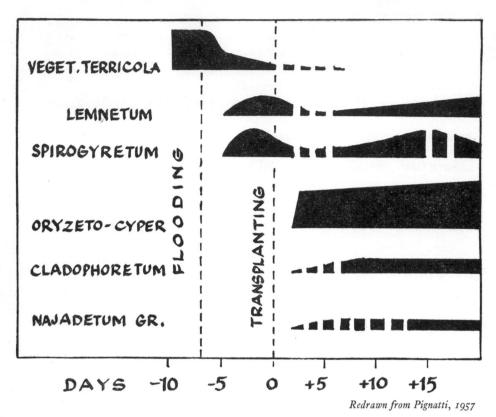

Redrawn from Pignatti, 1957

Fig. 42A.—Stage I. Development of the different associations considered during the formation—submersion and transplanting—of the rice field. The various associations are named to the left as explained in the text; the first dotted line refers to submersion (sommersione), and the second dotted line refers to the date of transplanting (trapianto)—all shown in relation to middle of June (date of transplanting).

species. Ubrizsy found no close and definite correlation between the nitrogen content of the site of the individual weed associations and the phytocoenoses living on that site. The balance between the ruderal phytocoenoses is rather labile, while environmental conditions change very suddenly on these sites, with the growths following each other as narrow bands (zonations), giving the impression of a mosaic (*see* Fig. 44). The scheme of successions described can, as the author states, give only a rough idea of the correlations and laws governing the developmental processes of the remarkably mobile and dynamic weed associations. Yet he concludes that a thorough knowledge of these processes and their laws should eventually enable man to exert a guiding influence upon the growth of herbage.

Oberdorfer (1954—*see* Ch. XI), in his study of weed associations in the lower Balkan area (northern Greece and some adjacent territories), has noted this controversy concerning nitrophily and the development of

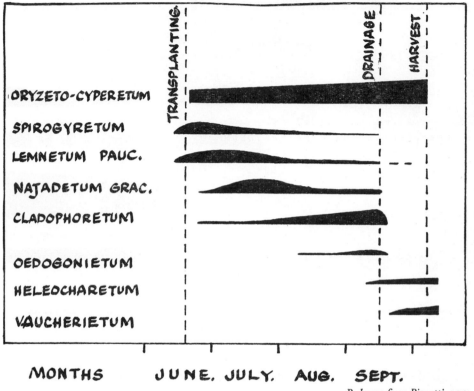

Redrawn from Pignatti, 1957

Fig. 42B.—Stage II. Development of the main associations composing the biocoenosis of the rice field during the summer. The vertical lines are, left to right, transplanting (trapianto), drying-off after draining (asciutta), and harvesting (mietitura). The associations are listed to the left using the nomenclature explained in the text. (Data from Pavia, Italy.)

weed associations. But he appears to recognize such nitrophilous associations in these more southern and arid regions in contrast to the northern regions; and also notes the erroneous assumption that plants associated with cultivated soils are cosmopolitan. He finds that the composition of the weed societies depends upon the structure of the local soils, their chemical nature and water content, and their aeration, as well as on the influence of climate. In the area studied he recognized six principle ruderal associations. These are illustrated in Fig. 41, which indicates their average height in centimetres, as well as their initiation and growth throughout the season. The nomenclature is similar to that described earlier

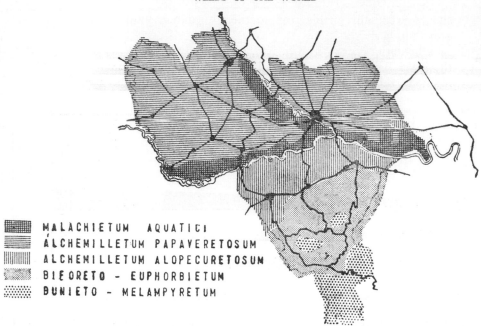

MALACHIETUM   AQUATICI
ALCHEMILLETUM PAPAVERETOSUM
ALCHEMILLETUM ALOPECURETOSUM
BIFORETO - EUPHORBIETUM
BUNIETO - MELAMPYRETUM

From Pignatti, 1957a

FIG. 43.—Distribution of the weed associations in the cereal-growing areas around Pavia, Italy. The five principal associations are named in the legend to the left of the map, and their names are derived from the following dominant species (named in the order of the legend): *Malachium aquaticum; Alchemilla arvensis, Matricaria chamomilla, Papaver (argemone, dubium, hybridum, rhoeas); Alchemilla arvensis, Matricaria chamomilla, Alopecurus myosuroides; Bifora radians, Euphorbia falcata;* and *Bunium bulbocastanum, Melampyrum arvense.* The names of the latter four associations are shortened on the map legend. The map shows the river Ticino flowing from the north and joining the Po river a short distance south-east of Pavia (shown by the largest black spot). To the north-west of Pavia is the city of Vigevano (shown by the second-largest black spot). The area shown by the map covers 2,957 sq. km.

and is indicated in the legend. The nitrophilous weed associations of Euro-Siberian Europe have been studied by Tüxen (1950).

Apart from studies of weed ecology based largely on the description of the vegetation, many others have been made of the development of an individual species or a group of species in relation to various factors of the environment. The weeds that are characteristic of one or more of six habitats in the Province of Quebec, Canada, are shown in the diagram reproduced in Fig. 45. One of the more important and far-reaching of these studies has been that of Heinz Ellenberg (Ellenberg, 1950; Coombe, 1952) of Hohenheim, Germany, as a result of which he provides a considerable number of autecological data for 244 field and garden weeds of West Germany. Ellenberg was particularly concerned with the soil indicator value of weeds, and presented a large body of data on the relation between the distribution of weed species and the environment.

Ellenberg divided his weed species into groups that were based on their 'ecological constitution' in relation to given environmental factors.

Thus his group R1 contains the species that are largely limited to strongly acid soils, R5 contains the species that are largely limited to neutral or alkaline soils, and RO consists of species that are apparently indifferent to the pH of the soil. Similar groupings are described in relation to the

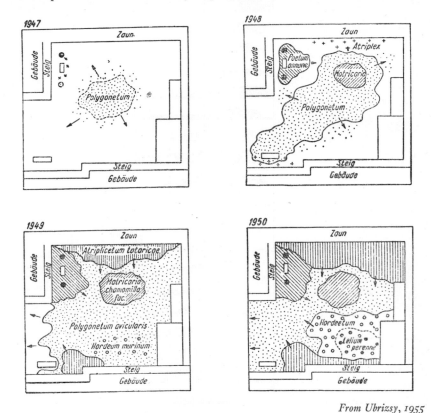

From Ubrizsy, 1955

FIG. 44.—The development of weed associations in an open courtyard, city of Budapest, Hungary, through the years 1947, 1948, 1949, and 1950. Conventional naming of the associations follows the species concerned: *Polygonum aviculare*; *Poa annua*; *Atriplex* spp.; *Matricaria* sp.; *Hordeum murinum*; and *Lolium perenne*.

water and the air contents of soils, to nitrogen status, to temperature and the continentality of climate, and to the degree of soil mellowness or friability, while further valuable information is given on life-form, rooting depths, etc. Ellenberg believes that an assemblage of species has a better indicator value than any one of those species can have alone, and he makes it clear that a weed community is no organism or individual, although there is a nexus of correlations of the community and its environment. Having listed the species of a given weed assemblage and assigned each— in so far as it has a known indicator value—to its place in a numbered group corresponding to its ecological 'demands', Ellenberg then finds the mean numbers for each group of environmental factors.

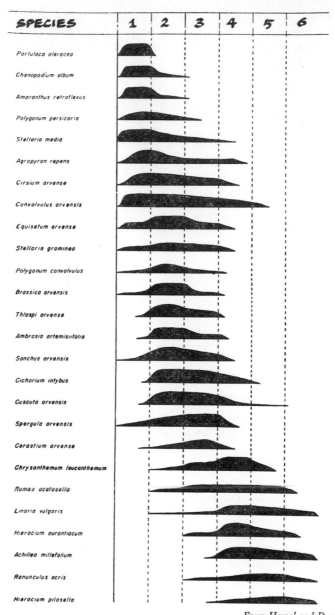

SPECIES | 1 | 2 | 3 | 4 | 5 | 6

Portulaca oleracea

Chenopodium album

Amaranthus retroflexus

Polygonum persicaria

Stellaria media

Agropyron repens

Cirsium arvense

Convolvulus arvensis

Equisetum arvense

Stellaria graminea

Polygonum convolvulus

Brassica arvensis

Thlaspi arvense

Ambrosia artemisiifolia

Sonchus arvensis

Cichorium intybus

Cuscuta arvensis

Spergula arvensis

Cerastium arvense

Chrysanthemum leucanthemum

Rumex acetosella

Linaria vulgaris

Hieracium aurantiacum

Achillea millefolium

Ranunculus acris

Hieracium pilosella

From Hamel and Dansereau, 1949

FIG. 45.—A chart showing the relative importance, and the distribution of a group of weeds in six different habitats in the Province of Quebec, Canada. The habitats are: 1, hoed or cultivated area; 2, cereal fields; 3, young prairie; 4, old prairie; 5, pasture; 6, abandoned land.

In a review of this work, Coombe (1952) cites a group of weeds from an asparagus field on the sandy plain of the upper Rhine near Schwetzingen. These were *Setaria viridis*, *S. glauca*, *Panicum sanguinale*, *Echinochloa crusgalli*, *Galinsoga parviflora*, *Urtica urens*, *Portulaca oleracea*, *Chenopodium album*, and *Solanum nigrum*. From Ellenberg's tables the reviewer derived the following:

(*a*) The 'Mean Temperature Number' (T) is 3, indicating moderate temperature requirements similar to that of species of which the northern limits correspond with those of *Quercus robur*.

(*b*) The 'Mean Water Relations Number' (W) is 3, corresponding to a well-aerated soil which is always well supplied with water but never waterlogged.

(*c*) The 'Mean Reaction Number' (R) is about 4, but is rather uncertain, as several of the species are indifferent to the pH of the soil, and hence belong to the group RO; however, it is suggested that they may prefer weakly acid conditions to alkaline ones.

(*d*) The 'Mean Nitrogen Number' (N) is $4\frac{1}{2}$, suggesting a soil that is very rich in nitrogen.

(*e*) The 'Mean Friability Number' (G) is 4, indicating a well-cultivated soil.

These examples indicate the detail with which the weed communities were analysed—primarily on a physiological basis. Otto Wehsarg, in his detailed work on weed biology (1954), cites Ellenberg's grouping for the weed species included. A series of studies by P. Jovet (1937, 1940, 1940*a*, 1940*b*, 1954*a*) of the weeds of the great and ancient city of Paris, and of the highways and railways leading into the city, comprise a unique group of phytosociological studies in relation to man's activities.

Apart from these studies of groups of weeds, there are many that cover in considerable detail all facets of the environment in relation to the development of a single species, i.e. their autecology. Examples include: Hofsten (1954—*see* Ch. VI) on *Taraxacum*, Harper (1957) on *Ranunculus*, and various other contributions in the series on the Biological Flora of the British Isles (published as supplements to the *Journal of Ecology*).

In the study of *Taraxacum* just referred to, Hofsten has illustrated the distribution of *Taraxacum* '*Vulgaria*' and certain associated plants in the area occupied by an extensive artillery field at Uppsala, Sweden (Fig. 46). Likewise, soil drillings to obtain an indication of the soil profile associated with each dominant species, etc., in this field were obtained, as indicated in Fig. 47.

In conclusion we may cite a question that might logically be raised at this point: 'Why are we interested in weed associations, when in most cases under good management they should not be permitted to become so far advanced?' The answer given here is the one that applies most appropriately to all questions concerning the value of fundamental

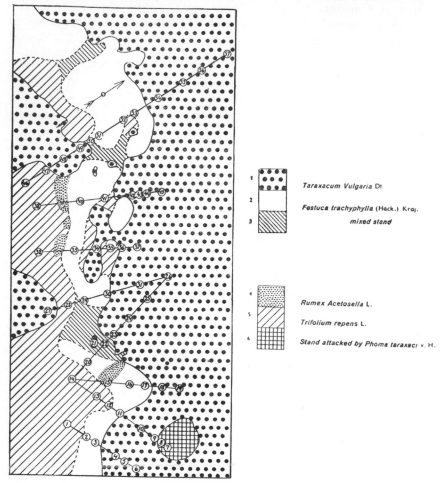

From Hofsten, 1954—see Ch. VI

Fig. 46.—Map of part of the artillery field at Uppsala, Sweden, showing the distribution of several species etc. of plants—principally *Taraxacum 'Vulgaria'*—and the numbers of the soil-drilling samples taken during the profile examination.

research: a given body of research must first be completed, and then, when the accumulated facts are properly at hand, applications may be evident. Herein lies one of the great dilemmas of modern science. As stated, it is not until the facts have been accumulated (no matter how erudite, or impractical, they may at first seem), that extensions to practicability may be made. Few individuals are sufficiently clairvoyant to bridge this gap, although some may succeed. Another fact which is quite often apparent, is that the reduction to practice is made by individuals other than those who produce the fundamental groundwork (the discovery of the *selective herbicidal-activity* of 2,4-D, is a prime example, cf. Ch. XII). In the case at hand it would appear that such data may be useful in improving the methods of weed control. One has only to study the weed association diagrams of Pignatti for rice fields (Fig. 42) to visualize quickly the different strata of competing growths in the field throughout the growing-season. It will perhaps then be realized how complex are the considerations for effective control when one or several cultural and/or chemical methods are contemplated.

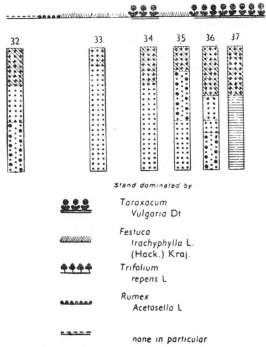

Stand dominated by

Taraxacum
Vulgaria Dt

Festuca
trachyphylla L.
(Hack.) Kraj.

Trifolium
repens L

Rumex
Acetosella L

none in particular

From Hofsten, 1954—see Ch. VI

FIG. 47.—Soil profiles along one of the diagonals shown in the preceding figure, together with the dominating species etc. growing in the immediate area of the drill-hole. *Trifolium repens* not shown in profile selected here. Profile No. 32 shows from the top downwards; mould and average sand; average sand; average to coarse sand. In No. 37; mould-average sand; clay. The author concluded that the soil-water relationships were more important factors than competition with *Festuca*.

The present-day widespread use of herbicides, both in non-crop and crop land, has an effect on the ecological relationships of the weeds associated with these particular environments. A more difficult assessment, that of the long-range effects on the character of the weed flora and the development of 2,4-D (or other herbicide) resistant weeds, has been considered in Chapter IX.

It is now a well-known fact that the use of the 2,4-D herbicides has altered the weed flora in a number of crops. Especially familiar is the increase in grasses after broad-leafed weeds have been controlled. Beatty

(1958, cf. Ch. XIII) has noted that, in spinach fields, henbit (*Lamium amplexicaule*) infestation increased after chickweed (*Stellaria media*) had been eliminated, while, after henbit was controlled, Virginia peppergrass (*Lepidium virginicum*) became a problem.

WORLD ASPECTS OF WEED DISTRIBUTION

It has earlier been pointed out that anthropophytes (man-encouraged plants) and apophytes (native species venturing into largely man-created habitats) are the two great groups from which the majority of weeds have been derived.

Levina's (1944) analysis of anthropochorology has revealed man's conscious and unconscious weed-promoting activities with regard to sowing, cultivation, and mechanical equipment. It is surprising how large a proportion of our autotrophic land weeds were used by man at some time or other for food, shelter, clothing, medicine, ornamentation, or amusement. Accordingly, many weeds may be regarded as cast-off plants—the discards, the remnants of man's usage and later abandonment—which have, through some of the most elaborate mechanisms operative in plant growth, survived, either changed or relatively unchanged through prehistoric and historic times down to the present, to become one of the serious plagues of modern agriculture.

The role of man in weed distribution has, of course, long been recognized. He has carried weeds throughout the globe during his travels, in his grain and seed shipments, with his armies, and by his movement of cattle and other animals. A large proportion of the widespread field-weeds of temperate Europe and North America have migrated in a westerly direction from the early centres of civilization in the eastern Mediterranean region—the same path as that followed by peoples migrating to new and distant lands.

The weed survey presented in these volumes has revealed that, while there are sizeable numbers of both pantemperate and pantropic weeds, the majority of weeds appear to be restricted to smaller areas, and to have been derived from the respective native floras. The manner in which many of our common weeds have evolved has already been considered in Chapter IX. The ready development of ecotypes, or physiological races adapted to various climatic conditions the world around, has occurred in *Stellaria media*, the common chickweed (Fig. 48), and is responsible for the world-wide distribution of this species. It has also occurred in *Taraxacum* and members of a number of other genera—cf. the ecotypes of *Poa annua* as described by Tutin (1957—*see* Ch. VII), and illustrated and described in our Volume II, in the part devoted to European weeds.

It is true, of course, that certain elements of the native floras the world around are of an adventive character, often termed 'nomad species'. These species contrast with the more stationary members which comprise the highly adapted and specialized forms that are so characteristic of many floras. Those nomad species, when venturing into more open habitats, frequently created by man, have been termed apophytes. From this reservoir of adventives, many of our most pernicious weeds undoubtedly have developed. While the role of man has been important in this connection, it should not be forgotten that certain other disruptive forces in nature have likewise played a part.

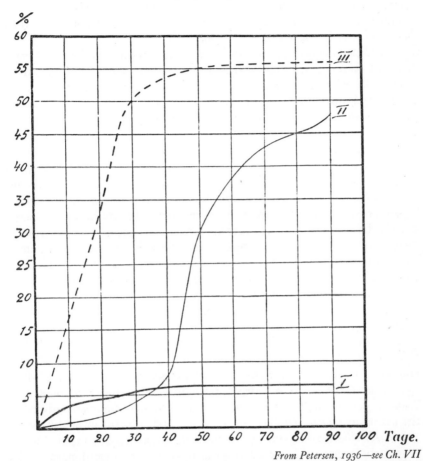

From Petersen, 1936—see Ch. VII

FIG. 48.—Graph showing the average percentage germination obtained throughout a 100-day period for lots of seed from three different ecotypes of *Stellaria media* : I, from northern latitudes (arctic, alpine); II, from middle latitudes (oceanic); III, from maritime situations in northern latitudes.

EXAMPLES OF PLANT DISPERSAL FROM THE PACIFIC ISLES

In his comments on the spread of weeds in many parts of the world, Merrill (1954) notes that of the 30 weeds recorded in Tahiti in 1769 few, if any, were of American origin, but that a surprisingly high percentage of these weeds are clearly of Indo-Malaysian origin. It is believed that the seeds of these weeds were carried along with soil from island to island which was used to transport the propagating-portions of basic food plants (since, other than fruit trees, these had to be grown from underground parts—tubers, rhizomes, corms). He further comments that a large number of the weeds recorded from India originated from plants developing in the Calcutta Botanic Garden from seeds in soil scattered in the garden from containers in which a large number of living economic species had been transported from various parts of Malaysia.

Dr. Merrill (1954) believes that it is certain that many now ubiquitous pantropic weeds, clearly of American origin, were not present in Tahiti or elsewhere in Polynesia proper at the time the first explorations were made by Europeans. Involved here are very aggressive species of *Cassia*, *Hyptis*, *Mimosa*, *Scoparia*, *Stachytarpheta*, etc., as well as such weedy shrubs and small trees as *Lantana camara*, *Acacia farnesiana*, *Leucaena glauca*, *Psidium guajava*, etc., all of which were conspicuous by their absence at the time the first botanical explorations were made in the Pacific islands. He notes, too, that of 64 species of troublesome weeds of Fiji listed in a published flora of 1873, 48 of these were common to America and Fiji, and only 16 were confined to Indo-Malaysia and Fiji. Thus the Pacific Islands have served as 'stepping stones' for the transmission of weeds between the two hemispheres—largely by way of man's travels. Dr. Merrill observes that this group of weeds was particularly aggressive in the new and virgin territory since they were introduced there without insect, fungus, and other enemies that kept them, more or less, in check in those parts of America from whence they came.

There were, in addition to the manifestly man-introduced weeds in Polynesia, another series from the Tahiti list of 1769 referred to above. Merrill (1954) believes that these are naturally of world-wide distribution —probably having attained their extended ranges in earlier geologic times, long before man became a factor. Species here include some sedges (*Kyllinga*, *Cyperus*, *Fimbristylis*), a few grasses, and *Ipomoea bona-nox*, *Operculina turpethum*, etc. Other species of wide distribution noted were *Ipomoea pes-caprae*, *Cassytha filiformis*, and *Hibiscus tiliaceus*. Species in the genera *Thespesia*, *Dodonaea*, *Canavalia*, and *Sophora* were also listed. While *H. tiliaceus* is generally considered a useful fibre plant, Merrill (1954) notes that its universal tropical distribution is attributable to its floating seeds.

EARLY TRADE ROUTES IN RELATION TO PLANT DISTRIBUTION

The subject of trade routes and plant distribution has been reviewed in an extensive fashion by Merrill (1954), and the material included below is taken from his publication. Since the close of the fifteenth century, man, intentionally or inadvertently, has been the greatest single factor in extending the ranges of plants. Up to about 460 years ago there were no cultivated economic species (except *Lagenaria*) and, apparently, none of the aggressive weeds common to either the temperate or tropical parts of the two hemispheres. For the northeastern United States and adjacent Canada 1,098 species are considered introduced and naturalized; while 4,425 are considered indigenous. A census of California plants in 1925 revealed that of the total of 4,019 species 292 were naturalized aliens— mostly from parts of the world with a Mediterranean type of climate, and all introduced within the past 200 years. The number 292 provides no proper concept of the vast numbers of individual and aggressive plants involved. This is true, too, of some particularly aggressive species of the eastern United States: for example, the Japanese honeysuckle, *Lonicera aponica*, unknown to the area as late as 1897; the giant foxtail grass, *Setaria faberii*, which since its introduction from China 30 years ago has become one of the most widely distributed and aggressive weeds; and the water chesnut, *Trapa natans*, which was first collected in America in 1878 in the fish ponds that existed until sometime after 1900 on the mall at Washington, D.C.

There were two early trade routes by which economic plants and weeds of Brazilian origin reached the Orient (1) by way of Brazil direct to the Cape of Good Hope and thence to India and (2) by way of Brazil to Cape Horn, then to Guam, and finally to the other parts of the Orient. These were developed soon after the discovery of Brazil in 1500. A few years earlier, in 1498, the Portuguese discovered the route to India by way of the Cape of Good Hope. Thus, according to Merrill (1954), about this time tropical American economic plants as well as numerous aggressive American weeds began to appear in the Orient. Three weeds of Brazilian origin are good examples here: *Heliotropium indicum*, *Malvastrum coromandelianum*, and *Mimosa pudica*.

Another important route involved in weed dispersal is the long-continued Acapulco-Manila galleon line. The first galleon crossed the Pacific in 1565, and the last reached Acapulco in Mexico in 1815—an interval of 250 years. It is believed that many Mexican economic plants and aggressive weeds reached the Orient by this trade route. For example, a list of plants from the Manila area (40 square miles) prepared in 1912, included about 1,000 species, of which 175 were from Mexico and Brazil. In the Guam area of 212 square miles, there were, in 1914, 550 known species, of which 113 were from Mexico and Brazil. These figures include both economic plants and weeds. Introductions have added greatly to the New Zealand flora as well. Of the 2,890 species comprising the total flora, some 1,760 are recognized as mostly indigenous, and about 1,125 as introduced and more or less naturalized.

COMPARISONS OF WEED FLORA OF THE OLD AND NEW WORLDS

The extent of weed distribution may be determined by analysing the origins of weed species for a specific area. Dr. John M. Fogg, Jr. (1945) has done this for the 242 weeds included in his work on the weeds of eastern temperate North America. Approximately 53 per cent are of European or Eurasian origin; 32·5 per cent are native to North America (although some of them occur in the Old World as well); 8 per cent come from eastern Asia or India; 5·5 per cent are indigenous to the tropical or subtropical portions of America; while only two species (less than 1 per cent) are derived from Africa. These last species comprise Johnson grass, sudan grass, and possibly carpet weed—which last is said to be native to Africa, but occurs in the tropics of the New World as well. Because of similarities of climate between parts of eastern Asia and eastern North America a number of weeds have been introduced that are particularly aggressive: *Setaria faberii, Hydrocotyle rotundifolia* (as a lawn weed in the vicinity of a number of American cities), and the Japanese knotweed, *Polygonum cuspidatum*, one of the most persistent and aggressive of all perennial weeds.

It is of interest to examine the opposite situation, how many weeds of foreign origin have been introduced into Asia? This has been determined for Japan by Kasahara (1954). Of 236 species of introduced plants, representing 55 families, 90 originated from Europe, 60 from North America, about 40 from other parts of Asia, 3 from Australia, and 2 from Africa. A group of 32 species, introduced from Europe through China in the early pre-historic era, was also recognized—species found mainly on the upland fields. Also noted were an additional 82 species that were introduced from south-eastern Asia and southern China some 2,000 years ago by an ancient group of people, who brought rice culture to Japan.

OCEANIC CURRENTS AND PLANT DISPERSAL

Another important phase of plant distribution, not seriously attributable to man's influence, is that related to the oceanic currents of the world (cf. Fig. 49). A number of well-known studies (Guppy, 1912, 1917; Barber, *et al.*, 1959; Ridley, 1930) have considered this form of distribution in considerable detail. Muir (1937) investigated this subject further, and also dealt with the influence of ocean currents on the strand vegetation of South Africa. While various types of plant fragments may float and remain viable for considerable periods of time in sea water, seeds are undoubtedly the most important agents in such dispersal. Muir recognized three groups of seed (or fruit) buoyancy: Group I, in which buoyancy is due to unoccupied space inside the seed or fruit (*e.g. Hibiscus, Ipomoea, Cassytha*, and many leguminous plants such as *Vigna, Caesalpinia*, and *Entada* (owing to their intercotyledonary cavity); Group II, in which buoyancy is due to the floating power of seed-contents (e.g. *Ximenia, Canavalia, Erythrina*, etc.); and Group III, in which buoyancy is due to aeriferous tissue in the testa or fruit-coat (e.g. *Scirpus, Terminalia, Wedelia, Cocos, Mucuna*, etc.).

An analysis of a consecutive series of 1,000 seeds from a forty-mile strip of temperate coast on the Riversdale beaches of South Africa,

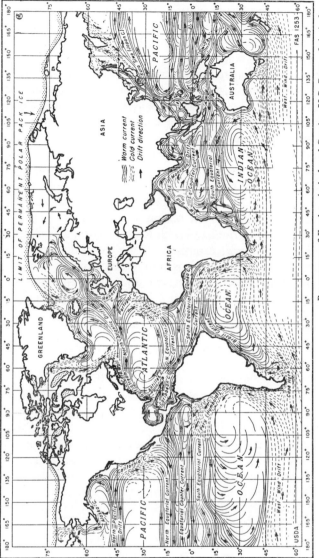

By courtesy of Foreign Agricultural Service, U.S. Dept. of Agriculture

FIG. 49.—Principal ocean currents of the world. Oceanic currents and floating ice have been considered in problems of plant dispersal throughout the world. An instance of the vast distances which plants and plant parts may be transported by water and oceanic currents is provided by Barber *et al.* (1959). A log (10 × 5 ft.) of *Nothofagus pumilio* drifted from Tierra del Fuego in South America to Tasmania and the Macquarie Islands, a distance of 10,000 miles, in the track of the westerly winds. Using the speed of the surface current in the Antarctic circumpolar drift as 15 cm./sec., the maximum time involved here would be over three years.

studied by Muir (1937), revealed that these seeds originated from some 17 plant genera. The most abundant seeds were of *Caesalpinia crista* (30 per cent), *Dioclea reflexa* (18 per cent), *Intsia bijuga* (17 per cent), *Entada gigas* (13 per cent), and four species of *Mucuna* (14 per cent), and there were smaller numbers of *Ipomoea* sp. (1·0 per cent) and *Cocos nucifera* (0·6 per cent). It is not clear from Muir's account as to what measures, if any, were taken to sieve out and identify the smaller seeds (which would no doubt include many weed types) from the drift debris; most attention was apparently given to the 'macro' seeds.

The distances involved with respect to Still Bay, South Africa, include some 4,000 miles from Java, 4,500 miles from Western Australia, and there are some 250 to 600 miles between Madagascar and the mainland of Africa. Experiments have demonstrated the viability of some seeds to be unimpaired after 500 days of floating in sea water. The time required for movement in the oceanic currents has been inferred from bottle-drift records (one such moved a distance of 1,269 miles in 161 days, or 7·9 miles per day). Guppy (1917) has stated that the traverse of seeds across the Indian Ocean, from south of Sumbawa to East Africa, may take eight months or less—according to the season of the year.

The monumental study of the late H. N. Ridley (1930), *The Dispersal of Plants Throughout the World*, examines all modes of dispersal, and, apart from water, includes wind, birds and other animals, adhesion, human agency, and mechanical means. This study will repay thorough examination by all who are interested in this important phase of plant geography. (*See also* Barrau, 1963.)

BIBLIOGRAPHY

(The Phytosociology and World Distribution of Weeds)

ADAMS, R. C. (1929). Weed succession on an abandoned roadway. *Proc. Iowa Acad. Sci.*, 36, 213.

ALBERTSON, F. W. (1937). Ecology of mixed prairie in west central Kansas. *Ecol. Monog.*, 7, 481–547.

ALLAN, H. H. (1950, publ. 1953). Classifying vegetation for the geographer. *Proc. 7th Internat. Bot. Congr.*, p. 653.

AMES, O. (1939). *Economic Annuals and Human Cultures*. Bot. Museum Harvard University, Cambridge, Mass., 153 pp.

ANON. (1938). The nature of weed competition. *Gard. Chronicle*, 103, 329.

ARCHIBALD, E. E. A. (1949). The specific character of plant communities. I. Herbaceous communities. *J. Ecol.*, 37(2), 260–73.

ARDISSONE, F. (1885). *La Vegetazione Terrestre Condierata nei Suoi Rapporti eol Clima.* Fratelli Dumolard, Milan, 190 pp.

AUFHAMMER, G., SPINDLER, F. & AMM, M. (1938). Der Einfluss von verschiedenartigen Besatz auf die Gütebeurteilung des Weizens. *Prakt. Bl. PflBau. Pflanzen-Schutz*, 16, 49–71.

AZZI, G. (1956). *Agricultural Ecology*. Constable, London, 420 pp.

BARBER, H. N., DODSWELL, H. E. & INGLE, H. D. (1959). Transport of driftwood from South America to Tasmania and Macquarie Island. *Nature, Lond.* 184, 203–4.

BARRAU, J. (ed.), (1963). *Plants and the Migrations of Pacific Peoples; a Symposium.* 10th Pacific Science Congress, Honolulu, 1961. Bishop Museum Press, Honolulu, Hawaii. 136 pp.

BATES, J. M. (1900). The flora of a neglected door-yard. *Asa Gray Bull.*, 8, 58–63.

BEAUVERIE, M. A. REYNAUD-. See REYNAUD-BEAUVERIE, M. A.

BECKING, R. W. (1957). The Zurich-Montpellier School of phytosociology. *Bot. Rev.*, 23, 411–88.

BELOZEROV, P. I. (1956). [In regard to the distribution of *Elodea canadensis* in the North (of U.S.S.R.)—in Russian.] *Bot. Zhur.*, 41, 262–3.

BEWS, J. W. (1927). Studies on the ecological evaluation of the Angiosperms. *New Phytol.*, 26, 65–84, 129–48, 209–31, 232–44, 273–94.

BHARADWAJA, R. C. (1956). On the distribution and origin of the genus *Ischaemum* Linn. *Sci. & Cult. (India)*, 21, 748–9.

BILLINGS, W. D. (1957). Physiological ecology. *Ann. Rev. Plant Physiol.*, 8, 375–92.

BINGHAM, M. T. (1937). A study of vegetational invasion and succession on a denuded area of the Cranbrook Estate, Bloomfield Hills, Michigan. *Michigan Acad. Sci. Pap.* 23, 101–8.

BISSET, W. J. (1953). Competition and weedicide studies of mintweed (*Salvia reflexa* Hornem.). *Austral. J. Agric. Res.*, 4, 249–55.

BLACKMAN, G. E. & TEMPLEMAN, W. G. (1938). Nature of the competition between cereal crops and annual weeds. *J. Agric. Sci.*, 28, 247–51.

—— HOLLY, K. & COX, G. E. (1951). Physiological and ecological studies in the analysis of plant environment. VI. *Ann. Bot.*, 15(57), 63–94.

—— & WILSON, G. L. (1954). Physiological and ecological studies in the analysis of plant environment. IX. Adaptive changes in the vegetative growth and development of *Helianthus annuus* induced by an alteration in light level. *Ann. Bot.*, n.s., 18, 71–94.

BLAIR, B. O. (1940). The ecology of a pasture in the Dakota sandstone formation in Ellsworth County, Kansas. *Trans. Kansas Acad. Sci.*, 52(1), 38–57.

BLAISDELL, J. P. (1949). Competition between sagebrush seedlings and reseeded grasses. *Ecology*, 30(4), 512.

BLASER, R. E., GRIFFITH, W. A. & TAYLOR, T. H. (1956). Seedling competition in establishing forage plants. *Agron. J.*, 48, 1–6.

BLUM, A. (1925). Beiträge zur Kenntnis der annuellen Pflanzen. *Bot. Archiv.*, 9, 3–36.

BÖCHER, T. W. (1950, publ. 1953). Cultivation experiments with *Geranium Robertianum*, *Veronica officinalis*, and *Prunella vulgaris*. *Proc. 7th Internat. Bot. Congr., Stockholm*, pp. 268–9.

BOTERENBROOD, A. J., DONSELAAR-TEN BOKKEL HUININK, W. E. A. VAN, & DONSELAAR, J. VAN. (1955). Quelques données sur l'écologie de la végétation des dunes et sur la fonction de l'enracinement dans l'édification des dunes à la este Méditerranéenne de la France. I and II. *Akad. Wetenschappen*, 58(Ser. C), 523–47.

BOYKO, H. (1955). Climatic, ecoclimatic and hydrological influences on vegetation. *U.N. Educ. Sci. & Cult. Organ. Arid Zone Res.*, 5, 41–46.

BRAUN-BLANQUET, J. (1932). *Plant Sociology.* (Trans. G. D. Fuller & H. S. Conrad.) McGraw-Hill, New York, 439 pp. (Version española por A. P. L. Diglio y M. M. Grassi. Buenos Aires, Acme Agency, 1950. 444 pp.)

BRENCHLEY, W. E. & HEINTZE, S. G. (1933). Colonization by *Epilobium angustifolium*. *J. Ecol.*, 21, 101–2.

BROWN, H. L. (1947). Coaction of Jack rabbit, cottontail and vegetation in a mixed prairie. *Trans. Kansas Acad. Sci.*, 50, 28–44.

BUCHLI, M. (1936). Ökologie der Ackerunkräuter der Nordostschweiz. *Beitr. Geobot. Landesaufn.*, 19, 354.

BUZACOTT, J. H. (1955). Weed succession in north Queensland. *Qd. Bur. Sugar Exp. Sta. Cane Growers' Quart. Bull.*, 19, 48–52.

CAIN, S. A. & EVANS, F. C. (1952). The distribution patterns of three plant species in an old-field community in south-eastern Michigan. *Michigan Univ. Lab. Vertebrate Biol. Contrib.* No. 52, 11 pp.

CANNON, H. L. (1957). Description of indicator plants and methods of botanical prospecting for uranium deposits on the Colorado plateau. *U.S. Geol. Surv. Bull.* No. 1030 M, 399–516.

CASSADY, J. T. (1940). Certain ecological characteristics of orange sneezeweed. *Ecology,* 21, 87–90.

CHRISTENSEN, E. M. (1954–55). Ecological notes on the mountain brush in Utah. *Proc. Utah Acad. Sci. Arts & Let.* 32, 107–11.

CLEMENTS, F. E. (1947–49). *Dynamics of Vegetation.* Wilson, New York, 296 pp.

—— , WEAVER, J. E. & HANSON, H. C. (1929). *Plant Competition.* Carnegie Inst., Washington, 340 pp.

COOMBE, D. (1952). Review of Ellenberg, H., *Landwirtschaftlichen Pflanzensoziologie.* Vol. 1. *Unkrautgemeinschaften als Zeiger für Klima und Boden.* Eugen Ulmer, Stuttgart, 1950, 141 pp. In *J. Ecol.,* 40, 409–10.

COOPER, J. P. (1951). Studies on growth and development in *Lolium.* II. Pattern of bud development of the shoot apex and its ecological significance. *J. Ecol.,* 39, 228–70.

COPELAND, E. B. (1912). Terrace weeds in the Philippines. *Sci. American,* 3 Feb., p.108.

CORNER, E. J. H. (1951). The Durian theory of the origin of the modern tree. *Ann. Bot.,* n.s., 13, 367–414.

COTTAM, C. (1950). The effects of uncontrolled introductions of plants and animals. *Internat. Tech. Conf. Protect. Nat., Proc. & Papers for 1949,* pp. 408–13.

CRESSLER, L. (1942). The effect of different intensities and times of grazing and the degree of dusting upon the vegetation of range land in west central Kansas. *Trans. Kansas Acad. Sci.,* 45, 74–91.

DAMMER, W. (1893). Die Verbreitungsausrustungen der Polygonaceen. *Bot. Jahrb.,* 15, 260–85.

DANSEREAU, P. (1951). Description and recording of vegetation upon a structural basis. *Ecology,* 32, 172–229.

—— (1957). *Biogeography: an Ecological Perspective.* Ronald, New York, 394 pp.

—— & LEMS, K. (1957). The grading of dispersal types in plant communities and their ecological significance. *Contr. l'Inst. Bot. l'Univ. Montréal* No. 71, 5–50.

DAUBENMIRE, R. F. (1959). *Plants and Environment: a Textbook of Plant Autecology.* Wiley, New York, 2nd edn., 422 pp.

DAWSON, G. W. P. (1951). A method for investigating the relationship between the distribution of individuals of different species in a plant community. *Ecology,* 32, 332–4.

DERSAL, W. R. VAN (1936). The ecology of a lawn. *Ecology,* 17, 515–27.

EBERHARDT, C. H. (1954). Ackerunkrautgesellschaften und ihre Abhängigkeit von Boden und Bewirtschaftung. *Z. f. Acker- und Pflanzenbau,* 97(4), 453–84.

EGLER, F. E. (1954). Philosophical and practical considerations of the Braun-Blanquet System of phytosociology. *Castanea,* 19, 45–60.

—— (1957). Vegetation science concepts. *Acta Geobot.,* 4, 412.

ELLENBERG, H. (1948). Unkrautgesellschaften als Mass fur den Säuregrad, die Verdichtung und andere Eigenschaften des Ackerbodens. *Ber. über Landtechnik Wolfratshausen,* No. 4.

—— (1948–49). Vorlesung uber allgemeinen Pflazensoziologie (Vegetationsgeographie Deutschlands). Winter-Sem.

—— (1950). Kausale Pflanzensoziologie auf physiologischer Grundlage. *Ber. Deutsch. Bot. Ges.,* 63, 24–31.

—— (1952). Physiologisches und ökologisches Verhalten derselben Pflanzenarten. *Ber. Deutsch. Bot. Ges.,* 65, 350–61.

EVANS, F. C. (1952). The influence of size of quadrat on the distributional patterns of plant populations. *Contrib. Michigan Univ. Lab. Vert. Biol.* No. 54, 15 pp.

—— & CAIN, S. A. (1952). Preliminary studies on the vegetation of an old-field community in south-eastern Michigan. *Contrib. Michigan Univ. Lab. Vert. Biol.* No. 51, 17 pp.

FERRARINI, E. (1954). [Research on the flora infesting crops in Italy—in Italian.] *Nuovo Giorn. Bot. Ital.*, n.s., **61**, 133–81.

FOGG, J. M., JR. (1945). *Weeds of Lawn and Garden, A Handbook for Eastern Temperate North America.* University of Pennsylvania Press, Philadelphia, 215 pp.

GIMINGHAM, C. H. (1951). The use of life form and growth form in the analysis of community structure, as illustrated by a comparison of two dune communities. *J. Ecol.*, **39**, 396–406.

GOOD, R. (1931). A theory of plant geography. *New Phytol.*, **30**, 149–71.

—— (1953). *The Geography of Flowering Plants.* Longmans, Green, London, 2nd edn., 452 pp.

GOODALL, D. W. (1953). Objective methods for the classification of vegetation. I. The use of positive interspecific correlation. *Austral. J. Bot.*, **1**, 39–63.

GREIG-SMITH, P. (1952). The use of random and contiguous quadrats in the study of the structure of plant communities. *Ann. Bot.*, n.s., **16**, 293–316.

GROSSE-BRAUCKMANN, G. (1954). Untersuchungen uber die Ökologie, besonders den Wasserhaushalt, von Ruderalgesellschaften. *Vegetatio*, Den Haag, **4**, 245–83.

GUPPY, H. B. (1912). *Studies in Seeds and Fruits.* Williams & Norgate, London, 528 pp.

—— (1917). *Plants, Seeds and Currents in the West Indies and the Azores.* Williams & Norgate, London, 531 pp.

HALL, T. F. (1940). The biology of *Saururus cernuus* L. *Amer. Midl. Nat.*, **24**, 253–60.

HAMEL, A. & DANSEREAU, P. (1949). L'aspect écologique du problème des mauvaises herbes. *Bull. Serv. Biogeogr.*, **5**, 1–41.

HANF, M. (1937–38). Pflanzengesellschaften des Ackerbodens. *Pflanzenbau*, **13**, 449–76; **14**, 29–48.

HARDY, M. (1920). *The Geography of Plants.* Clarendon Press, Oxford, 327 pp.

HARPER, J. L. (1957). Ecological aspects of weed control. *Outlook on agriculture*, **1**, 197–205.

—— (1959). The ecological significance of dormancy and its importance in weed control. *Proc. 4th Internat. Congr. Crop Prot.*, **1**, 415–420.

HASE, C. L. (1941). The effect of clipping and weed competition upon the spread of pasture grass seedlings. *Trans. Kansas Acad. Sci.*, **44**, 104–15.

HAUMAN-MERCK, L. (1928). Les modifications de la flore Argentine sous l'action de la civilisation (essai géobotanique humaine). *Mém. Acad. R. Belg. Cl. Sci.*, **9**(3), 1–99.

HAUSRATH, H. (1911). *Pflanzengeographische Wandlungen der deutschen Landschaft.* Leipzig and Berlin.

HÉDIN, L. (1945). Contribution à l'étude des formes biologiques des espèces prairiales. *Ann. Agron.*, **15**, 235–78.

—— (1951). Humidité du sol et comportement des espèces prairiales. (Abs.) *Ann. Agron.*, Sér. B., **2**, 382.

HEINRICHS, D. H. & BOLTON, J. L. (1950). Studies on the competition of crested wheatgrass with perennial native species. *Sci. Agric.*, **30**(10), 428–43.

HÖCK, F. (1897). *Grundzüge der Pflanzengeographie*, Breslau.

—— (1905). Hauptergebnisse meiner Untersuchungen über die Gesamtuerbreitung der in Norddeutschland vorkommenden Allerweltspflanzen. *Beih. Bot. Centralbl.*, **18**, II, 394–416.

—— (1910). Neue Ankömmlinge in der Pflanzenwelt Mitteleuropas. *Beih. Bot. Centralbl.*, **26**, II, 391–433.

—— (1914). Ergänzungen zu meinen Arbeiten uber Ankömmlinge in der Pflanzenwelt Mitteleuropas. *Beih. Bot. Central.*, **32**, II, 71–110.

HOEDTKE, I. (1942). Ökologie der Ackerunkräuter im östlichen Hügellande Schleswig-Holsteins. Staatsexamensarbeit, Kiel.

HØEG, O. A. & LID, J. (1929). Adventive plants in Spitsbergen. Kgl. Norske Videnskab. Selsk. Forhandl. (Trondhjem), 1, 176–8.

HOLMGREN, R. G. (1956). Competition between annuals and young bitterbrush (Purshia tridentata) in Idaho. Ecology, 37, 370–7.

HULBERT, L. C. (1955). Ecological studies of Bromus tectorum and other annual brome-grasses. Ecol. Monog., 25, 181–213.

JANNACCONE, A. (1953). [Investigations on the relation of associations and successions of black mustard—in Italian.] Ital. Agric., 80, 344–8.

JOËL, A. H. (1928–29). Weed distribution and crop character in relation to soil type in Saskatchewan. Sci. Agric., 9, 675–82.

JONES, E. W. (1954). Applied forest ecology. Quart. J. Forest., 48(1), 24–28.

JOVET, P. (1937). Evolution, après abandon de culture, des champs de Valois. Bull. Soc. Bot. Fr., 84, 184–95.

—— (1940). Remarques sur l'introduction et la propagation de quelques plantes par les voies de communication. C. R. Soc. Biogéogr., 17(145), 29–34.

—— (1940a). Plantes rudérales, adventices et naturalisées de Paris et de sa banlieue. Bull. Soc. Bot. Fr., 87, 286–99.

—— (1940b). Evolution des groupements rudéraux 'parisiens'. Bull. Soc. Bot. Fr., 87, 304–12.

—— (1954). Influence de l'écoupage sur la flore des pâturages basques. Ann. Fédér. Pyrén. d'Econ. Montagnarde, (1952), 18(1), 23–94.

—— (1954a). Paris, sa flore spontanée, sa végétation. Notices et Itinéraires du VIIIᵉ Congrès Internat. de Botanique, Paris, II-3, 21–60.

KASAHARA, Y. (1954). Studies on the weeds of arable land in Japan, with special reference to kinds of harmful weeds, their geographic distribution, abundance, life-length, origin, and history. Ber. Ohara. Inst., 10, 72–109.

KENDREW, W. G. (1953). The Climates of the Continents. Clarendon Press, Oxford, 4th edn., 607 pp.

KERNER VON MARILAUN, A. (1951). The Background of Plant Ecology. (Trans. H. S. Conard.) Iowa State Coll. Press, Ames, 238 pp.

KIELHAUSER, G. E. (1956). Ackerunkrautgesellschaften aus dem trockensten Teile des oberen tiroler Inntales. Vegetatio, Den Haag, 7, 9–14.

KIRCHNER, O., LOEW, E. & SCHRÖTER, C. (1908). Lebensgeschichte der Blütenpflanzen Mitteleuropas. Stuttgart.

KNOPP, R. (1954). Experimentalle Soziologie der höheren Pflanzen. 1. Einwirkung der Pflanzen aufeinander. Soziologie der Keimung und des aufwachsenden Bestandes. Eugen Ulmer, Stuttgart, 202 pp.

KRASHENINNIKOV, I. M. (1946). [An essay of phytogenetical analysis of some Eurasian groups of the genus Artemisia L. according to the paleogeographic features of Eurasia—in Russian, English summary.] In V. L. Komarov (Ed.) [Materials in the History of the Flora and Vegetation of the U.R.S.S.], Fasc. II, pp. 87–196.

KREH, W. (1932). Das Pflanzenkleid der Umgebung von Stuttgart. Jahr. Hefte Ver. Vaterl. Naturk. in Württemberg, 88, 37–73.

KUHN, K. (1937). Die Pflanzengesellschaften im Neckargebiet der Schwäbischen Alb., Ferdinand Rauhringen, 340 pp.

KUMMER, A. P. (1945). Role of weeds in maintaining the plains grassland. Chicago Nat., 8, 26–27.

LEVINA, R. E. K. (1944). [The question about anthropochory—in Russian.] Sovetsk. Bot., 1944(3), 42–46.

MACDOUGAL, D. T. (1953). Plant Ecology. Lea & Febiger, Philadelphia.

MADAUS, G. (1938). Pflanzenfreundschaft und Pflanzenfeindschaft. Umschau, 42, 260–4.

MARILAUN, A. KERNER VON. See KERNER VON MARILAUN, A.

MAYNE, W. W. (1952). Weeds as a problem in crop ecology. *Planters' Chron.*, 47, 515–20.

MERRILL, E. D. (1954). The botany of Cook's voyages. *Chron. Bot.*, 14, 161–383. (cf. 'Weeds', pp. 219–22; 'Early trade routes in relation to distribution', pp. 223–39).

MEUSEL, H. (1943). *Vergleichende Arealkunde.* Berlin, 2 vols.

MÖLLER, I. (1949). *Die Entwicklung der Pflanzengesellschaften auf den Trümmern und Auffüllplätzen.* Dissertation, Kiel, 711 pp.

MUIR, J. (1937). The seed-drift of South Africa and some influences of ocean currents on the strand vegetation. *Union of South Africa, Dept. of Agric. & Forestry, Bot. Survey Mem.* No. 16, 108 pp. (8 pls., 7 figs.).

NAUMANN, D. (1951). *Die Ackerunkrautgesellschaften des Bonner Raumes und ihre Beziehungen zum Standort.* Dissertation, Bonn, 99 pp.

NEWMAN, L. F. & NEWMAN, R. W. (1918). Some records of the seasonal flora of arable land under cultivation. *J. Ecol.*, 6, 178–88.

NORRIS, E. L. (1939). Ecological survey of the weed population of eastern Nebraska. *Nebraska Univ. Studies*, 39, 28–90.

OBERDORFER, E. (1954). Über Unkrautgesellschaften der Balkanhalbinsel. *Vegetatio*, Den Haag, 4, 379–411.

O'CONNOR, K. F. (1956). Influences of treading on grasslands. *Ph.D. Thesis, Cornell Univ.*, 194 pp.; *Dissert. Abst.*, 17, 4–5, 1957.

OLESEN, C. (1922). The ecology of *Urtica dioica*. *J. Ecol.*, 9, 1–18.

OOSTING, H. J. (1942). An ecological analysis of the plant communities of Piedmont, North Carolina. *Amer. Midl. Nat.*, 28, 1–126.

—— (1956). *The Study of Plant Communities. An Introduction to the Study of Ecology.* Freeman, San Francisco, 2nd. edn., 440 pp.

PAMMEL, L. H. (1909). Underground organs of weeds. *Proc. Iowa Acad. Sci.*, 16, 31–40.

—— & KING, C. M. (1929). Heights of weeds. *Proc. Iowa Acad. Sci.*, 36, 221–3.

PAPADAKIS, J. (1952). *Agricultural Geography of the World.* The Author, Buenos Aires, 118 pp.

PELTON, J. F. (1951). Outline for ecological life history studies in trees, shrubs, and stem succulents. *Ecology*, 32, 334–43.

PFEIFFER, E. (1945). Weeds and what they tell. *Org. Gard.*, Ser. II, 94 pp.

PHILLIPS, M. R. (1953). Studies on the quantitative morphology and ecology of *Eriophorum angustifolium* Roth. I. The rhizome system. *J. Ecol.*, 41, 295–318.

PIEMEISEL, R. L. (1951). Causes affecting change and rate of change in a vegetation of annuals in Idaho. *Ecology*, 32(1), 53–72.

PIGNATTI, S. (1957). La vegetazione delle risaie pavesi (studio fitosociologico). *Archiv. Botan. Biogeo. Ital.*, 33(1–2), 1–67.

—— (1957a). La vegetazione messicola delle colture di Frumento, Segale, e Avena nella provincia Pavia. *Atti Ist. Bot. Lab. Critt. Univ. Pavia* (ser. 5), 12, 243–319.

PLUMMER, G. L. (1954). *Cercis canadensis* L.; an ecological life history. *Dissert. Abst.*, 14(12), 2187–8.

POLUNIN, N. (1960). *Introduction to Plant Geography and Some Related Sciences.* Longmans, Green, London; McGraw-Hill, New York, 640 pp.

PORSILD, M. P. (1932). Alien plants and apophytes of Greenland. *Medd. om Grønland*, 92(1), 1–85.

QUANTIN, A. (1947). Les associations rudérales en Bourgogne méridionale. *Bull. Soc. Bot. France*, 94, 406–9.

RAUCHFUSS, F. L. (1956). The ecology of *Halogeton glomeratus* on Wyoming range lands. *J. Range Mangt.*, 9, 33.

RAUNKIAER, C. (Ed. A. G. Tansley) (1934). *The Life-forms of Plants and Statistical Plant Geography.* Clarendon Press, Oxford, 632 pp.

REYNAUD-BEAUVERIE, M. A. (1936). *Le Milieu et la Vie en Commun des Plantes.* Paris.

RICE, E. L. & PENFOUND, W. T. (1954). Plant succession and yield of living plant material in a plowed prairie in central Oklahoma. *Ecology*, 35, 176–80.

RIDLEY, H. N. (1930). *The Dispersal of Plants throughout the World.* Reeve, Ashford, Kent, 744 pp.

RIETZ, G. E. DU (1921). *Zur methodologishen Grundlage der modernen Pflanzensoziologie.* Diss. Wien, Uppsala, 272 pp.

RIMBACH, A. (1902). Physiological observations on the subterranean organs of some Californian Liliaceae. *Bot. Gaz.*, 33, 401–20.

ROTHMALER, W. (1955). *Allgemeine Taxonomie und Chorologie der Pflanzen.* W. Gronav Jena, 2nd. edn., 215 pp.

RÜBEL, E. (1936). Plant communities of the world. I. *Essays in Geobotany in Honor of William Albert Setchell*, Univ. California, Berkeley, 263–290.

SALISBURY, E. J. (1928). On the causes and ecological significance of stomatal frequency with special reference to the woodland flora. *Phil. Trans. Roy. Soc. London*, 216, 1–65.

—— (1929). The biological equipment of species in relation to competition. *J. Ecol.*, 17, 197–222.

SALZMANN, R. (1939). Untersuchungen uber die Ackerunkräuter in Gebietsen schweizerischer Kleegraswirtschaften. *Landw. Jahrb. Schweiz*, 53, 748–50.

SARFATTI, G. (1948). Sull'interpretazione della frequenza percentuale valutata col metodo di Raunkiaer. *Nuovo Giorn. Bot. Ital.*, 55, 588–92.

SAX, K. (1955). *Standing Room Only. The Challenge of Overpopulation.* Beacon Press, Boston, 206 pp.

SCHOEMAN, S. N. (1937). Sward density and weed invasion of woolly finger (Pretoria small) pastures under different grazing treatments. *S. Afr. J. Sci.*, 34, 218–23.

SCHRÖTER, C. (1937). Die Lebensbedingungen der Ackerunkräuter. *D. Naturwissenschaft.*, 25, 685–8.

—— & —— (1937). A quantitative analysis of the weed flora in arable land. *J. Ecol.*, 25, 213–21.

SINGH, B. N. & CHALAM, V. G. (1936). Unit of quantitative study of weed flora on arable lands. *J. Amer. Soc. Agron.*, 28, 556–7.

——, —— & DAS, K. (1937). Changing density of weed flora on arable land during the course of the 'rate' season. *J. Amer. Soc. Agron.*, 29, 204–12.

SINSKAIA, E. N. (1931). [The study of species in their dynamics and interrelation with different types of vegetation—in Russian, English summary.] *Bull. Appl. Bot. Genet. Pl. Breed.*, 25(2), 1–97.

SISSINGH, G. (1950). Onkruid-associaties in Nederland. Een sociologisch-systematische beshrijving van de klasse Rudereto-secalinetea Br.-Bl. 1936. *Versl. Landbouwkdg. Onderz.*, 's-Gravenhage, nr. 56.15, 224 pp.

SLIFE, F. W. & SCOTT, W. O. (1951). Giant foxtail—new cornbelt weed menace. *Crops & Soils*, 3(7), 22–23.

SMITH, H. D. (1944). The balance of nature upset by foreign importations. *Gard. Cl. Amer. Bull.*, ser. 9, No. 3, 5–14.

SPILLMAN, W. J. & CATES, J. S. (1908). Agronomic habits of rootstock producing weeds. *Proc. Soc. Agric. Sci.*, 29, 57–66.

STAPLEDON, R. G. (1916). Plant communities of farmland. *Ann. Bot.*, 30, 161–80.

STEVENS, O. A. (1944). Variations in kinds of weeds from year to year. *N. Dakota Agric. Exp. Sta. Bimon. Bull.*, 6(6), 6.

SUAREZ, O. R. (1947). Sobre comunidalles ruderales de la cornbrea de Grado (Asturias). *Farmacognosia* (Spain), 6, 167–94.

TADROS, T. M. & ATTA, B. A. M. (1958). The plant communities of barley fields and uncultivated areas of Mareotis (Egypt). *Vegetatio*, Den Haag, 8, 161–75.

TAJIMA, S. (1952). [Fundamental studies of weed control. I. Seasonal changes of kind, quantity and some other facts of weeds on arable land—in Japanese.] *Proc. Crop Sci. Soc. Japan*, 21, 115–16.

TALLON, G. (1958). La flore des rizières de la région d'Arles (Camarge, France) et ses répercussions sur la culture du riz. *Vegetatio*, Den Haag, 8, 20–42.*

TANSLEY, A. G. (1917). On competition between *Galium saxatile* L. (*G. hercynicum* Weig.) and *Galium sylvestre* Poll. (*G. asperum* Schreb.) on different types of soil. *J. Ecol.*, 5, 173–9.

TARAKANOV, K. N. (1950). [Ecological stages of development and forms of adaptation of some plant species—in Russian.] *Akad. Nauk USSR Inst. Lesa. Lab. Evoliuts. Ekol. Rast. Im. B. A. Kellera. Trud.*, 2, 48–75.

THELLUNG, A. (1925). Kulturpflanzeneigenschaften bei Unkräutern. *Veröff. Geobot. Inst. Zürich, Festschrift Schröter*, 3, 743–61.

TOMASELLI, R. (1951). Applicazione del metodo fitosociologico alla valutazione dell' efficacia dei discerbanti. *Humus*, 7(1), 23–29.

TURRILL, W. B. (1951). Some problems of plant range and distribution. *J. Ecol.*, 39, 205–27.

—— (1954). Mapping the ranges and distribution of taxonomic groups of plants. *Kew Bull.*, 1954, 1, pp. 59–64.

TÜXEN, J. (1953). Zur Systematik und Ökologie der Hackfruchtunkraut-Gesellschaften. *Mitt. Florist. Soziolog. Arbeitsgemeinschaft*, 4, 147–9.

TÜXEN, R. (1950). Grundriss einer Systematik der nitrophilen Unkrautgesellschaften in der eurosibirischen Region Europas. *Mitt. Florist. Soziolog. Arbeitsgemeins.*, 2, 94–175.

UBRIZSY, G. (1950). Les associations de mauvaises herbes rudérales de la Hongrie et les aspects agricoles du problème. *Acta Agron. Hung.*, 1, 107–23.

—— (1955). [Die ruderalen Unkrautgesellschaften Ungarns. II. Studien uber Okologie und Sukzession—in Russian, English summary.] *Acta Agron. Hung.*, 5, 393–418.

—— (1959). Phytozönologische Untersuchungen an Ackerunkrautgesellschaften mit besonderer Berucksichtigung der chemischen Bekämpfung. *Proc. 4th Internat. Congr. Crop Prot.* (Hamburg), 1957, I, 451–457.

UPHOF, T. J. C. (1920). Influence of temperature on the geographical distribution of *Opuntia*. *J. Ecol.*, 8, 41–53.

VAN DERSAL, W. R. *See* DERSAL, W. R. VAN.

VESTER, H. (1940). Die Areale und Arealtypen der Angiospermen-Familien. *Bot. Archiv*, 41, 203–75.

VON MARILAUN, A. KERNER. *See* KERNER VON MARILAUN, A.

VRIES, D. M. DE & ZANDSTRA, Z. (1952). [Field-weeds in the course of the year—in Dutch.] *Levende Natuur*, 55, 184–8.

WATT, A. S. (1947). Contribution to the ecology of bracken. IV. The structure of the community. *New Phytol.*, 46, 97–121.

—— (1947a). Pattern and process in the plant community. *J. Ecol.*, 35, 1–22.

WEAVER, J. E. (1954). A seventeen-year study of plant succession in prairie. *Amer. J. Bot.*, 41, 31–38.

—— & DARLAND, R. W. (1944). Grassland patterns in 1940. *Ecology*, 25, 202–15.

WEHSARG, O. (1954). *Ackerunkraüter; Biologie allgemeine Bekampfung und Einzelbekampfung*, 2nd. edn., Akademie-Verlag, Berlin, 294 pp.

WILLIAMS, C. B. (1943). Area and number of species. *Nature, Lond.*, 152, 264–7.

WITTMACK, L. (1892). Die Vertilgung der Wurzelunkräuter. *Jahrb. Deutsch. Landw. Ges.*, 7, 231–45.

* *See also* the exhaustive study: Miyawaki, A. (1960). Pflanzensoziologische Untersuchungen über Reisfeld-Vegetation auf den japanischen Inseln mit vergleichender Betrachtung Mitteleuropas. *Vegetatio*, Den Haag, 9, 345–402. Eng. summ. (12 tables, 16 figs., 107 refs.; *see* his fig. 16, p. 394 for a map of the principal rice-field plant associations of the world).

XII

THE CLASSIFICATION AND MODE OF ACTION OF HERBICIDES

INTRODUCTION

IT has often been said that there are three areas of major advance in agriculture that have been highly significant and far-reaching in their application to most aspects of agricultural endeavour throughout the world. These are: (i) the use of mineral fertilizers; (ii) the understanding and utilization of the principles of genetics in the improvement of plants and animals; and (iii) the use of pesticides, and appropriately here the plant growth-regulating substances—from 2,4-D to tordon. The great modern subject of herbicides is the principal concern of this and the following two chapters, for their use has resulted in vast improvements in the nature and economics of weed control. The other methods of weed control—mechanical and fire, as well as biological and ecological—will be dealt with in the last chapter of the present volume.

The historical aspects of the development of chemical weed control have been reviewed by a number of authors (Robbins *et al.*, 1952; and others cited below), and will only concern us briefly here. The literature on chemical weed-killers before the introduction of the growth-regulator types has been particularly well reviewed by Cook & Halferdahl (1937) and by Wilson (1944). Cook & Halferdahl compiled, in tabulated form, the findings of 339 investigators, and listed the publications of another 311. Wilson (1944) reviewed all aspects of noxious plant control as indicated by a bibliography of 409 items. With the advent of the growth-regulator type of herbicides, the following more detailed reviews and books have appeared, in chronological order (Akamine, 1948; Crafts & Harvey, 1949; Norman *et al.*, 1950—*see* Ch. XIII; Blackman *et al.*, 1951—*see* Ch. XIII; Thorup, 1951—*see* Ch. XIII; Nickell, 1952; Overbeek, 1952; Crafts, 1953—*see* Ch. XIII; Melnikov & Baskakov, 1954; Melnikov *et al.*, 1954—*see* Ch. XIII; Woodford *et al.*, 1958; Crafts, 1961; Klingman & Noordhoff, 1961; Audus, 1964).

Chemical methods of killing weeds in cereals began nearly seventy years ago, when G. Bonnet in France showed, in 1896, that a solution of copper sulphate (XLIII)* would kill charlock plants which were growing with cereals. Some sixteen years later, Rabaté (cf. 1934) demonstrated that

* These Roman numerals refer to those in Appendices I & II, where further details concerning the properties and uses of the individual herbicides will be found.— Ed.

284

dilute sulphuric acid could also be used for this purpose, and, in 1932, in France again, the first organic chemical, 'DN' (dinitro-*ortho*-cresol), was used to destroy weeds in cereals (cf. Wain, 1957). In the United States, Bolley (1908) was an early experimenter with differential herbicides, in North Dakota. The action of all of this group of chemicals may be describ-ed as caustic, or burning, in effect, there being little, if any, translocation.

With the introduction of the plant hormone era in plant physiology in the late 1920's and early 1930's (cf. Went, 1935; Went & Thimann, 1937), and with the chemical identity of the first active substance of this nature in plants established as 3-indoleacetic acid by Kögl *et al.* (1934—*see* Ch. XIII), the stage was set for spectacular advances in both the theoretical and applied fields (cf. Nielsen, 1930—*see* Ch. XIII; Boysen-Jensen, 1936—*see* Ch. XIII).

Accounts vary concerning the earliest dates that can be claimed for work on the growth-regulator herbicides (*see* Akamine, 1948), but, here, the sequence of events from the published record is followed. In 1942, Zimmerman & Hitchcock published their work with the substituted phenoxy acids, of which 2,4-D (I) is one: they were the first to demonstrate the physiological activities (in cell elongation, morphogenesis, root development, and parthenocarpy) of this group of compounds. This publication was preceded by a decade or so of work on the physiological activity of unsaturated gases, of indoleacetic and indolepropionic acids, and of *beta*-phenyl-propionic acid (Hitchcock, 1935) (cf. Crocker, 1948, Chapter 6, 'Plant Hormones' by P. W. Zimmerman). The original illu-stration, from the now classic paper of Zimmerman & Hitchcock, showing the effects of 2,4-D acid on plants, is reproduced in our Plate 15 (cf. Zimmerman & Hitchcock, 1942, p. 326).

The inquiry of a carnation grower in the Chicago area, as to 'What is the effect of illuminating gas on carnations?', essentially initiated the long and fruitful trail of events that led to the plant growth-regulating substances being discovered at the Boyce Thompson Institute in the 1930's, 1940's, and later. As related by the late Dr. William Crocker, the first Managing Director of the Institute, in his book *Growth of Plants—Twenty Years' Research at Boyce Thompson Institute* (1948), this first inquiry led to the research on ethylene at the University of Chicago (Crocker & Knight, 1908) and later at the Institute. The study of this gas, and of other physiologically active gases, absorbed a considerable share of the research efforts of Dr. Crocker and his colleagues, Drs. P. W. Zimmerman and A. E. Hitchcock, for many years thereafter, and led to work on lethal gases and on the indole compounds, the phenoxy com-pounds, the benzoic derivatives, and many others. In 1935 Drs. Zimmerman and Hitchcock were honoured with the American Association for the Advancement of Science award for 'A Notable Contribution to Science', for their paper *Responses of Plants to Synthetic Growth Substances (Phyto-hormones)* (American Association . . . , 1948, p. 66).

The late Dr. J. M. Beal (1944), at the University of Chicago, first worked only with 4-chloro phenoxyacetic acid on sweet pea plants, and noted the rapid translocation from the point of application, referring to such as 'telemorphic effects'; while in a second paper, published later in 1944 (Beal, 1944*a*), 2,4-D acid and 2,4,5-T acid (III) were studied in similar fashion as regards their effect on sweet pea, African marigold, and red kidney-bean. Again Beal noted the strong telemorphic effects and lethal action, and he concludes his discussion (p. 178) with the statement 'That these and similar experiments with growth-regulating substances are significant is beyond doubt, . . . because of the possibility of establishing for them economic and practical applications as growth stimulators, growth depressors, or herbicides'. How very right this forecast proved to be!

Mitchell & Hamner (1944, p. 482—*see* Ch. XIII), in the same June issue of the *Botanical Gazette* as published the first-cited article of Dr. Beal, in their study of the use of polyethylene glycols as carriers for growth-regulating substances (including 2,4-D), observed that 'Since these compounds . . . apparently travel for long distances through certain plants . . . they may prove highly effective as herbicides, even when applied in low concentration. It was also noted that certain of the weeds, particularly grasses, which were growing in soil treated with solutions of 2,4-dichlorophenoxyacetic acid, were differentially affected. This may be of importance in connection with the differential killing of weeds.' Later in that same eventful year of 1944 the first experiments designed to test the potentiality of the growth-regulators as herbicides were conducted by Hamner & Tukey (1944). They successfully used 2,4-D and 2,4,5-trichlorophenoxyacetic acid to kill bindweed (*Convolvulus arvensis* L.).

Marth & Mitchell (1944) of the United States Department of Agriculture, in their pioneer study on the differential herbicidal activity of 2,4-D, state (*op. cit.*, p. 224) that Dr. E. J. Kraus of the University of Chicago proposed in 1941 that the growth-inhibitory properties of these compounds be utilized in connection with weed control. It is also of interest to note that McNew & Hoffmann (1950) likewise had been working for some years with this group of compounds.

Concurrently in England, similar studies were under way (reportedly as early as 1940), in which the first growth-regulator to be tried (naphthaleneacetic acid), when applied at 25 lb./acre, was found to remove charlock from oats with little injury to the latter (Slade *et al.*, 1945). It is reported that these same workers had concluded in 1941 that 2-methyl--4-chlorophenoxyacetic acid (as the Na salt)—later called 'Methoxone' (II)—was one of the two most active compounds tested. 2,4-D, the other highly active compound found by Slade, Templeman & Sexton (1945), was used by Nutman *et al.* (1945—*see* Ch. XIII) at the Rothamsted Experimental Station in 1942, in further experiments to test the merits of this compound as a herbicide.

The first patent in the United States for 2,4-D herbicides was obtained in 1945 by F. D. Jones of the American Chemical Paint Co. (U.S. No. 2,390,941). An earlier patent for a growth-regulating substance had been obtained, however, by J. F. Lontz in 1943 (U.S. No. 2,322,761).

An examination of the 1945 patent of F. D. Jones discloses that it is a continuation-in-part of a prior application filed in March, 1944. Weeds are defined, and some examples are given. Included are such otherwise desirable plants as Japanese honeysuckle and 'lawn grasses growing on driveways'. He notes that many of the then available herbicides were hazardous to use, corrosive to equipment, and high in cost per acre. Furthermore, they killed only the tops of plants without any permanent damage to the roots. He notes that the new compounds ('halogenated phenoxy monocarboxylic aliphatic acids, their esters and salts') represent a wholly new class of systemic or translocated herbicides that must be used at much higher concentrations than have ever been used for plant-growth promotion. The herbicidal range of active ingredient is given as 0·1 to 0·04 per cent for aqueous preparations, and 0·2 per cent or higher for dust formulations. He notes that applications must be made to the leaves of weeds, with the best results obtained on sunny days when the temperature is over 70°F. He records that these substances kill in from two to three weeks, that large areas may be treated at relatively small expense, and that the treated areas are not rendered sterile. The twenty-seven claims included comprise, primarily, methods and compositions for killing weeds. Nowhere is there any claim or suggestion of *selective herbicidal activity*. No experimental data were included.

In a survey of the mechanisms of herbicide action, Overbeek (1962, 1964) notes that all of the principal herbicides now in use appear to act primarily on some phase or another of the growth process. He raises the question too, just why from a physiological point of view these herbicides are successful. The answer follows, he states, from the work of Crafts (1961) and his school. 'It is that a herbicide persists in the plant. At any rate its effect persists in the plant for a long time. Successful herbicidal chemicals are stable themselves, or their toxic reaction-products in the plant are stable. From a physiological point of view, one could therefore define a herbicide as a chemical that deranges the physiology of a plant over a period long enough to kill it.'

Classification of Herbicides*

Perhaps the most useful classification of herbicides is the one based on their general mode of action. This classification has been used by a number of authors, with minor changes (cf. Robbins *et al.*, 1952; Woodford, 1957). The present treatment follows, in a general form, this last author, though there are some newly introduced concepts. A chemical

* Full details for the majority of herbicides, including the purposes for which they are most useful, will be found in Appendices I & II (pp. 438–52).

classification is of value, however, for considering the chemical relation-ships of the various molecules. A concise chemical classification has been prepared by Woodford & Kasasian (1960), and is reproduced with certain adaptations in Table XI.

More recently, Brian (1964) has published a classification which com-prises an inorganic group, and two organic groups, one having *no* nitrogen, and one containing nitrogen. The classification essentially is similar to that presented in Table XI. One difference arises, however, in that Brian introduces two new groups, the bipyridylium quaternary salts, and the toluidines (both representing newly introduced herbicides, *see* Appendix II).

TABLE XI

A CHEMICAL CLASSIFICATION OF THE PRINCIPAL ORGANIC HERBICIDES
(Adapted from Woodford & Kasasian, 1960)

A. Chemicals with amide, thioamide, or amidine groups:

amide	$\diagdown \text{N}-\overset{\displaystyle \overset{O}{\|\|}}{\text{C}}-\text{C}-$	CBAA CDEA NPA MH
urea	$\diagdown \text{N}-\overset{\displaystyle \overset{O}{\|\|}}{\text{C}}-\text{N}\diagup$	DCU Fenuron Monuron Diuron
amidine	$\diagdown \text{N}-\overset{\displaystyle \overset{N}{\|\|}}{\text{C}}-\text{N}\diagup$	Simizine Amitrole
carbamate	$\diagdown \text{N}-\overset{\displaystyle \overset{O}{\|\|}}{\text{C}}-\text{O}-$	IPC Chloro IPC
thiocarbamate	$\diagdown \text{N}-\overset{\displaystyle \overset{O}{\|\|}}{\text{C}}-\text{S}-$	EPTC
dithiocarbamate	$\diagdown \text{N}-\overset{\displaystyle \overset{S}{\|\|}}{\text{C}}-\text{S}-$	CDEC SMDC DMTT

B. Substituted phenoxy and benzoic acids: MCPA, 2,4-D, TBA, etc.
C. Chlorine and methyl substituted acetic acids: TCA, Dalapon.
D. Chlorine and nitro substituted phenols: Dinoseb, Pentachlorophenol.
E. Unsaturated aliphatics: Allyl alcohol, Acrolein.
F. Miscellaneous: Endothal, Alanap, Dacthal.

Note: In Group A, the 'nitrogenous group', only this key nitrogen-containing portion of the respective molecule is shown.

The complete molecular structure for most of these may be found in Appendices I & II (pp. 438–52).

CONTACT HERBICIDES

This class has been referred to as the caustic herbicides. Their application results in a 'burning' of the tissues, and is primarily an effect of the very high concentrations employed: e.g. sulphuric acid, 5–70 per cent; iron sulphate, 20–30 per cent; and copper sulphate (XLIII), 1–5 per cent. The cellular reactions to these concentrations are non-specific, and bring about the denaturation and precipitation of protein in various ways (Currier, 1956—*see* Ch. XIII; Woodford, 1957).

(*i*) *Oils*. Herbicidal oils consist of two principal types: the light distillates (boiling range, 300–400°F.), used for the selective control of weeds in umbelliferous crops and among forest tree seedlings, and heavier distillates (boiling range, 400°–500°F.), containing a higher percentage (85 to 90) of aromatics and used for the non-selective control of weeds —particularly grasses—along railways, etc.

Oils have a considerably lower surface-tension than water (light stove-oil, 27·3 dynes/cm. as opposed to 73 dynes/cm. for water), and thus they readily spread over and 'wet' plant surfaces. This is also referred to as the spreading coefficient (cf. Stage, 1952, p. 46). This value, + 11·8, together with the value for the interfacial tension between water and oil, 32·9 dynes/cm., may be found for the light stove-oil, as well as other oils, in the reference cited. Such a flowing or 'creeping' action of oils is a useful one, as with high rates of application the oil will flow between the leaves and reach the basal growing-point of tall grasses. Oils of low viscosity appear to enter leaves through the stomata and permeate the intercellular spaces for considerable distances: they do not move through the vascular system. It is generally believed that bulk oil does not move into living cells; but after cells have been injured, oils may penetrate them.

The primary toxic effect of oils is due to a solvent action on the outer plasma membranes of the cells. The details are not fully understood, but Overbeek & Blondeau (1954—*see* Ch. XIII) suggest that the hydrocarbon molecules displace the fatty molecules and thus destroy the semi-permeability of the membrane, and similarly disturb other lipophases in the plant. Minshall & Helson (1949—*see* Ch. XIII), using a sensitive infra-red absorption apparatus, found that when a solvent oil was applied to plants, their photosynthesis ceased abruptly, while the respiration was not affected initially. As the submicroscopic structure of the grana of the chloroplast must be maintained for normal photosynthetic action (and this requirement does not hold for respiration), Overbeek & Blondeau suggest that the hydrocarbons, or other constituents of the oil, dissolve in the lipoid phase of the grana, thereby causing an increase in the distances between individual chlorophyll molecules and also other disruptions of the normal submicroscopic structures that are required for photosynthesis.

As is widely known, members of the Umbelliferae (such as carrot, parsnip, etc.) are free from injury by the lighter oils, such as Stoddard's solvent; accordingly this type of oil has been widely used in weeding carrots and conifer seedlings in forest nurseries. Overbeek & Blondeau (1954—*see* Ch. XIII) found that the plasma membrane of the cells of members of this family (Umbelliferae)—not only leaf cells, but root cells as well—are inherently resistant to oils, including paraffins and olefins.

(*ii*) *Dinitro Compounds*. Two members of the class of dinitro alkyl-phenols (or 'DN's') have been widely used as general or non-selective herbicides: 2,4-dinitro-6-*sec*-butylphenol (Dinoseb) (XIX), and 3,5-dinitro-γ-cresol (DNC). Their highly toxic nature to both plants and animals has been known for some time. It has been assumed that they interfere with some metabolic process that is common to both kingdoms. Apparently, the initial effect of low doses of these compounds is to prevent the formation of energy-rich phosphate bonds; this uncoupling leads successively to increased respiration, reduced growth, and often death. When higher concentrations, such as those employed at herbicidal levels, are used, additional mechanisms become apparent: respiration is inhibited (possibly by the action of flavo-protein enzymes), inhibition of fermentation follows, and proteins are denatured (Woodford, 1957).

A summary of the study by Fogg (1948) of the penetration of 3,5-dinitro-γ-cresol into *Sinapis* leaves, indicates some aspects of the mode of action and specificity, as well as some degree of selectivity, of this herbicide. Entry through the stomata was found to be unimportant; but lethal amounts may enter from aqueous solution by simple diffusion of the undissociated phenol through the epidermis, which behaves as a homogeneous lipid membrane. Lethal amounts may also enter the plant from a dry surface deposit, by gaseous diffusion through the stomata, or by diffusive penetration of the epidermis following sublimation. Movement of this chemical within the plant is slight and appears to be mainly by diffusion. On plants that are resistant to DNC the contact angle is greater than 100°, while such an angle on *Sinapis* leaves is much lower—63°. The area of contact is considerably less on resistant plants, owing to the more marked corrugation of their epidermal surface and a thicker cuticle, than in the case of *Sinapis*.

INHIBITORS OF CELL GROWTH

Those herbicidal chemicals which have been observed to interfere with some stage or stages of the process of cell division (i.e. mitosis) are grouped here.

(*i*) *Phenyl Carbamates*. The first member of this group, *N*-phenyl *iso*propylcarbamate, was selected by Templeman & Sexton (1946, 1946a—*see* Ch. XIII) as the most active growth-substance in a series of arylurethanes. The second important member, CIPC (isopropyl-*N*-

(3-chlorophenyl)carbamate) (XII), was introduced as an experimental weed-killer by E. D. Witman and A. J. D. Newton in 1951. These substances are applied as soil treatments at 4–8 lb./acre for the control of annual grasses and a few dicotyledonous weeds that grow during the winter in grass-seeded crops and lucerne.

Several investigators (Ennis, 1949—*see* Ch. XIII; Ivens & Blackman, 1949—*see* Ch. XII) have shown that the effects of IPC on the dividing cell are similar to those caused by colchicine, and often referred to as 'C-mitosis'. Spindle formation is inhibited, and the chromosomes fail to arrange themselves on the equatorial plane of the cell during metaphase. Cell elongation is also retarded, while the chlorophyll content of the whole plant increases by from 19 to 28 per cent and respiration is affected. At a concentration of 10^{-4} M, IPC almost completely inhibits the activity of certain respiratory enzymes, and Freed (1953—*see* Ch. XIII) has suggested that this might be connected with a blocking of cell division at the metaphase. As Woodford (1957) indicates, it is not clear whether the carbamates act directly on the dividing nucleus, or whether blockage at a particular stage of cell division is merely the result of a more fundamental action which may also influence cell elongation. Vegedex (2-chloroallyl-diethyldithiocarbamate) (XV) is effective as a pre-emergence application for grass control in a variety of crops. Another member of the group, Eptam (ethyl N,N-di-n-propylthiolcarbamate) (XVI), has proved useful both for pre- and post-emergence weed control on a great variety of crops (Crafts, 1961).

Moreland & Hill (1959; cf. Fig. 50) have investigated the inhibitory effects of IPC and three monochlorinated derivatives on the Hill reaction, finding the widely used herbicide CIPC to be the most inhibitory. The Hill reaction in the photosynthetic process has been used by a number of investigators to assay the effects of certain toxins and herbicides. R. Hill in 1937 showed that isolated chloroplasts from such plants as species of *Stellaria* and *Chenopodium* are able to form oxygen in the presence of light and ferric salts. Until recently it was generally agreed that this 'Hill reaction' was based on the photolysis of water, but the recent data of O. Warburg and G. Krippahl (cf. Gysin & Knüsli, 1960) postulate that the action of light in the Hill reaction is due to the splitting of carbon dioxide. Warburg and Krippahl's explanation of the Hill reaction is that ferric salts oxidize carbon to CO_2 in a dark reaction, and that, in the light, CO_2 is split into $C + O_2$. Other herbicides, such as Monuron and Simazine, inhibit the Hill reaction when in about the same dilutions, showing a 50 per cent inhibition at concentrations of 7×10^{-7} M.

The carbamate herbicides do not retain their identity in treated plants, but are converted to water-soluble forms—with some into the N-hydroxy derivative. The mechanisms basic to phytotoxicity are not known, although as noted above they are inhibitory to photosynthesis. Eptam as a liquid or vapour inhibits wax formation in the developing leaves of cabbage, and this inhibition accurs as long as a source of herbicide is available (Gentner, 1962; cf. Hilton *et al.*, 1963). The carbamates are predominantly soil-applied, and are effective through a soil medium. Absorption occurs through the developing epicotyl of grass seedlings, and root absorption occurs readily but seems of secondary importance to effective action of this group of herbicides. As inhibitors of cell division, their lethal action also occurs in the root meristems (Hilton *et al.*, 1963; Crafts 1964).

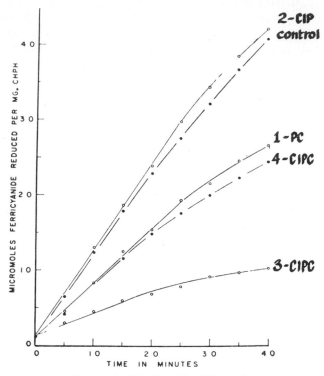

By courtesy of J. Agric. Food Chem.; from Moreland & Hill, 1959

Fig. 50.—Effect of isopropyl *N*-phenylcarbamate (IPC, here labelled 1-PC) and its mono-chlorinated derivatives (chloro IPC, etc.) at concentrations of 6×10^{-4} moles, on the Hill reaction of chloroplasts isolated from turnip greens (*Brassica* spp.). The micromoles of ferri-cyanide reduced per milligram of chlorophyll were plotted as a function of time during a 4-minute period. 3-CIPC, a herbicide that is now widely used, produced the greatest amount of inhibition at this concentration.

(ii) Trichloroacetic Acid (XXXI) *and Chloral Derivatives.* Ammonium trichloroacetate was introduced as a herbicide in 1947 (U.S.P. 2,393,086), and other derivatives were developed in 1949 (Barrons, 1949). These materials, with tillage, were especially effective against quack-grass (*Agropyron* spp.) at 40–50 lb./acre. It is noteworthy that the other large group of grass toxicants is believed to belong to this class of cell toxins. Most of the evidence for this rests on older work, performed with chloral hydrate $(CCl_3CH(OH)_2)$ as a polyploidizing and cytological reagent,

before the advent of work with colchicine. Work with chloral hydrate on *Vicia* and *Pisum* has been reported by Němec (1904—see Ch. XIII) and Küster (1935—*see* Ch. XIII); like the present-day derivatives, this substance proved particularly damaging to these leguminous plants. Trichloroacetic acid (XXXI) has long been known to be an effective protein precipitant.

Dr. L. P. Miller (1941—*see* Ch. XIII), at the Boyce Thompson Institute, studied the fate of trichloroethyl alcohol in a monocotyledonous plant (*Gladiolus*) and found that, through a possible detoxification process, this material was converted into a glycoside, β-2,2,2-trichloroethylgentiobioside, in the corms. Later, Miller (1942—*see* Ch. XIII) showed that chloral hydrate treatment of maize and dandelion plants resulted in the formation of β-2-trichloroethyl-D-glucoside in the tops and roots of both.

Incidentally, these studies trace the fate of applied growth-regulators such as ethylene chlorohydrin and chloral hydrate, and are among some early studies revealing one mode, at least, of the detoxification mechanisms of plants. During the course of these studies, a trichloroethylglycoside containing a C_{11} disaccharide had been obtained from dandelion (*Taraxacum officinale*) plants which had been treated with chloral hydrate. More recently (Miller, 1957), the monosaccharide components of this disaccharide have been identified as glucose and xylose, using the paper chromatographic technique. Just which of the disaccharides of glucose and xylose is involved is not known, but it was suggested that the most common of the naturally occurring ones is primeverose.

Another member of this group of herbicides is dichloral urea (DCU) (XX). Bis(1-hydroxy-2,2,2-trichloroethyl)urea was introduced as a selective pre-emergence herbicide in 1950 (King, 1950, U.S.P. 2,219,416). It has been successfully tested for control of annual grasses in cruciferous and cucurbitaceous crops, as well as in cotton, potatoes, tomatoes, and tobacco. When disked into the soil, it has been useful as a pre-planting treatment for grass control in sugar beets.

One of the newer herbicides within this group, Dalapon (2,2-dichloropropionic acid) (XXXII), may well act in a somewhat similar manner. Dalapon was introduced in 1953 (U.S.P. 2,642,354); it is a highly effective grass toxicant, and is superior to the trichloroacetates in that it is freely transported in the phloem and xylem and can be applied to either soil or foliage. The trichloroacetates have to be applied to the soil. Likewise, certain leguminous plants are highly sensitive to Dalapon and related types of herbicides.

Other theories of action have been reviewed by Woodford (1957). Trichloroacetic acid is known to react with 2,4-D in its effect on extension growth of root and shoot segments of the pea (Sen & Woodford, 1953). It is possible that these herbicides interfere with the natural auxins of plants. Trichloroacetic acid is absorbed by both susceptible and resistant species, but accumulates more in the latter—suggesting that the metabolic breakdown of the herbicide and its toxic effect may be related.

Redemann & Meikle (1955) have suggested that Dalapon might act as an antimetabolite to pyruvic acid, and tests have shown that enzyme systems involving pyruvate as a substrate (pyruvate oxidase and carboxylase) are inhibited by Dalapon. In these tests, however, inhibition was not great enough to be the primary cause of the herbicidal activity of Dalapon.

Dalapon along with TCA is not readily degraded in plants—but may be metabolized by various micro-organisms. Interference with pantothenate metabolism is partially responsible for the phytotoxic action of aliphatic acids. There is evidence that the primary effect of TCA may be on the formation of insoluble phosphate (presumably nucleic acids), on uptake of phosphate by roots inhibited by concentrations of Dalapon inhibiting growth, and the inhibition of phosphate esterification (Hilton et al., 1963). Flanagan & Langille (1963) have noted an unknown compound in quack-grass rhizomes following Dalapon applications. This unknown resembled phenol, and was found to be somewhat higher in concentration than was observed in the rhizomes of unsprayed plants. These authors and others have noted that stress is a causative factor in the induction of phenols.

As the primordial regions of stems and roots are the parts most readily affected, in both grasses and many species of leguminous plants, by this general group of compounds, the hypothesis of action as an inhibitor of cell division would appear to account best for many of these observations. An intriguing aspect is what common biochemical system occurs in members of the Gramineae and large numbers of the Leguminosae, rendering them so exceedingly susceptible to interference by $RCCl_3$ compounds and related substances.

'AUXIN-TYPE' GROWTH-REGULATING CHEMICALS

This group encompasses all herbicides that increase cell elongation in shoot tissue and have a physiological action resembling that of 3-indoleacetic acid (Woodford et al., 1958). The growth-regulating activity of the many substituted phenoxy acids (cf. Appendix I, pp. 438–40) is often very similar to that of one of the naturally occurring plant 'auxins', 3-indoleacetic acid (IAA). This latter compound has been observed to affect fruit development and abscission, cambial activity, root initiation, organ differentiation, phototropic and geotropic responses, and the growth of meristematic cells. Yet IAA is useless as a herbicide, presumably because the widely distributed indoleacetic acid-oxidase rapidly destroys or inactivates it in most plant tissues, soon after application (see Galston, 1956). The reason for this marked difference between one of these important naturally occurring 'auxins' and the synthetic group of 'auxins' such as the phenoxyacetic acids, is of great and fundamental significance.

While a number of theories have been advanced to explain the situation, none is completely convincing, and it seems likely that a better understanding of the herbicidal action of these compounds will have to await explanation of the action of the natural auxins (Woodford, 1957).

(*i*) *Phenoxyacetic Acids.* The largest tonnage of the organic herbicides used throughout the world at the present time consists of the substituted phenoxyacetic acids: 2,4-D (I) and 2,4,5-T (III)—as well as derivatives of MCPA (II)—in particular. 2,4-D and MCPA are widely used for the control of broad-leafed weeds in cereals, while 2,4,5-T is particularly useful as an arboricide. Fig. 51 indicates the yearly commercial production in the United States of 2,4-D acid and its esters.

MILLIONS OF POUNDS

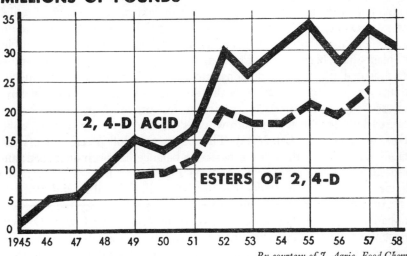

By courtesy of *J. Agric. Food Chem.*

FIG. 51.—Commercial production in the United States of the acid and ester derivatives of 2,4-dichlorophenoxyacetic acid (2,4-D). 2,4-D is among the top-tonnage products of the pesticides industry, exceeded only by copper sulphate, sodium chlorate, the aldrin-toxaphene group, and DDT. About one-half of all 2,4-D now used is in the form of amine salts; the other half is in the form of esters.

The commercial production in the United States of the combined 2,4-D and 2,4,5-T on an acid equivalent basis was 44·4 million lb. for the crop year 1959–60. In 1962 total *sales* of all forms of 2,4-D and 2,4,5-T were 53·7 million lb., while for 1963 all forms totalled 74·8 million lb. Total production was reported as 98·97 million lb. for 1962 and 190·94 million lb. for 1963 (*Synthetic Organic Chemicals*, U.S. Tariff Commission, 1964).

It has been observed that there is one major difference between 2,4-D and IAA: when 2,4-D is sprayed on plants it results in abnormal growth, whereas applications of IAA do not. It has been established that this effect of 2,4-D can be prevented completely by the simultaneous application of IAA and that, under certain conditions, treatment of plants with 2,4-D alone reduces their IAA content. These findings led Weintraub (1953) to postulate that the 'vital' action of 2,4-D is its effect on natural 'auxin' in the plant. Organized growth in leaves and stems depends upon the polarized division of meristematic cells, and this is controlled by IAA as well as by closely related auxins. If structurally related compounds, such as 2,4-D, competed with one or more of the natural auxins and in some manner brought about their deficiency, this might result in disorganized cell division, malformed leaves and stems, widespread derangement of metabolic and physical processes, and death. Woodford (1957) notes that this theory depends on the validity of the assumption, which is not yet generally accepted (cf. Audus & Thresh, 1956—see Ch. XIII), that 2,4-D influences IAA levels within the plant, and that such deficiencies result in abnormal cell division.

Despite this cited difference of opinion concerning the theory, there are a number of other relevant observations that have been made, and that may lend support to its validity. Various investigators have noted that many virus diseases in plants often result in considerable leaf malformation, formative effects, stringiness of leaves, etc.—many of which are almost identical with the effects produced by sub-lethal amounts of 2,4-D. The morphogenic effects of virus infections upon various species of plants have been reviewed by Kunkel (1954—see Ch. XIII). A number of included illustrations demonstrate these effects: e.g. 'shoestring' of tomato caused by infection with tobacco mosaic and carrot yellows viruses (in combination), and a similar malformation in tomato foliage caused by infection with potato witches'-broom virus (see Kunkel, 1954, Figs. 9 and 11—see Ch. XIII). These symptoms of infected plants certainly indicate that the normal hormone balance has been disturbed; and indeed, Grieve (1943—see Ch. XIII) found that tomato leaves, after being infected with spotted wilt virus, had a diminished 'auxin' content.

Additional evidence would appear to be provided by the effects of radiation upon plants. Gunckel & Sparrow (1954—see Ch. XIII) have reviewed the subject of aberrant plant growth as a result of exposure to ionizing radiation. Here again a number of illustrations depict these effects: e.g. stringiness and leaflet suppression in dahlia leaves, caused by two months of chronic gamma irradiation at 250 r. per day; and stringiness and suppression of blade tissue in *Nicotiana rustica*, also caused by gamma radiation, this time at 350 and 575 r. per day (Gunckel & Sparrow, 1954, Figs. 22 and 23; cf. Vlitos *et al.*, 1956, for effects on *Nicotiana tabacum*—see Ch. XIII). Reports in the literature suggest that 3-indoleacetic acid (and likely enough other 'auxins' as well) is destroyed by ionizing radiation (Skoog, 1935—see Ch. XIII; Gordon & Weber, 1950). Gamma irradiation studies on the stem-tip elongation of pinyon pine (*Pinus monophylla*) revealed that the low level of 15 r. inhibited stem-tip elongation, while vascular tissue anomalies occurred in the needles when exposed to dosages from 100 r. to below 50 r. (Brandenburg *et al.*, 1962; cf. Shields & Wells, 1962).

Another theory also depends on a comparison of effects of the natural and the synthetic auxins. It suggests that the main difference between IAA and 2,4-D might be due to the presence in plants of an enzyme that inactivates IAA when this auxin is present in excess, but leaves 2,4-D un-affected and therefore free to exert its toxic effects. Galston (1956) has shown that an IAA oxidase exists in brei prepared from roots and etiolated aerial portions of some plants, but its presence in intact living plants has apparently not been proved. As noted above, this oxidase system explains quite well why a tomato plant sprayed with IAA, which at first shows severe epinasty, will, after a few hours, recover to almost its normal appearance. While demonstration of this oxidase in intact plants would be desirable, it still does not appear critical for the support of this theory. Actually, as IAA or similar growth-substances control so many phases of plant growth, the triggering and release of the oxidase enzyme at the appropriate time and place must be a very specialized procedure—otherwise, moreover, the responses would not all proceed in orderly fashion. And it is just this orderly procedure of growth-substance interactions within the cell, that synthetic growth-substances, virus infections, radiation, and occasionally insect injury (with consequent gall formation), may drastically alter.

Still another theory has been put forward by D. J. Osborne (cf. Woodford, 1957), based on experiments with etiolated pea epicotyls. She proposes that the growth-promoting processes brought about by IAA are always associated with the production of an inhibitor which can protect the plant from its own auxin, and that such safety mechanisms do not exist for synthetic compounds; therefore, 2,4-D and related chemicals act as herbicides. Woodford (1957) notes that this is supported by the work of Ball & Dyke (1956—see Ch. XIII), who demonstrated that, if whole plants are treated for short periods with IAA, there is an initial stimulation of growth and then a fall to a growth-rate below that of the control. Similar treatment with 2,4-D results in stimulation but no sub-sequent growth inhibition.

Since growth-rate is dependent upon the rate of RNA production, and growth is often stimulated for a time by the application of 2,4-D, RNA pro-duction is also increased. The abnormal quality of such induced growth results from this hormonal imbalance. As kinins cause orderly cell divi-sions, it has been suggested that an auxin-kinin imbalance results in the abnormally induced growth observed with 2,4-D applications, which leads to the destruction of the plant (Overbeek, 1964). The differences in herbicidal activity of 2,4,5-T, MCPA and the chlorinated phenyl and ben-zoic acids are based on their chemical stability, persistence and mobility within the plant. F. W. Slife et al. (cf. Overbeek, 1964) found that 2,4,5-T is mobile for a much longer time than is 2,4-D. For example, the amount of $C^{14}O_2$ evolved from the biological decarboxylation of these herbicides was ten times greater for 2,4-D than for 2,4,5-T.

It appears that conversion to the free acid is necessary for 2,4-D, 2,4,5-T, etc. to exert herbicidal activity. The metabolic fate of phenoxy acids includes: (a) physical or chemical conjugation with cellular con-stituents, (b) degradation of the aliphatic acid side-chain of the molecule, and (*c*) ring hydroxylation. Aspartic and glucose-ester derivatives have been reported in wheat coleoptiles, and the latter is considered a detoxification product. Degradation of the side-chain does explain partially the 2,4-D resistance of some species. The resistance of *Galium aparine* to MCPA has been attributed to detoxification resulting from loss of both carbon atoms of the side-chain (Hilton *et al.*, 1963). Further aspects of the fate of herbicides in plants are considered in Ch. XIII.

Siegel & Porto (1961), in their study of oxidants, antioxidants, and growth regulation, have developed the Regulator-Antioxidant Hypothesis. Hormonal substances with antioxidant properties have been assigned a protective role of buffering the cell against cumulative damage by oxidants. Again, the stimulation of growth by growth regulators at low concentration, and its inhibition at high concentration, is illustrated by these authors. Growth is promoted under ordinary aerobic conditions, which become survival factors at elevated oxidant levels, and yet lose their effectiveness, or inhibit growth, when the oxidant level is reduced. Siegel & Porto concluded that bioregulatory antioxidants serve as protectants for specific structures or on the oxidation-reduction balance; they may serve as metabolic regulators by selectively blocking specific pathways, and moreover, as mobile electronic systems, antioxidants may act as cofactors in electron transport.

(*ii*) *Phenoxypropionic Acid.* It has been found (Lush, 1956) that the *alpha*-phenoxypropionic acids (MCPP and 2,4,5-TP) (IV) have a selective action that is different from those of the corresponding acetic derivatives. MCPP is much more toxic to *Galium aparine* (cleavers) than is MCPA, but it is less toxic to cereals than is MCPA. Thus a chemical of lower mammalian toxicity may now be used for this weed, whereas formerly the more dangerous sulphuric acid, DNC, or Dinoseb, were required for its control.

Woodford (1957) suggests that the changes in relative toxicity which arise from these minor modifications to the aliphatic side-chain are probably due primarily to the alteration in the physical properties of the molecule, and that this has a differential effect on retention, penetration, and perhaps also transport, of the molecule in different species.

(*iii*) *Phenoxybutyric Acids* (V, VI). Synerholm & Zimmerman (1947— *see* Ch. XIII) pointed out that only the chlorinated phenoxyacids with an even number of carbons in the aliphatic chain portions of their molecules had any appreciable growth-regulator activity. These authors explained this difference in activity on the basis of the *beta*-oxidation theory of the acid side-chain. This theory had earlier been introduced by Knoop in 1904 to explain the breakdown of fatty acids in the animal body. The above authors suggested that the low activity of the derivatives with the odd number of carbon atoms in the side-chain results from their oxidation by *beta*-oxidation to the corresponding inactive phenol, while the oxidation of the homologues with the even number of carbon atoms in their side-chains yields the correspondingly active phenoxyacetic acid.

Direct experimental evidence for this was found by Wain (1951). He treated flax plants with a range of homologous *gamma*-phenoxyalkyl-carboxylic acids of the general formula C_6H_5-O-$(CH_2)_n$COOH. After permitting these plants to absorb various chemicals by way of the roots, analysis for phenol showed its presence only in those plants that had been treated with acids having an odd number of carbon atoms in the side-chains.

Differences in the ability of crop and weed species to effect this conversion enable the compounds to be used in situations where the corresponding acetic acid homologue would be too toxic to the crop. Extending the side-chain by two methyl groups also influences penetration and selectivity. Experiences under the conditions prevailing in Great Britain have demonstrated that MCPB (VI) is particularly useful because it is less toxic than MCPA (II) to clovers, cereals, and peas, yet it is almost as toxic as MCPA to certain weeds, and so can be effective in situations where it is impracticable to use MCPA on these crops (Woodford, 1957).

(iv) Substituted Aryloxy Alkanols. This group has often been referred to as the 'sodium ethyl sulphates'. The principal herbicide in it is sodium 2-(2,4-dichlorophenoxy)ethyl sulphate (VII), now referred to commercially as Sesone (formerly a product of the Crag Agricultural Chemicals Division, Union Carbide Chemicals Co.). This compound, together with related ones, was first described in 1950 (King *et al.*, 1950). A review of the extensive research on this group of herbicides has been prepared (King, 1957; cf. Bracey, 1957—*see* Ch. XIV). The structures of Sesone and related compounds are indicated in the Appendix. It, of course, is homologous with the substituted phenoxyacetic acids and related structures. The only difference lies in the basic structure of the parent compounds, which, for Sesone, is 2,4-dichlorophenoxyethanol (with the terminal alcoholic group, —OH, of the side-chain), and, for 2,4-D, is 2,4-dichlorophenoxyacetic acid (with the terminal carboxyl group, —COOH, of the side-chain).

The two parent compounds just described ('ethanol' and the acid), are quite similar in their effects when once they are introduced into susceptible dicotyledonous plants. When applied as a surface spray, the 'ethanol' is not readily absorbed or translocated—in contrast to 2,4-D, which is. Root absorption of the two compounds appears to be of about the same order. However, when the sodium sulphate derivative of the 'ethanol' is prepared, all activity of any kind is lost (in the absence of soil). This derivative is Sesone, which requires non-sterile soil for its activation and use as a pre-emergence herbicide.

A detailed study of this biological activation was made by Vlitos (1953—*see* Ch. XIII), who found that *Bacillus cereus* var. *mycoides* was one among several common soil organisms that were capable of converting the inactive molecule to an active one which inhibited the germination of weed seeds. In fact, bacteria-free extracts were also capable of bringing about this activation, and it was suggested that an aryl sulphatase was the enzyme involved. As the original Sesone, or an aqueous preparation of it that has not touched soil, is inactive, no injury to plant foliage occurs following such contact or spray application. This is a most useful pre-emergence herbicide for application to newly cultivated and weed-free soil that is supporting established crops such as strawberries and asparagus cf. (Plate 17).

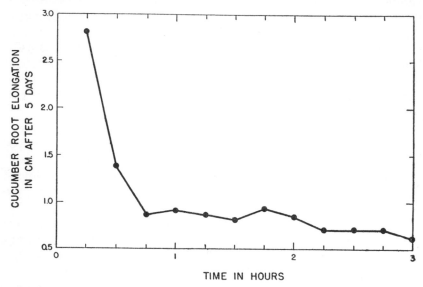

By courtesy of Boyce Thompson Institute for Plant Research; from Vlitos, 1953—see Ch. XIII

FIG. 52.—Length of time required for conversion of Sesone, sodium 2-(2,4-dichloro-phenoxy)ethyl sulphate (2,4-DES), to the active herbicidal form in non-sterile soil, as shown by its ability, when converted, of suppressing the elongation of cucumber seedling roots.

(v) Substituted Benzoic Acids. A number of derivatives of chlorinated benzoic acid (XXXIX) have come into extensive use for control of perennial weeds in non-crop or non-cultivated areas. They are especially useful for the group of weeds that possess varying degrees of resistance to 2,4-D—bindweed, Canada thistle, the woody climbers Smilax and honeysuckle, and such other woody plants as sumac, persimmon, and sassafras. Rates of application are, however, somewhat higher than for 2,4-D—generally from 20 to 40 lb./acre of acid equivalent in soil applications, and 8 lb./acre for foliage sprays. Drift hazards, and some residual action on such land as may be later cropped, are the main problems here. Nitrobenzoic and aminobenzoic acid derivatives (e.g. Dinoben and Amiben, respectively) are new introductions that appear promising, particularly as pre-emergence herbicides for strawberries and several other horticultural crops, respectively.

The substituted benzoic acids have a mild type of growth-regulator activity in comparison with that of 2,4-D. Their activity was first extensively explored by Dr. P. W. Zimmerman at the Boyce Thompson Institute.

The recently introduced herbicide Tordon (4-amino-3,5,6-trichloropicolinic acid) (LXVIII) (Hamaker *et al.*, 1963) has many of the physiological responses of the substituted benzoic acids and thus may tentatively be grouped in this class. It is possible that this new molecule could be considered an isostere of the benzoic and phenylacetic acid molecules.

INHIBITORS OF GROWTH AND OF TROPIC RESPONSES

Maleic hydrazide (MH) (XXXVIII) has been found to be a general inhibitor of plant growth, and specifically an inhibitor of respiration; its activity was first described by Schoene & Hoffmann (1949). MH is a selective herbicide which is effective against grasses (0·5–0·25 per cent), and can be translocated within plants, being toxic to meristematic tissue, and causing loss of apical dominance. It will prevent sucker (axillary shoot) development in tobacco, and also arrests sprouting in stored root crops, such as potato, carrot, onion, and beet (0·1–0·05 per cent). In addition, it may be used to prevent pollen germination at 0·025 per cent. It has been used chiefly to suppress the growth of grasses, i.e. as a 'herbistat' rather than as a herbicide.

Suggestions have been made that maleic hydrazide interferes with IAA activity. Investigations have confirmed that it is a competitive inhibitor of IAA and 2,4-D, and that it promotes the destruction of IAA by enzymes (Leopold, 1955—*see* Ch. XIII). The suspicion of Darlington & McLeish (1951) that MH might be carcinogenic, has not been confirmed by prolonged tests (Barnes & Magee, 1957).

Maleic hydrazide has been found (M. Shaw *et al.*, 1958) to prevent flowering in wheat, and to increase the oxygen consumption per unit of dryweight of the first leaves by 20 to 50 per cent (IAA increased oxygen uptake by only 10 to 15 per cent). Brian & Hemming (1957) have shown, in tests with peas, that MH prevents the response to gibberellic acid by gibberellic acid-sensitive plants, and that shoot reduction caused by MH is due primarily to blocking the activity of the postulated 'gibberellic acid-like hormone'. Weller *et al.* (1957) have found that thiols will form addition-compounds with MH, although these authors were unable to find any enzyme in living radish tissue that would catalyse such a reaction. The diethanolamine salt (40 per cent MH) has been the form generally used for field applications.

A striking inhibitor of geotropic and phototropic responses is *N*-1-naphthylphthalamic acid (XL). This is the only herbicide among a group of several compounds which interferes with tropic responses. Its herbicidal action, however, is not usually due directly to this effect. The growth-regulating properties of this substance were described by Hoffmann & Smith (1949—*see* Ch. XIII), and it was introduced as a herbicide in 1950. At 2–10 lb./acre, it prevents germination of seeds of grass and broad-leafed weeds, and appears particularly promising as a selective herbicide for use on cucurbit crops.

Templeman (1955) has discussed the possible use, as herbicides, of compounds that affect the geotropic and phototropic responses of plants, and he has drawn attention to 2,4,6-tribromophenylnitramine and 2-chloro-9-fluorenol-9-carboxylic acid. Triiodobenzoic acid (Zimmerman & Hitchcock, 1942, 1949) also influences geotropism, probably by its ability to control the activity and polarity of movement of IAA.

INHIBITORS OF CHLOROPHYLL FORMATION AND OF PHOTOSYNTHESIS

A number of compounds have been reported from time to time that suppress the development of chlorophyll in plants. They include sulphanilamide and streptomycin, some tetronic acid derivatives (Hamner & Tukey, 1951), certain substituted benzoic acid derivatives, carbamates, and O-methylthreonine. The only useful herbicide having this property is amino triazole (Amitrole) (XXXV). This chemical was introduced in 1954 as an experimental herbicide (U.S.P. 2,670,282).

(*i*) *Amino Triazole* (*Amitrole*, AT, *etc.*). Amino triazole has been most widely and successfully used in the control of certain perennial weeds, such as Canada thistle. Its ready absorption, and extensive and rapid translocation throughout the plant, has been investigated by Bondarenko & Williard (1957). Using carbon–14 labelled herbicide, and employing the autoradiographic technique, these authors detected maximum radioactivity in all parts of the Canada thistle test plant within forty-eight hours of treatment—the herbicide being located in and near the terminal apex of the stem and in the younger leaves. Studies by the senior author cited also involved examination of the decomposition rate of similarly labelled material in the soil. The rate of $C^{14}O_2$ evolution from the treated soil samples was measured daily, and was found to increase until the thirteenth day, when the maximum was reached. It then decreased rapidly until the forty-second day, and thereafter gradually until the experiment was terminated on the two-hundred-and-fortieth day, when extremely small amounts of $C^{14}O_2$ were evolved. In a field experiment, small amounts of the labelled material were found at the 1-in. level fourteen months after treatment.

The mode of action of amino triazole or Amitrole, (XXXV) has been extensively studied, and the following summary of recent research is taken from the review of Hilton *et al.* (1963). Amitrole-C^{14} studies show that it moves preferentially to, and accumulates in, meristematic or young expanding tissues (such as terminal buds, root-tips, young leaves and sprouts) and may by-pass mature tissues along the way. A number of metabolites of Amitrole have been found in plants—carbohydrate derivatives (with glucose), and amino-acid derivatives (alanine, glycine, serine). However, formation of such metabolites does not constitute the toxic act. The half-life of amitrole-C^{14} in maize was approximately eight days, and the C^{14} approached a zero concentration six weeks after application.

Amitrole forms chelates with certain essential metals (e.g. magnesium and iron) required by enzymes, and this may lead to growth inhibition. Since chlorosis symptoms are the most striking effects of Amitrole usage, some interference with porphyrin synthesis has been postulated. Amitrole also inhibits the development of leaf plastids. An interference with purine metabolism is also indicated from the evidence that Amitrole probably inhibits biosynthesis of histidine, riboflavin, possibly nucleic acids, and from the inhibition of 4-amino-imidazole hydrolase, an enzyme involved in purine metabolism (Hilton et al., 1963).

(ii) *Monuron* (CMU). This is perhaps the best known of the three commercially available phenyl-substituted ureas. The other two, Diuron (XXIII) and Fenuron (XXII), contain, respectively, two and no chlorine substitutions in the benzene ring. Monuron, 3-(*p*-chlorophenyl)-1,1-dimethylurea) (XXI) was introduced in 1951, by the E. I. du Pont de Nemours Co. (U.S.P. 2,655,445). These compounds are highly toxic and persist in the soil. Little foliage absorption occurs, most of the absorption being by the roots, with subsequent movement throughout the plant. Monuron (80 per cent active) is now used as a general herbicide for application to soil; it is used selectively in certain crops (cotton, asparagus, etc.) at 1 to 6 lb./acre, or non-selectively at 20 to 80 lb./acre.

The trichloroacetate derivatives of Monuron (XXI) and Fenuron (XXII)—Urox (XXVI) and Urab (XXV)—have been developed. They are intended primarily for rapid, non-selective control. They have greater solubility than the parent ureas, and thus are more rapid in their action. Urab is considered particularly useful for brush control and is available in granular and liquid formulations.

A review of the extensive work on the phenyl-substituted ureas has been published (Abel, 1957), while Woodford (1957) notes some of the newer advances in our knowledge. Seedlings treated with these compounds do not die until after they have developed cotyledons and leaves, and chlorosis (not correctable by iron applications) is the chief symptom of toxicity. Muzik et al. (1954) have shown that Monuron (CMU) is relatively non-toxic to roots, and that excised roots can be grown for many months in a nutrient culture containing enough Monuron to kill the whole plant.

V. H. Freed (cf. Gysin & Knüsli, 1960) made studies with radio-active Monuron and found that the amount which is taken up by a plant during growth decreases while the concentration of another unknown radioactive compound is increased. When this complex (the reaction product of herbicide with cell components) was hydrolysed it could be split; over 90 per cent of unchanged CMU was found, which indicates that no final breakdown of CMU takes place in the plant.

Several other workers have also shown that these compounds have a specific effect on the leaf; but not until Wessels & Veen (1956) demonstrated that Monuron and other substituted ureas are extremely effective inhibitors of the photochemical activity of isolated choloroplasts, was there any conception of the real mechanism and action of these chemicals. It has subsequently been confirmed by Cooke (1956) and by Spikes (1956 —see Ch. XIII) that Monuron inhibits the Hill reaction of photosynthesis at concentrations as low as 10^{-7} M. Thus for the first time a precise chemical step in the phytotoxic action of a group of chemicals was pinpointed. Moreland & Davis (1956—see Ch. XIII), likewise, have examined a long series of herbicidal chemicals for their effects on the Hill reaction.

Hilton *et al* (1963) note too that the site of action is the oxygen-liberating pathway— inhibiting photophosphorylation in systems in which O_2 is involved, possibly in some manner involving the cytochromes. They also may act as physical poisons, disrupting organized surfaces of cellular structures.

A newer urea derivative, cyclooctyldimethylurea (OMU), is claimed to have greater selectivity than other ureas, and has been widely tested in Germany and elsewhere for use on sugar beets, carrots, onions, peas, beans, and forest nurseries. Its solubility in water is about 15 p.p.m.— as compared with 4·8 for Neburon and 42 for Diuron. It is available as a mixture with butynyl (chlorophenyl)-carbamate, and is known as HS 55 (cf. Woodford & Kasasian, 1960).

(iii) Simazine (2-chloro-4,6-bis(ethylamino)-s-triazine) (XXVII). This is another of the herbicides which affect the photosynthetic process. It was first announced by Gast *et al.* in 1956 as a promising pre-emergence herbicide. At 2 lb./acre it has been used for the pre-emergence weeding of maize, tomatoes, grapes, and asparagus. At higher concentrations it acts as a soil sterilant.

An interesting feature of this herbicide is that it increases in toxicity when used in combination with soil. The herbicide has a very high selectivity to maize. Studies have shown that it is absorbed by the maize plants, but no measurable quantity can be detected in plants that have been treated with doses equivalent to 10 kg. per hectare. Gysin & Knüsli (1960) have suggested that the resistance of maize plants is due to a detoxification mechanism which hydrolyses the Simazine to 2-hydroxy-4,6-bis(ethylamino)-s-triazine as soon as it enters the plant. Roth (1957—see Gysin & Knüsli, 1960) showed that extracts of maize decompose Simazine, although they lose this property if heated to 80°C. for two hours; but similar extracts prepared from wheat had no such effect.

Further studies by Gysin & Knüsli (1960a) with radioactive Simazine have shown that, in the maize plant, there is a uniform distribution of the breakdown fragments which makes it likely that they are used by the plant, while in cotton and cucumbers the Simazine appears to be unchanged and therefore not metabolized by the plants. The fact that the CO_2 appears as an end-product of Simazine metabolism in the maize plant (which proves that the triazine ring is broken), the reactivity of the fragments formed from the original triazine ring, and the uniform distribution in the whole plant, make it likely that the metabolites of Simazine are used by the plant for further growth.

W. Roth's studies in 1957 have shown that a polyphenol fraction is present in maize which is able to metabolize Simazine *in vitro*. He found a high catalase activity in all Simazine-sensitive plants. On the other hand, plants with various degrees of resistance showed a significant content of polyphenols, often accompanied by high peroxidase activity. Roth postulates that the triazines interfere with the redox-potential level that is appropriate for the normal function which chlorophyll has to fulfil in the plant. If this level is maintained by catalase, Simazine seems to be able to destroy the equilibrium, but if peroxidase plus polyphenols predominate, Simazine would be or would become ineffective (Gysin & Knüsli, 1960).

Many of the less water-soluble triazines are effective only when absorbed by roots, and movement occurs with the transpiration stream to the leaves, accumulating at the leaf-tips and margins. Photosynthesis is probably the physiological system most sensitive to action of the phytotoxic triazines. Germination is not affected except at high concentrations of these herbicides. Severe reduction in transpiration-rates occurs soon after treatment with Atrazine and other inhibitors of photosynthesis, and probably results from stomatal closure (Hilton *et al.*, 1963).

The triazines inhibit starch and sucrose formation in leaves, O_2 release in leaves, and CO_2 utilization by plants. Processes involved in the dark CO_2 fixation were unaffected. Inhibition of photosynthesis and of the Hill reaction results from interference with mechanisms for O_2 production. The Hill-reaction activity of chloroplasts from Simazine-sensitive and Simazine-tolerant species *is inhibited equally*; thus the mechanism controlling selectivity lies outside the chloroplasts (Hilton *et al.*, 1963).

The nine most important substituted *s*-triazine herbicides have been grouped according to structural affinity by Woodford & Kasasian (1960), and are shown in Table XII. Further structural details for some of these may be found in Appendices I & II.

In the triazine group, Simatrin (cf. Table XII) appears to be the most promising of the 2-methylmercapto analogues. In comparison with Simazine, it has a much shorter soil persistence and a very different toxicity spectrum, being selective towards small grains, peas, beans, and rape.

305

TABLE XII

THE NINE MOST IMPORTANT SUBSTITUTED s-TRIAZINE HERBICIDES

(*From Woodford & Kasasian*, 1960)

s-TRIAZINES *

$$R_1 HN—C(=N—N)—NH R_2$$

(triazine ring with R_3 at top carbon, ring nitrogens N, N and N at bottom)

R₁	R₂ (R₃)	Cl	OCH₃	SCH₃
CH₃ CH₂	CH₃ CH₂	Simazine	Simetone	Simatrin
(CH₃)₂CH	(CH₃)₂CH	Propazine	Prometone	Propatrin
(CH₃)₂CH	CH₃ CH₂	Atrazine	Atratone	Atratrin

* 'S-triazines' sometimes written: '1,3,5-triazine' (*see* pp. 304, 444–5); further data for some of these molecules may be found in Appendices (pp. 444–5, 451.

OTHER TRANSLOCATED HERBICIDES

(*i*) *Chloroacetamides*. The pre-emergence herbicide, 2-chloro-N,N-diallylacetamide (Randox or CDAA) (XXXIV), was introduced in 1956 (Hamm & Speziale, 1956). It is one of a number of N-substituted *alpha*-chloroacetamides which have been tested and reported on by these authors. These compounds have to be applied to the soil at rates of 3 to 6 lb./acre, and all are highly toxic to grasses (especially *Setaria* spp., crabgrass, annual bluegrass, wild oats, and cheat grass). Some broad-leafed weeds, such as pigweed, carpet weed, purslane, etc., are controlled satisfactorily. Tests have shown selectivity to maize and onions.

The range of weeds killed by CDAA is limited, however, and efforts have been made to increase this range without limiting selectivity (such as control of grass weeds in soybeans, peanuts, maize, etc.). A product with increased efficiency employing a mixture of CDAA and trichloro-benzylchloride is now available.

In addition to the two amides, CDAA and CDEA, listed in the Appendix, several new ones are now available: examples are Karsil, N-(3,4-dichloro-phenyl)-2-methylpentanamide; Solan, N-(3-chloro-4-methylphenyl)-2-methylpentanamide; Dicryl, N-(3,4-dichlorophenyl)-methylacrylamide;

and a fourth compound, FW-734, which is N-(3,4-dichlorophenyl)-2-propionamide. Karsil, Solan (LVII), and Dicryl are all selective to umbelliferous crops, such as celery, carrots, parsnip, and parsley. Karsil is particularly effective in celery, carrots, parsley, parsnips, and strawberries, while Solan is suggested for use in tomatoes, and Dicryl in cotton and cucumbers. FW-734 is proving particularly effective for the selective control of a range of weeds of upland rice.

In the maize plant, a metabolism for Randox—which is, chemically, chloroacetic acid diallylamide—has been suggested, which involves hydrolysis at the chlorine locus to a hydroxyl group, and then scission to glycollic acid and diallylamine. These fragments may then react with plant constituents. As Randox is rather tolerant to maize, it was suitable for such metabolic studies. This reactivity of the chlorine atom in chloro-fatty acid amides is similar to that in a 2-chloro-4,6-bis-alkylamino-s-triazine, such as Simazine. Systems that are present in the maize plant could hydrolyse in both molecules at the chlorine locus to hydroxy-groups (Gysin & Knüsli, 1960a).

(ii) *Sodium Chlorate.* Sodium chlorate (XLVII) has been used for fifty years or more as a herbicide, and in recent years has been combined with other chemicals—organic and/or inorganic. It is taken up by roots and leaves and seems to be readily translocated. Its toxic effects are slow to develop, often localized to particular organs, and sometimes conditioned by light and nitrate supply. Recent work has established fairly definitely that poisoning is the result of the reduction in the plant of the chlorate to hypochlorite and chlorite. In 1947, E. Åberg suggested that the chlorate is reduced by the mechanisms which normally reduce nitrate in the plant. Woodford (1957) suggests that, as molybdenum is present in the enzyme which is responsible for converting nitrate to nitrite (and that plants suffering from molybdenum deficiency accumulate nitrate because of a decrease in nitrate reductase activity), it would be interesting to know whether a deficiency of molybdenum influences the toxic action of chlorate.

There are a considerable number of herbicidal molecules which are listed in the Appendices, and which are useful herbicides, yet the mode of action of which has not been elucidated. Thus they are not described in this chapter; but their particular uses may be found in Chapter XIV, devoted to usage, as well as in the comments in the Appendices.

BIBLIOGRAPHY
(The Classification and Mode of Action of Herbicides)

ABEL, A. L. (1957). The substituted urea herbicides. *World Crops*, 9(8), 328–30.
—— (1957a). The substituted urea herbicides. *Chem. & Ind.*, 1957, pp. 1106–12.
AKAMINE, E. K. (1948). Plant-growth regulators as selective herbicides. *Hawaii Agric. Exp. Sta. Circ.*, 26, 1–43.

ALLEN, W. W. (1950). Progress report on volatility of some esters of 2,4-D. *Proc. 3rd Annu. Sth. Weed Control Conf.*, pp. 7–12.

AMERICAN ASSOCIATION FOR THE ADVANCEMENT OF SCIENCE (1948). *Summarised Proceedings and Directory, 1940–1948.* Washington, 1219 pp.

ANON. (1957). Technical information: 'Mylone' 85W soil fumigant. A new 'Crag' Agricultural Chemical. *Carbide & Carbon Chemicals Co., New York*, 10 pp.

APPLETON, A. A. (1956). Substituted urea herbicides for agricultural use. *Canad. Nat. Weed Comt. East. Sect. Proc.* 1955, **9**, 134–9.

AUDUS, L. J. (Ed.) (1964). *The Physiology and Biochemistry of Herbicides.* Academic Press, London & New York, 555 pp.

BARNES, J. M. & MAGEE, P. N. (1957). The non-toxicity of maleic hydrazide for mammalian tissues. *Nature, Lond.*, **180**, 62–64.

BARRONS, K. C. (1949). TCA (trichloroacetic acid)—a promising new chemical for grass control. *Down to Earth* (Midland, Mich.), **4**(4), 8–9.

BARTLEY, C. (1957). Simazin and related triazine compounds as pre-emergence and post-emergence herbicides. *Agric. Chem.*, **12**, 34–36.

BARTLEY, T. R. (1958). Physical and chemical properties indicative of good hydrocarbon solvents for aquatic weed control in irrigation systems. *Proc. West. Weed Control Conf.*, **16**, 34–39.

BEAL, J. M. (1944). Some telemorphic effects induced in sweet peas by application of 4-chlorophenoxyacetic acid. *Bot. Gaz.*, **105**, 471–4.

—— (1944*a*). Further observations on the telemorphic effects of certain growth-regulating substances. *Bot. Gaz.*, **106**, 165–78.

BEREZOVSKIĬ, M. A. & KUROCHNINA, V. F. (1956). [Studying the effect of 2,4-dichlorophenoxyacetic acid on the conversion of phosphorus compounds in plants—in Russian.] *Moskov. Ordena Lenina Sel'skokhov. Akad. im. K. A. Timiriazeva Dok. TSKHA*, 1956(25), 182–7.

—— & —— (1957). [The influence of 2,4-dichlorophenoxyacetic acid upon phosphorus transformations in the plant—in Russian.] *Dok. Akad. Nauk SSSR.*, **113**(2), 458–61.

BOLLEY, H. L. (1908). Weeds and methods of eradication. *Bull. N. Dak. Agric. Exp. Sta.*, **80**, 513–73.

BONDARENKO, D. D. & WILLARD, C. J. (1957). Amino triazole appears to give control of Canada thistle (*Cirsium arvense*). *Ohio Farm & Home Res.*, **42**(305), 29–30.

BONNER, J. M. & BANDURSKI, R. S. (1952). Studies of the physiology, pharmacology, and biochemistry of the auxins. *Annu. Rev. Pl. Physiol.*, **3**, 59–86.

BRANDENBURG, M. K., MILLS, H. L., RICKARD, W. H. & SHIELDS, LORA M. (1962). Effects of acute gamma radiation on growth and morphology in *Pinus monophylla* Torr. & Frem. (Pinyon pine). *Radiat. Bot.*, **2**, 251–63.

BRIAN, P. W. & HEMMING, H. G. (1957). The effect of maleic hydrazide on the growth response of plants to gibberellic acid. *Ann. Appl. Biol.*, **45**, 489–97.

BRIAN, R. C. (1964). The classification of herbicides and types of toxicity. Pp. 1–37 in *The Physiology and Biochemistry of Herbicides* (L. J. Audus, Ed.). Academic Press, London & New York.

—— (1964*a*). The effects of herbicides on biophysical processes in the plant. Pp. 357–86 in *The Physiology and Biochemistry of Herbicides* (L. J. Audus, Ed.). Academic Press, London & New York.

BRITISH WEED CONTROL COUNCIL. (1958). Properties of herbicides. Pp. 209–31 in *Weed Control Handbook.* Blackwell, Oxford, 245 pp.

CARVELL, K. L. (1955). Translocation of ammate. *Forest Sci.*, **1**(Mar.), 41–43.

CLOR, M. A. & CRAFTS, A. S. (1957). Comparative translocation of C^{14}-labelled 2,4-D amino triazole and urea in cotton plants and subsequent leakage from roots. (Abs.) *Plant Physiol.*, **32**(suppl.), xliii.

COOK, W. H. & HALFERDAHL, A. C. (1937). Chemical weed killers. *Nat. Res. Coun. Can. Bull.* 18, 111 pp.

COOKE, A. R. (1956). A possible mechanism of action of the urea type herbicides. *Weeds*, 4, 397–8.

—— (1957). Influence of 2,4-D on the uptake of minerals from the soil. *Weeds*, 5, 25–28.

CRAFTS, A. S. (1957). The chemistry and mode of action of herbicides. *Advanc. Pest Control Res.*, 1, 39–79.

—— (1961). *The Chemistry and Mode of Action of Herbicides*. Interscience Pub., New York, 269 pp.

—— (1964). Herbicide behaviour in the plant. Pp. 75–110 in *The Physiology and Biochemistry of Herbicides* (L. J. Audus, Ed.). Academic Press, London & New York.

—— & HARVEY, W. A. (1949). Selective weed killers. *Calif. Agric. Coll. Ext. Circ.*, 157, 16 pp.

——, CURRIER, H. B. & DREVER, H. R. (1958). Some studies on the herbicidal properties of maleic hydrazide. *Hilgardia*, 27, 723–57.

—— & YAMAGUCHI, S. (1958). Comparative tests on the uptake and distribution of labelled herbicides by *Zebrina pendula* and *Tradescantia fluminensis*. *Hilgardia*, 27, 421–54.

CROCKER, W. (1948). *Growth of Plants. Twenty Years' Research at Boyce Thompson Institute*. Reinhold, New York, 459 pp.

—— & KNIGHT, L. I. (1908). Effect of illuminating gas and ethylene upon flowering carnations. *Bot. Gaz.*, 46, 259–76.

CROKER, B. H. (1953). Effects of 2,4-dichlorophenoxyacetic acid and 2,4,5-trichlorophenoxyacetic acid on mitosis in *Allium cepa*. *Bot. Gaz.*, 114, 274–83.

DARLINGTON, C. D. & McLEISH, J. (1951). Action of maleic hydrazide on the cell. *Nature, Lond.*, 167, 407.

DAY, B. E. (1952). The absorption and translocation of 2,4-dichlorophenoxyacetic acid by bean plants. *Plant Physiol.*, 27, 143–52.

FAWCETT, C. H., WAIN, R. L. & WIGHTMAN, F. (1958). Beta-oxidation of omega-(3-indolyl)alkanecarboxylic acids in plant tissues. *Nature, Lond.*, 181, 1387–9.

FLANAGAN, T. R. & LANGILLE, A. R. (1963). Phenol in quackgrass associated with dalapon. *Science*, 140, 179–80.

FOGG, G. E. (1948). The penetration of 3,5-dinitro-*o*-cresol into leaves. *Ann. Appl. Biol.*, 35, 315–30.

FREED, V. H. & MONTGOMERY, M. L. (1963). The metabolism of herbicides by plants and soils. *Residue Rev.*, 3, 1–18.

GALSTON, A. W. (1956). Some metabolic consequences of the administration of indoleacetic acid to plant cells. Pp. 219–33. In *The Chemistry and Mode of Action of Plant Growth Substances* (Wain, R. L. & Wightman, E., Eds.). Butterworth, London, 312 pp.

GORDON, S. A. & WEBER, R. P. (1950). The effect of x-radiation on indoleacetic acid and auxin levels in the plant. (Abs.). *Amer. J. Bot.*, 37, 678.

GYSIN, H. & KNÜSLI, E. (1960). Activity and mode of action of triazine herbicides. *Proc. 4th Brit. Weed Control Conf.*, 1958, pp. 225–33.

—— (1960a). Chemistry and herbicidal properties of triazine derivatives. *Advanc. Pest Control Res.*, 3, 289–358.

HAMAKER, J. W., JOHNSTON, H., MARTIN, R. T. & REDEMANN, C. T. (1963). A picolinic acid derivative: a plant growth regulator. *Science*, 141, 363.

HAMM, P. C. & SPEZIALE, A. J. (1956). Relation of herbicidal activity to the amide moiety of *N*-substituted chloroacetamides. *J. Agric. Food Chem.*, 4, 518–22.

—— & —— (1957). Effect of variations in the acyl moiety on herbicidal activity of *N*-substituted alpha-chloracetamides. *J. Agric. Food Chem.*, 5, 30–32.

HAMNER, C. L. & TUKEY, H. B. (1944). The herbicidal action of 2,4-dichlorophenoxyacetic acid and 2,4,5-trichlorophenoxyacetic acid on bindweed. *Science*, 100, 154–5.

HAMNER, C. L. & TUKEY, H. B. (1951). Chlorophyll inhibition and herbicidal action of 3-(alpha-imino-ethyl)5-methyl tetronic acid. *Bot. Gaz.*, 112, 525–8.

HANF, M. (1958). Unkrautwirkung von Phenoxy-Propionsäuren im Vergleich zu Phenoxy-Essigsäuren. *Gesunde Pflanzen*, 10(5), 1–7.

HAVIS, J. R. (1950). Herbicidal properties of petroleum hydrocarbons. *New York Agric. Exp. Sta. Memoir* 298, 20 pp.

HAY, J. R. (1956). Translocation of herbicides in marabu (*Dichrostachys nutans*). II. Translocation of 2,4-dichlorophenoxyacetic acid following foliage application. *Weeds*, 4, 349–56.

HELGESON, E. A. (1957). Herbicides (chemistry and uses). Pp. 24–50 in *Methods of Weed Control*. F.A.O., Rome, 189 pp.

HERBERT, R. A. & LINCK, A. J. (1957). The influence of 3-amino-1,2,4-triazole on the carbohydrate balance and respiration in Canada thistle (*Cirsium arvense*). (Abs.) *Pl. Physiol.*, 32(supp.), vi.

HILTON, J. L., JANSEN, L. L. & HULL, M. M. (1963). Herbicides. *Annu. Rev. Pl. Physiol.*, 14, 353–84.

HITCHCOCK, A. E. (1935). Indole-3-*n*-propionic acid as a growth hormone and the quantitative measurement of plant response. *Contr. Boyce Thompson Inst.*, 7, 87–95.

HOLLY, K. (1956). Penetration of chlorinated phenoxyacetic acids into leaves. *Ann. Appl. Biol.*, 44, 195–9.

HULL, H. M. (1957). Anatomical studies demonstrating phloem inactivation and its dependency upon the interaction of concentrations of 2,4,5-trichlorophenoxy-acetic acid and an anionic wetting agent. (Abs.) *Plant Physiol.*, 32(suppl.), xliii.

IVENS, G. W. & BLACKMAN, C. F. (1949). The effects of phenylcarbamates on the growth of higher plants. *Soc. Exptl. Biol. Sympos.*, 3, 266–82.

JAWORSKI, E. G. (1956). Biochemical action of CDAA, a new herbicide. *Science* 123, 847–8.

JONES, F. D. (1945). Methods and composition for killing weeds. U.S. Patent, 2,390, 941, 11 Dec. 1945, 5 pp.

KEAYS, J. W. & ZEDLER, R. J. (1957). A new herbicide, soil fungicide and nematocide called Mylone. *Proc. Northeast Weed Control Conf.*, 11, 58–64.

KING, L. J. (1950). Dichloral urea . . . and sodium 2,4-dichlorophenoxyethyl sulfate . . . as selective herbicides. *Proc. 4th Annu. Mtg. Northeast Weed Control. Conf.* (New York City), 302–9.

—— (1957 [1959]). Substituted aryloxy-alkanol derivatives for use as biologically activated pre-emergence herbicides. *Proc. 4th Int. Congr. Crop Prot.*, Hamburg, 1957, Bd. 1, 557–64.

—— & KRAMER, J. A., JR. (1951). Studies on the herbicidal properties and volatility of some polyethylene and polypropylene glycol esters of 2,4-D and 2,4,5-T. *Contr. Boyce Thompson Inst.*, 16, 267–78.

——, LAMBRECH, J. A. & FINN, T. P. (1950). Herbicidal properties of sodium 2,4-dichlorophenoxyethyl sulfate. *Contr. Boyce Thompson Inst.*, 16, 191–8.

KLINGMAN, D. L. (1953). Effects of varying rates of 2,4-D and 2,4,5-T at different stages of growth on winter wheat. *Agron. J.*, 45, 606–10.

KLINGMAN, G. C. & NOORDHOFF, L. J. (1961). *Weed Control: As a Science*. New York, John Wiley & Sons, 421 pp.

KNÜSLI, E. (1958). Nouvelles recherches sur les désherbants à base de triazines. *Phytiatrie-Phytopharm.*, 7(2), 81–92.

KOOPMAN, H. & UHLENBROEK, J. H. (1957). New s-triazine herbicides. *Nature, Lond.*, 180, 147–8.

LINDEN, G. (1957). The use of 2,4,5-T and related weedkillers. *World Crops*, 9(8), 325–7.

LONTZ, J. F. (1943). Composition and method. U.S. Patent 2,322,761.

LUSH, G. B. (1956). A new development in selective weed control. I. Introduction and weed control data. *Proc. Brit. Weed Control Conf.*, 3rd Meeting (Blackpool, England, 6–7 Nov.), pp. 625–32.

McNEW, G. L. & HOFFMANN, O. L. (1950). The growth-regulant, herbicidal and physical properties of 2,4-D and related compounds. *Iowa St. Coll. J. Sci.*, **24**, 189–208.

MARTH, P. C. & MITCHELL, J. W. (1944). 2,4-dichlorophenoxyacetic acid as a differential herbicide. *Bot. Gaz.*, **106**, 223–32.

——, DAVIS, F. F. & MITCHELL, J. W. (1945). Herbicidal properties of 2,4-dichlorophenoxyacetic acid applied in dusts containing hygroscopic agents. *Bot. Gaz.*, **107**, 129–36.

MELNIKOV, N. N. & BASKAKOV, J. A. (1954). Die chemischen Unkrautbekämpfungsmittel und die Stimulantia des Pflanzenwachstums. *Ergebnisse der Chemie*, **23** (H.2), 142–98 [also as separate publication, VEB Leipziger Druckhaus, Leipzig, 63 pp.; 685 refs., pp. 49–63].

MILLER, L. P. (1957). Monosaccharide components of an induced glycoside of trichloroethyl alcohol from dandelion (*Taraxacum officinale*) tops. *Contr. Boyce Thompson Inst.*, **19**, 113–15.

MITCHELL, J. W. & BROWN, J. W. (1946). Effects of 2,4-dichlorophenoxyacetic acid on the readily available carbohydrate constituents in annual morning glory. *Bot. Gaz.*, **107**, 120–9.

MORELAND, D. E. & HILL, K. L. (1959). The action of alkyl N-phenylcarbamates on the photolytic activity of isolated chloroplasts. *J. Agric. Food Chem.*, **7**, 832–7.

MUIR, R. M. & HANSCH, C. (1955). Chemical constitution as related to growth regulator action. *Annu. Rev. Pl. Physiol.*, **6**, 157–76.

MUZIK, T. J., CRUZADO, H. J. & LOUSTALOT, A. J. (1954). Studies on the absorption, translocation and action of CMU. *Bot. Gaz.*, **116**, 65–73.

NICKELL, L. G. (1952). The control of plant growth by the use of special chemicals, with particular emphasis on the plant hormones. In *Survey of Biological Progress*, vol. **2**, 141–95. G. S. Avery, Jr. (Ed.). Academic Press, New York.

NORMAN, A. G. (1954). The chemical nature of plant regulators. Pp. 29–43 in H. B. Tukey (Ed.), *Plant Regulators in Agriculture*. J. Wiley, New York, 269 pp.

ORGELL, W. H. & WEINTRAUB, R. L. (1956). Some principles involved in the foliar absorption of 2,4-D. *Plant Physiol.*, **31**(suppl.), xxi.

OVERBEEK, J. VAN (1952). Agricultural application of growth regulators and their physiological basis. *Annu. Rev. Pl. Physiol.*, **3**, 87–108.

—— (1962). Physiological responses of plants to herbicides. *Weeds*, **10**, 170–4.

—— (1964). Survey of mechanisms of herbicide action. Pp. 387–400 in *The Physiology and Biochemistry of Herbicides* (L. J. Audus, Ed.). Academic Press, London & New York.

PALFY, F., BARBAT, I. & PUIA, I. (1956). [Contributions à l'étude de l'efficacité du désherbant 2,4-D—in Romanian.] *Prob. Agric.* (Bucharest), **8**(5), 60–66.

POIGNANT, P. (1956). Quelques aspects du mode d'action et de la phytotoxicité sélective des auxines de synthèse. *Phytiatrie-Phytopharm.*, **5**(4), 213–28.

—— (1957). Le trichloroacétate de soude, anti-graminées sélectif; comment détruire le vulpin des champs dans les cultures de colza et de lin. *Phytoma*, **8**(84), 9–14.

POULOS, P. L. (1958). Neburon: newest of the substituted urea herbicides. *Proc., Northeast Weed Cont. Conf.*, **12**, 45–49.

RABATÉ, E. (1934). *La destruction des mauvaises herbes.* 3e edn. Paris.

RASMUSSEN, L. W. (1947). The physiological action of 2,4-dichlorophenoxyacetic acid on dandelion, *Taraxacum officinale*. *Plant Physiol.*, **22**, 377–92.

—— (1956). The effects of 2,4-D and 2,4,5-T applications on the stand density of Canada thistle (*Cirsium arvense* Scop.). *Weeds*, **4**, 343–8.

RAY, P. M. (1958). Destruction of auxin. *Annu. Rev. Pl. Physiol.*, **9**, 81–118.

REDEMANN, C. T. & MEIKLE, R. W. (1955). Inhibition of several enzyme systems by 2,2-dichloropropionate. *Arch. Biochem. Biophys.*, 59, 106–12.

RICE, E. L. (1948). Absorption and translocation of ammonium 2,4-D by bean plants. *Bot. Gaz.*, 190, 301–14.

ROBBINS, W. W., CRAFTS, A. S. & RAYNOR, R. N. (1952). *Weed Control*. McGraw-Hill, New York, 2nd. edn., 503 pp.

SCHOENE, D. L. & HOFFMANN, O. L. (1949). Maleic hydrazide, a unique growth regulant. *Science*, 109, 589–90.

SEN, G. & WOODFORD, E. K. (1953). Effects of trichloroacetic acid on the extension growth of root and shoot segments of *Pisum sativum*. *Nature, Lond.*, 171, 936–7.

SHAW, M., SAMBORSKI, D. J. & OAKS, A. (1958). Some effects of indoleacetic acid and maleic hydrazide on the respiration and flowering of wheat. *Canad. J. Bot.*, 36, 233–7.

SHAW, W. C. (1960). Recent developments in weed control research and herbicide utilization on a national scale. *Annu. Meet. Hawaiian Sugar Technol.*, 1960, pp. 25.

—— & GENTNER, W. A. (1957). The selective herbicidal properties of several variously substituted phenoxyalkylcarboxylic acids. *Weeds*, 5(2), 75–92.

—— & SWANSON, C. R. (1953). The relation of structure configuration to the herbicidal properties and phytotoxicity of several carbamates and other chemicals. *Weeds*, 2, 43–65.

SHIELDS, LORA M. & WELLS, P. V. (1962). Effects of nuclear testing on desert vegetation. *Science*, 135, 38–40.

SIEGEL, S. M. & PORTO, F. (1961). Oxidants, antioxidants, and growth regulation. Pp. 341–53 in *Plant Growth Regulation, Fourth International Conference on Plant Growth Regulation*. Iowa State University Press, Ames, Iowa, 850 pp.

SKVORTSOVA, L. A. (1957). [The influence produced by 2,4-dichlorophenoxyacetic acid on the colloid-chemical properties of a vegetable cell—in Russian.] *Akad. Nauk SSSR. Dokl.*, 114(1), 203–5.

SLADE, R. E., TEMPLEMAN, W. G. & SEXTON, W. A. (1945). Plant-growth substances as selective weed-killers. Differential effect of plant-growth substances on plant species. *Nature, Lond.*, 155, 497–8.

SMITH, F. G., HAMNER, C. L. & CARLSON, R. F. (1947). Changes in food reserves and respiratory capacity of bindweed tissues accompanying herbicidal action of 2,4-dichlorophenoxyacetic acid. *Plant Physiol.*, 22, 58–66.

STAGE, H. H. (1952). Use of petroleum oils in mosquito control. *Advanc. Chem.*, Ser. 7, 43–51.

TEMPLEMAN, W. G. (1955). The uses of plant growth substances. *Ann. Appl. Biol.*, 42, 162–3.

TUKEY, H. B., HAMNER, C. L. & IMHOFE, BARBARA (1945). Histological changes in bindweed and sowthistle following applications of 2,4-dichlorophenoxyacetic acid in herbicidal concentrations. *Bot. Gaz.*, 107, 62–73.

VOEVODIN, A. V. (1957). [The way dioecious plants answer to the application of the 2,4-D herbicide—in Russian.] *Akad. Nauk SSSR Dokl.*, 112(1), 148–51.

WAIN, R. L. (1951). Plant growth-regulating and systemic fungicidal activity: the aryloxyalkylcarboxylic acids. *J. Sci. Food Agric.*, 3, 101–6.

—— (1957). Selective weed control with MCPB. *Agriculture*, 63, 57–9.

—— & WIGHTMAN, F. (1957). Studies on plant growth-regulating substances. XI. Auxin antagonism in relation to a theory on mode of action of aryl- and aryloxy-alkanecarboxylic acid. *Ann. Appl. Biol.*, 45, 140–57.

WEAVER, R. J. & DEROSE, H. R. (1946). Absorption and translocation of 2,4-dichlorophenoxyacetic acid. *Bot. Gaz.*, 107, 509–21.

WEED SOCIETY OF AMERICA (1962). Report of the terminology committee, Weed Society of America. *Weeds*, 10, 255–71.

WEINTRAUB, R. L. (1953). 2,4-D mechanism of action. *J. Agric. Food Chem.*, 1, 250–4.

WEINTRAUB, R. L., REINHART, J. H., SCHERFF, R. A. & SCHISLER, L. C. (1954). Metabolism of 2,4-dichlorophenoxyacetic acid. III. Metabolism and persistence in dormant plant tissue. *Plant Physiol.*, **29**, 303–4.

WELDSTRA, H. (1953). The relation of chemical structure to biological activity in growth substances. *Annu. Rev. Pl. Physiol.*, **4**, 151–98.

WELLER, L. E., BALL, C. D. & SELL, H. M. (1957). Studies of maleic hydrazide interactions with thiol compounds. *Plant Physiol.*, **32**, 146–8.

WENT, F. W. (1935). Hormones involved in root formation. *Proc. 6th Int. Bot. Congr.*, **2**, 267–9.

—— & THIMANN, K. V. (1937). *Phytohormones. Experimental Biology Monographs.* Macmillan Co., New York, 294 pp.

WESSELS, J. S. C. & VAN DER VEEN, R. (1956). The action of derivatives of phenylurethan and of 3-phenyl-1,1-dimethylurea on the Hill reaction. *Biochim. Biophys. Acta*, **19**, 548–9.

WILDON, C. E., HAMNER, C. L. & BASS, S. T. (1957). The effect of 2,4-dichlorophenoxyacetic acid on the accumulation of mineral elements in tobacco plants. *Plant Physiol.*, **32**, 243–4.

WILLARD, C. J. & BERNARD, R. H. (1958). The effect of 2,4-dichlorophenoxyacetic acid (2,4-D) on wheat, oats, barley. *Res. Bull. Ohio Agric. Exp. Sta.*, **761** (1958), 24 pp.

WILSON, H. K. (1944). Control of noxious plants. *Bot. Rev.*, **10**, 279–326.

WOODFORD, E. K. (1957). The toxic action of herbicides. *Outlook Agric.*, **1**(4), 145–54.

—— & KASASIAN, L. (1960). Some new herbicides; developments in chemical weed control 1958–1960. *Chem. & Ind.*, 1960, 1118–25.

—— , HOLLY, K. & MCCREADY, C. C. (1958). Herbicides. *Annu. Rev. Pl. Physiol.*, **9**, 311–58.

ZIMMERMAN, P. W. & HITCHCOCK, A. E. (1942). Substituted phenoxy and benzoic acid growth substances and the relation of structure to physiological activity. *Contr. Boyce Thompson Inst.*, **12**, 321–43.

—— & —— (1949). Formative effects of several substituted phenoxy acids applied to *Kalanchoe*. *Contr. Boyce Thompson Inst.*, **15**, 421–7.

ZUKEL, J. W. (1955). Literature summary on maleic hydrazide. *MHIS No. 6C. Naugatuck Chem. Div., U.S. Rubber Co.*, 28 pp.

XIII

APPLICATION, ENTRY, AND ACTIVITY OF HERBICIDES

As there is now a very wide range of herbicides available, it is important to select the most appropriate one for any particular weed control problem, and, furthermore, to formulate and apply it in the most effective manner under the expected conditions of use. For example, among the many kinds of 2,4-D formulations, it is important to consider whether or not a derivative in an aqueous solvent system, or in some form of oil or other organic solvent system, would be the more suitable under specific weather conditions. Or might a low-volatile ester be somewhat more effective, and just as safe, as a non-volatile form such as an amine salt? It is also important to consider what selectivity, if any, is involved in the situation—on flax, might MCP be safer than 2,4-D? Or would 2,4-DB be more effective than 2,4-D in removing cleavers (*Galium* spp.) from small grains? These and related problems will be discussed below, principally in relation to their more fundamental aspects.

FORMULATION

The average user of herbicides is not prepared to modify existing formulations appreciably, or to prepare new ones. Within any one class of herbicides, there often exist a number of different formulations that might require special care in selection for a specific application. Generally, examples of 2,4-D-types are cited here, as they have been in use for a longer period of time, and offer a greater variety of formulations, than do other types.

The choice of a solid, liquid, or gaseous form, for the use of 2,4-D herbicides, is relatively limited. Aerial applications of the dust forms of 2,4-D are, in general, prohibited by law in most of the United States, because of the severe problem of their drift onto susceptible crops. Solid forms have also appeared in granular preparations for pre-emergence weeding, and in various types of pellet—such as those used for aquatic weed control. Among other herbicides, the solid form, or an emulsifiable suspension, is the only way in which dichloral urea, the various Monuron derivatives, Simazine, and the chlorate-borate-Monuron combinations, may be used. Where long residual action in the soil is desired, the solid forms of the several herbicides are generally preferable.

314

Among the 2,4-D group of herbicides, the liquid preparations constitute the largest volume of material used. They consist essentially of two groups: the water-soluble amine formulations, and the several kinds of esters that are soluble in either oil or some other organic solvent. Those which are soluble in organic solvents may be sprayed directly as an oil concentrate, as in aircraft spraying; or the concentrates may also contain an emulsifier, so that water-emulsifiable sprays of larger volume for ground spray-rigs (e.g. along rights-of-way) may be prepared. The relative merits of these two groups will be considered later in this chapter.

2,4-D is rarely used as a herbicide in the vapour form. In fact, the tendency in recent years has been to move almost completely away from such volatile forms as the 2,4-D butyl ester and into the less-volatile esters with longer alkyl side-chains,—such as the 2-ethylhexyl ester, etc. The problem of injury from vapour drift has been considered by a number of investigators, as have suitable analytical methods (Allen, 1950—*see* Ch. XII; Tafuro *et al.*, 1950; King & Kramer, 1951; and Leasure, 1958).

Perhaps the most precise physical measurements ever made on the volatility of 2,4-D esters are those of Miller *et al.* (1954), using radio-chemical techniques. They examined the highly volatile *n*-butyl ester, and two low-volatile esters—2-ethylhexyl ester and 2-(2-ethoxyethoxy) propyl ester—all labelled with carbon-14 in the carboxyl position. The average time required for 50 per cent loss of these three esters at room temperature was 10·5 minutes, 2·5 hours, and 9 hours, respectively (cf. Figs. 53 and 54).

There are, however, several herbicides that are used in a fumigant manner, whose vapours kill weed seeds or deeply-buried perennial roots. Methyl bromide and carbon disulphide have been widely used for this purpose, as has chloropicrin. The vapours of the solid, Mylone (XVII)*, are also reported to be effective against weeds and weed seeds in the soil (Keays & Zedler, 1957—*see* Ch. XII).

The factors affecting the performance of maleic hydrazide (XXXVIII)* have been examined in some detail by Smith *et al.* (1959) and may serve as an introduction to the problems involved. Studies using tracer, spectro-photometric, and chromatographic techniques, showed that maleic hydrazide is stable and non-volatile, and is efficiently translocated. Absorption is often slow, and this was particularly related to the relative humidity and the type of formulation: at low relative humidity, the herbicide was absorbed poorly from all formulations, whereas at moderate and high humidities, formulation differences were evident. The diethanolamine salt of maleic hydrazide was found to be the most practicable of the type that was absorbed efficiently (cf. Figs. 55 and 56). In tests on tobacco (where it is used to suppress axillary shoot development following topping

---

* Roman numerals refer to those in Appendices I and II (pp. 444–5, 451) where further details concerning the properties and uses of the individual herbicides will be found.—Ed.

of the plant), about half of the chemical applied as the diethanolamine salt might be expected to be absorbed in four days at 50 per cent relative humidity, or in one day at 100 per cent relative humidity. Tobacco plants growing in dry soil (presumably under moisture stress) absorb foliage-applied maleic hydrazide more slowly at a given humidity than do plants growing in wet soil under similar conditions.

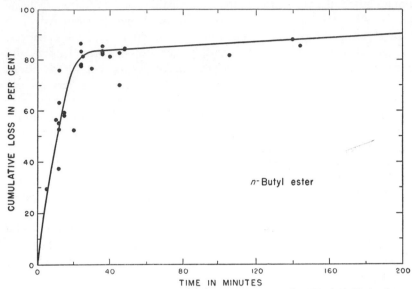

By courtesy of the Boyce Thompson Institute; from Miller, Weed & Hitchcock, 1954

Fig. 53.—Evaporation of *n*-butyl ester of 2,4-D (labelled with C^{14} in the carboxyl position) from nickel-plated planchets at room temperature, plotted against time in *minutes*. Data obtained from nine different runs. The average time required for 50 per cent loss of the ester was about 10·5 *minutes*. Thus the high volatility-rate here confirms the field experience, where, in the earlier days of the use of 2,4-D butyl ester, severe damage to neighbouring crops often occurred. Recent work has shown that substituted oleyl amine salts of 2,4-D can be used in areas near susceptible plants with less danger from volatility under high soil and air temperatures (145° F.) than any other form of 2,4-D.

APPLICATION, COVERAGE, AND SPRAY RETENTION

The selection of appropriate spraying equipment, including the choice of nozzle types, involves the more practical aspects of this subject, which are considered, under the various usages of herbicides, in Chapter XIV. Also, two recent works are noteworthy in this connection: *Crop Protection*, by G. J. Rose (1963), which is particularly good for application equipment and recommendations, while *Concentrate Spray Equipment, Mixtures and Application Methods*, by S. F. Potts (1958), is exceedingly well documented, covering many theoretical and basic aspects, though with due emphasis also on the applied phases. Concerning the correct nozzles to use, *see* Potts' Appendix No. IV, and Appendix IV of this volume.

Ennis *et al.* (1952), in Mississippi, examined various aspects of spray retention in considerable detail, and the following is largely a report of their results, though some reference is made, when appropriate, to the more recent work of others.

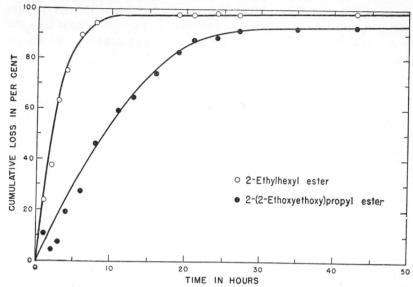

By courtesy of the Boyce Thompson Institute; from Miller, Weed & Hitchcock, 1954

FIG. 54.—Evaporation of the 2-ethylhexyl and the 2-(2-ethoxyethoxy)propyl esters of 2,4-D (labelled with C^{14} in the carboxyl position) from nickel-plated planchets at room temperature, plotted against time in *hours*. The average time required for 50 per cent loss of the esters was two and a half *hours* for the 2-ethylhexyl ester and nine *hours* for the 2-(2-ethoxyethoxy) propyl ester, confirming the field experience of greater safety with these long-chain esters.

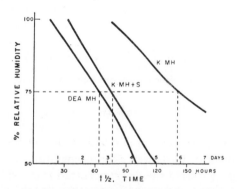

By courtesy of J. Agric. Food Chem., from Smith et al., 1959

FIG. 55.—Effect of relative humidity on $t\frac{1}{2}$ (time for 50 per cent absorption) for three formulations of maleic hydrazide: DEA MH (diethanolamine salt of MH); K MH + S (potassium salt of MH plus Sorbitol); and K MH (potassium salt of maleic hydrazide). The humectant, Sorbitol, minimizes crystallization of MH, and improves the absorption and activity of certain formulations.

1. *Effects of leaf pubescence:*—Pubescent and glabrous varieties of soybeans were sprayed with three concentrations (100, 250, and 500 p.p.m.) of 2,4-D acid, with and without 'Carbowax 1500'* (at 0·5 per cent). The

* A high-molecular-weight polyethylene glycol.

results showed that the 2,4-D in 0·5 per cent Carbowax 1500 was more inhibitory to all the varieties of soybean than were the wholly aqueous sprays of the growth-regulator. The question arose as to whether this might not be due to increased adherence of the spray (caused by the Carbowax). Another experiment was therefore conducted in which the plants under test were weighed before and after spraying. These results indicated that, on an average, there was about 23 and 36 per cent more spray retained by the pubescent and glabrous plants, respectively, when Carbowax 1500 was employed, than with the water sprays. Further statistical analysis of the data confirmed these findings: the better growth-inhibition was indeed due to the increased adherence of the Carbowax 1500 preparations.

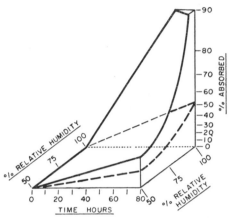

By courtesy of J. Agric. Food Chem., from Smith et al., 1959

FIG. 56.—Three-dimensional response surfaces for two maleic hydrazide formulations— per cent absorbed *v.* relative humidity and time. The solid line indicates the response surface of diethanolamine salt formulation of maleic hydrazide; the broken line indicates the response surface of the potassium salt formulation. Tests involved sprays of the respective formulations on potted tomato plants.

2. *Effects of leaf angle and leaf pubescence on spray retention :*—Glabrous and pubescent soybean leaves held (*a*) horizontally and (*b*) downwards at an angle of 45°, were sprayed individually with aqueous solutions containing a dye, and with Carbowax 1500 preparations also containing the dye. Rinsing and analysis of the dye concentrations revealed that, in every case, pubescent leaves retained more spray than did the glabrous leaves— at both of the angles studied, and similarly with the Carbowax 1500 under identical circumstances.

3. *Behaviour of wholly aqueous droplets impinging on leaf surfaces :*— Ennis *et al.* (1952) observed that wholly aqueous droplets frequently bounced from the leaves of the soybeans, irrespective of whether the leaves were pubescent or glabrous. Droplets (0·5–0·7 mm. in diameter) were accordingly applied to the leaf surfaces of some thirteen crops and weeds.

Oats, cabbage, and peanuts, essentially repelled all droplets, while these were retained by dandelion, mullein, tobacco, and potato. Variations, such as adherence to veins only, or to the margins of leaves, or even to the lower surface only, were observed. On some surfaces the droplets broke up into many minor droplets, which in some cases formed a circle of numerous satellite droplets.

4. *Behaviour of droplets containing surface-active agents:*—The addition of 'Tergitol 7',* at a concentration of 1 per cent, resulted in the retention of spray droplets on all the leaves that were studied. With use of a 5 per cent oil-emulsion instead of the Tergitol 7, cabbage and oat (but not peanut) still repelled the droplets.

5. *Behaviour of droplets of non-aqueous and other herbicidal formulations:*—Species which retained wholly aqueous (i.e. without a surfactant) droplets, also retained droplets of all the other 2,4-D formulations that were tested. Species that were difficult to wet with water, such as certain droplets of grasses (including maize and oats), and lespedeza, largely repelled the 2,4-D preparations.

6. *Effect of the waxy layer (bloom) on droplet behaviour:*—On removing the waxy layer (by rubbing the surface slightly with the finger) from the leaves of all the plants which otherwise repelled the droplets, complete droplet retention was obtained. In tests, several waxy substances spread thinly on glass slides (e.g. paraffin, tissue matte, beeswax, etc.), effected droplet retention—although the contact angles for these substances were larger than for some other substances which were tested. A further test involved the removal, with ethyl ether, of the waxy layer from cabbage leaves, and then re-depositing the wax on glass slides and on thin cellophane. The deposited film did not repel aqueous droplets. It is obvious that simulating the waxy film of leaves presents certain difficulties, and Ennis *et al.* concluded that the physical properties of the natural waxes on the leaves of cabbage, and possibly the resilience of the leaves, are important factors in repelling aqueous droplets. The rough, reticulate surfaces revealed by the electron microscope studies of Schieferstein & Loomis (1956), are certainly additional factors involved here.

7. *Spray output and spray retention:*—Brunskill (1956), in England, has examined in detail the factors controlling retention of liquid by leaves of *Pisum sativum* under conditions where the leaves were maintained in a horizontal plane and received drops of a uniform size that varied on different occasions. These studies also involved the measurement of surface-tension of the preparations employed. For example, the surface-tension of pure water is quite high (73 dynes/cm.), while that of many organic solvents, emulsions, and aqueous preparations of surface-active agents, is much lower.

* A surface-active agent (Tergitol).

Helqvist (1956), in his work on spraying rates and retention of herbicides in Sweden, studied methods of measuring the wettability of leaf surfaces. Wettability is a surface phenomenon: if a liquid is applied to a solid body, a surface of contact arises between the drop and the solid body. The shape of the drop depends on the properties of the liquid itself (largely on its surface-tension), on the solid, and also on the surrounding gaseous medium (air). These properties determine directly the 'angle of contact', or 'contact angle', which is the angle that the surface of the drop makes with the surface of the solid at the point of contact (Fig. 57), and is actually the angle which is formed by the tangent to the surface of the liquid and the tangent of the solid body (i.e. the leaf surface). Both tangents are drawn from the point where the gas, liquid, and solid phases meet. With a completely wetted surface, i.e. when the drop spreads out to a thin film over the solid body, the angle of contact will be = 0°. If the surface is less wettable, the contact angle will be larger, while for surfaces which are difficult to wet, it will approach 180°.

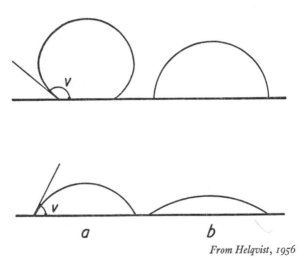

From Helqvist, 1956

FIG. 57.—The outlines of a liquid drop on the surface of a leaf of the pea (*Pisum sativum*) (*above*) (similar also for a drop on a leaf of *Chenopodium album*), and on a leaf of *Sinapis arvensis* (*below*). (*a*) Distilled water, having high surface-tension (73 dynes/cm.). (*b*) Distilled water with a surface-active agent, and low surface-tension (35 dynes/cm.). V = 'contact angle'— cf. Table XIII.

Helqvist used a combination of microscopic (after Fogg, 1947) and photographic techniques to determine the angle of contact on leaf surfaces, while the mathematical method of Mack (1940) was used for the calculation of these angles. Both 'receding contact angles' (decreasing angle of contact through evaporation of the droplet) and 'advancing contact angles' (the angle which the drop makes immediately after the liquid phase has come in contact with the solid phase) were recognized by Fogg (1947) and by Helqvist (1956). The latter type of angle was studied by both authors, and a few examples, taken from the work of Helqvist (1956), are given in Table XIII. As these data show, the contact angle for distilled water is high, and it is well known that the leaves

TABLE XIII

SURFACE-TENSION VALUES AND CONTACT ANGLES OF PURE WATER, AND AS MODIFIED BY THE ADDITION OF SURFACE-ACTIVE AGENTS, OR BY A HERBI-CIDE AT SEVERAL CONCENTRATIONS, OBTAINED FOR VARIOUS LEAF SURFACES.

(Prepared from the data of Helqvist, 1956)

Series	Concn., %	Surface-tension, in dynes/cm.	Contact angle in degrees (upper surface)
A. Distilled water	—	73·0	137·3[*]
B. Distilled water with surface-active agent	—	40·0	116·3[†]
C. Agroxone solutions of different concentrations[‡]	1	72·0	128·0
	5	62·5	116·0
	10	56·5	113·0
D. Agroxone solutions of different concentrations	0	72·8	129·5
	1	72·0	128·1
	5	62·5	123·1
	10	56·5	80·0

Notes: Contact angles on the upper surface of the leaf of *Chenopodium album* (Series A and B); of the same species with Agroxone solutions of different concentrations (Series C); contact angles for the upper surface of the leaf of flax (*Linum usitatissimum*), with Agroxone solutions of different concentrations (Series D).
    [*] Lower surface, 147·50
    [†] Lower surface, 123·80
    [‡] Agroxone (Na salt of MCP)

of *Chenopodium album* are difficult to wet with water. Even with the surface-tension reduced to 40 dynes/cm. by the addition of a surface-active agent, the drops make a large contact angle with the underlying surface. Helqvist further notes that the leaves of certain species show very little wettability—as, for example, many grasses such as cereals (which have a contact angle with pure water of about 150°), and also peas, flax, rape, and the weeds *Chenopodium album* and *Sonchus arvensis*. On the other hand, plants, the leaves of which are easy to wet include the potato, and the weeds *Sinapis arvensis* and *Galeopsis* spp., which have a contact angle with pure water of less than 90°.

8. *Other aspects of spray retention:*—Holley (1952) investigated the problem of volume and application rate, on the activity of translocated herbicides. His studies, as well as those of Helqvist (1956), have shown contradictory results, obtained in experiments with different volumes, as well as large differences in retention for these different application rates. Holley observed that the variation in the amount of toxicant which is retained at different volumes, is much greater than the variation in the phytotoxic effect of the herbicide. Rice (1948—*see* Ch. XII) stated that penetration into the plant occurs only while the herbicide is in solution on the surface of the plant, and that it ceases as soon as the herbicide crystallizes out on the plant's surface. With translocated herbicides, the amount of active substance which is absorbed by the plant depends upon how long the herbicide is in solution. In spraying with a high-volume rate, the herbicide will crystallize out more slowly than if a low volume of water is used. These results probably explain the difference in retention which occurs when different spray volumes are used.

Two factors are important in understanding these differences: the retention of the spray and the penetration by the herbicides. Temperature is also a factor, and investigators in the United States, England, and Sweden, have each done their work under different climatic conditions— apparently without controlling, or even stating, the temperature at which their spray retention studies were conducted. For application to tropical conditions, such information is quite vital.

9. *Aspects of spray drift:*—An important problem in studies bearing on suitable droplet size is that relating to drift under the average or normal conditions of field usage. This is particularly important with respect to the growth-regulator type of herbicides. Helqvist (1956) has considered some of these problems, which are summarized here. Brooks (1947) examined some of the risks, especially when the droplets are very small, and stated that droplets with a diameter of less than 50 microns are not desirable. With aircraft application, however, other aspects must be considered. This is an involved subject, that has been considered by a number of investigators.

The droplet sizes which occur in rain, mist, and clouds, are listed by Helqvist (after Brooks, 1947, and Gallwitz, 1952); they extend in diameter from about 1 mm. down to 5 microns. Extremely small droplets have less ability to fasten onto a surface than large ones, and evaporation loss is also important at the higher temperatures. Very large droplets cannot, on the other hand, adhere to plants that are refractive to wetting particularly if the surface-tension of the spray is high. The size of the droplets also influences the physical selectivity.

Gallwitz (1952) has made a division of fineness of spray into three size-classes: 'Spritzen' (droplet sizes from 150 to 300 microns), 'Sprühen' (droplet sizes from 50 to 150 microns), and 'Nebeln' (droplet sizes from

5 to 50 microns). He concludes that plant growth-regulators should not be sprayed in the form of these smaller droplets. In recent studies of the influence of drop size on the effectiveness of low-volume herbicidal sprays Ennis & Williamson (1963) found that with foliar applications at rates of 100 to 500 ml. per acre, the herbicidal toxicity increased as the particle diameter increased from 0.3 to 1.0 mm. (300 to 1,000 microns).

The fate of small droplets of about 200 microns in diameter, with aircraft application, is indicated in Fig. 58. Such small droplets are deposited farther outboard than the larger droplets (from 375 to 700 microns in diameter), and these smaller droplets, emerging from the point 75 per cent out to the wing-tip, are entrained in the trailing wing-tip vortex—thereby being dispersed over the countryside, far from the spray-swath.

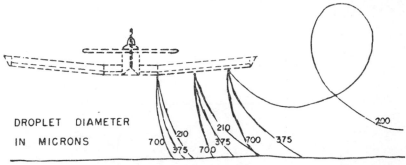

DROPLET DIAMETER
IN MICRONS

By courtesy of the Agricultural & Mechanical College of Texas

Fig. 58.—Computed paths of spray droplets of various sizes, dispensed from Ag-1 airplane flying at 20 ft. above the ground at the low speed of 58 miles per hour. Computations are given for nozzles located at three spanwise positions, 25, 50, and 75 per cent of the distance out to the wing-tip. They show that the smaller droplets, 210 microns in diameter, are deposited farther outboard than the larger droplets, and that the smaller droplets emerging from the point 75 per cent out to the wing-tip are entrained in the trailing wing-tip vortex.

10. *Low-volume spraying:*—Low-volume (10–25 gal./acre) spraying of cereals with growth-regulator types of herbicides has been widely used, both in the United States and in England, for removing weeds. The average droplet size is about 100 microns in diameter for low-volume spraying, when ground-borne sprayers are used. It is obvious that there would be greater spray drift from nozzles with small orifices; so, if drift is to be reduced, larger spray volumes, as well as larger droplet sizes, must be used. Helqvist (1956) advanced certain recommendations, as follows: if great precaution against spray drift from wind is needed, a volume rate of 40 litres/hectare should be used, while with contact herbicides sych as dinitro-ortho-cresol, much larger volumes must be used (such as 400 litres/hectare for cereals, and 600 to 800 litres/hectare for the same herbicide on a flax crop).

Helqvist's (1956) experiments in spring-sown cereals and linseed (flax) with MCPA did not show any difference in the weed-killing effect of MCPA between a low-volume rate (100 litres/hectare) and a high-volume rate (900 litres/hectare) with the droplet-size distribution that was used. However, it must be remembered that these studies were made under Swedish climatic conditions. The nozzle used was a Teejet 650067 (Spraying Systems Co.), which provided a flat fan-shaped jet, and at the pressure used (5 kg./sq. cm.) the average droplet diameter was 88 microns.

Low-volume spraying has been restricted, pretty much by necessity, to aircraft application. Problems of drift were encountered, among others, and even a light wind can alter the spray pattern. The results of some studies that were made at the Texas Agricultural and Mechanical College are shown in Fig. 59. Here the effect of a crosswind of up to 8 miles per hour upon a trapezoidal spray distribution pattern is vividly portrayed.

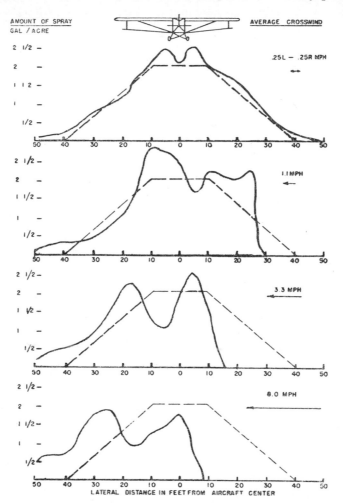

By courtesy of the Agricultural & Mechanical College of Texas

FIG. 59.—The effect of a crosswind of up to 8 miles per hour upon a trapezoidal spray distribution pattern applied from an aircraft.

A nearly 50 per cent displacement of the spray pattern occurred at 8 miles per hour.

Beatty (1958) has reported the use of certain inverted emulsions of the phenoxy acids, as brush-killer formulations for use in airplane applications. When the formulations are mixed with oil and water in various proportions, a viscous material similar to buttermilk or mayonnaise is produced. Particular attention has been paid to their drift characteristics. Beatty has described a centrifugal sprayer which has been developed and could vary volume and droplet size, and distribute very viscous materials that could not be sprayed from conventional equipment. Satisfactory results have been obtained with this new sprayer, using the invert emulsions and applying them by helicopter or fixed-wing aircraft. With application from a helicopter at a rate of 7 gal. of total volume per acre, and at the altitudes that are necessary to clear the steel towers which appear on rights-of-way, the invert emulsion material and sprayer reduced drift. The material has been applied at wind velocities well over the usually-considered limit of 5 miles per hour. In herbicidal activity, it appears equal, on most species, to conventional sprays, and is superior in translocating properties on mesquite; its use also appears encouraging on several hard-to-wet water weeds such as water-lettuce (*Pistia stratiotes*).

Mode of Entry into Plants

Perhaps the two most critical aspects of determining whether an otherwise potent herbicide will be effective in the eradication of a particular noxious plant form, are those of entry into the plant, and movement within the plant (especially into the root system). Apart from root absorption, the only way a herbicide can enter a plant is by passing through the cuticular layer of leaves and stems, or as a gas through the stomata. The cuticle covers all plant parts that are exposed to the air.

Our knowledge of the structure of the plant's cuticle has advanced considerably during the past few years—with the use of the electron microscope (Mueller *et al.*, 1954; Schieferstein & Loomis, 1956; Scott *et al.*, 1958), the separation of the cuticle from the cell-wall by pectic enzyme action (Orgell, 1954, 1955), and sorption studies (Orgell, 1957). A number of detailed chemical studies have also appeared (Skoss, 1955; Matic, 1956). Orgell (1957) considers the cuticle to be a layer of semi-lipoidal material outside the outer epidermal cell-wall. Using a replica technique, Mueller *et al.* (1954) and Schieferstein & Loomis (1956) have demonstrated the presence of rodlets and granules of wax-like substances. Macroscopic surface deposits of wax in the form of layers, plates, granules, and rods, e.g. bloom, are commonly observed. Lamellae of wax also occur within the body of the cutin layer which forms the main part of the cuticle. Cutin is believed to be a polymer consisting of oxidized unsaturated lipids (Priestley, 1943), or a polyester (Frey-Wyssling, 1953).

At the boundary between the cuticle and the outer epidermal cell-wall, a layer of pectic material is often noted. Ectodesmata have been observed in the outer epidermal cell-wall (Lambertz, 1954), but it was not known until quite recently that they extend into, and influence the properties of, the cuticle. Scott *et al.* (1958) describe the tubular epidermal cells of the leaves and roots of *Allium cepa*, noting that they are pitted on all cell faces including the outer wall, and concluding that wax and mucilage precursors, sheathing the root in fluid form, presumably extrude along the ectodesmata through the pits in the outer wall. It has also been proposed that hydrophyllic lamellae may be present in the cuticle of certain plants or parts of plants, e.g. apple leaves (Roberts & Southwick, 1948). Orgell (1957) has suggested that these structures, as well as cracks and insect injuries in the cuticle, may provide a pathway for the penetration of polar materials. A schematic diagram of a leaf epidermal cell, incorporating some of these more recent findings, has been prepared by Orgell (1957), and is here reproduced in Fig. 60. His studies indicate that the cuticle is contracted and uncharged in acid solution, but expanded and negatively charged in alkaline solution (cf. Fig. 61).

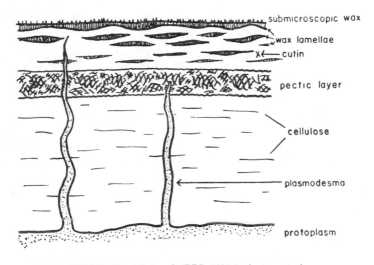

LEAF EPIDERMAL CELL OUTER WALL (schematic)

w·o

From Orgell, 1957

Fig. 60.—Diagrammatic representation (not to scale) of a leaf's outer epidermal cell-wall and cuticle—based on Anderson (1934), Roelofsen (1952), Frey-Wyssling (1953), Lambertz (1954), Mueller *et al.* (1954), and Schieferstein & Loomis (1956). The hydrophyllic lamellae, apparently interspersed among the wax lamellae, as proposed by Roberts *et al.* (1948), are not shown here.

In defining his studies on 'sorption', Orgell (1957) stated that substances may concentrate and become orientated at the interface between the cuticle and a solution by the process of adsorption, or they may enter into the bulk of the cuticle by the process of absorption. The term 'sorption' includes both of these processes. Penetration refers to the movement of a substance completely through the cuticle. These studies, conducted with a wide range of foliar-applied chemicals on isolated cuticle disks of apricot leaves, revealed that polar substances in aqueous solution move very slowly, if at all, through intact cuticle and into a layer of agar gel. As was pointed out, this does not indicate that such substances do

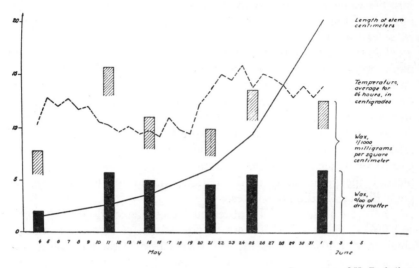

By courtesy of H. Frederiksen

FIG. 61.—An ontogenetic study of the development of cuticular wax on fibre flax (*Linum usitatissimum*). Studies based on nine crops grown in Denmark. The graph shows that the quantity of wax per unit area differs in relation to the height of the plant, to the temperature, and perhaps to other climatic factors. As there is a large quantity of wax on the flax plants when they are 2–3 cm. high, H. Frederiksen suggests that spraying at this very early stage (with MCPA) may be possible.

not penetrate intact cuticle on the plant, as the nature of the receiving medium of the plant must be considered. These studies might also indicate that the cuticle is altered in some imperceptible manner by the pectic enzyme treatment; that the ectodesmata may enter the cutin and be involved in the absorption and movement of foliar-applied materials (perhaps even with an expenditure of energy after the manner of Hoagland's theory of ion absorption by roots); or that the stomatal pores, breaks, and insect damage to the cuticle, are more important channels of entry than was formerly believed.

However, work by Crowdy & Jones, (1958), on the entry of sulphonamides into the leaves of wheat, has provided some entirely new concepts. Kramer (1957) recently reviewed a number of claims that the initial process by which a chemical enters plant tissue is diffusion. The development of the concept of 'free space' (*see* Crowdy & Jones, 1958) has provided support for the belief that the portion of plant tissue which is freely available for diffusion, and upon which the study of diffusion has tended to centre, is that area in the tissue which is more properly termed 'apparent free space'. This space (in percentage of tissue volume) averages about 23 ± 10 per cent for root tissues and some other structures (Crowdy & Jones, 1958). These last-mentioned workers state that this type of diffusion is essentially the movement of materials in aqueous solution on the surface of the plant, thence through a membrane and into the water in the free space. The importance of free water, or very moist conditions, for the uptake of chemicals from leaves, has been noted by several investigators.

Weintraub *et al.* (1954—*see* Ch. XII) reported that 2,4-D acid was more rapidly absorbed by turgid plant cells than by plants which were on the point of wilting, and it has been shown (Crowdy & Jones, 1958) that the entry of maleic hydrazide into leaves is markedly dependent upon atmospheric moisture—e.g. they found the time required for half the deposit on the leaves to enter the tissue to be 128, 25, and 2 hours, at relative humidities of 40, 70–75, and 100 per cent, respectively. As Crowdy & Jones (1958) state, conditions of high moisture may actually increase the permeability of the cuticle, in addition to increasing the possibility of diffusion of solutes.

Holly (1956—*see* Ch. XII) observed, in tests on sunflower (*Helianthus* sp.) leaves, that the highest rate of penetration of MCPA (Na salt) (II) obtained with glycerol present, was 4·3 per cent of the amount applied, per hour, over the four-hour period following application. He concluded that a very considerable fraction of the amount applied in commercial spraying of water-soluble formulations of these herbicides is, in fact, wasted by remaining on the leaf surface, from which it is washed off by the first rain after application. Absorption stops when the phenoxyacetic acid crystallizes out on the leaf surface. Glycerol is hygroscopic and prevents crystallization. In the comments on maleic hydrazide, it was also noted that Sorbitol was an antihumectant and prevented the crystallization of this particular herbicide.

The cuticle consists essentially of a hydrophyllic framework in which are embedded impermeable wax platelets; in conditions of high humidity, the framework will absorb water and swell. This will separate the wax platelets and increase the area available for diffusion (Overbeek, 1956; Crowdy & Jones, 1958). This view tends to provide an explanation of the experimental evidence that plants in arid regions, exposed situations, etc., can absorb water vapour and dew, and lose mineral salts and sulphonamides by leaching from leaves (Crowdy & Jones, 1958). In this new study of the sulphonamides, these last authors examined the diffusion constants based on Fick's law of diffusion, and indicated that this diffusion process is primarily physical. Certain assumptions were required here, so the role of the plasmodesmata, if any, has yet to be elucidated.

The isolated cuticle, being largely composed of lipoidal substances, might be expected to be soluble or partially so in oil-type solvents. Extensive studies (King, 1957) with a variety of such solvents which are usually obtainable in the laboratory, disclosed that this is not the case. The substances which most readily dissolved cuticle disks were found to be concentrated solutions of sodium ethylenediamine tetraacetate, as well as KOH.

Unpublished work performed at the Boyce Thompson Institute, by L. J. King & H. G. Cutler, demonstrated that separation of the epidermis and cuticle on both the upper and lower leaf surfaces of *Gardenia* spp. and a number of species of common weeds, could be readily accomplished by using the pectic enzyme technique of W. H. Orgell. While *Gardenia* is not a weed, its heavier type of cuticle is perhaps representative of *Eichhornia crassipes*, *Quercus*, etc. Herbicidally, *Gardenia* is still of interest as it has been used as a test or screening plant in the search for new herbicides that would be effective on woody plants. The gross appearance of these isolated *Gardenia* cuticle disks is shown in Plate 19(*a*), while photomicrographs of epidermis and cuticle from both the upper and lower leaf surfaces are shown in Plate 19(*b*). Micrometer measurements on frozen cross-sections of *Gardenia* cuticle *in situ* revealed that the upper cuticle averaged 8·6 microns, whilst the lower cuticle averaged a maximum of 7·8 microns and a minimum of 3·6 microns in thickness. (The two values for the lower cuticle are due to the fact that it appears in cross-section as a corrugated structure.) Light transmission studies of isolated leaf cuticle disks revealed a transmission of about 80 per cent for the upper cuticle, while the lower cuticle had an average value of 72 per cent transmission. These isolated portions offer many possibilities for elucidating some aspects of the penetration of cuticle by herbicides (Martin 1964).

While the recent research reviewed here throws considerable light on the process of 'sorption', it is not at all certain that the effects of various factors on this process necessarily parallel these effects on penetration. Crafts (1948*a*), in his theory of herbicidal action, suggested that substances which can exist in an ionized (more polar) and in an un-ionized (less polar) form, penetrate cuticle more readily in the less polar forms. We are still far from an understanding of the processes involved in penetration, and especially lacking in adequate supporting evidence.

Useful in any consideration of the uptake and distribution of applied herbicides are the symplast and apoplast concepts. As Crafts (1964) has recently stated the symplast concept considers that all of the living cells of the organized multicellular plant form a functionally integrated unit, and that the cells are interconnected by protoplasmic connections, the plasmodesmata. Soluble materials, including those of natural origin and function as well as those absorbed from outside the plant body, are moved throughout this protoplasmic network. Such movement is relatively slow, however, and may range from rates of a few millimetres to a few centimetres per hour. Once substances have entered the plant they may enter the translocation system of the plant where movement is much greater, of the order of 100 cm. or more per hour. By contrast the apoplast makes up the cell-wall structural frame-work that surrounds and supports the symplast. The xylem system is an important system here in conduction, and much higher rates are involved, up to a 100 m. per hour (Crafts, 1964 *see* Ch. XII).

The Plasma Membrane

Apart from the cuticle and the cell-wall, another barrier to penetration must be passed—the plasma membrane. The protoplast does not lie as a smooth layer against the inside of the cell-wall, but penetrates it with a multitude of thin strands, the ectodesmata. The outer walls of the epidermis also appear to have thousands of these plasmatic tentacles that extend to immediately beneath the cuticle. It has been claimed that these plasmatic tentacles rhythmically extend and contract, and, as noted earlier, their penetration into the cuticle *has not been clearly* established (Overbeek, 1956).

Overbeek has provided, in his review (1956), most of the ideas used in the following section. The plasma membrane is a very thin, yet relatively impermeable, membrane surrounding the outer surface of the protoplast and also of course the ectodesmata. This membrane is basically a lipoid layer 50 thick, with protein Åabsorbed on each side, though the protein-absorbing layer as a whole may attain a thickness of about 70 Å. It is believed that the protein stabilizes the lipoid layer. Overbeek recognized three steps in the penetration, through the lipoid layers, of a chemical from an aqueous solution: (*a*) entry into the membrane which involves breaking the hydrogen bonds that link the molecule to water, the overcoming of van der Waals' forces, and the formation by thermal agitation of a hole in the membrane through which the chemical then slips; (*b*) diffusion through the membrane which involves overcoming the van der Waals' forces between hydrocarbon chains and between hydrocarbon chains and the diffusion molecule; and (*c*) exit from the membrane, which is the same as (*a*) in reverse.

It is also noted that the presence of an aromatic solvent in the monolayer greatly increases permeability of the lipoid layer. As observed earlier, this is in agreement with the theory of the action of phytotoxic oils on plants, which holds that the lethal effect of hydrocarbons is attributable to their solubilizing entry between the lipoid molecules of the plasma membrane, thereby causing an abnormal increase in permeability. If other structures inside the protoplast are to be penetrated, the chemical must also penetrate the membranes surrounding them. These include the membrane about chloroplasts, the protein network envelope of the

330

nuclei, the double membranes of the mitochondria, and the membrane of the endoplasmic reticulum.

In two additional studies, Overbeek (1962, 1963—*see* Ch. XII) comments further on the action of herbicides on membranes. Investigators have noted the large number of chemicals (pentachlorophenol, dinitrophenol, dicoumarol, salicylate, azide, and ammonia) that are uncouplers of oxidative phosphorylation. These findings together with other evidence led P. Mitchell in 1961 to the conclusion that these uncouplers act on the membranes of the structures in which phosphorylation takes place. Indeed, he believes that the enzyme which facilitates ATP production is located in the centre of these lipoid membranes. It is known too that mitochondria, chloroplasts, and the endoplasmic reticulum consist of highly folded membranes. Uncoupling agents penetrate the membrane destroying its selective impermeability. With the discovery that dinitrophenol increases the current leak through membranes, and that this herbicide also depresses the transmembrane potential of oat coleoptile cells, Overbeek (1962) states that herbicides which act as uncouplers cause electric current to leak through the membranes of mitochondria and chloroplasts, just like herbicidal oils cause water and water soluble materials to leak through the plasma membrane of the cells.

MOVEMENT OF HERBICIDES IN PLANTS

The passage of the chemical to the site of herbicidal action is the next most critical phase. The first barriers to be met when the herbicide has passed through the cuticle of the leaf, or the superficial layer of the root are, respectively, the cells of the leaf mesophyll or of the root cortex. As Woodford (1957) notes, little is known about the cell-to-cell transport system that carries the herbicide along this chain of living cells and delivers it into the conducting tissues of either the phloem or the xylem. Nor is it known how closely the systems in the leaf and the root may parallel each other. However, it has been ascertained that the process in the leaf is a metabolic and not a physical one, and that it moves some chemicals faster than others. The rate of movement of 2,4-D between the leaf surface and the conducting tissue has been shown to be about 0·003 cm. per hour (Day, 1952).

The herbicide is distributed throughout the plant by its movement up and down in the conducting tissues of the xylem and phloem. Upward movement with the transpiration stream in the xylem is generally associated with entry through the roots, and downward movement with assimilates in the phloem after their entry from the leaves. Woodford (1957) notes that most of the chemicals that are able to enter the phloem can also pass from it into the xylem, and so are truly systemic in nature. Movement in the phloem depends upon the flow of certain metabolites from the leaves and, at its rate of 10–100 cm. per hour, is much faster

331

than the cell-to-cell movement in the leaf just noted above. Woodford contended that, in practice, it is probably the slower and more sensitive transport system of the leaf mesophyll which determines whether or not a herbicide is capable of reaching the phloem.

Overbeek (1956) has suggested that 2,4-D, applied as an aqueous spray to weeds in the field, undergoes a rapid absorption before it is taken into the interior of the plant. This absorption explains the extraordinary rate at which 2,4-D is bound to weeds—a fact which surprised the early users of 2,4-D herbicides. As we have seen above, some explanation may be found in the suggestions of Crowdy & Jones (1958) relative to the initial movement (and storage?) in the 'apparent free space' areas of living tissue. The studies on the complexing of applied biocides with certain cellular constituents (after the manner of detoxification) add additional evidence for the quick absorption that has been observed. 2,4-D persists in some plants for considerable periods of time—in dormant buds of two-year-old cherry trees for five months, and in apricot seeds for at least seven months (cf. Woodford et al., 1958).

In general, if a compound is taken up by the leaves it is transported out of those leaves via the phloem. When a compound is taken up through the root system, transport upwards into the aerial portions of the plant takes place through the xylem. Such widely different materials as phosphates and indoleacetic acid can move up through the xylem into the leaves, and from there may be rerouted via the phloem. As some of this routing involves downward movement, it has been suggested that such materials may possibly circulate through the plant (Overbeek, 1956). In a detailed review, Woodford et al. (1958) have drawn attention to certain pitfalls in current methods of research on the movements of herbicides within plants.

Weintraub et al. (1956) have reported on their studies of the translocation of radioactive 2,4-D and its relatives. They applied these 'tagged' materials to the leaves of various species, and studied the amount of export after twenty-four hours by analysing the tissues for carbon-14. Translocation in the broad-leafed types (garden bean, soybean, cotton) was from 5 to 70 times as great as in the cereals. It was found that the differences in susceptibility were of the same order as the differences in translocation, which suggests that translocation is an important factor in determining susceptibility and resistance. In a study of two varieties of field corn (maize), one being resistant to 2,4-D and the other susceptible, foliage applications of tagged 2,4-D were made, and it was found that the total amounts of C^{14} which had moved in twenty-four hours were virtually the same in both varieties. However, the distribution was found to be quite different. In the susceptible variety, about one-half of the mobile C^{14} had been exported from the blade and about one-third had moved out of the leaf altogether, whereas in the resistant variety only one-fifth had left the blade, and only one-sixteenth had been exported from the leaf!

A similar study performed on varieties of field maize revealed that about twice as much C^{14} was exported from the leaves of the susceptible varieties as from those of the resistant varieties.

Similar studies involving the time-course of movement disclosed that when the growth-regulator was applied near the tip of the leaf, distribution from this site of application continued for at least forty-eight hours. There was very little movement from blade to sheath after the first twenty-four hours. Export from the leaf appears to come to a halt within a few hours. It is of interest to note that substantial movement may take place within the treated leaf while very little export occurs. The block to movement appears to be at the point of insertion of the leaf at the node.

Studies of a similar character have been reported by Butts & Fang (1956). The tomato plant steadily increased its absorption until the seventh day, when 51·3 per cent was found to have been absorbed and translocated to other parts of the plant, while the pea plant showed no further absorption of 2,4-D after one day.

In his review, Crafts (1964 see Ch. XII) notes that compounds of the 2,4-D type are strongly accumulated within the symplast and translocated chiefly in the phloem. In contrast to this group are the substituted ureas and the symmetrical traizines that may penetrate the cuticle and move in the apoplast with the transpiration stream, but do not commonly enter the phloem. Amitrole (XXXV) is particularly interesting because of its ready mobility in both phloem and xylem. It is not accumulated actively within the symplast as is 2,4-D, and hence moves more freely. Crafts (1964) notes another category which includes Dalapon (XXXII), maleic hydrazide (XXXVIII), and 2,3,6-TBA (XXXIX) that are freely mobile in mesophyll and phloem and thus reach the roots of weeds. Here they apparently leak from the phloem into the xylem and move upward in the transpiration stream. Upon again reaching the leaves they may re-enter the symplast and recycle again, much as phosphorous circulates in the plant (Crafts, 1964).

FATE OF 2,4-D AND OTHER HERBICIDES WITHIN PLANT TISSUES

Butts & Fang (1956) sought to elucidate some of the biochemical aspects of resistance. They found that applied 2,4-D reacted with the plant tissue substrate to form 2,4-D protein complexes. The rate of this formation was far more rapid in resistant plants than in susceptible ones. When this 2,4-D protein complex was applied to the bean leaf, no absorption and no toxic effects were observed.

In a further study, this complex was injected into the stems of bean plants, as was also a sample of radioactive 2,4-D. It was found that the plant which received the 2,4-D protein complex treatment gave off $C^{14}O_2$ approximately three times as fast as the one receiving an equal amount of radioactivity in 2,4,-D. Butts & Fang concluded that 2,4-D protein complex is a product of a detoxification process and is perhaps an intermediate of the metabolism of 2,4-D. Hydrolysis of such complexes revealed the presence of at least twelve amino-acids.It should be noted here that Andreae & Good (1957) have also suggested that 2,4-D is phytotoxic to certain plants because, in these, it persists in the tissues by resisting degradation and by failing to form conjugation products.

The studies of Glastonbury *et al.* (1960) on the residual levels of 2,4-DB and the breakdown of its butyl ester in seedling alfalfa (lucerne) are also illustrative here. They used carbon-14 labelled compounds and a special isotope dilution technique, and by infra-red analysis found the limit of sensitivity at 1 p.p.m. In a series of field experiments, the persistence of 2,4-DB sodium salt on seedling lucerne at spray rates up to 3 lb. per acre was 7–28 days according to the initial dose and the growing conditions. When the very high spray rate of 4 lb. per acre was used, the limit of detection was not reached until forty-two days after spraying. The re-appearance of normal growth in the majority of plants occurred a few days before a concentration of 1 p.p.m. was reached. The breakdown of the ester form to 2,4-DB was complete in one experiment within twenty-four hours, whereas in another experiment the persistence of the ester form was four days—this difference being apparently related to different temperature levels. Thus, as might be expected, the persistence of 2,4-DB in plants treated with an ester form was longer than in plants which had been treated under the same conditions with the equivalent rate of the sodium salt, being sixteen days for the ester treatment and seven days for the sodium salt.

Bach & Fellig (1961) confirmed the finding of Butts & Fang (1956) that 2,4-D, upon application to bean plants, was converted to at least three compounds which were resolvable by paper chromatography. The former authors, using carboxyl-labelled 2,4-D, found that decarboxylation and release of $C^{14}O_2$ appear to constitute a minor path in the metabolism of 2,4-D by bean stems, and that most of the radioactivity was recovered in the form of a complex of unknown structure which yielded 2,4-D upon acid hydrolysis.

W. A. Andreae reported in 1959 that when radioactive 2,4-D was incubated with pea stems for twenty-four hours most of the 2,4-D which accumulated in the tissue was present as the metabolically unchanged 2,4-D. There were, however, small amounts of 2,4-D in a conjugated form—the 2,4-D probably being linked to aspartic acid by a peptide linkage.

Freed *et al.* (1961), in exploring the physico-chemical aspects of growth-regulator action, concluded that the primary event in the mechanism of action of the chlorophenoxyacetic acids is that of adsorption upon a protein surface, and that, as a consequence of this adsorption, the structure of the protein is modified, with a consequent change in its enzymatic activity. These authors believe that this theory of the molecular-level mechanism of action affords an explanation of how the same molecule may both stimulate growth at a low concentration and bring about inhibition at a higher concentration.

The fate of maleic hydrazide (XXXVIII) has been considered by Smith *et al.* (1959). In experiments using herbicide impregnated with carbon-14, most if not all of the carbon-14 that could be extracted from plants up to seven days from treatment was in the form of maleic hydrazide. In experiments lasting a week or longer, not all the carbon-14 had been accounted for. This unaccounted remainder may be lost to an un-extracted complex. It is known that maleic hydrazide can be bound as a protein complex or glycoside, and possibly oxidatively degraded.

The growth-inhibiting effect of maleic hydrazide on plants continues for many months after the original chemical application—e.g. Bermuda grass will remain inhibited for over a year. Residue measurements involving a colorimetric method have shown that normal levels have been found in potatoes and in the roots of turf grasses as long as eight months after treatment. It is thus apparent that at least part of the chemical in the plant tissues resists breakdown for long periods of time (Smith *et al.*, 1959).

PHYSIOLOGICAL EFFECTS FOLLOWING HERBICIDAL APPLICATIONS

Much has already been reviewed, in an earlier Chapter (Ch. XII), of the mode of action of the various herbicides. The particular biochemical processes affected were there noted, as well as any associated visible effects on the plants' growth and appearance. Sometimes very little growth occurs following the application of a particular herbicide, whereas, with certain others, considerable abnormal growth results. These effects are complex and often slow to develop, particularly if the toxicant is arriving at the site of action over an extended period and is not immediately lethal.

Woodford (1957) notes that the information which is available on the manner in which various herbicides alter the growth and composition of treated plants, tends to confuse rather than clarify an understanding of the mechanisms of the toxic action; for the interval between time of application and analysis is so long that the direct effect of the toxicant has been masked by subsequent processes. The ways in which 2,4-D and MCP can affect the growth of plants illustrates the diversity of the after-effects of treatment: changes in respiration, carbohydrate utilization, nutrient uptake, mitosis, cell elongation, cell differentiation, reduction in vital leaf-area and in the size of the plant, and many other processes. Death may result from the extended action of any one of these events; or it may be the effect of a combination of two or more, resulting in dwarfing or cessation of growth and a failure to compete with unsprayed crop-plants; or it may occur indirectly, as when the action of a toxicant paves the way for an attack by a pathogen. This last action appears to be an important consideration with the use of such pre-emergence chemicals as Sesone and 2,4-D, whose primary action is that of a germinative toxicant to the weed seed. With reduction in growth and the exposure of the young embryo or seedling, pathogens in the soil readily invade, causing death in these immature phases.

THE SELECTIVITY OF HERBICIDES

Much that has been reviewed up to this point has a decided bearing upon the problem of selectivity. It is certainly true that the most striking features of the new growth-regulator type of herbicide, such as 2,4-D, are the selectivity aspects—particularly with regard to the broad separation of largely susceptible dicotyledonous plants from the largely resistant monocotyledonous plants. Blackman (1950) has reviewed this problem of selectivity, and observes that the degree of toxicity at the cell level involves the amount and distribution of toxicant retained by the shoot, its penetration into the plant, its transport within the plant, and its possible differential accumulation. Environmental factors, as well as the method of toxicant application, were also mentioned as factors influencing selectivity.

Some aspects of the biochemical differences between 2,4-D-resistant and 2,4-D-susceptible plants were cited above from the work of Butts & Fang (1956), where the rate of the 2,4-D protein complex formation was found to be far more rapid in resistant plants than in susceptible ones.

Blackman (1950) notes that the selectivity of biocides, other than herbicides, is usually dependent upon metabolic differences between host and parasite, and that the selective action holds over a relatively wide range of dosage. However, most selective herbicides depend for their effectiveness not only on a difference of toxicity at the cell level, but also on all the factors which influence the amount of herbicide that reaches the site of toxic action. The dose required for selectivity is often critical. A number of investigators have noted that the growth-regulator type of herbicide follows the dosage-response curve of indoleacetic acid (cf. Audus, 1959). This graphical treatment indicates that, at very low concentrations (1×10^{-5} p.p.m.), there is actually a stimulation of root growth (likewise, increased stem elongation has been observed with very small quantities of 2,4-D), while at high concentrations (1,000 p.p.m.), inhibition of growth occurs. With some molecules that are alien to plant metabolism, such as 2,4-D, higher concentrations are not only inhibitory to growth but are also lethal.

Blackman (1961), in further examining the selective action of 2,4-D at the cellular level, employed *Pisum* stem sections as representative of the sensitive dicotyledonous plants and *Avena* sections as representative of the resistant monocotyledonous plants. He found that 2,4-D, after absorption, can be readily released from the stem tissues of susceptible, but not from those of resistant, species, and that this is compatible with the view that a restriction of movement after penetration into the shoot may in part confer resistance. Furthermore, selective action apparently rests on the extent to which the growth-regulator interferes with the organized pattern of cell growth and differentiation, and the factors which are grouped under the aegis of permeability allow the movement of 2,4-D out of some species more than others. Thus if the introduced growth-regulator persists in the tissues, only very small changes between or within cells are necessary to bring about ordered—or disordered—cellular development.

While such morphological differences as the protected growing-point (by the sheathing leaf-bases) in the Gramineae, and the exposed apical growing-region (as well as the axillary buds) in dicotyledonous plants, are important contributory factors to selectivity, much recent work has further elucidated the many biochemical mechanisms that are also involved in selectivity—especially at the cell level. The studies of Wain (1955) and Wain & Wightman (1957) have shown that, when some herbicidal chemicals such as 4(2,4-DB) were applied to one species of plant, a breakdown of the chemical occurred within the tissues, followed by a well defined response; but when the same chemicals were sprayed upon other species, there was no growth response whatever. This indicated that only certain species of plants were capable of breaking down this particular group of chemicals to release the potent growth-regulating substance—so destroying themselves. Such results as these indicated a new and fundamental basis on which selective weed control might operate—a selectivity which arises from differences in the chemical constitution of the plants themselves.

One of the first examples of such a type of activation—from an inactive to a highly active herbicide molecule—is that furnished by the conversion of Na 2-(2,4-dichlorophenoxy) ethyl sulphate (Sesone) to the principal active molecule, 2,4-dichlorophenoxyethanol, by the micro-organisms present in non-sterile soil (King et al., 1950—see Ch. XII), and particularly by Bacillus cereus var. mycoides (Vlitos, 1953). This is not only an excellent example of endotoxication with regard to the action of the micro-organisms, but also a good example of exotoxication with respect to higher plants. It might be stated that it is at the same time an exotoxic reaction with the micro-organisms, as a secreted enzyme, probably an arylsulphatase (Vlitos, 1953), can also effect the conversion upon the removal of the bacterial cell (cf. Fig. 62).

This same type of activation has been particularly evident with regard to the highly effective systemic insecticides and fungicides which are now being used for the control of these groups of agricultural pests.

Åberg (1964) in a recent review has discussed the susceptibility of plants to herbicides, and particularly the factors in the plant that modify the responses of a given species to treatment. Included among the factors are: stage of development of both weeds and crop plants; vigour and nutrient status; previous history (e.g. cultivation, injury, competition, etc.); health status (e.g. prevailing disease or insect attacks); varietal differences; and lastly, population trends and acquisition of immunity.

A recent review of selectivity in relation to formulation and application methods has been prepared by K. Holly (1964). Topics considered include selectivity and chemical structure; spray retention (role of plant factors and differential retention and the physical characteristics of the spray or selectivity); relationship to penetration into the shoot; and action through the soil. Recent penetration experiments with 2,4-D present evidence that it enters primarily through a number of specific sites, probably the guard cells and accessory cells, but not through the stomatal pores. Ectodesmata have been demonstrated which form a direct connection between epidermal cells and the external surface and are covered only by the cuticle. These are believed to play an important role in absorption by forming a pathway for transport of substances into the leaf (Holly, 1964). The outer wax layer of the cuticle is formed via the ectodesmata in the outer tangential cell walls of the epidermis. These ectodesmata also play an important role in building up cuticular layers (see Linskens, H.F., et al., 1965).

Among the soil factors related to selectivity, Holly (1964) includes: extended absorption of the herbicide by the plant roots; directional spray to hit the soil only; special formulations such as granular or pelletized compositions; adsorption; leaching and movement within the soil profile; adsorptive barriers on the crop seed or as a layer in the soil above the crop seed (such as activated carbon); soil factors and herbicidal volatility; differential absorption by various regions of the same root system; and root absorption differences among the various species. Herbicidal placement in relation to crop seed is an important selective feature.

The behaviour of herbicides within the plant is also a very important aspect of selectivity and this has recently been reviewed by R. L. Wain (1964). In addition to some of the better known aspects of selectivity two specific areas are treated: inactivation of chemicals in the plant (detoxication and differential detoxication) and conversion of inactive to active compounds in plants. Both of these areas have been studied extensively by Wain and his associates at Wye College. Reference has already been made in Ch. XII to the studies on β-oxidation of the side chain of 2,4-D and 2,4-DB derivatives and its relationship to selectivity. The review cited provides a thorough survey of this important field of herbicide research.

FATE OF HERBICIDES APPLIED TO THE SOIL

It is important to know something about the residual aspects of herbicides that have been applied to the soil, as pre-emergence applications to the soil for weed control are widely used. The residual aspects are particularly important where food crops, for man or animals, are involved. By contrast, it is also important in soil sterilization treatments to know just how long the chemical may remain effective and, consequently, when re-applications may have to be made.

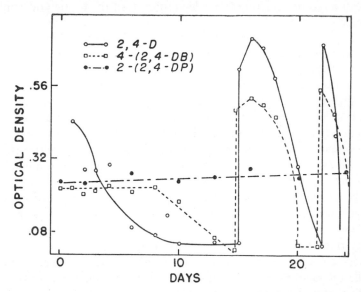

From Whiteside & Alexander, 1960

FIG. 62.—Spectrophotometric determination of the decomposition in a soil-culture medium of 2,4-D, 2-(2,4-DP) and 4-(2,4-DB). The herbicides were re-introduced into the medium at fifteen and twenty-two days. Note the much shorter time required for the metabolizing of the herbicides after these later introductions (except 2-(2,4-DP)).

The fate of the phenoxy group of herbicides in soil has been most extensively examined. By and large, the majority of the more commonly used derivatives have a relatively short life in the soil. Whiteside & Alexander (1960; cf. Fig. 62), in their special test-tube soil culture system, found that, at the first introduction of the herbicides into the medium, 2,4-D persisted for about 10 days and '2,4-DB' for about fifteen days, while following the second introduction they persisted for about eight and five days, respectively. In these studies, however, 2,4-DP was not altered but persisted throughout the twenty-five-day test period.

The trichloroacetates, as well as Dalapon, are among the more persistent of the newer group of herbicides. These are often used to control quack-grass in croplands, and their effects may still be evident in the following year when the treated land is planted to maize.

Where long-term soil sterilization is desired, herbicides that are long-lasting are the most suitable. Combinations of inorganics with organics (ureas and triazines) are also used. The arsenicals, as well as the borates and the borate-chlorate combinations, fall into this general long-lasting group. Persistence of inorganics for two or more years, depending upon the rate of application and the annual rainfall, is not uncommon.

A thorough examination of the many aspects of the fate of herbicides in the soil is now available in the Second Symposium of the British Weed Control Council, *Herbicides and the Soil*, edited by E. K. Woodford (1960), and in the recent reviews of Hartley (1964), and of Audus (1964) noted below.

The fate of herbicides in the soil has an important bearing on the length of effective activity, on the nature of the residual or degradation products, and on the relationship of residual products to the food-chain and to other aspects of our ecosystem (*see* Ch. XIV). Hartley (1964) has thoroughly reviewed the physical factors of the soil and herbicidal action. Topics included are the physics of transfer in the soil; mechanism of adsorption in the soil; herbicidal losses from the soil (evaporation, chemical decomposition, loss by cropping); herbicidal uptake; and transfer of dosage from soil to plant. The author cited notes that the results of pre-emergence application of herbicides have been very variable and that the outstanding disadvantage of pre-emergence application is the unavoidable dependence upon future weather, particularly rainfall. Irrigation provides one method of control of this variable, and G. S. Hartley reminds us that increasing knowledge of the 'soil-weather-plant-herbicide complex' must keep pace with irrigation developments.

The interactions of herbicides with soil micro-organisms is the subject of a thorough review by L. J. Audus in one chapter of the recent work, *The Physiology and Biochemistry of Herbicides* (1964). Two broad categories analysed include the effects of herbicides on soil micro-organisms, and the effects of soil micro-organisms on herbicides. The latter category alone can be considered here. Direct evidence for the role of micro-organisms in herbicidal detoxication is provided by steam-pressure soil sterilization experiments, and by the use of certain chemicals to block microbial metabolism. The use of such metabolic poisons as small concentrations of sodium azide (a cytochrome oxidase inhibitor) and of sodium fluoride (a respiration inhibitor) in a herbicide-perfused soil can completely prevent the breakdown of 2,4-D, MCPA, and 4-CPA in enriched soils (Audus, 1964).

Final proof of the role of bacteria is provided by isolation of the responsible organism. The results of many studies show that several orders of the true bacteria, the actinomycetes, and the lower fungi can all destroy herbicides in the soil. Predominant are the genera *Nocardia* and *Arthrobacter* which attack the phenoxy-type—and the chlorinated aliphatic herbicides. From studies available to date, Simazine seems not to be decomposed by bacteria but only by fungi and actinomycetes. Allyl alcohol can be decomposed in pure culture by species of soil organisms (*Pseudomonas* and *Nocardia*) adapted to a medium containing this herbicide. The persistence of herbicides in the soil and the possible danger of such pesticide residues in plants that serve as food for animals and man are problems of current concern and do require continued attention.

Audus (1964) notes that many soil microorganisms can acquire the capacity of utilizing alien chemicals as a food source, and thus many herbicides are rapidly degraded in the soil. The most popular herbicides have a low mammalian toxicity—and do, therefore, present a more favourable position in our ecosystem.

BIBLIOGRAPHY

(Application, Entry, and Activity of Herbicides)

ÅBERG, E. (1964). Susceptibility: factors in the plant modifying the response of a given species to treatment. *The Physiology and Biochemistry of Herbicides* (Ed. L. J. Audus), pp. 401–22. Academic Press, London & New York.

—— & GRANSTROM, B. (1956).Ogräsbekämpning med kemiska medel (Chemical weed control) 1956. Uppsala. Lantbrhögsk. och Stat. Jordbrförösk. *Särtryck och Smaskr.*, 91, rev., 31 pp.

AGRICULTURE RESEARCH SERVICE, United States Department of Agriculture. (1958). Interpretations of the Regulations for the Enforcement of the Federal Insecticide, Fungicide and Rodenticide Act. *Washington, USDA (Rev.)*, 44 pp.

ANDERSON, D. B. (1934). The distribution of cutin in the outer epidermal wall of *Clivia nobilis. Ohio J. Sci.*, 34, 9–19.

ANDREAE, W. A. & GOOD, N. E. (1957). Studies on 3-indoleacetic acid metabolism. IV. Conjugation with aspartic acid and ammonia as processes in the metabolism of carboxylic acids. *Plant Physiol.*, 32, 566–72.

ANON. (1950). New generations of farm weeds may prove resistant to 2,4-D. *Crops & Soils*, 3(1), 23.

AUDUS, L. J. (1959). *Plant Growth Substances*, 2nd. edn. Plant Science Monographs. (Ed. N. Polunin.) Leonard Hill, London, and Interscience, New York 553 pp.

—— (1964). Herbicide behaviour in the soil. *The Physiology and Biochemistry of Herbicides* (Ed. L. J. Audus), pp. 163–206. Academic Press, London & New York.

—— & THRESH, R. (1956). The effects of synthetic growth-regulator treatments on the levels of free endogenous growth-substances in plants. *Ann. Bot., Lond.*, 20, 439–59.

BACH, M. F. & FELLIG, J. (1961). The uptake and fate of C^{12}-labelled 2,4-dichlorophenoxyacetic acid in bean stem sections. In *Plant Growth Regulation*, Fourth International Conference on Plant Growth Regulation. Iowa State Univ. Press, Ames, Iowa, pp. 273–87.

BALL, N. G. & DYKE, I. J. (1956). The effects of indole-3-acetic acid and 2,4-dichlorophenoxyacetic acid on the growth rate and endogenous rhythm of intact *Avena* coleoptiles. *J. Exp. Bot.*, 7, 25–41.

BATES, G. H. (1955). *Weed Control.* Spon, London, 235 pp.

BEATTY, R. H. (1958 [pub. 1960]). Herbicides and the American farmer. *Proc. 4th Brit. Weed Control Conf.*, Brighton, pp. 86–96.

BIEBL, R. (1953). Resistenz pflanzlicher Plasmen gegen 2,4-D. *Protoplasma*, 42, 193–208.

BLACKMAN, G. E. (1950). Principles of selective toxicity and the action of selective herbicides. *Sci. Prog.*, 38, 637–51.

—— (1961). A new physiological approach to the selective action of 2,4-dichlorophenoxyacetic acid. In *Plant Growth Regulation*, Fourth International Conference on Plant Growth Regulation. Iowa State Univ. Press, Ames, Iowa, pp. 233–47.

——, TEMPLEMAN, W. G. & HALLIDAY, D. J. (1951). Herbicides and selective phytotoxicity. *Ann. Rev. Plant Physiol.*, 2, 199–230.

BLAIR, B. E. & GLENDENING, G. E. (1953). Intake and movement of herbicides injected into mesquite. *Bot. Gaz.*, 115, 173–9.

BOHME, L. (1957). Unkrautbekämpfung unter besonderer Berücksichtigung arbeits-wirtschaftlicher Erwägungen. *Mitschurin-Bewegung. Schulungsbeilage*, 4, 23 pp.

BOYSEN-JENSEN, P. (1936). *Growth Hormones in Plants* (English translation of *Die Wuchsstofftheorie* ... (1935), by G. S. Avery, Jr., & P. R. Burkholder). McGraw-Hill, New York, 268 pp.

BRITISH WEED CONTROL COUNCIL (1958). The mechanics of herbicide application. Pp. 145–163 in *Weed Control Handbook*, Blackwell, Oxford, 245 pp.

—— (1958a). Non-selective weed control. Pp. 131–8 in *Weed Control Handbook*, Blackwell, Oxford, 245 pp.

BROOKS, F. A. (1947). The drifting of poisonous dusts applied by airplane and land rigs. *Agric. Eng.*, 28, 233.

BRUNSKILL, R. T. (1956). Physical factors affecting the retention of spray droplets on leaf surfaces. *Proc. 3rd Brit. Weed Control Conf.*, Blackpool, 2, 593–603.

BUTTS, J. S. & FANG, S. C. (1956). Tracer studies on the mechanism of action of hormonal herbicides. *Conf. Radioactive Isotopes Agric.* (Papers), pp. 209–14.

CARNS, H. R. & ADDICOTT, F. T. (1964). The effects of herbicides on endogenous regulator systems. *The Physiology and Biochemistry of Herbicides* (Ed. L. J. Audus), pp. 343–56. Academic Press, London & New York.

CRAFTS, A. S. (1946). Selectivity of herbicides. *Plant Physiol.*, 21(3), 345–61.

—— (1948). Weed control in the tropics. *Science*, 107(2773), 196–7.

—— (1948a). A theory of herbicidal action. *Science*, 108, 85–86.

—— (1953). Herbicides. *Ann. Rev. Plant Physiol.*, 4, 253–82.

—— (1961). Improvement of growth regulator formulation. In *Plant Growth Regulation* Fourth International Conference on Plant Growth Regulation. Iowa State Univ. Press, Ames, Iowa, pp. 789–802.

—— & FOY, C. L. (1962). The chemical and physical nature of plant surface in relation to the use of pesticides and to their residues. *Residue Reviews*, 1, 112–39.

—— & HARVEY, W. A. (1949). Weed control, I, 289–320. *Advances in Agronomy*.

—— & —— (1955). Weed control by soil sterilization. *Calif. Agric. Exp. Sta. Circ.* 446, 20 pp.

—— & LEONARD, O. A. (1956). Translocation of herbicides. *Hilgardia*, 26(6), 287–415.

—— & RAYNOR, R. N. (1940). Principles of chemical weed control. In *The Control of Weeds* (Ed. R. O. Whyte), *Herbage Pub. Serv. Bull.*, 27, pp. 38–54.

—— & ROBBINS, W. W. (1962). *Weed Control* (3rd edn.), McGraw-Hill, New York & London, 671 pp.

CROWDY, S. H. & JONES, D. R. (1958). The translocation of the sulphonamides in higher plants. III. *J. Exp. Bot.*, 9, 220–8.

CURRIER, H. B. (1956). Effects of toxic compounds: inhibition, injury and death. *Handb. der Pflanzenphysiol.*, 2, 792–825.

DAY, B. E. (1952). Absorption and translocation of 2,4-dichlorophenoxyacetic acid by bean plants. *Plant Physiol.*, 27, 143–52.

——, JOHNSON, E. & DEWLEN, J. L. (1959). Volatility of herbicides under field conditions. *Hilgardia*, 28, 255–67.

DOUROS, J. D. & REID, J. J. (1956). Decomposition of certain herbicides by soil microflora. (Abs.) *Proc. Soc. Amer. Bact.*, 56, 23–24.

ENNIS, W. B. (1949). Histological and cytological responses of certain plants to some aryl carbamic esters. (Abs.) *Amer. J. Bot.*, 36, 823.

—— & WILLIAMSON, R. E. (1963). The influence of drop size on effectiveness of low-volume herbicidal sprays. *Weeds*, 11, 67–72.

——, ——& DORSCHENER, K. P. (1952). Studies on spray retention by leaves of different plants. *Weeds*, 1, 274–86.

EXER, B. (1958). Über Pflanzenwachstumsregulatoren. *Experientia*, 14, 136–7.

FABRE, R. & TRUHAUT, R. (1954). *Toxicologie des products phytopharmaceutiques.* Société d'Edition d'Enseignement Supérieur, Paris, 272 pp.

342

FANG, F. C. (1958). Absorption, translocation, and metabolism of 2,4-D-1-C^{14} in pea and tomato plants. *Weeds*, 6, 179–86.

—— & BUTTS, J. S. (1954). Studies in plant metabolism. IV. Comparative effects of 2,4-dichlorophenoxyacetic acid and other plant growth regulators on phosphorus metabolism in bean plants. *Plant Physiol.*, 29, 365–8.

——, FREED, V. H., JOHNSON, R. H. & COFFEE, D. R. (1955). Absorption, translocation, and metabolism of radioactive 3-(p-chlorophenyl)-1, dimethylurea (CMU) by bean plants. *J. Agric. Food Chem.*, 3, 400–2.

FISCHNICH, O., PAZOLD, A. & THIELEBEIN M. (1954). Awendung von Maleinsäure-hydrazid bei einigen Kulturpflanzen, *Angew. Bot.*, 28, 88–113.

FOGG, G. E. (1947). Quantitative studies on the wetting of leaves by water. *Proc. Roy. Soc. London*, Ser. B, 134, 503–22.

FREED, V. H. (1953). Herbicidal mechanism—mode of action other than oxyalkyl acids. *J. Agric. Food Chem.*, 1, 47–51.

—— (1958). The chemistry and reactions of herbicides as related to their use. *Proc. West. Weed Control Conf.*, 16, 18–27.

——, REITHEL, F. J. & REMMERT, L. F. (1961). Some physical-chemical aspects of synthetic auxins with respect to their mode of action. In *Plant Growth Regulation*, Fourth International Conference on Plant Growth Regulation, Iowa State Univ. Press, Ames, Iowa, pp. 289–306.

FREY-WYSSLING, A. (1953). *Submicroscopic Morphology of Protoplasm*, 2nd Eng. edn. Elsevier Publ. Co., New York, 411 pp.

GALLWITZ, W. (1952). Spritzen-Sprühen-Nebeln-Stäuben. *Landtechnik*, 5, 150–5.

GESHELE, E. E. (1956). [Experiment in chemical control of weeds in Siberia—in Russian.] *Gosudarstvennoe Izdatelstvo Selskokhoziaistvennoi Literatury*, Moskva, pp. 215–19.

GLASTONBURY, H. A., STEVENSON, MARGARET D. D & BALL, R. W. E. (1960). 2,4-DB and its butyl ester: residual levels in seedling lucerne. *Proc. Fourth British Weed Control Conf.* (1958), pp. 33–38.

GOOR, G. A. W. VAN DER (1950). Weed control with synthetic hormones. *Gen. Agric. Res. Sta. Contrib.*, Indonesia, No. 108, 45 pp.

GOTAAS, H. B. (1956). *Composting, Sanitary Disposal and Reclamation of Organic Wastes*. World Health Organization, Palais des Nations, Geneva, 205 pp.

GREENHAM, C. G. (1957). Studies on phytocides. *Aust. J. Biol. Sci.*, 10, 180.

GRIEVE, B. J. (1943). Auxin levels, etc. *Aust. J. Exp. Biol. Med. Sci.*, 21, 89.

GUNCKEL, J. E. & SPARROW, A. H. (1954). Aberrant growth in plants induced by ionizing radiation. *Brookhaven Symposia in Biol.*, 6, 252–80.

GUSTAFSSON, M. (1960). [Residues of pesticides in crop and soil—in Swedish, English summary.] *J. Roy. Swed. Acad. of Agric. & For.*, Suppl. No. 4, 107 pp., lit. pp 89–107.

HACCIUS, B. & LINDEN, G. (1956). Untersuchungen zur 2,4-D-Persistenz in pflanzlichen Geweben. *Zeit. Bot.*, 44, 145–52.

HANNA, L. W. (1958). *Hanna's Handbook of Agricultural Chemicals*, 2nd edn. Forest Grove, Oregon, 489 pp. (Herbicides pp. 207–55).

HARTLEY, G. S. (1964). Herbicide behaviour in the soil. *The Physiology and Biochemstry of Herbicides* (Ed. L. J. Audus), pp. 111–61. Academic Press, London & New York.

HELQVIST, H. (1956). The effect of volume application rate on the retention and activity of herbicides. *Ann. Roy. Agric. Col. of Sweden*, 22, 41–92.

HOFFMANN, E. & SCHMELING, B. VON (1953). Zur Wirkung der 2,4-dichlorophenoxy-essigsäure auf den Stoffwechsel bzw. Fermentgehalt der Pflanze. *Naturwissen-schaften*, 40, 23–24.

HOFFMANN, O. L. & SMITH, A. E. (1949). A new group of plant growth regulators. *Science*, 109, 588.

HOFSTEN, C. G. VON (1946). Ogräsproblemet (the weed problem). *Lantbruksveckan*, 5, 162.

HOLLEY, R. W. (1952). Studies of the fate of radioactive 2,4-dichlorophenoxyacetic acid in bean plants. II. A water soluble transformation product of 2,4-D. *Arch. Biochem. Biophys.*, 35, 171–5.

HOLLY, K. (1964). Herbicide selectivity in relation to formulation and application methods. *The Physiology and Biochemistry of Herbicides* (Ed. L. J. Audus), pp. 423–64. Academic Press, London & New York.

HULL, H. M. (1960). A tabular summary of research dealing with translocation of foliar-applied herbicides and selected growth regulators. *Weeds*, 8, 214–31.

JENSEN, P. BOYSEN-. *See* BOYSEN-JENSEN, P.

KENSINGTON SCI. MUSEUM, LONDON (1936). The physiological action of weed killers and other plant poisons. *Sci. Libr. Bibliographical Series*, No. 235.

KIERMAYER, O. (1964). Growth responses to herbicides. *The Physiology and Biochemistry of Herbicides* (Ed. L. J. Audus), pp. 207–33. Academic Press, London & New York.

KING, L. J. (1952). Germination and chemical control of the giant foxtail grass (*Setaria faberii*). *Contr. Boyce Thompson Inst.*, 16, 469–87.

—— (1952a). Unpublished data.

—— (1956). Unpublished data.

—— (1957). Unpublished data.

—— & KRAMER, J. A. (1951). Studies on the herbicidal properties and volatility of some polyethylene and polypropylene glycol esters of 2,4-D and 2,4,5-T. *Contr. Boyce Thompson Inst.*, 16, 267–78.

KÖGL, F., HAAGEN-SMIT, A. J. & ERXLEBEN, H. (1934). Über ein neues Auxin (Heteroauxin) aus Harn. 11 Mitteilung über plflanzliche Wachstumsstoffe. *Hoppe-Seyl. Z.*, 229, 90–103.

KRAMER, P. J. (1957). Outer space in plants. *Science*, 125, 633–5.

KRAUS, E. J. (1954). The significance of growth regulators in agricultural practice. *Amer. Sci.*, 42, 439–60.

—— & MITCHELL, J. W. (1947). Growth-regulating substances as herbicides. *Bot. Gaz.*, 108, 301–50.

KUNKEL, L. O. (1954). Virus induced abnormalities. *Brookhaven Sym. in Biol.*, 6, 157–73.

KÜSTER, E. (1935). *Die Planzenzelle*. Gustav Fischer, Jena, 672 pp.

LAMBERTZ, P. (1954). Untersuchungen über das Vorkommen von Plasmodesmen in den Epidermisaussenwänden. *Planta*, 44, 147–90.

LEASURE, J. K. (1958). A study of some bioassay methods for herbicide volatility. *Weeds*, 6, 310–14.

LEOPOLD, A. C. (1955). *Auxins and Plant Growth*. Univ. Calif. Press, Berkeley and Los Angeles, 354 pp.

LEVI, E. (1955). Some aspects of the toxicity of CMU to plants. *Austral. J. Agric. Res.*, 6, 27–32.

LINSER, H. (1951). Unkrautbekämpfung auf hormonaler Basis. *Bodenkultur*, 5, 191–222.

—— (1964). The design of herbicides. *The Physiology and Biochemistry of Herbicides* (Ed. L. J. Audus), pp. 483–505) Academic Press, London & New York.

—— & PRIMOST, E. (1951). Uber die Verwendbarkeit von Holzfässern bei der hormonalen Unkrautbekampfung. *Pflanzenschutzberichte*, 6, 161–77.

LINSKENS, H. F., HEINEN, W. & STOFFERS, A. L. (1965). Cuticula of leaves and the residue problem. *Residue Rev.*, 8, 136–78.

LUCKWILL, L. C. (1955). Herbicides. *Soc. Chem. Indus. Rep. Prog. Appl. Chem.*, 40, 676–80.

McCready, C. C. (1960). The translocation of herbicides in plants. *Proc. 5th Brit. Weed Control Conf.*, Brighton, England, pp. 655–7.

Mack, G. L. (1936). The determination of contact angles from measurements of the dimensions of small bubbles and drops. I. The spheroidal-segment method for acute angles. *J. Phys. Chem.*, 40, 159–67.

—— & Lee, G. A. (1940). The determination of contact angles from measurements of the dimensions of small bubbles and drops II. The sessile drop method for obtuse angles. *J. Phys. Chem.*, 40, 169–176.

Martin, J. T. (1964). Role of cuticle in the defense against plant disease. *Ann. Rev. Phytopath.*, 2, 81–100. (118 refs.)

Matic, M. (1956). The chemistry of plant cuticles: a study of cutin from *Agave americana* L. *Biochem. J.*, 63, 168–76.

Mayer, F. (1957). Zur Wirkungsweise von Trichloracetat auf die höhere Pflanze. *Zeit. für Naturforschung*, 12B, 336–46.

Melnikov, N. N., Baskakov, J. A. & Bokarev, K. S. (1954). [*Chemistry of Herbicides and Plant Growth Stimulators*—in Russian.] Moscow, 381 pp.

Miller, L. P. (1941). Fate of chloral hydrate absorbed by growing plants of *Lagenaria leucantha*. *Contrib. Boyce Thompson Inst.*, 12, 167–9.

—— (1942). Synthesis of Beta-2-trichloroethyl-D-glucoside and its isolation from corn and dandelion plants treated with chloral hydrate. *Contrib. Boyce Thomp. Inst.*, 12, 465–70.

—— (1955). Growth regulants, their nature and action. Pp. 193–213 in *Handbook of Food and Agriculture* (Ed. F. C. Blanck), New York Reinhold. 1039 pp.

——, Weed, R. M. & Hitchcock, A. E. (1954). Comparative volatility of the n-butyl, 2-ethylhexyl, and 2-(2-ethoxyethoxy) propyl esters of 2,4-D. *Contrib. Boyce Thompson Inst.*, 17, 397–400.

Minshall, W. H. & Helson, V. A. (1949). The herbicidal action of oils. *Proc. Amer. Soc. Hort. Sci.*, 53, 294–8.

Mitchell, A. E. (1954). Equipment and methods for the application of plant regulators. Pp. 227–44 in *Plant Regulators in Agriculture* (Ed. H. B. Tukey). John Wiley, New York.

Mitchell, J. W. & Hamner, C. L. (1944). Polyethylene glycols as carriers for growth regulating substances. *Bot. Gaz.*, 105, 474–83.

—— & Linder, P. J. (1963). Absorption, translocation, exudation, and metabolism of plant growth-regulating substances in relation to residues. *Residue Reviews*, 2, 51–76.

Moreland, D. E. & Davis, J. C. (1956). The effects of certain herbicidal chemicals on the activity of an amylase enzyme—a preliminary report. (Abs.) *Proc. South. Weed Conf. 9th Meeting*, 150–1.

Mueller, L. E., Carr. P. H., & Loomis, W. E. (1954). The submicroscopic structure of plant surfaces *Amer. J. Bot.*, 41, 593–600.

Muir, R. M., Hansch, C. H. & Gallup, A. H. (1949). Growth regulation by organic compounds. *Plant Physiol.*, 24, 359–66.

Nemec, B. (1904). Uber die Einwirkung des chloral hydrate auf die Kern und Zelltheilung. *Jb. Wiss. Bot.*, 39, 645–730.

Nex, R. W. & Swezey, A. W. (1954). Some chemical and physical properties of weed killers. *Weeds*, 3, 241–53.

Nielsen, N. (1930). Untersuchungen über einen neuen wachstumsregulierenden Stoff: Rhizopin. *Jahrb. Wiss. Bot.*, 73, 125–191.

—— (1930a). Undersøgelser over et nyt Plantevaekststof Rhizopin. *Diss. København*, 99 pp.

Noone, J. A. (1959). Pesticides, some observations on their regulation. *Agr. Chem.*, 14(8), 47–49, 103.

345

NORMAN, A. G., MINARIK, C. E. & WEINTRAUB, R. L. (1950). Herbicides. *Ann. Rev. Plant Physiol.*, **1**, 141–68.

NUTMAN, P. S., THORNTON, H. G. & QUASTEL, J. H. (1945) Inhibition of plant growth by 2,4-dichlorophenoxyacetic acid and other growth substances. *Nature, Lond.*, **155**, 498–500.

OPATOWSKI, I. & CHRISTIANSEN, A. M. (1948). On herbicidal actions. *Bull. Math. Biophys.*, **10**(2), 57–61.

ORGELL, W. H. (1954). The isolation and permeability of plant cuticle. (*Doctoral thesis, Univ. of Calif.*, 171 pp.)

—— (1955). The isolation of plant cuticle with pectic enzymes. *Plant Physiol.*, **30**, 78–80.

—— (1956). Problems of uptake and movement of herbicides. *Abst. Weed Soc. Amer.* (1956 Meeting) p. 40.

—— (1957). Sorptive properties of plant cuticle. *Proc. Iowa Acad. Sci.*, **64**, 189–98.

OVERBEEK, J. VAN (1956). Absorption and translocation of plant regulators. *Ann. Rev. Plant Physiol.*, **7**, 355–72.

—— (1956a). Studies on the relation between molecular structure and penetration of growth regulators into plants. *The Chemistry and Mode of Action of Plant Growth Substances* (Ed. Wain, R. L. & Wightman, F.), pp. 205–10, Academic Press, N.Y., 1956.

—— & BLONDEAU, R. (1954). Mode of action of phytotoxic oils. *Weeds*, **3**, 55–65.

PARKIN, A. (1955). The weed unlocks its own doom. *Fmrs. Wk.* (London), **42**(17), 89–90.

PFEIFFER, R., BRUNSKILL, R. T. & HARTLEY, G. S. (1955). A variable dosage sprayer for agricultural experiments. *Nature, Lond.*, **176**, 472.

POTTS, S. F. (1958). *Concentrate Spray Equipment, Mixtures and Application Methods.* Dorland, Caldwell, New Jersey, 598 pp.

PRESTON, S. W. & THOMPSON, B. J. (1956). The significance of formulation and its relationship to selective herbicide efficiency. *New Zealand Weed Control Conf. Proc.*, **9**, 128–34.

PRIESTLEY, J. H. (1943). The cuticle in angiosperms. *Bot. Rev.*, **9**, 593–6.

PUTTARUDRIAH, M. (1956). Notes on the preliminary experiments with weedicides. II. *Mysore Agric. J.*, **31**(3), 146–51.

QUEBEC DEPARTMENT OF AGRICULTURE. INFORMATION AND RESEARCH SERVICE. (1958.) Manuel d'emploi des herbicides, 36 pp.

RASTORGUEVA, I. (1956). [In regard to the role of microflora in weed control—in Russian.] *Moskov. Ordena Lenina Sel'skokhoz. Akad. im K. A. Timiriazeva. Sborn. Studencheskikh Nauch.-Issled.*, **5**, 110–16.

RAUCOURT, M. & BEGUE, H. (1945). *Formulaire Phytopharmaceutique.* Imp. Nationale, Paris.

RAUTENSHTEIN, I. I. (1956). [Second conference on phytocides—in Russian.] *Mikrobiologia*, **25**(6), 757–60.

ROBBINS, W. W., CRAFTS, A. S. & RAYNOR, R. N. (1952). *Weed Control* (2nd edn.). McGraw-Hill, New York & London, 503 pp. [for details of later (3rd) edition see CRAFTS & ROBBINS, 1962].

ROBERTS, E. A. & SOUTHWICK, M. D. (1948). A microchemical examination of McIntosh apple leaves showing relationship of cell wall constituents to penetration of spray solutions. *Plant Physiol.*, **23**, 621–33.

ROELOFSEN, P. A. (1952). On the microscopic structure of cuticular cell walls. *Acta Bot. Neerlandica*, **1**, 99–114.

—— & HOUWINK, A. L. (1951). Cell wall structure of staminal hairs. *Protoplasma*, **40**, 1–22.

ROSE, G. J. (1957). Ultra-low-volume spraying in Africa. *World Crops*, **9**(2), 60–62.

—— (1963), *Crop Protection.* Leonard Hill, London, 490 pp. 2nd edn.

SCHIEFERSTEIN, R. H. & LOOMIS, W. E. (1956). Wax deposits on leaf surfaces. *Plant Physiol.*, **31**, 240–7.

SCOTT, F. M., HAMNER, K. C., BARKER, E. P. & BOWLER, E. (1958). Electron microscope studies of the epidermis of *Allium cepa*. *Amer. J. Bot.*, **45**(6), 449–60.

SEXSMITH, J. J., HOPEWELL, W. W., ANDERSON, D. T., RUSSELL, T. C. & HURTIG, H. (1957). Characteristics of spray deposits resulting from aircraft application of oil-carrier sprays. *Canad. J. Plant Sci.*, **37**(2), 85–96.

SIEGEL, S. M. (1962). *The Plant Cell Wall*. Pergamon Press, Oxford and Macmillan Co., New York, 123 pp.

SKOOG, F. (1935). The effect of X-irradiation on auxin and plant growth. *J. Cell. Comp. Physiol.*, **7**, 227–70.

SKOSS, J. D. (1955). Structure and composition of plant cuticles in relation to environmental factors and permeability. *Bot. Gaz.*, **117**, 55–72.

SLADE, R. E., TEMPLEMAN, R. G. & SEXTON, W. A. (1945). Plant growth substances as selective weed-killers. *Nature, Lond.*, **155**, 497–8.

SMITH, A. E., ZUKEL, J. W., STONE, G. M. & RIDDELL, J. A. (1959). Factors affecting the performance of maleic hydrazide. *J. Agric. Food Chem.*, **7**, 341–4.

SPIKES, J. D. (1956). Effects of substituted ureas on the photochemical activity of isolated chloroplasts. *Plant Physiol.*, **31**, Suppl. xxxii.

SUNK, K. A. (1956). Residual activity of 3-amino-1,2,4-triazole in soils. *J. Agric. Food Chem.*, **4**, 57–60.

SYNERHOLM, M. & ZIMMERMAN, P. W. (1947). Preparation of a series of ω-(2,4-dichloro-phenoxy)-aliphatic acids and some related compounds with a consideration of biochemical role as plant growth regulators. *Contrib. Boyce Thompson Inst.*, their **14**, 369–82

TAFURO, A. J., VAN GELUWE, J. J. D. & CURTIS, L. E. (1950). Drift and volatility comparison of an amine salt and ester form of 2,4-D under field conditions. *Proc. North-eastern States Weed Control Conf.*, pp. 31–35.

TEMPLEMAN, W. G. & SEXTON, W. A. (1946). The differential effect of synthetic plant growth substances and other compounds upon plant species. I. Seed germination and early growth responses to α-naphthylacetic acid and compounds of the general formula aryl OCH$_2$COO R. *Proc. Roy. Soc. London*, Ser. B, **133**, 300–13.

—— & —— (1946a). The differential effect of synthetic plant growth substances and other compounds upon plant species. II. Seed germination and early growth responses to some arylcarbamic esters and related compounds. *Proc. Roy. Soc. London*, Ser. B, **133**, 480–5.

THIMANN, K. V. (1935). On the plant growth hormone produced by *Rhizopus suinus*. *J. Biol. Chem.*, **109**, 279–91.

THOMPSON, H. E., SWANSON, E. P. & NORMAN, A. T. (1946). New growth regulating compounds. I. Summary of growth inhibitory activities of some organic compounds as determined by three tests. *Bot. Gaz.*, **107**, 476–507.

THORUP, S. (1951). [The Danish Weed Research Station 1946–8—in Danish.] *Tidsskr. Planteavl.*, **54**, 553–627.

TIBBITS, T. W. & HOHN, L. G. (1954). Accumulation and distribution of TCA in plant tissues. *Weeds*, **3**, 146–51.

TUKEY, H. B. & HAMNER, C. L. (1945). A new principle in weed control. *Farm Res.*, Cornell, **11**(3), 3, 16.

UBRIZSY, G. (1957). [Phytocoenological studies of weed associations, with special reference to the use of herbicides—in Hungarian.] *Növénytermelés*, **6**(3), 257–74.

U.S. GOVERNMENT, BUREAU OF RECLAMATION. (1941). *Weed Manual*. Federal Security Agency, Civ. Conserv. Corps., Washington, 158 pp.

VAN DER GOOR, G. A. W. *See* GOOR, G. A. W. VAN DER.

VAN OVERBEEK, J. *See* OVERBEEK, J. VAN.

VENKATARAMANI, K. S. (1956). Chemical weedkillers. *United Planters' Assoc. South. India Sci. Dept. Tea Sect.*, Bull. 16, 12 pp.

VLITOS, A. J. (1953). Biological activation of sodium 2-(2,4-dichlorophenoxy) ethyl sulfate. *Contrib. Boyce Thompson Inst.*, 17, 127–49.

——, MEUDT, W. & BEIMLER, R. (1956). The role of auxin in plant flowering. IV. A new unidentified naturally occurring indole hormone in normal and gamma irradiated Maryland Mammoth tobacco. *Contrib. Boyce Thompson Inst.*, 18, 283–49.

VON HOFSTEN, C. G. *See* HOFSTEN, C. G. VON.

WAIN, R. L. (1955). A new approach to selective weed control. *Ann. Appl. Biol.*, 42, 151–7.

—— (1955a). The chemical regulation of plant growth. *Agric. Prog.*, 30(2), 81–89.

—— (1964). The behaviour of herbicides in the plant in relation to selectivity. *The Physiology and Biochemistry of Herbicides* (Ed. L. J. Audus), pp. 465–81. Academic Press, London & New York.

—— & WIGHTMAN, F. (1957). Studies in plant regulating substances. Auxin antagonism in relation to a theory on mode of action of aryl- and aryloxyalkane carboxylic acids. *Ann. Appl. Biol.*, 45, 140–57.

WEINTRAUB, R. L. (1956). Relation of chemical structure to herbicidal action. *Weed Soc. Amer. Abstr.* for 1956, pp. 41–42.

——, REINHART, J. H. & SCHERFF, R. A. (1956). Role of entry, translocation, and metabolism in specificity of 2,4-D and related compounds. *Conf. Radioactive Isotopes Agr.* (Papers), 1956, 203–8.

WENT, F. W. (1926). On growth-accelerating substances in the coleoptile of *Avena sativa*. *Proc. Kon. Akad. Wetensch.* (Amsterdam), 30, 10–19.

—— (1928). Wuchsstoff und Wachstum. *Rec. Trav. Bot. Néerl.*, 25, 1–116.

—— (1935). Auxin, the plant growth hormone. *Bot. Rev.*, 1, 162–82.

—— & THIMANN, K. V. (1937). *Phytohormones*. Macmillan, New York, 294 pp.

WERNER, R. (1931). [Versuche zur Verwendung chemischer Methoden bei der Unkrautbekämpfung—in Russian.] *J. Agric. Sci. S.E. & USSR*, 9, 133–55.

WESTMAN, J. R. (1957). Some experiences with the aquatic weed problem in the State of New Jersey. *Proc. Northeast. Weed Control Conf.*, 11, 243–6.

WHITESIDE, J. S. & ALEXANDER, M. (1960). Measurement of microbiological effects of herbicides. *Weeds*, 8, 204–13.

WILSON, H. K. (1944). Control of noxious plants. *Bot. Rev.*, 10, 279–326.

WOODFORD, E. K. (1957). The toxic action of herbicides. *Outlook on Agric.*, 15, 145–54.

—— (1958). How a selective herbicide works. *World Crops*, 10(8), 277–80.

—— (Ed.) (1960). *Herbicides and the Soil*. Second symposium of the British Weed Control Council. Blackwell Scientific Publications, Oxford, 88 pp.

—— HOLLY, K. & McCREADY, C. C. (1958). Herbicides. *Ann. Rev. Plant Physiol.*, 9, 311–58.

WORT, D. J. (1964). Effects of herbicides on plant composition and metabolism. *The Physiology and Biochemistry of Herbicides* (Ed. L. J. Audus), pp. 291–334. Academic Press, London & New York.

—— (1964a). Responses of plants to sublethal concentrations of 2, 4-D, without and with added minerals. *The Physiology and Biochemistry of Herbicides* (Ed. L. J. Audus), pp. 335–42. Academic Press, London & New York.

WYSSLING, A. FREY-. *See* FREY-WYSSLING, A.

YEO, R. R. (1955). Modern weed control applicators. *New Mexico Agric. Expt. Sta. Bull.* 391, 24 pp.

YOUNG, P. D. (1956). A short history of chemical weed control in Puerto Rico: what is a weed? *Sugar J.*, 18(12), 54–56.

ZAHNLEY, J. W. (1956). 50 years of progress in weed control. *Kansas Bd. Agric. Bien. Rep.*, 29, 86–87.

ZUKEL, J. W., SMITH, A. E., STONE, T. M. & DAVIES, M. E. (1956). Effect of some factors on rate of absorption of maleic hydrazide. (Abst.). *Plant Physiol.*, 31(supl.), xxi.

XIV

THE USES OF HERBICIDES

INTRODUCTION

WEED control of some type is required annually in the United States on about 140 million acres of row crops (weeded intensively), about 230 million acres of drilled crops (with moderate weeding), one billion* acres in hay, pasture and range (with limited weed control), 30 million acres in connection with railroads and highways, and about 33 million single-family homes requiring some weed control. About 85 million acres in crops were treated with herbicides in 1961, costing $90 million for chemicals alone. Control of bush and woody plants in Texas was practised in 1961 on 1·5 million acres of which about 0·7 million of these acres were chemically treated, on the remainder, mechanical methods were utilized. It is also reported that the 1961 production of 2,4-D- and 2,4,5-T-type herbicides in the United States was approximately 94·8 million lb., of which about one-tenth was exported (Shepherd 1962).

A recent survey (Saunders *et al.*, 1962) states that losses caused by weeds in the United States are believed to equal the combined losses from insects and diseases and to rank second only to those caused by soil erosion. Losses from weeds and costs of controlling them on agricultural lands are estimated to be about $3.8 billion each year.

R. H. Beatty, in his essay *Herbicides and the American Farmer* (1958, published 1960), has pointed out that in the United States the cost of farm labour has increased 400 per cent during the past 25 years, and that in the same time there have come to be fewer men available for farm work. The farmer's profit margin has become smaller and the need for greater efficiency increasingly urgent. Chemical weed-control has helped considerably in solving the problems of labour shortage and increased costs. The labour requirements of the Mississippi cotton-grower for mechanical weed-control range from twenty to forty-one man-hours per acre, but the use of herbicides on cotton reduced this to about five man-hours per acre, and also increased yields somewhat, leading to an average gain of $21.00 per acre. The gains from controlling weeds chemically in rice are very much greater, running as high as $400.00 per acre in foundation stock which moreover commands a premium price. In Oregon, controlling

* An American billion i.e., one thousand millions is meant here. The British etc., billion is one million millions.—Ed.

big sagebrush (*Artemisia tridentata*), infesting rangelands, with herbicides costing $2.25 to $3.25 per acre, has given a net gain that is estimated at $1.68 an acre. If such a treatment were applied on one-quarter of the 96 million acres of range infested with big sagebrush, an annual gain of over $40 million might be realized, and control might be effective to some degree for at least ten years; thus the actual gain would be about ten times the figure indicated. On such huge areas, spraying is often the only practical way to control encroaching vegetation which can reduce the value of the land to the point where 10 acres are required to carry a single steer.

Beatty has noted that the advantages of chemical weed-control become apparent to more American farmers every year, and that now more acres are sprayed for weed control than for the control of insects and diseases combined. In 1957 the area sprayed for weed control amounted to over 35 million acres of farmland. Typical data from the State of North Dakota illustrate the rapidity of this development; there nearly three times as many acres of farmland were treated with chemicals for selective weed-control in 1957 as in 1953. About 70 per cent of this acreage in North Dakota was treated by farmers with their own or borrowed equipment, and about 30 per cent by custom sprayers or operators. Herbicides have been particularly useful in the high-cash crops, such as vegetable crops. In 1956 in the United States some 5 million acres of vegetables were grown with a value on the farm of over $1.5 billion. Values vary from an average of $150.00 per acre for those vegetables which are canned, frozen, or dried, to an average of $375.00 for those which are grown for the fresh market. Thus there has been a great demand for herbicides in vegetable crops requiring extensive and expensive hand-weeding, such as onions, beets, spinach, and most of the other vegetable crops.

Weed control must be looked upon as part of the whole farm programme however, and not as an isolated practice related only to a specific crop. It has been noted, for instance, that certain farmers using a Simazine spray with good results on maize remarked that, by being freed from cultivating, they were able to produce better hay. Thus the cost of spraying does not have to be charged to one crop, but should be considered as part of the whole—with benefits that are indirect as well as direct.

INTERNATIONAL PROGRESS IN CHEMICAL WEED CONTROL

In a recent assessment of progress, Woodford (1960) notes that, between 1953 and 1956, the most rapid increase in the consumption of 2,4-D and related herbicides occurred in Austria and Italy. Large increases must also have taken place in other European countries, such as Yugoslavia, and in tropical and semi-tropical countries. In Canada the acreage sprayed increased from 500,000 in 1947 to 13 million three years later, when 20–30 per cent of the total cereal crop was being sprayed. W. C. Shaw (1960) has provided us with similarly startling figures for the expansion of use of herbicides in the United States, where in 1959 about 50 million acres of crop land were treated, which was more than double the area treated in 1949. Included were: 19 million acres of small grains; 2 million acres of sorghum; one million acres of cotton; $\frac{1}{2}$ million acres each of soybeans and rice; 2 million acres of pastures; and 4 million acres of rangeland. About 16 million acres of corn (maize) were treated with herbicides at a cost of some $36 million annually. The benefit accruing from the elimination of cultivation alone amounted to $12 million annually. Reference to 2,4-D production in the United States has already been made (cf. Fig. 51). Woodford has noted that in 1957 there were 600 tons of 2,4-D produced in the U.S.S.R., and that the amount was to be increased to the calculated requirement of 10,000 tons.

In an assessment of educational and research aspects it was noted that textbooks on weed control have been published in Denmark (Frederiksen *et al.*, 1950), Holland (Riepma, 1955), Norway (Korsmo & Vidme, 1954), Germany (Wehsarg, 1954), U.S.A. (Robbins *et al.*, 1952 cf. Ch. XIII), U.S.S.R. (Kott, 1955), Czechoslovakia (Hron, 1957), and the U.K. (British Weed Control Council, 1958). Others include Kurth (1963), (1936), Crafts & Robbins (1962, cf. Ch. XIII), and Klingman & Noordhoff (1961, cf. Ch. XII). The number of full-time professional officers employed in the United States Department of Agriculture on weed control increased from seventeen in 1951 to sixty in 1958, and the annual expenditure for this purpose at the Agricultural Experiment Stations in the Agricultural Research Service has risen from approximately $800,000 to $2,300,000 during the same period. *Weed Abstracts* during the two years 1956 and 1957 abstracted 2,000 papers each year, of which the top four in country of origin included: U.S.A. 37 per cent, United Kingdom 13 per cent, and Germany and U.S.S.R. 6 per cent each. In a survey of weed control conferences Canada is credited with having the first organization especially set up to consider weeds, the Associate Committee on Weed Control (formed in 1924). The first weed control conference in the U.S.A. was the western one in 1938, and the first such British conference was held in 1953. Six countries or groups of countries have held weed control conferences for the first time since the second British one of 1956: France, Yugoslavia, East Africa, U.S.S.R., Italy, and East and Central and South Africa.

There are two technical journals devoted exclusively to weeds and weed control, *Weeds* (published by the Association of Weed Control Conferences in the United States), and *Weed Research*, the official journal of the European Weed Research Council. The former was established in 1951, and the latter in 1961. *Advances in Pest Control*, an annual publication beginning in 1957, and *World Review of Pest Control* (1962 to date) are additional sources of information.

INTRODUCTION TO CHEMICAL METHODS

The application of a chemical to control weeds in a specific crop can only be made successfully providing the crop has a high degree of resistance or tolerance to the chemical in question. If this is the case, then the herbicide so used is regarded as a selective herbicide for this specific crop. Herbicides applied to the newly-cultivated soil surface in seeded crops prior to both weed and crop emergence are termed 'pre-emergence herbicides'. Herbicides applied as an over-all spray to crops after emergence are termed 'post-emergence herbicides'. One of the best examples of the former type is the use of Simazine on newly-planted maize, while the use of 2,4-D on young maize plants (and small grains), as well as the use of oils on carrot seedlings, are examples of the second type.

In the *Weed Control Handbook* (Woodford & Evans, 1963, *see* Ch. I) eighty-seven specific herbicides are listed. As Overbeek (1964, *see* Ch. XII) has noted in actual practice today some three-quarters of all chemical weed control is achieved with just three chemicals and their homologues and analogues. These herbicides are 2,4-D (the most widely used), Simazine and Diuron. The remaining quarter comprise six principal chemicals: Dinoseb, naphthylphthalamic acid, Dalapon, CDAA, chloro IPC, and Amitrole.

A survey prepared by the United States Department of Agriculture (Saunders *et al.*, 1962) showed that in 1959 pre-emergence herbicides were more extensively used than post-emergence herbicides on cotton, soybeans, peanuts, and sugar beets, whereas post-emergence herbicides were more widely used on small grains, corn, rice, and some other crops (*see* Appendices I & II). The average cost per acre of pre-emergence herbicides and their application was about twice as much as those of post-emergence treatments.

HERBICIDES FOR FIELD CROPS*

Seeded Crops

Among the field crops on which herbicides have been used most successfully are the small grains, including wheat, oats, rice, and maize. In the United States and Canada, already in 1952, 17 million acres of small grains were sprayed with 2,4-D preparations. For the post-emergence control of broad-leafed weeds in small grains, the ester or amine salt of 2,4-D, or MCPA, at $\frac{1}{4}$ to $\frac{1}{2}$ lb. in 5 to 20 gal. of water per acre is applied after the cereals are well tillered—usually when they are 10 to 20 cm. high—but before they joint or reach the boot stage. Certain weeds, such as Canada thistle and sow thistle, may be effectively inhibited but not necessarily killed by such treatment. Grasses, and such perennial weeds as horse-nettle and milkweed, will not be controlled in this manner. It

* Full details of most of the herbicides cited will be found in Appendices I and II. *See also* Woodford (1963).

has been suggested that, in the western Great Plains and Intermountain regions, 2,4-D should be applied at $\frac{1}{2}$ to 1 lb. per acre to control most weeds infesting small grains. Applications of 2,4-D or MCPA to cereal crops in the early seedling stages prior to tillering, or during the late jointing, boot, or early heading stage, may result in serious reductions in yield, lowered germination of grain, changes in protein content of the grain, and lowered quality of products made from the treated crops (cf. Figs. 63 and 64 for cereals, and 65 for flax).

▨ Herbicide can be safely used
☐ Herbicide should *not* be used

HERBICIDE	AUTUMN-SOWN CEREAL TREATED IN SPRING	SPRING WHEAT Not Undersown E	L	Undersown E	L	SPRING BARLEY Not Undersown E	L	Undersown E	L	SPRING OATS Not Undersown E	L	Undersown E	L
MCPA	▨	▨		▨		▨				▨	▨		
2,4-D	▨	▨		▨		▨				▨			
MCPB	▨	▨	▨	▨	▨	▨	▨			▨	▨	▨	▨
2,4-DB	▨	▨	▨	▨	▨	▨	▨			▨	▨	▨	▨
CMPP	▨	▨		▨		▨				▨			
CP-1815	▨	▨		▨		▨				▨			
DNC	▨	▨		▨		▨				▨			
dinoseb	▨	▨		▨		▨		▨				▨	
SMA	▨	▨		▨		▨				▨			

E = Early: cereals, 2-4 leaves on main shoot
L = Late: cereals, 5 leaves to beginning of shooting

From Fryer, 1958

FIG. 63.—Herbicides for selective weed-control in cereal crops, and situations in which the different herbicides can be used (in Great Britain). CMPP = (alpha-(4-chloro-2-methyl-phenoxy) propionic acid); CP-1815 = a mixture of MCPA and 2,3,6-trichlorobenzoic acid; SMA = sodium monochloroacetate.

For the control in maize of such common weeds as pigweed, ragweed, lamb's-quarters, cocklebur, and other broad-leafed annual weeds, the ester or amine salt of 2,4-D at $\frac{1}{4}$ to $\frac{1}{2}$ lb. in 5 to 20 gal. of water per acre, is applied when the weeds are small and the maize is 4 to 24 in. high. Some injury to maize from 2,4-D applications has been noted, especially if the treatment is applied under conditions favouring rapid growth. Applications should be avoided when temperatures are high and the maize is growing at the maximum rate. One should avoid cultivation for several days after treatment, in order to reduce stalk breakage if brittleness develops.

The herbicide Simazine may be used for the pre-emergence control of both broad-leafed weeds and annual grasses at 2 to 4 lb. per acre sprayed in 20 to 40 gallons of water per acre at the time of planting or shortly after, but prior to crop and weed emergence.

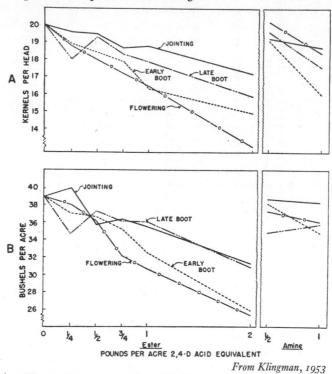

From Klingman, 1953

FIG. 64.—Three-year average number of kernels per head (A) and yield in bushels per acre (B) of Pawnee winter wheat as affected by 2,4-D applications at four stages of growth. Tests conducted at Lincoln, Nebraska. Yield reductions were relatively minor on the average when rates of application were not greater than a total of $\frac{1}{2}$ lb. of 2,4-D ester or 1 lb. of 2,4-D amine in all stages of growth.

Weeds are a serious problem in most land devoted to maize production, and particularly so if the fields are located on alluvial soils. Under these latter conditions weed growth may become so abundant that severe reduction in the growth of the maize may result; consequently it is advisable to use a herbicide in the early stages of growth when the weeds are quite small. Weeds are most easily controlled when they are small. Cultivation, especially deep cultivation, can injure the young maize plants through root pruning. Early use of a herbicide permits a delay in cultivation until the maize plants are large enough to facilitate rapid cultivation, when the weeds in the drill row can be covered with soil.

Pre-emergence applications for the control of annual grasses and broad-leafed weeds by, preferably, using the ester form of 2,4-D at 1 to 2 lb. in 5 to 20 gal. of water per acre, may be made at any time after planting but prior to emergence. However, treatment is not advised on sandy soils. A

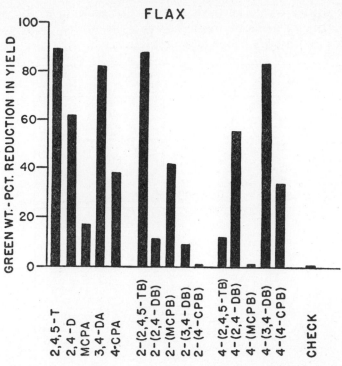

FLAX

From Shaw & Gentner, 1957

FIG. 65.—The effect of several phenoxyalkylcarboxylic acids at ½ lb. per acre on flax (*Linum usitatissimum* cultivar, Cascade). TB = trichlorophenoxybutyric acid; DB = dichlorophenoxybutyric acid; MCPB = methylchlorophenoxybutyric acid. The data show considerable tolerance to MCPA, less tolerance to 2-(MCPB), but very high tolerance to 4-(MCPB). Data from greenhouse studies at Beltsville, Maryland.

lower rate of application is used on loam soils and a higher rate on clay soils; on muck soils and heavy clay soils that are high in organic matter, 2 to 4 lb. of 2,4-D per acre may be required for weed control. Pre-emergence treatments are especially valuable when excessive rainfall prevents cultivation for extended periods after maize emerges (cf. Fig. 66).

For soybeans, a pre-emergence application of a dinitro (DNBP) compound at rates of 4–8 lb. may be made just after planting. Cotton may be weeded by applications of CIPC (chloroisopropylphenyl carbamate) at 4–12 lb., or by Diuron or Monuron at 1·5–2 lb., in 20–40 gal. of water per acre applied during the planting operation. Dalapon is used for Johnson grass control (Pl. 16). Weeds in peanuts may be controlled by Sesone at 3 lb. in 20 gallons of water applied during the planting operation, or at any time thereafter until emergence (cf. review of Sesone by King, 1959, cf. Ch. XII). For a review of weed control in the principal crops of the southern United States *see* Ennis (1955).

In Iowa experiments (Staniforth *et al.*, 1963) the ten-year average soybean yield reduction of 3·8 bu. per acre from weed competition despite normal control methods suggests that under normal conditions the new cost of herbicide treatment would not exceed the value of the soybeans lost through failure to control weeds.

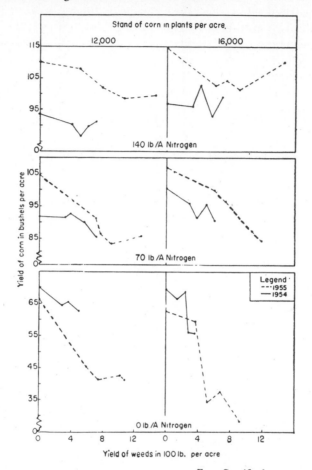

From Staniforth, 1957

Fig. 66.—Relationship of yield of mature foxtail weed (*Setaria lutescens*) to the resulting corn (maize) yield reductions with two rates of nitrogen fertilizer application and two corn plant populations. Tests in north-central Iowa. In 1955 the total rainfall for the period from May 15 to September 15 amounted to 12 in.—approximately half of the same period in 1954.

A number of procedures have been worked out for sugar-cane, and these have been summarized by Helgeson (1957g). Pre-emergence sprays of 2,4-D, at about 2 lb. per acre, made soon after planting, will control most grass seedlings as well as broad-leafed weeds. Grass seedlings, may

Note—Herbicidal methods for weeding cotton include; preplanting treatment (none recommended); preemergence: CIPC or diuron on sandy loam to clay loam, monuron on heavy clay soil, none used on extremely sandy soils; postemergence: herbicidal naphthas, diurons, and tentatively—DMA (disodium monomethylarsonate), DMA plus dicryl, and linuron (*see Miss. Agric. Exp. Sta. Bull.* 681, 1964 and the new 'triband' concept (ref. p. 437)).

be controlled by TCA at 10 to 15 lb. per acre, or by Dalapon. Various formulations of Monuron (*p*-chlorophenyl dimethylurea) are also useful for pre-emergence applications, at about 4 lb. of active ingredient per acre, immediately after the cane is planted. Such sprays have given excellent weed-control for periods of up to 21 weeks without harm to the cane. Post-emergence applications may be used at these same dosages for many weeds, but the more resistant will require fortified oil emulsions of the hormone herbicides. These last will have to be directed towards the base of the sugar-cane plants, as the oils damage the sugar-cane leaves. Helgeson (1957*g*) also presents a concise review of the present practices in the chemical weeding of *Hevea* rubber with particular reference to the control of lalang grass (*Imperata cylindrica*).

One of the most ancient of weed-control practices coincides with an important cultural requirement of rice, namely water. Flooding with water during most of the growth period of rice after transplanting provides a high degree of weed control. However, certain weeds that are tolerant to flooding may present a problem, e.g. species of *Zizania, Cyperus, Sagittaria, Juncus, Phragmites, Echinochloa* (cf. Fig. 67), etc.

By courtesy of Shiu-ying Hu and the Arnold Arboretum, Harvard University

FIG. 67.—Illustration of *Echinochloa crusgalli* copied from the Chinese herbal, *Pen Ts'ao Kang Mu*, of Shih Chen Li, published about 1590. The ideograph reads 'Pai', i.e. 'a weed (a bad or low-grade grass) in a grain field'. This is one of the most universally distributed weeds, and is particularly noxious wherever rice is grown. It is used as a famine food by the Chinese. While it is undoubtedly represented by a plethora of ecotypes and varietal taxa throughout the world, it is still recognizable from this figure.

An important feature of control is cultural, i.e. alternating other crops with the rice. However, 2,4-D may be used on rice, as is the practice in Louisiana, where the spray is applied about three to six days before flooding, when the rice plants are 3 to 4 weeks old. Rates of up to 0·75 lb. of 2,4-D (acid equivalent of an amine formulation) may be applied with little injury to the rice. After the plants have been flooded for several weeks, rates of up to 1·5 lb. per acre have been applied without serious injury. The rice plant is similar to the other small grains in that it appears that the proper stage for herbicidal application is the fully tillered stage. For discussions on rice weeding, *see* Helgeson (1957g) and the studies of Kasahara and co-workers (Kasahara *et al.*, 1955, 1956; Kasahara & Hirata, 1956) in Japan, and for rice weeds *see* R. E. Williams (1955–56).

A recent development indicates that water grass (*Echinochloa crusgalli*) in rice may be controlled by 3,4-dichloropropionanilide (DPA) when used as a foliage spray at the 2-4-leaf stages of the weed seedlings.

An important feature of weed control in seeded crops is a preventive one. This is achieved by using the cleanest seed obtainable—i.e. free from noxious weed-seeds (cf. Ch. XV). In an earlier chapter, reference has already been made to primitive seed-cleaning methods, especially winnowing, and how such methods perpetuated and extended the weeds associated with a particular crop. In fact, such methods exerted a selective influence, and encouraged the development of such satellite weeds.

Control of Wild Oats

Wild oats (*Avena fatua* and *A. ludoviciana*) are widespread in grain-growing temperate regions the world around. Wild oats, naturally, are so close in growth-habit to cultivated oats, that to provide any measure of control of them in this crop presents formidable problems. Wild oats shatter badly just at harvest time, so that, with crop harvesting, the pest is further disseminated. However, a number of new selective chemical methods have recently been introduced, and, although the results are preliminary, the prospects appear good for the eventual control of wild oats.

Carbyne (4-chloro-2-butynyl *N*-(3-chlorophenyl)carbamate) [XIII], applied as a post-emergence spray, gave good control of wild oats in grain crops when applied in the 1- to 2-leaf stage at a rate of 1·2 lb. per acre, and in the 3-leaf stage at either 15 gal. or 30 gal. per acre. No adverse effects were noted on wheat, barley, rapeseed, or flax—but Fortune oats appeared to be as susceptible as wild oats. Carbyne is not an eradicant of wild oats, but it does provide economic control.

Avadex (2,3-dichloroallyl di-isopropylthiolcarbamate, *cis* and *trans* mixture) [XIV] in Canadian trials in 1959 provided 99 per cent control of wild oats when applied at a rate of 1·6 lb. per acre, but did not damage barley below 3·6 lb. per acre. The herbicide was applied as a pre-planting treatment in water, from 10 to 14 gal. per acre, and was incorporated with the use of a double-disk down to a depth of 2–3 in. immediately after spraying. Some crops were seeded immediately after spraying; in others, seeding was delayed for up to fifteen days. Rapeseed, barley, and flax, were undamaged at application rates of 6 lb. per acre, and wheat was undamaged at rates below 2·5 lb. per acre. The herbicide is active in the soil during six to eight or more weeks, and selectively kills the wild oats as they germinate.

Avadex is commercially available in Canada, and is recommended by the authorities for the control of wild oats in flax and for trial use in barley, sugar beet, rapeseed, and sunflower. Both Avadex (Diallate) and Carbyne (Barban) control a number of annual grasses other than wild oats, and wheat seems to be more susceptible to injury than barley.

HERBICIDES FOR VEGETABLE CROPS

Vegetable crops present a variety of weed problems because of their diversity in duration, in habit, and in the season of the year when they are grown. Their response to the currently used herbicides is frequently similar to that of the weeds which commonly occur in them, so that there are at present a limited number of chemical methods of weed control available for those crops (cf. Appendix III, pp. 453–8).

Two vegetable crops, carrots and asparagus, have had the distinction of being weeded by chemical means for a longer period of time than any other crops. Calcium cyanamide has been used on asparagus in the United States and Europe for a great many years, and carrot weeding by the use of petroleum fractions has been widely practiced in the United States since the introduction of this method by Dr. Robert Sweet at Cornell University, followed by related studies in California. At various times, recommendations for the control of weeds in onions through using sprays of sulphuric acid have appeared. However, such methods were not widely employed because of the hazard to operators and the corrosion of equipment (cf. Jones & Mann, 1963).

Apart from the crops just mentioned, a number of newer herbicides have been developed for weed control in a variety of other vegetable crops. A relatively new material, CDAA [No. XXXIV in Appendix], has been successfully used as a pre-emergence herbicide on seeded onions grown on muck soils infested with annual grasses, purslane, chickweed, redroot, ragweed, and lamb's-quarters. Rates of Randox at $\frac{1}{2}$ gal. (6 lb. per gallon of active ingredient) in 20 to 60 gal. of water can be sprayed per acre at any time from immediately after planting until one to two days before emergence. Chloro IPC at 4–6 lb. of active ingredient per acre in 20–60 gal. of water has also been successfully used as a pre-emergence application. While established asparagus beds had formerly been weeded with calcium cyanamide, two herbicides, Sesone and Monuron (or Karmex W), have been more widely used latterly, Sesone is quite safe on asparagus, and because it is water-soluble is easy to apply with a low-volume pressure sprayer. It is applied as a pre-emergence spray on light sandy soil at a rate of from $2\frac{1}{2}$ to 3 lb. per acre, in 35 to 40 gal. of water. Monuron has also been successfully used at $1\cdot2-1\cdot6$ lb. of active ingredient per acre, in 30 to 100 gal. of water. Two applications of Monuron per year may be made to clean, or recently cultivated soil; the first application should be before the cutting season begins, the second at the end of the cutting season.

In tests in New Jersey, EPTC (ethyl N,N-di-n-propylthiolcarbamate) [XVI], used both as a spray and on a granular carrier, provided satisfactory weed control, with no injury or yield reductions, in tomatoes and potatoes. Applications of EPTC at 6 lb. per acre as a pre-planting treatment provided excellent control throughout the growing-season, with only a hilling cultivation at lay-by. Eptam added after the last cultivation also gave satisfactory control of annual grasses until harvest. This herbicide is, at the present time, one of the most specific chemical control agents for the widespread and pernicious nut-grasses (*Cyperus* spp.). As the herbicide is volatile, it is necessary to incorporate it into the soil soon after application. Investigations have revealed that its activity was inversely proportional to the adsorptive capacity of the soil, and that absorptive capacity was five times greater in air-dry soil than in the same soil at field capacity.

HERBICIDES FOR ORNAMENTAL, FRUIT, AND NURSERY CROPS

Ornamentals comprise a vast range of plant species that include annual, perennial, and woody, as well as bulbous and rhizomatous plants. Sesone [VII] has been one of the most successful and widely used herbicides for the pre-emergence control of weeds in these plantings. A number of publications have shown the usefulness of Sesone, not only in liner nursery stock but also in established plantings (cf. the review by King, 1959). Carlson *et al.* (1951), in Michigan, found that Sesone at 4 lb. per acre destroyed 89 per cent of the weeds when applied before the emergence of gladiolus.

As both resistant and susceptible species of ornamental plants are frequently interplanted, and the areas involved are often small, the chemical control of weeds, in nursery plantings, presents considerable difficulties. The areas to be treated often involve plantings that are held over during more than one winter season. Because of this, a number of winter-annual weeds may be quite troublesome. Among these are common chickweed (*Stellaria media*), annual bluegrass (*Poa annua*), and certain other species which germinate at about the same time in the fall of the year.

Sesone has been used as a spray, applied to the soil at 3 to 4 lb. per acre, for the pre-emergence control of many annual broad-leafed weeds and also grasses. As the herbicide is not particularly effective on emerged weeds, it is important that it be applied to newly-cultivated and weed-free soil. Recent usage on weeds that were just emerging, has also provided satisfactory control.

Control of weeds in beds of annual garden flowers has presented a number of difficulties. Most of these plants are quite susceptible to injury by 2,4-D, and therefore in no case should this be used around such plants. A few new chemicals have shown some promise of the control of weeds growing among annual garden flowers.

In the United States, weed growth in new plantings of strawberries has been particularly troublesome. Sesone has been found to provide excellent control of weeds when applied after the strawberry plants have become established, usually five to seven days after planting. These applications should be made over the entire area every ten days to two weeks, or longer, as needed for adequate weed control. On light soils, $2\frac{1}{4}$ lb. of active ingredient in 35–40 gal. of water are used per acre, while on heavier loam soils 2·7 lb. of active ingredient may be used for application during the dormant season. One gallon of Sinox PE (3 lb. of DNOSBP) per acre may be used for weed control during the dormant season. At this time of the year over-wintering weeds, such as chickweed, often become a severe problem. The Sinox should be applied during the winter season when the temperatures are above freezing. If weeds are heavily matted, it may be necessary to make a second application three or four weeks later.

Commercial and home-garden plantings of small fruits such as raspberries, blackberries, currants, and blueberries, often become seriously infested with weeds. Sesone is quite valuable if applied to newly-cleaned plantings before any weed-seeds germinate, but should not be applied when canes are emerging. Sinox PE may be applied after the weeds are up, but works most effectively if the weeds are still very small.

In raspberries and blackberries, for control of winter annual grasses and broad-leafed weeds in the autumn or early winter, CIPC may be used at 4 to 8 lb. in 20 gal. of water per acre prior to weed emergence. This is particularly effective also in controlling chickweed (*Stellaria media*) after emergence (Danielson *et al.*, 1961).

WEED CONTROL IN FORAGE CROPS, PASTURES, AND RANGELANDS

In the northeastern United States, many grain-fields are under-seeded to leguminous plants, including alfalfa and clovers (Ladino, red, or alsike), as well as to bird's-foot trefoil. These fields become infested with mustard, yellow-rocket, and other broad-leafed weeds. Where the grain is not seeded with mixed legumes, such weed infestations can be eliminated with the use of 2,4-D; however, 2,4-D should not be used when legumes are present. Formulations of MCP [II] may be used at the rate of

1·03 lb. of acid equivalent per acre in 5–6 gal. of water when red clover is 2–3 in. in height, and preferably before the mustard comes into bloom. When legumes are not present, MCP may be used at $\frac{1}{4}$ lb. of acid equivalent per acre, in 5–6 gal. of water. Recent work has also indicated that some of the new 2,4-DB [V] preparations may be similarly used. Grass control in alfalfa is indicated graphically in Fig. 68.

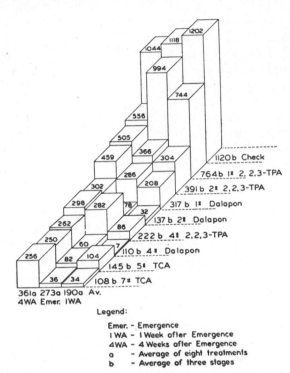

Legend:
Emer. - Emergence
I WA – I Week after Emergence
4WA – 4 Weeks after Emergence
a   - Average of eight treatments
b   - Average of three stages

From McCarty & Sand, 1958

FIG. 68.—Yield of weedy grasses in pounds of oven-dry matter per acre harvested early in July, as affected by chemical treatment at three stages of the growth of alfalfa. Each bar represents an average of four replications for two years. Tests made at Lincoln, Nebraska. TPA = Na salt of 2,2,3-trichloropropionic acid.

Weeds in pastures and hay-fields present a serious problem, and year after year decrease the value of these fields. Not only are annuals a particular problem, but perennials become even more of a problem owing to the long-continued use of the land without cultivation. When legumes are not present, applications of 2,4-D at $\frac{3}{4}$ to $1\frac{1}{8}$ lb. of acid equivalent per acre in 10–15 gal. of water may be made when the weeds are small and growing actively. In many pastures, wild onion and garlic (*Allium* spp.) become a serious problem, and these weeds may prohibit pasturing by dairy cattle for whole periods during the season because of the risk of tainted milk. A low-volatile ester of 2,4-D at $1\frac{1}{8}$ to $1\frac{1}{2}$ lb. of acid equivalent per acre in 10–15 gal. of water may be used in the early spring, when the onion and garlic plants are small and growing actively. Repeat applications over a period of years may be necessary for complete eradication of these obnoxious plants. Areas sprayed with 2,4-D should not be pastured for at least ten days after spraying. Pasture renovation by chemical means with Dalapon, TCA, etc., has been successful (cf. Fig. 69).

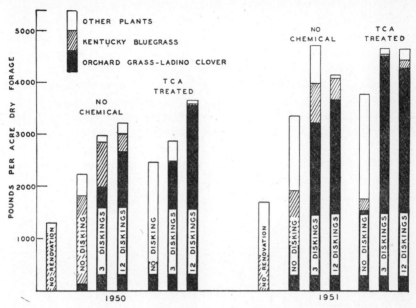

From Sprague, 1952

FIG. 69.—Total yield per acre during 1950 and 1951 of orchard grass-Ladino clover, Kentucky bluegrass, and other plants, from areas renovated with different chemical and tillage treatments in August, 1949. M.S.D. 5 per cent = 346 lb.; 1 per cent = 472 lb. Tests conducted in northern New Jersey on unploughable pastures show that three diskings of the TCA-treated (dead) sod produced almost as good a seed-bed as 12 diskings (the recommended number), and the yields of forage during the second season were almost identical. The herbicide treatment reduces tillage requirements for seed-bed preparation, lessens competition, and encourages seedling establishment. (Note: Dalapon at 10 lb. [8·5 lb. active ingredient] per acre in 50–100 gallons of water has now largely replaced the use of TCA for this purpose.)

Vast areas of grazing land in the western and southwestern areas of the United States, as well as many types of valuable grazing lands in many other parts of the world, may, because of over-grazing or certain non-controllable environmental factors such as drought periods, etc., come to suffer the dominance of undesirable herbacious, perennial, or woody plant species. Quite often, these species are native to the region and normally grow in non-pastured areas, along streams, etc. Many of these invading plants, especially the larger bush and tree forms, by their shading and occupation of extensive land areas, prevent the growth and development of the valuable range-grasses.

As such vast areas are generally involved, aircraft applications of herbicides, at low gallonage, are commonly made. This method has been particularly successful for the control of sand sagebrush (*Artemisia* sp.)

and mesquite (*Prosopis* sp.) where spray volumes as low as 3 gal. per acre of 2,4-D have been employed. These sprays of 2,4-D and 2,4,5-T are quite selective, and therefore little, if any, damage occurs to the more valuable range-grasses. If, however, leguminous plants are present, then these herbicides may cause damage to such plants.

The following recommendations have been made (Klingman *et al.*, 1958; Danielson *et al.*, 1961) for the control of these noxious rangeland plants in the western United States: (1) for sand sagebrush (*Artemisia filifolia*), use a 2,4-D ester at the rate of 1 lb. per acre in oil, or in an emulsion of 1 gal. of diesel oil and 2–4 gal. of water, applied in May or June to the foliage when the plants are growing rapidly and have made 6–8 in. of new growth; (2) for big sagebrush (*Artemisia tridentata*), use 2,4-D ester at 1½–2 lb. per acre in 5 gal. of oil, water, or oil-water emulsions, when bunch-grasses are heading; (3) for mesquite (*Prosopis juliflora*), use 2,4,5-T at ¼ to ½ lb. per acre in oil, or in an emulsion of 1 gal. of diesel oil and 3 gal. of water, applied to foliage in the spring; (4) for shinnery oak (*Quercus havardii*), use repeated applications of a 2,4-D ester at 1 lb. per acre in oil, or in an emulsion of 1 gal. of diesel oil and 2–4 gal. of water,

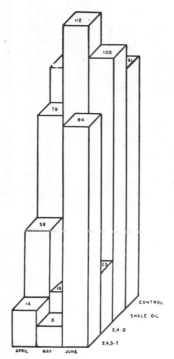

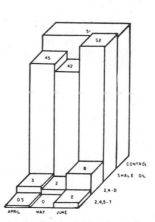

From Robertson & Cords, 1956

FIG. 70.—Average percentage survival of two age-classes of big sagebrush (*Artemisia tridentata*) one year after being sprayed with 2,4-D at 2 lb. per acre, 2,4,5-T at 1 lb. per acre, or shale oil at 50 gallons per acre, at three dates each. *Left*: shrubs more than 4 in. high in an old mature stand. *Right*: young shrubs more than 4 in. high in crested wheat-grass. Tests made in central Elko County, Nevada (elevation, 5,400 ft. precipitation average 9·13 in.).

applied to foliage; (5) for post oak (*Quercus stellata*), blackjack oak, (*Quercus marilandica*), and other associated woody plants, use 2,4,5-T ester or 2-(2,4,5-TP) ester at 2 lb. per acre in an emulsion of 1 gal. of diesel oil and 4 gal. of water, or in 5 gal. of diesel oil, repeating applications for two to three consecutive years and using then 1 to 2 lb. of either chemical; (6) for buckbrush (*Symphoricarpos vulgaris*), use repeated applications of 2,4-D ester at 1–2 lb. per acre in an emulsion of 1 gal. of diesel oil and 3 gal. of water, or in 4 gal. of diesel oil. The results of several experiments for sagebrush control are given in Figs. 70, 71 and 72. The critical time for spraying mesquite in Texas is shown in Fig. 73, while the influence of mesquite control on the gain in weight of steers is indicated in Fig. 74.

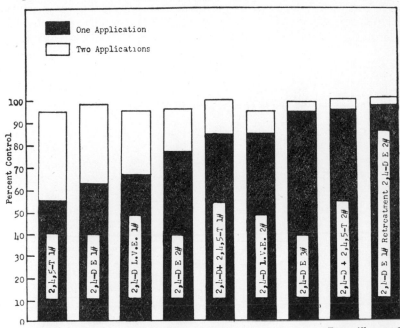

From Alley, 1956

FIG. 71.—Percentage of big sagebrush (*Artemisia tridentata*) controlled with 2,4-D, 2,4,5-T, and mixtures of 2,4-D and 2,4,5-T, with one application in 1952. The two-application series included the original treatments plus 2 lb. of 2,4-D ester per acre sprayed the following year. Applications were made in 1951 and 1952 to plots originally treated with 1 lb. of 2,4-D ester which were followed by 2 lb. of 2,4-D ester. Tests made in northwestern Wyoming (elevation 8200 ft., average annual precipitation 20 in.).

There may be times when it would be more practicable to apply foliage sprays with ground equipment (rather than from aircraft) for the control of the above species; depending on the tolerance of the particular species, 2,4-D, 2,4,5-T, or 2-(2,4,5-TP), should be applied at 3 lb. per 100 gal. of water, per acre, when the plants are at the full-leaf stage and during the three to four week period thereafter. For the control of mixed brush, ammonium sulphamate at $\frac{3}{4}$ lb. to 1 gal. of water per acre may be applied first to the foliage as a wetting spray.

365

The use of arboricides in modern forestry practice is increasing—especially to remove undesirable broad-leafed trees from conifer plantings, and for miscellaneous weeding-out operations. For the extensive literature on this subject, *see* the items on the control of woody plants in the bibliography terminating this chapter.

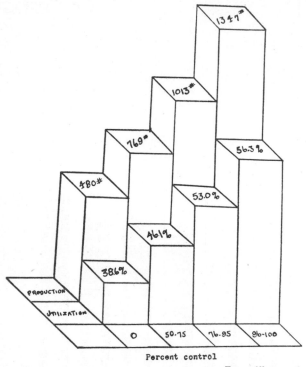

From Alley, 1956

FIG. 72.—1953–54 average air-dry grass production and utilization of grasses on sagebrush control plots sprayed in 1952–53. Tests made in northwestern Wyoming. Values of 76 to 95 per cent control appeared to be the logical amount of sagebrush which should be controlled to give maximum return in production and livestock utilization per dollar invested.

Aerial applications for woody-plant control may be made if the area involved warrants it. Esters of 2,4-D, 2,4,5-T, and 2,4,5-TP, or brush-killer mixtures of these herbicides, are generally used. Where selectivity is not required, ammonium sulphamate, Monuron, or Simazine, may also be used. Where aerial applications are not feasible, individual treatments may be employed, using one of the following methods. Basal-bark applications are made to the base and to the ground-line portions of trees and shrubs 15 cm. (6 in.) or less in diameter. They are made either in the dormant period or in the growing-season, and are sprayed on in high concentrations in oil (e.g. 4 lb. of active ingredient in 25 gal. of kerosene). Typical responses to either foliage or basal applications are indicated in Table XIV. Such concentrates may also be painted on the surface of

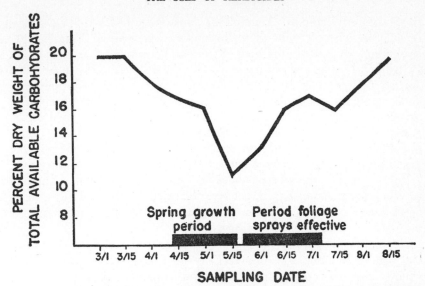

From Fisher & Quinn, 1959, by courtesy of Texas Agricultural Experiment Station

FIG. 73.—Average total available carbohydrate content of mesquite (*Prosopis juliflora*) root tissues at bi-weekly intervals during 1953–56. Aerial application of 2,4,5-T for control has been most effective from 20 May to 15 July, when the carbohydrate content of the roots is being replenished rapidly—i.e. at the time of the greatest translocation from the leaves into the root system. Tests made at Spur, Texas. [Readers in countries where it is usual to place the number of the day before that of the month should note that, as commonly in America, the opposite is done in this figure.—Ed.]

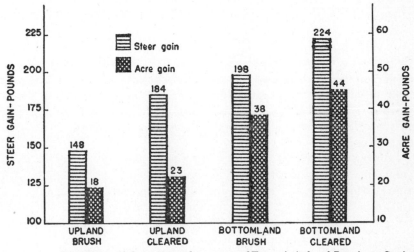

From Fisher & Quinn, 1959, by courtesy of Texas Agricultural Experiment Station

FIG. 74.—Influence of mesquite (*Prosopis juliflora*) control (combination of mechanical and chemical) on the gain in weight of yearling steers, and the acre-gain in weight during a 156-day period annually through 1945–56, at Spur, Texas, on upland and bottomland pastures. For the over-all period of study, the annual acre-gain was increased an average of 18 per cent by the control of mesquite. The values are averages for the years 1945–56.

freshly cut tree-stumps. Ammonium sulphamate [XLVIII], in crystal form, or in a concentrated water solution, may also be used. Various types of cuts may be made in the bark of trees and chemicals thus introduced. By frilling the trees and placing 2,4,5-T in the frill, the trees can be killed and stump sprouting prevented. To frill a tree, make overlapping axe cuts completely around the base of the tree 20–60 cm. above ground and then fill this frill with a 2,4,5-T concentrate, such as was mentioned above. A deeper girdle may be cut into the tree, for trees above 30 cm. (12 in.) in diameter, and be similarly treated. Notches may also be made near the ground-level of larger trees and herbicides applied to prevent re-sprouting.

Aerial applications of herbicides on mixed hardwoods in Louisiana revealed that at a rate of 5 gal. per acre the most effective was the butoxy-ethanol ester of 2,4,5-T. These were applied in an oil-water emulsion at the rate of 2 lb. per acre (Peevy & Burns, 1959).

The difficulties of herbicidally killing large trees is well illustrated by the work of Hodgson *et al.* (1962). Control of large (50–60 ft. tall) black willow trees (*Salix nigra*) growing along irrigation canals in Utah was achieved by yearly applications of undiluted herbicide in either areas chopped, or holes bored into the base of the trees. 2,4-D and ammonium sulphamate [XLVIII] were separately applied in 1948, with further treatment in 1949, 1950, and 1951. Ammonium sulphamate was applied at the rate of 2 full tablespoons per hole for 14 holes per tree (a total of 28 full tablespoons per tree), and the following year (1949) only 50 per cent of the normal amount of growth was noted. With a second treatment in 1949 at the same rate no regrowth was observed the following year (1950). When 2,4-D isopropyl ester was similarly applied at the rate of 6 full tablespoons per tree a 15 per cent regrowth was noted the following year. A second application at the same rate in 1949 revealed no regrowth the following year (1950). These treatments, together with some variations on these rates, were applied to 15 trees. None died during the first year after application. In 1952, after four treatments in four years 7 of the 15 originally treated black willow trees were dead. Six trees showed a little to 5 per cent of the original wood still living, another had 10 per cent still alive, and another 25 per cent alive.

A very useful guide for brush control is the table of 'Susceptibility of common woody species to herbicide treatments' (cf. U.S. Dept. Agric., 1961), which lists 182 species and their responses to foliage sprays, and to basal and stump sprays, for three herbicides. Included are data for 4 species of ash (*Fraxinus*), 5 species of *Ceanothus* (all susceptible to herbicides), 10 species of currant (*Ribes*) (all susceptible), 10 species of gooseberry (*Ribes*) (nearly all susceptible), 14 species of oak (*Quercus*) (generally susceptible to foliage sprays of ammonium sulphamate and to basal and stump sprays of 2,4,5-T ester), 6 species of *Rosa* (generally intermediate to resistant to many herbicides), and 5 species of willow (*Salix*) (quite susceptible to all herbicides listed).

TABLE XIV

RESPONSES OF SOME WOODY SPECIES OF THE TEMPERATE ZONE OF THE NORTHERN UNITED STATES TO EITHER FOLIAGE OR BASAL APPLICATIONS OF HORMONE HERBICIDES (from data obtained in Wisconsin, cf. Peterson & Buchholtz, 1958).

Kind of woody genus	Foliage Applications 2 lb. acid equivalent per 50 gal. water. 50–100 gal. spray needed per acre to wet foliage		Stump or Basal Treatment 1 lb. acid equivalent in 10 gal. light oil or kerosene. Cover thoroughly to ground-level.	
	2,4-D or ester	2,4-D and 2,4,5-T esters	2,4-D ester	2,4-D and 2,4,5-T esters

(x = Plant affected but no root-kill   xx = Partial kill but retreatment needed   xxx = Usually complete kill)

Common name	Genus	2,4-D or ester	2,4-D and 2,4,5-T esters	2,4-D ester	2,4-D and 2,4,5-T esters
Alder	*Alnus*	xxx	xxx	xxx	xxx
Ash	*Fraxinus*	x	xx	x	xxx
Basswood	*Tilia*	x	xx	x	xx
Birch	*Betula*	x	xx	x	xx
Blackberry	*Rubus*	x	xxx	—	—
Box elder	*Acer*	xxx	xxx	xxx	xxx
Cherry	*Prunus*	xx	xxx	xx	xxx
Cottonwood	*Populus*	xx	xxx	xx	xxx
Elm	*Ulmus*	xx	xxx	xx	xxx
Gooseberry	*Ribes*	x	xxx	—	—
Grape	*Vitis*	xxx	xxx	xxx	xxx
Hawthorn	*Crataegus*	x	x	xxx	xxx
Hazel bush	*Corylus*	xxx	xxx	xxx	xxx
Hickory	*Carya*	x	xx	x	xxx
Lilac	*Syringa*	x	xx	x	xxx
Locust (black)	*Robinia*	xx	xxx	xx	xxx
Locust (honey)	*Robinia*	xx	xxx	xx	xxx
Maple (hard)	*Acer*	x	xx	x	xxx
Maple (soft)	*Acer*	xx	xxx	xx	xxx
Mulberry	*Morus*	x	xx	xx	xx
Oak*	*Quercus*	x	xx	x	xx
Osage orange	*Maclura*	x	xx	x	xx
Plum	*Prunus*	x	xx	x	xxx
Poison ivy*	*Rhus*	xx	xxx	xx	xxx
Poplar	*Populus*	xx	xxx	xx	xxx
Prickly ash	*Xanthoxylum*	xx	xxx	xx	xxx
Raspberry	*Rubus*	x	xxx	—	—
Rose	*Rosa*	x	xxx	—	—
Sumac	*Rhus*	xxx	xxx	xxx	xxx
Virginia creeper	*Parthenocissus*	xx	xxx	xx	xxx
Willow	*Salix*	xxx	xxx	xxx	xxx

* In addition use Ammate as spray for quick kill of poison ivy. Use Ammate in the dry form to kill oak stumps.

Control of Herbaceous Perennial Weeds

Perennial weeds are among our most noxious forms, because they may reproduce vegetatively as well as by seed production. Therefore, it is all the more important to use the most effective chemical control-measure available for the eradication, if possible, of any new infestations. To prevent their dissemination into new and distant areas is one of the prerequisites of effective weed-control. The methods of control are too diverse to describe individually here. But many such methods will be found, together with the species involved, in the check-lists for various regions almost throughout the world, and some examples are indicated in Figs. 75 and 76.

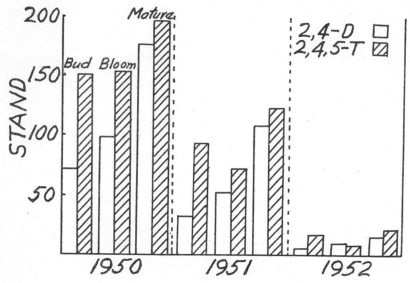

From Rasmussen, 1956

FIG. 75.—Canada thistle (*Cirsium arvense*) stand after successive treatments with 2,4-D and 2,4,5-T at bud, bloom, and mature stages of growth (rates of application of 1·2, 2·4, and 3.6 lb. of each of the two herbicides per acre at each respective stage). Tests made near Pullman, Washington (average annual precipitation 21 in.).

Chemical control of perennial weeds essentially involves at least three types of applications: (1) non-selective foliage sprays for plants that are not growing in, or near, useful plants—for susceptible broad-leafed species use repeated treatments at ½ to 2 lb. of 2,4-D per acre, and for more resistant species use from 1 to 4 lb. of 2,4-D per acre; (2) for selective foliage sprays for the control of perennial weeds in crops, *see* some of the tables etc., or consult the recommendations of local authorities; (3) applic-ations of soil sterilants may be made on land that is not to be cultivated and cropped for a period of years—use sodium chlorate at 3–10 lb. per square rod,* or borax at 20–40 lb. per square rod, or mixtures of the two at 6–20 lb. per square rod. The arsenicals may be used on the shallower-rooted grasses and sedges, but are much less effective on deep-rooted broad-leafed species. Erbon [XI] may be applied at 80–160 lb. per acre. Surviving plants should be retreated again in subsequent years. Tem-porary soil toxicants, which are generally volatile compounds, are also available.

* 1 rod, pole, or perch = 5½ yd., 1 sq. rod being 30¼ sq. yd.—Ed.

Perennial grasses and sedges require more specialized forms of chemical treatment than do other perennial weeds. Some grasses (Johnson grass, Bermuda grass, and quack-grass) may be most easily and economically controlled by frequent cultivation, every two or three weeks, during the

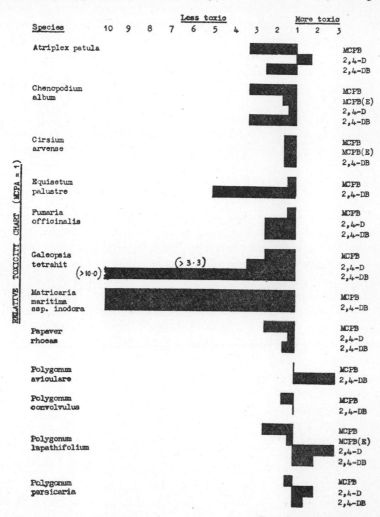

From Fryer & Chancellor, 1956

FIG. 76.—The toxicity of MCPB, 2,4-D, and 2,4-DB, to some annual and perennial weeds as compared with the toxicity of MCPA (which has been taken as 1). Blacked areas to the left of 1 indicate the extent to which the compound is less toxic than MCPA (5 = 1/5 as toxic). Blacked areas to the right of 1 indicate the extent to which the compound is more toxic than MCPA (2 = twice as toxic). Tests conducted in the vicinity of Oxford, England.

growing-season. However, the amount of cultivation that is necessary can be greatly reduced by applying TCA at 25–50 lb., or Dalapon at 10–20 lb., per acre, as a foliage and soil-surface treatment before ploughing, or disking, in late autumn or early spring. Spot-spraying with Dalapon

371

at $\frac{1}{4}$ lb. per gal. of water, or with TCA at $\frac{1}{4}-\frac{1}{2}$ lb. about once a month during the growing-season, will effectively control small patches of the more common grasses.

Along roadsides, ditch banks, in fence rows, and on other uncultivated areas, soil-sterilant chemicals may provide the most effective means of controlling the more usual perennial grasses and sedges. The substituted urea herbicides (Monuron, etc.), at 20–80 lb. per acre, usually give excellent control of these species. Sodium chlorate at 4–10 lb. per square rod, or borax at 20–40 lb. may also be quite effective.

Simazine [XXVII] may also be used at 20–80 lb. of active ingredient per acre, in 40 or more gal. of water, spraying being done in the spring before the plants have become established. For species that are hard to kill, and on heavy soils, use the higher rate. Ammate at about 28 to 38 lb. in 50 gal. of water, when applied as a thorough drench to the foliage, will provide a very rapid kill. It is relatively non-toxic to humans and animals, and so can be used around the home or farm.

As a pre-planting treatment, EPTC [XVI] is effective for control of the nut-grasses (*Cyperus* spp.). It is suggested that suppression is obtained with application at 6–10 lb. per acre in 20–40 gal. of water as a pre-planting soil incorporated treatment. For control of horsetail (*Equisetum* spp.) on non-crop land Amitrole is suggested at 3–6 lb. and is applied when the plants are 12–18 in. tall (Danielson *et al.*, 1961).

From the early reports now available (Pengelly, 1963) Tordon (4-amino-3,5,6-trichloropicolinic acid) [LXVIII] appears to be highly effective for the control of otherwise difficult-to-kill perennial weeds and woody plants. These include Canada thistle (*Cirsium arvense*), bindweed (*Convolvulus arvensis*), Russian knapweed (*Centaurea repens*), bracken (*Pteridium aquilinum*), field horsetail (*Equisetum arvense*), etc. The woody plants controlled include several species of maple (*Acer* spp.), white poplar (*Populus alba*), black locust (*Robina pseudo-acacia*), sassafras (*Sassafras albidum*), willows (*Salix* spp.), cherries (*Prunus* spp.), mesquite (*Prosopus juliflora*), poison oak (*Rhus diversiloba*), etc.

THE CONTROL OF AQUATIC PLANTS

Many species of emerged, submerged and floating aquatic plants, are naturally distributed wherever bodies of fresh water occur. A great many of these plants are native to the areas in which they grow, and are commonly not considered to be troublesome in their natural habitats. However, when these plants invade aquatic habitats which are used or constructed by man, such as bodies of water that are employed for recreation, transportation, irrigation, reservoir, and other public purposes, they often become troublesome and harmful and, therefore, are classed as weeds.

In the water-distribution and drainage systems in the irrigated sections of the western United States, submerged aquatic weeds have caused numerous and often serious problems. Such invading plants interfere, directly or indirectly, with the delivery of irrigation water, and moreover cause losses from seepage and evaporation. They have also contributed to the collection of silt, to canal breaks, and to other difficulties. These problems are generally encountered, and are often most serious, during the warm growing-season, when irrigation water is urgently needed for crops. From surveys made in 1947–48, Balcom (1949) reported that irrigation-water losses resulting from aquatic and ditch-bank weeds in the seventeen western United States were estimated at 1,272,480 acre-feet annually, with a value of nearly \$25¼ million.

Mechanical methods such as underwater cutting devices are widely used in the larger canals that are infested with southern naiad (*Najas guadalupensis*), coontails (*Ceratophyllum* spp.), and bladderworts (*Utricularia* spp.). However, with removal by this method, or by hand, or by machine raking, the regrowth problem is generally magnified. Control by the emulsifiable aromatic oils in concentrations ranging from 20 to 200 p.p.m., depending on the weed species, the solvent, and the degree of infestation, has been found to be economical for farm canals and ditches.

A study, for the control of submerged aquatic weeds in irrigation channels in the western United States, has been prepared by Bruns *et al.* (1955). A summary of their recommendations, for the control of the more important species encountered, is presented in Table XV. Precise equipment was found to be necessary to deliver the required rate of herbicide into the channels, and similarly, it was essential to know the rate of water flow in the channels. Results were best if applications were made at water temperatures of 70°F., and if the water velocities in the channels were from 22·5 to 37·5 cm. (0·75 to 1·25 ft.) per second. It was also found that such weed-control was more economical in smaller channels (carrying up to 50–70 cubic ft. per second). Thirty minutes was found to be the optimum time for introducing aromatic solvents into the channel, while applying the same amount during a sixty-minute period gave equally good results, and a fifteen-minute introduction appeared to be effective for a distance of no more than ¾ mile. Applications of high concentrations of 1,600 p.p.m. and 2,400 p.p.m. during shorter periods usually gave unsatisfactory control for the first ¼ to ½ mile below the point of introduction, but frequently gave excellent results ¾ to 1 mile below it.

These aromatic solvents include a number of organic solvents, petroleum naphthas, and paint thinners. Some of these are effective herbicides without chlorination or ethylation. The most effective ones had a flash point of not less than 80°F., distillation ranging between 278° and 420°F., and an aromatic content of not less than 85 per cent (Bruns *et al.*, 1955).

It was found that the treatment with aromatic solvents was not appreciably injurious to the perennial root systems of the submerged aquatic weeds. The control of weeds was temporary, or seasonal, permitting

TABLE XV

RATES OF AROMATIC SOLVENT USUALLY NEEDED TO CONTROL DIFFERENT
SPECIES OF SUBMERGED AQUATIC WEEDS (from Bruns *et al.*, 1955).

Species	Usually controlled with—		
	Concen-tration	Intro-duction time	Amount of solvent
	P.p.m.	Minutes	Gal./c.f.s.*
Filamentous algae	150	15	1·0
White water-crowfoot (*Ranunculus* *aquatilis*)	300–400	30	4·0–5·4
Waterweed (*Elodea* [*Anacharis*] *canadenis*)	400–600	30	5·4–8·1
Horned pondweed (*Zannichellia palustris*)	400–600	30	5·4–8·1
Leafy pondweed (*Potamogeton foliosus*)	400–600	30	5·4–8·1
Sago pondweed (*P. pectinatus*)	600	30	8·1
Richardson pondweed (*P. richardsonii*)	740	30	10·0
Gigantic sago pondweed (*P. pectinatus* var. *interruptus*)	740	30	10·0
American pondweed (*P. nodosus*)	740	30	10·0
Water stargrass (*Heteranthera dubia*)	740 or more	30	10·0 or more

* Gallons per cubic foot per second.

the unimpeded flow of water through the channels during a major portion of the season. Weed regrowth the following year was generally comparable with the original infestation. Thus, the search for more effective and permanent control measures is still being pursued. Recent work in California has shown the value of Acrolein [XXIX] for the control of submerged aquatics in irrigation channels (cf. Fig. 77).

Acrolein is, however, a highly reactive water-soluble chemical product that has proved very effective for controlling submerged aquatic weeds in irrigation and drainage channels. The chemical is toxic to mammals, and to fish and other aquatic animal life. It is highly volatile, flammable, and its vapour is a powerful irritant to the eyes and respiratory passages. Because of these properties, the chemical must be metered or pumped from the closed container into the water of the channel without contact with the air. Licensed operators with especially adapted equipment are needed for such applications (Danielson *et al.*, 1961).

One of the most spectacular and widespread of floating aquatic weeds is the water-hyacinth (*Eichhornia crassipes*). This plant is found in most subtropical and tropical regions of the world, where it obstructs the flow of water and navigation and provides breeding places for insects and other pests, meanwhile decreasing the desirable aquatic life in freshwater bodies. The control of this plant has been studied in the United States by Hitchcock *et al.* (1949*a*, 1950, 1950*a*), Zimmerman *et al.* (1950, 1950*a*, 1952), and others. These studies were conducted in the State of Louisiana, where special control methods were worked out (cf. Plate 18). The weed has also become a serious problem in the Congo River, but with an extensive and well-planned programme of 2,4-D applications, its near-eradication has been achieved (cf. Kirkpatrick, 1958).

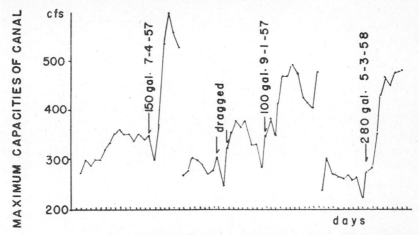

From Overbeek, Hughes & Blondeau, 1959, by courtesy of Science

FIG. 77.—Beneficial effects of the herbicide Acrolein, through controlling submerged weeds (*Potamogeton crispus*), on the water-carrying capacity of a large irrigation canal in Kern County, California. The computed maximum capacity in cubic feet per second is plotted against time. The horizontal units are single days. The three trials which are reported refer to the same canal. The amount of Acrolein in gallons, and the date of treatment, are shown. The increase in water flow is due to destruction of submerged water-weeds. [Readers in countries where it is customary to place the number of the day before that of the month should note that, as commonly in America, the opposite is done in this figure.—Ed.]

It is suggested (Danielson *et al.*, 1961) that for the control of such floating weeds as water-hyacinth and water-lettuce (*Pistia*), that the amine salts or low volatile esters of 2,4-D at 1 to 4 lb. in 2 to 150 gal. of water per acre be utilized. The higher volumes of spray often give better results. Sprays should be applied at low pressure with large nozzles to reduce spray drift. To ensure proper wetting of leaves use oil, or an oil-water emulsion as a spray.

N. W. Pirie (1960) of the Rothamsted Experimental Station has stressed the need for finding uses of water-hyacinth. It has been used as cattle and pig food, and to some extent for human consumption. The concensus of opinion now, however, appears to be that there is no need to pursue experiments on utilization because of the danger of dissemination of the seeds of *Eichhornia* through its use as cattle food and compost. Davies (1959) states that mats of water-hyacinth exceed many metres in depth in parts of the White Nile, interfering with navigation and native fishing.

For the proper use of herbicides in bodies of water it is essential that a close estimation of the volume of water in the area to be treated be obtained. Measure the average length (L), average width (W), and average depth (D), then multiply L × W × D which will give the cubic feet of water in the body of water. Then, for example, 1 lb. of copper sulphate may be used (for algal control) for each 16,000 cubic ft. of water. Ponds which overflow should have the water level lowered for three days to prevent loss of treated water. Ponds fed by large streams should not be treated because the control will be poor (Grange League Federation, 1962–63).

For the control of submerged rooted aquatics, granular 2,4-D formulations such as 'Aqua-Kleen' have proved effective. For the control of susceptible water weeds (water milfoil, water stargrass, white waterlily, and yellow waterlily or spatterdock) use 5 lb. of 'Aqua-Kleen 10' (10 per cent 2,4-D butoxyethanol ester) per 2,200 square feet of surface area; for hard-to-kill water-weeds (bushy pondweed, pondweeds (*Potomogeton* spp.), coontail, water-chestnut, and waterweed) apply double the amount stated above. The best results are obtained with applications made in the early spring, or applications made on ice in late winter. Water from such treated ponds should not be used to irrigate 2,4-D-susceptible plants. It is reported that the 2,4-D will probably dissipate within three weeks after reaching the bottom of the pond, although this is not a certainty (Grange League Federation, 1962–63).

There are a number of other floating plants that frequently become noxious. Water-lettuce (*Pistia stratiotes*) is distributed in many of the habitats occupied by water-hyacinth, and likewise provides a favourable breeding ground for mosquitoes in particular. It is common in Florida, in Central America, and in the irrigation systems of Egypt, India, and many other countries. Its foliage, like that of cabbage, rapidly sheds aqueous applications of 2,4-D; but control has been obtained by using oil as a carrier for 2,4-D, and by employing a surface-active agent.

The control of submerged aquatics in bodies of water that are used for fishing and for other forms of recreation, presents one of the most difficult problems in the entire field of weed control, because the safety of persons using these facilities, as well as of the fish and other wild life, is most important. Many years of experience with the veteran herbicide, copper sulphate [XLIII], has shown its reliability and safety when properly used. Copper sulphate will control a large number of species of algae at concentrations varying from 0·5 to 1·0 p.p.m.

An invaluable guide to the principles of aquatic plant control has been provided in a most thorough manner by T. F. Hall (1961) of the Wilson Dam, Alabama. The following material is condensed from this publication. The control of a plant implies a reduction in the area it covers so that it does not offer a serious problem when duly controlled. Since water-borne reproductive structures move mainly downstream control measures should proceed from upstream to downstream to lessen new infestations downstream.

Eradication means the elimination of the species from the natural region or drainage basin. Eradication may or may not be economically practical, and may even be impossible. Prevention of initial introductions of these noxious plants should be attempted where possible by plant quarantine laws. The time to attempt eradication of an introduced species is shortly after its initial introduction. Control efforts are much less costly than eradication. The possibility of the reintroduction of the species should also be considered before undertaking eradication.

A thorough study of the biology of the noxious plants in question should always be conducted. A knowledge of reproductive habits, for example, provides the clues to the proper timing for herbicidal applications or other control methods. The selection of a practical control measure must rest on reliable answers to such questions as 'what, when, where and how?' The more detailed and comprehensive the answers are to these questions the greater will be the refinements possible in the control procedures. (*See* Yeo (1964) and Timmons (1963)).

Sometimes the control of aquatic plants evokes conflicts of interest, but some of these problems may be resolved within practical limits by building on mutual interests and over-all objectives. An example cited is the current practice for promoting waterfowl food plants by setting areas of wetlands back to earlier stages of colonization. This may be accomplished by mechanical or herbicidal control of undesirable woody species, or by flooding followed by lowering of the water level in the summertime to promote the growth of desirable marginal food plants.

Hall (1961) states that once a practical procedure has been determined there are four steps in placing a species under control and maintaining it in this condition: '(1) properly define the locations and extent of the plants to be controlled, (2) apply an effective control method, (3) maintain surveillance in the area under control for locating resprouting colonies or further colonization, and (4) make early retreatment of the new growth.'

An extensive compilation, *Aquatic Herbicide Data* (Lawrence, 1962), is now available which provides in tabular form responses of some 43 species of submerged weeds, 14 species of emergent weeds, some 76 species of marginal weeds, as well as 9 species of floating and miscellaneous weeds—all to some 102 herbicides and herbicidal products. This summarization is based on a bibliography of 253 items. In addition, data are provided on the responses of some 102 species of algae. Toxicological data are included also for pond fishes and fish-food organisms.

The author of the above work states that the problems arising from the presence of aquatic plants have increased greatly in the twentieth century because of the expanded development and utilization of man-made ponds, lakes, and irrigation channels. Many of the plants provide breeding habitats for mosquitoes and snails. Water-hyacinths, however, tend to inhibit the breeding of the *Anopheles* mosquito.

Aquatic herbivorous animals also have been used successfully for the control of noxious water plants, and several examples are cited in some

377

detail in Chapter XV. Herbivorous fish of the genus *Tilapia* belonging to the sunfish family, have been introduced from Africa into Hawaii, and have successfully and economically controlled weeds in irrigation ditches. In British Guiana the native manatee (*Trichechus manatus*, class Mammalia) has successfully controlled aquatic vegetation in canals and irrigation schemes.

HERBICIDES FOR LAWNS AND SPORTS AREAS

The turf areas that are used for lawns and for sports represent a highly specialized ecological state. While nutrition and water supply are generally adequately provided for, growth conditions are highly restricted through dense planting, close mowing, and treading action. This growth restriction thus determines, in large measure, the character of the plant species—not only those that are planted for the turf, but also those that invade and become successfully established as weeds.

In their useful *Suggested Guide for the Chemical Control of Weeds*, Danielson *et al.* (1961) have listed some important agronomic and maintenance techniques for effective weed control in lawns and other turf areas: (1) adequate fertilization based on fertility needs as established by a soil analysis; (2) planting turf grasses best adapted to the soil and location; (3) mowing most turf grasses to a height of $1\frac{1}{2}$ to $2\frac{1}{2}$ in.; (4) use of proper water practices (infrequent but thorough wetting of soil); and (5) controlling insects and diseases. Such practices should result in a vigorous lawn, and these, supplemented by improved methods of weed control, are important in obtaining a weed-free lawn.

The differences in climate between the northern and southern sections of the United States have necessitated the use of two radically different types of grass. Turf in the more northern regions is composed mostly of Kentucky bluegrass (*Poa pratensis*), or of bent-grasses (*Agrostis* spp.); these grow best in the spring and autumn, and become less aggressive, or even dormant, during the hot summer period. This, unfortunately, is one of the failings of this group of grasses, as during this dormant period undesirable species of crabgrass (*Digitaria* spp.) appear in the thinner and more open turf, and will thrive and grow most luxuriously during the hot, dry periods of middle and late summer. In the southern regions, Bermuda and carpet grasses (*Cynodon dactylon*, *Axonopus compressus*, and *A. affinis*) make their best growth in the hot summer months and are dormant in the cooler seasons. The weed problem is more serious in the middle region between the north and the south; for in the far northerly regions of the United States and Canada, crabgrass is not a problem.

Some of the more troublesome lawn weeds belong to the genera *Digitaria*, *Plantago*, *Trifolium*, *Taraxacum* (dandelions), *Stellaria* and *Cerastium* (chickweeds), and *Sagina* (sandworts), as well as to species of

Bellis, *Holcus*, *Cyperus*, *Allium*, *Polygonum*, *Veronica*, etc. The early widespread use of 2,4-D in the United States resulted in the control of most of the broad-leafed species (cf. Monteith, 1940; Klingman & Noordhoff, 1961, cf. Ch. XII).

The amount of land occupied by turf-grass in certain areas reaches a surprisingly high figure. Actual data are, however, quite scanty. The Southern California Golf Association has prepared (1954) a turf-grass survey of Los Angeles County which is quite revealing. This county, comprising 4·08 thousand square miles (55 per cent of which is mountains or desert), 46 cities, and a population of 4·8 million in 1954, had a turf-grass area which was estimated at 63,490 acres. A selection of some of these data is given in Table XVI.

TABLE XVI

TURF-GRASS SURVEY OF LOS ANGELES COUNTY, CALIFORNIA

Type of turf-grass area	Number	Turf-grass acreage
Cemeteries	62	1,400
Churches	3,218	184·7
Parks and athletic fields	135	2,522·4
Public properties	—	441·9
Factories	575	39·6
Golf courses and driving ranges	63	3,163·0
Private residences	1·13 million	50,681·0
Other types of residences	131,200	3,835·0
Schools and colleges	1,223	1,077·6
Miscellaneous	—	137·8

This survey showed that the average lawn area for single-family dwellings was 1,953 sq. ft. The total annual maintenance costs of all of the area indicated above is given as $90·4 million (including water, fertilizer, etc., and labour). Were it not for the necessity of irrigation at certain seasons of the year in many places, the total area would be considerably larger.

While 2,4-D has been widely used on lawns for the control of a large number of weed species, some have proved to be resistant. Occasionally the resistant weeds became more prominent after 2,4-D has eliminated some of the competitors. Recent tests in Ohio have shown that one application of Silvex (2-(2,4,5-trichlorophenoxy)propionic acid), at 1·5 lb. of active ingredient per acre, not only controlled the weeds that were usually controlled by 2,4-D, but also common chickweed (*Stellaria media*), meadow chickweed (*Cerastium arvense*), ground-ivy (*Nepeta herderacea*), and white clover (*Trifolium repens*). Other weeds that may be controlled by Silvex are wood-sorrels (*Oxalis* spp.), mouse-ear chickweed (*Cerastium vulgatum*), and yarrow (*Achillea millefolium*). At the rate which is recommended for lawn weed control, this herbicide will injure neither common Kentucky bluegrass nor the Merion variety. Bent-grass, however, may be seriously injured.

In the southern United States, both St. Augustine grass and centipede grass are widely-used turf-grasses, but they have become injured (especially the former) by the 2,4-D and 2,4,5-T herbicides, while both are injured by the organic arsenicals that are used for crabgrass control. A mixture of Simazine (2-chloro-4,6-*bis*(ethylamino)-*s*-triazine) at 2–4 lb. per acre and 4-(2,4-dichlorophenoxy)butyric acid (4-(2,4-DB)) at 1–2 lb. per acre, was effective in controlling established broad-leafed weeds, and the activity of residual Simazine controlled annual grasses and annual broad-leafed species for a period of a few weeks after application. *Dichondra* and most northern turf-grasses are susceptible to injury from the use of Simazine.

Equal in intensity to the effort at the control of broad-leafed weeds with 2,4-D in lawns, has been the search for effective control agents (either pre-emergence or post-emergence) for the control of crabgrass (*Digitaria* spp.). In the north-central and the north-eastern United States, this annual grass is a serious competitor of the lawn grasses which are used in these regions. With the occurrence of hot dry weather in mid- and late-summer, *Digitaria* usually dominates the average lawn. A veritable spectrum of herbicides exists that is effective in the control of this most noxious weed.

A newly introduced product for the pre-emergence control of crabgrass in turf is Zytron (*O*-(2,4-dichlorophenyl)-*O*-methylisopropyl-phosphoramidothioate). Autumn application is claimed to prevent the setting of viable seed. It is effective against a number of annual grasses and broad-leafed weeds (including *Oxalis* spp.), but perennials appear to be resistant. Dacthal [XLI] is another product that is used, in autumn or spring, for the pre-emergence control of crabgrass in turf.

The Use of Soil Sterilants

The use of the term 'soil sterilant' is not quite justified as, even with chemical treatment, soil sterilization is not entirely accomplished. However, the treatment does result in the removal of weed infestations for considerable periods of time—i.e. a disinfestation. Not only are established perennials killed, but in many cases the weed seeds infesting the area are also destroyed, or if they are not, the residue of chemical present results in their destruction during the early stages of germination.

Quite often the removal of permanent vegetation for extended periods of time is essential for reducing fire hazards. This is especially true around oil-storage and other chemical storage tanks, along railroads, in lumber yards, around grain elevators, and around special mechanical installations, etc. Soil sterilization is also employed in roadways, driveways, along irrigation ditches and canals, etc. Sometimes the use of such methods has to be balanced against the destructive forces of soil erosion. In tropical regions of heavy rainfall, complete denudation of the soil is not generally recommended. However, in the regions of more moderate

380

rainfall, this is not a serious problem, as the outlying areas are generally covered with vegetation and the eroding soil, if any, is not carried far.

Chemicals, that are relatively insoluble and will withstand the leaching action of rain and percolating soil-water, are needed for soil sterilization. With the introduction of the newer organics, various substituted ureas, triazines and uracils are also proving successful. Some preparations of borate-chlorate-Monuron are now available for soil sterilization use. Some of the most detailed and long-range tests of this nature have been sponsored by the Association of American Railroads.

Soil sterilants are generally used to control all vegetation on an area, and since few, if any, chemicals alone will kill all species of plants at rates of application that would be economically feasible, herbicide mixtures are finding wider use in this application. In addition to the more commonly used inorganics, such herbicides as Monuron, Diuron, and Simazine at 10–80 lb. per acre are utilized. Mixtures of these with 2,4,5-T, 2,4-D, Silvex [IV], Dalapon, or TCA, and with such fortifying agents as the herbicidal oils, the dinitro compounds [XIX], and pentachlorophenol [XVIII], may be used for control of vegetation on ditchbanks, railroad rights-of-way, industrial sites, and on other noncultivated areas. Such treatments as are suggested will render most soils unproductive for periods of from thirty days to four years or more depending on the chemicals used, the soil type, and a number of soil properties and climatic factors (Danielson *et al.*, 1961).

THE CONTROL OF SPECIAL GROUPS OF WEEDS

Under certain conditions, very specialized methods of chemical control of weeds may be required. This is especially true of the control of undesirable epiphytic plant growth. Reference has already been made, in Chapter II, to the use of certain growth-regulator sprays to remove bromeliads and other 'air plants' from grapefruit plantations in the West Indies. There may be times, too, when *Tillandsia* (Spanish-moss) should be removed from trees, and the host tree sprayed so that it does not become reinfected.

Another specialized use, and one which requires a very high degree of selectivity, is the chemical control of the phanerogamic, or flowering, parasitic plants. This group of plants, and their destructiveness to economic plants, has also been reviewed in Chapter III. Some of the more promising chemical control work with the mistletoes such as *Loranthus* spp. and *Ameyma pendula* has been by tree-injection as reported by Greenham (1957) and his associates in Australia. Selective control of the *Ameyma* was obtained with about 10 per cent 2,4-D (triethanolamine) on 7 species of *Eucalyptus* trees. However, tests on *E. maculata* gave unsatisfactory results. Injection into fewer, but deeper holes, than the one shallow hole per in. of tree diameter at breast height, increased host injury and decreased mistletoe kill; increasing dosage rates gave similar results. About one-half of the parasites remaining after the first application, were killed by re-treatment at the same rate two years later. Where rapid reinfestation occurs, a treatment giving 80 per cent kill, with re-treatment every five years, is probably better than an initial treatment giving 99 per cent kill. Applications at lower cost have been made with a modified axe and a drenching gun.

In Maine, tests with maleic hydrazide and with MCPA were unsatisfactory in controlling dwarf-mistletoe (*Arceuthobium pusillum*) infesting *Picea glauca* and *P. rubra*; this parasite also occurs on the slower-growing *P. mariana* of acid bogs.

Fenac (2,3,6-trichlorophenylacetic acid) is a persistent chemical and has given the best results when applied to the soil. It is claimed to be effective on quack-grass and *Convolvulus*. Its most recent application seems to be for the control of parasitic witchweed (*Striga asiatica*). In the presence of this chemical, the parasite fails to establish the necessary contact with the host plant (maize, *Digitaria* spp., etc.) and dies. Several thousand acres in the infested area (North Carolina-South Carolina region) were treated in 1960.

The susceptibility of individual weed species to the principal herbicides now in use will be found grouped by major geographic regions in later volumes of this series. Extensive listings of herbicidal susceptibilities are also available in the following works: Helgeson (1957); Klingman & Noordhoff (1961, *see* Ch. XII); Klingman & Shaw (1962); and Audus (1964, *see* Ch. XII).

The Use of Growth Suppressants

Growth suppressants should also be considered in any vegetation control programme. In many situations the suppression of noxious plant growth may be preferable to outright lethal action and eradication. This would be the case where a living vegetal cover is needed for the prevention of the more serious forms of soil erosion in areas of excessive rainfall. The use of growth suppressants would be useful along certain rights-of-way where an attractive, yet nearly dormant cover, would find greater public acceptance. The existence of a living yet dwarfed vegetal cover would also preserve wild-life habitats. This too is an important aspect of community goodwill that is essential where extensive vegetation control programmes involve, or impinge, upon, public lands or rights-of-way. Few substances are yet available, however, that could be used economically and yet be effective for extended periods of time. Newly developed growth suppressants are quite likely to be forthcoming in the not too distant future.

As noted earlier, maleic hydrazide [XXXVIII] has been employed as a growth suppressant for grasses. Two quaternary ammonium carbamates

(4-hydroxy-5-isopropyl-2-methylphenyl trimethyl ammonium chloride, 1-piperidine carboxylate), or 'Amo-1618'; and 'CCC' or 2-chloroethyl trimethyl-ammonium chloride, as well as 'Phosfon' (2,4-dichlorobenzyl-tributyl phosphonium chloride) are additional substances that are growth depressants, but not necessarily herbicidal.

Investigations of Cathey and Marth (1960) have shown that 'CCC' has the broadest spectrum—retarding the growth of some 50 plant species of agronomic or horticultural interest. 'Amo-1618' and 'Phosphon' persisted in the soil while 'CCC' did not. In general these substances delayed germination of seeds; root development was initially inhibited (but not so by flowering time); internodal growth was less on most plants; and the main stem of some treated species grew in essentially a rosette fashion. The control of flower initiation by photoperiod and temperature was unaffected, however, and the flowering time of most species was not noticeably altered. The chief use of the substances just named, particularly 'Phosphon', has been the more localized applications to produce shorter stemmed forms of certain more desirable horticultural specimen-plants—namely, Easter lilies, chrysanthemums, and poinsettias. Their application for use in the field is, for the present at least, limited by their cost.

HERBICIDES AND THE ENVIRONMENT

Considerable attention is being given to the role of all types of pesticides, including herbicides, in the ecosystem of the human environment and the associated and ancillary animal and plant environments. The pesticide residue problem on the portions of plants and animals consumed by man has long been the concern of agriculturalists and agricultural chemists. A vast body of analytical procedures in this area is to be found in the *Journal of the Association of Official Agricultural Chemists*, and summarized at intervals in the *Official Methods of Analysis* of the Association.* Likewise, the *Journal of Agricultural and Food Chemistry* contains articles dealing with analytical techniques for pesticide residues. More recently the serial publication, *Residue Reviews*, has been established to evaluate the increasing amount of information in this area. V. H. Freed (1964) has recently reviewed the methods for determination of herbicides and plant growth regulators, and both Hartley (1964) and Audus (1964) have examined this group of substances from the standpoint of their behaviour in the soil. Crafts (1964) has considered the behaviour of herbicides within the plant.

Of greater contemporary concern, perhaps, is the influence of pesticides, including herbicides, on our ecosystem, and particularly on the elaborate and complicated food-chain relationships of all living organisms which compromise the biological world. Public attention, at least, was more sharply focused upon this problem following the publication of the

* For a summary of the work of this association *see* the article by W. Horwitz in *Residue Rev.*, 7, 37–60, 1964.

controversial book of Rachel Carson, *Silent Spring* (1962). The ultimate fate and disposition of the many types of pesticide molecules, both inorganic and organic, are of paramount importance. The report prepared by the President's Science Advisory Committee, *Use of Pesticides* (Weisner, 1963) has indicated the areas where research is urgently needed. Likewise, the several reports of the National Academy of Sciences (1962–63) on pest control and wildlife relationships demonstrate where research is needed. The American ecologist, Dr. F. E. Egler, has more recently (1964) in an extensive survey considered pesticides in relation to our ecosystem. It will be some time, however, before sufficient analytical data are available to formulate sound and objective evaluations of both the useful and the deleterious aspects of pesticides that are so urgently needed for the high level of agricultural production required by our exploding population.

BIBLIOGRAPHY *
(*The Uses of Herbicides*)

[3] ADDICOTT, F. T. & CARNS, H. R. (1964). Abscission responses to herbicides. *The Physiology and Biochemistry of Herbicides* (Ed. L. J. Audus), pp. 277–89. Academic Press, London & New York.

[1-7] ADVANCES IN PEST CONTROL (vol. 1, 1957 to date). Academic Press, New York

[4] AGADZHANIAN, G. K. (1956). [Biology of Johnson grass (*Sorghum halepense*) and measures for controlling it—in Russian.] *Akad. Nauk Armianskoĭ SSR. Izv. Biol. Sel' skokhoz. Nauk.*, 9(1), 43–47.

[1] AHLGREN, G. H., KLINGMAN, G. C. & WOLF, D. (1951). *Principles of Weed Control*. John Wiley & Sons, New York. 368 pp.

[5] AKHURST, C. G. (1935). Use of weed killers in the control of natural covers. *J. Rubb. Res. Inst. Malaya*, 6, 111–20.

[5] —— (1953). Chemical weed control on rubber estates in Malaya. *Plant Protect. Overseas Rev.*, 4, 5–14.

[1] ALIEV, A. (1956). [Effectiveness of using overground sprayers in weed control on plantings of grain crops—in Russian.] *Moskov. Ordena Lenina Selskokhoz. Akad. im. K. A. Timiriazeva Sborn. Studencheskikh Nauch.-Issled Rabot*, 5, 104–9.

[3] ALLEN, H. P. (1954). Weed control in grassland. *C.R. Congr. Internat. Phytopharm.*, 3(2), 689–98.

[4] —— & SMITH, W. N. (1954). The effect of CMU and PDU on Lalang-grass (*Imperata cylindrica*) in Malaya. *Proc. Brit. Weed Cont. Conf.* 1954, 509–22.

[4] —— & —— (1956). Weedkiller trials on Lalang (*Imperata cylindrica*) in Malaya. *Outlook Agric.*, 1(2), 70–74.

* In this bibliography, a good many references to the uses of herbicides in many of the countries of the world have been included.

The bibliography of this chapter was submitted in 7 sections which have now been consolidated into a single general sequence. The original section to which each book or paper previously belonged is indicated by a prefixed superior numeral, through use of which the individual sections can readily be reconstructed, as follows:

[1] Field Crops
[2] Horticultural, Vegetable, Ornamental, Fruit, Nursery
[3] Forage Crops, Pastures, Rangelands
[4] Herbaceous Perennials (including Grasses)
[5] Specialized Areas, Rights-of-way, Woody Plants, Soil Sterilization
[6] Aquatic Plant Control
[7] Lawns and Play Areas. —Ed.

[3] ALLEY, H. P. (1956). Chemical control of big sagebrush (*Artemisia tridentata*) and its effect upon production and utilization of native grass species. *Weeds*, 4, 164–73.

[1] ANDREEVA-FETVADZHIEVA, N. (1956). [Die Anwendung von 2,4-D als Herbizid bei der Reiskultur—in Bulgarian.] *Bulgar. Akad. na Nauk. Bot. Inst. Izv.*, 5, 263–92.

[6] ANON. (1929). Weeds and water. *Farming S. Africa*, 4, 152.

[6] —— (1946). Control of weeds on irrigation systems. *U.S. Dept. Interior, Bur. Reclamation Rept., Washington, D.C.*, 71 pp.

[6] —— (1947). Malaria control on impounded water. *U.S. Public Health Service, Tennessee Valley Authority & Fed. Sec. Agency, Washington D.C.*

[5] —— (1948). New weed killer for southern pines. *Amer. Nurseryman*, 87(1), 36–37.

[4] —— (1956). New weed killer for control of grass. *Plant. Bull. Rubber Res. Inst. Malaya*, n.s., 23, 27–28.

[5] AREND, J. L. (1954). Chemical herbicides as tools in forest management. *Amer. Foresters Proc.*, 1954, 194–8.

[1-7] ASSOCIATION OF AGRICULTURAL CHEMISTS (1963). *Manual of Official Methods of the Association of Agricultural Chemists*. Williams & Wilkins, Baltimore.

[5] ATKINS, E. S. (1956). The use of chemicals to release white pine (*Pinus strobus*) reproduction. *Canad. Dept. North. Aff. & Natl. Res., Forest Res. Div., Tech. Note* 37, 9 pp.

[6] AUTOLENE LUBRICANTS CO. (1948). Modern methods of eradicating water weeds from canals. *Denver*, 15 pp.

[6] BALCOM, R. B. (1949). *Control of Weeds on Irrigation Systems*. U.S. Govt. Print. Off., Washington, 140 pp.

[6] —— (1953). Control of aquatic weeds. *Proc. Northeast. Weed Control Conf.*, 7, 5–9.

[6] BANFIELD, G. L. (1955). Weed control in drains. *Proc. N. Z. Weed Control Conf.*, 8, 77–80.

[6] BARANEK, P. (1952). The weed control program on irrigation systems. *Proc. West. Weed Cont. Conf.*, 13, 62–71.

[1] BARANOV, M. S. (1956). [Weeds of cereals and measures for controlling them—in Russian.] *Alma-Ata, Kazakhskoe Gosudarstvennoe Izdatelstvo*.

[6] BARBER, Y. M. (1955). *Experiments in Control of Needlerush with Herbicides: Observations on Plant Succession*. M.S. Thesis, North Carolina State College.

[2] BARBIER, M. & TRUPIN, F. (1956). Utilisation des Monuron et Diuron comme herbicides dans les plantations d'ananas. *Fruits*, 11, 443–6.

[5] BARRONS, K. C. (1952). Vegetation control on industrial lands. *Advances in Agron.*, 4, 305–27.

[5] —— (1954). Plant regulators for vegetation control on noncrop land. Pp. 216–26 in *Plant Regulators in Agriculture* (Ed. H. B. Tukey), John Wiley, New York.

[1] BEATTY, R. H. (1960). Herbicides and the American farmer. *Proc. Fourth British Weed Control Conf.* (1958), *Soc. Chem. Ind.*, London, pp. 86–96.

[3] BELKOV, V. P. & ZELAND, M. G. (1956). [Changes in the grass stand and soil during the use of chemical measures for brush control on pastures—in Russian.] *Agrobiologiia*, 4, 128–32.

[5] BENNETT, J. M. (1957). Chemical control of conifers on utility right-of-way. *Proc. Northeast Weed Control Conf.*, 11, 329–35.

[5] BERGESON, E. D. & LORENZ, R. W. (1957). Seasonal effectiveness of 2,4,5-T basal sprays for eradicating ribes in white pine (*Pinus strobus*) blister rust control in Illinois. *J. Forest.* 55, 17–19.

[6] BICKLEY, W. E. & CORY, E. N. (1955). Water caltrop (*Trapa natans*) in the Chesapeake Bay. *Bull. Assoc. Southeastern Biologists*, 2, 27–28.

[6] BIRKAIA, A. F. & GUDZHABIDZE, N. I. (1957). [Application of herbicides to control weeds in drainage canals in Colchis—in Russian.] *Gidrotekh. i. Melior.*, 9(4), 41–48.

[5] BOLAR, M. D. (1956). Tree girdling in Arkansas. *Soil Conserv.*, 21, 225–6.

O

[1] BONDARENKO, D. & WILLARD, C. J. (1958). Chemical weed control in field crops. *Ohio Agric. Col. Ext. Bull.* 370, 46 pp.

[6] BONDUR, A. I. (1956). [Eradication of stiff vegetation on (fish) ponds with the aid of herbicides—in Russian.] *Nauk. i peredovoi opyt v Sel'skom. Khoz.*, 6, 45.

[3] BOWEN, M. S. (1958). Eleven years of a systematic ragweed control program. *Proc. Northeast Weed Control Conf.*, 12, 313–16.

[6] BOYER, B. B. (1947). *Aquatic Weed Control Manual.* The Cloroben Corp., Jersey City, N.J., 21 pp.

[1-2] BRACEY, P. (1957). Recent advances in residual pre-emergence herbicides. *World Crops*, 9(7), 298–300.

[6] BRAGG, K. K. (1951). An introduction to the aquatic weed problem. *Proc. Canad. Natl. Weed Comt. East. Sect.* 4, 106–11.

[4] —— (1956). Response of bulrush (predominantly *Scirpus americanus*) to herbicidal sprays of Dalapon, amino triazole, and DB compounds. *Proc. Canad. Natl. Weed Comt. East. Sect.*, 9, 95.

[5] BRAMBLE, W. C. (1957). Recent advances in woody brush control in rights-of-way. *Proc. Natl. Shade Tree Conf.*, 33, 180–6.

[5] —— BYRNES, W. R. & WORLEY, D. P. (1957). Progress report no. 4. Effects of certain common brush control techniques and materials on game food and cover on a power line right-of-way. *Proc. Northeast Weed Control Conf.*, 11, 219–26.

[1] BROOKINS, W. W. (1944). *Weeds in Flax.* Central Fibre Corp, Pisgah, N. C., 21 pp.

[6] BRUNS, V. F. & FARMER, W. H. (1950). Aromatic solvents for waterweeds. I. & II. *Reclam. Era* (Washington D.C.), 36, 79–80, 96–97.

[6] ——, RASMUSSEN, L. W. & WOLFE, H. H. (1955). The use of aromatic solvents for control of submersed aquatic weeds in irrigation channels. *U.S. Dept. Agric. Circ.* 971, 33 pp.

[1-7] BUCHHOLTZ, K. P. (1962). Weed control—a record of achievement. *Weeds*, 10,167–9.

[4] —— & PETERSON, D. R. (1957). Control of quackgrass with Dalapon. *Down to Earth*, 12(4), 4–5.

[1] —— & —— (1961). Weed control in field crops. *Wisconsin Agric. Ext. Serv. Circ.*, 447, 13 pp.

[5] BUCKLEY, T. A. (1951). Notes on the control of trees and weeds by phytocides. *Malayan Agric. J.*, 34, 27–31.

[5] BULL, H. & CAMPBELL, R. S. (1950). Recent research in poisoning southern weed hardwoods. *S. Weed Control Conf.* 1950, 7 pp.

BURG, F. W. ZUR. *See* ZUR BURG, F. W.

[2] BYCHKOVA, Z. (1955). [Chemical method of controlling weeds in flax plantings—in Russian.] *Zemledelie*, 3(7), 98–100.

[5] CAMPBELL, R. S. & PEEVY, F. A. (1950). Chemical control of undesirable southern hardwoods. *J. Range Mgmt.*, 3(2), 118–24.

[5] CARLSON, A. E. (1951). Chemistry assumes increasing importance in forest management. *S. Pulp & Paper Mfr.*, 14(10-A). 7, 10, 12.

[2] CARLSON, R. F., MOULTON, J. E. & KRONE, P. R. (1951). Further developments in weed control in gladiolus. *Mich. Agric. Exp. Sta. Quart. Bull.*, 33, 269–74.

[7] ——, —— & —— (1954). Plant regulators in weed control in lawn, garden, orchard and nursery. Pp. 170–83 in *Plant Regulators in Agriculture* (Ed. H. B. Tukey). John Wiley, New York.

[1-7] CARSON, RACHEL. (1962). *Silent Spring.* Houghton Mifflin, Boston; Hamish Hamilton, London, 368 pp.

[5] CARVELL, K. L. (1956). The use of chemicals in controlling forest stand composition in the Duke Forest. *J. Forest.*, 54, 525–30.

[5] —— & BERTHY, H. P. (1955). A guide to killing woody plants in West Virginia. *West Virginia Agric. Exp. Sta. Circ.* 98, 7 pp.

[3-5] CATHEY, H. M. & MARTH, P. C. (1960). Effectiveness of quaternary ammonium carbamates and a phosphonium in controlling growth of *Chrysanthemum morifolium*. *Proc. Amer. Soc. Hort. Sci.*, 76, 609–19.

[6] CHACKO, P. I. (1952). The bladder-wort, *Utricularia fleruosa* Vahl, as a competitor for fish food. *39th Indian Sci. Congr. Proc. Pt. III*, 21.

[5] CHAIKEN, L. E. (1950). Control of undesirable hardwoods. (Abs.) *Assoc. S. Agric. Workers Proc.*, 47, 91–92.

[5] ——(1951). Tree poisoning with 2,4,5-T in frills. *Forest Farmer*, 10(9), 9, 12.

[5] —— (1951a). Chemical control of inferior species in the management of loblolly pine. *J. Forest.*, 49, 695–7.

[5] —— (1952). Control inferior tree species. *Unit*, 41(1), 33–36.

[5] —— (1952a). Control inferior tree species. *S. Lumberman*, 184(2306), 38–39.

[5] —— (1952b). The control of weed trees in forest management. *Proc. S. Weed Conf.*, 5, 135–6.

[6] CHANCELLOR, A. P. (1958). The control of aquatic plants and algae. *Bull. Min. Agr., Fish and Food*, London, 20 pp.

[1-4] CHESALIN, G. A. (1957). [Chemical method of weed control—in Russian.] *Kukuruza*, 2(3), 35–38.

[6] CHIPMAN CHEMICAL ENGINEERING CO. (1954). Control weeds in ponds and lake. Bound Brook, N.J.

[2] CHMORA, S. (1956). [Utilization of certain fractions of petroleum products as herbicides in carrot plantings—in Russian.] *Moskov. Ordena Lenina Selskokhoz. Akad. im. K. A. Timiriazeva. Sborn. Studencheskikh Nauch. -Issled. Rabot*, 6, 82–87.

[1] CHOW, N. P., SZE, W. B. & CAHO, T. T. (1956). [Studies on the use of chemical weed killers in the sugarcane fields of Taiwan (second report—in Chinese).] *Formosa Sugar Exp. Sta. Rep.*, 14, 16–35.

[5] CHURCH, T. W. (1955). Weeding—an effective treatment for stimulating growth of northern hardwoods. *J. Forest.*, 53, 717–19.

[1] CIFERRI, R. (1956). [Four years of observation on selective herbicides and rice—in Italian.] *Riso*, 5(12), 10–12.

[4] CLARE, K. E. (1961). The use and control of vegetation on roads and airfields overseas. *Dept. Sci. Ind. Res. Road Res. Lab. Tech. Paper* No. 52, 41 pp.

[1] COLEMAN, P. G., HAYNES, D. W. M. & HITCHCOCK, J. L. B. (1956). Observations on the control of weeds in padi fields by the use of herbicides. *Malayan Agric. J.*, 39(3), 191–9.

[5] CONSTABLE, D. H. (1952). Testing of tree killing substances on *Hevea brasiliensis*. I. *Rubber Res. Inst. Ceylon Quart. Circ.*, 28, 26.

[3] CORNELIUS, D. R. & TALBOT, M. W. (1955). Rangeland improvement through seeding and weed control on east slope Sierra Nevada and on southern Cascade Mountains. *U.S. Dept. Agric. Handbook*, 88, 51 pp.

[4] COSTER, C. (1932). Eenige waarnemingen omtrent groei en bestrigding van alangalang (*Imperata cylindrica* Beauv.). *Tectona* (Buitenzorg), 25(4), 383–402.

[4] —— (1932a). [Some observations on the growth of *Imperata cylindrica* Beauv. and its extermination—in Dutch, English Summary.] *Proefstation voor het Bosohwegen, Korte mededeelingen*, Buitenzorg, No. 26.

[5] COTTA, A. (1951). Il bastadume. *Schweiz. Zeitschr. Forstw.*, 102, 221–7.

[5] COULTER, L. L. (1954). Some aspects of right-of-way brush control with 2,4,5-T and 2,4-D. *Weeds*, 3, 21–27.

[5] —— (1955). Herbicides useful to foresters in aerial brush control. *U.S. Forest Serv. Lake States Forest Exp. Sta. Misc. Rep.*, 39, 1–7.

[4] COUPLAND, R. T. & SELLECK, G. W. (1957). The place of life history studies with perennial weeds. *Proc. Canad. Natl. Weed Comt. West. Sect.*, 10, 61–66.

[1] CRAFTS, A. S. & EMANUELLI, A. (1955). La erradicacion de yerbajos en la cana de azucar. *Industr. Azucarera*, 61, 409–15.

[5] CROSSLEY, D. I. (1950). Chemical thinning of young stagnating lodgepole pine stands. *Canad. Forest Res. Div. Silvicult. Leaflet* 42, 2 pp.

[1] DADD, C. V. (1957). The cultural and chemical control of wild oats. *Agric. Rev.*, 2(10), 36–39.

[4] DANHOF, G. N. (1940). [An attempted solution of the lalang-grass problem in the Lampong district—in Dutch.] *Tectona*, 33(2/3), 197–225; *Bergenehires*, 14, 584–92, 610–17.

[1-7] DANIELSON, L. L., KLINGMAN, D. L., SHAW, W. C., TIMMONS, F. L. & ENNIS, W. B., JR. (1961). Suggested guide for chemical control of weeds. *U.S. Dept. Agric., Agric. Res. Service Special Report*, 22–67. Washington, D.C. 60 pp.

[3] DARROW, R. A. & McCULLY, W. G. (1958). Pellet application of Fenuron for the control of post and blackjack oaks. *Texas Agric. Exp. Sta. Prog., Rep.*, 2041, 4 pp.

[6] DAVIES, W. (1959). Effects of the water hyacinth (*Eichhornia crassipes*) in the Nile Valley. *Nature, Lond.*, 184, 1085–6.

DAVIS, A. E. SANGER. *See* SANGER-DAVIS, A. E.

[6] DAY, B. E. & SWEZEY, A. W. (1956). Control of *Phragmites* with Dalapon. *Down to Earth*, 11(4), 17–19.

[5] DAY, M. W. (1957). Killing undesirable trees—a comparison of methods. *Michigan Agric. Exp. Sta. Quart. Bull.*, 39(4), 487–690.

[1-4] DEATRICK, E. P. (1930). The spotting method of weed eradication. *Science*, 71, 487–8.

[7] DEFRANCE, J. A. & WISNIEWSKI, A. J. (1956). Control of crabgrass (*Digitaria*) and other common lawn weeds. *Plants & Gard.*, 12, 102–9.

[2] DENISEN, E. L. (1956). Weed control in small fruits. *Iowa Book Agric.*, 2, 165–8.

[1-7] DESMOND, ANABELLE (1963 [1962]). How many people have ever lived on Earth? *Smithsonian Inst. Rep.* 1963, pp. 545–65 (originally in, *Population Bull.* 18 (1)).

[1-4] DEWEY, L. H. (1896). Legislation against weeds. *U.S.D.A. Div. Bot. Bull.* No. 47.

[6] DICKERSON, L. M. (1955). Some practical pointers on weed control in small ponds. *Va. Comm. Game & Inland Fish. Ed. Leaflet* 17, 11 pp.

[5] DIETZ, S. M. & LEAD, L. D. (1930). Methods of eradicating buckthorn. *U.S. Dept. Agric. Circ.* 133, 15 pp.

[6] DIVEKAR, M. V. (1956). Weed control in the submerged areas of Kolhapur. *Deccan Sugar Technol. Assoc. (India) Ann. Conv.*, 13(1), 72–75.

[1-2] DOOTJES, E. (1955). [Control of weeds on arable land—in Dutch] *Netherlands. Rlandbconsschap. v. Noordelijk Zuid-Holland, Verslagen en Meded.*, 2, 73–80.

[6] EATON, M. E. D. (1954). The maintenance of irrigation and drainage channels with special reference to weed control. *Trans. Inst. Comm. Irrigation & Drainage, Second Congr.* 1954, Vol. 2 (Cf. Pesticides Abs. & Summ. Sect. C2(4), 36 (1956)).

[1-3] EGGEBRECHT, H. (1962). *Unkräuter im Feldbestand; eine Bestimmungsbuch.* 3 Aufl. von C. Tittel Radebeul, Neumann, 296 pp.

[6] EGGINTON, G. E. & ROBBINS, W. W. (1920). Irrigation water as a factor in the dissemination of weed seeds. *Colorado Agrig. Exp. Sta. Bull.* 253, 25 pp.

[6] EGGLER, W. A. (1953). The use of 2,4-D in the control of water hyacinth and alligator weed in the Mississippi Delta, with certain ecological implications. *Ecology*, 34, 409–14.

[1-7] EGLER, F. E. (1964). Pesticides—in our ecosystem. *Amer. Scient.*, 52, 110–36.

[6] ELLIS, M. M. (1937). Detection and measurement of stream pollution. *U.S. Dept. Commerce, Bur. Fisheries Bull.* 22, 72 pp.

[1-2] ENNIS, W. B. (1955). Weed control in principal crops of the Southern United States. *Advanc. Agron.*, 7, 252–97.

[5] EVANS, S. (1954). Weed control on state highways. *Proc. Natl. Shade Tree Conf.*, 30, 241–6.

[6] EVERHART, M. (1950). Biological effects of nitrosine used for control of weeds in hatchery ponds. *Prog. Fish Culturist*, 12, 135–40.

[5] FARRER, R. P. (1951). The use of selective herbicides in forestry in general and in nursery work in particular. *Empire Forestry Rev.* (London), 30, 66–71.

[6] FASSETT, N. C. (1951). *Callitriche* in the New World. *Rhodora*, 53(630), 137–55.

[1] FERTIG, S. N. (1950). The use of 2,4-D for the control of weeds in field crop rotations. Ph.D. Thesis, Cornell Univ., 570 pp.

FETVADZHIEVA, N. ANDREEVA-. *See* ANDREEVA-FETVADZHIEVA, N.

[3] FISHER, C. E. & QUINN, L. (1959). Control of mesquite on grazing lands. *Texas Agric. Exp. Sta. Bull.* 935, 24 pp.

[5] FORBES, R. D. (Ed.) (1955). *Forestry Handbook*. Ronald Press, New York.

[4] FORSTER, R. (1957). [The use of Dalapon weedkiller against *Imperata brasiliensis* Trin.—in Portuguese.] *Bragantia*, 16(note), I–III.

[4] FRAZIER, J. C. (1948). Principal noxious perennial weeds of Kansas, with emphasis upon their root systems in relation to control. *Kansas Agric. Exp. Sta. Bull.* 331, 45 pp.

[1-7] FREDERIKSEN, H., GRØNTVED, P., & PETERSEN, H. I. (1950). [*Weeds and Weed control*— in Danish.] Kgl. Danske Landhusholdningsselskab, Copenhagen. 320 pp.

[1-7] FREED, V. H. (1964). Determination of herbicides and plant growth regulators. *The Physiology and Biochemistry of Herbicides* (Ed. L. J. Audus). pp. 39–74. Academic Press, London & New York.

[5] FRYER, J. D. (1955). The role of arboricides in bush and forest eradication. *J. Sci. Food & Agric.*, 6, 73–78.

[1] —— (1958). Choosing the best herbicides for cereals. *Agriculture*, 64, 585–92.

[1-4] —— & CHANCELLOR, R. J. (1956). The relative toxicity of MCAPA, 2,4-D and 2,4-DB to weeds. *Proc. Brit. Weed Control Conf.* 3(1), 357–77.

[3] FUELLEMAN, R. F. & GRABER, L. F. (1938), Renovation and its effect on the populations of weeds in pastures. *J. Amer. Soc. Agron.*, 30, 616/23.

GANCEDO, A. P. GARCIA. *See* GARCIA GANCEDO, A. P.

[1-2] GARCIA CABEZON, A. (1956). Herbicida selectivo para umbelfferas. *Agricultura* (*Madrid*) 26, 735–7.

[1-2] GARCIA GANCEDO, A. P. (1955). Algunas experience realizadas con fiitohormonas sobre diversas especies vegetales. *Inst. Bot. A. J. Cavanilles*, An. 13, 79–94.

[6] GAY, P. A. (1958). *Eichhornia crassipes* in the Nile of the Sudan. *Nature, Lond.*, 182, 538.

[1-7] GENTNER, W. A. (1963). 1963 Field evaluation of chemicals for their herbicidal properties. *U.S. Dep. Agric. Crops Res. Div. Publ.* 75–63. 38 pp.

[5] GEORGE, J. L. (1962). Some primary and secondary effects of herbicides on wildlife, pp. 40–73, *in* McDermott, R. E. & Byrnes, W. R., *Herbicides and their Use in Forestry*, School of Forestry, Pennsylvania State Univ., Univ. Park, Penn. 128 pp.

[1-7] GERMAN FEDERAL REPUBLIC. (1961). *Naturschutz- Tierschutz- und Jagdrecht*; *Fischerei und Kulturpflanzenschutz*. Kommentar von Albert Lorz. Munchen, Bech, 466 pp.

[1] GHARABAGHY, V. (1956). [Weeding out sugar beet bushes—in Iranian.] *Iran. Ext. Serv. Bull.* 12, 8 pp.

[7] GOETZE, N. (1955). Some factors affecting the chemical control of velvet grass, *Holcus lanatus*, in sods of Astoria bentgrass, *Agrostis tenuis*. *Agron. Abs.*, 47, 74.

[6] GONZALES, A. J. (1955). Malas hierbas y plantas nocivas en los canaverales. *Asoc. de Téc. Azucareros de Cuba Mem. de la Conf. Anu.*, 29, 27–36.

GONZALES, R. SOSA *See* SOSA GONZALES, R.

[3] GOODRUM, P. D. & REID, V. H. (1956). Wildlife implications of hardwood and brush controls. *Trans. N. Amer. Wildlife Conf.*, 21, 127–41.

[5] GOOR, C. P. VAN (1955). [Chemical weed control in forestry—in Dutch.] *Nederland. Heidenmaatsch. Tijdschr.*, 66, 98–106.

[1-7] GORTER, C. J. & VAN DER ZWEEP, W. (1964). Morphogenetic effects of herbicides. *The Physiology and Biochemistry of Herbicides* (Ed. L. J. Audus), pp. 235–75. Academic Press, London & New York.

[1] GRANGE LEAGUE FEDERATION (1962–63). *Chemical Weed Control Guide.* Cooperative G.L.F. Exchange Inc., Ithaca, New York. 82 pp.

[1] —— (1963). *Chemical Weed Control Guide,* 1963–1964. Cooperative G. L. F. Exchange, Inc., Ithaca, New York, 34 pp.

[5] GRANO, C. X. (1953). Chemical control of weed hardwoods (*Quercus falcata*). *S. Lumberman,* **186** (2332), 46–47.

[7] GRAU, F. V. (1951). Open letter to green chairmen about *Poa annua. U.S.G.A. J. and Turf Mgmt.,* **4**(3), 27–29.

[6] GREELEY, J. R. (1950). Water weeds. *New York State Conserv.,* **5**, 14–15.

[1] GREENHAM, C. G. (1957). Studies on phytocides. II. Tests of chlorinated aryloxy-methylphosphorous and phosphorous acids as poisons and auxins. *Austr. J. Biol. Sci.* **10**, 180–1.

[4] GRIEG, J. L. (1937). The use of chemicals for the eradication of lalang grass. *Malayan Agric. J.* (Kuala Lumpur), **25**, 363–93.

[1-4] GUDNASON, A. (1956). [Preparations for eradication of weeds—in Icelandic.] *Freyr,* **52**, 249–52.

[1] GUZMAN, V. L. (1955). Herbicidal control of weeds in sugar cane growing in muck soil. *Soil Sci. Soc. Florida Proc.,* **15**, 53–59.

[5] HACKETT, D. P. (1952). Experiments in the chemical control of hardwoods in north-eastern forests. *Proc. Northwest. Weed Control Conf.,* **6**, 311–19.

[5] HAIG, I. T. (1950). The control of undesirable hardwoods in southern forests. *Forest Farmer,* **9**(11), 9, 11, 14.

[5] HAINES, A. (1940). The uses and control of natural undergrowth on rubber estates. *Planting Manual No. 6, Rubber Res. Inst. of Malaya,* 37 pp.

[5] HALL, C. W. (1953). Controlling upland hardwoods in South Carolina. *Clemson Agric. Coll. S.C. Ext. Circ.* 385, 11 pp.

[6] HALL, T. F. (1961). Principles of aquatic plant control. *Advances in Pest Control* **4**, 211–47.

[5] HAMILTON, L. S. & MORROW, R. R. (1955). Killing undesirable woody plants with chemicals. *Cornell. Univ. Coll. Agric. Dept. Conserv. Mimeo. Leaflet* 9 (rev.), 5 pp.

HANNFELT, M. JUHLIN- *See* JUHLIN-HANNFELT, M.

[7] HANSEN, A. A. (1921). Lawn pennywort; a new weed. *U.S. Dept. Agric. Circ.* 165, 6 pp.

[6] —— (1925). Notes on the control of water weeds. *J. Amer. Soc. Agron.,* **17**, 119–20.

[4] HANSON, N. S. (1956). Dalapon for control of grasses on Hawaiian sugar cane lands. *Down to Earth,* **12**(2), 2–5.

[1] HAQ, A. (1955). Weed flora of paddy fields and its control in eastern Uttar Pradesh. *Science & Culture,* **21**, 277–8.

[6] HARPER, H. J. & DANIEL, H. R. (1934). Chemical composition of certain aquatic plants. *Bot. Gaz.,* **96**, 186–9.

[5] HAWKES, C. L. (1952). Something new in weed tree control. *Proc. West. Forestry & Conserv. Assoc.,* **43**, 45–46.

[5] —— (1953). Planes release tree plantation. *J. Forest.,* **51**, 345–8.

[1-7] HELGESON, E. A. (1957). Control of aquatic and ditchbank weeds. Pp. 78–84 in *Methods of Weed Control.* F.A.O., Rome, 189 pp.

[1-7] —— (1957a). Some principles of weed control. *Methods of Weed Control,* FAO, Rome, pp. 1–5.

[1-7] —— (1957b). Chemical methods of weed control. *Methods of Weed Control,* FAO, Rome, pp. 20–23.

[1-7] —— (1957c). Equipment for weed control. *Methods of Weed Control,* FAO, Rome, pp. 51–77.

[6] HELGESON, E. A. (1957*d*). Reaction of plant species to certain herbicides (alphabetical listing). *Methods of Weed Control*, FAO, Rome, 159–84.

[5] —— (1957*e*). Control of woody plants. Pp. 85–94 in *Methods of Weed Control*. F.A.O., Rome, 189 pp.

[7] —— (1957*f*). Control of weeds in grassland and turf. Pp. 95–96 in *Methods of Weed Control*. F.A.O., Rome, 189 pp.

[1] —— (1957*g*). Weed control in field crops. Pp. 97–113 in *Methods of Weed Control*. F.A.O., Rome, 189 pp.

[2] —— (1957*h*). Weed control in horticultural crops. Pp. 114–25 in *Methods of Weed Control*. F.A.O., Rome, 189 pp.

[4] —— (1957*i*). Control of some important weeds (largely perennial). Pp. 126–54 in *Methods of Weed Control*. F.A.O., Rome, 189 pp.

[1] HES, J. W. (1951). [The question of lalang grass in rice fields—in Dutch.] *Econ. Weekbl. v. Indonesia*, **17**, 180.

[5] HICKMAN, K. V. (1956). Aerial sprays to aid forestry. *Conserv. Volunteer*, **19**(109), 8–10.

[7] HITCHCOCK, A. E. & ZIMMERMAN, P. W. (1947). Response and recovery of dandelion and plantain after treatment with 2,4-D. *Contrib. Boyce Thompson Inst.*, **13**, 471–92.

[6] ——, KIRKPATRICK, H. & ZIMMERMAN, P. W. (1949). Comparative activity of hormone-like substances as herbicides and their future possibilities with special reference to water weeds. *Proc. Northeast. Weed Control Conf.*, **3**, 14–19.

[6] ——, —— & —— (1950). Practical control of water hyacinth with 2,4,-D applied by helicopter and other equipment. *Proc. Northeast. Weed Control Conf.*, **4**, 263–5.

[6] ——, ——, —— & EARLE, T. T., (1949*a*). Water hyacinth, its growth, reproduction, and practical control by 2,4-D. *Contrib. Boyce Thompson Inst.*, **15**(7), 363–401.

[6] ——, ——, —— & —— (1950*a*). Growth and reproduction of water hyacinth and alligator weed and their control by means of 2,4-D. *Contrib. Boyce Thompson Inst.*, **16**, 91–130.

[6] HODGSON, J. M., BRUNS, V. F., TIMMONS, F. L., LEE, W. O., WELDON, L. W. & YEO, R. R. (1962). Control of certain ditchbank weeds on irrigation systems. *U.S. Dep. Agric. Res. Serv. Prod. Res. Rep.* **60**, 64 pp.

[5] HOLT, V. (1952–53). Weed growth in plantations. *Sylva* (Edinburgh), **33**, 19–20.

[6] HOPE, A. (1927). The dissemination of weed seeds by irrigation water in Alberta. *Sci. Agric.*, **7**(7), 268–76.

[5] HOSNER, J. F. & MINCKLER, L. S. (1957). Chemical debarking offers means of utilizing pine thinnings. *J. Forest.*, **55**(6), 458–60.

[6] HOTCHKISS, N. & DOZIER, H. L. (1949). Taxonomy and distribution of North American cattails. *Amer. Mid. Nat.*, **41** (1), 237–54.

[1] HRON, F. (1957). [The Control of Field Weeds—in Czech.] Prague. 159 pp.

[5] HUBBARD, R. A. (1955). Brush disposal—brush chippers. *Proc. Natl. Shade Tree Conf.* **31**, 174–6.

[5] HUCKENPAHLER, B. J. (1954). Poisoning versus girdling to release underplanted pines in north Mississippi. *J. Forest.*, **52**, 266–8.

[6] HUGHES, E. C. (1956). Effect of soil sterilants on water smartweed (*Polygonum hydropiperoides*) in drainage ditches in the Fraser Valley. *Res. Rep. Natl. Weed Comt., West. Sect., Dec. 1956*, p. 78.

[6] —— (1956*a*). Control of bog rush (*Juncus effusus*) in pastures. *Res. Rep., Natl. Weed Comt., West. Sect., Dec. 1956*, p. 84.

[2] HUYSMANS, C. P. & GONGGRIJP, J. (1951). [Chemical weed control in tea—in Dutch.] *Bergcultures*, **20**, 209, 211, 213.

[3] HYDER, D. N., SNEVA, F. A., CHILCOTE, D. O. & FURTICK, W. O. (1958). Chemical control of rabbitbrush (*Chrysothamnus*) with emphasis upon simultaneous control of big sagebrush (*Artemisia tridentata*). *Weeds*, **6**(3), 289–97.

[6] INGRAM, W. M. & TARZWELL, C. M. (1954). Selected bibliography of publications relating to undesirable effects upon aquatic life by algicides, insecticides, weedicides. *U.S. Public Health Serv., Publ. Health Bibliog.*, Ser. 13, 28 pp.

[1] ISELY, D. (1960). *Weed Identification and Control in the North Central States.* Iowa State Univ. Press, Ames, 2nd edn., 400 pp.

[5] IURKEVICH, I. D. & MISHNEV, V. G. (1956). [Chemical method for the care of young forests—in Russian.] *Lesn. Khoz.*, 10, 9–14.

[6] JACKSON, H. W. (1951). Weed control in small ponds. *Virginia Agric. Exp. Sta. Bull.* 425, 30 pp.

[6] JACOBS, D. L. (1947). An ecological life-history of *Spirodela polyrhiza* (greater duckweed) with emphasis on the turion phase. *Ecol. Monog.*, 17, 437–69.

[6] —— (1950). Ecological and taxonomical status of Georgia duckweeds, *Wolffiella.* Abstract, *Tennessee Acad. Sci. J.*, 25, 228.

[1-7] JAGOL, R. B. & JOHNSTON, M. (1949). The use of plant growth-regulating substances as weed killers. *Malayan Agric. J.*, 32, 304–14.

[1] JAHN, S. (1952). Über die Bindung bestimmter Unkräuter an die Wintergetreidearten. *Mitt. Floristisch-Soziolog. Arbeitsgemein*, 3, 113–22.

[5] JARVIS, J. M. (1957). The effectiveness of ammonium sulphamate for killing defective tolerant hardwoods. *Forestry Chron.*, 33(1), 51–53.

[6] JENKINS, B. C. (1955). Wildlife habitat development with herbicides in Michigan. *Proc. North Carolina Weed Control Conf.*, 12, 58.

[1-7] JOHNSON, O., KROG, N. & POLAND, J. L. (1963). Fungicides and herbicides. *Chem. Week.* 92 (22), 55–90.

[1-2] JONES, H. A. & MANN, L. K. (1963). *Onions and Their Allies.* World Crops Series. (Ed. N. Polunin). London, Leonard Hill; New York, Interscience. 286 pp.

[6] JONES, K. W. & ANDREWS, F. W. (1952). The chemical control of water weeds in the Gezira area of the Sudan. I. *Ann. Appl. Biol.*, 39, 120–8.

[6] JOSHI, L. M., PANTALU, V. R. & PADMANATHAN, S. Y. (1950). Control of water hyacinth with hormone herbicides. *Indian Farmer*, 11, 545–6.

[5] JUHLIN-HANNFELT, M. & DUTHRIE, E. C. (1927). Methods of weed control in forest nurseries (Abs.). *Int. R. Agric.*, 18, 1240–2.

[3] KALENICH, W. (1951). Bibliography on brush control. *Southwest. Res. Inst., Range Mgmt. Sect., Agr. Div., San Antonio*, 59 pp.

[1] KASAHARA, Y. & HIRATA, M. (1956). [On the control of weeds on the field of rush (*Juncus effusus* L. var. *decipiens* Buch.) after rice crop with CIPC—in Japanese.] *Nogaku Kenkyu*, 44(3), 105–18.

[1] ——, HIRATA, M., HARO, S. & TAKEDO, M. (1956). [Studies on the control of weeds on the field of winter cereals after rice crop. III—in Japanese.] *Nogaku Kenkyu*, 43, 181–212.

[1] ——, KINOSHITA, O. & HIRATA, M. (1955). [Studies on the control of weeds on the fields of winter cereals after rice crop. I-II.—in Japanese.] *Nogaku Kenkyu*, 43, 73–104.

[3] KENNEDY, P. B. (1927). An alkali forage weed—*Bassia hyssopifolia. J. Amer. Soc. Agric.*, 19, 750.

[1-7] KING, L. J. (1943). Responses of *Elodea densa* to growth-regulating substances. *Bot. Gaz.*, 105, 127–51.

[1-7] KINGSBURY, J. M. (1964). *Poisonous Plants of the United States and Canada.* New Jersey, Prentice-Hall. 626 pp.

[6] KIRKPATRICK, H. (1958). Eradication and control of water hyacinth (Eichhornia); results of a campaign in the Belgian Congo in 1955–57. *World Crops*, 10(8), 286–8.

[1] KLINGMAN, D. L. (1953). Effects of varying rates of 2,4-D and 2,4,5-T at different stages of growth on winter wheat. *Agron. J.*, 45, 606–10.

[3] —— (1956). Weed control in pastures in the North Central Region. *Weeds*, 4, 369–75.

[1-7] KLINGMAN, D. L. & SHAW, W. C. (1962). Using Phenoxy herbicides effectively. *Fmrs. Bull. U.S. Dep. Agric.* No. 2183, 24 pp.

[*1] ——, ——, TIMMONS, F. L., ALDRICH, K. J., DANIELSON, L. L. & ENNIS, W. B., JR. (1958). Weed control in field crops. Pp. 17–23 in *Suggested Guide for Chemical Control of Weeds*, U.S. Dept. Agric., Washington.

[2] ——, ——, ——, ——, —— & —— (1958*a*). Weed control in horticultural crops. Pp. 24–30 in *Suggested Guide for Chemical Control of Weeds*. U.S. Dept. Agric., Washington.

[3] ——, ——, ——, ——, —— & —— (1958*b*). Weed control in forage crops, pastures, and rangelands. Pp. 31–36 in *Suggested Guide for Chemical Control of Weeds*. U.S. Dept. Agric., Washington.

[4] ——, ——, ——, ——, —— & —— (1958*c*). Control of herbaceous perennial weeds in cropland. Pp. 37–38 in *Suggested Guide for Chemical Control of Weeds*. U.S. Dept. Agric., Washington.

[5] ——, ——, ——, ——, —— & —— (1958*d*). Control of weeds along fencerows, ditchbanks, roadsides, utility lines, and other noncultivated areas. Pp. 39–40 in *Suggested Guide for Chemical Control of Weeds*. U.S. Dept. Agric., Washington.

[6] ——, ——, ——, ——, —— & —— (1958*e*). Control of aquatic weeds. Pp. 41–42 in *Suggested Guide for Chemical Control of Weeds*. U.S. Dept. Agric., Washington.

[7] ——, ——, ——, ——, —— & —— (1958*f*). Weed control in lawns and other turf areas. Pp. 43–46 in *Suggested Guide for Chemical Control of Weeds*. U.S. Dept. Agric., Washington.

[5] KOLAR, M. (1957). [Forest thinning—in Hebrew.] *La-Yaaran*, 7(1/2), 10–12.

[4] KOROBATOV, V. A. (1956). [Peculiarities of vegetative propagation of perennial weeds and their control—in Russian.] *Ministerstvo Selskogo Khoz. Sbornik materialov. po phlopkovodstvu*, pp. 64–70. Azerbaidzhanskoe Gosudarstvennoe Izdztel'stvo, Baku.

[1-4] KORSMO, E. & VIDME, T. (1954). [*Weeds in Present-day Agriculture*—in Norwegian.] A.-S. Norsk Landbruks Forlag, Oslo, 635 pp.

[1-7] KOSESAN, W. H. (1964). *Spray Manual*. Tech. Bull. No. 25, Oregon State Highway Dept., Salem. 50 pp.

[1-7] KOTT, S. A. (1955). [*Weeds and their Control*—in Russian.] Selkhozgiz, Moscow, 384 pp.

[1-4] KRAUS, E. J. (1954. The significance of growth regulators in agricultural practice. *Amer. Sci.*, 42, 439–60.

[5] KRYKHANOV, L. (1957). [Practices in brush control in Karelia—in Russian.] *Zemledelie*, 5(5), 52–55.

[1-7] KURTH, H. (1963). *Chemische Unkrautbekampfung*. G. Fischer, Jena, 302 pp. *Zw. Aufl.*

[2] KURUP, P. G. (1955). Weed control in coconut gardens. *Indian Cent. Coconut Comt. Bull.*, 9, 40–42.

[5] LARSON, W. H. (1952). Airplane spraying for weed trees. *West. Forestry & Conserv. Assoc. Proc.*, 43, 46–47.

[3] LAUWERS, T. (1956). Le désherbage des prairies. *Liège Inst. Prov. de Coop. Agric. Bull.*, 25, 8–12.

[6] LAWRENCE, J. M. (1962). *Aquatic Herbicide Data*. Agricultural Research Service, United States Dept. of Agriculture, Washington, D.C. *Agricultural Handbook No. 231*. 133 pp.

[1] LEASURE, J. K. (1955). Chemical weed control experiments with cotton 1951–54. *Tennessee Agric. Exp. Sta. Bull.* 240, 11 pp.

[6] LEE, W. O. & TIMMONS, F. L. (1956). Control of cattail by various chemical treatments. *West. Weed Cont. Conf. Res. Prog. Rep.*, pp. 81–82.

[4] LEMAISTRE, J. (1956). La lutte contre l'*Imperata. Fruits*, 11, 380–3.

* Cf. Danielson, L. L., *et al.* (1961) revised edition p. 388.

[3,5] LEONARD, O. A. & HARVEY, W. A. (1956). Chemical control of woody plants in California. *California Agric. Exp. Sta. Bull.* 755, 39 pp.

[6] LEVARDSON, N. O. (1951). Weed control in Michigan lakes. *Michigan Conserv.*, 20(3), 11–14.

[6] LEWIS, N. R. (1932). Head loss in flow through fine screens. *Agric. Engng.*, 13, 144.

[1] LINNIK, E. F. (1956). [Chemical weeding of fibre flax—in Russian.] *Lën i Konoplia*, 7, 45–46.

[1] LONGCHAMP, P. (1956). Le désherbage du riz. *Journées du Riz.*, 5, 47–57.

[1] — (1956a). Le désherbage du riz. *Bull. d'Inform. des Rizicult. de France*, 49, 11–16.

[1] ——, BLANCK, A. & MIQUEL, L. (1956). Récherches préliminaires sur l'action des désherbants à base de 2,4-D sur le riz. *Bull. d'Inform. des Rizicult. de France*, 44, 16–22.

[1] LOPINOT, A. C. (1963). Aquatic weeds and their identification and methods of control. *Illinois Fish. Bull.* No. 4, 47 pp.

LORZ, A. *See* GERMAN FEDERAL REPUBLIC (1961).

[3] LYMAN, R. J. (1950). Tucumcari tumbleweed (*Cirsium*) trap. *Reclam. Era*, 36, 138–9.

[1-7] LYNES, F. F. (1935). Statistical analyses applied to research in weed eradication. *J. Amer. Soc. Agric.*, 27, 980–7.

[1] McCARTY, M. K. & SAND, P. F. (1958). Chemical weed control in alfalfa. *Weeds*, 6, 152–60.

[5] McDERMOTT, R. E. & BYRNES, W. R. (eds.) (1962). *Herbicides and their Use in Forestry*. Proc. Forestry Symposium, 1960. Penn. State Univ., Univ. Park, Penn., 128 pp.

[6] MacMULLAN, R. A. & HARGER, E. M. (1955). Control of undesirable plants in waterfowl projects. *Proc. North Cent. Weed Cont. Conf.*, 12, 58–59.

[1-7] MAKAROVA, V. A. (1955). [*Weed Control*—in Russian.] Rostovskoe Knizhnoe Izdatelstvo, *Rostovna-Donu*, 59 pp.

[5] MAKI, T. E. & ALLEN, R. M. (1952). Use of allyl alcohol for weed control in forest nurseries. *J. Forestry*, 50, 470–1.

[2] MANII, A. (1956). [Controlling weeds in orchards—in Iranian.] *Iran. Ext. Serv. Bull.* 10, 12 pp.

[3,5] MANLEY, K. & WALKER, C. F. (1956). Brush control and reseeding for range improvements in central California. *J. Range Mgmt.*, 9, 278–80.

[6] MARTIN, A. C. (1955). Another water chestnut infestation. *J. Wildlife Mgmt.*, 19, 504–5.

[6] ——, ERICKSON, E. C. & STEENIS, J. H. (1957). Improving duck marshes by weed control. *U.S. Dept. Interior, Fish & Wildlife Serv. Circ.* 19, 60 pp.

[5] MASERA, M. (1955). [Research on plant hormone type products used for brush control in mountain areas. I—in Italian.] *Milan. U. Facol. di Agr. Ann.*, n.s., 4, 253–62.

[1] MATERIKINA, E. (1956). [Weed control in millet plantings—in Russian.] *Zemledelie*, 4(7), 109–10.

[6] MATHESON, R. (1930). Utilization of aquatic plants as aids in mosquito control. *Amer. Nat.*, 64, 58–86.

[3] MAYES, J. (1920). The practical control of weeds in Missouri meadows and pastures. *Missouri State Bd. Agric. Mo. Bull.*, 18(6), 35 pp.

[1-4] MELNICHUK, A. S. (1956). [Chemical control of weeds in the Ukraine—in Russian.] *Zasch. Rast. ot Vred. i Boleznei*, 1(4), 33.

[6] MERCER, A. D. (1948). Control of water hyacinth (*Eichhornia crassipes*) in the Rewa delta. *Agric. J.* (Fiji), 19, 72–73.

[6] MICHIELS, A. & DUSTIN, A. (1956). Quelques acquisitions dans le domaine du contrôle de la végétation aquatique. *Ghent. Landb Hogesch. Meded.*, 21(3), 627–41.

[5] MILLER, R. S. B. (1957). Some aspects of coniferous advance growth release by herbicide application. *Pulp & Paper Mag. Canada*, 58(3), 357–9, 361–2.

[3] MIUGE, S. G. (1956). [Pasture poisonings and chemical control measures against poisonous plants.—in Russian] *Zhivotnovodstvo*, 8, 75–78.

[5] MOLIN, N. & TEAR, J. (1956). [Experiments with chemical weed control in forest nurseries—in Swedish.] *Meddl. Stat. Skogsförsoks.*, 46(6), 16 pp.

[6] MONSANTO CHEMICAL COMPANY (1956). The chemical control of aquatic weeds. *Monsanto Tech. Serv. Bull.*, 7 pp.

[7] MONTEITH, J. (1940). Weed control in turf. Pp. 55–67 in *The Control of Weeds* (Ed. R. O. Whyte), *Herbage Pub. Ser. Bull.* 27.

[1-4] MONTERREY, A. (1956). Los productos quimicos incrementan la productividad de las siembras de algodón. *Agronomica* (Monterrey), 48, 2–7.

[6] MOYLE, J. (1949). Some chemical factors influencing the distribution of aquatic plants in Minnesota. *Amer. Mid. Nat.*, 34(2), 402–20.

[5] MULLISON, W. R. (1952). Brush control. *Plants & Gard.*, 8, 53–55.

[6] MURDOCK, H. R. (1952). Controlled pollution is the best method known to date for eradicating large areas of aquatic plants. *Industr. Engng. Chem.*, 44(2), 97A–99A.

[1-7] NARAYANAN, T. R., & MEENAKSHISUN-DARAM, D. (1957). Studies on weed control by herbicides: observations on the phytocidal action of chemical herbicides on some weeds in Madras State. *Madras Agric. J.*, 44(3), 81–88.

[1-7] NATIONAL ACADEMY OF SCIENCES (1962–63). Pest control and wildlife relationships. *Nat. Acad. Sci. Publ.* 920, A. B. C. I. 28 pp; II 53 pp; III 28 pp.

[1-7] NATIONAL RESEARCH COUNCIL (1962–63). New Developments and problems in the use of pesticides. *Nat. Res. Coun. Publ.* 1082. 82 pp. Washington, D.C.

[6] NORMAN, I. W. (1958). C.M.U. makes channel cleaning easy. *Dairy Farming Digest*, 5(4), 33–35.

[7] NYLUND, R. E. & STADTHERR, R. (1956). Studies on the control of crabgrass in bluegrass lawns. *Weeds*, 4, 264–74.

[6] OBORN, E. T. (1954). Control of aquatic weeds that impede flow of western irrigation waters. *Weeds*, 3(3), 231–40.

[6] O'BRIEN, G. E. & TATE, H. D. (1956). Dichlone as a control for submersed aquatic weeds. *Weed Soc. Amer. Abs.*, p. 66.

[6] OGDEN, E. C. (1943). The broad-leaved species of *Potamogeton* of North America north of Mexico. *Rhodora*, 45, 57–105, 109–63, 171–214.

[1-4] OLSEN, H. K. & STAPEL, C. (1955). [Review of chemical control of weeds, plant diseases and pests in agriculture—in Danish.] *Landbrugets Informationskontor, København*. 39 pp.

[3] OLSON, H. C. (1952). 'Stinkweed' flavour in cream and butter (Abs.). *J. Dairy Sci.*, 35, 485.

[1-7] OVERBEEK, J. VAN (1947). Use of synthetic hormones as weed killers in tropical agriculture. *Econ. Bot.*, 1, 446–59.

[1-4] —— (1954). Plant regulators for weed control in the tropics. Pp. 202–15 in *Plant Regulators in Agriculture* (Ed. H. B. Tukey). John Wiley, New York.

[6] —— (1958). New herbicide for aquatic weed control. *Proc. Fourth British Weed Control Conf.*, pp. 1–2.

[6] ——, HUGHES, W. J. & BLONDEAU, R. (1959). Acrolein for the control of water weeds and disease-carrying water snails. *Science*, 129, 335–6.

[5] PAGE, T. J. (1953). Weeding the woods; unwanted weed trees now can be controlled in valuable timber stands by treatment with Esteron. *Dow Diamond*, 16(5), 25–27.

[6] PARISH, S. B. (1913). Plants introduced into a desert valley as a result of irrigation. *Plant World*, 16, 275–80.

[6] PARK, F. D. R. (1955). Experience of the Dade County Water Conservation District in controlling water hyacinths and water weeds. *Proc. Soil Sci. Soc. Florida*, 14, 140–53.

[5] PEARSE, C. K. (1951). New trends in control of noxious range plants. *J. Forestry*, 49, 498–500.

[5] PEEVY, F. A. (1951). New poisons for undesirable hardwoods. *J. Forestry*, 49, 450.

[5] PEEVY F. A. & BURNS, P. Y. (1959). Effectiveness of aerial applications of herbicides for hardwood control in Louisiana. *Weeds* 7, 463–9.

[5] —— & CAMPBELL, R. S. (1949). Poisoning southern upland weed trees. *J. Forestry*, 47(6), 443–7.

[3-4] PENGELLY, R. (1963). A new systematic herbicide. *Proc. Sixteenth N.Z. Weed Cont. Conf.* (1963), pp. 139–42.

[1] PENNSYLVANIA AGRICULTURAL EXPERIMENT STATION, EXTENSION SERVICE (1963). *1963 Agronomy Guide*. Univ. Park, Penn., 22 pp.

[5] PETERSON, D. R. & BUCHHOLTZ, K. P. (1958). Controlling brush, stumps, and small trees with chemicals. *Wisconsin Agric. Exp. Sta. Ext. Circ.*, 564, 7 pp.

[5] PILLAI, A. K. (1953). The poisoning of *Ficus* trees in the dry zone. *Ceylon Forester*, n.s. 1, 124.

[6] PIRIE, N. W. (1960). Water hyacinth: a curse or a crop? *Nature, Lond.*, 188, 23.

[3] RABOTNOV, T. (1956). [Use of 2,4-D preparation for improvement of pastures overgrown with brush—in Russian.] *Kolkhoz. Proizvodstvo*, 16(9), 25.

[4] RASMUSSEN, L. W. (1956). The effects of 2,4-D and 2,4,5-T applications on the stand density of Canada thistle (*Cirsium arvense* Scop.). *Weeds*, 4, 343–8.

[1] RATAJ, K. (1956). [Use of 2-methyl-4-chlorophenoxyacetic acid for destroying weeds in fibre flax—in Russian.] *Za Sotsialist. Selskokhoz. Nauk. Ser. A, Agron-Zootekh.*, 5(4), 339–84.

[4] REA, H. E. (1958). Spot-spraying Johnson grass (*Sorghum halepense*). *Texas Agric. Coll. Ext. Bull.* 902, 14 pp.

[4] REHBEIN, C. A. (1958). Further steps in the control of reed grass (*Phragmites communis*). *Queensland Bur. Sugar Exp. Sta. Cane Growers' Quart. Bull.*, 22(1), 12–13.

[6] REIMER, C. A. & CUTLER, W. A. (1955). Further studies on the use of Dalapon for the control of cattail. *Proc. North Carolina Weed Cont. Conf.*, 12, 60–61.

[5] RENNERFELT, E. (1951). [On use of poison hormones in American forestry—in Swedish.] *Skogen*, 38, 118–19.

[3] REUSS, L. A. (1958). Costs of clearing land and establishing improved pastures in central Florida. *Florida Agric. Exp. Sta. Bull.* 600, 40 pp.

[2] REVELO, P. M. A. & SALDARRIAGA, V. A. (1956). Represión des las malezas del cultivo de la papa, en la sabana de Bogotá. *Agric. Trop.*, 12, 787–93.

[1] ——, —— & POSADO, O. L. (1956). Represión de malezas en los cultivos de trigo, en la sabana de Bogotá. *Agric. Trop.*, 12, 437–45.

[1-7] RIEPMA, P. (1955). [*Weed Control*—in Dutch.] J. B. Walters, Groningen, 225 pp.

[1] RIES, S. K. (1958). Chemical weed control for vegetables and small fruits. *Michigan Agric. Exp. Sta. Ext. Folder* F-24.

[1] RIOS, P., MONTILLA, J. A. & RINCÓN, D. J. (1956). Herbicidas en cultivos de papa, caña de azucar, cebolla y zanahoria. *Co. Shell de Venezuela Serv. Shell para el Agric. Ser. A., Informe* 5, 41 pp.

[3] ROBERTSON, J. H. & CORDS, H. P. (1956). Survival of big sagebrush (*Artemisia tridentata*) of different ages after treatment with selective herbicides. *Weeds*, 4, 376–85.

[1] ROCHE, W. (1951). The importance of weed control in sugar beet production. *Beet Grower*, 5, 98–100.

[1] ROSS, M. R. (1943). The weeds in certain field crops at Knapp farm. *J. Tennessee Acad. Sci.*, 18, 334–49.

[1] ROTH, W. (1957). [Comparative study of the response of maize and wheat to the herbicidal substance, Simazine—in French.] *C.R. Acad. Sci.* (Paris), 245, 942–4.

[1] ROW, V. V. (1955). The effect of spraying MCPA (sodium 2-methyl-4-chlorophenoxyacetic acid) to suppress *Cyperus rotundus* L. on the yield of wheat crop grown in an infested field. *Indian Acad. Sci. Proc. Sect.* B, 41, 65–68.

[5] ROY, D. F. (1956). Killing tan oak (*Lithocarpus densiflorus*) in northwestern California. *U.S. Forest Serv. Calif. Forest & Range Expt. Res. Notes* 106, 9 pp.

[4] Rozhkov, A. I. (1955). [Comparative testing of the ways to destroy *Daphne glomerata* —in Russian.] *Erivan. Inst. Zhivotn. Trud.*, 5, 223–32.

[6] Rudd, R. & Genelly, R. (1957). Pesticides: their use and toxicity in relation to wildlife. *California Dept. Fish & Game Bull.* 7, 209 pp.

[1] Ryker, T. C. (1948). Weed control in rice with 2,4-D. *Louisiana Agric. Exp. Sta. Bull.* 427, 8 pp.

[1-7] Saburova, P. V. & Petunova, A. A. (1960). [*The Use of Herbicides in Agriculture*—in Russian.] Gosudarst. Izdatel. Sel'sko-Khoz, 78 pp.

[1] Safra, R. & Konik, B. (1957). [Control of dodders in bast-fiber crop plantings—in Russian.] *Len i Konoplia*, 2(4), 26–28.

[3] Samgin, P. A. (1956). [Chemistry for the control of willow brushwood on pastures— in Russian.] *Nauk. Pered. Opyt v Selsk. Khoz.*, 9, 28–30.

[5] Sampson, A. W. & Schultz, A. M. (1956). Control of brush and undesirable trees. I, II. *Unasylva*, 10, 19–29; 179–229.

[5] —— & —— (1957). Control of brush and undesirable trees. IV. Conservation in land clearing. *Unasylva*, 11, 19–25.

[6] Sands, N. H. (1933). Notes on certain submerged aquatic weeds in padi fields. *Malayan Agric. J.*, 24, 175–6.

[4] Sanger-Davis, A. E. (1937). Control of resam (*Gleichenia linearis* Burm.). *Malayan Forester*, 6, 140–1.

[1-7] Saunders, J. M. Danielson, L. L., Ennis, W. B., Jr., Klingman, D. L., Shaw, W. C., Timmons, F. L. & Strickler, P. E. (1962). *A Survey of Extent and Cost of Weed Control and Specific Weed Problems*. U.S. Dep. Agric. Res. Serv. No. 34–23, 65 pp.

[1-7] Savchenko, E. N. (1961). [*Handbook of Chemical Weed and Pest Killers*—in Russian.] Goudarst. Izdatel. Sel'sko-Khoz. Lit. Ukr. SSR, Kiev, 328 pp.

[6] Schofield, R. C. (1956). Control of weeds in irrigation races. *Proc. N.Z. Weed Cont. Conf.*, 9, 110–4.

[5] Schroppel, H. (1957). Ein Beiträg zur Kenntnis des Ackerhohlzahnes mit Berücksichtigung sebiner Bekämpfung. *Z. Acker- u. Pflanzenbau*, 100, 367–78.

[5] Schweizer, J. (1952). [Killing old *Hevea* stands with sodium arsenite—in Dutch.] *Bergcultures*, 21, 340, 343; 345; 347, 349.

[6] Seale, C. C. (1949). The control of aquatic weeds by chemical methods in the Florida Everglades. *Proc. Soil Sci. Soc. Florida*, 9, 100–7.

[6] Segadas-Vianna, F. (1949). A phytosociological and ecological study of cattail stands in Oakland County, Michigan. *Bull. Ecol. Soc. Amer.*, 30(4), 60.

[4] Shafer, N. E. (1954). Soil applications of 2,4-D for the eradication of deep-rooted perennial weeds. *Down to Earth*, 9(4), 12–13.

[1] Shaw, H. R., Conrad, P. F., Amundsen, R. F. & Tutton, S. M. (1947). Weed control by 2,4-D with notes on application by airplane. *Hawaiian Pltrs. Rec Ord.*, 51, 155–75.

[3] Shaw, R. G., Holmes, G. D. & Miller, A. D. (1957). Problems of land reclamation. *Agric. Rev.*, 3(2), 31–36.

[1] Shaw, W. C. (1960). Mimeographed communication. U.S. Dept. of Agriculture, Washington, D.C.

[1] —— & Gentner, W. (1957). The selective herbicidal properties of several variously substituted phenoxyalkylcarboxylic acids. *Weeds*, 5, 75–92.

[1-7] Shcheglov, I. V. (1956). [Chemical control of weeds—in Russian.] *Selsk. Khoz. Povolzhia*, 1956(5), 75–76.

[1-7] Shepherd, H.N. (1962). *The pesticide situation for 1961–62.* Agricultural Stabilization & Conservation Service. U.S. Dept. Agric. Washington, D.C. 22 pp.

[1] Shipinov, N. A. (1958). Chemical weed control in the USSR. *Proc. 9th Int. Conf. Quar. Plant Prot.* Moscow, 13 pp.

[3] SILKER, T. H. & DARROW, R. A. (1956). Hardwood control and increased forage production in scrub hardwood-pine stands treated with aerial applications of 2,4,5-T and Silvex. *Texas Agric. Exp. Sta. Prog. Rep.* 1852, 5 pp.

[5] SIMPSON, A. W. (1956). Lucha contra el matorral y los arboles inútiles. *Tierra* (Mexico), 11, 877, 922–3.

[2] SITTON, B. G. & LEWIS, W. A. (1954). Chemical control of blackberry plants and volunteer tung trees in the tung orchard. *Amer. Tung News*, 5(5), 6–7.

[2] ——, —— & POTTER, G. F. (1954). Suggestions on chemical control of seedlings, briars. *Amer. Tung News*, 5(6), 8–9.

[6] SMITH, E. V. (1940). Control of spatterdock in ponds. *Trans. Amer. Fish. Soc.*, 70, 363–8.

[6] —— & SWINGLE, H. S. (1941). The use of fertilizer for controlling pond weed, *Najas guadalupensis. Trans. Sixth N. Amer. Wildlife Conf.*, pp. 245–51.

[6] SOIL SCIENCE SOCIETY OF FLORIDA (1949). Symposium: The control of aquatic plants from the standpoint of water management and irrigation in the lakes, rivers, and canals of the South. *Proc. Soil Sci. Soc. Florida*, 9, 1–115.

[6] SOSA GONZALES, R. (1956). Control de la vegetación sumergida en canales de riego. *Agron. Trop.* (Maracay), 5, 253–8.

[4] SOUTH, F. W. (1923). Eradication of sensitive plant (*Mimosa pudica*). *Malayan Agric. J.*, 10, 237.

[7] SOUTHERN CALIFORNIA GOLF ASSOCIATION (1954). Turf grass survey of Los Angeles County, California. Los Angeles, Calif., 6 pp.

[1-7] SPANKHUIZEN, J. C. VAN DER L. VAN (1956). [Chemical weed control in Indonesia— in Dutch.] *Bergcultures*, 25, 463, 465, 467, 469, 471, 473, 475, 477, 479–80.

[4] —— & SADJIARTO, S. D. R. (1957). [The 'wiping' of lalang in rubber plantations— in Dutch.] *Bergcultures*, 26(9), 187–9.

[6] SPEIRS, M. M. (1948). Summary of literature on aquatic weed control. *Canad. Fish Culturist*, 3(4), 20–32.

[3] SPRAGUE, M. A. (1952). The substitution of chemicals for tillage in pasture renovation. *Agron. J.*, 44, 405–9.

[1] SPRINGER, P. F. (1957). Effects of herbicides and fungicides on wildlife. *N.C. Pesticide Manual*, pp. 87–106. N.C. Agric. Exp. Sta. Raleigh, N.C.

[5] SRIVASTAVA, T. N. (1951). Studies of the differential toxicity of herbicides to tree species. *Indian Forester*, 77, 109–17.

[5] —— (1951a). The application of selective herbicides to forestry practice. II. *Indian Forester*, 77, 176–91.

[1] STAMPER, E. R. & CHILTON, S. J. P. (1951). Johnson grass control in sugarcane. *Weeds*, 1, 32–42.

[1] STANIFORTH, D. W. (1957). Effects of annual grass weeds on the yield of corn. *Agron. J.*, 49, 551–5.

[1] ——, LOVELY, W. G. & WEBER, C. R. (1963). Role of herbicides in soybean production. *Weeds*, 11, 96–98.

[6] STAUFFER, R. E. (1950). Butterworts (*Pinguicula*) and bladderworts (*Utricularia*). *N.Y. Bot. Gard. J.*, 57, 133–44.

[6] STEENIS, J. H. (1956). Progress report on *Phragmites* control. Papers presented at charter meeting of *Weed Society of America*, January 5, 1956.

[1-7] STELZNER, S. (1938). Zur Bekämpfung der Ackerunkräuter. *Forschungsdienst*, 5(5).

[6] STEPHENS, J. C. (1955). Review of methods and formulations for aquatic weed control. *Proc. Soil Sci. Soc. Florida* 1954, 14, 122–6.

[6] ——, CRAIG, A. L. & HARRISON, D. S. (1957). Controlling submersed water weeds with emulsifiable solvents in south Florida. *Florida Agric. Exp. Sta. Circ.* S-97, 14 pp.

[6] STILES, W. B. (1956). Summary of weed control on national wildlife refuges. *U.S. Dept. Interior, Fish & Wildlife Service*, Mimeographed, 23 pp.

398

[2] STOECKLER, J. H. (1952). Control of weeds in forest nurseries with mineral spirits. *Advances in Chemistry Series*, 7, 84–90.

[6] STOUT, O. V. P. (1934). Irrigation of weeds and other noncrop plants costly and unprofitable. *U.S. Dept. Agric. Yrbk.* 1934, 250–3.

[5] SUGGITT, J. W. & GRUNDY, W. M. (1956). Chemical brush control. *Proc. Natl. Shade Tree Conf.*, 32, 112–20.

[6] SURBUR, E. W. (1949). Control of aquatic plants in ponds and lakes. *U.S.D.A. Fish and Wildlife Service, Fishery Leaflet* 344, 26 pp.

[5] SWAIN, L. C. (1954). Economical tree killing. *New Hampshire Agric. Exp. Sta. Bull.* 408, 15 pp.

[1,2] SWEET, R. D. (1957). Chemical weeding of vegetables. *N.Y. (Cornell) Agric. Exp. Sta. Ext. Bull.*, 980, 44 pp.

[6] SWINGLE, H. S. & SMITH, E. V. (1947). Pond weeds and their control. *Alabama Agric. Exp. Sta. Bull.*, 254, 24–28 (revised).

[6] TAYLOR, A. R. A. (1954). Control of eel-grass (*Zostera marina*) in oyster culture areas. *Canad. Fisheries Res Bull. Gen. Ser.* 23, 3 pp.

[5] TEXAS AGRICULTURAL & MECHANICAL COLLEGE (1956). *Handbook on Aerial Applications in Agriculture.* Short Course Office, Texas A. & M., 146 pp.

[6] THOMPSON, M. M. (1952). Water and weeds! *Golden Gard.*, 16(9), 10–11, 23.

[6] TIMMONS, F. L. (1949). Irrigation makes weeds grow too! *What's New in Crops and Soils*, 1(8), 4 pp.

[6] —— (1958). Profits from research on control of aquatic and ditchbank weeds on irrigation systems. *Proc. West. Weed Cont. Conf.*, 16, 41–46.

[6] —— (1963). Studies on control of common cattail in drainage channels and ditches. *Tech. Bull. U.S. Dep. Agric.* No. 1286, 51 pp.

TITTEL, C. (1962). *See* EGGEBRECHT, H.

[1] UBRIZSY, G. (1962). [New directions and problems in chemical weed control—in Hungarian.] *Budapest. Magyar Tudo. Akad. Agrtudo. Ostzta'ly. Kozlem.* 20(1/2), 17–27.

[6] UHLER, F. M. (1954). Water chestnut menaces upper section of Chesapeake Bay. *Maryland Sportsmen*, 12(9), 4–5.

[5] UNITED STATES DEPT. AGRIC. (1961). Chemical control of brush and trees. *Farmers' Bull.* 2158, 23 pp.

[2] UNITED STATES DEPARTMENT OF AGRICULTURE. (1963). Controlling lawn weeds with herbicides. *Home Gdn. Bull.* No. 79, 16 pp.

[3] —— & UNITED STATES DEPARTMENT OF THE INTERIOR (1959). *Handbook, Chemical Control of Range Weeds* U.S. Government Printing Office, Washington D.C. 96 pp.

[6] VAAS, K. F. (1951). Notes on the water hyacinth (*Eichhornia crassipes*) in Indonesia and its eradication by spraying with 2,4-D. *Agric. Res. Sta. (Bogor, Indonesia) Gen. Contrib.* 120, 59 pp.

VAN GOOR, C. P. *See* GOOR C. P. VAN

VAN OVERBEEK, J. *See* OVERBEEK, J. VAN.

[1] VARENITSA, E. T. & BIRIUKOVA, V. S. (1956). [Weed control on foxtail millet fields —in Russian.] *Selek. i Semen*, 21(3), 44–49.

[3] VARLET, G., VALLEZ, H. & LACOMBE, G. (1955). Essais démonstratifs de désherbage et de 'débroussaillage' chimiques sur pâturages permanents en Franche-Comté. *Phytoma*, (881), 28–34.

[1] VELASCO, J. R. (1954). Some aspects of weeds in rice fields and their control. *Agric. & Industr. Life*, 16(3), 14–15.

[1] —— (1958). A study on the effect of herbicide on weeds in rice fields. *Proc. Pacific Sci. Cong.*, 8(4B), 65–106.

[4] VENKATARAMANI, K. S. (1956). The control of *Imperata* grass. *Planters' Chron.*, 51, 293–4.

[1] VERMA, R. D. & BHARDWAJ, R. B. L. (1958). A better way of tackling weeds in sugarcane. *Indian Farming* 83, 29–31.

VIANNA, F. SEGADAS-. *See* SEGADAS-VIANNA, F.

[6] VIRGINIA POLYTECHNIC INSTITUTE (1951). Weed control in small ponds. *Virginia Polytech. Inst. Bull.* 425 (revised).

[1] VOEVODIN, A. V. & TARNOVICH, N. K. (1956). [Raising the efficiency of the chemical method of controlling the weeds of grain crops—in Russian.] *Vsesoiuzn. Akad. Sel'skokhoz. Nauk. im. V. I. Lenina Dokl.*, 21(6), 18–21.

[1-7] VOITOV, P. I., LADONIN, V. F. & CHERNYSHOVA, N. N. (1961). [*Use of Herbicides for Weed Control*—in Russian.] Moskov. Rabochii, Moscow, 68 pp.

[1] WEHSARG, O. (1954). [*Field Weeds*—in German.] Akademie Verlag, Berlin, 294 pp.

[6] WEIGHT, W. K. (1956). Aquatic weed control practice in potable water supply reservoirs. *Weeds*, 4, 235–40.

[7] WEISER, N. A. (1955). Crabgrass *vs.* the human race. *Golf Course Rptr.*, 23(8), 7–8.

[1-7] WEISNER, J. B. (Chairman) (1963). *Use of pesticides*. The White House, Washington D.C. 25 pp. Prepared by the President's Science Advisory Comm., J. B. Weisner, Chairman.) (Publ. also in *Residue Rev.*, 6, 1–22, 1964.)

[5] WEITZMAN, S. & LINDAHL, R. R. (1956). Eliminate worthless trees! *Va. Forests*, 11(4), 4–7.

[3] WELDON, L. W., BOHMONT, D. W. & ALLEY, H. P. (1958). Re-establishment of sagebrush (*Artemisia tridentata*) following chemical control. *Weeds*, 6(3), 298–303.

[6] WESTMAN, J. R. (1957). Some experiences with the aquatic weed problem in the State of New Jersey. *Proc. Northeast. Weed Cont. Conf.*, 11, 243–6.

[1] WESTMORELAND, W. G. & KLINGMAN, G. C. (1956). Small grain chemical weed control. *North Carolina State Agric. Col. Ext. Folder* 105, 6 pp. (revised).

[6] WILBER, C. P. P. (1942). Aquatic weed control. *Parks & Recreation*, 25, 296–9.

[1] WILD, H. (1962). *Harmful aquatic plants in Africa and Madagascar*. Scientific Council for Africa South of the Sahara. Public. No. 73, Int. Pub. Service, 69 pp.

[1] WILLARD, C. J. (1954). Plant regulators for weed control in field crops. Pp. 184–201 in *Plant Regulators in Agriculture* (Ed. H. B. Tukey). John Wiley, New York.

[1] WILLIAMS, J. H. (1954). Differential varietal response of oat varieties to 2,4-dichloro-phenoxyacetic acid. *Agron. J.*, 46, 565–9.

[6] WILLIAMS, R. E. (1955–56). Weeds in rice. *Rice J.*, 1955: 53, 19; Jan. 1956: 8–9; Feb. 1956: 8; March 1956: 8–9; April 1956: 14; May 1956: 24; June 1956: 34–35; July 1956: 59, 22–23; Aug. 1956: 17; Nov. 1956: 20–28.

[6] —— (1956). Weeds in rice. *Rice J.*, 59(12), 20–26, 28.

[6] WILLIAMS, R. H. (1956). *Salvinia auriculata* Aubl. : The chemical eradication of a serious aquatic weed in Ceylon. *Trop. Agric.* (St. Augustine), 33, 145–57.

[6] WILSON, M. & FINNEY, G. M. (1950). Controlling cattail (*Typha*) with 2,4-D. *Reclam. Era*, 36, 108–9.

[6] WILSON, T. M. (1929). Weed control in irrigation canals, New South Wales, Australia. *Reclam. Era* (U.S.), 20(9), 137.

[3] WILTSE, M. G. & CHURCHILL, B. R. (1954). Chemical control of downy brome-grass (*Bromus tectorum* L.) in an established alfalfa field. *Agron. J.*, 46, 160–2.

[6] WINNE, W. T. (1935). A study of the water chestnut, *Trapa natans*, with a view to its control in the Mohawk River. *M.S. Thesis, Cornell University*.

[1] WOODFORD, E. K. (1960). A survey of international progress in chemical weed control. *Proc. Fourth British Weed Control Conf.*, 1958, Soc. Chem. Ind. (London), pp. 2–9.

[6] —— (ed.) (1963). *Crop production in a weed-free environment*. Symp. of the Brit. Weed Cont. Coun. 2., Blackwell, Oxford. 114 pp.

[1-7] WORLD REVIEW OF PEST CONTROL (vol. 1. No. 1. 1962, to date quarterly). World Review of Pest Control, 95 Wigmore St. London, W.1. England.

[3] WURGLER, W. (1955). Déstruction des broussailles dans les pâturages de montagne. *Landwirt. Jahrb. der Schweiz*, 69, 771–82.

[6] YEO, R. R. (1964). Life history of common cattail (*Typa latifolia*). *Weeds*, 12, 284–88.

[6] YOUNGER, R. R. (1958). Preliminary studies using Kuron as an aquatic herbicide. *Proc. Northeast. Weed Cont. Conf.*, 12, 332–7.

[5] ZAHARIADI, C. (1956). Die Bekämpfung der Unkräuter im Hilsenfruchtanbau durch chemische Mittel. *Rev. Biol.*, n.s., 1, 257–64.

[1] ZAHNLEY, J. W., ANDERSON, L. E. & RUSS, O. G. (1957). Controlling weeds in Kansas. *Kansas Agric. Exp. Sta. Bull.* 390, 36 pp.

[5] ZAVIEZO, M. S. (1956). Aplicacion de herbicides en plataciones forestales. *Chile Maderero*, 6(3), 55.

[6] ZIMMERMAN, P. W. (1952). Water weeds. *Plants & Gardens*, 8, 56–57.

[6] —— , HITCHCOCK, A. E. & KIRKPATRICK, H. M., JR. (1950). Control of water hyacinths. *Boyce-Thompson Inst. Prof. Paper*, 2(9), 75–86.

[6] ——, —— & —— (1950a). Practical control of water hyacinth with 2,4-D. *Agric. Chem.*, 5(2), 45–47, 49, 81, 83–85.

[7] ZUKEL, J. W. (1953). Progress report on grass inhibitors for highway areas. *Ohio State U. Short Course Roadside Developmt.*, 12, 96–98.

[5] —— & EDDY, C. O. (1957). Pesticide use on highway areas. *Agric. Chem.*, 12(7), 38–39.

[6] ZUR BURG, F. W. (1949). Effect of certain herbicides on the water hyacinth and other aquatic plants. *Proc. Soil Sci. Soc. Fla.*, 9, 92–99.

XV

NON-CHEMICAL METHODS FOR THE CONTROL OF WEEDS

CONTROL BY SOIL CULTIVATION

As suggested by Sauer (1952), early agriculture probably began in wooded lands. Here primitive cultivators, by killing the trees, could readily open up spaces for planting, whereas they could not so well dig in sod or eradicate vigorous stoloniferous grasses. Sauer, like some other authors, believes that the cradle of earliest agriculture was in southeastern Asia, and that it developed from the earlier fishing economy of the Mesolithic period. This sedentary habit, together with the culture of plants, is believed to have developed after the last deglaciation in the Neolithic period. Until recently, much of our information on these early farmers came from the pollen studies of Johannes Iversen (*see* Ch. I) and others, and from archaeological remains in Europe. The origin of this early agriculture is believed by Sauer (1952) to lie farther east, and to have involved at first merely the planting of portions of plants (i.e. vegetative propagation) such as yams. The planting of seeds came later. One of the oldest known agricultural villages has recently been excavated in Iraq, and a dating of charcoal from it by the radiocarbon technique indicates an age of 9,000 years.

Perhaps a qualifying statement should be added to Sauer's theory. It is well known that since the time of the ancient Egyptians, river-bank habitats have provided another 'cleared' area for agriculture. With the seasonal rise and fall of the water-level of the river, a flood-free period is available for man's use. This periodically inundated zone is relatively free of forest growth and other woody plants, or can be kept free of such growth with a minimal amount of hand labour. On the other hand, the growth of herbaceous weeds becomes a severe problem. The fertility and high productivity of these areas, as well as of flood plains or 'bottom lands', have sustained peoples of many cultures throughout the world. Such river-bank agriculture is known in Honduras, and along the Amazon and its tributaries in Brazil. The American Indian, in some regions, however, utilized clearings in upland forested areas for his crops.

At any rate, the first attempts at removing competing plants from these early cultivated plots must have been strictly mechanical—i.e. by hand removal and by the use of primitive tools. The repeated stirring of the soil, either by hand or by crude implements, to prevent the appearance of new noxious growths, probably came at a somewhat later date. With the opening and clearing of otherwise covered areas, and the introduction of soil tillage, the growth of competing plants, or weeds, provided additional problems.

Thus from the very earliest period of agriculture, cultivation of the soil, combined with hand removal, was the only effective method of weed control. And this method was used almost exclusively, in one form or another, until the early part of the twentieth century, when the introduction of chemical methods indicated that other procedures might be possible. The use of fire, grazing animals, and flooding (as in rice culture), were also found by early man to provide some degree of weed control. Earlier parts of this volume have dealt with these new chemical techniques. But, promising and effective though they are, there are times when mechanical removal, or tillage, appears more feasible. Often, the land has to be cultivated in preparation for seeding, and this provides some measure of weed control at the same time. Anyway, this same tillage of the soil also stimulated the germination of the weed seeds (or the spreading of vegetative portions), resulting in a perpetuation of the weed problem. This apparent dilemma can be resolved, at least in part, by a combination of chemical and tillage methods.

Russell (1950) has observed that the agriculture of northwestern Europe has been centred on the mouldboard plough, an implement which, when properly used, cuts and inverts a furrow and leaves the surface completely bare of all vegetation. This form of ploughing can bury surface rubbish, applied manure, and mineral fertilizers. By it, weeds are often prevented from germinating, at least under conditions of cool weather, or are often killed. However, this method has the limitation of leaving the soil bare and often open to severe erosion. An alternative method has been to scratch, or cultivate, the surface without turning a furrow—much along the lines developed six, or more, thousand years ago in the Middle East and Egypt. The use of a plough that is like a cultivator tine to which wide sweeps are attached, or with rotary-rod weeders cutting some two inches below the soil surface, has been referred to in the United States as 'stubble mulch farming'. It tends to be most suitable for the drier regions where, by such a tillage operation, weeds are cut off and quickly dry out, with virtually no possibility of re-rooting. The weeds are left as trash on the soil surface and serve as a mulch in conserving water and preventing, in part, the growth of new weeds.

Of course, hand-hoeing has long been an effective and decisive method of weed control, whereby the young weed seedlings are cut off below ground-level, or may be covered with soil. Mechanical cultivators do practically the same thing, loosening and partly turning the soil, so that young weeds are uprooted and buried in a layer of soil in such a way that they rarely recover. In recent years, with the knowledge that cultivation also damages surface crop-roots, fewer and shallower cultivations are being employed.

However, cultivation and/or combinations of it with chemical applic-ations, present a problem of greater magnitude when long-standing infestations of perennial weeds are involved. The control of quack-grass (*Agropyron repens*), field bindweed (*Convolvulus arvensis*), and Johnson grass (*Sorghum halepense*), provides a small, but convincing, group of examples from North America.

Because quack-grass regenerates from even very small portions of its extensive underground system of rhizomes, complete eradication requires unremitting effort extending over several years. Summer fallow with frequent cultivations has been effective, providing the summer is rela-tively dry—thus allowing the exposed rhizomes to be dried out and killed. However, with valuable land, such fallowing may not always be possible. Thus TCA (sodium trichloroacetate) at 18–27 lb. per acre of active in-gredient in 40 or more gallons of water, sprayed in the autumn on soil that has been ploughed five to ten days previously, has been effective. This treatment should be followed by a thorough disking and harrowing. Dalapon may also be used at 8·5 lb. of active ingredient per acre in 40 or more gallons of water in the spring when the quack-grass is 10 to 15 cm. high. Ploughing should then follow after five to seven days, with planting of certain tolerant crops scheduled some three to four weeks from the date of Dalapon application. Potatoes, however, may be planted immedi-ately after ploughing (Grange League Federation, 1958).

Phillips & Timmons (1954) have summarized the control work on field bindweed conducted in Kansas from 1935 to 1952, and their findings may be summarized as follows. Intensive fallowing usually eliminated the bindweed in two seasons or less, provided cultivations were performed at the proper time and with proper implements. Cultivation operations per-formed twelve days after each bindweed emergence resulted in bindweed eradication with an average of 16·2 cultivations (optimum depth, 10 cm. [4 in.]). For practical use, it appears that cultivation operations should be performed every two weeks during the first two to three months of the treatment, or until the bindweed has been weakened and emerges more slowly than before. The interval of time may then be safely lengthened to three weeks. The cultivation operations should continue until 15 September or 1 October in this region, to prevent partial recovery of the bind-weed.

One year of intensive fallowing and three crops of wheat, seeded early in October after intensive cultivation between harvest and seeding each year, eradicated bindweed in three to four years and proved to be practi-cable for the Hays, Kansas, area. This method requires no change from the conventional practices of progressive wheat farmers, other than timely and thorough cultivation at two- to three-week intervals when the land is not in crop.

Of the various soil-sterilant chemicals tested, sodium chlorate appears to be the most satisfactory—at least, where using it creates no serious fire hazard. Applications of 3 or 4 lb. per square rod, followed by re-treatment in subsequent years, has generally proved to be the most economical method.

Bindweed stands may be greatly reduced with 2,4-D; but even repeated applications will not, in all cases, completely eradicate established stands. The best results have been obtained with application when the weed is well-emerged and growing vigorously—following a short period of intensive cultivation—at the rate of 1 lb. of 2,4-D acid equivalent per acre (in any formulation). Bindweed seedlings continue to emerge in large numbers for many years after the original stand has been eradicated. Proper use of 2,4-D may help considerably in preventing this reinfestation. The annual rainfall during this experimental period (1935–52) averaged 23.4 in. (Phillips & Timmons, 1954).

Johnson grass, though primarily a weed of the southern United States, has, in recent years, been reported in such northern areas as the southern lowlands of Illinois, and New Jersey. In the North, the rhizomes are usually killed in the winter by freezing. Again with Johnson grass, summer fallow with numerous cultivations (three to eight times at two- to four-week intervals) has been successful, as has overgrazing for a period of several years. No chemical treatment of heavy infestations in growing crops is possible at present. In light infestations, spot treatment of the crowns with a naphtha-type oil two to six times per season, greatly suppresses growth; or a wetting spray, prepared by dissolving one pound of Dalapon in 4 gal. of water, may be applied instead. Suppression of seed production is very important.

Adams (1952), in England, has reviewed some aspects of the cultural control of weeds. Light cultivation in early autumn will result in a crop of seedlings which are killed by later frosts. Another light cultivation, before sowing the next crop in the spring, will again reduce the seed content of the soil, and any seedlings will thus be killed before the crop is planted. This is a useful method of starving out the weeds, but is not recommended on poor and light soils. Heavy dressings of organic manure, and liming, will reduce some species—e.g. *Equisetum arvense*—through competition with vigorous crop plants. Repeated cutting will weaken such weeds as bracken, nettle, and willow-herb; but it is always important to plant a crop to replace the weeds that are eradicated.

MECHANICAL CLEARING OF LAND

With the availability of many kinds of diesel- or gasoline-powered mobile equipment, new and faster methods of land clearing have been developed. Winches of various types are now available for attachment to tractors, and are considered a very promising method of removing trees up to 45 cm. (18 in.) in diameter—at least in the lighter, sandy soils.

For removal of roots that might re-sprout, a machine is used which cuts the roots beneath the surface. These cutters are designed as V-shaped blades and may be mounted to the circle of a motor grader. For handling large material, the sweeps are usually attached to a tool bar mounted upon, or pulled behind, a track-type tractor. Rolling coulters are often used with them, to prevent material from dragging up on to the root-cutter shank and to reduce the amount of grass that is torn up as the root cutters are pulled through the soil. If the land is to be left for pasture, the cut roots are left in the soil to decompose; but if the land is to be used for crops, it is raked and the collected material is burned.

Tree-cutters are also available for handling trees from 20 to 25 cm. (8 to 10 in.) in diameter. One recently-developed machine can be used on trees 50 cm. in diameter, but is used most economically on trees 30 cm. in diameter. The trees can be cut off flush with the ground at travelling speeds ranging from two to three miles per hour—as the terrain and other factors permit. This speed is needed to get the shearing that is required, such equipment being widely used for dam, reservoir, and power-line right-of-way clearing.

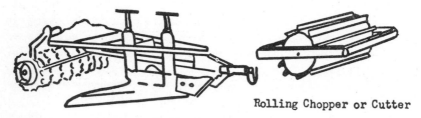

Rolling Chopper or Cutter

Undercutter
(Pull-tool with V-plane blade and trailed disk)

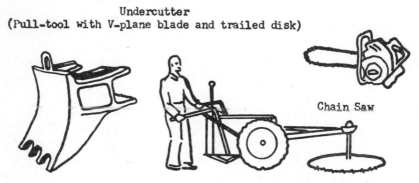

Chain Saw

Detachable Stumper

Movable Bandsaw

By courtesy of Florida Agricultural Experiment Station

Fig. 78.—Examples of land-clearing equipment.

The chain-dozing and high-balling methods are accomplished by pulling a length of anchor chain, varying in length from 60 to 150 m. (200–500 ft.), between two tractors or teams of tractors. The U-shaped chain pattern is pulled from the ends and knocks down the trees as it comes in contact with them—so long as the tractors have sufficient power. A modification of this makes use of a huge steel ball, 2·4–3 m. in diameter, which is fastened through its centre and in the centre of the chain—to keep the latter off the ground for higher chain contact against the trees.

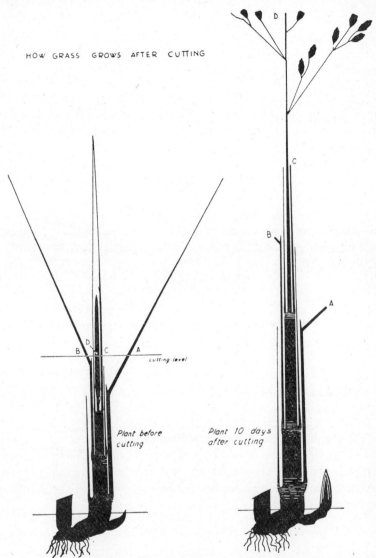

HOW GRASS GROWS AFTER CUTTING

cutting level

Plant before cutting

Plant 10 days after cutting

Drawing by Cocucci; by courtesy of Missouri Botanical Garden and G. B. Van Schaack

FIG. 79.—Illustration of the growth (meristematic) regions of members of the grass family (Gramineae), and of the change in position of the several structures marked A, B, C, and D (originally all at the same level in the plant on the left) ten days later (*see* plant on right), after the cutting of all structures at the level shown. Growth in grasses occurs not only from above, that is from terminal buds as in other plants, but also from below from intercalary meristems, shown in the figure as horizontally hatched.

Regular soil-moving, bulldozer, and free-dozing machines, that will knock over trees in one or two attempts, are also available. A detachable stumper machine is available which can be fastened to the frame of an angle-dozer and used to remove stumps of trees with fibrous root systems. Rakes are available in a variety of sizes, to handle almost any kind of debris. Rotary cutters and rolling shoppers are also available for cutting, or shredding up, smaller growth. The rotary cutters are used to keep pipeline and telephone rights-of-way clear. Sometimes, in combination with these land-clearing methods, chemical or tree-poisoning methods are used (Anon., 1951b, 1956). A range of land-clearing equipment is shown in Fig. 78.

A very common method of controlling weeds along roadsides is by machine mowing; in former times, hand scything was employed. The grazing of animals, especially sheep, achieves a similar degree of control. It is well known, of course, that, owing to the peculiar growth of grasses from intercalary meristems (and from underground portions as well), only a very short period of control is attained. For, in a short time, regrowth readily occurs (cf. Fig. 79).

Mechanical methods also include the use of certain barriers, such as plastic sheeting or stone or other mulches on the soil surface, to prevent the germination and establishment of weeds (cf. Krylov, 1956; Sonvil, 1957; Streich, 1931).

CONTROL BY FLOODING

Flooding by water is an age-old technique for weed control in paddy rice culture (cf. Arai & Miyahara, 1956). However, this method is sometimes used for the control of perennial weeds in other crop-lands. In California, the infested area is surrounded by dykes and is then covered with 15 to 25 cm. (6 to 10 in.) of water for several weeks in the summer. This method has been effective against wild morning-glory, camel-thorn, hoary cress, and white horse-nettle. In one area in California, a 13-acre field infested with Russian knapweed was flooded for sixty days and the weed thereby killed. Occasionally, submergence for three to five weeks has given satisfactory control. This method is more effective in sandy soils than in the heavier types. At the same time that weed control may be achieved, other pests, such as nematodes, and also soil fungi, may be brought under control.

CONTROL BY FIRE

The use of fire is another age-old method of removing undesirable vegetation. This method still finds useful applications in many situations throughout the world. Fire may be used on large acreages under controlled conditions, or it may be used in the form of a 'flame cultivator', or 'weed burner', where small, directed burners burn off the weeds and spare the crop.

In California a combination of the use of fire, followed by the grazing of goats on the new- or re-growth areas, has proved an effective method of weed control in some regions. Weed burners have been used along irrigation ditches, and Lowry (1955) describes such burners that use butane or propane gas. In burning green material, about 3 miles per hour can be covered, while with dead, or dry, material about 5 to 6 miles per hour can be burned. The costs in New Mexico on small ditches average $8.70 per mile, whereas similar ditches in Texas that are free from Johnson grass cost only $7.80 per mile. In Louisiana, six burners consuming together 9–10 litres of fuel per hour required eight hours to destroy weeds in 10–12 hectares.

Fire has been used as a method of controlling velvet mesquite (*Prosopis velutina*), burroweed (*Aplopappus tenuisectus*), and cholla (*Opuntia fulgida*), on southern ranges (Humphrey, 1949), and of eliminating stands of Medusa-head (*Elymus caput-medusae*) in California (Furbush, 1952). 'Farming by fire' is a regular method in certain sections of the Sudan, where the natives burn off the natural dead-grass growth and such new grass growth as has appeared. They then plant this land to sorghum or perhaps sesame (J. R. Thomson, 1950). Firing the land is, of course, also a method of stimulating new plant growth, such as that of grasses etc., for use as forage—for both domestic and wild animals. A number of investigations have shown that fire serves as a stimulus for the germination of certain plant seeds, and few other conditions will stimulate such growth (cf. Went *et al.*, 1952., *see* Ch. VI). H. H. Bartlett (1955) has prepared an extensive review of fire in relation to primitive agriculture and grazing in the tropics.

Prevention of Weed Infestations by the Use of Clean Crop Seed

An important feature of weed control in seeded crops is a preventive one. This is principally accomplished by using the cleanest seed obtainable—i.e. free from noxious weed seeds. In the United States, the Federal Seed Law has set up specifications for crop seeds and the permissible weed-seed content for all inter-state shipments. In addition, the individual States have stringent laws regulating the noxious weed seed permissible in seed sold for sowing. Nearly all of these States maintain seed laboratories where seeds are examined and then certified for sale. The magnitude of the weed-seed problem in the wheat country in the northern United States is evident from Plate 21. References to works on seed-cleaning methods and the disposal and identification of weed seeds are given at the end of this chapter.

Ecological Control of Weeds

This is control by using plant ecological methods, and is sufficiently different and long-range in plan and scope to be discussed separately from the other categories of biological control and to be treated here as a separate section. In most instances, ecological control falls into the general scope of the 'replacement control' of Piemeisel (1945), who defined this area of control as that '. . . which employs an indirect means of getting rid of pests through changes in vegetation. The changes involve replacement of weeds and other ephemeral plants by a more desirable cover of grasses or native perennials. With this replacement of weed pests by other plants, other ends are achieved, such as control of those insects and small animals which depend on the weeds for development of high numbers, and also, better or increased forage and better protection of the soil surface against erosion.' Piemeisel further points out that this replacement method differs from biological control in that the latter method employs a natural means, but depends on direct destruction of the pest by a predator or parasite, and is aimed at a specific pest. In replacement control and ecological control, no actual destruction *per se* is involved, but rather discouragement of initial establishment and development by an astute selection of initial plantings to occupy the problem area.

The replacement control concept of Piemeisel is perhaps more inclusive than the general definition of ecological control. It also envisages the control of auxiliary and associated fungus and insect pests at the time when their hosts and other noxious forms of vegetation are removed from the scene by these replacements, or by replanting techniques.

The problem of long-range planting coupled with a minimum of effort on the part of man in spot chemical treatment, pruning, and the like, is all envisaged in some current right-of-way ecological control methods, and similarly along super-highways and in parkways and similar areas. This phase of control is being critically evaluated by the Connecticut Arboretum through its right-of-way demonstration area. This area was established in 1953 on a 450-metres sector of the Connecticut Power Company right-of-way that crosses the Connecticut Arboretum.

In this area, the vegetation is being manipulated in order to produce those cover types which yield the maximum wildlife benefits and the greatest stability, with the lowest cost over the years, that will still satisfy the requirements of the utility concerned. On the right-of-way, two types of plant community are recognized—a shrub-land and a sprout-hardwood commmunity. This latter is adjacent to the forest-edge paralleling the lines. To achieve this situation, different management techniques are used for the three zones shown in the diagram in Fig. 80: (*A*) directly under the wires; (*B*) in the strips beyond the outer wires; and (*C*) in the forest-edge paralleling the wires.

In zone *A*, greenbrier (*Smilax* spp.) has been stem-killed with high concentrations of hormone herbicides to make room and allow other shrubby plants to form a cover, while in zone *B* the potential danger trees will be removed (i.e. those which are likely to grow into the wires).

Selective cutting can be done, or tree poisoning by basal treatments. The shrubby masses both in *A* and *B* will prevent tree invasion, and yet provide cover for wildlife (cf. Egler, 1952, 1954, 1958; Niering, 1957).

From Niering & Egler, 1957

FIG. 80. Controlled vegetation zones along power-lines in Connecticut: A, central strip of herbaceous plants, grasses, sedges and low shrubs; B, larger shrubs and low understory trees (the far edge of B adjoining the forest-edge C is feasible for *Viburnum lentago* (*see* Niering & Egler, 1955)). Advances over the sketch shown above are to be found in Fig. 3 of the latter publication, and in Fig. 1 of Goodwin & Niering, 1959.

THE BIOLOGICAL CONTROL OF WEEDS BY INSECTS

The suppression of the growth of noxious weeds—or their elimination —by the application of biological measures comes under the category of biological control. These biological measures may involve the use of phytophagous insects, of fungi or other plant disease agents, of parasitic flowering plants, of herbivorous fishes, or of grazing cattle or other animals—or the use of competitive cropping, auxiliary competitive planting, or ecological control. This last category has been considered in the preceding section. Until fairly recently, there was no extensive or critical review of this general field—most notably with regard to control by insects. This has been remedied by the appearance of the reviews by Evans (1952) and Huffaker (1957), and by the two volumes, *The Principles of Biological Control* (Sweetman, 1958), and *Biological Control of Insect Pests and Weeds* (DeBach, 1964).

Cameron (1935), in surveying the natural enemies of ragwort (*Senecio jacobaea*) in New Zealand, listed five main principles underlying the biological control of weeds: (1) As accidentally introduced insects often have an extremely destructive effect on plants of economic value, purposely introduced species of a suitable nature may exercise a similarly destructive effect on plants of no value—i.e. weeds. (2) The selected insect should preferably be effective against the weed in its home country, although an insect which is comparatively harmless in one environment may be more virulent in another, and vice versa. (3) The insects must be more or less specific, or have a restricted host-range. If the weed in question is isolated systematically and physiologically from the plants that are of economic value, the problem is greatly simplified; if, on the other hand, it is closely allied, then more specialized insects, such as

411

root-borers, seed-feeders, etc., and not leaf-feeders, should be employed. Leaf-feeders seem, on the whole, to be less specific in their habits than root-borers, etc. (4) The possibility of a change of host plant, or alternate feeding, must be eliminated by exhaustive tests of the insects (including starvation experiments) on economic plants, especially on those allied to the weed species. (5) Parasites of the insect must, so far as possible, be eliminated before it is exported. If the insects have been exposed to the attack of parasites in the field before collection, great care must be exercised in the country receiving the insects to see that all parasites which make their appearance there are destroyed.

The first concerted efforts in the use of introduced insects for the control of weeds were those of R. C. L. Perkins and A. Koebele in the early 1900's in Hawaii. These workers were concerned with the noxious pasture weed, *Lantana camara*, and out of more than a hundred possible enemies of *Lantana*, only eight were successfully introduced into the Islands, owing to the poor transportation facilities at that time.

The most outstanding example of the control of a weed pest through the agency of insect attack is the destruction in Australia of the prickly-pear cacti, *Opuntia inermis* and *O. stricta*, by the Argentine moth-borer, *Cactoblastis cactorum*. The first prickly-pear was introduced to Australia with the first colonists in 1788, and the species was probably *O. vulgaris*, a native of Brazil. This species has become established in all States of the Commonwealth, usually in the form of overgrown hedges—becoming a minor pest in an area in North Queensland. *O. inermis* was introduced prior to 1839, and, with the opening up of the country for grazing, was planted in 1850 to 1875 for hedge purposes, or was grown as a potential fodder plant, at many points in Queensland and New South Wales. *O. stricta* was probably imported about 1860, and its establishment and later extension followed the same sequence as those of *O. inermis*.

From 1900 onwards the spread of prickly-pear was rapid. In 1925 the peak of invasion was considered to have been reached when some 60 million acres were affected and the rate of increase was about 1 million acres annually; about five-sixths of the occupied area was in Queensland, and the remaining one-sixth was in New South Wales. Approximately one-half of the 60 million acres were occupied by dense prickly-pear, growing to a height of 0·9 to 1·5 metres (3 to 5 ft.), and completely covering the ground to the exclusion of all grasses and other herbage. The remaining acreage had a more scattered infestation. An area of very scattered prickly-pear often becomes a dense mass within three to four years. Dense prickly-pear was estimated to contain in bulk 500 to 800 tons of plant material per acre.

The heavily infested area possesses an annual rainfall of from 50 to 75 cm. (20 to 30 in.) and constitutes good sheep and cattle grazing land, while large areas near railway lines are suitable for dairying and the growing of cereals and cotton. At the time of maximum infestation, the value of the land, before it could be improved for production purposes, varied generally between 5s. and 30s. per acre. However, mechanical or chemical prickly-pear eradication could not be accomplished for less than £10 per acre. Herein lay the great problem, and year by year more land became abandoned and holdings and homesteads deserted.

In 1912, Queensland initiated some investigation of the insect pests of these cacti, and recommended the introduction of insect and disease agencies from America. In 1920 the Commonwealth Prickly-Pear Board was formed, and explorations and investigations in North and South America were continued until around 1937. About 150 different kinds of insects that were restricted, or apparently restricted, to cactus host-plants, were discovered. Some five species of insects (including a bug, a cochineal, and a red spider) were introduced in the early studies, and resulted in a thinning of stands. Since 1927, success has been due to *Cactoblastis cactorum;* for of the former introductions, only the cochineal (*Dactylopius opuntiae*) has maintained its existence, and caused some destruction of the fruit and young plants.

C. cactorum, from Argentina and Uruguay, belongs to a group of Phycitidae containing 17 genera and some 50 species—all of which tunnel as larvae in the stems or fruits of prickly-pear and other cacti. There are two generations annually—a shorter summer and a longer winter (larval) generation. The moths are nocturnal and free-flying, and the eggs (as many as 300 per individual) are generally deposited in the immediate vicinity of the point of emergence from the pupal stage. The larvae are heavy feeders on the internal tissues of the cladodes (slabs or 'leaves'), thus causing a breakdown of the tissues—followed by pathogenic organisms which cause the final decay. As a result, a large area of dense prickly-pear frequently collapses completely during a period of a few weeks. Two or more waves of succulent regrowth may occur before the infestation is eradicated, or is reduced to scattered proportions.

The first liberation of the egg stage was early in 1926, and by the time the distribution was completed in 1930, some 3 billion eggs had been used. The success of this method was apparent almost from its introduction. By 1930 to 1932, the vast stands of prickly-pear throughout Queensland, and in districts of New South Wales, were reduced to decayed pulp in a most spectacular manner. Regrowth did occur, but at the end of 1934 these large areas had been brought under control. Two forms resistant to insect attack have been noted: a chlorotic 'yellow pear', which is low in nitrogen, and a robust, thick-jointed form with an abnormally high carbohydrate content. Despite this, the former great bulk of the weed in Queensland has been reduced by 95 per cent, while that in New South Wales has been reduced by at least 75 per cent (Dodd, 1940, 1940a).

The control of St. John's-wort, *Hypericum perforatum*, in the western United States, by the introduction of the European chrysomelid beetle, *Chrysolina gemellata,* has likewise been a most successful operation. This

413

weed is a native of Europe, and is so named because it blooms on or about 24 June, the feast of St. John the Baptist. It is a perennial growing from 0·3 to 1·5 m. (1 to 5 ft.) high, and was first reported in the United States in 1793 from near Lancaster, Pennsylvania. By 1900 it had spread to California, in the northern part around the Klamath River—hence the origin of the other common name, 'Klamath weed'. By 1929 it had occupied some 100,000 acres of previously useful range-land, and by 1940 the infestation had extended to about 250,000 acres. Wherever this weed grew, land values depreciated.

The weed not only competes with forage plants, but it contains a photosensitizing agent that is injurious to cattle and sheep, should they feed solely on it.* In the period prior to the introduction of 2,4-D, the chemical control of this weed did not appear feasible or economical, as the range-lands involved were too extensive and too inaccessible. From 1920, the Commonwealth of Australia began to seek insect enemies of the plant. In England and southern France, they found that the weed was attacked by two leaf-feeding beetles, a root-borer, and a gall-fly. After exhaustive feeding trials, the desirable insects were released in Australia, and by 1944 the results were encouraging. The first introductions into California were of two species of leaf-feeding beetles which were finally released in the field during 1945–46. These species became readily established, and by 1948 it was no longer necessary to import them.

Within two years it became apparent that, of the two species, *C. gemellata* from southern France was multiplying much the more rapidly. The adult beetles of this species emerge in April and May from their pupal cells just beneath the surface of the soil. They feed voraciously on the weed foliage, but by the latter part of July they go into a resting stage and seclude themselves in the soil, or under stones or debris. The weed, likewise, is in a more or less dormant condition during this period. With the autumn rains, the plants renew growth and the beetles again feed on the foliage. About mid-October, the adults mate and the females begin to lay eggs which later hatch into larvae. All three forms—adults, eggs, and larvae—are found throughout the winter. The larvae may completely destroy the trailing growth of the weed that had been produced in the late season following the rains. Early in the spring, the plants produce upright shoots that eventually bear flowers. The larvae at about this time complete their feeding and enter the soil, burrowing to a depth of about 2·5 cm. (1 in.), where they develop into pupae—thus completing the one-year life-cycle of the insect.

The living beetles are collected generally from the flowering heads of the weed and transported to new areas. Experience disclosed that it was necessary to release from 2,000 to 10,000 adult beetles in a circle not more

---

* Photosensitization results from animals feeding upon such plants as St. John's-wort (*Hypericum perforatum*), as well as rape (*Brassica napus*) and buckwheat (*Fagopyrum esculentum*). White-pigmented portions of the animal's body become overly sensitive to sunlight, resulting in blistering of the skin and other complications.

than 1·8 m. (6 ft.) in diameter. This density increases the mating possibilities and ensures a more rapid rate of increase than if the beetles were
spread thinly over a larger area. When they have devoured all the plants
of this weed in the immediate vicinity, they must move on, for they feed
on nothing else. Data show that they may move more than a quarter of a
mile in one month. Both the root-borer and the gall-fly have also been
successful in the control of this weed, often in areas and at times of the
year when the beetles are not present, or are not active.

The competitive ability of this weed is reduced by these leaf-eating
beetles, and it generally does not survive more than three years of such
feeding. With the destruction of the weed by the beetles, desirable forage
plants have returned to the infested areas. Many thousands of acres in
California now have the capacity to support more livestock, land values
have risen, and expenditure for the control of this weed has become
negligible. Owing to the high rate of reproduction of the beetles and their
ability to locate readily any new infestations, the insect controls will
perpetuate themselves.

Other examples of biological control noted since the above was written
may be cited. *Trirhabda nitidicollis* (Coleoptera) has been described as a
pest of rabbitbrush (*Chrysothamnus nauseosus*) in New Mexico (Massey &
Pierce, 1960). In Germany Böning & Bollow (1959) have described
infestations of *Gastroidea viridula* (Coleoptera) in relation to the control
of *Rumex obtusifolius*, and Muller (1960) has listed the same pest as useful
for biological weed control in pastures in Switzerland. In the western
United States Pringle & Arnott (1960) note that 50 per cent kill of sagebrush (*Artemisia tridentata*) has been obtained with the beetle, *Trirhabda
pilosa*. Biological control of Scotch broom (*Cytisus scoparius*) by *Leucoptera
spartifolicella* in California has been reported by Mobley (1960). Harris
(1961) in Canada has reported the control of toadflax (*Linaria vulgaris*)
by *Brachypterolus pulicarius* and *Gymnactron antirrhini* (Coleoptera).
Biological control of the puncture vine (*Tribulus terrestris*) in California
with imported weevils (*Microlarinus* spp.) has been reported by Huffaker
et al. (1961). The control of St. John's-wort in Chile with *Chrysolina
hyperici* and *C. quadrifemina* has been reported by Villaneuva & Fauré
(1959). A. P. Dodd (1961) in Australia has described the control of crofton
weed (*Eupatorium adenophorum*) with *Procecidochares utilis* (Diptera) and
the fungus *Cercospora eupatorii*.

A review of the biological control of insects and weeds in Australia
and Australian New Guinea is provided by F. Wilson (1960); while a decade
of biological control work in Fiji is evaluated by O'Connor (1960). Other
reviews or general works on the biological control of weeds include publications of DeBach (1959, 1964), Rademacher (1960), Mellini (1961),
Yakhontov (1961), and Huffaker (1962).

The introduction and release of an insect species for the control of a
specific weed is a precarious venture. In such a programme, one phase

is important above all—as is indicated in the following quotation from J. R. Williams which prefaces a paper of Huffaker (1957): 'The critical phase of biological control work against weeds is the selection of species that will not harm other plants, or at least useful plants. All other considerations are subordinate, and a suitable species for introduction into a country against a weed is one that is safe to introduce, irrespective of its other characteristics.'

CONTROL BY FUNGAL, OR OTHER DISEASES, OR PARASITIC SEED PLANTS*

A large number of fungus, bacterial, and virus diseases, of noxious plants, have been studied in some detail, with the hope that they might be utilized in the control and eradication of the noxious host. The following examples are illustrative: *Fusarium* disease of prickly-pear (Carpenter, 1944); thistle-rust which checks the spread of California thistle (Cockayne, 1916); a fungus parasite (*Physalospora* sp.) of *Opuntia robusta* in Italy (Gervasi, 1941); some eleven fungus diseases of *Opuntia lindheimeri* in North America, as described by Wolf (1912); some moderate control was reported for *Rubus fruticosus* in South Africa by the rust, *Kuehneola albida* (Wager, 1947); a virus disease of the tropical *Emilia scabra* (Loos, 1941); the fungi *Corticium* sp. and *Mycosphaerella* sp. were thought by M. J. F. Gregor (1932) to offer possibilities of control of bracken in Scotland; Brod (1955) studied in some detail the fungus *Cercospora mercurialis* on the common weed *Mercurialis annua* in Germany, but concluded that this parasite was not a suitable control agent, owing to the vigour of the weed and the long incubation period of the fungus; similarly, Hofsten (1954,—*see* Ch. II) studied *Phoma taraxaci* as a parasite of the common dandelion (*Taraxacum* spp.), but could not isolate strains that were sufficiently virulent to control this weed.

Some further studies have described the possibilities of the biological control of dodder (*Cuscuta* spp.) by several of its fungus parasites (*Alternaria* and *Cladosporium*) (Rudenko and Rudakov, 1959; Rudakov, 1960, 1961). Hamblyn (1959) reports that manuka blight (*Eriococcus orariensis*) is losing its effectiveness in the control of *Leptospermum scoparium* in North Island, New Zealand.

It appears that, in a great many cases where the disease agent (pathogen) is closely associated with the life-cycle of the weed in question—where indeed it probably evolved along with the weed—it is not really suitable for use in control or eradication. This is especially true if the disease agent is used in the same region in which both it and the host have developed under the same environmental conditions. However, if the

---

* For the latter control in nature *see* the note on *Cuscuta* serving as a check on the rampant vine *Mikania* (Compositae) (p. 51). F. L. Wellman (Parasitism among neotropical phanerogams, *Ann. Rev. Phytopath.*, 2, 43–56, 1964, 66 refs.) has noted the fungus infections of these parasites, and that *Cassytha* and *Cuscuta* dodders are never observed together in nature, but under culture *Cuscuta* is apparently able to overwhelm *Castsytha*.

disease agent is taken into a new environment and applied to an ecotype, or to a species related to the original host, there may be greater possibilities of control, if conditions are not too adverse. At best, these diseases of weeds do serve to keep them under some degree of control; and of course, from a survival standpoint, lethal action to the host has not been reached in this pseudo-symbiotic relationship of host and disease agent.

CONTROL BY ANIMAL FEEDING

The grazing of animals, particularly cattle, sheep, and goats, has long been known to be an effective way of keeping down the growth of many kinds of noxious plants. Stahler & Carlson (1947) reported that grazing sheep somewhat reduced the stand of field bindweed (*Convolvulus arvensis*), but this practice was less effective than was the grazing of infested land on which crops were being grown. In Oregon, Angell (1950) reported the control of tansy (*Tanacetum*) by grazing sheep; while in Portugal, sheep control weeds in the coffee plantations (Boggi, 1953). Geese are used in the weeding of mint fields in the northwestern part of the United States. They thrive on the weeds but do not eat the mint. Judd (1898) referred to birds as weed destroyers, and stated that some 50 species in the United States were effective. This may be so, but on the other hand the amount of viable seed distributed by many birds must more or less nullify any control value they may exert.

In California, a combination of fire and goat grazing has been used to control some of the woody shrubs infesting valuable grazing lands, while in New Zealand, Wright (1927) has examined the value of goats for weed control. Geese, too, in recent years have been widely proposed for use in weeding in the United States—particularly for crabgrass etc., control in strawberry beds (Rayner, 1951; Andrus, 1952; Hash, 1952). Geese have also been reported to remove grasses from bicolor lespedeza (Anon., 1951a), and to be useful in cotton as well (Bilfrey & Carter, 1952).

Several species of fish (and an aquatic mammal, too) have been observed to keep certain undesirable aquatic plants under control. The carp *Cyprinus* sp. has been so used (Sweetman, 1935). The unsightly and clogging weeds *Hydrilla* spp. are believed to have been controlled in ponds in Ceylon into which the gouramy fish (*Osphronemus olfax*) of Java was introduced. These fishes are known to be greedy feeders on water weeds. The control of pond weeds by the use of herbivorous fishes has been evaluated by Swingle (1957).

Tilapia mossambica, an herbivorous fish belonging to the sunfish family, was introduced from South Africa in 1955 by the Territorial Board of Agriculture and Forestry in Hawaii, for the control of aquatic vegetation. Since that time the extensive ditch system has been stocked successfully with over 75,000 fish. It is prolific, spawning at intervals as short as six weeks, depositing anywhere from 50 eggs, when young, to almost 2,000 eggs when older. These fishes thrive in either fresh or

P   417

brackish, and clear or muddy water. Through their burrowing in the bottoms of the ditches to form saucer-shaped spawning nests, the roots of aquatic plants are disturbed and destroyed. This, in addition to the herbivorous nature of the fish, destroys the vegetation—including weedy grasses, submerged and emergent aquatics, and algae. Whereas the cost of ditch weed control at Kekaha rose steadily to a total of $5,194 for chemicals and labour in 1954, that cost, due to the fish, was reduced to $25.25 in 1956, and to a negligible figure in 1957. Another species, *Tilapia zilli*, also introduced by the Board, promises to be effective in ditches that are heavily infested with grasses.

Studies in Alabama (Shell, 1962) utilized the following herbivorous fish: Israeli strain of the common carp, *Cyprinus carpio*; the Nile tilapia, *Tilapia nilotica*; and the Java tilapia, *T. mossambica*. The Israeli carp and either the Nile or the Java tilapia in ponds containing only 3 fish species virtually eliminated aquatic weeds, but when stocked with established populations of such game fish as the largemouth bass and bluegills the results were less encouraging. These herbivorous fish are not in themselves the total answer to the problem, concludes E. W. Shell.

W. H. L. Allsopp (1960) of the Fisheries Laboratory, Georgetown, British Guiana, has observed that manatees (*Trichechus manatus*, order Sirenia) are voracious consumers of aquatic vegetation. During 1959–60 it was found that two manatees $7\frac{1}{2}$ ft. long were capable of clearing a canal 22 ft. wide and 1,600 yd. long in seventeen weeks. They effectively kept reservoirs clear of such aquatic plants as *Cabomba*, *Elodea* (*Anacharis*), *Leersia*, and *Utricularia*. They can clear trenches which are covered with grass or *Nymphaea*, *Nelumbo*, and *Eichhornia*, as well as submerged aquatics. These mammals are harmless to fishes and other water animals. The only risk in their wide use appears to be that they may be slaughtered for their meat, and legislation is required to ensure their complete protection. The manatees are found in the rivers of British Guiana, and more recently have been distributed in several canals and irrigation schemes throughout the country.

Perhaps it is of interest at this point to note that certain aquatic plants have developed specialized structural features which appear to serve as protective measures against herbivorous animals. A notable example is that of the giant water-lily of the Amazon, *Victoria regia*. The giant floating leaves at or just under the surface of the water are heavily barbed, as are the long petioles extending to the root system, and, likewise, the large flower-buds.

COMPETITIVE CROPPING

Throughout the years, many practices have been developed with regard to the time of crop planting and the growing of certain crops together—considerations which are directed, to some degree, towards the control of weeds. In Minnesota, Robinson & Dunham (1954) have studied the use of companion crops for weed control in soybeans. Soybeans sown with a grain drill in non-cultivated rows 15 cm. (6 in.) apart, and with winter wheat or winter rye as companion crops, yielded as much as, or more than, soybeans grown without companion crops.

By virtue of their spreading habit, grasses have been used to control various types of weeds. The following will serve as illustrations: in Michigan, bromegrass is an effective agent in quack-grass control (Wolcott, 1951), and crested wheat-grass has been reported as helpful in controlling bindweed; in North Dakota, the growth of winter rye has provided improved weed control. Various leguminous plants have also been used in this fashion: in New South Wales, alfalfa has assisted in the control of skeleton weed (*Chondrilla juncea*) (Ross & Taylor, 1935), while the same crop has been reported to smother Canada thistle in the Middle-West (Burger, 1925); in New South Wales, again, subterranean clover has been found to smother St. John's-wort (*Hypericum* sp.) (G. C. Bartlett, 1936), while in the southern United States, Johnson grass control has been reported through using Singletary peas. Other broad-leafed crops, such as sunflowers, have been reported to be effective as a 'cleaning crop' which outgrows and suppresses weeds (Shewell-Cooper, 1951), while in Canada, two crops of buckwheat may be grown in one year and assist in the control of quack-grass and sow-thistle.

In Ceylon, the questionable recommendation of cultivating *Passiflora foetida* and *Mikania scandens* (both rapidly-growing vines) to keep down other weeds, apparently in the Royal Botanical Gardens, has been made by Bamber (1909). Perhaps this growth would serve, much as that of Japanese honeysuckle (*Lonicera japonica*) sometimes does in parks and woodlands (with cutting and mowing), to exclude other noxious growths. Sayupatham (1954), in Siam, reported on a grass (*Pollinia ciliata*) that will eradicate cogon grass (*Imperata cylindrica*). Other writers have examined some different aspects of this form of biological control: Buzacott (1955) in Mauritius, Cates (1923, 1934) and Suggs (1956) in the United States of America, and Struve (1926) in the U.S.S.R.

Penngift crown-vetch *Coronilla* (*Vicia*) *varia* (Leguminosae), planted on highway slopes and cuts, has been found to keep out weed infestations, no mowing being needed. These slopes become 'zero-maintenance' items, provide erosion control, and the crown-vetch blossoms will offer a blanket of beauty for much of the year. It will thrive in rocky, 'sterile' subsoil, and responds well to the modern method of 'hydroseeding', in which seeds, fertilizer, limestone, and an inoculant, are all mixed with water in a 1,000-gallon slurry tank and then sprayed on slopes of all degrees. Many tracts on highway slopes which have been covered with this plant for ten years or more still show only a trace of weeds, and these are largely limited to areas on which there has been some disturbance of the cover.

419

BIBLIOGRAPHY*

(Non-chemical Methods for the Control of Weeds)

[1] ADAMS, R. (1952). Some aspects in the cultural control of weeds. *J. Roy. Hort. Soc.*, 77(5), 178–82.

[2] ALEXANDER, W. B. (1919). *The Prickly Pear in Australia.* Inst. Sci. & Industry, Melbourne, Bull. No. 12, 48 pp.

[2] —— (1926). Variation of the acclimatized species of prickly pear (*Opuntia*). *Proc. Roy. Soc. Queensland*, 38, 47–54.

[1] ALLEN, E. F. & BEWLAY, E. W. (1949). Investigations on the mechanical cultivation of padi at Chenderong Balai, 1948–49. *Malayan Agr. J.*, 32, 208–22.

ALLISON, D. V. (1957). Root plowing proves best; methods of killing brush and re-establishing native grasses. *Cattleman*, 43(8), 40–42, 44.

[1] —— & RECHENTHIN, C. A. (1956). Root plowing proved best method of brush control in south Texas. *J. Range Mgmt.*, 9, 130–3.

[2] ALLSOPP, W. H. L. (1960). The manatee: ecology and use for weed control. *Nature, Lond.*, 188, 762.

[1] ALMOD, F. L. & KING, N. J. (1955). Weed control in sugar cane; relative merits of herbicides and cultivation. *S. African Sugar J.*, 39, 559, 561, 563.

[2] ALPATOV, V. V. (1956). [Biological control of weeds—in Russian.] *Priroda*, 45(10), 96.

[2] ANDRUS, M. (1952). Experience with geese in the strawberry plantation. *Mich. Hort. Soc. Annual Rep.* 1951, 81, 76–80.

[2] ANGELL, G. N. (1950). Sheep control tansy (*Tanacetum*); pasturing sheep on tansy, a control measure in Lincoln County, Oregon. *Oregon Farmer*, 73, 861, 872.

[2] ANON. (1915–16). Insects attack weeds in Minnesota. *Minnesota Agr. Exp. Sta., Rep. State Entomolog.* 1915–16, pp. 135–52.

[1] —— (1919). Killing weeds with live steam. *Sci. Amer.*, 120, 599, 13–14.

[4] —— (1923). The contamination of milling wheat: the effects of strong-scented weed seeds. *Agr. Gaz. N.S. Wales*, 34, 628.

[2] —— (1930). Control of ragwort by the cinnabar moth in New Zealand (*Myria jacobacae*). *Garden. Chron.*, 88, 268.

[4] —— (1932). Ninety-six trains of sixty cars each are required to haul weed seeds from western Canada to Port Arthur each year. *Canad. Chem. & Metall.* 1932, 230.

[2] —— (1938). Eradication of prickly pear. (Provisions of proclamation No. 161 of 1938 issued under the Weeds Act, 1937.) *Farming S. Africa*, 13, 347, 355.

[2] —— (1940). Opuntias in South Africa. *Farming S. Africa*, 15, 119–28.

[2] —— (1941). *Opuntia.* C.S.I.R., Australia, *14th Report*, 1939–40, 102 pp.

[1] —— (1941a). Weed destruction by flaming. *Int. Sugar J.*, 1941, 142–3.

[4] —— (1943). Agricultural seed. *Kansas State Bd. Agric. Rep.*, 62(256), 32 pp.

* The Bibliography of this chapter was submitted in 4 sections which have now been consolidated into a single general sequence. The original section to which each book or paper previously belonged is indicated by a prefixed superior numeral, through use of which the individual sections can readily be reconstituted, as follows:

[1] Mechanical and Fire;
[2] Biological Control;
[3] Ecological Control;
[4] Weed Seeds.   —Ed.

[2] ANON. (1949). Imported beetles show promise in war on western range weed. *Crops & Soils*, 1(7), 26.

[4] —— (1949*a*). Nebraska noxious weed districts install seed-treating machines. *Agr. News Letter*, 17(2), 27.

[1] —— (1950). Mechanizing agriculture: flame cultivation. *Agr. Econ.*, 2(3), 7.

[2] —— (1950*a*). St. John's wort, a dangerous weed. *Farming S. Africa*, 25, 61–63.

[2] —— (1951). Geese for weed control in strawberry fields. *Amer. Nurseryman*, 94(4), 40–41.

[2] —— (1951*a*). Geese cut the grass (in bicolor lespedeza). *Soil Conserv.*, 16(7), 166.

[1] —— (1951*b*). Mechanized land clearing. *World Crops*, 3(6), 232–3.

[2] —— (1952). Goatweed beetles doing fine job. *Idaho Agr.*, 37(1), 6.

[2] —— (1954). Gleotinia. *Trans. Brit. Mycol. Soc.*, 37, 29–32.

[2] —— (1955). Control of weeds by plant-eating insects. *Rur. Res. C.S.I.R.O.*, 11, 10–15.

[1] —— (1956). Advanced designs in land-clearing equipment. *World Crops*, 8, 137–41.

[2] —— (1957). Can insects fight halogeton? *Agr. Research*, 5(10), 10–11.

[1] ARAI, M. & MIYAHARA, M. (1956). [Studies on weed control by submergence in rice cultivation. I–II.—in Japanese.] *Proc. Crop Sci. Soc. Japan*, 24, 163–5.

[1] ARNOLD, K., BURCHAM, L. T., FENNER, R. L., & GRAH, R. F. (1951). Use of fire in land clearing; controlled burns must be planned and organized to obtain effectiveness, safety and low cost. *Calif. Agr.*, 5(5), 11–12 (cont.).

[1] ——, ——, —— & —— (1951*a*). Use of fire in land clearing. *Calif. Agr.*, 5(6), 13–15.

AYYAR, T. V. RAMAKRISHNA. *See* RAMAKRISHNA AYYAR, T. V.

[2] BAIRD, A. B. (1956). Biological control of insect plant pests in Canada. *Abs. Tenth Int. Congr. Entomol.* (Montreal), Aug. 17–25.

[2] BALACHOWSKY, A. (1951). Los insectos auxiliares fitofagos. *Siembra (Madrid)*, 7(4), 17–19.

[2] BAMBER, M. K. (1909). The cultivation of *Passiflora foetida* and *Mikania scandens* to keep down other weeds. *J. Roy. Bot. Garden Ceylon*, 4 (16), 141.

[1] BARNARD, R. C. (1954). The control of lalang (*Imperata arundinacea* var. *major*) by fire protection and planting. *Malayan For.*, 17, 152–6.

[1] BARR, H. T. (1947). Flame cultivation. *Louisiana Agr. Exp. Sta. Bull.* 415, 15 pp.

[2] BARTLETT, G. C. (1936). Subterranean clover smothers out St. John's wort in the Mannus Valley. *Agr. Gaz. N.S. Wales*, 47, 554, 576.

[1] BARTLETT, H. H. (1955). *Fire in Relation to Primitive Agriculture and Grazing in the Tropics: Annotated Bibliography.* Univ. Michigan Bot. Gardens, Ann Arbor, 568 pp.

[4] BARTLETT, S. & BLAXTER, K. L. (1943). Straw pulp; recent experiments. *J. Min. Agr.*, 50, 224–6.

[4] BEAL, W. J. (1910). Seeds of Michigan weeds. *Michigan Agr. Exp. Sta. Bull.*, 260, 101–82.

[2] BEESON, C. F. G. (1934). Prickly pear and cochineal insects. *Indian Forestry*, 60, 203–5.

[4] BELLUE, MARGARET K. (1945–47). *Weed Seed Handbook.* Series I–VIII. *Calif. State Agric. Bull.* 34 (1945), 27–34, 76–83, 116–23; 35 (1946), 13–20, 87–94, 159–66; 36 (1947), 27–30, 31–38.

[2] BENJAMIN, M. S. & OLD, A. N. (1939). Chemical composition of prickly pear. Relation to parasitism by *Cactoblastis. Agr. Gaz. N.S. Wales*, 50, 240, 276.

[4] BER, W. & KRESTNIKOWA-SYSSOEJWA, A. (1935). [Die thermische Sterilisation des Bodens als Unkrautbekämpfungsmethode—in Russian.] *Chemis. Soz. Landw.*, 7, 85–94.

[2] BESS, H. A. & HARAMOTO, F. H. (1956). Biological control of Pamakani, *Eupatorium adenophorum*, in Hawaii. *Abs. Tenth Int. Congr. Entomol.* (Montreal), Aug. 17–25.

[2] BILFREY, K. & CARTER, H. H. (1952). The goose in the cotton patch. *Prog. Farmer, Mis.-Ark.-La.*, 67, 15, 147.

[2] BIRD, J. J. (1951). 'Goose-berry' management. *Proc. Tennessee State Hort. Soc.*, 46, 25–26.

[2] BISWAS, K. (1950). Note on the cactus plants of India. *Poona Orientol.*, 15(14), 143–5.

[1] BLAISDELL, J. P. (1950). Effect of controlled burning on bitterbrush on the upper Snake River plains. *Intermt. For. & Range Exp. Sta. Res. Paper* 20, 3 pp.

[2] BODENHEIMER, F. S. (1932). Über die Ausrottung von *Opuntia* spp. durch *Dactylopius* spp. auf Grund einiger Beobachtungen auf Ceylon. *Zentralbl. f. Bakter.*, 86, 155–60.

[2] BOGGI, A. (1953). [The use of sheep in controlling weeds on coffee plantations—in Portuguese.] *Chacaras e Quintais*, 87, 692–4.

[2] BÖNING, K. & BOLLOW, H. (1959). Massenauftreten des Ampferblattkäfers (*Gastroidea viridula* DEG.) und andere Schadenserreger an grossblättrigen Ampferarten (*Rumex obtusifolius*) zugleich ein Beitrag zur biologischen Unkrautbekämpfung. *Pflanzenschutz*, 11, 109–14.

[3] BORDEN, R. J. (1941). Weed control methods influence subseqent weed types. *Hawaiian Planters Rec.*, 45, 150–4.

[2] BORELL, A. E. (1952). Daddy Pope's geese. *Soil Conserv.*, 18, 27–29, 47.

[2] BRANDHORST, C. T. (1943). A study of the relationship existing between certain insects and some native western Kansas forbs and weedy plants. *Trans. Kansas Acad. Sci.*, 46, 164–75.

[1] BRAUN, H. (1934). [Why control weeds?—in German.] *Mitt. Landw.*, 49, 401.

[1] BRENCHLEY, W. E. & WARINGTON, K. (1945). The influence of periodic fallowing on the prevalence of viable weed seeds in arable soil. *Ann. Appl. Biol.*, 32, 285–96.

[2] BROD, G. (1955). Studien über *Cercospora mercurialis* Posser in Hinblick auf eine biologische Bekämpfung des Schutt-Bingelkrautes (*Mercurialis annua* L.). *Phytopathol. Z.*, 24, 431–42.

[1] BROWN, B. A. (1930). Effect of time of cutting on the elimination of bushes in pastures. *J. Amer. Soc. Agron.*, 22(7), 603.

[4] BROWN, E. (1905). Weeds commonly found with commercial bluegrass seeds. *U.S. Dep. Agr. Bull.*, 84, 32.

[2] BUGBEE, R. E. & REIGEL, A. (1945). The cactus moth, *Melitara dentata* (Grote), and its effect on *Opuntia macrorhiza* in western Kansas. *Amer. Midl. Nat.*, 33, 117–27.

[4] BUNTING, L. (1933). Noxious weeds found in crop seeds. *California Dep. Agr. Mo. Bull.*, 22, 283–5.

[4] BURCHARD, O. (1892). Über einige Unkrautsamen, welche unter Umständen für die Provenienzbestimmung ausländischer Saatwaren wichtig sind. *Landw. Vers. Stationen*, 41, 449–52.

[4] —— (1900). *Die Unkrautsamen der Klee- und Grassaaten mit besonderer Berücksichtigung ihrer Herkunft.* Paul Parey, Berlin, 100 pp.

[2] BURGER, A. A. (1925). Kill the Canada thistle by smothering with alfalfa. *Wallace's Farmer*, 50, 822.

[4] BURNS, G. P. & PETERSEN, A. K. (1916). Agricultural seed. Concerning weeds and weed seeds. *Vermont Agr. Exp. Sta. Bull.*, 200, 3–79.

[2] BUZACOTT, J. H. (1955). Weeds to control weeds. *Queensland Bur. Sugar Exp. Sta. Cane Growers' Q.B.*, 19, 52–56.

[1] CABLE, D. R. (1961). Small velvet mesquite (*Prosopis chilensis*) seedlings survive burning. *J. Range Mgmt.*, 14, 160–1.

[2] CAMERON, E. (1935). A study of the natural control of ragwort (*Senecio jacobaea* L.). *J. Ecol.*, 23, 266–322.

[4] CAPITAINES, L. (1910). Étude des graines des Papaveracées d'Europe. *Rev. Gén. Bot.*, 22, 432–5.

[2] CARPENTER, C. W. (1944). Fusarium disease of the prickly pear. *Hawaiian Planters Rec.*, 48, 59–63.

[4] CARTER, A. S. (1946). Weed survey based on seed laboratory reports. *Proc. Ass. Off. Seed. Anal.*, 36, 101–3.

[1] CATES, J. S. (1912). The weed factor in the cultivation of corn. *U.S. Dep. Agr. Bur. Plant Ind. Bull.* 257, 35 pp.

[2] —— (1923). Fighting weeds with weeds. *Country Gent.*, 89, 10.

[2] —— (1934). Weed killing crops—crop mysteries. *Country Gent.*, 100, 7.

[2] CHATER, E. H. (1931). A contribution to the study of the natural control of gorse (*Ulex*). *Bull. Ent. Res.*, 22, 225–35.

[1] CHILDRESS, D. L. (1954). Cabling semi-desert ranges. *Ariz. Cattle.*, 9(10), 6–8.

[2] CLARK, L. R. & CLARK, N. (1952). A study of the effect of *Chrysomela hyperici* Forst. on St. John's wort (*Hypericum*) in the Mannus Valley., N.S.W. *Austral. J. Agr. Res.*, 3, 29–59.

[2] COCKAYNE, A. H. (1916). California thistle rust as a check on the spread of California thistle. *Int. Rev. Sci. & Pract. Agr.* (Rome), 7(3), 451.

[2] COCKERELL, T. D. A. (1929). Biological control of the prickly pear. *Science*, 69, 328–9.

[1] COLEMAN, F. (1954). The control of weeds by tillage. *J. Inst. Brit. Agr. Engrs.*, 10, 3–12.

[1] —— (1954a). Weed seed dispersal by machinery. *Proc. Brit. Weed Control Conf.*, 1, 295–300.

[2] COLLINS, W., JR. (1945). Crested wheat grass helping control bindweed. *Soil Conserv.*, 10, 182–3.

[2] COOK, C. W. (1942). Insects and weather as they influence growth of cactus on the Central Great Plains. *Ecology*, 23, 209–14.

[1] COOK, L. (1939). Burning for brush control. *S. Africa J. Sci.*, 36, 270.

COOPER, W. E. SHEWELL-. *See* SHEWELL-COOPER, W. E.

[4] CORNER, E. J. H. (1951). The leguminous seed. *Phytomorphology*, 1, 117–50.

[2] COSTELLO, E. F. (1941). Prickly pear control on shortgrass range in the central Great Plains. *U.S. Dep. Agr. Leaflet* 210, 6 pp.

[1] CRUZ, S. R., MIGUEL, G., JUMALON, F. & BLANCO, D. T. (1959). Experiments on weeding by flame. *Araneta J. Agric.*, 6(1), 51–57.

[2] CUNNINGHAM, G. H. (1927). Natural control of weeds and insects by fungi. *J. Agr. N. Zealand*, 34, 244–51.

[2] CURRIE, G. A. & FYFE, R. V. (1937). The fate of certain European insects introduced into Australia for the control of weeds. *J. Council Sci. & Ind. Res., Australia*, 11, 289–301.

[2] —— & GARTHSIDE, S. (1932). The possibility of the entomological control of St. John's wort in Australia. *Prog. Rep., Council Sci. & Ind. Res., Australia*, No. 29, 28 pp.

[1] DABNEY, T. E. (1921). Fighting the water hyacinth. *Sci. Amer.*, 125, 260.

[1] DADD, C. V. (1957). The cultural and chemical control of wild oats. *Agr. Rev.*, 2(10), 36–39.

[2] DANIELS, L. B. (1941). White grub found destroying cactus plants is identified; is an aid in range improvement. *Colorado Farm. Bull.*, 3(2), 12–13.

[2] DAVID, A. L. & MUTHUKRISHAN, T. S. (1953). The prickly pear cochineal: observations on its natural hosts and enemies in South India. *Indian J. Entomol.*, 15 (14.III), 219–24.

[2] DEBACH, P. (1959). Biological control of insect pests and weeds. *J. Appl. Nutr.*, 12, 120–4.

[2] —— (1964). *Biological Control of Insect Pests and Weeds*. Reinhold, New York, 930 pp.

[2] DECARY, R. (1930). La destruction des cactus par une cochenille à Madagascar: ses conséquences économiques et sociales (*Dactylopius coccus*). *Ann. Soc. Linn. Lyon*, 75, 101–17.

[4] DEFRANCE, J. A. (1943). The killing of weed seed in compost by the use of certain fertilizers and chemicals. *Proc. Amer. Soc. Hort. Sci.*, 43, 336–42.

[4] DEGEN, A. VON (1926). Die charakteristischen Unkräutsamen der ungarischen Rotklee- und Luzernensamen. *Budapest*, 9 pp.

[2] DENT, T. V. (1942). The biological control of exotic weeds. *Indian Forester*, 68(7), 357–60.

[2] DESHPANDE, V. C. (1935). Eradication of prickly-pear by cochineal insects in the Bombay Presidency. *Agr. & Livestock India*, 5, 36–42.

[1] DETERRE, J. (1931). [Complete weed-eradicating fertilizers—in French.] *Engrais*, 46, 47–49.

[1] DIEFFENBACH, E. M. (1940). Electrical weed control. *Agr. Eng.*, 21, 486, 488.

[2] DODD, A. P. (1926). The campaign against prickly-pear in Australia. *Nature, Lond.*, 117, 625–6.

[2] —— (1929). The progress of biological control of prickly-pear in Australia. *Commonwealth Prickly-Pear Bd.*, *Brisbane*, 44 pp.

[2] —— (1933). The present position and future prospect in relation to the biological control of prickly-pear. *J. Council Sci. Ind. Res.*, 6, 8–13.

[2] —— (1936). The control and eradication of prickly-pear in Australia. *Bull. Entomol. Res.*, 27, 503–22.

[2] —— (1940). The biological control of prickly-pear in Australia. In '*The Control of Weeds*' (Ed. R. O. Whyte). *Herbage Publ. Ser. Bull.*, 27, 131–43.

[2] —— (1940a). The biological campaign against prickly-pear. *Commonwealth Prickly-Pear Bd.*, *Brisbane*, 117 pp.

[2] —— (1961). Biological control of *Eupatorium adenophorum* in Queensland. *Austral. J. Sci.*, 23, 356–65.

[2] DOULL, K. M. (1955). The biological control of noxious plants and insects. *Rural Educ. Bull.*, 10, 98–128.

[1] DROTTY, S. (1929). [Harrowing to control weeds in cereals—in Swedish, English summary.] *Medd. Centralanst. Försöksv. Jordbruksområdet*, 348, 23 pp.

[2] DU TOIT, E. (1937). Prickly-pear eradication. *Farming S. Africa*, 12, 411–13.

[2] DU TOIT, R. (1942). The spread of prickly-pear in the Union. *Farming S. Africa*, 17, 300–4.

[2] —— (1950). Lantana as a weed. *Farming S. Africa*, 25, 163–4.

[4] DYMOND, J. R., ARCHIBOLD, E. S. & ELFORD, F. C. (1915). Grain screenings . . . with results of feeding experiments. *Canad. Dep. Agric.*, *Ottawa*, 44 pp.

[1] EDWARDS, D. C. (1942). Burning for brush control. *Emp. J. Exp. Agr.*, 10, 219.

[4] EGGINK, H. J. (1950). [Preliminary investigation on the occurrence of weed seeds in cleaned seed samples—in Dutch.] *Maandbl. Landouwvoorl. Dienst*, 7, 304–12.

[4] EGGINTON, G. E. (1921). Colorado weed seeds. *Colorado Agr. Exp. Sta. Bull.* 260, 91 pp.

[3] EGLER, F. E. (1950). Herbicide effects on Connecticut vegetation, 1949. *Bot Gaz.*, 112, 76–85.

[3] —— (1951). Brush control, an aspect of 'plant community management'. *Elect. Light & Power*, 29(3), 98–9, 151 (also in *Proc. Northeast Weed Cont. Conf.*, 5 (Supplement), 73–5, 1951).

[3] —— (1951a). The unsuitability of certain grasslands as rights-of-way vegetation cover. *Proc. Northeast Weed Cont. Conf.* 5, 251–4.

[3] —— (1952). Herbicide effects on Connecticut vegetation, 1950. *J. Forestry*, 50, 198–204.

[3] —— (1954). Vegetation management for rights-of-way and roadsides. *Smithsonian Institution (Washington, D.C.) Report for 1953*, pp. 299–322.

[3] —— (1958). Science, industry, and the abuse of rights-of-way. *Science*, 127, 573–80.

[2] ELAM, F. L. (1952). Goats cleared our brush. *West. Livestock J.*, 30(42), 37, 46, 51, 55.

[1] ELLIOTT, F. C. (1954). Mechanical weed control. *Cotton Gin & Oil Mill Press*, 35(17), 43–44.

[2] ELLIS, H. (1951). Fighting weeds with beetles. *Farm J.*, 65(4), 29.

[2] EVANS, J. W. (1942). The gorse weevil. *Tasmanian J. Agr.*, 13(1), 15–18.

[2] EVANS, J. W. (1952). *Injurious Insects of the British Commonwealth (except the British Isles, India and Pakistan); with a Section on the Control of Weeds by Insects.* Comm. Inst. Entomol., London, 242 pp.

[4] EVERSON, L. E. (1942). Weed trends in Red and Alsike clover seed since 1911. *Proc. Ass. Off. Seed Anal.* (1942), pp. 68–69.

[4] —— (1952). Weed garlic (*Allium vineale*) bulblets in Kentucky bluegrass. *Ass. Off. Seed Anal. News Letter*, 26, 13–15.

[4] —— (1956). Noxious weed seeds in Iowa oats and red clover samples. *Proc. Iowa Acad. Sci.*, 63, 252–8.

[1] FAIL, H. (1956). The effect of rotary cultivation on rhizomatous weeds. *J. Agr. Eng. Res.*, 1(1), 68–80.

[1] FLAY, A. H. (1952). The control of grassy weeds by mechanical aids. *Proc. New Zealand Weed Control Conf.*, 5, 17–23.

[2] FRANZ, J. (1956). Bibliographie concernant la lutte biologique. *Entomophaga*, 1, 107–12.

[1] FRIESEN, H. A. (1955). The place of cultural and chemical weed control methods. *Proc. West. Canad. Weed Control Conf.*, 8, 21–26.

[2] FULLAWAY, D. T. (1954). Biological control of cactus in Hawaii. *J. Econ. Entomol.*, 47, 696–700.

[2] —— (1956). Biological control of *Opuntia megacantha* and *Lantana camara* in Hawaii. *Abs. Tenth Int. Congr. Entomol.* (Montreal), Aug. 17–25.

[1] FURBUSH, P. B. (1952). Controlled burnings most effective method of eliminating stands of Medusa-head weed (*Elymus caput-medusae*). *Calif. Cattleman*, June, 1952.

[2] FYFE, R. V. (1937). The lantana bug, *Teleonemia lantanae* Distant. *J. Council. Sci. Ind. Res.* (Melbourne), 10, 181–6.

[4] GAERTNER, E. E. (trans. and arr.) (1954). Two keys for the identification of 'seeds' based on the works of W. Beyerinek and J. Scurti. Research Council of Ontario, Toronto, 22 and 23 pp.

[2] GARDNER, T. R. (1956). Biological control of insect and plant pests in the Trust Territory and Guam. *Abs. Tenth Int. Congr. Entomol.* (Montreal), Aug. 17–25.

[1] GATES, F. C. & SEWELL, N. C. (1925). Tillage and weeds. *Ecology*, 6, 138–42.

[2] GERVASI, A. (1941). Su un fungo parasita di *Opuntia robusta* Wendl.: *Physalospora opuntiae robustae* n.sp. *Riv. Pat. Veg.* (Pavia), 31, 3–12.

[2] GEYER, J. W. (1941). The biological control of the 'rondeblaar' prickly-pear. *Farming S. Africa*, 79, 4 pp.

[2] GIBSON, A. (1914). The burdock gelechiid, an insect seed destroyer. *Ottawa Nat.*, 28, 96.

[4] GIRSCH, A. (1941–43). Origin of clover and grass seed by weed seed content. *Proc. Int. Seed Test. Ass.*, 13, 147.

[2] GOODWIN, R. H. & NIERING, W. A. (1959). The management of roadside vegetation by selective herbicide techniques. *Conn. Arbor. Bull.*, 11, 4–10. (*See* Fig. 1 for new selective method.)

[1] GRANDFIELD, C. O. (1930). The relation of organic food reserves to the effect of culling pasture weeds at different stages of growth. *J. Amer. Soc. Agron.*, 22, 709–13.

[2] GRANGE LEAGUE FEDERATION (1958). *Chemical Weed Control Guide.* Cooperative GLF Exchange Inc., Ithaca, New York, 63 pp.

[2] GREAT BRITAIN: COMMONWEALTH INSTITUTE OF BIOLOGICAL CONTROL (1952). The work of the Commonwealth Institute of Biological Control. *Brit. Agr. Bull.*, 5(19), 53–57.

[2] GREAT BRITAIN: DISCUSSION ON THE BIOLOGICAL CONTROL OF WEEDS (1954). *Commonwealth Ent. Conf. Rep.*, 6, 95–101.

[4] GREGER, J. (1927). *Mikroskopie der landwirtschaftlichen Unkrautsamen, mit besonderer Berücksichtigung der Frucht- und Samenschaden.* P. Parey, Berlin, 117 pp.

[2] GREGOR, M. J. F. (1932). The possible utilization of disease as a factor in bracken control. *Scot. Farm. J.*, 46, 52–59.

[2] GROOT, P. VAN DER (1940). Biological control of prickly-pear in the Palu Valley (N. Celebes). *Landbouw* (Buitenzorg), 16, 413–29; *Meded. Alg. Proefstat. Landb. Buitenzorg*, nr. 43, 17 pp.

[2] HAMBLYN, C. J. (1959). Manuka blight losing effectiveness in North Island. *New Zealand J. Agric.*, 99(2), 119, 121, 123.

[2] HAMLIN, J. C. (1924). Biological control of prickly-pear in Australia: contributing efforts in North America. *J. Econ. Entomol.*, 17, 447–60.

[2] —— (1926). Biological notes on the important *Opuntia* insects of the United States. *Pan Pacific Entomol.*, 2, 97–105.

[2] —— (1928). *Copidryas cosyra* Druce, an enemy of cactus on the west coast of Mexico. *J. Econ. Entomol.*, 21, 939–40.

[2] —— (1932). An inquiry into the stability and restriction of feeding habits of certain cactus insects. *Ann. Entomol. Soc. Amer.*, 25, 89–120.

[1] HARDY, E. A. (1931). Machinery for weed control. *Agr. Eng.*, 12(10), 369–73.

[1] —— (1938). Tillage in relation to weed root systems. *Agr. Eng.*, 19, 435–8.

[1] HARRINGTON, J. B. (1954). The control of wild oats (*Avenua fatua*) by cultural methods. *Saskatchewan Univ. Coll. Agr. Ext. Bull.* 131, 4 pp. (revised).

[2] HARRIS, P. (1961). Control of toadflax (*Linaria vulgaris*) by *Brachypterolus pulicarius* L. and *Gymnactron antirrhini* Payk. (Coleoptera) in Canada. *Canad. Ent.*, 93, 977–81.

[1] HART, G. H. (1950). Brush burning—California blazes a trail on reclaiming to grass. *West. Livestock J.*, 29(22), 35, 48–51, 59–60.

[1] HARTLEY, C. W. S. (1949). An experiment on mechanical methods of Lalang eradication. *Malayan Agr. J.*, 32, 236–52.

[4] HARZ, C. O. (1885). *Landwirtschaftliche Samenkunde*. Paul Parey, Berlin, 1371 pp.

[2] HASH, T. R. (1952). Geese in the berry planting. *W. Va. Agr. Coll. Ext. Misc. Publ.* 12, 7 pp.

[2] HEALD, F. D. & LEWIS, I. M. (1912). A blight of the mesquite. *Trans. Amer. Micr. Soc.*, 31, 5–10.

[2] HEINZE, K. (1956). Blattläuse als biologischer Bekämpfungsfaktor bei der Bekämpfung von Unkräutern. *Z. Pflanzen. u. Pflanzenschutz*, 63, 689–93.

[1] HELGESON, E. A. (1957). Cultural and mechanical methods of weed control. Pp. 6–19 in *Methods of Weed Control*. F.A.O., Rome, 189 pp.

[1] HILLI, A. (1932). [The effect of depth of ploughing on the weed condition of cultivated soils—in Finnish.] *Maat. Aikak.* (Helsinki), 4, 60.

[1] HODGSON, J. M. (1950). Electrocution of weeds, widely advertised, not successful in Idaho field experiments. *Crops & Soils*, 3(3), 25.

[3] —— (1958). Control of perennial weeds by competitive croppping and cultural management. *Proc. West. Weed Control Conf.*, 16, 90–96.

[4] HOEFLE, O. M. (1932). Weeds seeds found in vegetable seeds. *New York Agr. Exp. Sta. Bull.* 616, 15 pp.

[1] HOLEKAMP, E. R. (1954). Weed control by flame cultivation. *Prog. Agric. Arizona*, 6, 4.

[4] HOLLISTER, B. A. (1921). The relation between the common weeds of Michigan and those found in commercial seed. *Mich. Acad. Sci. Rep.*, 22, 187–98.

[2] HOLLOWAY, J. K. (1952). Biological control of Klamath weed (*Hypericum perforatum*) in California. *Proc. West. Weed Cont. Conf.*, 13, 33–35.

[2] —— (1956). The biological control of Klamath weed in California. *Abs. Tenth Int. Congr. Entomol.* (Montreal), Aug. 17–25.

[2] —— (1957). Weed control by insects. *Sci. Amer.*, 197(1), 56–62.

[2] —— & HUFFAKER, C. B. (1952). Insects to control a weed. *U.S. Dep. Agric. Yearbook 1952*, 135–40.

[2] HOLLOWAY, J. K. & HUFFAKER, C. B. (1953). Establishment of a root borer and a gall fly for control of Klamath weed. *J. Econ. Entomol.*, **46**, 65–67.

[2] HOWARD, L. O. (1926). The work of the Prickly-Pear Board in Australia. *J. Econ. Entomol.*, **19**, 872.

[2] HOY, J. M. (1960). Establishment of *Procecidochares utilis* Stone (Diptera: Trypetidae) on *Eupatorium adenophorum* Spreng. in New Zealand. *New Zealand J. Sci.* **3**, 200–9.

[2] HOYT, A. S. (1950). Insects build a pasture of 60 million acres. (*Cactoblastis cactorum* for prickly-pear control.) *Cattle Digest*, **1**(3), 57–58.

[2] HUFFAKER, C. B. (1951). The return of native perennial bunchgrass (*Danthonia californica*) following the removal of Klamath weed (*Hypericum perforatum* L.) by imported beetles (*Chrysolina* spp.). *Ecology*, **32**, 443–58.

[2] —— (1953). Quantitative studies on the biological control of St. John's wort (Klamath weed) in California. *Proc. Pacific Sci. Congr. 1949*, 7(4), 303–13.

[2] —— (1956). The principles of biological control of weeds. *Abs. Tenth Int. Congr. Entomol.* (Montreal), Aug. 17–25.

[2] —— (1957). Fundamentals of biological control of weeds. *Hilgardia*, **27**, 101–57.

[2] —— (1962). Some concepts on the ecological basis of biological control of weeds. *Canad. Ent.*, **94**, 507–14.

[2] ——, RICKER, D. W. & KENNETT, C. E. (1961). Biological control of puncture vine (*Tribulus terrestris*) with imported weevils (*Microlarinus* spp.). *Calif. Agric.*, **15**(12), 11–12.

[1] HUMPHREY, R. R. (1949). Fire as a means of controlling velvet mesquite (*Prosopis velutina*), burroweed (*Aplopappus tenuisectus*), and cholla (*Opuntia fulgida*) on southern Arizona ranges. *J. Range Mgmt.*, **2**, 175–82.

[2] HURST, F. (1951). Clean as a floor—sheep hoe sugar-cane. *Progr. Farmer* (Miss.-Ark.-La. ed.), **66**, 15, 96.

[2] HUTSON, J. C. (1926). Prickly-pear and cochineal insects. *Trop. Agric. (Trinidad)*, **47**, 290–2.

[4] HYDE, E. O. C. (1950). Weed seeds in agricultural seed. *New Zealand Dep. Agr. Bull.* 316, 48 pp.

[2] IMMS, A. D. (1929). Remarks on the problem of biological control of noxious weeds. *Trans. Fourth Int. Congr. Entomol.* (1928), 10–17.

[2] —— (1931). Biological control. II. Noxious weeds. *Trop. Agric. (Trinidad).* **8**, 124–7.

[2] —— (1941). The prickly-pear problem in Australia. *Nature, Lond.*, **148**, 303–5.

[4] ISELY, D. (1951). Seeds of *Bromus secalinus* and *commutatus*. *Proc. Iowa Acad. Sci.*, **58**, 155–63.

[4] ——, WEST, D. & POHL, R. W. (1951). Seeds of agricultural and weedy *Bromus*. *Iowa State Coll. J. Sci.*, **25**, 531–48.

[4] —— & WRIGHT, W. H. (1954). Noxious weed seeds. II. *Iowa State Coll. J. Sci.*, **28**, 521–86.

[1] IVANOV, P. K. & KIREEV, V. N. (1954). [Agrobiological basis of the control of Canada thistle on Volga soils under irrigation—in Russian.] *Agrobiologiya*, No. 6, 3–9.

[2] JACQUES, C. (1933). Le *Cactoblastis cactorum*. *Rev. Agr. Nouvelle-Calédonie* (1933), 1085–94.

[1] JALAS, J. (1952). A parallel cultivation experiment on *Oxytropis campestris* ssp. *sordida* (Willd.) Hartm. *Suomalassen Elain- ja Kasvitet. Seuran Vanamon. Tiedonnanot*, **7**, 39–43

[2] JEPSON, F. P. (1930). Present position in regard to the control of prickly-pear (*Opuntia dillenii* Haw.) in Ceylon by the introduced cochineal insect *Dactylopius tomentosus* Lamk. *Trop. Agric. (Perideniya)*, **75**, 63–72.

[2] JOHANSSON, S. (1962). Insects associated with *Hypericum perforatum* L. I. Host plant and Coleoptera. *Opus Ent.*, **27**, 128–46.

[2] JOHNSTON, T. H. (1924). The relation of climate to the spread of the prickly-pear. *Trans. Roy. Soc. South Australia*, 48, 269–96.

[2] JUDD, S. D. (1898). Birds as weed destroyers. *U.S. Dep. Agric. Yearbook 1898*, pp. 221–32.

[4] KAMENSKY, K. W. (1930). [Morphologisch-anatomische Unterscheidungsmerkmale der Unkrautsamen aus den Familien Liliaceae und Iridaceae—in Russian.] *Bull. Appl. Bot. Genet. & Plant Breed.*, 25, 59–108.

[1] KAUL, B. N. (1951). Weed control by good husbandry. *Allahabad Farm.*, 25(4), 137–41.

[1] KEEPING, G. S. & MATHESON, H. D. (1949). Mechanical spraying for the eradication of Lalang. *Malayan Agr. J.*, 32, 253–9.

[2] KELLEY, S. G. (1931). The control of Noogoora and Bathurst burr by insects. *J. Council Sci. Ind. Res., Australia*, 4, 161–72.

[2] —— (1937). The use of insects for the control of noxious weeds. *Kansas State Bd. Agr. Quart. Rep.*, 55(217-A), 34–38.

[1] KELTON, E. (1952). Greasewood, blackbrush, it's still bad around Fort Stockton (Tex.); they're controlling it with a super stalk cutter. *Soil & Water Mag.*, 1(9), 18–19.

[1] KHIL, G. T. (1955). [Deep plowing-method of controlling perennial weeds—in Russian.] *Zemledelie*, 3(7), 109.

[1] KOIE, G. (1951). [On the extirpation method considered from a biological standpoint of weeds in nursery—in Japanese.] *Trans. Jap. Forestry Soc.*, 59, 81–83.

[4] KORSMO, E. (1935). *Weed Seeds*. Gyldendal Norsk Forlag, Oslo, 175 pp.

[1] KRASULIN, V. P. (1935). [Stubble burning as a method of weed control—in Russian, German summary.] *Khim. Sotsial. Zemled.*, 11–12, 120–4.

[2] KRAUSS, M. L. H. (1955). Notes on insects associated with Lantana in Cuba. *Proc. Hawaiian Entomol. Soc.*, 15, 123.

[1] KRYLOV, S. V. (1956). [Mulch paper—in Russian.] *Moskov. Ordena Lenina Selskokhoz. Akad. im. K. A. Timiriazeva Dok. TSKHA*, 1956(25), 133–6.

[2] KUNHIKANNAN, K. (1930). Control of cactus in Mysore by means of insects. *J. Mysore Agr. Exp. Un.*, 11, 95–98.

[4] LAKON, G. (1916). [Some information concerning the recognition of the Italian origin of red clover and alfalfa seed—in German.] *Landw. Jahrb.*, 49, 137–45.

[2] LALONDE, L. M. (1957). New observations on toadflax (*Linaria vulgaris*) and on its biological control in the Province of Quebec. *Proc. Canad. Nat. Weed Comt. East. Sect.* (1956), 10, 62–63.

[2] LEACH, J. G. (1940). *Insect Transmission of Plant Diseases*. McGraw-Hill, New York, 615 pp.

[1] LEGGETT, H. W. (1953). Cultural control of wild oats. *Proc. West. Canad. Weed Control Conf.*, 7, 51–53.

[2] LEVER, R. J. A. W. (1960). Lantana bug, introduced into some Pacific islands. *World Crops*, 12, 256.

[4] LEWIS, N. G. (1943–44). Seed science and weed control. *Proc. Ass. Off. Seed Anal.* (1943, 1944), 84–86.

[2] LOCKWOOD, S. (1933). The relation of weeds to insect pests. *Calif. Dep. Agric. Bull.*, 22, 279–82.

[2] LOOS, C. A. (1941). A virus disease of *Emilia scabra*. *Trop. Agric. (Trinidad)*, 97, 18–21.

[1] LOWRY, O. J. (1955). Hot weeds. *Reclam. Era* (1955), 71–75.

[4] LUTMAN, A. S. & HILLS, J. L. (1930). Agricultural seed; fifteen years of agricultural seed inspection. *Vermont Agric. Exp. Sta. Bull.* 322, 20 pp.

[1] LYLE, C. C. (1956). Weed control by mechanical and cultural methods. *Proc. Canad. Nat. Weed Comt. East. Sect.* (1955), 9, 18–22.

[1] McCreath, J. B. & Martin, D. J. (1954). Bracken cutting on West of Scotland farms; an economic and botanical survey of past work. *West Scot. Agr. Coll. Econ. Dep. Rep.* 15, 45 pp.

[4] McCullough, J. C., Seed Co. (1950). *Farm and Grass Seed* Manual (2nd edn.) (Compiled by W. E. Ward.) Cincinnati, Ohio, 148 pp.

[1] McKell, C. M., Wilson, A. M. & Kay, B. L. (1962). Effective burning of rangeland infested with medusahead *(Elymus caput-medusae)*. *Weeds*, 10, 125–131.

[2] McLeod, J. H. (1952). Biological control of *Hypericum perforatum* L. *Brit. Columbia Agron. Ass. Conf. Rep.*, 6, 54–57.

[2] —— (1953). Progress report on biological control of *Hypericum perforatum* L. (Abs.) *Brit. Columbia Agron. Ass. Conf. Rep.*, 7, 85.

[2] —— (1955). Progress report on the biological control of goatweed *(Hypericum perforatum* L.). *Brit. Columbia Agron. Ass. Conf. Rep.* (1955), p. 28.

[4] MacMillan, C. (1902). Suggestions on the classification of seeds. *Bot. Gaz.*, 34, 224.

[1] Maitland, V. K. (1933). The eradication of lantana with elephants in the Melghat Division. *Indian Forester*, 59, 84–90.

[2] Manuel, C. G. (1935). A beneficial meaner bird *(Munia cabanisi)*, destroyer of weed seeds in rice crops. *Philippine J. Sci.*, 58, 193–212.

[2] Marcovitch, S. (1917). Insects attacking weeds in Minnesota. *Sixteenth Rep. Minnesota State Entom.*, 1915–16, pp. 135–52.

[4] Martin, A. C. & Barkley, W. (1961). *Seed Identification Manual.* Univ. of California Press, Berkeley, 221 pp.

[2] Massey, C. L. & Pierce, D. A. (1960). *Trirhabda nitidicollis* a pest of rabbitbrush *(Chrysothamnus nauseosus)* in New Mexico. *J. Range Mangt.*, 13, 216–17.

[1] Masson, H. (1948). [Burning for brush control—in French.] *L'Agronomie Tropicale*, 3, 174.

[4] Mauldin, M. P. (1941). The weed impurities found in some seed samples of grasses utilized in soil conservation. *Amer. J. Bot.*, 28(10), 17.

[2] Mayton, E. L., Smith, E. V. & King, D. (1945). Nutgrass eradication studies. IV. Use of chickens and geese in the control of nutgrass, *Cyperus rotundus* L. *J. Amer. Soc. Agron.*, 37, 785–91.

[2] Mellini, E. (1961). [The use of phytophagous insects in the control of noxious plants—in Italian.] *Prog. Agric.* (Bologna), 7, 747–56.

[2] Merwe, C. R. van der (1931). Prickly pear and its eradication. *Union S. Africa Dep. Agric. Sci. Bull.* 93, 32 pp.

[2] —— (1932). Eradication of jointed cactus. *Farming S. Africa*, 7, 21–23.

[4] Meyer, K. (1942). Die Unkrautsamen der Saaten landwirtschaftlicher Kulturpflanzen. *Arzneipfl.-Umschau* (Pharm. Ind. 9, H.15), F20, 157–61.

[2] Miller, D. (1929). Control of ragwort through insects: experimental work with cinnabar moth *(Thyria jacobaeae)*. *N. Zealand J. Agric.*, 39, 9–17.

[2] —— (1936). Biological control of weeds. *N. Zealand J. Sci. & Technol.*, 18, 581–4.

[2] —— (1939). Control of weeds by insects. Effect on blackberry, ragwort and periperi. *N. Zealand J. Agric.*, 58, 37, 39.

[2] —— (1940). Biological control of noxious weeds of New Zealand. *Herbage Publ. Ser. Bull.*, 27, 153–7.

[2] —— Clark, A. F. & Dumbleton, L. J. (1937). Biological control of noxious weeds and insects in New Zealand. *N. Zealand J. Sci. & Technol.*, 18, 579–93.

[1] Mimaud, J. (1957). Une application de désinfection du sol par la chaleur: la destruction de l'Oxalis tubereux. *Phytoma*, 86, 17–19.

[2] Mobley, L. (1960). Biological control of Scotch broom *(Cytisus scoparius)*. *Calif. Dep. Agr. Bull.* 49(3), 193–194.

[2] Moiseev, A. D. (1950). [Flies of the genus *Dicraeus* as pests of crested wheatgrass *(Agropyron cristatum)* seeds—in Russian.] *Doklady Vsesoiuzn. Akad. Selskhoz. Nauk*, 5(12), 33–38.

[2] MOORE, R. M. & CASHMORE, A. B. (1943). The control of St. John's wort (*Hypericum perforatum* L. var. *angustifolium* D.C.) by competing pasture plants. *Council, Sci. Ind. Res. Bull. Austr.* 151, 23 pp.

[1] MUIR, J. (1952). Mechanical brush clearing the West's 'great white hope'. *West. Livestock J.*, 30(48), 37, 56–57.

[2] MULLER, W. (1960). Der Blackenkäfer (*Gastroidea viridula*). *Grüne*, 88, 886–7.

[4] MURLEY, M. R. (1951). Seeds of the Cruciferae of northeastern North America. *Amer. Midland Nat.*, 46, 1–81.

[4] MURSIL, ALBINA F. (1950). Some brief notes on the identification of seeds of foxtail millet. *Proc. Ass. Off. Seed Anal.*, 40, 55–57.

[4] —— (1964). *Identification of Crop and Weed Seeds.* U.S. Dep. Agric. Handbook No. 219, Washington, D.C., 171 pp. (43 pl.).

[4] MYERS, A. (1941). Common seed impurities of lucerne. *Agr. Gaz. N.S. Wales*, 52, 454–9.

[2] NAUDE, T. J. (1955). Biological control of jointed cactus (*Opuntia aurantica*). *Farming S. Africa*, 30, 259–60, 272.

[2] —— (1955a). Biological control of prickly pear (*Opuntia megacantha*). *Farming S. Africa*, 30, 493–4, 523.

[2] NICHOLSON, A. J. (1950). Progress in the control of *Hypericum* by insects (*Chrysomela gemellata, C. hyperici, Agrilus hyperici.*). *Proc. Eighth Int. Congr. Entomol.* (Stockholm), pp. 96–99.

[3] NIERING, W. A. (1957). The Connecticut Arboretum right-of-way demonstration area progress report. *Proc. Northeast. Weed Control Conf.*, 11, 203–8.

[3] —— (1958). Principles of sound right-of-way vegetation management. *Econ. Bot.*, 12, 140–4.

[3] —— & EGLER, F. E. (1955). A shrub community of *Viburnum lentago*, stable for twenty-five years. *Ecology*, 36, 356–60.

[3] —— & —— (1957). Public utility rights of way—vegetation management. Mimeographed, New London, Conn. 6 pp.

[2] NIKOLSKAIA, M. N. (1935). [Pistacia-seed-eating Chalcidids and their parasites (Hymenoptera, Chalcididae)—in Russian.] *Crop Protection*, 1, 81–87.

[2] NOVITZKY, S. (1951). [The organization of biological control for plant parasites and weeds in Europe—in Italian.] *Conf. Internat. pour l'Examen des Moyens de Lutte contre les Parasites des Plantes. Allocutions, Proc.-Verb., Rap., Commun. et Résolutions*, 1, 430–4.

[2] NOWINSKI, M. (1955). Das Problem der Unkräuter und ihre Bekämpfung auf biologischer Grundlage—in Polish, German summary.] *Poznańskie Towar. Przyjaciól Nauk. Wydz. Mat.-Przyrodiniczy. Komis. Biol. Prace*, 18, 146 pp.

[2] OATES, A. V. (1956). Goats as possible weapons in the control of thorn bush. *Rhodesian Agr. J.*, 53, 61–85.

[2] O'CONNOR, B. A. (1950). Biological control of insects and plants in Fiji. *Fiji Dep. Agric. J.*, 21, 43–54. (Includes a list of beneficial insects introduced into the Fiji Islands.)

[2] —— (1960). Pest and disease control—a decade of biological control in Fiji. *Fiji Dep. Agric. J.*, 30, 44–54.

[4] PALMER, E. L. (1916). A seed key to some common weeds and plants. *Proc. Iowa Acad. Sci.*, 23, 335–94.

[4] PAMMEL, L. H. (1898). The histology of the caryopses and endosperm of some grasses. *Trans. Sci. St. Louis*, 8, 199–220.

[4] —— & DOX, A. W. (1917). The protein content and microchemical tests of the seeds of some common Iowa weeds. *Proc. Iowa Acad. Sci.*, 24, 527–32.

[4] —— & KING, C. M. (1910). Results of seed investigations for 1908 and 1909. *Iowa Agric. Exp. Sta. Bull.*, 115, 154–75.

[4] PARKINSON, S. T. & SMITH, G. (1914). 'Impurities of Agricultural Seeds, with a Description of Commonly Occurring Weed Seeds and a Guide to their Identification.' Ashford, England and Bishopgate, Canada, 105 pp.

[2] PAVLYCHENKO, T. K. (1942). The place of crested wheat grass, *Agropyron cristatum* L., in controlling perennial weeds. *Sci. Agric.* (Ottawa), **22**, 459–60.

[2] —— (1944). The place of crested wheat grass in controlling perennial weeds. *Saskatchewan Univ. Coll. Agric. Ext. Bull.* 109, 4 pp.

[2] PEDERSEN, M. W. (1942). A survey of biological destruction of cactus on Nebraska range land. *J. Amer. Soc. Agron.*, **34**, 769–70.

[2] PENHALLOW, R. (1952). A commentary on biological control. *Proc. Int. Grassland Congr.*, **6**, 573–7.

[2] PERKINS, R. C. L. & SWEGEY, O. H. (1924). The introduction into Hawaii of insects that attack *Lantana*. *Exp. Sta. Hawaiian Sugar Planters' Ass., Entomol. Serv. Bull.* 16, 83 pp.

[2] PETIT, G. (1929). Sur l'introduction à Madagascar du '*Dactylopius coccus* Costa' parasite de l'*Opuntia vulgaris* Mill. *Compte. Rend. Acad. Agric.*, France, **15**, 410–16.

[2] PETTEY, F. W. (1934). *Cactoblastis cactorum*: Government's policy with regard to distribution of the insect. *Farming S. Africa*, **9**, 138–9, 150.

[2] —— (1941). How to make the best use of *Cactoblastis* and cochineal insects. *Farming S. Africa*, **16**, 1 p.

[2] —— (1943). Control of cochineal in spineless cactus plantations. *Farming S. Africa*, **18**, 4 pp.

[2] —— (1943a). Prickly-pear eradication by insects and felling of plants. *Farming S. Africa*, **18**, 4 pp.

[2] —— (1948). The biological control of prickly pears in South Africa. *S. Africa Dep. Agric. Sci. Bull.*, 163 pp.

[2] —— (1953). Boring beetles of prickly pear in South Africa and their importance in the control of *Opuntia megacantha*. *S. Africa Dep. Agric. Sci. Bull.* 340, 1–36.

[2] —— & MARAIS, S. J. S. (1950). The cochineal (*Dactylopius opuntiae*), and the problem of its control in spineless cactus plantations. I. Its history, distribution, biology, and achievements in the control of prickly pear (*Opuntia megacantha*) in South Africa. II. The control of cochineal in spineless cactus (*O. fusicaulis*) plantations. *S. Africa Dep. Agric. Sci. Bull.* 296, 34 pp.

[2] PHILLIPS, E. P. (1938). Jointed cactus and its eradication. *Farming S. Africa*, **13**, 216–17.

[2] —— (1940). Opuntias in S. Africa. *Farming S. Africa*, **15**, 119–28.

[1] PHILLIPS, W. M. & TIMMONS, F. L. (1954). Bindweed (*Convolvulus arvensis*)—how to control it; results of bindweed control experiments at the Fort Hays Branch Station, Hays, Kansas, 1935 to 1952. *Kans. Agric. Exp. Sta. Bull.* 366, 40 pp.

[2] PIEMEISEL, R. L. (1945). Natural replacement of weed hosts of the beet leafhopper as affected by rodents. *U.S. Dep. Agric. Circ.* 739, 48 pp.

[3] —— (1954). Replacement control; changes in vegetation in relation to control of pests and diseases. *Bot. Rev.*, **20**, 1–32.

[3] —— & CARSNER, E. (1951). Replacement control and biological control. *Science*, **113**, 14–15.

[4] PIETSCH, A. (1937). Unkrautsamen und Unkrautfrüchte. *Kosmos, Gesellschaft der Naturfreunde* (Stuttgart), 16 pp.

[4] PLANT PROTECTION LTD. (1953). Soil steamed in frames to kill weeds. *Grower*, **39**, 1018–19.

[4] PORTER, R. H. (1949). Recent developments in seed technology. *Bot. Rev.*, **15**, 221–344.

[2] POWELL, T. (1952). A new science: biological weed control. *Org. Farmer*, **3**(7), 34–37.

[2] PRINGLE, W. L. & ARNOTT, D. A. (1960). Beneficial beetles; study reveals 50 per cent kill of sagebrush. *Res. Farmers*, **5**(4), 15.

[2] PUTTARUDRIAH, M. (1953). Achievements in the field of biological control of insects and weed pests. *Mysore Agric. J.*, 29(3/4), 92–99.

[4] QUACKENBUSH, F. W., CARTER, A. S., SHENBERGER, L. C. & BALBACH, P. (1955). Inspection of agricultural seeds. *Indiana Agr. Exp. Sta. Circ.* 418, 63 pp.

[2] QUEENSLAND: PRICKLY PEAR LAND COMMISSION (1925–32). First to Eighth Annual Reports, Brisbane.

[2] RADEMACHER, B. (1960). Aussichten einer biologischen Unkraut- und Schädlings-bekämpfung. *Hohenheim. Landwirt. Hochsch. Reden. u. Abhandle.*, 11, 27–55.

[2] RAMAKRISHNA AYYAR, T. V. (1931). Control of the prickly-pear by the cochineal insect. *Nature, Lond.*, 128, 837.

[2] —— (1931a). The Coccidae of the prickly-pear in South India and their economic importance. *Agric. & Livestock India*, 1, 229–37.

[4] RATHER, H. C. (1930). Weed problems in relation to the production and marketing of farm seeds. *J. Amer. Soc. Agron.*, 22, 409–16.

[2] RAYNER, H. J. W. (1951). Using geese in strawberry production. *Delaware State Bd. Agr. Bull.*, 40(5), 90–92.

[4] REGILIS, K. & NORMANTAS, K. (1941). [Beiträge zur Kenntnis der Unkräuter in Litauen. II. Die Unkrautsamen in Getreide—in Latvian, German summary.] *Vilniaus Univ. Bot. Sodo Rastai* 1941, 1, 65–112 (15 Tab.).

[1] RENSBURG, H. J. VAN (1952). Burning for bush control. *East Africa Agric. J.*, 17, 119–29.

[1] REUSS, L. A. (1958). Costs of clearing land and establishing improved pastures in Central Florida. *Florida Agric. Exp. Sta. Bull.* 600, 40 pp.

ROBERTSON, J. H. & CORDS, H. P. (1957). Survival of rabbitbrush, *Chrysothamnus* spp. following chemical, burning, and mechanical treatments. *J. Range Mangt.*, 10(2), 83–89.

[2] ROBINSON, R. G. & DUNHAM, R. S. (1954). Companion crops for weed control in soybeans. *Agron. J.*, 46, 278–81.

[4] ROGENHOFER, E. (1952). Einige seltenere Unkrautsamen im Saatgut. *Wien Bundesanst. f. Pflanzenbau u. Samenprüf. Jahrb.* (Wien), 1951, pp. 69–71.

[2] ROSS, H. & TAYLOR, T. P. (1935). Skeleton weed and its control by lucerne. *Agric. Gaz. N.S.W.*, 46, 15–17.

[2] RUDAKOV, O. (1960). [*Alternaria*—an enemy of dodder—in Russian.] *Sels'k. Khoz. Kirgizii*, 1960(4), 42–43.

[2] —— (1961). [*Fungus parasite of dodder, Alternaria cuscutacidae, its culture and use*—in Russian.] Frunze, Izdatel'stvo AN Kirgizskoi SSR, 1961, 65 pp.

[2] RUDENKO, A. & RUDAKOV, O. (1959). [Biological control of *Cuscuta*—in Russian.] *Sel'sk. Khoz. Kirgizii*, 1959(11), 27–28.

[1] RUSSELL, (Sir) E. J. (1950). *Soil Conditions and Plant Growth* (8th edn., Rev. by E. W. Russell). Longmans, Green, London, 635 pp.

[1] SADATI, H. (1956). [Cultivation and cultivators—in Persian.] *Iran. Ext. Serv. Bull.* 18, 28 pp.

[1] SAMPSON, A. W. & SCHULTZ, A. M. (1956). Control of brush and undesirable trees. II. Equipment for mechanical brush clearing. *Unasylva*, 10, 117–29.

[1] SANDERS, H. G. (1954). Cultivations and weed control. *Proc. Brit. Weed Control Conf.*, 1, 15–21.

[1] SAUER, C. O. (1952). *Agricultural Origins and Dispersals*. Bowman Memorial Lecture, ser. 2. American Geographical Society, New York., 110 pp.

[2] SAXENA, J. S. & SINGH, J. P. (1962). Biological control of baroo (*Sorghum halepense*). *Indian Farming*, 11(11), 27.

[2] SAYUPATHAM, T. (1954). [A cogon eradicating grass—in Siamese, English summary.] *Kasikorn*, 27, 154–6.

[4] SCHAPER, P. (1936). *Beiträge zur mikroskopischen Diagnostik der wichtigsten Carophyll-aceensamen unter besonderer Berücksichtigung ihres Verkommens als Unkrautbesatz in Saatwaren und Futtermitteln.* Diss., Univ. Hamburg 1936, 100 pp.

[4] SCHOENICHEN, W. (1923). Mikroskopische Untersuchungen zur Biologie der Samen und Früchte. *Biologische Arbeit* H. 17. Freiburg i. Br. (Th. Fisher), 48 pp. (95 Fig.)

[2] SCHONLAND, S. (1924). The jointed cactus. *Union S. Africa Dep. Agric. J.*, 9, 46–225.

[4] SEED WORLD (Chicago) (1940). Weeds and weed seeds, common, poisonous; with commonly used crop seeds. *Seed World* (Chicago), 74 pp.

[2] SELLERS, W. F. (1952). The collection of the cactus weevil, *Cactophagus spinolae* (Gylh.), in Mexico and its dispatch to South Africa. *Bull. Entomol. Res.*, 43, 43–50.

[1] SHELL, E. W. (1962). Herbivorous fish to control *Pithophora* sp. and other aquatic weeds in ponds. *Weeds*, 10, 326–7.

[4] SHEVELEV, N. I. (1928). [Methods of separating weed seeds from the soil—in Russian.] *Bull. Appl. Bot. Gen. Plant Breed.*, 19, 305–14.

[2] SHEWELL-COOPER, W. E. (1951). Success with sunflowers; a good cleaning crop which outgrows the weeds and gives them little or no chance of survival. *Field*, 198, 471.

[1] SHINER, E. (1952). Will horsepower solve our brush clearing problems? *Farmer-Stockman*, 55(12), 14, 43.

[1] SILKER, T. H. (1955). Procedures for prescribed burning in pine-hardwood stands and slash pine plantations for the control of undesirable hardwoods. *Texas Forest Serv. Circ.* 47, 6 pp.

[2] SILVESTRI, F. (1932). The biological control of insect and weed pests. *J. South-Eastern Agr. Coll.*, 30, 87–96.

[1] SIMEONOV, B. & STOLANOVA, I. (1958). [The influence of some agrotechnical measures upon the weediness in Dobrudja District—in Bulgarian.] *Nauch Trudove, Ser. Rastenievud*, 3(1), 7–322.

[2] SIMMONDS, F. J. (1949). Initial success of attempts at the biological control of the weed *Cordia macrostachya* (Jacq.) R. et S. in Mauritius. *Trop. Agric. (Trinidad)*, 26, 135–6.

[2] SIMMONDS, H. W. (1929). Lantana bug, *Teleonemia lantanae*. *J. Dep. Agric. Fiji*, 1, 16–21.

[2] —— (1929a). Visit to Taveuni by government entomologist. *J. Dep. Agric. Fiji*, 1, 21–22.

[2] —— (1931). Noxious weeds and their control in Fiji. 2. Biological control. *J. Dep. Agric. Fiji*, 4, 29–31.

[2] —— (1932). Weeds in relation to agriculture. *J. Dep. Agric. Fiji*, 5, 58–62.

[1] SINGH, B. N., DAS, K. & CHALAM, G. V. (1937). The effectiveness of cultural treatment on the control of grass weeds. *Emp. J. Exp. Agric.*, 5, 63–68.

[2] SINGH, T. C. N. (1953). Biological eradication of *Saccharum spontaneum* L. *Proc. Fourth Ind. Sci. Congr.* Pt. III, p. 146.

[1] SMIRNOV, B. M. (1952). [The agrotechnics of fallow on soils infested with wild oats in the Southeastern SSR—in Russian.] *Sovet. Agron.*, 8, 77–81.

[1] —— (1953). [Control of perennial weeds (by tillage)—in Russian.] *Zemledelie*, 1, 108–11.

[1] SMITH, C. W. (1940). Cultural control of bindweed. *Agr. Eng.*, 21, 468.

[2] SMITH, H. S. (1947). Biological control of weeds in the United States. *Proc. Entomol. Soc. Wash.*, 49, 169–70.

[2] —— (1953). The initiation of the biological control of weeds in the United States. *Proc. Pacific Sci. Congr.* (1949), 7(4), 294.

[2] SMITH, J. M. (1952). Biological control of weeds in Canada. *Proc. Canad. Nat. Weed Comt. East. Sect.* (1951), 5, 95–97.

[2] —— (1955). Biological control of common St. John's wort (*Hypericum perforatum*) in British Columbia in 1954. *Proc. Canad. Nat. Weed Comt. East Sect.* (1954), 8, 84–88.

[2] —— (1955a). Biological control of weeds. *Proc. West Canada Weed Control Conf.*, 8, 65.

[2] SMITH, J. M. (1956). Biological control of Klamath weed, *Hypericum perforatum* L., in British Columbia. *Proc. Tenth Int. Congr. Entomol.* (Montreal), Abs. 165, p. 155.

[2] SMITH, R. C. (1938). A preliminary report on the insects attacking bindweed, with special reference to Kansas. *Trans. Kansas Acad. Sci.*, 41, 183–91.

[2] SOKOLOFF, V. P. (1951). Biological control of weeds in compacted soil cultures. *Science*, 114, 271–4.

[1] SOMES, H. A. & MOOREHEAD, G. R. (1950). Prescribed burning does not reduce yield from oak-pine (*Quercus pinus*) stands of southern New Jersey. *U.S. Forest Serv. Northeast. Forest Exp. Sta. Paper* 36, 19 pp.

[1] SONVIL, W. A. (1957). Plastic control of weeds; California strawberry growers cover beds with polyethylene. *Amer. Fruit Grower, West. Ed.*, 77(10), 11.

[4] STAHL, C. A. (1938). The occurrence of weed seeds in commercial vegetable seeds. *Proc. Ass. Off. Seed Anal.*, 30, 64–67.

[2] STAHLER, L. M. & CARLSON, A. E. (1947). Controlling field bindweed by grazing with sheep. *J. Amer. Soc. Agron.*, 39, 56–64.

[4] STEVENS, O. A. (1919). Weed seeds in analyses. *Seed World*, 5, 243.

[4] —— (1931). Impurities of North Dakota *Bromus inermis* seed. *North Dakota Agric. Exp. Sta. Bull.* 247, 16 pp.

[4] STONE, A. L. (1915). The weed content of seeds. *Proc. Ass. Off. Seed Anal.* (1914), pp. 23–27.

[4] —— (1915a). State seed inspection and weed control, 1914. *Wisconsin Agric. Exp. Sta. Bull.* 254, 3–39.

[1] STONE, E. C. & JUHREN, G. (1951). The effect of fire on the germination of the seed of *Rhus ovata*. *Amer. J. Bot.*, 38(5), 368–72.

—— & —— (1954). Mechanical clearing better for old stands of chamise; burning hastens revegetation. *California Cattleman*, 1954 (Jan.), 22–23.

[1] STREICH, A. (1931). [Weed eradication and plant growth under paper or pulp sprays—in German.] *Fortschr. Landw.*, 6, 246–8.

[2] STRUVE, V. P. (1926). [On some crops subduing weeds—in Russian.] *Bull. Appl. Bot. Genet. & Plant Breeding* (Leningrad), 16, 171–9.

[2] SUBRAMANIAN, T. V. (1934). The Lantana seedfly in India, *Agromyza ophromyia lantanae* Froggatt. *Indian J. Agric. Sci.*, 4, 468–70.

[2] SUGGS, D. D. (1956). Weed control by grass competition. *Reclam. Era*, 42, 1–3.

[2] SWEETMAN, H. L. (1935). Successful examples of biological control of pest insects and plants. *Bull. Entomol. Res.*, 26, 373–7.

[2] —— (1936). *The Biological Control of Insects.* Chapter on Weed Control, by H. L. Sweetman. Comstock Publ. Co., Ithaca, N.Y., 461 pp.

[2] —— (1958). *The Principles of Biological Control.* Brown, Dubuque, Iowa, 572 pp.

[2] SWINGLE, H. S. (1957). Control of pond weeds by the use of herbivorous fishes. *Proc. South. Weed Control Conf.*, 10, 11–17.

[2] TAMBE, G. C. & WAD, Y. D. (1938). Biological eradication of kans (*Saccharum spontaneum*) in field patches. *Agric. & Livestock India*, 8, 397–406.

[1] TANNEHILL, G. F. (1951). Control of hardwood underbrush by bulldozing. *J. Forestry*, 49, 776–8.

[2] TAYLOR, D. M. (1961). Flame cultivation—how to cut weed control costs as much as 85 per cent. *West. Crops and Farm Mangt.*, 10(2), 22A–22B.

[1] THAKUR, C., NEGI, N. S. & SINGH, H. N. (1955). Tillage control of nut grass (*Cyperus rotundus*) in relation to its organic reserves. *Proc. Bihar Acad. Agric. Sci.*, 4, 67–74.

[1] —— & SINGH, H. N. (1954). Tillage method of controlling nut grass. *Proc. Indian Sci. Congr. Assoc.*, 41(3, Abs.), 239–40.

[4] THIERET, J. W. (1956). The seeds of *Veronica* and allied genera. *Lloydia*, 18, 37–45.

[2] THOMPSON, W. R. (1930). The principles of biological control. *Ann. Appl. Biol.*, 17, 306–338.

[1] THOMSON, J. R. (1950). Farming by fire. (Weed control in central Sudan.) *World Crops*, 2, 396–7.

[4] THOMSON, R. B. & SIFTON, H. B. (1922). *A Guide to the Poisonous Plants and Weed Seeds of Canada and the Northwestern United States.* University of Toronto Press, Toronto, 169 pp.

[4] TILDESLEY, W. T. (1947). Weed seeds. *Canad. Nat.*, 9, 133–7.

[2] TILLYARD, R. J. (1927). Biological control of St. John's wort. *New Zealand J. Agric.*, 35, 42–45.

[2] —— (1927a). Summary of the present position as regards biological control of noxious weeds. *New Zealand J. Agric.*, 24, 85–90.

[2] —— (1927b). The principles of biological control in economic entomology. I, II. *Nature, Lond.*, 119, 202–5, 242–3.

[2] —— (1929). The biological control of noxious weeds. *Trans. Fourth Int. Congr. Entomol.* 1928, (Ithaca), 2, 4–9.

[2] —— (1929a). The biological control of noxious weeds. *Roy. Soc. Tasmania, Papers & Proc.* 1929, pp. 51–86.

[2] —— (1933). The entomological control of weeds in the Pacific Region. *Proc. Fourth Pacific Sci. Congr.* (Canada), pp. 3547–57.

[2] TIMMONS, F. L. (1942). The dissemination of prickly pear seed by jack rabbits. *J. Amer. Soc. Agron.* (Geneva), 34, 513–20.

[1] —— & BRUNS, V. F. (1951). Frequency and depth of shoot-cutting in eradication of certain creeping perennial weeds. *Agron. J.*, 43, 375.

TOIT, E. DU. *See* DU TOIT, E.

TOIT, R. DU. *See* DU TOIT, R.

[2] TOOKE, F. G. C. (1930). Insects in relation to prickly pear control. *S. Afric. J. Nat. Hist.*, 6, 386–93.

[1,3] TORIYAMA, K. & TOYOKAWA, R. (1956). [Studies on weed control. I. Rotation system and weed control—in Japanese.] *Proc. Crop Sci. Soc. Japan.*, 25, 22–23.

[1] TRAVERS, S. J. (1950). Weed control by good husbandry. *J. Min. Agr.*, 57, 264–70.

[2] TRYON, H. (1912). Insects for checking the growth or dissemination of Lantana. *Queensland Agr. J.*, Dec. 1912, No. 6.

[4] TRYTI, G. (1924). [New ways of determining the origin of seed—in Norwegian.] *Tidsskr. Norske Landb.*, 31, 188–99.

[2] TURNER, G. T. & COSTELLO, D. F. (1942). Ecological aspects of the prickly pear problem in eastern Colorado and Wyoming. *Ecology*, 23, 419–26.

[1] TWISSELMAN, C. (1958). Brush burning and air pollution. *California Cattleman*, April 1958, pp. 16–18.

[4] ULBRICH, E. (1928). *Biologie der Früchte und Samen (Karpobiologie).* J. Springer, Berlin, 230 pp.

[4] UNITED STATES DEPARTMENT OF AGRICULTURE (1961). *Seeds, The Yearbook of Agriculture*, 1961. U.S. Government Printing office, Washington, D.C. 591 pp.

VAN DER GROOT, P. *See* GROOT, P. VAN DER.

VAN DER MERWE, C. R. *See* MERWE, C. R. VAN DER.

VAN RENSBURG, H. J. *See* RENSBURG, H. J. VAN.

[2] VILJOEN, P. R. (1941). Jointed-cactus eradication policy. *Farming S. Africa*, 16, 335.

[2] VILLANEUVA, H. L. & FAURÉ, G. O. (1959). Biological control of St. John's wort in Chile. *FAO Plant Protect. Bull.*, 7, 144–6.

[4] VOLKART, A. (1922). Die Herkunftsbestimmung der Saaten. *J. Essais Semences*, 1, 32–43.

VON DEGEN, A. *See* DEGEN, A. VON.

[2] WAGER, C. A. (1947). Can rust kill the bramble? *Farming S. Africa*, 22, 831–2.

[4] WAHLEN, F. T. (1928). A survey of weed seed impurities of agricultural seed produced in Canada, with special reference to the determination of origin. *Compt. Rend. Assoc. Internatl. Essais Semences*, 1928(3), 19–66.

[2] WAIN, R. L. (1960). Some developments in research on plant disease and weed control. *J. Roy. Agric. Soc. Eng.*, **121**, 117–24.

[2] WEBER, P. W. (1955). Recent liberations of beneficial insects in Hawaii. IV. *Proc. Hawaiian. Entomol. Soc.*, **15**, 635–8.

[2] —— (1957). Recent introductions for biological control in Hawaii. II. *Proc. Hawaiian Entomol. Soc.*, **16**, 313–14.

[4] WELCH, G. B. (1954). Seed processing equipment. *Mississippi Agr. Exp. Sta. Bull.* 520, 23 pp.

[4] WELTON, F. A. (1941). Killing weed seeds. *Iowa State Hort. Soc. Rep.*, **76**, 214–17.

[4] WHITE, J. W. (1950). Observations on seed cleaning. *Proc. Canad. Nat. Weed Comt.* (*East. Sect.*), **3**, 86–87.

[4] —— (1951). The disposal of weed seed screenings. *Proc. Canad. Nat. Weed Comt.* (*East. Sect.*), **4**, 57–58.

[1] WIANT, D. E. (1939). Mechanical equipment for weed control. *Agr. Eng.*, **20**, 15–16.

[2] WIDDIFIELD, R. B. (1953). Grow winter rye for better control. *N. Dakota Agric. Coll. Ext. Circ.*, A-199, 8 pp.

[1] WILLARD, C. J. (1954). Eradicating quack-grass by cultural methods. *Ohio Agric. Coll. Ext. Leaflet* L-43, 4 pp.

[2] WILLIAMS, J. R. (1948). A preliminary account of the project for the control of *Cordia macrostachya* (Jacq.) Roem. and Shult. in Mauritius. *Rev. Agric. Maurit.*, **27**, 214–33.

[2] —— (1951). The control of the black sage in Mauritius by *Schematiza cordiae* Barb. (Coleoptera, Galerucidae). *Bull. Entomol. Res.*, **42**, 455–63.

[2] —— (1954). The biological control of weeds. *Commonweath Entomol. Conf. Rep.*, **6**, 95–98.

[2] —— & WIEHE, P. O. (1960). The control of black sage (*Cordia macrostachya*) in Mauritius: the introduction, biology and bionomics of a species of *Eurytoma* (Hymenoptera, Chalcidoidea). *Bull. Entomol. Res.*, **51**, 123–33.

[2] WILLIAMS, W. E., FLOURNOY, R. E. & MEYERS, L. (1953). Johnson grass control using Singletary peas. *Amer. Soc. Sugar Cane Technol. Proc.* 1946/50, pp. 8–10.

[4] WILSON, A. C. (1919–20). Tolerance limits in weed seeds. *Proc. Ass. Off. Seed Anal.*, *12th & 13th Meetings.*

[4] WILSON, A. M. (1949). The prevalence of weed seeds in seed grain. *Proc. West. Canad. Weed Control Conf.*, **3**, 154–6.

[2] WILSON, F. (1943). The entomological control of St. John's wort (*Hypericum perforatum* L.) with particular reference to the insect enemies of the weed in southern France. *Austr. Counc. Sci. Ind. Res. Bull.* 169, 87 pp.

[2] —— (1950). The biological control of weeds. *New Biol.*, **8**, 51–74.

[2] —— (1953). Some aspects of the control of weeds by insects. *Proc. Pacific Sci. Congr.* (1949), 7(4), 294–9.

[2] —— (1953a). Progress in the entomological control of St. John's wort (*Hypericum perforatum*) in Australia. *Proc. Pacific Sci. Congr.* (1949), 7(4), 300–3.

[2] —— (1960). A review of the biological control of insects and weeds in Australia and Australian New Guinea. *Commonwealth Inst. Biol. Control Tech. Commun.* **1**, 102 pp.

[2] —— & CAMPBELL, T. G. (1943). Recent progress in the entomological control of St. John's wort. *J. Counc. Sci. Ind. Res., Australia*, **16**, 45–56.

[2] WILSON, H. K., LARSON, A. H. & STAHLER, L. M. (1945). Competitive crops effective in stopping field bindweed. *Minnesota Farm Home Sci.*, 2(3), 4–5.

[4] WINTON, A. L. (1903). American wheat screenings. *Connecticut Agric. Exp. Sta. Rep.*, **26**, 339–58.

[4] WOESTEMEYER, V. (1953). Feed grain inspection protects against weeds. *Kansas Bd. Agr. Bien. Rep.*, **38**, 116–17.

[2] WOLCOTT, A. R. (1951). Bromegrass as an effective agent in quack-grass control. *Michigan State Coll. Quart. Bull.*, 33(4), 343–50.

[2] WOLF, F. A. (1912). Some fungus diseases of the prickly-pear, *Opuntia lindheimeri* Engelm. *Ann. Mycologici*, 10, 113–34.

[4] WOODBRIDGE, M. E. (1939). List of weed seeds found in alfalfa and clover seeds. *Farm Research (N.Y.)*, 5, 12.

[2] WRIGHT, R. (1927). Goats and noxious weed control. *J. Agric. New Zealand*, 35, 295–7.

[2] YAKHONTOV, V. V. (1961). [Biological control of weeds—in Russian.] *Zasch. Rast. ot Vred. e Boleanei*, 1961(8), 50–51.

[1] YOUNG, R. S. & COLLEDGE, E. (1948). Burning for brush control. *Emp. J. Exp. Agric.*, 16, 76.

[2] ZADE, A. (1913). [A cover crop as a factor in restricting certain weed seeds—in German.] *Fühlings Landw. Ztg.*, 62, 777–85.

ADDENDUM

Recent works noted while this volume was in press.

BACHTHALER, G. (1963). *Chemische Unkrautbekampfung auf Acker und Grünland.* München, 107 pp.

BRUN-HOOL, J. (1963). *Ackerunkraut-Gesellschaften der Nordwestschweiz.* H. Huber, Bern. 146 pp. (Diss. Tech. Hochs., Zurich).

CALDERBANK, A. & CROWDY, S. H. (1962). Bipyridylium herbicides. *Soc. Chem. Indus. Rpt. Prog. Appl. Chem.*, 47, 536–42.

DONALD, C. M. (1963). Competition among crop and pasture plants. *Adv. Agron.*, 15, 1–118.

ENNIS, W. B., JR., SHAW, W. C., DANIELSON, L. L., KLINGMAN, D. L. & TIMMONS, F. L. (1963). Impact of chemical weed control on farm management practices. *Adv. Agron.*, 15, 161–210.

GUTENMANN, W. H. & LISK, D. T. (1964). Herbicide mechanisms: conversion of 4-(2,4-DB) to 2,4-dichlorophenoxycrotonic acid (2,4-DC) and production of 2,4-D from 2,4-DC in soil. *J. Agric. Food Chem.*, 12, 322–3.

HOLSTUN, J. T., WOOTEN, O. B., PARKER, R. E. & SCHWEIZER, E. E. (1963). Triband weed control—a new concept in cotton. *Agric. Chem.*, 19(4), 24–6, 123–4.

JAMES, N. I. & LUND, S. (1965). Induction of male sterility in barley with potassium giberellate and other plant growth regulators. *Agron. J.*, 57, 269–72.

KOLEV, I. D. (1963). *Weeds of Bulgaria* (including control methods). In Bulgarian. Sofia. 566 pp.

KZN, P. R. (1963). The influence of volume rate and droplet size on the efficiency of herbicidal sprays. *J. Rubber Res. Inst. Malaya*, 18, 4–14. (Useful for the tropics.)

LOPINOT, A. C. (1963). Aquatic weeds: their identification and control. *Ill. Fish. Bull.* (Springfield), 4, 1–47.

MACLEOD, D. G. (1963). The parasitism of *Cuscuta*. *New Phytol.*, 62, 257–63.

MALZEV, A. I. (1962). [*Weeds of the USSR and their control*—in Russian.] Edn. 4. Leningrad. 271 pp.

ORTH, H. (1962). *Chemische Unkrautbekampfung in Gartenbau.* München. 146 pp.

POHL, R. W. & LOOMIS, W. (1963). Ecesis of a weed flora. *Iowa Acad. Sci. Proc.*, 70, 55–58.

ROBERTS, H. A. (1963). The problem of weed seeds in the soil. *Brit. Weed Cont. Council, Proc. Symp.*, 1963, 73–82.

SHAW, W. C. (1964). Weed science—a revolution in agricultural technology. *Weeds*, 12, 153–62.

TAYLOR, J. (1964). Invert emulsions; the inside out sprays. *Weeds & Turf*, 3(1), 12–13.

UNITED STATES CONGRESS, SENATE, COMMITTEE ON INTERIOR AND INSULAR AFFAIRS (1963). *Phreatophyte control on the Pecos River Basin, New Mexico and Texas.* U.S. Govt. Printing office, Washington, D.C. 48 pp.

ZWEIG, G. (ed.) (1964). *Analytical methods for pesticides, plant growth regulators and food additives.* Vol. 4. Herbicides. Academic Press, N.Y. 269 pp.

APPENDIX I

PROPERTIES AND USES OF HERBICIDES*

No.	Compound	Common or abbreviated names	Formula	Molecular weight	Melting point (°C.) or physical state	Formulation and uses
	PHENOXY-TYPE COMPOUNDS (-ACETIC, -PROPIONIC, -BUTYRIC, ETC.)					
I	2,4-dichlorophenoxyacetic acid	2,4-D		221·0	138–42	Solutions of esters and amine salts; post-emergence—in cereals, in turf areas for broad-leafed weeds or combined with 2,4,5-T for woody plant control.
II	4-chloro-2-methylphenoxy-acetic acid	MCPA; MCP; Methoxone		200·6	118–20	Sodium salt or amine formulations; water-soluble; selective in cereals and certain leguminous plants in post-emergence applications, safer on the seedling. Also used in rice and flax. For control of broad-leafed weeds only.
III	2,4,5-trichlorophenoxyacetic acid	2,4,5-T		255·5	154–7	Emulsifiable concentrate of ester, often combined with 2,4-D ester; over-all spray in water. For control of woody plants in hedgerows, pastures, roadsides; poison-ivy, brambles, mesquite; horse-nettle.

*For a comprehensive listing of chemical and physical properties of herbicides see Nex & Swezey (1954, 1961) (ref. Ch. XIII), see also Report Terminology Committee, Weeds 10, 255–71, 1962, and for use of approved names and structures see footnote to Subject Index.

	Name	Common name	Structure	M.W.	State	Notes
IV	2-(2,4,5-trichlorophenoxy)-propionic acid	2-(2,4,5-TP); Silvex	CH_3, $OCHCOOH$ on 2,4,5-trichlorophenoxy ring	269·5	179–81	Emulsifiable concentrate; iso-octyl ester etc. For control of broad-leafed weeds in turf; for woody plants including mesquite, *Quercus*, poison-ivy, and brambles; for submerged and emergent aquatic weeds; for broad-leafed weeds in rice.
V	4-(2,4-dichlorophenoxy)-butyric acid	4-(2,4-DB)	$OCH_2CH_2CH_2COOH$ on 2,4-dichlorophenyl ring	249·1	Solid	Ester or amine salt; selective control of broad-leafed weeds in alfalfa, clover, flax, beans, peas.
VI	4-(4-chloro-2-methylphenoxy) butyric acid	4-(MCPB)	$OCH_2CH_2CH_2COOH$ on 4-chloro-2-methylphenyl ring	228·7	Solid	Amine salt; selective control of weeds in leguminous crops.

PHENOXYETHYL SULPHATES AND RELATED COMPOUNDS

	Name	Common name	Structure	M.W.	State	Notes
VII	Sodium 2-(2,4-dichloro-phenoxy)ethyl sulphate	2,4-DES; Sesone	$OCH_2CH_2OSO_2ONa$ on 2,4-dichlorophenyl ring	309·1	Solid	Water-soluble; for pre-emergence; asparagus, strawberries, peanuts, potatoes, nursery stock. Safe on foliage.

439

No.	Compound	Common or abbreviated names	Formula	Molecular weight	Melting point (°C.) or physical state	Formulation and uses
VIII	Sodium 2-(2,4,5-trichloro-phenoxy)ethyl sulphate	2,4,5-TES; Natrin	$OCH_2CH_2OSO_2ONa$ (2,4,5-trichlorophenoxy structure)	343·6	Solid	Water-soluble; similar to No. VII; more residual; safer on certain transplanted crops.
IX	2-(2,4-dichlorophenoxy)ethyl benzoate	2,4-DEB; Sesin	$OCH_2CH_2O_2C$ (2,4-dichlorophenoxy ethyl benzoate structure)	311·2	74	Wettable powder or emulsifiable concentrate; more resistant to leaching under irrigation than Sesone, but otherwise, for use on same crops.
X	Tris-(2,4-dichlorophenoxy-ethyl)phosphite	2,4-DEP; Falone	$(Cl\dots OCH_2CH_2O)_3P$ (2,4-dichlorophenoxyethyl structure)	649·13	Solid	Emulsifiable concentrate; granular; pre-emergence weed control in peanuts, strawberries, ornamentals, asparagus.
XI	2-(2,4,5-trichlorophenoxy) ethyl 2,2-dichloropropionate	Erbon	$OCH_2CH_2OCCCl_2CH_3$ (2,4,5-trichlorophenoxy structure)	366·5	Solid	Emulsifiable concentrate; for non-selective control at high rates; soil sterilization.

CARBAMATES

	Name	Common names		State	Description	Structure
XII	Isopropyl N-(3-chlorophenyl)-carbamate	CIPC; Chloropropham	213·7	Solid	Emulsifiable concentrate; pre-emergence, selective for spinach, onions, cole crops, established stands of only alfalfa and clover; controls chickweed, smartweed, purslane, most annual grasses.	(structure)
XIII	4-chloro-2-butynyl N-(3-chlorophenyl)carbamate	Carbyne; Barban (in part)	258·1	75	Emulsifiable concentrate; post-emergence control of wild oats in wheat, barley, rapeseed, flax.	(structure)
XIV	2,3-dichloroallyl di-isopropyl-thiolcarbamate	Avadex Diallate	270·22	150°C. at 9 mm. Hg	Emulsifiable concentrate; pre-emergence; disked-in soil pre-planting treatment for control of wild oats in wheat, barley, rapeseed, flax.	(structure)
XV	2-chloroallyl diethyl-dithiocarbamate	Vegedex; CDEC	223·8	Liquid	Emulsifiable concentrate; pre-emergence control of annual weeds (including grasses) in maize, beans, celery.	(structure)
XVI	Ethyl N,N-di-n-propylthiol-carbamate	Eptam; EPTC	189·4	Liquid	Granular carrier; pre-emergence, and as a spray for pre-planting use on tomatoes and potatoes; highly specific for nutgrass (Cyperus spp.) control.	(structure)

No.	Compound	Common or abbreviated names	Formula	Molecular weight	Melting point (°C) or physical state	Formulation and uses
XVII	3,5-dimethyltetrahydro-1,3,5-2 H-thiadiazene-2-thione	Mylone; DMTT Dazomet		162·3	105	Wettable powder; worked into soil as a fumigant; fungicide, nematocide, weed killer; on ornamentals; tobacco and vegetable seed-beds.
SUBSTITUTED PHENOLS						
XVIII	Pentachlorophenol	PCP		266·3	190-1	Emulsifiable concentrate; rapid top-kill of weed species; for ditchbank weed control.
XIX	2,4-dinitro-6-sec-butylphenol [2-sec-butyl-4, 6-dinitrophenol]	Dinoseb; DNBP; 'Dinitro'		240·2	38-42	Water-soluble amine salts, also granular form; pre-emergence in beans, maize, potatoes.
SUBSTITUTED UREAS						
XX	Dichloral urea; [1,3-bis(2,2,2-trichloro-1-hydroxyethyl)urea]	DCU	$CCl_3CHOHNHCNHCHOHCCl_3$ (with O)	354·9	Solid	Wettable powder; pre-emergence oil treatment; control of grass weeds in sugar-beets.

442

	Name	Common name	Structure			Notes
XXI	3-(p-chlorophenyl)-1,1-dimethylurea	CMU; Monuron	O, CH_3, CH_3, NHCN, Cl	198·7	167–74	Wettable powder; for pre-emergence control or for control of weed seedlings in well-established crops of sugar-cane, pineapple, asparagus, and citrus grown in certain areas.
XXII	3-phenyl-1,1-dimethylurea	Fenuron	O, CH_3, CH_3, NHCN	164·2	136	Pelleted product for dry application to the soil for control of woody plants in fence-rows, drainage ditches, utility and railroad rights-of-way; for control of bindweed and for use in other non-cultivated areas.
XXIII	3-(3,4-dichlorophenyl)-1,1-dimethylurea	Diuron	O, CH_3, CH_3, NHCN, Cl, Cl	233·1	150–5	Wettable powder; for pre-emergence control or for control of weed seedlings in well-established crops of sugar-cane, pineapple, peppermint (lay-by), irrigated cotton (at lay-by), alfalfa (dormant), perennial grass crops, certain small berry crops, and grapes.
XXIV	1-n-butyl-3-(3,4-dichloro-phenyl)-1-methylurea	Neburon	O, H, CH_3, NCN, CH_3, Cl, Cl, $CH_3CH_2CH_2CH_2$	275·2	102–3	Wettable powder; pre-emergence; in nursery plantings of certain woody ornamental plants for control of annual weeds and grasses—in arborvitae, *Chamaecyparis*, *Euonymus*, firethorn, *Forsythia*, honeysuckle, juniper, pine, privet, yew.

No.	Compound	Common or abbreviated names	Formula	Molecular weight	Melting point (°C.) or physical state	Formulation and uses
XXV	3-phenyl-1,1-dimethylurea trichloroacetate	Urab; Fenuron TCA		326·5	Solid	Soil sterilant at high rates (100–200 lb. per acre).
XXVI	3-(p-chlorophenyl)-1,1-dimethyl urea trichloroacetate	Urox; Monuron TCA		361·1	Solid	Soil sterilant at high rates (100–200 lb. per acre).

TRIAZINES

No.	Compound	Common or abbreviated names	Formula	Molecular weight	Melting point (°C.) or physical state	Formulation and uses
XXVII	2-chloro-4,6-bis(ethylamino)-1,3,5-triazine	Simazine		201·7	225	Wettable powder; pre-emergence for annual weeds and grasses in maize; for quack-grass control; for soil sterilization.

XXVIII	2-chloro-4-ethylamino-6-isopropylamino-1,3,5-triazine	Atrazine		215·7	173-5	Wettable powder; pre-emergence in maize; for quack-grass and nutgrass control; for soil sterilization.
UNSATURATED ALIPHATICS						
XXIX	Acrylic aldehyde	Acrolein	$CH_2 = CHCHO$	56·06	B.P. 52·5	Water-soluble; injected into irrigation channels for control of aquatic weeds.
XXX	2-propen-1-ol	Allyl alcohol	$CH_2 = CHCH_2OH$	58·08	B.P. 96-97	Water-soluble; fumigation of seed-beds often combined with a nematocidal agent, in tobacco, etc.
CHLORINATED ALIPHATIC ACIDS						
XXXI	Trichloroacetic acid	TCA	CCl_3COOH	163·4	57	Sodium salt; water-soluble; temporary soil sterilant; for quack-grass and other grasses; little translocation.
XXXII	2,2-dichloropropionic acid	Dalapon; Dowpon	CH_3CCl_2COOH	165·0	193-7	Sodium salt; water-soluble; post-emergence control of grasses in railroad ballast, industrial areas, drainage ditches, and sugar-cane; translocated.

445

No.	Compound	Common or abbreviated names	Formula	Molecular weight	Melting point (°C.) or physical state	Formulation and uses
AMIDES						
XXXIII	2-chloro-N,N-diethylacetamide	CDEA	CH_3CH_2 ... $NCCH_2Cl$ ... CH_3CH_2 (O)	149·6	Liquid	Emulsifiable concentrate; for pre-emergence control of grass weeds.
XXXIV	2-chloro-N,N-diallylacetamide	Randox; CDAA	$CH_2=CHCH_2$ ... $NCCH_2Cl$ ... $CH_2=CHCH_2$ (O)	173·7	Liquid	Emulsifiable concentrate; for pre-emergence control of annual weeds (including grasses) in certain vegetable crops (beans, onions, etc.), and corn, sorghum.
MISCELLANEOUS (organic)						
XXXV	3-amino-1,2,4-triazole	Amitrole ATA	$HN-N$, $HC \quad CNH_2$, N	84·1	153-4	Water-soluble salt; perennial weeds; prolonged soil sterilization; particularly useful for poison-ivy control.
XXXVI	N-(3,4-dichlorophenyl)-methacrylamide	Dicryl	Cl–(ring)–Cl ... $NCC=CH_2$, $H \quad CH_3$ (O)	230·09	127-8	Emulsifiable concentrate; post-emergence for weeds in cotton.

XXXVII	3,6-endoxohexa-hydro-phthalic acid, etc.*	Endothal-Na	230·1	116		Sodium salt; water-soluble; now useful as a defoliant and desiccant.
XXXVIII	Maleic hydrazide [1,2 dihydropyridazine-3,6-dione]	MH	112·1	296–8		Liquid concentrate of ammonium salt; for retarding growth of perennial grasses along roadsides; i.e. suppresses regrowth of pruned trees.
XXXIX	2,3,6-trichlorobenzoic acid†	Trysben (in part); 2,3,6-TBA; Zobar (in part) Benzac	225·5	125·6		Water-soluble dimethylamine salt, other chlorinated benzoic acids (tetra-chloro-, etc.) also present; both foliage and root absorption. For non-selective control of noxious perennial weeds (bindweed, leafy spurge, Canada thistle, Russian knapweed, bur ragweed, and other broad-leafed weeds); woody vines (trumpet vine, honeysuckle, *Smilax*) and other woody plants (conifers, roses, sumac, persimmon, sassafras).

* Recently renamed, 7-opabicyclo-[2.2.1] Leptane-2,3-dicarbopylic acid.
† Amiben (a liquid formulation containing 2 lb. per gallon of the ammonium salt of 3-amino-2,5-dichlorobenzoic acid) at 1½ gal. per acre in 12 to 15 gal. of water has been suggested for pre-emergence weed (particularly for grasses) control in soybeans.

447

No.	Compound	Common or abbreviated names	Formula	Molecular weight	Melting point (°C.) or physical state	Formulation and uses
XL	N-1-naphthylphthalamic acid	NPA; Alanap	[structure: naphthalene with —CONH— and —COOH on benzene ring]	291·3	175–185	Various formulations; pre-emergence in asparagus, cucurbit crops.
XLI	Dimethyl 2,3,5,6-tetra-chloroterephthalate	Dacthal DCPA–dimethyl	[structure: benzene ring with COOCH$_3$, 4 Cl, COOCH$_3$]	331·98	156	Wettable powder; long residual pre-emergence control of crabgrass and other weeds in turf.
MISCELLANEOUS (inorganic)						
XLII	Calcium cyanamide	Cyanamide	$CaCN_2$	80·1	Solid	Granular applications on asparagus, before spear emergence, for control of germinating annual weeds; has fertilizer use and value.
XLIII	Copper sulphate	Blue vitriol	$CuSO_4 . 5H_2O$	249·7	Solid	Water-soluble; algicide, and for control of submerged and floating vegetation in bodies of water.

XLIV	Potassium cyanate	KOCN	81·1	315	Water-soluble; post-emergence weed control in onions; also controls crab-grass.
XLV	Sodium arsenite	mixture of Na_3AsO_3, $NaAsO_2$, and $Na_4As_2O_5$	—	Solid	Water-soluble; limited use for control of submerged vegetation in static water; for soil sterilization, long-residual action.
XLVI	Sodium tetraborate	$Na_2B_4O_7 . 10H_2O$	381·4	Solid	Applied dry as soil treatment for soil sterilization; long-residual action (1–2 years.)
XLVII	Sodium chlorate	$NaClO_3$	106·5	248–50	Dry, or in aqueous solutions; non-selective for control of all vegetation; soil sterilization; because of fire hazard, often combined with borates or calcium chloride; residual.
XLVIII	Ammonium sulphamate AMS Ammate	$(NH_4)OSO_2NH_2$	114·1	130	Water-soluble; non-selective for control of all vegetation about buildings, fence-rows; both contact and trans-located; particularly useful for control of poison-ivy; short residual activity.

Q

APPENDIX II

SUPPLEMENTARY DATA ON RECENTLY INTRODUCED HERBICIDES

No.	Compound	Common or abbreviated names *	Formulation and uses
	PHENYLACETIC AND BENZOIC ACID DERIVATIVES *		
XLIX	2,3,6-trichlorophenylacetic acid	Fenac	Acid, salts, or esters; pre-emergence use in sugar-cane, asparagus, corn, for parasitic witchweed (*Striga*); effective on perennials, including quack-grass.
L	2,6-dichlorobenzonitrile	2,6-DBN; Dichlobenil; Casoron	Liquid; non-selective for control of germinating weed seeds; not for pre-emergence in seeded crops; well tolerated by established plants, thus useful in transplanted crops; suggested for orchard and berry-fruit areas, around ornamental shrubs and in nurseries; in established pastures to control seedling weeds, and for total weed control.
LI	2,3,6-trichlorobenzyloxy-propanol	Tritac 10 G	Emulsifiable concentrate, granular forms; non-selective for control of deep-rooted, perennial, broad-leafed weeds: field bindweed, Canada thistle, Russian knapweed, leafy spurge, bur ragweed, toadflax, etc.; for use on non-crop land, such as rights-of-way, fence-rows, industrial sites; long residual action in soils; use care in preventing transfer of herbicide to desirable vegetation and crops; low volatility.
	CARBAMATES †		
LII	Methyl-N-(3,4-dichlorophenyl) carbamate	Swep	Emulsifiable concentrate; pre-emergence control of broad-leafed weeds and grasses in corn, peas, peanuts, lima beans, snap beans, rice, soybeans, cotton.
LIII	Ethyl N,N-diisobutyl thiol-carbamate	R-1910	Emulsifiable liquid, granular forms; for pre-planting use in field and sweet corn; incorporate into soil with rotary hoe or disc immediately after application; controls broad-leafed and grass weeds.
LIV	Ethyl 1-hexamethylene imine carbothiolate	Ordram	Emulsifiable liquid, granular forms; for pre-emergence control of wild oats, barnyard grass, sprangletop in rice, barley and wheat; applied prior to emergence of weeds, incorporated into soil mechanically or by flooding.
	SUBSTITUTED UREAS		
LV	3-(3,4-dichlorophenyl)-1-methoxy-1-methyl urea	Linuron	Wettable powder; for both pre- and post-emergence weed control; effective as directed spray on young barnyard grass (*Echinochloa crusgalli*); post-emergence on peas, carrots; pre-emergence on beans, carrots, parsnips.

* Others belonging to this category include: 2,4-dichlorophenyl-4-nitrophenyl ether; 2-methoxy-3,6-dichlorobenzoic acid (Banvel D; Dicamba); 2-methoxy-3,5,6-trichlorobenzoic acid; 3-nitro-2,5-dichlorobenzoic acid (Dinoben); 4,6-dinitro-2-sec-butyl phenylacetate (Aretit).
† Others belonging to this category are n-propyl N-ethyl-N-(n-butyl)thiolcarbamate (Tillam; PEBC); n-propyl N,N-di-n-propylthiolcarbamate (R-1607); 3-(hexahydro-4,7-methanoindan-5-yl)-1, 1-dimethylurea (Norea).

No.	Compound	Common or abbreviated names	Formulation and uses
	AMIDES		
LVI	N,N-dimethyl-2,2-diphenyl-acetamide	Diphenamid; Dymid	Wettable powder, granular forms; pre-emergence control of annual weeds in direct-seeded and transplant tomatoes, peppers, tobacco, Irish potatoes, sweet potatoes, and strawberries; intermediate in soil-leaching characteristics; highly adsorbed on organic soils.
LVII	N-(3-chloro-4-methylphenyl)-2-methylpentanamide	Solan	Emulsifiable concentrate; primarily for post-emergence control of both broad-leafed and grass weeds in tomatoes, also in carrots and celery; useful for control of annual bluegrass (*Poa annua*) and chickweed (*Stellaria media*) in evergreen-tree nurseries.
	QUATERNARY AMMONIUM COMPOUNDS		
LVIII	1,1'-ethylene-2,2'-dipyridylium dibromide	Diquat	Suggested for post-emergence weed control in certain bush fruits; promising for control of submerged, floating and emerged aquatic weeds.
LIX	1,1'-dimethyl-4,4'-dipyridylium dichloride (or, dimethyl sulphate derivative)	Paraquat	Suggested for post-emergence use on dormant raspberries, black currants, and in tree fruits; effective on grasses, sedges, reeds; promising for control of submerged, floating, and emerged aquatic weeds; desiccant activity.
	DIAZINES AND TRIAZINES		
LX	5-bromo-3-isopropyl-6-methyluracil	Hyvar Isocil	Wettable powder; use as soil sterilant; some members of Compositae family resistant; certain grasses (*Paspalum*) resistant; promising for fern (*Pteridium esculentum*).
LXI	5-bromo-3-sec-butyl-6-methyl-uracil	Hyvar X Bromacil	Wettable powder; water-soluble powder (Hyvar x-ws); non-selective for control of grasses and broad-leafed annual and perennial weeds on industrial sites, etc.; residual activity.
LXII	1-phenyl-4-amino-5-chloro-pyridazone-6	Pyramin; Pyrazon; PCA	Wettable powder; for pre- and early post-emergence, and pre-plant soil incorporation; control of annual broad-leafed weeds in sugar-beets, table beets, possibly spinach.
LXIII	2-methoxy-4,6-bis(isopropyl-amino)-1,3,5-triazine	Prometone	Emulsifiable concentrate; contact herbicide; non-selective; for most annual and many perennial broad-leafed weeds and grasses; industrial areas, etc. for total weed control.
LXIV	2-chloro-4,6-bis(isopropyl-amino)-1,3,5-triazine	Propazine	Pre-emergence for many annual broad-leafed weeds and grasses in sorghum grown for seed.
LXV	4,6-bis(isopropylamino)-2-methyl-thio-1,3,5-triazine	Prometryne	Suggested for post-emergence broad-leafed weed control in young wheat (three-leaf stage); pre-emergence in potatoes.
	TOLUIDINES		
LXVI	N,N-di-(n-propyl)-2,6-dinitro-4-trifluoro-p-toluidine	Trifluralin	For pre-emergence weed control in *Brassica* crops.
LXVII	N,N-di-(n-propyl)-2,6-dinitro-p-toluidine	Dipropalin	Suggested for pre-emergence use, or against seedling grass weeds in established turf grasses.

MISCELLANEOUS *

No.	Compound	Common or abbreviated names	Formulation and uses
LXVIII	4-amino-3,5,6-trichloropicolinic acid	Tordon	Highly water-soluble potassium and triisopropylamine salts; readily absorbed by plant foliage, translocated through the plant; for control of woody species, deep-rooted perennial weeds: California thistle (Cirsium arvense), bindweed (Convolvulus arvensis), Russian knapweed (Centaurea repens), bracken fern (Pteridium aquilinum); for broad-leafed weeds in turf; most grasses tolerant to foliage sprays.
LXIX	N-(2-(O,O-diisopropylthio-phosphoryl) ethyl)-benzenesulphonamide	Betasan	Emulsifiable concentrate, granular forms; for certain grasses and broad-leafed weeds; selective for alfalfa, Brassica spp., cotton, lettuce, cucurbits, rice; for pre-emergence control of annual grasses and broad-leafed weeds on well-established Dichondra and grass lawns—particularly for crabgrass, annual bluegrass, pigweed; residual action in soil.
LXX	O-(2,4-dichlorophenyl)-O-methyl isopropyl-phosphoramidothioate	Zytron; DMPA	Emulsifiable concentrate, granular forms; pre-emergence for crabgrass control in turf; for grass control in rice; promising for pre-emergence weed control in cotton, corn, soybeans, peanuts, peas, beans.
LXXI	Diphenylacetonitrile	Diphenatrile	Applied pre-emergence; controls seedling grasses in herbaceous and woody ornamental plantings.
LXXII	3,4-dichloropropionanilide	Propanil	Highly selective for grass weeds in rice.

* Others belonging to this category include: ethyl xanthogen disulphide (Herbisan; EXD); 4-hydroxy-3,5-dinitro-n-pentasulfone (Sultropin); and the older herbicides for crabgrass control in lawns: phenylmercuric acetate, dimethylarsinic acid and disodium monomethylarsonate.

APPENDIX III

CHEMICAL WEED CONTROL SUGGESTIONS FOR VEGETABLE CROPS, STATE OF WISCONSIN, U.S.A.*

All rates are expressed in pounds of acid equivalent or of active ingredient per acre. Apply the amounts specified below in 40 gal. of water solution per acre unless otherwise stated.

Crops	Chemical	Rate per acre	Time of Application	Weeds controlled	Remarks
Asparagus seedlings (plant beds)	Dinitro (DNBP)	1–2 lb.	Pre-emergence to asparagus	Small annuals	Best when weeds are sprouted and just emerged
	Stoddard Solvent	75–100 gal.			
Asparagus (established beds)	Monuron (Telvar)	2 lb.	Before emergence and after cutting	Annuals	Apply to clean soil after disking in spring and after last cutting
	Alanap (NPA)	8 lb.			
	Dalapon	10 lb.	Before 1st cutting and 3 weeks later if needed	Quack-grass	Grass should be 6 to 8 in. high when treated
Beans (snap)	Eptam (EPTC)	3–4 lb.	Pre-planting or at planting	Annual grasses	Work into soil immediately after application
Beans (snap and lima)	Dinitro (DNBP)	6–9 lb.	Pre-emergence	Annuals	Use high rate when applying at planting time; lower rate just before emergence
		1½–2½ lb.	On day of emergence	"	May use band spray and save on cost

* Prepared by John A. Schoenemann, Extension Specialist in Vegetable Crops, in cooperation with Staff Members of the Departments of Agronomy and Horticulture, by courtesy of Wisconsin Agricultural Experiment Station, *Special Circular 55*, 1963.

Crops	Chemical	Rate per acre	Time of Application	Weeds controlled	Remarks
Beets	TCA	8 lb.	Pre-emergence	Annual grasses	Do not use tops for food or feed
	Common salt	200–400 lb.	Post-emergence	Annuals	Use 200 gal. water per acre and when weeds are small
	Endothal	6 lb.	Pre-emergence	,,	
Cabbage Broccoli and Cauliflower	TCA	8 lb.	Pre-emergence	Annual grasses	Use pre-emergence on direct seeded crop
	CDEC (Vegedex)	4 lb.	Pre-emergence and post-emergence	Annuals	Use pre-emergence on direct seeded crop, or immediately after transplanting. Don't apply in over 80°F. temperature. For post-emergence, follow with light irrigation
Carrots	Stoddard Solvent	75–100 gal.	Before carrots are ¼ in. in diameter	Annuals	Use before weeds are 2 in. high. Spray at night or when wind is down and humidity high
Celery	CDEC (Vegedex)	6 lb.	After transplanting	Annuals	Sprinkle irrigate after application for best results
Lettuce	CDEC (Vegedex)	3–4 lb.	Pre-emergence	Annuals	Plant slightly more seed to allow for reduced plant stand. Sprinkle irrigate after application. Use liquid or granules

Onions (Pre-emergence)	CIPC	4–8 lb.	Pre-emergence	Annuals	Use 4–6 lb. on heavy mineral soil; 8 lb. on muck
	Monuron (Telvar)	1·6 lb.	Pre-emergence	Annuals	Only on old, very well drained muck soils
	Monuron at [mixed with] CIPC at	1 lb. / 4 lb.	Pre-emergence	Annuals	
	CDAA (Randox)	4–6 lb.	Just before onion emergence	Annuals	Heavy rains may cause reduction in stand and stunting
	CIPC plus CDAA (Randox)	4 lb. of each mixed	Pre-emergence	Annuals	
Onions (Post-emergence)	CIPC	6–8 lb.	Loop stage	Annuals	Do not apply in flag stage. Do not use if CIPC was applied pre-emergence
		8 lb.	Onions with 3 or more leaves	Annuals	Direct spray at base of crop. Residue may injure fall-sown grain. Apply no later than 30 days before harvest
	Monuron (Telvar)	1·6 lb.	Onions with 3 or more leaves	Annuals	Direct spray at base of plant. Will not kill well-established weeds
	Monuron at [mixed with] CIPC at	1 lb. / 4 lb.	,,	Annuals	

Crops	Chemical	Rate per acre	Time of Application	Weeds controlled	Remarks
Onions (post-emergence) (cont'd)	CDAA (Randox)	4–6 lb.	Onions with 3 or more true leaves	Annuals	Caution: direct spray at base of crop. Use no later than 45 days before harvest
	CIPC plus CDAA (Randox)	4 lb. of each mixed	,,	Annuals	Direct spray at base of crop. Use no later than 45 days before harvest
Peas	DNBP	1 lb.	Weeds 1–3 in. high	Annual broad-leafed	Use at least 20 gal. water per acre
	MCPA (amine)	¼ lb.	Peas 4 to 8 in. high	Broad-leafed weeds	Use at least 20 gal. of water per acre. May delay maturity 1–4 days. Avoid use on early varieties
	Dalapon plus DNBP	1 lb. each	Weeds 1 to 3 in. high	Annuals	Use mixture of these two chemicals in at least 20 gal. of water per acre

Potatoes (DNBP)	Dinitro (DNBP)	2–3 lb.	Wait to apply just as first potato plants emerge	Annuals	For killing small emerged weeds. Use lighter rate indicated on sandy soils having low organic matter content. Caution: Early applications shortly after planting can injure plant stand if rain and high temperatures follow application
	2,4-D	2 lb.	Pre-emergence	Broad-leafed weeds	Use on muck and peat soils only
	Diuron (Karmex)	0·8 lb.	Pre-emergence	Annuals	Use on muck and peat soils only
	Dalapon [Pre-plant]	5 lb. (spring) or 10 lb. (fall)	Apply before ploughing; Wait 4 days before ploughing and planting	Quack-grass	Not for fields intended for red varieties. Label registration allows a maximum of 7·4 lb. in spring followed by only 3·7 lb. per acre after last cultivation
	Dalapon [pre-emergence]	5 lb.	Before potatoes come up but after grasses emerge	To retard quack-grass and control annual grasses	Not for red varieties. Do not use if pre-plant treatment was applied
	Dalapon [plus DNBP]	3 lb. of each mixed	After grasses and annuals emerged but before potatoes come up	Retards quack-grass and controls annual grasses	Use if broad-leafed weeds as well as grasses are a problem. Not for red varieties. Do not use if pre-plant application was used

Crops	Chemical	Rate per acre	Time of application	Weeds controlled	Remarks
Potatoes (cont'd)	Dalapon [post-emergence]	5 lb. (Do not exceed 3·7 lb. if pre-plant treatment was used)	Apply just as potatoes emerge or any time up to last cultivation	Retards quack-grass and controls annual grasses	Not for red varieties. May retard potato plants slightly. Do not use if pre-emergence application was made
	Eptam	4–6 lb.	Pre-planting or at planting	Annuals	Work into soil immediately after application. May give some quack control at the higher rate
Sweet Corn (i.e. Maize)	Atrazine	1–4 lb.	Pre-emergence	Annuals	Use higher rate on heavy soils. Use one pound rate on sandy soils. Row treatment will reduce cost. *See* caution under Atrazine below
	2,4–D amine	½ lb.	Corn not over 6 in. high	Broad-leafed	Apply as over-all spray
	2,4–D ester	⅓ lb.		,,	
	2,4–D amine or ester	1 lb.	Corn over 12 in. high	,,	Use drop nozzles. Stalks may become brittle. Do not cultivate for at least one week.
	Atrazine	2 lb.	Post-emergence weeds not over 2 in.	Annuals	Not always effective on annual grasses, some control of quack. Safe for corn. Caution: Residue left in soil may affect some crops such as beets or beans in following years

APPENDIX IV

CHOOSING THE CORRECT SPRAY NOZZLE TIP (*by courtesy of Grange League Federation*, 1958) (*See* Ch. XV); *and Spraying Systems, Inc.*

Gal. per acre desired	Suggested crop to spray	Nozzle Size to Use	
		Tee Jet	Mon-arch
5–10	Seeded grains	8001	22
10–15	Maize, grains not-seeded, winter wheat, grass pastures and hayfields	8002	35
30–40	Beans, strawberries, asparagus, maize, grains, spinach, alfalfa, clover, peas, onions, potatoes, legume and grass seedings, vine crops, cruciferous crops	8004 11004* 8003E†	59
40–50	Directional spraying of onions, maize, etc.	11006*	X
75–80	Potatoes, peas, carrots, brush control	8010	X
100–200	Potatoes, peas, onions, beets, brush control, vineyards, thorn apple	8015	99

* These are 110°-angle nozzles especially made to be used for post-emergence directional spraying where it is desirable to spray the soil only and to keep the spray off the plant's foliage.
† The 'E' series nozzles are to be used if band applications are made.

The figures are for a 20-in. nozzle spacing and for 40 lb. pressure at 4 miles per hour ground-speed. Four miles per hour is equivalent to 352 ft. per minute, or 107·3 metres per minute.

Conversion Factors

Measures of Weight—Avoirdupois to Metric

1 dram (dr.)	27·344 grains	1·772 grams
1 ounce (oz.)	16 drams	28·3 grams
1 pound (lb.)	16 ounces	0·454 kilogram
1 stone (st.)	14 pounds	6·350 kilograms
1 quarter (qr.)	2 stones	12·701 kilograms
1 hundredweight (cwt.)	4 quarters	50·802 kilograms
1 (long) ton	20 hundredweight	1·016 tonnes

Metric to Avoirdupois

1 milligram (mg.)		0·015 grain
1 gram (gm.)	1,000 milligrams	0·564 dram
1 kilogram (kg.)	1,000 grams	2·205 pounds
1 quintal (qt.)	100 kilograms	220·5 pounds
1 tonne	1,000 kilograms	0·984 ton

U.S. Weights to Metric

1 pound	16 ounces	453·592 grams
1 cental	100 pounds	45·359 kilograms
1 (short) ton	20 centals	0·907 tonne

Metric to U.S. Weights

1 quintal (qt.)	100 kilograms	2·205 centals
1 tonne	1,000 kilograms	1·102 (short) tons

Measures of Length—British to Metric

1 inch (in.)		5·400 millimetres
1 foot (ft.)	12 inches	230·480 centimetres
1 yard (yd.)	3 feet	0·914 metre
1 mile	1,760 yards	1·609 kilometres

Metric to British

1 micron (μ)	1/1,000 mm. (1/1,000,000 m.)	1/25,400 inch
1 millimetre (mm.)		0·039 inch
1 centimetre (cm.)	10 mm.	0·394 inch
1 decimetre (dm.)	10 cm.	3·937 inches
1 metre (m.)	10 dm.	1·094 yards
		3·281 feet
		39·370 inches
1 kilometre (km.)	1,000 m.	0·621 mile

Measures of Area (Based on 1 metre = 39·370 inches)
British to Metric

1 square inch (sq. in.)		6·452 sq. centimetres
1 square foot (sq. ft.)	144 sq. in.	0·093 sq. metre
1 square yard (sq. yd.)	9 sq. ft.	0·836 sq. metre
1 acre	4840 sq. yd.	0·405 hectare
1 square mile	640 acres	2·590 sq. kilometres
		258·998 hectares

CONVERSION FACTORS

Metric to British

1 square millimetre (sq. mm.)		0·00155 sq. inch
1 square centimetre (sq. cm.)	100 sq. mm.	0·155 sq. inch
1 square decimetre (sq. dm.)	100 sq. cm.	0·108 sq. foot
1 square metre (sq. m.)	100 sq. dm.	1·196 sq. yards
1 hectare (ha.)	10,000 sq. m.	2·471 acres
1 square kilometre (sq. km.)	100 ha.	0·386 sq. mile

Measures of Volume—British to Metric

1 cubic inch (cu. in.)		16·387 cu. centimetres
1 cubic foot (cu. ft.)	1,728 cu. in.	28·317 cu. decimetres
1 cubic yard (cu. yd.)	27 cu. ft.	0·765 cu. metre
1 bushel (bu.)	2,219·3 cu. in.	0·364 cu. metre

Metric to British

1 cubic centimetre (cc. = ml.)		0·061 cu. inch
1 cubic decimetre (cu. dm.)	1,000 cu. cm.	0·035 cu. foot
1 cubic metre (cu. m.)	1,000 cu. dm.	1·308 cu. yards
		2·750 bushels

Measures of Capacity—I. Based on 1 Imperial gallon (British) = 4·546 litres
(used for both liquid and dry measure)
British to Metric

1 pint (pt.)		0·568 litre
1 quart (qt.)	2 pints	1·136 litres
1 gallon (gal.)	4 quarts	4·546 litres
1 peck (pk.)	2 gallons	9·092 litres
1 bushel (bu.)	4 pecks	36·368 litres

Metric to British

1 millilitre (ml. = cc.)		0·0610 cu. inch
1 centilitre (cl.)	10 ml.	0·0176 pint
1 decilitre (dl.)	10 cl.	0·176 pint
1 litre (l.)	10 dl.	1·760 pints

II. Based on 1 U.S. gallon (liquid measure) = 3·785 litres
U.S. to Metric

1 pint (pt.)		0·473 litre
1 quart (qt.)	2 pints	0·946 litre
1 gallon (gal.)	4 quarts	3·785 litres

Metric to U.S.

1 millilitre (ml. = cc.)		0·0610 cu. inch
1 centilitre (cl.)	10 ml.	0·021 pint
1 decilitre (dl.)	10 cl.	0·211 pint
1 litre (l.)	10 dl.	1·057 quart

Note: 1 British pint, quart, or gallon = 1·201 U.S. (liquid) pints, quarts, or gallons respectively.

1 U.S. (liquid) pint, quart, or gallon = 0·833 British pint, quart, or gallon, respectively.

III. Based on 1 U.S. quart (dry measure) = 1·1012 litres
U.S. (dry measure) to Metric

1 pint (pt.)	33·600 cu. in.	0·5506 litre
1 quart (qt.)	2 pints	1·101 litres
1 peck (pk.)	8 quarts	8·810 litres
1 bushel (bu.)	4 pecks	35·238 litres

Metric to U.S. (dry measure)

1 litre (l.)		0·908 quart
1 dekalitre (dkl.)	10 l.	0·284 bushel
1 hectolitre (hl.)	10 dkl.	2·838 bushels

Temperature

0° Centigrade (= Celsius) = 32° Fahrenheit

The following formulae connect the two major thermometric scales:

Fahrenheit to Centigrade: $°C = 5/9 \ (°F - 32)$

Centigrade to Fahrenheit: $°F = (9/5 \ °C) + 32$

SUBJECT INDEX*

Abandoned land, 266
Aberrant plant growth, following exposure to ionizing radiation, 296
Abies concolor, 167
Abscission, 294
Absinthin, 251, 252
Absorbing-anchoring roots, 163
Absorption of nutrients by weeds, 174
Abutilon, 162, 243
— *avicennae*, 237
— *theophrasti*, 259
Abyssinia, 23
Acacia, 37, 58
— *farnesiana*, 272
Acapulco-Manila galleon line, 273
Acceleration of seed expulsion, 56
Accidental epiphytes, 42
Acer, 369, 372
— *rubrum*, 42
— *saccharum*, 42
3-acetyl-6-methoxybenzaldehyde, 252
Achillea, 82
— *millefolium*, 266, 379
— — illustration from Aztec herbal, *Pl. 6b*
Achromobacter, 104
Achyrachaena mollis, 84
Achryanthes, 39
— *aspera*, 174
Acidophile, weed growth and, 170
Acnida tamariscina, 179
Acrolein, 288, 374, 375, 445
Acropetalous roots, 164
Acropolis of Athens, synanthrope plants of, 17
Acrylic aldehyde, 445
Actinea odorata, 94
Adsorption upon, growth regulator, 334
Advances in Pest Control, 351, 384
Adventitious roots, 163, 164
Adventive plants, 42
Aegean Sea, 17
Aegilops, 238
— *squarrosa*, 238
Aeginetia indica, 61, 62
— — effect of parasitization of sugarcane on sucrose content, 61
Aelfred, use of 'weed', 2
Aerial applications, 367
Aeriferous tissue, 274
Aeroallergens, 114

Aeschynomene, 38
Afghanistan 3, 19, 23
Aframomum (*Amomum* sp.), 19
Africa, 19, 94, 274, 276, 351, 378
— hominid centre, 20
— mistletoes of, 57
— poisonous plants of, 92
African marigold, 286
— oil palm (*Elaeis guineensis*), 43
After-ripening of seed, 124
Ageing and susceptibility to herbicides, 239
Aggression, 24
— of weeds, Tab. I, 8
Agricultural ecotypes, 234
— *Index*, xxiv, 20
— origins, Sauer's theory of, 402
— production, high level needed, 384
— Research Service, U.S. Department of Agriculture, 20, 341
— soils, 128
Agromyzid fly (*Ophiomyia strigialis*), 67
Agronomic seeds, 124
Agropyron, 238, 250, 251, 292
— *cristatum*, 167
— — weight per acre of roots, 167
— — total root length, 167
— *pauciflorum*, total root length, 167
— *repens* (quack-grass), 35, 95, 165, 170, 186, 213, 249, 259, 266, 404
— — teletoxicity, 259
— *tenerum*, 95
Agrostemma githago (corncockle), 36, 91, 116, 117, 134, 135, 139, 141, 259
Agrostis, 378
— *alba*, 99, 171
— *tenuis*, 171
Agroxone, 321
Air plants, 43, 381
— pressure for sprays, 459
Aircraft, 213
— application, and droplet size, 322, 323
— — herbicides, 363
— — low-volume spraying, 324
— seed dispersal by, 15, 220
— spraying, 315
Alabama, 14, 376, 418
Alanap, 288, 448, 453
Alanine, 303
Alaska, 178
Alchemilla arvenis, 261, 267

* A few herbicides, indicated by asterisk, are indexed for identification purposes only, and are not mentioned in the text proper. Further data on these may be found in the latest handbooks of D. H. Frear (*see* Ch. I), in the frequently revised herbicide lists published in *Weeds* or on the back cover of *Weed Abstracts*. The works here cited, including Audus (1964, *see* Ch. XII), may be consulted for the common names and abbreviations approved by the respective organizations (Weed Society of America, British Standards Institution, etc.).

Alchemilleto-Matricarietum chamomillae Papaveretosum, 261
Alchemilletum Alopecuretosum, 264
— Papaveretosum, 261, 264
Alcohol, allyl, 288, 340, 445
3-aldehydo-4-methoxy-acetophenone, 251, *see* Tab. x
Alder, 369
Alfalfa [lucerne] (*Medicago sativa*), 150, 166, 184, 244, 291, 361, 362, 441, 443, 452
— seed, 50
— spray nozzle tips for, 459
— weed control in, 362
Algae, 261, 374
— control of, 376
Algicide, 448
Alhagi maurorum, 181
Alien plants, 16
Aliphatic acids, chlorinated, 445, 446
Aliphatics, unsaturated, 445
Alkaloid, 251
Allelopathy, Tab. I, 9, 249, 253
Allium, 133, 362, 379
— *see also* onion
— *cepa*, 326
— *oleraceum*, 117
— tainting of milk, 93
— *vineale* in Sweden, 259
Allyl alcohol, 288, 340, 445
Alnus, 369
— *glutinosa*, 42
Alopecurus alpinus, 178
— *myosuroides*, 149, 264
Alphaterthienyl, 252
Alpine, 271
Alsike clover, 361
Altai, 237
Alternaria, 100, 416
Aluminium, 171
Amaranth, 23
Amaranthaceae, 171
Amarantheto-Atriplictum tartaricae, 260
Amaranths, the grain of, 12
Amaranthus, 100, 128, 131, 140, 141, 164, 173, 217, 243
— *blitum*, 174
— *caudatus*, 12
— *cruentus*, 12
— *dubius*, 12
— *edulis*, 12
— *hybridus*, 12, 251, 259
— *leucocarpus*, 12
— *powellii*, 12
— *quitensis*, 12
— *retroflexus*, 13, 63, 84, 96, 106, 128, 129, 143, 162, 177, 178, 179, 180, 266
— *spinosus*, 174, 177
— *viridis*, 174
Amazon region, 402
Ambrosia, 114, 128, 129
— *artemisiifolia* (low ragweed), 100, 139, 188, 266
— bibliography of, 114
— — flowering under short day, *Pl. 10*
— — pollen-producing flowers, *Pl. 7(b)*
— *elatior*, 102, 129
— *trifida* (giant ragweed), 100, 125, 139, 188

Ambrosia trifida, flowers and pollen of, *Pl. 7(b)*
America, 10, 272, 273, 274
American Association for the Advancement of Science, 285, 308
— holly (*Ilex opaca*), 126
— Indian, 14, 80, 81, 402
— — camp sites, 17
— Institute of Crop Ecology, 210-11
— *Journal of Pharmacy*, xxii
— pondweed (*Potomogeton nodosus*), 374
Ametryne (4-ethylamino-6-isopropylamino-2-methylthio-1, 3, 5-triazine),
Amiben, 447
Amides, 288, 451
Amidine, 288
Amine formulations of 2, 4-D, 315
— (oleyl) salts of 2,4-D, 316
Aminobenzoic acid derivatives, 300
3-Amino-1,2,4-triazole (Amitrole), 302, 446
3-Amino-2,5-dichlorobenzoic acid (amiben), 447
4-Amino-imidazole hydrolase, 303
4-Amino-3,5,6-trichloropicolinic acid, 452
Amitrole, 288, 302, 372, 446
— chelates of, 303, 446
— mobility in both phloem and xylem, 333
Ammania, 38
Ammate, 369, 372, 449
Ammi visnaga, 82
Ammonia, 331
Ammonification, 175
Ammonium sulphamate (ammate), 41, 366, 368, 449
— — for control of mixed brush, 365
— thiocyanate for dodder control, 50
— trichloroacetate (TCA, in part), 292
Amo-1618, 383
Amomum sp., 19
AMS (ammonium sulphamate), 449
Amyema pendula, 381
Anabasis, 183
Anabiosis, 181
Anacardiaceae (*Rhus, Semecarpus, Anacardium*), 102
Anacardium, 102
— *occidentale*, 59
*Anacharis, see Elodea
Anagallis arvensis, 213
Analysis of the meaning of ideograph for weed, 5
Anchor chain, 406
Anchored hydrophytes with floating leaves, 38
— submerged hydrophytes, 38
Anderson weed classification system, 32
Andropogon, 99
— *gerardi*, 185
— *halepensis*, 133
— *sorghum*, 180
Anemone coronaria, 34
Anemophilous plants, 35
Angelica, root for good luck charm, 84
Angiosperm seed, 115
Angle of contact, 320
Anglo-Saxon, 2, 4
Animal excreta, 249
— feed, 80
— feeding, weed control by, 417

Animal grazing, 79
— *weedy*, 48
Animals, aquatic herbivorous, 377
Annual bluegrass (*Poa annua*), 360, 451, 452
— grasses, 441
— weeds, 35, 36, 212
Annuals, 17, 229
Anopheles quadrimaculatus, 102, 377
Antarctic circumpolar drift, 275
Antennaria, 128
Anthemis cotula, 36, 139
— *tinctoria*, 139
Anthers of ragweed, dehiscence of, 100
Anthesis, 188
Anthoxanthum odoratum, 99
Anthropochores, 33
Anthropochorology, 270
Anthropophytes, 15, 20, 33, 270
Antibiotics, 249
Antihumectants, 328
Antioxidants, 298
Ants, feeding of, 218
— seed, dispersal by, 213
Apera spica-venti, 134
Aphis gossypii, 98
— *maidis*, 97, 106
Apical meristem, 35, 407
— stem growth, 187
Aplopappus tenuisectus, 409
Apocynum, 82
— *cannabinum*, 85
Apogamy, 232
Apomictic species, 205, 219, 235
Apomixis, Tab. I, 226, 232
Apophytes, 15, 33, 270, 271
Apoplast, 329
Apothecaries, 81
Apparent free space, 328
Apple replant problem, 252
— root-bark, 253
— — — extracts, effect on apple seedlings, *Pl. 13*
— — residues, 253
— — seedlings, 253
— — effect of apple root-bark extracts on, *Pl. 13*
— tree replanting, 250
Application equipment, 316
Apricot seeds, 332
Aqua-Kleen, 376
Aquatic Herbicide Data, 377
— plants, control of, 38, 372, 373, 376
— weed control, 448
— weeds, 439, 445, 451
Aquilegia canadensis, 209
Ara trees, 44
Arabidopsis, 220
— *thalina*, biochemical mutant ecotypes, 234
Arabian seaboard, 57
Arabic weed names, xviii
Arachis hypogaea, Tab. II, 67, 252; *see* peanuts
Araliaceae, 40
Arboricides, 295, 366
Arborvitae, 443
Arceuthobium (dwarf mistletoes), 52, 54, 124
— on digger pine (*Pinus sabiniana*), 57

Arceuthobeum, medicinal use of, 57
— *americanum*, 55
— — on lodgepole pine and jackpine, 54
— *campylopodum*, on pine, spruce fir, hemlock and larch, 54
— *douglasii* on Douglas-fir, 54
— *minutissimum* on *Pinus excelsa*, 54
— *occidentale*, 57
Arceuthobium oxycedri, life history of, 55
— *pusillum*, on spruce, 54
— — herbicidal control of, 382
— *vaginatum* on *Pinus ponderosa* var. *scopulorum*, 54
— — *f. cryptopodum*, seed expulsion of, 56
Arctic Archipelago, 178
— regions, 153, 271
Archeophytes, 33
Areca catechu, 44
Arenaria serpyllifolia, 11
— *tenuifolia*, 206
— *trinervia*, 206
Argemone mexicana, 174
Argentina, 61, 189, 190, 413
Argentine moth borer, 412
Arid regions, plant absorption of water vapour, 328
Aridity, 153
Arizona, 185, 190
— dwarf mistletoe of, 55
Arjona, 60
— *tuberosa*, 61
Armenian weed names, xviii
Armies and weed introductions, 270
Army, weeds in fodder of, 16
Aromatic content of oils, 373
— oils, 289
Arsenic pentoxide, 103
Arsenicals, 339, 370
Artemisia, 16, 100, 183, 363
— *absinthium*, 251, 252
— *filifolia*, 164, 367
— *tridentata* (sagebrush), 80, 174, 350, 364, 365, 415
— — control of by 2,4-D and 2,4,5-T esters, 365
Arthrobacter, 340
Artichoke, Jerusalem, 23
Articulation of floret, 236
Artillery field, weeds of, 267, 268
Aryan invasion, 19
Arylsulphatase, enzyme in activation of Sesone, 300, 337
Arylurethanes, 290
Arundo, 250
Asclepiadaceae, 132
Asclepias, 82
— *curassavica*, 104
— *glaucescens*, 104
— *neglecta*, 104
— *syriaca*, 214
Ash (*Fraxinus*), 42, 368, 369
Asia, 3, 188, 237, 274, 402
— Minor, 212, 237
Asparagus, 82, 209, 267, 303, 304, 359, 439, 440, 443, 448, 450, 453
— spray nozzle tip for, 459
Aspartic acid, linkage of 2,4-D to, 334

Aspartic ester derivatives, 298
Asplenium nidus, 44
Assam, Flora of, 57
Association of Agricultural Chemists, 383, 385
— of American Railroads, 381
Aster, 128
— yellows, 97
Asthma, 102
Astragalus, 92
Atlacide, 61, 62
— for dodder control, 50
Atlantic Islands, 22
Atmosphere, rust spores and pollen in, 101
ATP, 331
Atratone, 306
Atratrin, 306
Atrazine, 305, 306, 445, 458
Atriplex, 125, 265
— *confertifolia*, 184
— *dimorphostegia*, 125
— *nitens*, 177
— *patula*, 207, 371
— — nitrate content of, 178
August, month of weeds, 2
Australia, 18, 22, Tab. II, 67, 68, 93, 175, 228, 274, 276, 381, 412, 414
— poisonous plants of, 93
Australian tar tree (*Semecarpus australiensis*), 102
Austria, 350
Autecology, 267
Autolene Lubricants Co., 385
Autopolyploidy, 229
Autoradiographic technique, 302
Autotrophic land weeds, 79, 226, 270
— plants, 51
Auxins, 249, 296
— naturally occurring, 294
— synthetic group of, 294
Auxin-type growth-regulating chemicals, 294
Autotoxic effects, 251
Auxochores, 214
Avadex (2,3-dichloroallyl di-isopropylthio-carbamate), 358, 441
Avena, 175, 251, 336
— see also oats
— *fatua* (wild oats), 35, 83, 116, 120, 133, 139, 147, 236, 259, 358
— — seed microflora, 259
— — total root length, 167
— *ludoviciana*, 120, 236, 358
— *sativa*, 236, 237, 252
Award of American Association for the Advancement of Science, 285
Awn, function in seed burial, 143
Awned seeds, 142
Axonopus affinis, 378
— *compressus*, 378
Azide, 331
Azolla, 38
Aztec herbal, plant illustration from, Pl. 6(a)

Babylonia, 237
Baccharis glutinosa, 184
Bachhaavia, host of dodder, 50

Bacillus, 104
— *cereus* var. *mycoides*, 299, 337
Back-crossing, 226, 227, 231
Bacteria, function in activation of Sesone, 300
— in latex of plants, 103
Bacterial diseases, 416
Bacterium angulatum, 96
Balkan Peninsula, 15
Balkans, 263
Ball moss (*Tillandsia recurvata*), 43
Ballast dumps, 34
Ballochores, 214
Bamboo (*Bambusa*), 102
Bambusa, 102
Banana, 23
Band spraying applications, nozzle tips for, 459
Bankers, class of aquatic plants, 39
Banvel D, 450
Barban, 359, 441
Barbarea vulgaris, 97, 145, 187, 259
Barberry (*Berberis vulgaris*), 96, 123
Barbing in *Victoria regia*, protection against herbivorous fish, etc., 418
Barley (*Hordeum vulgare*), 66, 148, 251, 358, 359, 441, 450
Barnyard grass (*Echinochloa crusgalli*), 148, 450
Barochores, 214
Barred sagebush (*Artemisia tridentata*), 174
Barriers to germination, 121
Basal-bark herbicide applications, 366, 368, 411
Basket-sieving, in seed cleaning, 83
Basophile, weed growth and, 170
Basswood, 369
Basuto tribe, 95
Bats, fruit dispersal by, 44
Beaches, seeds found along, 274
Bean, mungo, 23
Beans, 66, 304, 305, 441, 442, 445, 450, 452
— spray nozzle tips for, 459
Bedstraw (*Galium aparine*), 11
Bees, 203
Beeswax, 319
Beets, 301, 454
— seedling of, 237
— spray nozzle tips for, 459
Beetle, chrysomelid, 413
Beetles (*see also* Coleoptera), 414
Beggar Tick, 119
Begonia itatiaiensis, 215
Beijerinchia, 45
Belgium, 193
Bellis, 379
Belly plants, 35
Belonoliamus gracilis, 99
Bemisia, 97
Bent-grasses (*Agrostis*), 378, 379
Benzac, 447
Benzoic acid derivatives, 285, 288, 300, 302, 450
Berberis vulgaris, 96, 123
Bermuda grass (*Cynodon dactylon*), 10, 35, 99, 213, 378
Berry crops, 443
— fruits, 450

Beta, origin of name, 237
— *vulgaris*, 236
— — ssp. *maritima*, 237
Beta-oxidation theory, 298
Betasan, 452
Betula, 99, 191, 369
Bible, 12
— tares of, 2, 91
Bibliographie der Deutschen Zeitschriften-literatur, xxiv, 25
— *der fremdsprachigen Zeitschriftenliteratur*, xxiv, 25
— *der Pflanzenschutz Literatur*, xxiii, 25
Bibliography of Agriculture, xxiii, 25
— *of Soil Science, Fertilizers and General Agronomy*, xxiv, 25
— *of Tropical Agriculture*, xxiii, 25
Bicolor lepedeza, geese used for weeding in, 417
Bidens pilosa, 62
Biennials, 17, 31, 153
Bifora radians, 264
Biforeto-Euphorbietum, 264
Bifurco-monaxial root, 164
Bindweed, 443, 447, 450, 452
— (*Convolvulus arvensis*) 7, 36, 186, 216, 286, 300, 372, 417
— control of, 404
— seedlings of, 405
— use of 2,4-D, 405
Biochemical aspects of herbicide resistance, Tab. I, 8, 333
Biocides, complexing of with cellular constituents, 332
— selectivity of, 336
Biocoenosis, 263
Biogeochemical data, 247
Biological Abstracts, xxiii, 25
— activation of Sesone, 299
— — by *Bacillus cereus* var. *mycoides*, 299
— characteristics of weeds, Tab. I, 8, 9
— clock, 127
— competition, 18
— *Control of Insect Pests and Weeds*, 411
— control, possibility of for *Arceuthobium*, 57
— — of weeds by insects, 411
— decarboxylation, 297
— systems theory, 128
Bioregulatory antioxidants, 298
*BiPC (1-methylprop-2ynyl N-(3-chloro-phenyl)carbamatc)
Biotin, 234
Biotypes, *see* ecotypes
Bipyridylium quaternary salts, 288
Birches (*Betula*), 10, 99, 369
Birds, 60
— flower pollination by, 60
— seed dispersal by, 220
— weed control value, 417
— — destroyers, 417
Bird's foot trefoil, 361.
Bird's-nest fern (*Asplenium nidus*), 44
2,4-*Bis* (ethylamino)-6-methyl-1,3,5-mercap-to-triazine, (simetryne)
Bis (1-hydroxy-2,2,2-trichloroethyl) urea [DCU; Dichloral Urea], 293
2,4-*bis* (isopylamino)-6-1,3,5-methylmer-capto-(prometryne)-triazine

Bittersweet (*Celastrus scandens*), 42
Bitterweed (*Actinea odorata*), 94
Black locust (*Robina pseudoacacia*), 372
— willow trees (*Salix nigra*), 368
Blackberries (*Rubus*), 37, 361, 369
Blackcurrants, 451
Blackjack oak (*Quercus marilandica*), 365
Black root rot (tobacco), 252
Black-walnut trees (*Juglans nigra*), 251
Bladderworts (*Utricularia*), 373
Blister-rusts, 61
Bloom, of leaves, *see also* waxy layer
Blue paint for body from woad, 4
— vitriol, 448
Blueberries, 361
Bluegrass, annual (*Poa annua*), 360
— Kentucky (*Poa pratensis*), 171, 306
Bodenmudigkeit, 250
Bodies, human, unearthed from bogs, 11
Body, painted blue with woad, 4
Boerhaavia erecta, 107
Boisduvalia densiflora, 84
Bombed sites, 220
Boraginaceae, 218
Borate-chlorate combinations, 339
Borates, 339
Borax, 370, 372, 449
Botanical Gazette, 286
— prospecting, 167
Botanisches Zentralblatt, xxiii-iv, 27
Bottle drift records, 276
Bottom lands, 402
Bouteloua, 234
— *curtipendula*, 190
Box elder, 369
Boyce Thompson Institute, xxiv, xxvi, xxvii 252, 329
Bracken fern, 452
— (*Pteridium aquilinum*), 215, 372, 405, 416
Brachypodium pinnatum, 170
Brachypterolus pulicarius, 415
Bracts, chloride-ion in, 125
Brambles, 438, 439
Brasenia, 39
Brassica, 129, 151, 164, 292, 452
— *arvensis*, 13, 80, 266
— *campestris*, 13, 80, 145, 237
— crops, 451
— *elongata*, 145
—*juncea*, 80, 145
— *napus*, 249, 414
— *nigra*, 80, 98, 129, 181
— *rapa*, 249
Brazil, 94, 273, 402, 412
— poisonous plants, 93
— -Paraguay, 23
Bread wheat, 23
Breeding habitats for mosquitoes, 377
— — for snails, 377
Brevi-monaxial roots, 164
Bricks, adobe, weed seeds in 13
British Guiana, 378, 418
— Isles, 16
— Weed Control Council, 308, 342
— West Indies, 45
Broad bean, 63
Broad-leafed weeds, 35, 36, 269

Broccoli, 179, 453
Brodiaea lactea, 165
Bromacil, 451
Bromegrass, 218, 244
— use in quack-grass control, 419
Bromelia fastuosa, 215
Bromeliaceae, 43, 45
Bromeliads, 381
— role in malaria, 45
— tanks of, 45
5-Bromo-3-*sec*-butyl-6-methyluracil (Bromacil), 451
5-Bromo-3-isopropyl-6-methyluracil, 451
5-Bromo-3-*sec*-butyl-6-methyluracil, 451
5-Bromo-3-isopropyl-6-methyluracil, 451
*Bromoxynil (3,5-dibromo-4-hydroxybenzonitrile)
Bromus, 175
— *arvensis*, 117
— *inermis*, weight per acre of roots, 167
— *mollis*, 11
— *secalinus*, 117, 148,
— *squarrosus*, 133
Broomrape (*Orobanche ramosa*) on tomatoes, Pl. 5(*a*)
Browse, 79
Brush control, 303
— — with 2,4-D along power-line right-of way, Fig. 80
— — spray nozzle tips for, 459
Brush-killer formulations, 325
Buckbrush (*Symphoricarpos vulgaris*), 365
Buckthorn (*Rhamnus catharticus*), 97
Buckwheat (*Fagopyrum esculentum*), 23, 414
— for control of quack-grass and sow thistle, 419
Bud, vegetative, 232
Bulbine, 51
Bulbils, 230
Bulbous plants, 360
Bulbs, 164, 230
Bulldozer for tree removal, 408
Bulrushes, 80
Bunga (*Aeginetia*), 61, 62
Bunieto-Melampyretum, 264
Bunium bulbocastanum, 264
Buoyancy, 217
— seed, 274
Bur ragweed, 447, 450
Burial in soil, 244
Burma, 23, Tab. II, 67
Burning, 289
— experiments, for control of Tsetse fly, 103
Burr medic (*Medicago denticulata*), 175
Burroweed (*Aplopapus tenuisectus*), 409
Bush fruits, 451
Butoxyethanol ester of 2,4,5-T, 368
Buttonweed, 119
*Buturon(*N'*-(4-chlorophenyl)-N-isobutinyl-N-methylurea)
1-*n*-butyl-3-(3,4-dichlorophenyl)-1-methyl-urea (neburon), 443
n-butyl ester of 2,4-D, 315, 316, 317
Butynyl (chlorophenyl)-carbamate, 304

Cabbage, 131, 319, 376, 454
— waxy layer from, 319

Cabomba, 39, 418
Cacao trees, 45
Cactaceae, 37
Cacti, biological control of, 412
— insect pests of, 413
— resistant to insect attack, 413
Cactoblastis cactorum, 412, 413
Cactus, prickly pear (*Opuntia*), 412, 416
Caesalpinia, 274
— *crista*, 276
— *pyramidalis*, 148
Caesar, woad reference from, 4
Cakile maritima, 207
Calandrinia elegans, 83
Calcium, 244-7
— cyanamide, 359, 448
— in soil, 170
Calcutta Botanic Garden, weed introduction, 272
California, 3, 41, 63, 92, 184, 220, 233, 273, 375, 408, 409, 414, 415, 417
— thistle (*Cirsium arvense*), 372, 416, 452
— walnut, dwarf mistletoe on, 55
Cambial activity, 294
Camelina sativa, 116, 117, 118, 237
Camel-thorn, 408
Camp-followers, 16
Camphor, 51
Campsis, 39
— *chinensis*, 42
— *radicans*, 42
Camptosema, 94
Canada, 14, 95, 96, 152, 190, 191, 243, 264, 266, 273, 350, 352, 359, 378, 415
— first weed control organization in, 351
Canada thistle (*Cirsium arvense*), 36, 168, 186, 204, 213, 220, 300, 302, 352, 419, 447, 450
— — control of, 370
Canadian Northwest Territories, 178
Canals, 373
Canary grass, 119
Canavalia, 272, 274
Cancer therapy, 81
Cane sorghums, 65
Cannabis, 19
— *sativa*, 189
Caparol, new name for Prometryne, 451
Capeweed (*Cryptostemma calendula*), 175
Capitulum, 122, 203, 207
Capsella, 82, 200
— *bursa-pastoris*, 36, 63, 84, 97, 114, 117, 139, 170, 186, 213, 219
Capsicum annuum, 62, 63
Carbamates, 288, 302, 450
Carbon-14, 302
Carbon dioxide, radioactive as tracer, 297
— activated, 338
— disulphide, 315
— isotope of, 297
Carbowax 1500, 317
Carboxylase, 294
Carbyne (4-chloro-2-butynyl N-(3-chloro-phenyl) carbamate), 358, 441
Carcinogenic properties, 303
Cardamine hirsuta, 212
Cardaria draba, 213

Carduus, 129
— *acanthoides*, 146, 204
— — var. *acanthoides*, 227
— *nutans*, 227
Carex, 85, 133, 217
— *bigelowii*, 215
— *capillaris*, 165
— *irrigua*, 165
— *plantaginea*, 214
— *vesicaria*, 165
Caribbean, poisonous plants of, 93
Carnation, 285
Carob, 182
Carotenoid pigment in dodder, 51
Carpet grasses, 378
— weed (*Mollugo verticillata*), 274, 306
Carrots, 290, 301, 304, 307, 352, 359, 450, 451, 454
— spray nozzle tips for, 459
— yellow virus of, 296
Carya, 99, 369
Cashew (*Anacardium occidentale*), 59
Casoron, 450
Cassia, 272
— *occidentalis*, 174
Cassytha, 42, 51, 274, 416
— *filiformis* (woevine), 51, 272
Castor oil plant (*Ricinus communis*), 1, 10, 23, 132
Casuarina, 60
Catalase, 305
Catch crops, 66
Catechol, derivatives of, 102
Cat's-ear (*Hypochaeris radicata*), 204
Cattails (*Typha*), 184, 377
Cattle, 63, 270, 414, 417
— feed, 80
— grazing land, 412
Caucasus, *A. oxycedri* in, 56
Cauliflory, 44
Cauliflower, 454
Caustic herbicides, 289
CBAA, 288
CDAA or Randox, (2-chloro-*N*,*N*-diallyl-acetamide, 306, 346, 359, 454, 455
CDEA, 288, 446
CDEC, 288, 441, 454
Ceanothus, 368
— *integerrima*, 83
Cecropia, 40
Celastrus, 39
— *scandens*, 42
Celery, 307, 441, 451, 457
Cell division, abnormal, caused by 2,4-D, 296
— elongation, 285, 291
— growth, inhibitors of, 290
— to-cell transport system, 331
Cellulose, 326
Celtic word, *glas* ('blue'), 4
Cemeteries, turf-grass area of, 379
Cenchrus pauciflorus, 148
Centaurea, 17
— *cyanus*, 11, 16, 117, 134, 135, 139
— *diffusa*, 146
— *jacea*, 146
— *repens*, 372
— *scabiosa*, 146, 166

Centipede grass, 380
Central Africa, Tab. II, 67, 103
— America, 12, 22, 105, 235, 376
— Azores, *A. oxycedri* in, 56
— Europe, 16
Centralized roots, 165
Centranthera humifusa, 64
Centres of diversity of crop plants, 23
Centrifugal sprayer, 32-5
Centro-multiformal roots, 165
Centro-uniformal roots, 165
Centunculus, 173
Cephalaria syriaca, 237
Cerastium, 378
— *arvense*, 266, 379
— *vulgatum*, 171, 379
Ceratiola ericoides, 51
Ceratophyllum, 39, 373
Ceratopteris, 39
Cercospora eupatorii, 415
— *mercurialis*, 416
Cereal crops, 10, 61, 65, 210, 219, 236, 251, 261, 264, 266, 285, 295, 298, 299, 323, 412
— — adverse effects of herbicides on, 353
— — herbicides for selective weed control in, 353
Cereals, contact angle of pure water on foliage, 321
— first herbicides for, 284
— weed control in, 438
Ceterach, 181
Ceylon, 51, 419
Chaerophyllum bulbosum, 116
Chain pattern, U-shaped, 406
Chain-dozing, for tree removal, 406
Chalk quarries, woad in, 4
Chamaecyparis, 443
Chamaephytes, 34
Chamaescyce, 104
Channels, water velocities in, 373
Charcoal, 10
— radiocarbon dating of, 402
Charlock (*Brassisa* spp.), 284, 286
Cheat grass (*Bromus secalinus*), 119, 306
Cheiroline (*gamma*-methyl-sulphonyl-propyl-iso-thiocyanate), 93
Chemical and physical properties of herbicides, 438
— and tillage methods, combination of, 403
— conjugation, 297
— methods of weed control, 352
— storage tank areas, 380
— weed control, international progress in, 350
— weed-killers, literature of, 284
Chenopodiaceae, 17, 122, 171, 177
Chenopodietum muralis, 260
Chenopodium, 13, 16, 80, 82, 100, 128, 129, 137, 173, 191, 243, 291
— *album*, 11, 13, 117, 139, 169, 174, 175, 177, 178, 180, 191, 251, 266, 267, 320, 321, 371
— —, competition, 259
— — nitrate levels of, 179
— *glaucum*, 11, 191
— *murale*, 13

Chenopodium, photo-periodic responses of, 191
— *rubrum,* 191
— *salinum,* 191
— *serotinum,* 175
Cherries (*Prunus*), 332, 369, 372
Chess (*Bromus secalinus*), 148
Chickasaw plum (*Prunus angustifolia*), 14
Chickweed, 441
— (*Cerastium*), 378
— Chinese name for, 176
— common (*Stellaria media*), 171, 269, 359, 360, 361, 451
Chicory (*Cichorium intybus* var. *glabratum*), 16
Chile, 3, 5, 23, 415
Chilean tarweed, 23
Chilli, 63
China 3, 5, 19, 22, 23, 230, 237, 249, 273, 274, 357
— mistletoe in, 53
Chinese herbal, *Kang Mu,* 357
— ideographs for weed, 5
— millet, 230
— name for chickweed, 176
Chironax melanocephalus, 44
Chloral hydrate, 292, 293
*Chloramben (3-amino-2,5-dichlorobenzoic acid) [amiben]
Chlorate reduction, to hypochlorite and chlorite, 307
— -borate-CMU combinations, 314
— toxic action of, 307
*Chlorazine (2-chloro-4,6-*bis* (diethylamino)-1,3,5-triazine)
*Chlordane (1,2,4,5,6,7,10,10-octachloro-4,7 8,9-tetrahydro-4,7-methyleneindane)
Chlorinated aliphatic acids, 445, 446
Chloris, Tab. II, 67
Chloroacetamides, 306
Chloroacetic acid diallylamide, 307
2-chloroallyl diethyldithiocarbamate, 291
2-chloro-4,6-*bis*-alkylamino-*s*-triazine, 307
2 -chloro -4,6 -*bis*(ethylamino) -1,3,5 -triazine (Simazine), 304, 444
2-chloro-4,6-*bis* (isopropylamino)-1,3,5-triazine, 451
*4-Chloro-2-butynyl m-chlorocarbanilate (revised name for Barban),
4-Chloro-2-butynyl *N*-(3-chlorophenyl) carbamate (barban), 441
2-Chloro-*N,N*-diallylacetamide (Randox or CDAA), 306, 446
2-Chloro-*N,N*-diethylacetamide (CDEAA), 446
*2-Chloro-4-diethylamino-6-ethylamino-1,3, 5-triazine (Trietazine)
*2-Chloro-4-diethylamino-6-isopropyl-amino-1,3,5-triazine (Ipazine)
*2-Chloro-4,6-*bis* (diethylamino)-1,3,5-triazine (Chlorozine)
2-Chloro-4,6-*bis* (isopropyl-amino)-1,3,5-triazine (Propazine), 451
2-chloro-4-ethylamino-6-isopropylamino-1,3, 5-triazine (Atrazine), 445
2-chloroethyl trimethyl-ammonium chloride, 383
2-chloro-9-fluorenol-9-carboxylic acid, 302
Chlorogalum pomeridianum, for soap, 84

Chloro IPC, *see* CIPC
4-Chloro-2-methylphenoxyacetic acid *see* 2-methyl-4-chlorophenoxyacetic acid
α-(4-chloro-2-methyl-phenoxy) propionic acid, 353
N-(3-chloro-4-methylphenyl)-2-methylpent-anamide, 451
3′-Chloro-2-methyl-*p*-valerotoluidide (newest name for, Solan), 451
4-chlorophenoxyacetic acid (4-CPA), 286
3-(*p*-chlorophenyl)-1, 1-dimethyl urea (Monuron), 443
3-(*p*-chlorophenyl)-1,1-dimethyl urea trichloroacetate (Monuron TCA), 444
Chloropropham (CIPC), 441
Chloroplasts, 291
— grana of, 289
Chlorophyll, 291, 305
— a and b, in dodder, 51
— formation, inhibitors of, 302
Chloropicrin, 315
Chlorosis, 248
— in Amitrole usage, 303
— symptom of toxicity, 303
*Chloroxuron(*N*′-4-(4-chlorophenoxy) phenyl-*NN*-dimethylurea)
*Chlorpropham, *see* CIPC
Cholla (*Optunia fulgida*), 409
Choretum, 60
Christisonia wrightii, 62
Christmas season, mistletoe use, 53
Chromatography for separation of a soil-plant residue extract, *Pl. 14*
— technique, 284, 251, 253
Chromosomes, 291
— evolution of, 228
Chrysanthemum, 128, 383
— *leucanthemum,* 97, 175, 266
— *segetum,* 170
Chrysolina gemellata, 413, 414
— *hyperici,* 415
— *quadrifemina,* 415
Chrysothamnus nauseosus, 415
Churches, turf-grass area of, 379
Cichorium intybus var. *glabratum,* 16, 146, 266
Cicuta, 82
Cinnamon, 51
CIPC (isopropyl *N*-(3-chlorophenyl)-carbamate), 50, 288, 291, 355, 356, 359, 361, 441, 455, 456
Circaea quadrisulcata, 214
Cirsium arvense, 36, 117, 134, 139, 141, 166, 168, 169, 186, 204, 238, 266, 371, 372
— — control of, 370
— —, ecotypes, 259
— *ciliatum,* 146
— *lanceolatum,* 13
— *palustre,* 146
— *setosum,* 146
Cissus, Tab. II, 67
Citron, 58
Citrullus, 132
Citrus, 443
Citrus decumana, 58
— *maxima,* 58
— *reticulata,* 58
Citrus trees, spreading decline of, 98

Civil War camp-sites, *Viola* sp. of, 17
Cladodes, 413
Cladophoretum, 262, 263
Cladosporium, 100, 416
Clay soils, 172, 355
— — weeds of, 173
Clean crop seed, use of, in prevention of
  weed infestations, 409
Cleaning crop, 419
Cleavers (*Galium*), 298, 314
Cleistogamous flowers, 212
Cleome, Tab. II, 67, 173
— *viscosa*, 174
Climbers, 39
Climbing buckwheat (*Polygonum scandens*),
  125
Clover, 441
— spray nozzle tips for, 459
— *Trifolium*, 85, 173, 250, 299, 361
Clouds, droplet sizes of, 322
Club-root disease (*Plasmodiophora brassicae*),
  95
Clusia, 39, 40
Cluster bean (*Cyanopsis*), 19
CMU [Monuron] (*p*-chlorophenyl dimethyl-
  urea), 303, 357, 443
$C^{14}O_2$, 297
Cockle, 91
Cocklebur (*Xanthium canadense*), 122, 191,
  353
Cocos nucifera, 44, 274, 276
Coffee, 23
— forests, 19
— plantation, weed control by sheep, 417
— trees, 45
Coffee-weed (*Cassia tora*), 120
Cogon Grass (*Imperata cylindrica*), 35, 419
Coins with plant illustrations from Cyrene,
  Pl. 6(a), 13
Colchicine, 291
Cole crops, 441, 451
Coleoptera, 106, 415
— (*Gastroidea viridula*), 415
— (*Trirhabda nitidicollis*), 415
Coleoptile, 133
— node, 147, 149
Coleus, 19
Collembola, 106
Colonial bent (*Agrostis tenuis*), 171
Colorado, 79, 92, 105, 167
— potato beetle (*Leptinotarsa decemlineata*),
  105
Columbus grass, 65
Columella, 2
Combretum, 103
Commandra, 60
Commelina, 39
— *benghalensis*, 174
— *nudiflora*, 98
Commiphora, 103
Common black mustard (*Brassica nigra*), 98
— carp, 418
— chickweed (*Stellaria media*), 176, 379
— dandelion (*Taraxacum*), 416
— ragweed [or low ragweed] (*Ambrosia art-
  emisiifolia*), 100
— salt as a herbicide, 454

Companion crops, 419
Competing plants, growth, 403
Competition, 206, 225, 247
— failure of in plants following herbicidal
  application, 335
— genetic factors, 152
— as 'interference', 225
— for nutrients, 244
— at seedling stages, 150-2
— for space, 243
— of weeds, Tab. I, 8
— wheat and wild mustard, *Pl. 9(a)*
— of wheat and wild oats, *Pl. 9(b)*
Competitive cropping, 244, 418
Compositae 12, 17, 51, 122, 145, 146, 167,
  171, 173, 191, 203, 204, 207, 213, 218,
  252
— biology of, 220
— capitulum, 220
— origin of, 220
— resistant to herbicide, 451
— seedlings of, 146
Conception, pharmacological control of, 81
Condiment plants, 19
Confederate violet, 17
Conflicts of interest in control of aquatic
  plants, 377
Congeliturbation, 153
Congo, 94
— River, 375
Conifers plantings of, 366
— weed control in 447
— seedlings of, 290
Conium maculatum, 93
Conjugation products, failure to form in
  2,4-D resistant plants, 334
Connecticut, 99, 411
Contact angle, determination of, 290, 320
— dermatitis, 102
— herbicides, 289
Contractile roots, 163, 165, 167
*Contributions from the Boyce Thompson
  Institute*, xxvii, 26
Control measures of weeds, Tab. I, 8, 94
— of weeds in vegetable crops, Appendix III,
  453
Convallaria, 125
Conversion of inactive to active compounds
  in plants, 338
Convolvulus, 129
— *arvensis* 7, 36, 117, 169, 174, 186, 216, 266,
  286, 372, 404, 417
Coontails (*Ceratophyllum*), 373, 376
Copper sulphate, 289, 448
— — for algae control, 376
— — the first herbicide, 284
— — safety of, 376
Coppiced willows, 42
Coptic language, 2
Coral Gardens and their Magic, 87
Cordia, 82
Coriandrum sativum, 237
Corms, 164, 272
Corn (maize), 181, 351, 352, 445, 452
— aphid (*Aphis maidis*), 97
— cockle (*Agrostemma githago*), 11, 36, 91
— yields and weed growth, 356

471

Cornus florida, 212
Coronilla (*Vicia*) *varia*, 419
Corrodentia, 106
Corrugated structure of cuticle, 329
Corticium, 416
Corylus, 369
— *avellana*, 123
Cost of controlling weeds, 243
— lawn, 379
Cotton, 23, 107, 293, 303, 305, 307, 332, 349, 351, 352, 355, 412, 443, 446, 459, 452
— aphis (*Aphis gossypii*), 98
— herbicides, for, 356
— Johnson grass control in cotton with dalapon, *Pl. 16*
Cottonwood (*Populus*), 184, 369
Cotyledons, 36, 146
Coussapoa, 40
Coverage of herbicides, 316
Cowpeas, 64, 66
4-CPA (4-chlorophenoxy-acetic acid), 340
Crabgrass (*Digitaria* spp.), 35, 66, 97, 99, 148, 171, 211, 212, 246, 306, 378, 380, 448, 449, 452
Crag sesone, xxvii, 212
Crataegus 14, 228, 369
— *monogyna*, 228
— *oxycantha*, 82, 208, 228
Creeping action of oils, 289
— fern (*Drymoglossum heterophyllum*), 44
Crepis, 232
— *tectorum*, 117
Crested wheat-grass (*Agropyron cristatum*), 167, 364
Cretan flaxweed (*Silene cretica*), 11
Crimson Clover, 120
Crofton weed (*Eupatorium adenophorum*), 415
Cronartium ribicola, 97
Crop plants, centres of diversity, 23, 24
— — evolution of, 31
— — injurious effects of weeds on, 243
— — origin from weeds, 235
— — rotation of, 249
— — stage of development and herbicide, 337
— — transplanted, 440
— — use as competitive weed control method, 418
— —, in weed-free environment, 352
Crop-seed cleaning methods, 236
Crop seeds, associated weed seeds, 116, 118-20
Crotalaria, 99, 174
— *spectabilis*, 174
Croton setigerus, 84
Crown buds, 37
Crown-vetch, ground cover for weed control, 419
Cruciferae, 3, 6, 17, 115, 167, 177, 207
— seedlings of, 145
Cruciferous crops, 293
— — spray nozzle tips for, 459
Crystallization of herbicide on plant surface, 322
Cryptophytes, 34
Cryptostemma calendula, 175
Cuba, 97

Cucumber, 300, 305, 307
Cucumber vine, 179
Cucumis trigonus, 237
Cucurbit crops, 293, 302, 448
Cucurbitaceae, 132, 167
Cucurbits, Tab. II, 67, 452
Cultigens, 12
Cultivars, 15
Cultivated areas, weeds of, 266
— beet (*Beta vulgaris*), 236
— plants, 19
— — abandoned, 18
— — regions of the world, 23
— — seeds of, 129
Cultivation of crops, costs of, 243
Curare (*Strychnos*), 94
Curled dock (*Rumex crispus*), 129
Currant (*Ribes*), 361, 368
Cuscuta, 42, 49, 129, 416
— *arvensis*, 266
— *campestris*, 51
— *epithymum*, 139
— — photosynthesis in, 51
— *hyalina*, 50
— *lupuliformis*, 51
— *pentagona*, 49
— *polygonum*, 50
— *reflexa*, 51
Cuscutaceae, 49
Custard apple, 58
Cuticle, 290, 338
— chemical composition, 325
— disks from *Gardenia* leaves, *Pl. 19a*
— herbicidal penetration of, 329
— hydrophyllic framework of, 328
— structure of, 325
— thickness of, 329
— wax layer, 338
— wetting of, 153
Cutin, 326
Cutworms (*Prodenia*), 107
— (*Xylomiges*), 107
Cyanamide, 448
Cyanogenetic glycoside, 251
Cyanopsis, 19
Cyanotis cucullata, Tab. II, 67
Cyclochores, 214
Cyclooctyldimethylurea (OMU), 304
Cyclophorus adnascens, 44
*Cycluron (N'-cyclo-octyl-NN-dimethylurea)
Cymanchum, 131
— *acutum*, 132
Cynodon, 99, 250
— *dactylon*, 10, Tab. II, 67, 99, 174, 378
— —, ecotypes, 259
Cyperaceae, 35, 51, 168, 171
Cyperus, 36, 129, 184, 261, 272, 357, 360, 372, 379
— *esculentus*, 35, 213, 259
— *rotundus*, 174, 213
Cypripedium acaule, 214
Cyprinus, 417
Cyprinus carpio, 418
Cyrene, coins from, *Pl. 6a*
Cystopteris bulbifera, 215
Cytochrome oxidase inhibitor, 340
Cytochromes, 304

Cytogenetics, 1
Cytisus scoparius, 415
Czechoslovakia, 172, 351

2,4-D, 45, 269, 286, 288, 295, 297, 358, 376, 379, 381, 438, 457
— acid [*see*, generally, 2,4-dichlorophenoxy-acetic acid]
— activity on tomato plants, *Pl. 15*
— amine, 458
— binding of to cellular constituents, 332
— butoxyethanol ester, 376
— butyl ester, 315, 316, 317
— with C^{14}, 316-17
— conjugated form, 334
— in control of mistletoe, 55
— in control of witchweed, 66
— dissipation of, 376
— distribution in resistant varieties of corn, 332
— distribution in susceptible varieties of corn, 332
— ester, 315, 316, 317, 365, 458
— fate of within plant tissues, 333
— formulation of, 314
— isopropyl ester, 368
— metabolism of, 334
— molecular-level mechanism of action, 335
— movement rate of, 331
— oleyl amine salts, 316
— patent, 287
— penetration experiments, 338
— persistence in plants, 332
— protein complexes, 333
— radioactive, 316-17
— weeds resistant to, 269
— and 2,4,5-T for removal of brush from rights-of-way, *Pl. 22*
Dacthal, 288, 488
— for control of crabgrass in turf, 380
Dactylis glomerata, Tab. II, 67, 99, 123, 150
Dactyloctenium, 99
Dactylopius opuntiae, 413
Dahlia, 296
Dahlstedtia, 94
Dairy cattle, 362
Dalapon (2,2-dichloropropionic acid), 288, 293, 333, 355, 356, 362, 363, 371, 381, 404, 405, 445, 453, 456, 457, 458
— for control of Johnson grass in cotton, *Pl. 16*
Dalbergia sissoo, 58
Dandelion (*Taraxacum officinale*, etc.), 2, 37, 80, 98, 172, 213, 217, 293, 319, 378
— contractile root of, 168
— nectar of, 203
— seed production of, 205
— vegetative reproduction of, 168
Danthonia penicillata, 142
Dark CO_2 fixation, 305
Darnel (*Lolium temulentum*), *Pl. 1*, 2, 18, 91, 116, 118, 119, 236
Darwinian concepts, 24
Datura fastuosa var. *alba*, 62
— *stramonium*, 92

Daucus, 83, 128
— *aureus*, 34
— *carota*, 37, 166
— *pusillus*, as a talisman in gambling, 84
Daulia afralis (Lepidoptera), 61
Day-length (*see also* photoperiodism), 188, 211
— and germination, 135
Dazomet, *see* DMTT
2,4-DB, 334, 362
— persistence of in plants, 334
4-(2,4-DB), 439
2,6-DBN, 450
DCPA-dimethyl, 448
DCU [dichloral urea], 288, 442
De Civitas Dei, 2
Deam Arboretum, 209
Death, 290, 296
— from herbicides, 335
2,4-DEB, 440
— biological, 297
Decarboxylation and release of $C^{14}O_2$ from labelled 2,4-DB, 334
Decentralized roots, 165
Decentro-multiformal roots, 165
Decentro-uniformal roots, 165
Decomposition of 2,4-D in soil, 339
— of 2-(2,4-DB) in soil, 339
Definition of herbicide, 287
Defoliants chemical, 447
— in control of tsetse flies, 103
Defoliation, seasonal, 188
Deforestation, 16, 17
Degradation of the aliphatic acid side chain, 297
Degree of nitrophily, formula for, 177
Dehiscence of anthers in ragweed flowers, 100
Delaware, 80
Delay of maturity in peas, 456
Delphinium nudicaule, 84
Dendrophthoe falcata (*Loranthus falcatus*), 68
Denmark, 10, 11, 327, 351
Dentaria diphylla, 214
*2,4-DEP (tris-(2,4-dichlorophenoxyethyl) phosphite)
Depauperate plants, 35, 152, 208
— — of *Saxifraga tridactylites*, *Pl. 11*
Derris, 94
2,4-DES, 439
Desert annuals, 35
— regions, 166
— species, 125
Desiccant activity, chemical for, 447, 451
*Desmetryne (4-isopropylamino-6-methyl-amino-2-methylthio-1,3,5-triazine)
Desmochores, 214
Desmodium glutinosum, 214
— *triflorum*, 64
Detachable tree-stump remover, 406
Detoxification of herbicides in plants, 293, 304, 332, 334, 338
Devil's weed (*Isatis tinctoria*), 3
Dew, 183
Dew-absorbers, 183
Di-allate (2,3-dichloroallyl di-isopropylthiol-carbamate), 359, 441
Diallylamine, 307

Diaspores, 215
Diazines, 451
Dicaeum flammeum, 60
Dicamba, 450
Dichlobenil, 450
Dichloral urea (DCU), 293, 442
2,3-dichloroallyl di-isopropylthiolcarbamate (Avadex), 441
2,6-dichlorobenzonitrile, 450
2,4-dichlorophenoxyacetic acid [2,4-D], 286, 295, 299, 317, 328, 438
— commercial production of, 295
4-(2,4-dichlorophenoxy)-butyric acid [4-(2,4-DB)], 355, 380, 439
2,4-dichlorophenoxyethanol, 299
2-(2,4-dichlorophenoxy)-ethyl benzoate [2,4-DEB], 440
2,4-dichlorophenoxyethyl butyrate, 315, 316, 317
3-(3,4-dichlorophenyl)-1,1-dimethyl urea, (Diuron), 443
N-(3,4-dichlorophenyl)-methyacrylamide, (Dicryl), 446
3-(3,4-Dichlorophenyl)-1-methoxy-1-methyl urea (Linuron), 450
o-(2,4-Dichlorophenyl)-*o*-methyl isopropyl-phosphor-amidothioate (Zytron), 452
2,4-dichlorophenyl-4-nitrophenyl ether, 450
N-(3,4-dichlorophenyl)-2-propionamide, 307
3,4-dichloropropionanilide (DPA), 358, 452
2,2-dichloropropionic acid (Dalapon), 293, 445
Dichondra, 10, 380, 452
Dichotomophthora portulaceae, 96
Dicotyledonous plants, 17, 34, 35, 229, 337
— — 2,4-D-susceptible, 336
— — emergence from soil of, 132
— — sensitive, 336
Dicoumarol, 331
Dicryl (*N*-(3,4-dichlorophenyl)-methylacryl-amide), 306, 356, 446
Dictionary of American English on Historical Principles, 7, 26
Dicyclic growth, 5
Diesel oil, 68
Diethanolamine salt of MH, 301, 317
Differential detoxication, 338
Digger pine (*Pinus sabiniana*), 85
Digitaria, 35, 66, 80, 138, 141, 149, 152, 162, 243, 378, 380, 382
— *ischaemum*, 35, 171, 212
— *sanguinalis*, Tab. II, 97, 99, 167, 139, 148, 171, 212
Digitalis purpurea, 187
*6,7-Dihydrodipyrido (1,2-a:2',1'-c) pyrazi-dinium salt (revised name for Diquat)
1,2-Dihydropyridazine-3,6-dione (MH; maleic hydrazide), 447
N-(2-(*o,o*-diisopropylthio-phosphoryl) ethyl)-benzene-sulphonamide, 452
Dimethyl arsenic acid, 452
N,N-Dimethyl-2,2-diphenylacetamide (Di-phenamid), 451
*1,1'-Dimethyl-4,4'-bipyridinium salt (rev-ised name for Paraquat)
1,1'-Dimethyl-4,4'dipyridylium dichloride (*or*, dimethyl sulphate derivative) [Para-quat], 451

Dimethyl 2,3,5,6-tetrachloroterephthalate, 448
3,5-Dimethyltetrahydro-1,3-5,2 H-thiadiaz-ine-2-thione (Mylone), 442
Dimorphism, 189
— seasonal, 152
— seeds, 207
Dimorphotheca pluvialis, 207
4,6-Dinitro-*o-sec*-butyphenol (DNBP), 290, 442
3,5-Dinitro-*o*-cresol (DNC), 285, 290, 323
Dinitro herbicide, 381, 442, 453, 456, 457
Dinitrophenol, 331
2,6-Dinitro-*N,N*-di-*n*-propyl-*p*-toluidine, *see* *N,N*-di-(*n*-propyl)-2,6-dinitro-*p*-toluidine
2,6-Dinitro-*N,N*-di-*n*-propyl-*aaa*-trifluoro-*p*-toluidine, *see* *N,N*-di-(*n*-propyl)-2,6-dinitro-4-trifluoro-*p*-toluidine
Dinoben, 300, 450
Dinoseb, 288, 290, 442
Dioclea reflexa, 276
Diodea, 99
— *teres*, 174
Dioecious plants, 189
Dioscorea anthropophagorum, 94
Dioscorides, herbal of 4, 12
Diospyros, 52
Diphenamid, 451
Diphenatrile, 452
Diphenylacetonitrile, 452
Diploid, 230
N,N-di-(*n*-propyl)-2,6-dinitro-*p*-toluidine (Dipropalin), 451
N,N-di(*n*-propyl)-2,6-dinitro-α,α,α-tri-fluoro-*p*-toluidine (Trifluralin), 451
Diptera, 106, 415
Diquat, 451
Directional spraying, nozzle tips for, 459
Dischidia gandichandi, 44
Diseases, weeds as hosts for, 10
Disodium monomethylarsonate, 452
Dispersal, 203
— types of seeds, 214
— of weed seeds, 128
Disposal of weed seeds, 409
Dissemination of weeds, 216, 218, 219
Disseminules, 215
Distichlis spicata, 184
Disturbed habitat, 226
Ditches, weed control along, 442
— weeds of, 372, 373
Dithiocarbamate, 288
Diuron, 288, 303, 355, 356, 443, 457
Divari-monaxial root, 164
Diversity, centres of, 23
DMA (disodium monomethylarsonate), 356
DMPA, 452
DMTT, 288, 442
DN (Dinitro-ortho-cresol), 285
DNBP, 442, 453, 456, 457
DNC (3,5-dinitro-*o*-cresol), 285
*DNOC (2-methyl-4,6-dinitrophenol) [DNC]
Dobruja, 17
Docks (*Rumex*), 100, 118, 119, 120
Dodder (*Cuscuta*), 49, 50, 119, 416
— control of, 50
— mill for seed cleaning, 50

Dodder over-wintering of stem pieces, 50
— photosynthesis in, 51
— reproduction by stem-pieces, 50
— seed, 49
— seedling, 50
Dodecatheon hendersonia, flowers of, 85
Dodonaea, 272
Dogwood (*Cornus florida*), 212
Dolichos lablab, Tab. II, 67
Domestic animals, 213
Domestication of plants, origin of, 18
Dormancy, breaking of, 12, 15
— of weed seeds, 119
Dormant fruit plants, 451
Dosage-response curve of indoleacetic acid, 336
Dose, 336
Double dormancy, 126
Dowpon, 445
Draba verna, 96
Drabok, 92
Drainage ditches, 443
Drepanocladetum, 261
Drepanocladus fluitans, 261
Droplets behaviour effect on waxy layer, (bloom), 319
— containing surface active agents, behaviour of, 319
— impinging on leaf surfaces, 318
— of non-aqueous formulations, behaviour of, 319
— satellite, 319
— shape of, 320
— size and physical selectivity, 322
— in the trailing wing-tip vortex of aircraft, 323
Droppings of animals, seed dispersal by, 213
Drop-seed grass (*Sporobolus cryptandrus*), 148
Drought, 17
— resistance, 181
Drug plants, 19
Dry-land farming, 185
Drymoglossum heterophyllum, 44
— *piloselloides*, 44
Drynaria quercifolia, 44
Dune plants, root systems of, 166
Dunk Island, North Queensland Australia, 40
Durian (*Durio zibethinus*), 59
Durio zibethinus (durian tree), 59
Dust-storms, seed dispersal by, 217
Dwarf forms, 152
— mistletoes (*Arceuthobium* spp.), 54
— — causing witches'-broom, *Pl. 2a*
— — details of plants, *Pl. 3, 4*
— — herbicidal control of, 382
— — killing lodgepole pine, *Pl. 2b*
— — seed expulsion of, 56
Dwarfing of horticultural plants, 383
Dwarfing, by toxic action, 248
Dye plants, 3, 12
Dyer's woad (*Isatis tinctoria*), 3
Dyeweed (*Isatis tinctoria*), 2
Dymid, 451
Dyssodia papposa, 164

Early maturity, 162
Earthworm activity, 128, 213

East Africa, 37, 64, 103, 351
East Indies, 52
Easter lilies, 383
Eastern tropical South America, 22
Ecesis, 115
Echinocactus, 164
Echinochloa, 243, 357
— colona, Tab. II, 67
— crusgalli, Tab. II, 67, 117, 148, 168, 259, 267, 357, 450
Ecleptic acid, 252
Eclipta alba, 174
Ecological control of weeds, 409
— expression of weeds, Tab. I, 8, 9
Ecology, 1, 267
Economic Botany, 82, 88
Ecosystem, 340
— herbicides in, 383
Ecotypes, 15, 121, 170, 190, 191, 233, 270, 271, 357, 416
— agricultural, 234
— biochemical mutant, 234
— flowering of, 189
— formation, 24
Ectodesmata, role in absorption of herbicides, 326, 329, 330, 338
Egg, unreduced in apomixis, 232
Egg-plant, 105
Egypt, 63, Tab. II, 67, 95, 218, 376, 403
Egyptian language, etc., 2, 402
— tombs, plants of, 45
— words for *herba*, etc., 1
Eichhornia, 38, 39, 375, 418
— *crassipes*, 259, 329, 374
— — control with 2,4-D, *Pl. 18*
Einkorn wheat, origin of, 238
Elaeis guineensis, 43
Elaiosomes, 218
Electric current leaking through membranes, 331
Electron transport, cofactors, 298
Eleocharis, 261
Eleusine corocana, 19
Elms (*Ulmus*), 10, 99, 369
Elodea (*Anacharis*), 39, 120, 418
— — *canadensis*, 374
Elymus arenarius, 215
— *caput-medusae*, 259, 409
Elytranthe, 59, 60
— *barnesii*, 59
— *globosa*, 59
Embryos of fruits and seeds, 56, 86, 125, 144
Emergence from soil of dicotyledonous plants, 131, 132
Emergent amphibious hydrophytes, 38
Emilia scabra, 416
Emmer wheat, 236
Emotional attitudes towards plants, 19
Empetraceae, 51
Empetrum nigrum, 215
Emulsions inverted, 325
Encelia farinosa, 251, 252
Encouraged weeds, 19
Endogenous rhythm, 127, 143
Endosperm of dwarf mistletoe (*Arceuthobium vaginatum f. cryptopodum*), 56
Endothal, 288, 447, 454

Endotoxication, 337
Endozoochory, 218
3,6-Endoxohexahydrophthalic acid (Endothal), 447
Enforced dormancy, 127
England, 3, 4, 43, 79, 137, 208, 220, 322, 323, 371, 405, 414
Engystomops sp. ('weedy' animal), 48
Entada, 274
— *gigas*, 276
— *scandens*, 40
Entêg, 2
Entoma, xxii, 26
Entomophily, 44
Environment and herbicides, 383
Environmental dormancy, 127
Enzyme technique for cuticle separation, 325
Epicotyl dormancy, 125
— of grass seedlings, 292
Epidermis, 290
— penetration of, 290
Epigeal emergence of seeds, 131
Epilobium cephalostigma, 136
Epiphytes, 10, 40, 42, 124
— control of, 381
— relation to malaria, 102
Ephemerophytes, 34
Epoekophytes, 33
Eptam (ethyl *N,N*-di-*n*-propylthiolcarbamate), 291, 360, 372, 441, 453, 458
EPTC, 288, 360, 372, 441
Equipment, land clearing, 406
Equisetum, 372
— *arvense*, 266, 372, 405
— *palustre*, 371
Eragrostis, 149
— *cilianensis*, 217
— *ferruginea*, 136
— *major*, 148
Erbon, 370, 440
Erechtites hieracifolia, 238
Eremochloa, 99
Ergasiolipophytes, 33
Ergasiophygophytes, 33
Ergasiophytes, 33
Ergot (*Claviceps*), 91
Erigeron canadensis, 35, 106, 117, 251
— *microthecum*, 164
Eriococcus orariensis, 416
Erodium cicutarium, 13
Eruca sativa, 237
Erunco, 2
Erwinia, 104
Eryngium fluminense, 215
Erysimum cheiranthoides, 244
Erythrina, 45, 274
Ethiopia, 19
Ethiopian coffees, 19
Ethnobotany, 85, 86
2-(2-ethoxyethyoxy) propyl ester of 2,4-D, 315, 316, 317
Ethyl-*N,N*-diisobutyl thiolcarbamate, 450
Ethyl-1-hexamethylene imine carbothiolate, 450
Ethyl *N,N*-di-*n*-propylthiolcarbamate (EPTC), 291, 441
Ethyl xanthogen disulphide (EXD), 452

Ethylene, 285
— chlorohydrin, 293
1,1'-ethlyene-2,2'-dipyridylium dibromide (Diquat), 451
2-ethylhexyl ester of 2,4-D, 315, 316, 317
Eucalyptus, 40, 60, 381
— *maculata*, 381
Euclea divinorum, 103
Euonymus, 443
Eupatorium, 82
— *adenophorum*, 415
— *rugosum*, cause of milk sickness, 94
Euphorbia, Tab. II, 67, 104
— *amygdaloides*, 206
— *brasiliensis*, 104
— *cactiformis*, caustic latex, 94
— *exigua*, 206
— *falcata*, 264
— *gloriosa*, 166
— *helioscopia*, 206
— *hermentiana*, as a lightning-bolt arrester and protector, 94
— *hirta*, 104, 174
— *peplus*, 175, 206
— *pilulifera*, 177
— *thymifolia* ecotypes, 259
— *virgata*, 166
Euphorbiaceae, 104, 173
Euphrasia, 64
Europe, 3, 10, 22, 42, 79, 105, 188, 211, 233, 237, 264, 270, 274, 359, 403, 414
— weed flora of, 16
European mistletoe (*Viscum album*), 53
— pear orchards, mistletoe in, 53
Evapo-transpiration, 182
Evening primrose (*Oenothera biennis*), 119, 129
Evergreen nurseries, 451
Evolution of domestication, 18
EXD, 452
Exocarpus, 60
Exotoxication, 337
Experiment Station Record, xxiii, 26
Expulsion of seeds, 56
— mechanism, 214

Factories, turf-grass area of, 379
Facultative stranglers, 40
Faeces (excreta, etc.), seed dispersal by means of, 63
Fagopyrum esculentum, 237, 414
— *tartaricum*, 237
Falone, 440
False wild oats, 120
Famine food, 357
Farm hygiene, 220
Farming by fire, 409
Farm-land weeds, 18
Far-red radiation, 141
Fate of phenoxy herbicides in soil, 339
Fatigue-relieving plants, 19
Federal Register, xx
Federal Seed Law, 409
Fenac (2,3,6-trichlorophenylacetic acid), 382, 450
Fence-rows, 372, 443, 449

Fenoprop, *see* 2,4,5-TP
Fenuron, 288, 303, 443
— TCA, 444
Fermentation, inhibition of, 290
Ferns, 42, 144
— control of, 451
— rhizosphere of, 44
Fertile crescent, 19
— forms, 232
— hybrids, 226
Fertility levels, 244
Fertilization, 232
Fertilizer and herbicide, 448
Fertilizers, 218, 249
Ferula, *Pl. 6a*
Fescue, 118
Festuca trachyphylla, 268, 269
Fetish plants, 94
Fibre plants, 19, 272
Fibrous rhizomes, 165
Fick's law of diffusion, 328
Ficus, 39, 40, 44, 107
— *bengalensis*, 44, 165
— *benjamina*, 44
— *elastica*, 44, 183
— *hochstetteri*, 104
— *indica*, 44
— *ribes*, 44
Field bindweed (*Convolvulus arvensis*), 404
— corn, 450
— *Crop Abstracts*, xxiii, 26
— capacity of soil, 360
— crops, herbicides for, 352
— horsetail (*Equisetum arvense*), 372
Figs (*Ficus*), 39, 58, 104
Fiji, 272, 415
Fimbristylis, 64, 272
— *miliacea*, Tab. II, 67
Finland, 42
Fire, 10, 20
— hazard of sodium chlorate, 449
— hazards, reducing by weed control, 380
— in primitive agriculture, 409
— stimulus for germination, 409
— weed control by, 408
Firethorn, 443
Fireweed (*Kochia scoparia*), 217
Fish, 39, 97
— aquatic plant control by, 417
— culture, 38
— herbicide toxicological data for, 377
— herbivorous, 378, 411, 417
— ponds, 273
— soapwort, 84
Fishing, 376
— economy, 402
Fixed-wing aircraft in herbicide applications, 325
Flag stage of onions, 455
Flagelliflory, 44
Flame cultivator, 408
Flash point of aromatic solvents, 373
Flavanone (3_1, 4_1, dihydroflavanone), 252
Flavo-protein enzymes, 290
Flax (*Linum usitatissimum*), 116, 117, 251, 299, 321, 323, 355, 358, 438, 441
— — cuticular wax of, 327

Flax roots, HCN liberated from, 251
— spraying at young stages, 327
Flea-repellant plant, 85, 181, 184
Fleshy rhizomes, 165
Floaters, aquatic plants, 39
Floating ice in plant dispersal, 275
— hydrophytes, 38
— seeds, 272
Flooding, 16, 357, 377, 450
— weed control by, 408
Flood-plains, 20, 402
Flora, arable-land, 16
Flora of Assam, 57
— native, 15, 270
— naturalized, 15
— of Kansas, 34
— waste ground, 16
Floral agriculture, 19
Florae, Vocabularium Nocentium, xviii
Floret, articulation of, 236
Florida, 51, 52, 98, 174, 376, 406
— aquatic plants of, 39
— wild cotton, 217
Flour, prepared from grain amaranth seeds, 12
Flow of water through channels, 374
Flower beds, control of weeds in, 361
— initiation, control of, 383
Flowering parasites, 49, 416
Flower-picker birds (*Dicaeidae*), 60
Flowers, cleistogamous, 212
— of ragweed (*Ambrosia artemisiifolia*), 100
Fluorescence of scopoletin, *Pl. 12b*
Fodder, 2
Foliage, abscission, 191
— absorption of water vapour, 328
— area, 243
— malformation, 296
— mesophyll, transport system of, 332
— pubescence, effects on spray applications, 317
— selection for in development of beet, 236
— spray retention, relation to leaf angle, 318
— sprays, 365
— — non-selective, 370
— — selective, 370
— stringiness of, 296
— surface, wettability of, 320
— water-vapour absorption by, 183
— waxy film of, 319
— wetting of, 375
Folklore of plants, 86
Food, 12, 13
— and Drug Administration (FDA), xx
— plants, 19
— supplies, emergency, 79
Food-attractiveness of weeds to insects, Tab. I, 8
Food-chain relationships, 383
Forest nurseries, 290, 304
— tree seedlings, 289
Forestry practice, use of arboricides, 366
Formative effects, 296
Formica spp., 219
Formosa (Taiwan), 61, 62
Formulation, 314
Forsythia, 212, 443

Foxtail (*Setaria sp.*), 148
— (*Setaria lutescens*), 356
— grass (*Setaria viridis*), 217
— — comparison with the derived millet (*S. italica*), *Pl. 12a*
Fragaria, 99, 128
— *vesca*, 34
— *virginiana*, 215
France, 351, 414
Franseria tomentosa, 169
Fraxinus, 42, 368, 369
Free-dozing machines for tree removal, 408
Freezing and thawing, 153
French beans, 64
French words for weed, 2
Frenchweed (*Thlaspi arvense*), 94
Frilling of trees, 368
Fruit crops, herbicides for, 360
— development of, 294
— passion, 23
Fruits 6, 19, 361
— bush, 451
Fumaria officinalis, 213, 371
Fumigant, herbicide, 442
— herbicidal action of Mylone in soil, *Pl. 23*
Fungi, weed control by, 416
Fungicides, 442
— systemic, 337
Fungus spores, 100
Fusarium disease, 57, 64, 416

Galeopsis, 321
— *tetrahit*, 371
Galinsoga, 162, 243
— *parviflora*, 97, 120, 207, 267
Galium, 16, 42, 300, 314, 439
— *aparine*, 138, 298
— *boreale*, 139
— *mollugo*, 134, 139
Gall formation, 297
Gall-fly, 414, 415
Galla potatoes (*Coleus sp.*), 19
Gambling talisman (*Vicia americana*), 85
Garden bean, 332
— sorcery, 87
Gardenia, 329
— cuticle disks, *Pl. 19a*
Gardens, primitive, 18
Garlic (*Allium*), 362, 363
Gases, lethal, 285
— physiologically active, 285
Gastroidea viridula, 415
Geese in weeding bicolor lespedeza, 417
— — — cotton, 417
— — — strawberry beds, 417
— — — mint fields, 417
Genes, infiltration of in hybridization, 228
Genetic origin of weeds, 226
Genotypes, 226, 235
Geochronology, 13
Geophytes, 34
Geosubspecies, 233
Geotropic responses, 294, 301
Geovariety, 233
Geranieto-Silybetum, 260
Geranium, 82

German words for weed, 2
Germany, 42, 79, 96, 98, 169, 170, 177, 252, 264, 267, 304, 351, 415, 416
— Federal Republic, 389
— weeds and moisture in, 172
Germination, 130
— alternating temperatures effect of, 123
— barriers to, 121
— crabgrass, 211
— day length effect on, 135, 136
— effects of pH, 142
— effect of environmental factors on, 135
— inhibitors, 125
— light requirement, 124
— mechanisms, 131, 217
— periodicity of, 143
— seed structures facilitating, 142
— soil moisture effects, 135
— and soil nitrate levels, 142
— stages of, 131
— temperature requirements, 134
Germinative toxicant, 336
Ghana, 103
Giant foxtail grass (*Setaria faberii*), 35, 124, 125, 273
— ragweed (*Ambrosia trifida*), 100, 125, 188
— — flowers of, *Pl. 7a*
— — growth along roadside, *Pl. 7b*
Gibberellins, 284, 301
Gieseckia, host of dodder, 50
Gila River, 185
Ginger, 23
Girdling of trees, 368
Gladiolus, 293, 360
Glas, Celtic word for 'blue', 4
Glastum, Roman word for woad, 4
Glechoma (*Nepeta*) *hederacea*, 233
GLF (Grange League Federation, Ithaca, N.Y.), xxi
Glossinia, 103
— *morsitans*, 103
— *palpalis*, 103
— *tachinoides*, 103
Glucose, 293, 303
Glumes, 212
Glycerol as antihumectant, 328
Glycine, 303
Glycine max., 167, 180
Glycollic acid, 307
Glyodin fungicide, xxvii
Gmelina arborea, 58
Goats, grazing of, for weed control, 63, 409, 417
Gobi Desert, 130
Goitre and thioglycosides, 93
Goitrogens, 93
Golden nematode of potato (*Heterodera rostochiensis*), 98
Goldenrod (*Solidago*), 100
Golf Association, Southern California, 379
— courses and driving ranges, turf grass area of, 379
Gooseberry (*Ribes*), 368, 369
Goosefoot (*Chenopodium*), 101
Gorki Province, Russia, 51
Gossypium hirsutum, 217
Gothic word for *Isatis*, 4

478

Grain (see also cereals), 13, 270, 314
— changes in protein content with spraying, 353
— elevator areas, 380
— mango, 23
— screenings, 80
— shipment of, 16
— winnowing of, Pl. 8
Grains of paradise (Amomum), 19
— seeded, spray nozzle tips for, 459
Gramineae (see also grasses), 17, 18, 35, 51, 61, 124, 133, 167, 171, 218, 250, 294, 337, 407
— seedlings of, 148
Grange League Federation, 376, 390, 404, 425, 459
— — — Chemical Weed Control Guide, 1963-64, xxi
Granular carrier for herbicides, 360
— herbicide, 448, 450, 451, 452
Grape, 61, 304, 369, 443
Grapefruit trees, 45
Grasses, 100, 220, 269, 291, 294, 335, 352, 356, 359, 451, 452, 457
— adventive roots, 138
— annual, 454
— coleorhiza of, 147
— control, 362, 445, 446
— for control of weeds, 419
— coronal roots, 138
— crops, spray nozzle tips for, 459
— epicotyl, 147
— growing point of, 289
— meristematic growth in, 407
— mesocotyl elongation, etc., 147
— nodal root, 138, 147
— perennial, 20
— photoperiod response of, 190
— populations, 249
— retardant, 447
— seed, 147
— seedling, anatomy of, 147
— seedlings, emergence, 132
— — epicotyl of, 292
— seminal root, 147
— sheathing leaf-bases, 35
— shoot of, 147
— stoloniferous, 402
— suppressants for, 301
— weeds, 306
Grassland, 153, 245
Grass-seeded crops, 291
Grauballe Man, stomach contents of, 11
Grazing animals, 411
— — seed dispersal by, 218
— — damage to forest rejuvenation, 16
— land, 37, 363
Greasewood (Sarcobatus vermiculatus), 184
Great Britain, 228, 229
Greece, 16, 263
Greek words for weed, 2
Green foxtail (Setaria viridis), 148
Greenlands, 178, 229
Grey mould (Botrytis cinerea), 96
Ground covers for weed control, 419
— ivy (Nepeta hederacea), 379
Groundcherry (Physalis heterophylla), 97

Groundcherry (Physalis subglabris), 97
— (Physalis virginiana), 97
Groundnuts (peanuts) [Arachis hypogaea], 23, 64, 66, 306, 319, 352, 355, 439, 440, 450, 452
Ground-speed of sprayer, 459
Growth-forms, 191
Growth inhibitors, 286, 301, 447
— regions (meristematic), of grass family, 407
— regulator, adsorption upon a protein surface, 334
— — herbicides, 285
— — herbicides, literature of, 284
— suppressants, use of, 382
*GS-14260, (2-tert-butylamino-4-ethyl-amino-6-methylthio-1,3,5-triazine)
Guar, cluster bean (Cyanopsis), 19
Guava, 23, 158
Guiana, 39
— Indians, 82
Guttiferae, 40
Gymnactron antirrhini, 415

Habitat, of weeds, 32
Haiti, 106
Half-epiphytes, 4
Halogeton glomeratus, 92, 170
Halophytes, 17, 171
Haloxylon, 183
Hamamelis virginiana, 42
Han dynasty, 5
Hand-hoeing, for weed control, 403
Hand-scything, 408
Hand-weeding, 244
Hard seeds, 121
Harmful weeds, Tab. I, 9
Harnstrauch, 61
Harrisina brillans, 41
Harvest, duration of, 209
Hashish, 19, 105
Haustorium, of mistletoe, 53
Hawaii, 52, 102, 378, 412, 417
Hawthorn (Crataegus oxycanthus), 208, 228, 369
Hay, 124, 349, 354
— bales, weeds in, 16
— fever, 99, 102, 189
Hayfields, spray nozzle tips for, 459
— weeds in, 362
Hazel, 10
— bush, 369
— seeds (Corylus avellana), 123
Heat units and crop growth, 209
Height of weeds, 243
Helenium microcephalum, 102
— tenuifolium, 102
Heleocharetum, 261, 263
(H)Eleocharis, 261
Helianthus, 83, 232, 328
— annus, 229
— rigidus, 251
— tuberosus, 230
Helicopter, 325
Heliotropeto-Chrozophoretum, 260
Heliotropium indicum, 273
Helminthosporium, 95

Hemicryptophytes, 34
Hemi-parasites, 68
Hemizonia luzulaefolia, 83
Hemp (*Cannabis*), 19, 23, 101, 105
Henbit (*Lamium amplexicaule*), 36, 141, 269
Hepatica acutiloba, 214, 215
Herb, 1
— gardens, 81
— shops, 81
Herba, 2, 6
Herbaceous paeony, 125
— perennial weeds control of, 369
Herbal, Chinese (*Kang Mu*), 357
Herbalists, 81
Herbarium, longevity of seeds in, 130
Herbicide-perfused soil, 340
Herbicides, 269
— activity of, 314, 315, 316
— aircraft applications of, 363
Herbicides and the American Farmer, essay, 349
Herbicides analysis of, 383
— application of, 314-316
— behaviour within the plant, 338
— in cereals, first use of, 284
— chemical classification of, 288
— — and physical properties of, 438
— classification of, 284, 287
— common names of, 438
— contact, 289
— coverage, 316
— crystallization on plant surface, 322
— definition of, 287
— differential, 286
— in ecosystem, 383
— entry into plants, 314, 315, 316
— and the environment, 383
— fate in the soil, 338
— and fertilizers, 448
— for field crops, 352
— formulae of, 438
— formulation of, 314, 438
— for fruit crops, 360
— fumigant type, 315
— growth regulator type, 285
— inhibitors of cell growth, 290
— inorganic, 448, 449
— for lawns and sports areas, 378
— literature of growth regulator type, 284
— low mammalian toxicity, 341
— mechanism of action, 284, 287
— melting point of, 438
— metabolizing of in soil, 339
— mode of entry into plants, 325
— molecular weight of, 438
— movement into the plant, 325, 331
— — — root system, 325
— nitrogenous group, 288
— for nursery crops, 360
— organic, 446, 447, 448, 452
— for ornamental crops, 360
— persistence in the plant, 287
— — in soil, 340
— physiological effects following application, 335
— placement of, 338
— pre-emergence, 340

Herbicides pre-planting, 450
— properties and uses of, Appendix I, 438
— recent, Appendix II, 450
— resistance to, 238
— selectivity of, 336
— soil-incorporated, 450
— spray retention, 316
— toxicity and droplet size, 323
— translocated, 306
— triazine type, 306
— in tsetse fly control programme, 103
— uses of, 438
— for vegetable crops, 359
— volatility of, 338, Figs. 53, 54
Herbisan, 452
Herbistat, 301
Herbivorous animals, control of noxious aquatic plants, 377
— fishes, 411, 417
Hermaphroditic flowers, 203
Herodotus, plants in writings of, 12
Herpetomonas (*Leptomonas*), *ganorae*, 104
Hesiod, plants mentioned in, 12
Heteranthera dubia, 374
— *glycines*, 98
— *rostochiensis*, 98
— *tabaccum*, 99
Heteroecious rust, 61
Heteromorphic propagules, 207, 208
— seeds, 122
Heteromorphy of seeds, Tab. I, 8
Heterosis, 152
Heterotrophic plants, 49
Hevea brasiliensis, 104
Hevea rubber, 357
*3-[5-(3a,4,5,6,7,7a-hexahydro-4,7-methano-indanyl)]-1,1-dimethylurea (Norea)
Hexaploid, 230, 233
Hibernating structure, 213
Hibiscus, 274
— *tiliaceus*, 272
*Hibor (liquid herbicide containing sodium chlorate, sodium metaborate, and bromacil)
Hickory (*Carya*), 99, 369
Hides, shipment of, 16
— and seed dispersal, 218
Hieracium, 232
— *aurantiacum*, 266
— *pilosella*, 266
Hierbas malas, 7
Hieroglyphics, Egyptian for *herba*, etc., 1
Hierbas malas, 2
High-alpine regions, 153
High-balling for tree removal, 406
Highways, 267, 349
Hill reaction of photosynthesis, mechanism of, 291, 292
— — Monuron inhibits, 304
Hippocratic writings, plants listed in, 12
Hippomane mancinella, irritating nature of sap, 104
Histidine, 303
Hoagland's theory of ion absorption, 327
Hoary cress (*Cardaria draba*), 213, 408
Hoed areas, weeds of, 266
Hoeing for weed control, 244
Holcus, 379

Holcus lanatus, 11
—— host for club-root disease, 95
Hold area, 266
Holland, 11, 98, 175, 351
Homer, plants mentioned in, 12
Homes, turf area of single family, 340
Homoptera, 106
Honduras, 402
Honey plant, 205
Honeysuckle (*Lonicera japonica*), 300, 443, 447
Hop, 23
Hordeeto-Sisymbrietum, 260
— orientalis, 260, 261
Hordeum, 175
— *leporinum*, 261
— *murinum*, 265
— *pratense*, 148
— *vulgare*, 237
Horned pondweed (*Zannichellia palustris*), 374
Horse-nettle (*Solanum carolinense*), 92, 97, 352, 438
Horsetail (*Equisetum* spp.), 372
Horticultural Abstracts, xxiii, 27
Horticultural plants, dwarfing of, 383
— seeds, 124
Host plants of insects, classification of, 105
— and parasite, metabolic differences between, 336
— tree, 40
Hoya, 104
Human excreta as fertilizer in China, 249
— fertility, plants affecting, 81
Humidity and flowering of common or low ragweed (*Ambrosia artemisiifolia*), 100
Hungary, 261, 265
Hybrid, interspecific, 227
— populations, 227
— seeds, 152
— swarms, 227
Hybridization, 227
— introgressive, 230
Hydram, 450
Hydrangea, 82
Hydrilla, 417
Hydrochloa, 39
Hydrocotyle, 39
— *rotundifolia*, 274
Hydrocyanic acid, liberation from flax roots, 251
—— in *Prunus*, 93
Hydrophytes, 38, 165
Hydropiper, 173
Hydroseeding, 419
4-Hydroxycoumarin, 65
p-Hydroxybenzoic acid, 253
p-Hydroxyhydrocinnamic acid, 253
2-Hydroxy-4,6-*bis*(ethylamino)-*s*-triazine,304
4-Hydroxy-5-isopropyl-2-methylphenyl trimethyl ammonium chloride, 1-piperidine carboxylate, 383
5-Hydroxynaphthoquinone (juglone), 252
Hygrophila, 38
Hygrophyte, 219
Hygrorhiza, 38
Hymenoptera, 106

Hypericum, 151, 419
— *perforatum*, 413,
Hyperparasitism, 59
Hypochaeris radicata, 204
Hypogeal emergence of seedlings, 131
Hyptis, 272
Hyvar, x, 451

IAA (indole-3-acetic acid), 295, 301, 302
— content, reduction by 2,4-D, 295
— oxidase, 297
Ice Age, 233
— floating, 275
Iceland, 178
Idaho, 3, 92
Ideograph for weed, analysis of, 5
Ideographs Chinese and Japanese for weed, 6
Ilex opaca, 126
Illinois, 96, 405
— University of, 249
Illustrierte Flora von Mittel-Europa, 34
Inhibition, 141
Immigration, dispersal by, 15
Immortelle trees (*Erythrina*), 45
Immunity, 57
— acquisition of, 338
Impatiens capensis, 214
— *sultani*, 51
Imperata, 250
— *cylindrica*, 35, 357, 419
Independent weeds, 32
Index Kewensis, xix, 28
India, 13, 19, 22, 52, 61, 64, Tab. II, 67, 80, 218, 247, 273, 274, 376
— cereal rusts of, 97
— phanerogamic parasites, of, 68
Indian hemp, *Apocynum cannabinum*, 85
— medicinal plants, 82
— Ocean, 276
Indiana, 169, 209
— tomato mosaic in, 97
Indians of Mendocino County, Northern California, 83
Indicator value of species, 265
Indigo, 3
Indigofera, Tab. II, 67
Indo-Burma, 23
Indole-3-acetic acid (IAA), 285, 294, 336
Indolepropionic acid, 285
Indo-Malaya, etc., 22, 40, 271-2
Indonesia, 19, 44
Induced dormancy, 127
Industrial areas, 445, 450, 451
Influence of one plant upon another, 248
Infra-red analysis of C[14] labelled 2,4-DB, 334
Inherent dormancy, 127
Inhibitors of cell division, 294
— of growth, 301
— of tropic responses, 301
Injected herbicide, 445
Injurious interactions of weeds and crop plants, 243
Injury and herbicide susceptibility, 338
Innate dormancy, 127
Insecticides, systemic, 337
Insect-pollinated flowers, 60

R

Insects associated with weeds, 105
— attraction of weeds for, 8
— biological control of weeds, by, 411
— plant injury by, 297
— pollination by, 203
— resistance to insecticides, 238
— repellants, to 85
Institut für Pflanzenschutz, 252
Intercalary meristems, 407
Intercotyledonary cavity in floating seeds, 274
Interfacial tension, 289
Interference (competition), 225
International Bulletin of Plant Protection, xxiii, 28
International progress in chemical weed control, 350
Interplanetary vehicles, possible dispersal by, 15
Interspecific hybridization, 226
Introgression, 20
— multiple, 232
Introgressive hybridization, 230
Intsia bijuga, 276
Inverted emulsions as herbicidal sprays, 325
Ionized forms of herbicides, 329
Ionizing radiation, effect on auxin levels, 296
— — effect on plant growth, 296
Iowa, 106, 168, 356
*Ipazine (2-chloro-4-diethylamino-6-isopropylamino-1,3,5-triazine)
IPC (isopropyl *N*-phenylcarbamate), 288, 291
Ipomoea, 38, 274, 276
— *batatas*, Tab. II, 67
— *bona-nox*, 272
— *pes-caprae*, 215, 272
Iran, 237
Iraq, 1, 402
Iridaceae, 133
Iris, 133
Irish potatoes, 451
Iron, 303
— Age, 11
— sulphate, 289
Irrigated areas, weed control in, 440
Irrigation, 38, 171, 236, 379, 454
— channels and ditches, 39, 213, 373, 445
— developments of, 340
— and seed dispersal, 218
Isatis tinctoria, 2, 3
Isle of Lero, 17
Isocil, 451
4,6-*bis*(isopropylamino)-2-methylthio-1,3,5-triazine (Prometryne), 451
Isopropyl *N*-(3-Chlorophenyl)-carbamate (CIPC), 50, 288, 359, 441
— *N*-phenylcarbamate, 290, 292
Isostere, Tordon an example of, 301
Israel, 183
Israeli carp, for aquatic weed control 418
Italian word for weed, 2
Italy, 42, 67, 261, 264, 350, 351, 416
— weeds and moisture in, 172
Itchwood tree (*Semecarpus vitensis*), 102
Iva, 100
— *angustifolia*, 102

Jack fruit, 58
Japan, 3, 19, 22, 61, 80, 136, 171, 203, 229, 233, 274
Japanese honeysuckle (*Lonicera japonica*), 41, 273, 287, 419
— ideographs for weed, 5
— knotweed (*Polygonum cuspidatum*), 274
Jatropha, 148
Java, 23, 276
— tilapia, fish for aquatic weed control, 418
Jeffersonia diphylla, 209
Jerusalem artichoke, 23
Johnson grass (*Sorghum halepense*), 35, 118 119, 203, 213, 274, 355, 404, 405, 409
— — distribution of, 405
— — control by using Singletary peas, 419
Journal of Agricultural and Food Chemistry, 349, 383
Journal of the Association of Official Agricultural Chemists, 349, 383
Journal of Ecology, 267
Juglans cinerea, 214
— *nigra*, 251, 252
Juglone, toxic agent from *Juglans*, 252
Jujube (*Ziziphus* sp.), host for flowering parasite, 58
Juncaceae, 35, 168
Juncus, 85, 184, 220, 357
— *bufonius*, 117, 173
— *effusus*, 259
— *tenuis*, 220
Juniper, 443
Jussiaea repens, 38, 165
Justicia quinqueangularis, 66
Jutland, 11
Juvenile phases of plants, 152

Kaffir-corn, 65
Kaka, Egyptian word, 1
Kang Mu, Chinese herbal, 357
Kansas, 100, 152, 217
Kapok, plantation of Java, *Loranthus* infestations, 59
Karakum desert, 182
Karmex, 381, 457
— W, 359, 360
Karsil [*N*-(3,4-dichlorophenyl)-2-methylpentamide], 306
Kensington Science Museum, London, 344
Kentucky bluegrass (*Poa pratensis*), 123, 171, 378, 379
Kenya, 67, 103
Kerosene, 366
Kew Gardens, 219
Kinetin, 65
Kinins, 297
Klamath River, 414
— weed, 414
Knocking over trees, methods of, 408
Kochia indica, 183
KOCN, 449
Korsmo weed classification system, 32
Kuehneola albida, 416
Kuvi, 87
Kyllinga, 272

Labiatae, xxxii
Labrador, 178
Lactone, 251
Ladino clover, 361
Lagenaria, 272
L'Agronomie Tropicale, xxiv, 20
Lagundi (*Vitex negundo*), 59
Lake Dweller wheats, 238
— Windermere, 12
Lalang grass (*Imperata cylindrica*), 35, 357
Lallemantia iberica, 116
Lamb's-quarters (*Chenopodium*), 246, 353, 359
Lamium album, 42
— *amplexicaule*, 141, 213, 269
— *purpureum*, 186, 213
Land clearing equipment, 406, 408
— mechanical clearing of, 405
Landman, 10
Landscape, disfigurement of, 7
Landslides, 20
Langsat (*Lansium domesticum*), 59
Language, Egyptian, 1
— Latin, 2
Lansium domesticum, 59
Lansomes (*Lansium domesticum*), 59
Lantana camara, 272, 412
Lapland, 178
Lappa major, 11
Large trees, killing difficulties, 368
Latex, bacteria and protozoa in, 103
Latin words for weed, etc., 4
Lauraceae, 51
Laurel (*Umbellularia californica*), as flea repellant, 85, 181, 184
Lava-flows, 20
Lavandula, xxxii
Lawn, see also turf
Lawn grasses, 171, 287
— weeds, 170
— weed-free, 378
Lawns, area of in Los Angeles County, California, 379
— herbicides for, 378
Layering, 165
Leaching and movement within the soil of herbicides, 338
Lead arsenate, 43
Leaf-feeding beetles etc., 412, 414, 415
Leafy pondweed (*Potamogeton foliosus*), 374
— spurge, 447, 450
Leaves, see foliage
Leersia, 418
Legumes, 362
— spray nozzle tips for, 459
Leguminosae, 132, 167, 171, 173, 294
Leguminous plants, 274, 294, 361, 364, 438, 439
— — injury with chloral hydrate, 293
— — sensitive to dalapon, 293
— — in weed control, 419
Leipzig, plants of the city dumps, 177
Lemna, 38, 39, 261
Lemnetum, 261, 262, 263
Leontodon, 128
— *autumnalis*, 117, 171
Lepidium, 141

Lepidium virginicum, 36, 129, 136, 270
Lepidoptera, 106
Leptinotarsa decemlineata, 105
Leptomonas davidi, 104
Leptospermum scoparium, 416
Lespedeza, 99, 119
— dodder (*Cuscuta pentagona*), life history, 49
Lesquerella, 227
— *densipilia*, 227
— *lescurii*, 227
Lethal action of 2,4-D, 336
Lettuce (*Lactuca*), 20, 23, 98, 452, 454
— Grand Rapids, 141
— seed, 124
Leucaena glauca, 272
Leucoptera spartifolicella, 415
Lianas, 39
Lichens as epiphytes, 42
Life-form, 191, 265
— of plants, 34
— of weeds, 32
Life-span of seeds, 130
— of weeds, 32
Light soils, 361
— stove-oil, 289
Ligulate flower, 204
Lilac (*Syringa*), 369
Liliaceae, 133, 148
Lima beans, 209, 450, 453
Lime-pits, woad in, 4
Limnobium, 39
Limnophyton, 38
Linamarin, 251
Linaria vulgaris, 266, 415
Linnaeus, 12
Linseed, see flax
Linuron, 356, 450
Linum nodiflorum, 34
— *usitatissimum*, 237, 251, 321, 355
— — cuticular wax of, 327
Lipoid layer, 330
Liriodendron tulipifera, 42
Lithospermum, 82
— *linearifolium*, 164
— *ruderale*, 81
Littoral zone, 35
Livestock, plants poisonous to, 92
Lloydia, 82, 89
Loam soils, 361
Lobelioideae, origin of compositae, 220
Location of weeds, Tab. 1, 8
Locust, black (*Robinia pseudo-acacia*), 369
— honey (*Gleditsia triacanthos*), 369
Lodgepole pine killed by dwarf-mistletoe, Pl. 2b
Lolium, 147
— *temulentum*, Pl. 1, 2, 11, 13, 18, 91, 116, 117, 236
— — var. *muticum*, 116
— *perenne*, 265
Longevity of seeds in herbarium, 130
— of weed seeds in soil, 129
Longi-monaxial roots, 164
Lonicera, 39
— *japonica*, 41, 273, 419
Loranthaceae, 45, 52
Loranthus, 52, 60, 124, 381

Loranthus ampullaceus, 58
— *falcatus* (*Dendrophthoe falcata*), 68
— *ferrugineus*, 59
— *grandifrons*, 59
— *involucratus*, 58
— *longiflorus*, 58
— — var. *falcatus*, 58
— parasite, 59
— *pentandrus*, 59
— *pentapetalus*, 59
— *philippensis*, 58
— *scurrulus*, 58
— *secundiflorum*, 58
— *tetrandrus*, 60
Louisiana, 357, 368, 374, 409
Lousewort, 64
Low ragweed (*Ambrosia artemisiifolia*), Pl. *10*, 188
— — flowers *of*, Pl. *7a*
Low-temperature requirement, 122
Low-volume spraying, 323
Lucerne, see alfalfa
Lukban (*Citrus maxima*), 58
Lumber yard areas, 380
Lumbering operations, 39
Lupinus, 99
Luzula forsteri, 206
— *multiflora*, 206
Lychnis vespertina, 11
Lycium arabicum, 183

Machine mowing, 408
Maclura, 369
Macquarie Islands, 275
Madagascar, 64, 68, 276
— mistletoes of, 54
Madia dissitiflora, 83
Magnesium, 244-5-6-7, 303
Mahonia, 96
Maine, 382
Maize, 23, 61, 65, Tab. II, 67, 131, 174, 181, 183, 245, 246, 247, 261, 293, 304, 305, 306, 333, 350, 352, 382, 441, 442, 444, 445, 450
— chemical composition of, 246
— nozzle tips for, 459
— stalk breakage and brittleness of, 353
Malachietum aquatici, 264
Malachium aquaticum, 264
Malachra, 38
Malanthropophyte (*i.e.* weed), 15, 219
Malaria, relation to Bromeliads, 45
— — to epiphytes, 102
Malaya, 23, 43, 44
Malaysia, 272, 273
Maleic hydrazide (MH), 288, 301, 315, 316, 328, 333, 447
— — absorption of, 315-16-17
— — degradation in plants, 335
— — diethanolamine salt, 315
— — fate of, in plants, 335
— — growth suppressant for grasses, 382
— — persistence of in plants, 335
— — supression of axillary shoots of tobacco by, 315
— — translocation of, 315-17

Malerba, 2, 7
Malezas, 2
Malus sylvestris, 252
Malva rotundifolia, cause of pink yolk colour, 94
Malvastrum coromandelianum, 273
Mamalian toxicity, herbicides low in, 341
Mammals, aquatic for control of aquatic weeds, 418
Man, activities of, 267
Man-conditioned communities, 18
Man-created habitats, 20
Man-dispersal, 220
Man-disrupted habitats, 20
Man, role of in weed distribution, 270
Manatee (*Trichechus manatus*) for control of aquatic weeds, 378, 418
Manchineel tree (*Hippomane mancinella*), 104
Manchuria, 130
Mandarin orange (*Citrus reticulata*), 58
Manganese content of weeds, 247
Mangifera indica, 58
Mango grain, 23
— trees (*Mangifera indica*), 58
Manna, parasitization by *Striga*, 65
Manual of Official Methods, 383
Manuka blight (*Eriococcus orariensis*), 416
Manure, viability of seeds in, 218
Maple (*Acer*), 372
— (hard), 369
— (soft), 369
Maquis plants, 182
Marijuana (*Cannabis*), 19, 105
Marsh-elders (*Iva*), 100
Mascarene Islands, 22
Massachusetts, 234
Mat plant, 37
Matchbox-bean liana, *Entada scandens*, 40
Materia medica, 81
Matricaria, 265
— *chamomilla*, 261, 264
— *inodora*, 135, 139
— *maritima*, 371
— *matricarioides*, 139
Maturity dates, 209
— of peas, delay of, 456
Mauritius, Tab. II, 67
Mauvaise herbe, 2
Maypop (*Passiflora incarnata*), 14
Mayweed (*Anthemis cotula*), 36
MCPA, etc., 286, 288, 289, 295, 297, 327, 328, 362, 438, 456
2-(MCPB), 355
4-(MCPB), 299, 355, 439
MCPS, see Sodium 2-methyl-4-chlorophenoxy-ethyl sulphate
Meadow chickweed (*Cerastium arvense*), 379
— nematode (*Pratylenchus*), 98, 99
Mean nitrogen number, 267
— soil friability number, 267
— soil reaction number, 267
— temperature number, 267
— water relations number 267
Mebrosideros, 40
Mechanical clearing of land, 405
— control of vegetation, 407
Mecoprop (dl2-(4-chloro-2-methylphenoxy) propionic acid) [MCPP]

Medicago denticulata, 175
— *lupulina*, 34
— *sativa*, 166
Mediterranean, 23, 35, 60
Medusa-head (*Elymus caput-medusae*), 259, 409
Megalithic settlements in England, 12
Meiosis, 232
Melampyrum arvense, 264
Melandrium album, 166
Melasma brasiliensis, 64
Meliaceae, 59
Melilotus, 83
— *alba*, 174
— *indicus*, 34
— *infestus*, 34
Membrane of endoplasmic reticulum, 331
— of mitochondria, 331
Mercurialis annua, 212, 416
Merion bluegrass, 379
Meristematic cells, polarized division of, 295
Meristems, apical, 407
— intercalary, 407
Mesilla Valley, 184
Mesocotyl, 149
Mesolithic period, 402
Mesophyte, 164, 219
Mesquite (*Prosopis juliflora* etc.), 37, 184, 325, 364, 367, 372, 438
— carbohydrate of roots at bi-weekly intervals, 367
Metabolic differences between host and parasite, 336
Metabolites, rate of flow, 331
Metallic ores, 247
Metaphase, 291
Methoxone, *see also* MCPA, 286, 438
2-Methoxy-3,6-dichlorobenzoic acid, 450
2-Methoxy-4-ethylamino-6-isopropylamino-1,3,5-triazine (Atratone), 306
2-Methoxy-4,6-*bis*(ethylamino)1,3,5-triazine (Simetone), 306
2-Methoxy-4,6-*bis*(isopropylamino)-1,3,5-triazine (Prometone), 451
2-Methoxy-3,5,6-trichlorobenzoic acid (Tricamba), 450
Methyl bromide, 315
2-Methyl-4-chlorophenoxyacetic acid, 286, 438
2-(2-Methyl-4-chlorophenoxy) butyric acid [2-(MCPB)], 355
4-(2-Methyl-4-(chlorophenoxy) butyric acid [4-(MCPB)], 355
*1-(2-Methylcyclohexyl)-3-phenylurea(active ingredient in Tupersan TM)
*Methyl 3,4-dichlorocarbanilate (Swep)
Methyl-*N*-(3,4-dichlorophenyl) carbamate, 450
o-Methylthreonine, 302
Metonymy, 2
Mexican medicinal plants, 82
Mexico, 13, 23, 105, 190, 235, 273
*MH, *see* maleic hydrazide
Michigan, 100, 129, 360
Microflora of *Avena* seed, 259
Microlarinus, 415
Micromeria, 181

Microorganisms, in soil and interactions with herbicides, 340
Middle East, 403
Mikania, 42, 416
— *scandens*, 51, 419
Military camps, 16
— operations, dispersal by, 15
Milk sickness, 94
— tainting of, 94
Milkweed, 352
Millet, 23, Tab. II, 67, 179, 181
Millet (*S. italica*) compared with foxtail grass (*Setaria viridis*), *Pl. 12a*
Mimic weeding act, 87
Mimosa, 272
— *pudica*, 273
Mindanao Island, 59
Minnesota, 152, 211
Mint, geese for weeding in, 417
Missiles, possible dispersal by, 15
Mississippi, 349
— Agricultural Experiment Station, 118-20
Missouri Botanical Garden, 407
Mist, droplet sizes of, 322
Mistel, origin of word, 54
Mistletoe (*see also, Phoradendron, Viscum*), 381
— age of, 52
— cultivation in England, 54
— dwarf (*see Arceuthobium*)
— state flower of Oklahoma, 53
Modern science, dilemma of, 268
Molecular-level mechanism of action of 2,4-D, 335
Mollugo, 243
Molybdenum, 307
Monarch spray nozzles, 459
Monasteries, Cistercian, 12
Monkeys, 19
Monochasma, 64
Monochloroacetic acid, 64
Monocotyledons (*also*, monocots), 17, 229
— 2,4-D-resistant, 336
— emergence from soil of, 133
— resistance of, 336
— weeds of this group, 34
Monoecious plants, 189
Monsanto Chemical Company, 399
Monstera deliciosa, 215
Montana, 92
Month of weeds, August, 2
Montpellier, la flore adventice de, 32
— seaport area of, 32
— weed-aliens of, 16
Monuments, plant design on, 13
Monuron [CMU], 3-(*p*-chlorophenyl)-1,1-dimethylurea, 288, 303, 314, 355, 356, 366, 372, 381, 453, 455
Moraceae, 40
Morning-glory (*Convolvulus arvensis*), 118, 120, 169, 408
orphogenesis, 285
Morphological expression of weeds, Tab. I, 8, 9
Morphology, adaptive, 214
Morus, 369
Mosaic disease of sugar-cane, 106

Mosquitoes, 45
— breeding grounds, 376
— — habitats for, 377
— malaria-carrying, 102
Mosses, 42
Moth mullein (*Verbascum blattaria*), 129
Mouldboard plough, 403
Mt. Scopus, 182
Mouse-ear chickweed (*Cerastium vulgatum*), 379
Movable bandsaw, for tree removal, 406
Movement, time-course of, 333
Mozambique, Tab. II, 67
Muck soils, 355, 359, 455, 457
Mucuna, 274, 276
Mud, 213
Mulberry (*Morus*), 58, 369
Mulch, 403
Mulches for weed control, 408
Mule, cultivating with, 36
Mullein, 319
Multiformal, 164
Multiple germinations, 133
— introgression, 232
Mungo bean, 23
Munumunu, Polynesian term for weeds, 87
Mustard (*Brassica*, *Sinapis*), 1, 361, 362
Mutation, 18, 40
Mycosphaerella, 416
Mylone, 315, 442
— use as herbicidal fumigant in soil, *Pl. 23*
Myriophyllum, 39
Myrmecochorous plants, 218
Myrtaceae, 40

Nagpur, India, 38
Naiad (*Najas guadalupensis*), 373
Najadetum, 261, 262, 263
Najas, 39, 261
— *guadalupensis*, 373
Naphthaleneacetic acid, 286
Naphthas, herbicidal, 356
N-1-naphthylphthalamic acid (NPA), 301, 448, 488
Naptalam, 288
Narcissus poeticus, 34
Narrow-leaf vetch, 120
Narrow leafed weeds, 35
Natal, 65, 82
National Academy of Sciences, 384, 395
— Agricultural Chemical Association, xx
— Research Council, 395
Natrin, 440
Natural forces, dissemination by, 217
— hybridization, 227
— selection, 40, 217
— — on weed seedling, 153
Naturally occurring auxins, 294
Nature (London), 10
Die natürliche Pflanzenfamilien (Engler and Prantl), 13
Navigation, 38
N-(2-(*o,o*-diisopropylthiophosphoryl)ethyl)-benzene-sulphonamide, 452
Near East, 19
Nebeln, droplet size, 322

Nebraska, 185, 354
Neburon, 443
Nectar, 203, 205
Negev Desert, 125
Nelumbo, 418
— *nucifera*, 130
Nematocide, 442, 445
Nematodes, 408
— cysts of, 252
— larvae of, 252
Neolithic agriculture, 11
— cereal, 237
— period, 402
Neophytes, 33
Neotropical phanerogamic parasites, 416
Nepeta, 233
— *hederacea*, 379
Nephrolepis acutifolia, 44
— *exaltata*, 44
Neptunia oleracea, 38
Nest epiphytes, 44
Nettles (*Urtica*), 105, 405
Neurospora, 232
Neutrophile, weed growth and, 170
Nevada, 81, 92, 175, 364
New England, 14
New Jersey, 360, 405
New Guinea, 87, 415
New Mexico, 13, 184, 409, 415
New South Wales, 412
New York City area, 212
— — State, 98, 99, 100
— — — pollen records from, 101
New World, 12, 45, 274
— — weed flora of, 273
New Zealand, 22, 80, 273, 411, 416, 417
Nicotiana, 145
— *rustica*, Tab. II, 67, 296
— *tabacum*, Tab. II, 67, 296
Nigeria, Tab. II, 67
Night spraying, 454
Nile, flooding of, 36
— tilapia fish for aquatic weed control, 418
Nippur, 1
Nitrate content, toxicity to animals, 178
— leaching from soil, 247
— levels and tillage, 175
— reductase activity, 307
— in soils, 247
Nitrification, 15, 175, 177
Nitrifying nodules, 64
Nitrobacter, 175
Nitrobenzoic acid derivatives, 300
3-nitro-2,5-dichlorobenzoic acid, 450
Nitrogen, 244, 245, 246, 247, 288
— -fixing bacteria, 45
— number, mean, 267
—relationships and weed growth, 175
— -substituted *alpha*-chloroacetamides, 306
Nitrophilous associations, 263
— habitats, 15
— plants, 175, 176, 177
— weeds, Tab. I, 8
Nitrophily, 262
Nitrosomonas, 175
N,N-dimethyl-2,2-diphenyl-acetamide (Diphenamid), 451

N,N-di-(*n*-propyl)-2,6-dinitro-*p*-toluidine (Dipropalin), 451
N,N-di-(*n*-propyl)-2,6-dinitro-α,α,α-trifluoro-*p*-toluidine (Triflurolin), 451
Nocardia, 340
Nodding thistle (*Carduus nutans* var. *nutans*), 227
Noaea, 183
Nomadic camps, 16
— movements, 16
— species, 20, 270
Non-floral agriculture, 19
Non-food plants, 19
Non-stranglers, 40
Non-weedy taxa, 15
*Norea (3-[5-(3a,4,5,6,7,7a-hexahydro-4,7-methanoindanyl)]-1, 1-dimethylurea)
Norse, 12
North Africa, 3, 16, 22, 60, 95
— America, 13, 14, 16, 22, 37, 40, 234, 270, 274, 416
— Carolina, 49, 65, 96, 99
— Dakota, 190, 350, 419
— Pole, 100
— Queensland, 412
Northern Asia, wild plant region of, 22
Norway, 218, 351
— mistletoes of, 5
Nothochlaena, 181
Nothofagus pumilio, 275
Noxious vines, 42
— plants, lexicon, xviii
Nozzles, 316
— orifices of, 323
— spray tips, 459
NPA, Tab. XI, 288, 448, 453
Nucleic acids, 123, 294, 303
Nucleotide synthesis, 123
Nursery crops, herbicides for, 360
— plantings, 443
— stock, 360, 439
Nutgrasses (*Cyperus rotundus*, etc.), 36, 213, 360, 372, 441, 445
Nutrients, absorption by weeds, 174
— competition for, 244
— status of, 338
— uptake by maize, 246
— uptake by weeds, 173, 246
Nymphaea, 418

Oak-leafed fern (*Drynara quercifolia*), 44
Oaks (*Quercus*), 10, 99, 368, 369
— worship of, 86
Oats, (*Avena*), 23, 66, 116, 118, 120, 179, 247, 250, 261, 286, 319, 352
— scopoletin in seedlings revealed by ultraviolet light, *Pl. 12(b)*
Obligatory stranglers, 40
Oceania, 19
Oceanic currents and plant dispersal, 274
— — and seed dispersal, 281
— — of the world, 275
Octoploid, 230
Oedogenietum, 263
Oekiophytes, 34
Oenothera biennis, 106, 129

Official Methods of Analysis, 383
Ohio, 379
Oil, shale, 364
— diesel ('Powerine'), 68
Oils, 289, 381
— aromatic, 373
— naphtha-type, 405
— spreading coefficients, 289
— storage area, weed control in, 380
— toxic effect of, 289
Oklahoma, mistletoe state flower of, 53
Okra, 23
Old Aegean continent, 17
Old World, 14
— — weed flora of, 273
Olea chrysophylla, 103
Oleander, 82
Olefins, 290
Oleyl amine salts of, 2,4-D, 316
Olive (*Olea*), 181, 182
— trees, mistletoe on, 53
Oncidium variegatum, 45
Oncopeltus quadriguttatus, 104
Onion (*Allium*), 245, 301, 304, 306, 359, 363, 441, 445, 449, 455
— flag stage of, 455
— spray nozzle tips for, 459
Onkruid, Dutch name for weed, 5
Onopordetum illyrici, 260
Onset of Dormancy, 120
Oonopsis, 92
Operculina turpethum, 272
Ophiobolus, 95
— *graminis*, 95
Ophiomyia strigialis, 67
Opuntia, 80
— *fulgida*, 409
— *inermis*, 412
— as fodder plant, 412
— *lindheimeri*, 416
— *robusta*, 416
— *stricta*, 412
— *vulgaris*, 412
Orange Free State, 65
Orchard grass (*Dactylis glomerata*), 123, 150
Orchards, 450
— poison ivy in, 41
Orchidaceae, 12
Orchids, 12, 43
Ordram, 450
Oregon, 3, 5, 92, 349, 417
Organ differentiation, 294
Organic matter, oxidation rates of, 247
Organisms, 383
Orient, 273
Oriental migration of plants, 17
Origin of domestication, 18
— of weed species, 226, 273
Ornamental crops, herbicides for, 360
— plants, 19, 442, 450, 452
Orobanchaceae, 61, 68
Orobanche, 115
— biological control of, 64
— *cernua* var. *desertorum*, 62
— *crenata*, 63
— *elatior*, 139
— *minor*, 115

Orobanche picridis, 139
— *ramosa*, 63
— — (broomrape) on tomatoes, *Pl. 5(a)*
Oryza sativa, 261
Oryzeto-Cyperetum, 261, 262, 263
Osage orange (*Maclura pomifera*), 369
Osphronemus olfax, 417
Osyris, 60
— *alba*, 61
Over-wintering, 120
— of seeds, 126
Ovulation, 81
Ovule, 232
7-Oxabicyclo-(2.2.1)heptane-2,3-dicarboxylic acid (newer name for Endothal), 447
Oxalate, in *Halogeton*, 170
— poisonous principle, 92
Oxalic acid, 252
Oxalis, 42, 165, 252, 379, 380
— *stricta*, 250
Ox-eye daisy (*Chrysanthemum leucanthemum* var. *pinnatifidum*), 97
Oxford English Dictionary, 2, 5, 10, 14, 29
Oxidants, 298
Oxidase, indoleacetic acid, 297
Oxidative phosphorylation, uncouplers of, 331
β-oxidation of 2-4-D, and 2,4-DB, 338

Pacific islands, 22, 102
— North-west, weeds of, 3
Paddy (*see also* rice)
— rice culture, 38, 408
— — roots, respiration of, 167
Paint, body, 4
Paired seeds, 122
Pakistan, phanerogamic parasites of, 68
Palaeobotany, 13
Palmetto (*Sabal* spp.), 37
Palms, 43
Panama, 60
— Canal Zone, 104
Panic grass (*Panicum depauperatum*), 148
Panicum, Tab. II, 67, 152, 250
— *capillare*, 148, 180, 214, 215, 217
— *depauperatum*, 148
— *maximum*, Tab. II, 67
— *miliaceum*, 11
— *purpurascens*, 39
— *sanguinale*, 267
— *virgatum*, 148
Pantemperate weeds, 270
Pantothenate metabolism, interference of Dalapon, 294
Pantropic weeds, 270
Papaver, 151, 259, 261
— *argemone*, 264
— *dubium*, 264
— *hybridum*, 264
— *radicatum*, 215
— *rhoeas*, 264, 371
Paper chromatography, 248, 251, 253
— — use in separation of materials in a soil extract, *Pl. 14*
Pappus, of Compositae, 204, 217
Papyrus Ebers, 1

Para grass (*Panicum purpurascens*), 39
Paraffin, 290, 319
Paraquat, 451
Paraguay, 23
Parasites, 10, 416
Parasitic habit, Tab. I, 9
— seed plants, 49, 67, 124, 381, 416
— vine, 60
Parasitism, 35
Parks and athletic fields, turf-grass area of, 379
Parsley, 307
Parsnip, 23, 290, 307, 450
Parthenium hysterophorus, 102
Parthenocarpy, 285
Parthenocissus, 369
Parthenogenesis, 232
Paspalum, 39, 250
— resistant to herbicide, 451
— *dilatatum*, 10, Tab. II, 67
Passiflora foetida, 419
— *incarnata*, 14
Passion fruit, 23
Pastinaca sativa, 117
Pastures, 2, 128, 266, 349, 351, 367, 450
— renovation by chemical means, 363
— spray nozzle tips for, 459
— weeds in, 362
Patagonia, 61
Patent, 2,4-D, 287
— growth regulatory substances, 287
Pathogenic fungi, 251
Pathogens, attack by, following use of herbicides, 336
PCA, 451
PCP, 442
Pea (*Pisum sativum*), 66, 209, 293, 299, 304, 305, 321, 333, 334
Peach tree, 251
— — replanting, toxic soil residues and, 250
Peanuts (groundnuts) [*Arachis hypogaea*], 23, 64, 66, 306, 319, 352, 355, 439, 440, 450, 452
Pear trees, mistletoe on, 52, 54
Pearl millet (*Setaria* sp.), 19
Peas, 450, 452, 456
— spray nozzle tips for, 459
Peat soils, 457
PEBC, 450
Pecan trees, 43
— — mistletoe on, 52
Pecos River delta, 184
Pectic enzyme technique, for cuticle removal, 329
— layer, 326
Pedicularis palustris, 64
— *sylvatica*, 218
Peganum, 183
Pelleted herbicide, 443
Pelophiles, weeds of clay soils, 173
Pen Ts'ao, 357
Penetration, through the cuticle, 327
Penicillin, 249
Pennisetum, Tab. II, 67
Pennsylvania, 414
— Agricultural Experiment Station, Extension Service, 396

Pentachlorophenol, 288, 331, 381, 442
Pentateuch, plants listed in, 12
Peppergrass (*Lepidium virginicum*), 36, 119, 270
Peppermint, 443
Peppers, 451
Perennial weeds, 36
— — control of, 369, 446
— — roots of, 168
Perennials, 17, 153, 229
Peridermium pyriforme, 61
Periploca, 94
Permanent wilting point, 137
Permitted weeds, 19
Peroxidase activity, 305
Persia, 23
— *Arceuthobium oxycedri* in, 56
— wheat of, 238
Persimmon (*Diospyros*), 300, 447
— mistletoe on, 52, 54
Persistence of 2,4-DB in plants, 334
— of herbicides in soil, 339
— of weeds, Tab. I, 8
Peru, 23
Pesticides, 284, 383
— molecules of, fate of in ecosystem, 384
— residues, xx, 383
— tolerances, xx
Pests, 10
Petis, 44
Petunia hybrida, 106
pF, definition, 137
pH, of soil, 169,
Phanerogamic epiphytes, 43
— parasites, 49, 124, 381, 416
— — review of, 67
Phanerophytes, 34
Pharmacognosy, xxxii
Phenol, 284, 294, 298, 299
— induction in plants by dalapon, 294
— induction in plants by stress, 294
Phenology, 134, 208, 227, 238
— differences of plants in relation to, 239
— substituted, 442
Phenoxy acids, 288
— compounds, 285, 438
—monocarboxylic aliphatic acids, 287
Phenoxyacetic acids, 295
Gamma-phenoxyalkylcarboxylic acids, 299
Phenoxybutyric acids, 298
Phenoxyethyl sulphates, 439
Phenoxypropionic acids, 298
Phenyl carbamates, 290
Phenylacetic acid derivatives, 450
1-Phenyl-4-amino-5-chloropyridazone, 451
3-Phenyl-1, 1-dimethylurea, (Fenuron), 443
3-Phenyl-1, 1-dimethylurea trichloroacetate (Fenuron TCA), 444
Phenylmercuric acetate (PMA), 452
β-Phenyl propionic acid, 285
Philanthropophyte, 15
Philippines, 22, 61
— medicinal plants of, 82
Phleum arenarium, 206
— *boehmeri*, 206
— *pratense*, 99, 206
Phloem, 331

Phloretin, 252, 253
Phlorizin, 252, 253
Phloroglucinol, 253
Phlox amoena, 231
— *bifida*, 231
Phoma taraxaci, fungus parasite of common dandelion, 416, Fig. 46
Phoradendron, 52, 82
— *flavescens*, 52, 60
— *libocedri*, on cedar, 52
Phosfon (2,4-dichlorobenzyltributyl phosphonium chloride), 383
Phosphate bonds, 290
— esterification, inhibition of, 294
Phosphorus, 244, 245, 246, 247
— circulation in plants, 333
Phosphorylation (oxidative), uncouplers of, 331
Photochemical activity, inhibitors of, 304
Photomicrographs of cuticles from *Gardenia*, *Pl. 19(b)*
Photoperiod, 383
— autumnal, 191
— and flowering of low ragweed, *Pl. 10*
Photoperiodic ecotypes, 191
— response of grasses, 190
Photoperiodism, 187
Photophosphorylation, inhibitors of, 304
Photoreaction, reversible in seeds, 124
Photosensitization, 414
Photosynthesis, inhibitors of, 302
Photo-thermal growth development curve, 211
— units, 210, 211
Phototropic responses, 294, 301
Phragmites, 357
— *communis*, 165
Phreatophytes, 38, 167, 183
Phycitidae, 413
Phyllanthus niruri, 174
Phymatotrichum, 95
— *virginiana*, 97
— *subglabris*, 97
— *subglabrata*, host of *Bacterium angulatum*, 96
— *heterophylla*, 97, 214, 215
Physalospora, 416
Physical and chemical properties of herbicides, 438
— selectivity, and droplet size, 322
Physiological expression of weeds, Tab. I, 8, 9
— races, 15, 121, 270
Phytocoenoses, 262
— transient, Tab. I, 8
Phytomachia orobanchia, 64
Phytomonas, 104
Phytonicides, 250
Phytophagous insects, 411
Phytosociology of weeds, 260
Phytotoxins, 250, 252
Picea glauca, 382
— *mariana*, 382
— *rubra*, 382
*Picloram (4-amino-3,5,6-trichloropicolinic acid)
Pigweeds (*Amaranthus*), 12, 13, 96, 100, 101, 217, 246, 306, 353, 452

Pigweeds (*Chenopodium*), 100
Picts, ancient tribe of, 4
Piedmont fruit-belt, 41
Pileo-monaxial root, 164
Pileus, 164
Pinang (*Areca catechu*), 44
Pines (*Pinus*), 61, 443
Pineapple, 443
Pinole seeds, 83
Pinus banksiana, life history of, 55
— *contorta*, Pl. 2b.
— *monophylla*, 296
— *ponderosa*, 167, Pl. 2a
— *sabiniana*, 57, 85
— *strobus*, 42
Pinyon pine (*Pinus monophylla*), 296
Pistia, 38, 39, 102, 375
— *stratiotes*, 325, 376
Pistillodium of ragweed flower, 100
Pisum, 293, 336
— *arvense*, 237
— *sativum*, 319, 320
Plagioborthrys campestris, seeds used as pinole, 84
Plano-monaxial roots, 164
Plant Protection Ltd., 43
Plant Science Literature, xxiii, 29
Planta Medica, 82, 90
Plantago, 16, 37, 42, 82, 100, 129, 220, 378
— competition, 259
— *lanceolata*, 11
— *major*, 10, 11, 117, 129, 167
— *maritima*, 234
— *minor*, 10
Plantains (*Plantago*), 10, 100, 119
Plants, absorption of water vapour by, 328
— clothing uses, 18
— construction use of, 19
— (crop) evolution of, 31
— (cultivated) regions of the world, 23
— in demonology aspects, 86
— dispersal by ocean currents, 274, 275
— domesticated, 17
— food use, 18
— hairs of, 100
— hormones of, 285
— horticultural, 18
— in magic lore, 86
— medicinal uses, 18
— migration of, 17
— in mystical rites, 18
— ornamentation uses, 18
— quarantine laws for, 377
— remains from Swiss Lake dwellings, 11
— shelter uses, 18
— stand reduction of, 454
— (wild) regions of the world, 22
Plasma membrane, 330
Plasmodiophora brassicae, 95
Plastic sheeting as barrier to weed growth, 408
Platycerium, 44
Platyptillia, 61
Pleistocene glaciation, and weed origins, 48
Pliny, *herba* use of, etc., 2
Plough, mouldboard, 403
Plum, 369
Plumbago, 181

Plumeless thistle (*Carduus acanthoides*), 204, 227
Plumose pappus, 204
PMA, *see* phenylmercuric acetate
Po river, Italy, 264
Poa, 42, 124, 129, 131, 138, 175, 232
— *annua*, 13, 117, 129, 134, 178, 186, 191, 265, 270, 360
— *pratensis*, 99, 123, 171, 378
Pogogyne parviflora, 85
Pogonochores, 214
Poinsettias, 383
Poison-ivy, 37, 369, 438, 439, 446, 449
Poison oak (*Rhus diversiloba*), 40, 372
Poison-sumac, 37
Poisonous plants, 91
Poisons, Tab. I, 9, 94
— metabolic, 340
Polarity, 302
Pollarded willows, 43
Pollen, 10, 80, 99, 100, 189, 205
— atmospheric, etc., 101
— grass, 12
— germination, prevention of, 301
— release of ragweed (*Ambrosia artemisiifolia*), 100
— sacs of ragweed flowers, 100
— studies, 402
Pollination, 203, 217
— of dwarf mistletoe, *Arceuthobium oxycedri*, 55
Pollinosis allergies, 99
Polyaxial roots, 164
Polyethylene glycols, 286, 317
Polygonaceae, 171
Polygonum, 38, 39, 42, 82, 129, 183, 259, 379
— *amphibium*, 230
— *aviculare*, 84, 117, 170, 265, 371
— *convolvulus*, 175, 178, 266, 371
— *cuspidatum*, 230, 274
— *hydropiper*, 117, 129, 173
— *filiforme*, 230
— *japonicum*, 230
— *lapathifolium*, 11, 371
— *orientale*, 230
— *persicaria*, 250, 266, 371
— *reynoutria*, 230
— *scandens*, 125
— *virginianum*, 50
— *viscosum*, 230
— *viviparus*, 215
Polymorphic forms, 232
Polynesia, 272
— term for weeds used in, 87
Polyphenols, 305
Polyploidizing reagent, 292
Polyploids, 206, 228, 229, 235
— coefficient of, 229
Polypodium virginianum, 214
Pomegranate, 58
Pompeii, plant remains from, 13
Ponderosa pine, *Arceuthobium* on, 54
Pondweed, gigantic sago [*Potamogeton pectinatus* var. *interruptus*], 374
Pondweeds (*Potamogeton*), 1, 374, 376
Poplars (*Populus*), 369
— mistletoe on, 53

Poppies (*Papaver*), 261
Population, 7
— dynamics of weeds, 19, 20
— exploding human, 384
— of weeds, Tab. I, 9
Populus, 191, 369
— *alba*, 372
— *deltoides*, 234
— *trichocarpa*, 234
Porphyrin synthesis, interference with, 303
Portugal, 417
Portulaca, 129, 173, 243
— *oleracea*, 96, 129, 139, 174, 177, 179, 180, 266, 267
— host for *Dichotomophthora portulaceae*, 96
Portulacaceae, 149
Posoqueria, 40
Post oak (*Quercus stellata*), 365
Post-emergence, 153
— herbicides, extent of use, 352
Potamogeton, 39, 376
— *crispus*, 375
— *foliosus*, 374
— *nodosus*, 374
— *pectinatus*, 374
— *pectinatus* var. *interruptus*, 374
— *richardsonii*, 374
Potassium, 244, 245, 246, 247
— cyanate (KOCN), 449
— nitrate, effects on germination, 142
— salt of maleic hydrazide, 317
Potato (*Solanum tuberosum*), 23, 105, 198, 293, 301, 319, 321, 335, 360, 404, 439, 441, 442, 451, 457
— sensitivity of roots to poor aeration, 168
— spray nozzle tips for, 459
— witches'-broom virus, 296
Potentilla glandulosa, 233
Pouroma, 40
Poverty-weed (*Franseria tomentosa*), 169
Powerine (diesel oil), 68
Prairie, 266
Pratylenchus, 99
— *penetrans*, 252
Precis orithya, 66
Pre-emergence, 153
— herbicides, 336
— — disadvantage of application, 340
— — extent of use, 352
Prehistoric man, 79
Prehominids, 19
Pre-planting herbicide, 450
Pressure, air for spraying, 459
Preventive measures, weed control, 358
Prickly ash, 369
Prickly-pear cactus (*Opuntia*), 412, 416
— — spread of, 412
Prickly sida (*Sida spinosa*), 118, 120
Primary dormancy, 121
— root systems, 163
Primates, uses of plants by, 19
Primeverose, 293
Primitive agriculture, weed control, 86
Primrose, 120
Principles of Biological Control, 411
Private residences, turf grass area of, 379
Privet, 443

Procecidochares utilis, 415
Prodenia, 107
Prometon, 306, 451
Prometryne (recently renamed, Caparol), 451
Propagation of weeds, 212
Propagules, 7, Tab. I, 8, 215
— heteromorphic, 207, 208
Propanil, 452
Propatrin, 306
Propazine, 306, 451
2-propen-1-ol (allyl alcohol), 445
Properties and uses of herbicides, Appendix I, 438
Propham, *see* IPC
n-Propyl *N*-ethyl-*N*-(*n*-butyl) thiolcarbamate (Tillam), 450
Prosopia, 37, 364
— *juliflora*, 184, 364, 367, 372
— *stephaniana*, 181
— *velutina*, 409
Prostrate growth forms, 191
Proteaceae, 228
Protein, denaturation of, 289, 290
— precipitation of, 289
— surface, absorption of 2,4-D on, 334
Proto-agriculture, beginnings of, 19
Protocoronospora, fungus of mistletoe, 53
Protozoa in latex of plants, 103
Prunus, 369, 372
— *angustifolia*, 14
— hydrocyanic acid in, 93
— *serotina*, 93
Prunella vulgaris, 171, 233
Psammophiles, weeds of sandy areas, 173
Pseudomonas, 340
Pseudo-symbiotic relationship, host and disease agent, 417
Psidium guajava, 272
Psittacanthus schiedeanus, 60
Pteridium, 171
— *aquilinum*, 215, 372
— *esculentum*, 451
— *latiusculum*, 170
Pterochores, 214
Pterophorid moth, 61
Public health, 38
— properties, turf-grass area of, 379
Puccinia graminis, 96
Puerto Rico, 45
— — *Casytha filiformis* in, 52
Puncture vine (*Tribulus terrestris*), 415
Purine, 65
— metabolism, enzyme in, 303
— — interference, 303
Purslane (*Portulaca oleracea*), 96, 306, 359, 441
Pwakova, Polynesian for 'big weeds', 87
Pyralid moth, 61
Pyramin, 451
Pyrazon, 451
Pyrostegia venusta, 215
Pyruvate oxidase, 294
Pyruvic acid, dalapon as an antimetabolite of, 294

Quack-grass (*Agropyron repens*), 35, 95, 186, 213, 216, 249, 292, 339, 457, 458

Quack-grass control of, 419, 444, 445, 450
— rhizomes, 294
— stolons, 250
— teletoxicity, 259
Quarantine laws, plant, 377
Quaternary ammonium carbamates, as plant
    dwarfing agents, 382
— — compounds, 451
Quebec Department of Agriculture, 346
Queensland, Tab. II, 67, 93
— Prickly Pear Land Commission, 432
Quercitrin, 252, 253
Quercus, 99, 329, 368, 369, 439
— *alba*, 214
— *baruensis*, 60
— *havardii*, 364
— *marilandica*, 365
— *stellata*, 365
Quintral pest (*Loranthus tetrandrus*), 60

R-1910, 450
Rabbitbrush (*Chrysothamnus nauseous*), 415
Radiation, 297
— ionizing, 266
Radioactive carbon dioxide, 297
Radiocarbon, dating of charcoal, 402
— — — amaranth seeds, 13
— — technique, 402
Radish, 23
Rafflesia, flowering parasite, 68
Ragee millet (*Eleusine corocana*), 19
Ragweed (*Artemisia*), 99, 101, 353, 359,
    Pls. 7*a,b*
— bibliography of, 114
— common, (*Ambrosia artemisiifolia*), pollen
    release of, 100
— pollen, 101
Ragwort (*Senecio jacobaea*), 411
Railroad, 267, 349
— rights-of-way, 34, 41, 443
Rain, droplet sizes of, 322
— forests, strangling figs of, 40
Randox or CDAA (2-chloro-*N*-*N*-diallylacet-
    amide), 306, 307, 359, 446, 455
Range, 349
— grasses, 363
— weeds, 79
Rangeland, 351
Rank growth of weeds, Tab. I, 8
Ranunculus, 234, 267
— *acris*, 235, 266
— *aquatilis*, 374
— *bulbosus*, 235
— *eisenii*, 83
— *repens*, 11, 175, 216, 235
Rape, 23, 250, 305, 321
— (*Brassica napus*), 249, 414
— (*Brassica rapa*), 249
Rapeseed, 358, 359, 441
Raphanus, 146
— *raphanistrum*, 145, 175
Rapistrum rugosum, 93, 207
Raspberries, 361, 369, 451
Rate of herbicide movement, 330
— of movement, translocation stream, 330
Raunkaier, system of, 34

Rauwolfia, 94
— alkaloids, 82
— *serpentina*, 82
Receding contact angles, 320
Recent herbicides, Appendix II, 450
Recombination, 226
Recreation, 376
Recycling of herbicides in plants, 333
Red clover, 119, 150, 361
— kidney-bean, 179, 286
— light, 141
— spider, 412
Redox-potential interference of by triazines,
    305
Redroot (*Amaranthus*), 359
Redtop (*Agrostis alba*), 171
Reduction of plant stand, 454
Reeds, control of, 451
— Egyptian hieroglyphics known for, 1
Refuse, disposal of, 15
Regulator-Antioxidant Hypothesis, 298
Report Terminology Committee, Weed
    Society of America, 438
Reproduction, 203
— vegetative, 7
Reproductive capacity of weeds, Tab. I, 8
— habits, 377
Reseda lutea, 166
Residences, turf grass area of, 379
Residual aspects of herbicides in soil, 338,
    449, 451, 452
— pre-emergence, 448
Residue Reviews, 383
Residues, pesticide, 340
Resistance, 7
— biochemical aspects of, Tab. I, 8, 333
— to herbicides, 238, 332
— related to restriction of herbicide move-
    ment, 337
Respiration, 290
— inhibitor, 340
— rate, 168
Retama, 183
Rhamnus catharticus, 97
Rhamphicarpa, 64
Rhinanthus crista-galli, 64
Rhine River, 267
Rhizoctonia, 96
— *solani*, 66
Rhizomes, 164, 230, 272
Rhizomatous plants, 360
Rhizosphere, 248
Rhizophora mangle, 215
Rhodesia, Tab. II, 67
Rhododendron, 184
Rhus, 37, 39, 102, 369
— *diversiloba* (poison oak), 7, 40, 372
— *radicans*, 40
— *toxicodendron*, 102
Rhynchosia, Tab. II, 67
Ribes, 97, 368, 369
Riboflavin, 303
Ribulose-1,5-diphosphate carboxylase, 51
Rice (*see also*, paddy), 23, 38, 61, 64, 65, Tab.
    II, 67, 261, 262, 263, 269, 274, 283,
    307, 349, 351, 352, 357, 358, 438, 439,
    450, 452

Rice culture, 16
— tillering, 358
Richardson pondweed (*Potamogeton richard-sonii*), 374
Ricinus (Euphorbiaceae), 146
— *communis*, 1, 10, 23, 132
Rights-of-way, 443
— brush removal with 2,4-D, and 2,4,5-T, *Pl. 22*
Ring hydroxylation, 298
Rio Grande River, 185
Ripening, 211
Ritual plants, 19
River-bank agriculture, 402
RNA (ribonucleic acid) production, rate of following 2,4-D application, 297
Roadsides, etc., 41, 372, 380
Robenhausen, Swiss lake dwellings, 11
Robinia, 369
— *pseudo-acacia*, 372
Rocks, water-supplying capacity of, 182
Rolling chopper or cutter, for tree control, 406, 408
Rolling coulters, for tree control, 406
Roman Empire, 18
Roman world, 16
Romans, 4
Rooiblom (Striga), 65
Root absorption of herbicides, 299
— borers, 412, 414, 415
— cutters, 406
— development, 285
— — depth of, 166, 265
— dormancy, 125
— initiation, 294
— insects associated with in Iowa, 106
— meristems, 292
— parasites, 49
— physiology of, 167
— pruning, in maize, following deep cultivation, 354
— secretions, 65, 250
— systems, 162
— — classification of, 163
— — removal of, 406
— tensile strength of, 153
— toxic substances from, 151
— zone, 248
Rorippa palustris, 145
— *sylvestris*, 175
Rosa, 368, 369
Rose, 369, 447
— seed, dormancy of, 121
Rosemary (*Ceratiola ericoides*), *Cassytha* parasitic on, 51
Rosette, 4, 37, 191
Rosewood, 58
Rotary cutters, for tree control, 408
Rothamsted Experimental Station, 250, 286, 375
Row crops, 349
Royal Botanical Gardens of Ceylon, 419
— Swedish Academy of Sciences, xxvi
Rubber, 44, 59
— tree (*Hevea brasiliensis*), 59, 104
Rubiaceae, 40
Rubus, 37, 42, 152, 232, 369

Rubus fruticosus, 416
Rudbeckia, 82
— *hirta*, 97
Ruderal associations, 262
— flora, 17
— phytocoenoses, 262
— successions, 261
Ruderals, 16, 42
Ruellia strepens, 152
Rumex, 100, 129, 136
— *acetosa*, 170
— *acetosella*, 11, 117, 153, 169, 170, 175, 266, 268, 269
— *crispus*, 13, 84, 117, 129, 217
— *obtusifolius*, 415
Runcatio, 2
Runciatio, 2
Runcina, 2, 86
Runcinate, 2
Runco, 2
Runners, 230
Rush, 1
Russia (*see also*, U.S.S.R.), 2, 63, 92, 105, 166, 182, 211
— flora of, xviii
— weed names of, xviii
Russian knapweed (*Centaurea repens*), 372, 408, 447, 450, 452
— thistle (*Salsola kali* var. *tenuifolia*), 181
Rust spores in atmosphere, 101
Rusts, 95
Ruta graveolens, 82
Rye (*Secale cereale* etc.), 20, 66, 210, 211, 212, 252, 419
Ryegrass, 118

s-triazines (symmetrical triazines)[1,3,5-, triazines], 306
Sabal, 37
Saccharum, 250
— *spontaneum*, 35
Sacred lotus (*Nelumbo nucifera*), 130
Sagebrush (*Artemisia tridentata*, etc.), 80, 350, 364, 365, 366
Sagina, 378
— *procumbens*, 117
Sagittaria, 357
Sago pondweed (*Potamogeton pectinatus*), 374
St. Augustine grass, 380
St. Augustine's writings, 2
St. John the Baptist, feast of, 414
St. John's-wort (*Hypericum perforatum*), 413, 414, 419
Sakat ribu-ribu (creeping fern), 44
Salicylate, 331
Saline soils, 171
Salix, 50, 184, 369, 372
— *alba*, 42
— *lasiolepis*, 85
— *nigra*, 368
Salt, common (sodium chloride), 454
Saltcedar (*Tamarix gallica*), 184
— (*Tamarix pentandra*), 37
Saltgrass (*Distichlis spicata*), 184
Salsola autrani, 183
— *inermis*, 183

Salsola kali, 181
— *kali* var. *tenuifolia*, 180
— *pestifer*, 128
— *vermiculata*, 183
Salvia, xxxii
— *columbariae*, 84
— *dumetorum*, 182
— *nemorosa*, 166
Salvinia (fern sp.) in Kariba Lake, 259
San Diego County, California, 41
Sand sagebrush (*Artemisia filifolia*, etc.), 363, 364
Sandalwood, 58
Sandbur (*Cenchrus pauciflorus*), 148
Sandwort (*Arenaria serpyllifolia*), 11
Sandworts (*Sagina*), 378
Sand-dunes, 20
Sandy soil, 360, 457
Sanguinaria, 125
Sanicula menziesii, root for good luck, 84
Sanseveria, Tab. II, 67
Sanskrit plant names, 19
Santa Catarina, Brazil, 45
Santalaceae, 60
Santalum, 60
São Paulo, Brazil, 45
Sapi, to scratch, 87
Sarcobatus vermiculatus, 184
Sarcochores, 214
Sarcostemma, 104
Saskatchewan, 128
Sassafras (*Sassafras albidum* etc.), 42, 51, 300, 372, 447
Satellite weed, 18, 23, 116
Sauer's theory of agricultural origins, 402
Savannah, 37, 105
Saxifraga granulata, 206
— *tricuspidata*, 215
— *tridactylites*, 206
— — depauperate plants of, *Pl. 11*
Scandinavian element, 14
Schefflera, 40
Schools and colleges, turf grass area of, 379
Scirpus, 85, 184, 274
Scleranthus annuus, 169
Sclerochores, 214
Sclerophyllous plants, 182
Scleropyrum, 60
Sclerotium rolfsii, 95
Scoparia, 272
Scopoletin(7-oxy-6-methoxycoumarin), 65, 251, 252
— — in plant roots, 65
— revealed in oat seedlings by ultraviolet light, *Pl. 12(b)*
Scotch broom (*Cytisus scoparius*), 415
Scotland, 416
Screening, 117
Scrophularia nodosa, 216
Scrophulariaceae, 64, 68
Sculptures, plant designs on, 13
Scything, hand, 408
Sea onion (*Urginea maritima*), 94
— water, seed viability in, 276
Seasonal dimorphism, 152
Secale, 20
— *anatolicum*, 212

Secale cereale, 211, 212, 237
Secomone, 104
Secondary dormancy, 126
Sedges (*Carex*), 64, 133, 451
Seed, 115
— agronomic, 124
— Angiosperm, 86
— (*Arceuthobium*, mistletoe) expulsion of, 56
— awned, 142
— buoyancy, 274
— burial, depth of, 138
— charred amaranth, 13
— cleaning, 119
— cleaning methods, 409
— cleaning by winnowing, 83, 117, 236
— closely-aggregated, 151
— corn-cockle, 91
— death of, 144
— depths of emergence, 139
— dimorphic, 207
— disjuncter, 219
— dispersal, 216
— — by ants, 213
— — by dust storms, 217
— — by mud on footwear, 220
— — by pocket gopher, 220
— dissemination, 217
— of dwarf mistletoe (*Arceuthobium*), 55
— expulsion of dwarf-mistletoe, 56
— — velocity of, 56
— feeders, 412
— floating, 272
— habit, 86
— heteromorphy of, Tab. I, 8, 122
— inhibitory substances from, 138
— low temperature treatment of, 125
— microflora of *Avena*, 259
— number per plant, 139
— production, 203, 208
— reservoir in soil, 212
— size, 115
— soil burial experiments, 129
— storage of, 86
— surface area of, 117
— voilure coefficient of, Tab. IV, 139
— water-buoyancy of, 217
— weight, 115, 139, 206
Seed World, xx, 30, 433
Seed-beds, 445
— tobacco, 442
— vegetable, 442
Seed-case, winged, 3
Seed-coat, impermeability of, 122
Seed-leaves, 152
Seedlings, arrested growth, 149
— establishment of, 144
— growth and botanical composition, 150
— — effect of shading, 151
— — effect of stand, 151
— — soil factors, 150
— growth-habit of, 150
— mortality, 151, 153
— pathogenic factors, 154
— stages, competition, 150-2
— survival, 153
Selection, 228
Selective cutting, 411

Selective herbicidal activity, 287
— — — of 2,4-D, 269
Selectivity and chemical structure, 338
— factors influencing, 336
— from differences in chemical constitution of plants, 337
— soil factors related to, 338
Self-injury, 253
Self-pollination, 186, 226
Semecarpus (Anacardium), 102
— *atra*, 102
— *australiensis*, 102
Senecio, basal genus of, Compositae, 220
— *burchellii*, 92
— *ilicifolius*, 92
— *jacobaea*, 411
— *vulgaris*, 212, 213
Senmit, 1
Sensitive plant (*Mimosa pudica*), 273
Septogloeum, parasitic on, 57
Serine, 303
Serjania, 94
Sesame, 409
Sesbania, 38
Sesone (Na 2-(2,4-dichlorophenoxy)ethyl sulphate), 64, 337, 355, 359, 360, 361, 439
— biological activation of, 299, 300
— for pre-emergence weed control in strawberries, Pl. 17
Setaria, 19, 35, 148, 306
— *faberii*, 35, 124, 125, 138, 139, 230, 259, 273, 274
— *geniculata*, 230
— *glauca*, 138, 171, 267
— *italica*, Pl. 12(a), 11, Tab. II, 67, 139, 180, 181
— *lutescens*, 174, 230, 250, 256, 259
— taxonomic monograph, 259
— *viridis*, Pl. 12(a), 117, 139, 148, 217, 230, 259, 267
Seville orange, 58
Sevin insecticide, xxvii
Sex hormones, 81
Shade, effect on seed size, 206
Shading, 244
Shale oil, 364
Shape of weed seeds, 116
Shattering of seeds, 118, 358
Shepherd's purse (*Capsella bursa-pastoris*), 36
Shinnery Oak (*Quercus havardii*), 364
Shipping, dispersal by, 15
Short day plants, 191
Shoshone Indians, 81
Sheep, 414, 417
— grazing land, 412
— migrating, 16
Siam-Malaya-Java region, 23
Sicily, 104
Sida carpinifolia, 97
— *cordifolia*, 97
— *veronicaefolia*, 97
Side-oats grama (*Bouteloua curtipendula*), 190
Sierra Leone, 97
Silage, seed viability in, 218
Silene, 151
— *cretica*, 11

Silene cucubalus, 214
— *noctiflora*, 152
— *pendula* var. *compacta*, 153
Silent Spring, 384
Silk-cotton tree, 59
Silt, collection of, 373
Silvex, (2(2,4,5-trichlorophenoxy)propionic acid), 379
Silybum marianum, 146
Simatrin, 305, 306
Simazine, 288, 291, 304, 306, 314, 350, 354, 366, 372, 380, 381, 444
— decomposed by fungi, 340
— hydrolysis of, 304
— radioactive, 305
— resistance to decomposition by bacteria, 340
— sensitive plants, 305
— tolerant species, 305
Simetone, 306
*Simetryne(4,6-bis-ethylamino-2-methylthio-1,3,5-triazine)
Sinapis, 164, 290
— *arvensis*, 117, 123, 128, 134, 135, 136, 145, 162, 178, 320, 321
— (*Brassica*) *arvensis*, 139
— *dissecta*, 145
Singletary peas, 419
Sinkers, 39
— of mistletoe, 53
Sinox (2-methyl-4,6-dinitro-phenol), 361
Siphonostegia, 64
Sisal, 107
Sissoo, 58
Sisymbrium altissimum, 128, 214
— *officinale*, 145
— *orientalis*, 261
— *thalianum*, 96, 117
Sium latifolium, 165
Size of spray nozzles for different crops, 459
Skeleton weed (*Chondrilla juncea*), 419
Skin blistering of, 414
Skin-sensitizing index, 102
Sleeproot, narcotic properties, 84
Small grains, 305, 351, 352
Smartweed, 441
SMDC, 288
Smilacina, 125
Smilax, 39, 300, 447
— *herbacea*, 214
Smyrnium, 132
Snails, breeding habitats for, 377
Snap beans, 99, 450, 453
Sodium arsenite, 449
— azide, 340
— chlorate, 307, 370, 372, 404, 449
— — fire hazard of, 449
— chloride as a herbicide, 454
— — in soil, 171
— 2-(2,4-dichlorophenoxy) ethyl sulphate (Sesone), 299, 337, 437
— ethyl sulphates, 299
— ethylenediamine tetra-acetate, solvent for cuticle, 329
— fluoride, 340
— 2-methyl-4 chlorophenoxyethyl sulphate, see MCPC

Sodium N-methyldithiocarbamate (SMDC), 288
— monochloroacetate, 353
— tetraborate, 449
— trichloroacetate, 404
— 2-(2,4,5-trichlorophenoxy)ethyl sulphate [2,4,5-TES; Natrin], 440
Soil, 13, 248
— accumulative heat units of, 209
— adsorptive capacity of, 360
— aeration, 171, 140
— agricultural, 128
— cultivation of, 15
— — and weed dispersal, 213
— denudation, 380
— drillings, 267-8
— erosion, 16, 185, 349
— — and weed control, 380
— fertility, 249
— friability number, mean, 267
— fungi, 408
— herbicides fate in, 338
— — applicator for sub-surface, Pl. 20(a)
— leaching of herbicides from, 451
— moisture, and weed growth, 172
— organisms in decomposition of herbicides, 300
— pH of, 169, 170
— profile, 267-8
— reaction, 169, 249
— — number, mean, 267
— — weed growth and, 170
— relative humidity in, 137
— Science Society of Florida, 398
— 'sickness', 250
— surface, alternate wetting and drying of, 137
— — disturbance of, 140
— tillage, 403
— toxins, 249
— type and structure and weed growth, 172
— weed seed population of, 128
Soil-born diseases, 95
Soil-incorporated herbicide, 450, 451
Soil-moving machines, 408
Soil-sterilant chemicals, 338, 339, 340, 370, 372, 380, 444, 445, 446, 449, 451
Soil-weather-plant-herbicide complex, 340
Solan (N-(3-chloro-4-methylphenyl)-2-methylpentanamide), 306, 451
Solanaceae, 105, 167, 177
— sensitivity of roots to poor aeration, 168
Solanum, 42, 63, 105, 129
— burbankii, 99
— carolinense, 92, 97, 259
— dulcamara, 98, 99, 106
— integrifolium, 99
— nigrum, 99, 175, 267
— rostratum, 98, 99, 105, 164
— sarachoides, host of Verticillium alboatrum, 96
— triflorum, 98
— tuberosum, 105
— xanthii, 98
— xanthocarpum, 174, 177
Solidago, 100
Solvents, aromatic, 373

Sonchus, 96, 170
— arvensis, 117, 226, 229, 321
— asper, 13
— oleraceus, 229
Sophora, 272
Sopubia, 64
Sorbitol, 328
Sorghum, 64, Tab. II, 67, 118, 181, 250, 351, 409, 445, 451
Sorghum halepense (Johnson grass), 203, 213, 404
— — control of in cotton with Dalapon, Pl. 16
— —, morphology and development, 259
Sorption, 326
South Africa, 22, 64, 65, Tab. II, 67, 92, 95, 274, 276, 416, 417
— America, 12, 275
— — western tropical, 22
— Carolina, 99
— Russia, 17
Southern California Golf Association, 379, 398
— celery mosaic virus, 97
Southwestern Asia, 22
Sow thistle, 352
— — control of, 419
Soybeans (Glycine max), 64, 66, 99, 120, 167, 179, 244, 306, 317, 318, 332, 351, 352, 355, 419, 450, 452
— cyst nematode (Heterodera glycines) of, 98
— pubescent and glabrous plants, 318
— root respiration of, 168
— tillage for weed control, Pl. 20(b)
— in United States, 99
Space, competition for, 243
Spacing of spray nozzles, 459
Spain, 60
Spanish word for weed, 2
— bayonet (Yucca angustifolia), 148
— moss (Tillandsia), 43, 381
Spatterdock (Nuphar), 376
Spergula arvensis, 11, 266
— linicola, 237
— penandra, 11
Sphaeranthus, 38
Spinach, 23, 97, 269, 441, 451
— spray nozzle tips for, 459
Spindle formation, inhibition of, 291
Spirochaeta roubaudi, 104
Spirodela, 38
Spirogyretum, 261, 262, 263
Spitsbergen, 178
Spontaneity of weeds, Tab. I, 9
Spontaneous apophytes, 20, 34
Sporobolus cryptandrus, 148
Sporochores, 214
Sports areas, herbicides for, 378
Spotted wilt virus of tomatoes, 296
Sprangletop, 450
Spray, adherence of, 318
— drift, aspects of, 322
— — from wind, 323
— nozzle spacing, 459
— — tips, 459
— output, 319
— pattern, alteration by wind, 324

Spray pattern, displacement of, 325
— — retention, 319, 322
— — of herbicides, 316
— — leaf angle effect, 318
Sprayer, ground speed of, 459
Spraying, directional, nozzle tips for, 459
— equipment, 316
— low-volume, 323
— Systems Inc., 459
Spreading decline of citrus trees, 98
— roots, 37
Spring barley, 353
— oats, 353
— wheat, 353
Spritzen, drop size, 322
Sprühen, drop size, 322
Squill (*Urginea*), 94
Stachys palaestina, 182
Stachytarpheta, 272
Stag's-horn fern (*Platycerium*), 44
Stanleya, 92
Starch, 305
Steel ball, for tree control, 407
Steer, acres required to feed, 350
Steers, gain in weights, 365, 367
Stellaria, 131, 186, 291, 378
— *boraeana*, 206
— *graminea*, 266
— *holostea*, 206
— *media*, 11, 42, 95, 97, 117, 129, 134, 139,
    141, 170, 171, 176, 178, 186, 191, 206,
    212, 213, 219, 226, 266, 270, 271, 360,
    361, 379
— — nitrogen content in, 82
Stem parasites, 49
Stem-rust of wheat (*Puccinia graminis*, var.
    tritici), 96
Stenocephalis agilis, 104
Sterile forms, 232
Sterilization, soil, 440
Steroid, 81
Sticky seeds, 220
Sting nematode (*Belonolaimus gracilis*), 99
Stinging nettle (*Urtica dioica*), 176
Stink-grass (*Eragrostis cilianensis*), 217
— (*Eragrostis major*), 148
Stipa humilis, 61
Stoddard's solvent, 290
Stoloniferous grasses, 402
Stolons, 164
Stomach contents of Grauballe man, 11
Stomata, 289, 290
— closure of, 305
— entry of herbicides, 325
— photomicrographs of from *Gardenia* leaves,
    Pl. 19(b)
Stone mulch for weed control, 408
Strand vegetation, 274
Stranglers, 39
Strangling figs (*Ficus* spp.), 40
Stratification, 125
Strawberries, 301, 307, 361, 439, 440, 451
— pre-emergence weed control with Sesone,
    Pl. 17
— spray nozzle tips for, 459
Stream-banks, 20
Streamflow, effect of vegetation on, 184

Streptomycin, 302
Stress, causative factor for induction of
    phenols, 294
Striga, 115, 212
— distribution of species, Tab. II, 67
— *asiatica* (witchweed), *Pl. 5(b)*, 64, 65, Tab.
    II, 67, 382
— *curvifolia*, Tab. II, 67
— *densiflora*, Tab. II, 67
— *euphrasioides*, Tab. II, 67
— — biological control of, 66
— *gesnerioides*, Tab. II, 67
— *hermonthica*, 67
— *lutea*, Tab. II, 64, 67, 252
— *orobanchoides*, 65
— *parviflora*, Tab. II, 67
— *senegalensis*, Tab. II, 67
Strophanthus, 94
Struggle for existence, 24
Struthanthus marginatus, 60
Strychnos, 94
Stubble mulch farming, 403
Stump, removal of, 408
— sprays for tree killing, 368
Stupefying fish, plants for, 84
Submerged aquatic weeds control of, 374, 376
Submicroscopic wax of leaves, 326
Substituted aryloxy alkanols, 299
Subterranean clover, 419
— fungi, 68
Sucrose formation, inhibition of, 305
— loss of by parasitism, 61
— per cent in diseased (*Aeginetia indica*)
    sugar cane, 61
— — — in healthy sugar cane, 61
Sudan, 64, Tab. II, 67, 409
— grass, 65, 274
Sugar-beans, 64
Sugar beets, 251, 293, 304, 352, 359, 442, 451
Sugar cane, 61, 64, Tab. II, 67, 87, 238, 356,
    443, 445, 450
— — parasitic diseases of, 62
— — parasitization by *Aeginetia indica*, loss
    of sucrose by, 61
— — root parasite, 61
— maple, 191
*Suggested Guide for Chemical Control of
    Weeds*, 378
Sulphanilamide, 302
Sulphonamides, entry into wheat leaves, 327
Sulphuric acid, 285, 289, 359
— — for dodder control, 50
Sumac, 300, 369, 447
Sumatra, Tab. II, 67
Sump Weed, 119
Sunfish family, 378, 417
Sunflower (*Helianthus*), 23, 83, 181, 359
Sunlight sensitivity, 414
Surface-active agents, effect on spray reten-
    tion, 319
— — use of, 376
Susceptibility to herbicides, 332
Suspended hydrophytes, 38
Sweden, 42, 134, 135, 136, 153, 205, 213, 267,
    268, 322
Sweet corn, 450, 458
— peas, 286

Sweet potatoes, 23, 66, 451
Swep (methyl 3,4-dichlorocarbanilate), 450
Swiss Lake Dwellings, Robenhausen, plant remains, 11
Switch grass (*Panicum virgatum*), 148
Switzerland, 42, 53, 170, 415
Symbolic plants, 86
Symphoricarpos vulgaris, 365
Symplast, concept of, 329
Synanthropes, 16, 17
Synchytrium, 95
Synedrella nodiflora, 207
Synthetic group of auxins, 294
Syringa, 369
Systemic fungicides, 337
— herbicides, 287
— insecticides, 337
— movement, 331

2,4,5-T, 41, 103, 286, 295, 297, 365, 381, 438
— commercial production of, 295
Table beets, 451
Tagetes erecta, 252
Tahiti, 271, 272
Tainted milk, 362
Taiwan (Formosa), 61, 62
Talisman, plant as, 84
Tamarind, 58
Tamarix gallica, 184
— *pentandra*, 37
Tanacetum, 417
Tanganyika, 103
Tannins, 84
Tapioca, 23
Taraxacum, 37, 42, 120, 128, 131, 137, 143, 153, 167, 172, 173, 205, 213, 217, 232, 267, 270, 378, 416
— *fasciatum*, 137
— *kok-saghyz*, 63, 252
— *lapponicum*, 215
— *officinale*, 117, 170, 171, 203, 204, 214, 219, 293
— *vulgaria*, 268, 269
Tares of the Bible, 2, 91
Taro, 87
Tarweed, 83
— Chilean, 23
Tasmania, 93, 275
Taxonomy, 1
2,3,6-TBA, *see* 2, 3,6-trichlorobenzoic acid, 288, 333, 447
TCA (trichloroacetic acid), 288, 356, 362, 363, 371, 381, 445, 454
Tea bush, 57, 58
Teak, 57, 59
Technische Hochschule, Stuttgart-Hohenheim, 252
Tee Jet spray nozzles, 459
Teff, 65
Telemorphic effects, 286
Teletoxicity, 152, 248, 252, 254, 259
Teletoxins, Tab. I, 9
Telvar, 359, 381, 453, 455
Temperature, 17
— and flowering of common or low ragweed (*Ambrosia artemisiifolia*), 100
— mean number, 267

Temperature and spray retention, 322
— summation, 209
— and weed growth, 185
Tennessee, 227, 231
Tephrosia, Tab. II, 67
Terminalia, 274
Terminology Committee Report, Weed Society of America, 438
2-*tert*-butylamino-4-ethylamino-6-methylthio-1,3,5-triazine, (GS-14260), 1
Tertiary times, 17
2,4,5-TES, 440
Tetraploid, 229, 230, 233
— wheat, 237
Tetronic acid derivatives, 302
Texas, 43, 92, 95, 102, 190, 323, 324, 365, 367, 409
— Agricultural and Mechanical College, 323-4, 399
Textbooks on weed control, 351
Thames River, 220
Thellung classification scheme, 32
Themeda, 149
Theophrastus, 12
Theory of herbicidal action, 329
Thermoperiodism, 187
Therophytes, 34
Thesium humile, 60
Thespesia, 272
Thiamine, 234
Thielavia basicola, 64
Thiocarbamate, 288
Thioglycosides, plant, 93
Thiols, 301
Thiotriazines, *see* GS-14260
Thistle-rust, 416
Thlaspi arvense, 94, 117, 128, 139, 213, 266
Thorn apple, spray nozzle tips for, 459
Thorns, Tab. I, 9
Threshold temperature for flowering, 209
Thymelaea, 183
Thymus, 181
Tibet, 3
Tilapia, fish for aquatic weed control, 378
— *mossambica*, 417, 418
— *nilotica*, 418
— *zilli*, use in aquatic grass control, 418
Tilia, 369
Tillage methods, 216
— for weed control in soybean field, *Pl. 20(b)*
Tillam, 450
Tillandsia, 381
— *recurvata*, 43
— *usneoides*, 43
Timing devices, 127
— mechanisms for weed emergence, 238
Timothy, 252
Tips, spray nozzle, 459
Tissue matte, 319
Tissues, apparent free space in, 327
Tlalquequetzal (*Achillea millefolium*) from an Aztec herbal, *Pl. 6(b)*
Toadflax (*Linaria vulgaris*), 415, 450
Tobacco, 23, 63, 64, 66, 99, 105, 251, 293, 301, 316, 319, 445, 451
— cyst nematode (*Heterodera tabaccum*), 99
— mosaic virus, 296

Tobacco seed-beds, 442
— seeds of, 116
— suppression of axillary shoots by maleic hydrazide, 315
Tobago, 45
Tollund Man, stomach contents (plant), 11
Toluidines, 288, 451
Tomato, 23, 63, 97, 99, 105, 131, 187, 252, 293, 297, 304, 307, 333, 360, 441, 451
— plants, 2,4-D activity on, *Pl. 15*
Tombs, Egyptian, 13
Tordon, (4-amino-3,5,6-trichloropicolinic acid), 284, 301, 372, 452
— an isostere of benzoic or phenylacetic acid, 301
Tortula, 260
Total weed control, 451
Tovara virginiana, 214
Toxic soil residues in orchards, 250
— substances from roots, 250
Toxicological data, for pond fishes, 377
Toxin production, 250
2-(2,4,5-TP), 365, 439
2,2,3-TPA (2,2,3-trichloropropionic acid), 362
Tractors, 406
Trade routes and plant distribution, 272
Trampling, 261
Trans-Caucasia, 237
Trans-cinnamic acid, 252
Transhumance, 16
Transient phytocoenoses, Tab. I, 9
Translocated herbicides, 287
Translocation, 332
Transmembrane potential, 331
Transpiration rates reduction of by Atrazine, 305
— stream, 331
— of weeds, 180
Transplanted crops, 440, 450
Transport system of leaf mesophyll, 332
— — cell to cell, 331
Transvaal, 65
Trap crop, 64, 66, 252
Trapa, 38
— *natans*, 273
Treading action of animals, 35
— and shrubs, 366
Trees, control with steel ball, 407
— crowns of, 39, 41, 42
— cutters for, 406
— frilling technique, 368
— fruits of, 451
— girdling of, 368
— herbicide application to stumps, 368
— injection of, 381
— killing of, 402
— paeony, 125
— poisoning, 408, 411
Trianthera, host of dodder, 50
Triazine herbicides, 305, 306, 444, 445, 451
2,4,6-tribromophenylnitramine, 302
Tribulus, 132
— host of dodder, 50
— *terrestris*, 415
*Tricamba(2-methoxy-3,5,6-trichlorobenzoic acid)

Trichechus manatus, herbivorous mammal, 378, 418
Trichloroacetates, 293
— soil persistence, 339
Trichloroacetic acid (TCA), 292, 293, 445
2,3,6-Trichlorobenzoic acid (2,3,6-TBA), 353, 447
Trichlorobenzylchloride, 306
Trichloroethyl alcohols, fate of in a monocotyledonous plant, 293
β-2,2,2-Trichloroethylgentiobioside, 293
β-2-Trichloroethyl-D-glucoside, 293
Trichloroethylglycoside, 293
2,4,5-Trichlorophenoxy acetic acid (2,4,5-T), 286, 438
Trichlorophenoxybutyric acid [4-(2,4,5-TB], 355
2-(2,4,5-Trichlorophenoxy) ethyl-2,2-dichloropropionate (Erbon), 440
2-(2,4,5-Trichlorophenoxy)-propionic acid, (Silvex), 439
2,3,6-Trichlorophenylacetic acid (Fenac), 450
2,2,3-Trichloropropionic acid, sodium salt of, 362
Trichomes, Tab. I, 9
Tridax procumbens, 62
*Trietazine(2-chloro-4-diethylamino-6-ethylamino-1,3,5-triazine)
*α,α,α-Trifluoro-2,6-dinitro-N,N-dipropyl-p-toluidine (revised name for Trifluralin)
Trifluralin, 451
Trifolium, 85, 378
— *parryi*, 165
— *repens*, 250, 268, 269, 379
— *virescens*, 83
Triiodobenzoic acid, 302
Trillium, 125
*Trimeturon (N'-(4-chlorophenyl)-ONN-trimethylisourea)
Trinidad, 45
Triple-action pesticide, 442
Triploid, 233
Trirhabda nitidicollis, 415
— *pilosa*, 415
Tris-(2,4-dichlorophenoxy-ethyl) phosphite (2,4-DEP; Falone), 440
Tritac, 450
Triticum vulgare, 180, 237
— — weight per acre of roots, 167
— *dicoccum*, 237
Trobriand Islands, 87
Tropic responses, inhibitors of, 301
Tropical Africa, 22
— regions, 247
— skin ulcers, 104
Troublesome plants, 24
Trouser turn-ups, seeds in, 220
True epiphytes, 43
Trumpet creeper (*Campsis radicans*), 42
— vine, 447
Trypanosomiasis, 103
Trysben, 447
Ts'ao, Chinese word for weed, 6
Tsetse flies (*Glossinia*), 103
— — control of in relation to vegetation control, 103
Tubers, 230, 272

Tubular flower, 204
Tufted growth, 191
Tulipa oculis, 34
— *praecos*, 34
*Tupersan TM, (principal ingredient, 1-(2-methylcyclohexyl)-3-phenylurea)
Turf, 438, 439, 448, 451, 452
— ecological state of, 378
— (grass) survey of Los Angeles County, California, 379
Turkestan, 237
Turkey-mullein, 84
Turkish women winnowing grain, *Pl. 8*
— weed names, xviii
Turnip weed (*Rapistrum rugosum*), 93
Turnips, 96, 292
Tussilago farfara, 259
Tussocks, 191
Tylenchus semipenetrans, 98
Typha, 80, 184, 337
— *latifolia*, control in channels, ditches, 377
— —, life history, 377
— rhizomes of, 80
Tza ts'ao, Japanese word for weed, 5, 6

Ulmus, 99, 369
Ultra-violet light, 251
— — reveals scopoletin in oat roots, *Pl. 12b*
Umbelliferae, 17, 132, 290
Umbelliferous crops, 289
— — selectivity of Chloroacetamides to, 307
Umbellularia californica, 85
Umred, India, 38
Undercutter, 406
Underground elongation, 131
Undesirable weeds, Tab. I, 9
Ungava, 178
Uniformal root system, 164
Union Carbide Chemicals Company, xxvii
United States, 13, 23, 43, 52, Tab. II, 67, 92, 96, 99, 102, 105, 190, 211, 230, 243, 273, 322, 323, 349, 350, 351, 352, 359, 361, 363, 364, 372, 373, 378, 415, 417
— — amount of ragweed pollen, 101
— — Department of Agriculture, 66, 249, 286, 351, 352, 368, 399
— — Department of the Interior, 399
— — *Dispensatory*, 81
— — Government, Bureau of Reclamation, 347
— — hay fever regions of, 100
— — Weather Bureau, 211
University of Chicago, 285, 286
— — Michigan, 102
Un-ionized forms of herbicides, 329
Unkraut, 2, 5
Unsaturated aliphatics, 445
Unsightly weeds, Tab. I, 9
Upland cereals, 36
Upper and lower seeds in *Xanthium* fruits, 123
Upstream vs. downstream in aquatic plant control, 376
Urab, 303, 444
Uranium ores, 167
Urea, 288

Urea, effect on germination, 142
— herbicides, 442, 443, 444
— substituted, 442, 450
Urginea, as poisonous plant, 94
— as weeds, 95
— *altissima*, 94
— *burkei*, 94
— *capitata*, 94
— *macrocentra*, 94
— *maritima*, 94
Urox, 303, 444
Urtica, 16, 177
— *dioica*, 176
— *pilulifera*, 17
— *procera*, 215
— *urens*, 175, 213, 267
Urticeto-Ecballietum, 260
Uruguay, 413
Urushiol, toxicant of poison-ivy, 102
Use of Pesticides, 384
Useless weeds, Tab. I, 9
Uses, ceremonial, 12
— and properties of herbicides, Appendix I, 438
U.S.S.R.(Union of Soviet Socialist Republics), 351
— (*see also* Russia), 105
Ustilago utriculosa, on dock-leafed persicary, 96
Utah, 92, 184
Utensil-producers, 19
Utility rights-of-way, 443
Utricularia, 39, 373, 418

Vaccinium oxycococcus, 214
Van der Waals' forces, 330
Varietal differences, 338
Vascular epiphytes, 43
Vaucherietum, 263
Vegedex (2-chloroallyldiethyldithiocarbamate), 291, 441, 454
Vegetable crops, 19
— — herbicides for, 359
— — weed control of, Appendix III, 543
— seed-beds, 442
Vegetation, mechanical control of, 407
Vegetative propagation, 402
— reproduction, 226
— spread, 216
Velocity of seed expulsion, 56
Velvet mesquite (*Prosopis velutina*), 409
Venezuela, poisonous plants of, 93
Verbascum, 187
— *blattaria*, 129
Vermont, 80
Vernalization, 187
Veronica, 38, 219, 379
— *agrestis*, 213
— *hederifolia*, 212
— *peregrina*, 250
Verticillium alboatrum, 96
Vetches (*Vicia*), 99
Viburnum lentago community, 411
Vicia, 99, 293
— *americana*, for good luck while gambling 85

Vicia angustifolia, 117
— *cracca*, 131, 132
— *faba*, 63
— *sativa*, 92, 237
Victoria regia, 418
Vigna, 99, 274
— *unguiculata*, Tab. II, 67
Vine crops, spray nozzle tips for, 459
Vines, noxious, 39, 42
Viola, 17
Vineyards, 41
— spray nozzle tips for, 459
Virgil, reference to *herba*, 2
Virginia, 3
— apple orchards, 41
— creeper, 369
— Polytechnic Institute, 399
— western, 5
Virus diseases, 296, 297, 416
— — epidemiology of, 98
— — symptoms resembling 2,4-D effects, 296
Viscin cells of dwarf mistletoe (*Arceuthobium vaginatum* f. *cryptopodum*), 56
Viscosity, oils, 289
Viscum (mistletoes), 52, 59, 60, 124
— *album*, 53
— — in forests of Southern Europe, 53
— *articulatum*, 59
— *cruciatum*, 53
— Indian species, 54
— Indo-Malay species of, 54
— monograph on, 54
Vitex negundo, 59
— *orientale*, 58
Vitis, 39, 41, 369
— *girdiana*, 41
Vitrum, Latin word for woad, 4
Vocabularium Nocentium Florae, xviii
Voilure coefficients, 117
— concept, 116
Volatile herbicides, sub-surface soil applicator for, Pl. 20(a)
Volume of water in lakes, estimation of, 375
Vuurbossie (*Striga*), 65

Wad, 4
Waidso, 4
Waidt, 5
Wallrothiella, parasitic on *Arceuthobium*, 57
Walnuts, mistletoe on, 54
Washington, 370
Water, contact angles, 321
— currents, 213
— economy, 182
— level, lowering of, 377
— relations of weeds, 180
— requirements of weeds, 180
— seed dispersal by, 217
— surface-tension values of, 321
— volume estimation of in lake, 375
Water chestnut (*Trapa natans*), 273, 376
— grass, 358
— lettuce (*Pistia stratiotes*), 102, 325, 375, 376
— milfoil 376
Water-buoyancy of seeds, 217

Water-hyacinth (*Eichhornia crassipes*), 82, 374, 375
— — (*Eichhornia crassipes*) control with 2,4-D, Pl. 18
Water-level management, 102
Water-lily of the Amazon (*Victoria regia*), 418
Waterlilies, 376
Water-relations number, mean, 267
Water-stargrass (*Heteranthera dubia*), 374, 376
Water-table, 166
Waterweed (*Elodea* [*Anacharis*] *canadensis*), 374, 376
Wax formation, inhibition of, 291
— lamellae, 326
— layer (bloom), effect on droplet behaviour, 319
— leaf, 325, 326, 327
— platelets, 328
Wedelia, 274
Weed Abstracts, xxiv-v, 31, 351
— *Control Handbook*, 352
Weed, definitions of, 1, 6
— animal example, 48
— flora, 269
— — of New World, 273
— — of Old World, 273
— free land, 244
— Japanese ideograph for, 5
— lettuce, 20
— oats, seed shattering of, 236
— Polynesian term for, 87
Weed Research, 351
— seeds, disposal of, 409
— — in soil, 128
— Society of America, 312
— — — Terminology Report of, 6, 438
— tree, 37
Weeda, 2, 3
Weeding ceremony in Trobriand Islands, 87
— magic of, 87
Weeds (Journal of the Weed Society of America), xxiv, 31, 351
Weeds, absorption of nutrients, 174
— aggression of, Tab. I, 8
— annual, 185
— aquatic, 38, 373
— and associated insects, 105
— associations of, 265
— biological characteristics of, Tab. I, 8, 9
— — control by insects, 411
— biology of, 267
— burner for, 408, 409
— classification of, 32
— communities of, 153, 267
— competition of, Tab. I, 8
— control by animal feeding, 417
— — by chemical methods, 352
— — by fire, 408
— — by flooding, 408
— — in forage crops, 361
— — by hand-hoeing, 403
— — measures of Tab. I, 8, 9
— — of in vegetable crops, Appendix III, 453
— — in pastures, 361
— — in rangelands, 361

Weeds, corn yield reduction by, 356
— cost of controlling, 349
— development of, 162
— dispersal and soil cultivation, 213
— dissemination of, 216
— — by man, 219
— ecological control of, 409
— — expression of, Tab. I, 8, 9
— endemic, 16
— ensiling of, 80
— establishment of, 115
— flat and spreading types, 173
— food attractiveness of, Tab. I, 8
— as food for humans, 80
— food-tainting, 93
— germination, 115
— growth of, 162
— harmful aspects, Tab. I, 9, 91
— hayfield, 230
— hosts for fungus and bacterial diseases, 95
— — for nematodes, 98
— — of virus diseases, 97
— injurious effects of, 243
— as interceptors of rainfall, 185
— introduced, 16
— life-cycle of, 416
— losses from, 349
— morphological expression of, Tab. I, 8, 9
— nitrophilous, Tab. I, 8
— nutritive value of, 79
— origins of, 14
— — of crop plants from, 235-7
— — and Pleistocene glaciation, 48
— of the Pacific Northwest, 3
— pantemperate, 270
— pantropic, 270
— parasitic, 49
— pasture, 230
— persistence of, Tab. I, 8
— phenology of, 212
— physiological expression of, Tab. I, 8, 9
— phytosociology of, 260
— populations of, Tab. I
— prevention of by use of clean crop seed, 409
— propagation of, 212
— rank growth of, Tab. I, 8
— reproductive capacity of, Tab. I, 8
— resistance of, Tab. I, 8
— row-crop, 230
— satellite, 23
— seed structure, 115
— seedling ecesis, 115
— seeds of, 80
— — removed from wheat in North Dakota, Pl. 21
— societies of, 263
— species, origins of, 273
— spontaneity of, Tab. I, 9
— stage of development and herbicide, 337
— timing mechanisms for emergence, 238
— undesirable, Tab. I, 9
— — location of, Tab. 1, 8
— unsightly, Tab. I, 9
— useless, Tab. I, 9
— uses of, 79
— wild growth of, Tab. I, 8

Weeds world distribution of, 260, 270
Weed-seed screenings, oil from, 80
Weedt, 2, 3
Weet, 2
Weod, 2, 4
West Africa, Tab. II, 67
West Indies, 12, 22, 39, 64, 106
West Virginia, 41
Western Europe, 237
— grape skeletonizer (Harrisina brillans), 41
— rye-grass (Agropyron tenerum), 95
Wetland hydrophytes, 38
Wettability of leaf surfaces, measurement of, 320
Weyt, 2, 5
Wheat, 66, 116, 148, 162, 212, 236, 237, 247, 251, 261, 304, 327, 352, 358, 404, 409, 419, 441, 450, 451
— ancient Egyptian, 31
— bread, 23
— effect of 2,4-D spray on at various growth stages, 354
— fields, 128
— grass for control in bindweed, 419
— piles of weed seeds removed from, Pl. 21
— preventing flowering in, 301
— rust (Puccinia gramminis), 96
— seeds, 137
— spray nozzle tips for, 459
— and wild mustard, competition between, Pl. 9(a)
— — oats, competition between, Pl. 9(b)
White bud, zinc deficiency, 174
— clover seed, 50
— — (Trifolium repens), 379
— Dutch Clover, 119
— fly (Bemisia), 97
— horse nettle, 408
— Nile, 375
— oak (Quercus lobata), acorns, 84
— pine blister-rust (Cronartium ribicola), 97
— poplar (Populus alba), 372
— water-crowfoot (Ranunculus aquatilis), 374
— waterlily, 376
Wieden, Dutch verb, to weed, 5
Wild barley (Hordeum pratense), 118, 148
— carrot (Daucus carota), 37
— geranium, 120
— grape (Vitis girdiana, etc.), 41, 43
— greens, 80
— growth of weeds, Tab. I, 8
— mustard, 120
— — and wheat, competition between, Pl. 9(a)
— oats (Avena fatua, etc.), 35, 120, 139, 187, 306, 441, 450
— — used for food, 83
— — (Avena ludoviciana), 120
— — control of, 358
— — and wheat, competition between, Pl. 9b
— onion, 118, 119, 362
— pines, 45
— plant regions of the world, 22, 24
— plants, medical uses of, 81
— — seeds of, 129
— winter pea, 119
Wildlife, 39, 376

Wildlife American, 79
— food of, 42
— herbicide safety to, 376
Willow (*Salix*), 184, 369, 372
— (*Salix lasiolepis*), poles from, 85
Willow-herb, 405
Willows, mistletoe on, 53
Wilt, 183
Wilting, 248
Wind dispersal, 17, 220
— pollination, 203
— spray drift from, 323
— velocities, 324, 325
Wind-throws, 20
Winnowing, as seed cleaning method, *Pl. 8*, 83, 117, 236
Winter-annual weeds, 36, 187
Wisconsin Agricultural Experiment Station, 453
Witch-grass (*Panicum capillare*), 148
Witches'-broom, *Pl. 2(a)*
Witchweed (*Striga*), 65
— distribution of species, Tab. II, 67
— (*Striga asiatica*), *Pl. 5(b)*, 382
— (*Striga lutea*), 252
Woad, 2, 3, 4
— comparative philology of, 4
Woad-crops, 4
Woed-monath (*August*), 2
Woevine (*Cassytha*), 51
Wood borers, 42
Wood-sorrel (*Oxalis*), 379
Woody plants, 37, 438, 439, 443
— — control of 364, 365, 366, 367, 368, 369
Woody vines, 37, 447
Wool mills, 34
— seed dispersal by, 220
Wool-adventive flora, 18
World, cultivated plant regions of, 23
— distribution of weeds, 260
— ocean currents of, 275
— wild plant regions of, 22
World List of Scientific Periodicals, xxiii, 31
World Review of Pest Control, 351, 400
World-wide distribution of weeds, 272
Wormseed mustard (*Erysimum cheiranthoides*), 244
Wormwoods (*Artemisia*), 100
Wyethia longicaulis, 83
Wyoming, 92, 365

Xanthium, 126, 140, 146, 191
— *canadense*, 122
— fruits, 123
— *italicum*, nitrate levels of, 179
— *orientale*, 34
— *speciosum*, 102
— *spinosum*, 63
Xanthoxylum, 369
Xenophon, Anabasis plants from, 12
Xeric growth adaptation, 37
Xeromorphic plants, 182
— structure, 17
Xerophyte, 164, 219
Ximenia, 274
Xylem system, 330, 331
Xylomiges, 107
Xylorrhiza, 92
Xylose, 293

Yam, 23, 402
— Kuvi, 87
Yarrow (*Achillea millefolium*), *Pl. 6(b)*, 379
Yellow rattle, 64
— waterlily, 376
Yellow-rocket (*Barbarea vulgaris*), 361
Yerba delpescado (*Croton setigerus*), 84
Yerbas nocivas, 2
Yew, 443
Yucca, 148, 166
— *angustifolia*, 148
Yugoslavia, 350, 351
Yuki Indians, 57

Zannichellia palustris, 374
Zea mays, 165, 180
Zeitschrift fur Pflanzenkrankheiten, xxiv, 31
Zinc absorption by weeds, 173
— deficiency, white bud, 174
— contents of weeds, 247
— sulphate, 174
Zinnia, 10
Zizania, 357
Ziziphus (jujube fruit tree), 58
Zobar, 447
Zoochory, 16
Zoysia, 10
Zygophyllaceae, 132
Zygophyllum dumosum, 183
Zytron, (*O*-(2,4-dichlorphenyl)-*O*-methylisopropyl-phosphoramidothioate), 380, 452

AUTHOR INDEX

Aamisepp, A., 254
Aamodt, O. S., 107, 154, 192
Aase, H. C., 241
Abel, A. L., 238, 307
Åberg, E., xxx, 337, 341
Abrams, G. J. von. *see* Von Abrams, G. J.
Achey, D. M., 69
Adachi, A., 203, 225
Adams, R., 205, 420
Adams, R. C., 276
Addicott, F. T., 342, 384
Addy, S. K., 69
'Agadzhanian, G. K., 384
Agarwala, S. B. D., 66, 69
Agati, J. A., 62, 69
Agnew, A. D. Q., 259
Agogino, G. A., 13, 24, 154
Ahlgren, G. H., 384
Akamine, E. K., 284-5, 307
Akhurst, C. G., 384
Albertson, F. W., 276
Alcala, R. P., xxx
Aldrich, K. F., 393
Aleksandrov, F., 51, 69
Alex, J. F., 221
Alexander, M., 339
Alexander, W. B.,
Aliev, A., 384
Allan, H. H., 276
Allard, H. A., Pl. 10, 188-9, 192, 195
Allen, E. F., 420
Allen, H. P., 384
Allen, R. M., 394
Allen, W. W., 308, 315
Alley, H. P., 365-6, 385, 400
Allison, D. V., 420
Allsopp, W. H. L., 418, 420
Almod, F. L., 420
Alpatov, V. V., 420
Altstatt, G. E., 107
Amen, R. D., 127-8, 154
Ames, O., 85-86, 88, 276
Amm, M., 276
Amundsen, R. F., 397
Anderson, D. B., 326, 341
Anderson, D. T., 347
Anderson, E., xxx, 17-19, 20, 24, 32, 46, 230-2, 234, 235, 238, 239
Anderson, L. E., 401
Andreae, W. A., 334, 341
Andreeva-Fetvadzhieva, N., 385
Andrews, F. M., xxx
Andrews, F. W., 69, 392
Andrews, S. R., 69
Andrus, M., 417, 420
Angell, G. N., 417, 420
Anić, M., 61, 69

Anon (1954), 14
Anstead, R. I., 44, 46
Anzalone, B., 42, 46
Appleton, A. A., 308
Arai, M., 408, 421
Arashi, K., 192
Arber, Agnes, 46
Archer, W. A., 80, 90
Archibald, E. E. A., 276
Archibold, E. S., 424
Ardissone, F., 276
Arend, J. L., 385
Armstrong, S. F., 254
Arndt, F., xxx, xxvii
Arnold, H. C., 254
Arnold, K., 421
Arnott, D. A., 431
Arny, A. C., 192
Arthur, J. M., 187, 192
Artist, R. C., 169, 192
Aslander, A., 192
Atkeson, F. W., 154
Atkins, E. S., 385
Atkins, W. R. G., 192
Atta, B. M., 282
Audus, L. J., 284, 296, 308, 311, 336, 341, 344, 348, 382, 383
Atwood, A. C., xvii, 27
Aufhammer, G., 276
av Segerstad, F. Hård. *See* Hård av Segerstad, F.
Ayyar, T. V. Ramakrishna. *See* Ramakrishna Ayyar, T. V.
Azzi, G., 276

Babcock, E. B., 234
Bach, M. F., 334, 336
Bachelard, H. S., 107
Bachthaler, G., 437
Badianus, J., xxix
Badwar, B. L., 108
Bailey, E. H. S., 192
Bailey, E. Z., 7, 25
Bailey, I. W., 200, 225
Bailey, L. F., 157
Bailey, L. H., 7, 10, 25
Bailey, V., 107
Bailey, W. W., 25
Baird, A. B., 421
Baird, G., 93, 112
Bait, J., 201
Baker, H. G., 226, 234
Baker, K. F., 50, 69
Baker, R. G. Sanzen. *See* Sanzen-Baker, R. G.
Bakke, A. L., 181, 192, 221, 254
Balachowsky, A., 421

504

Balbach, P., 432
Balcom, R. B., 254, 373, 385
Baldrati, I., 69
Ball, C. D., 109, 313
Ball, N. G., 297, 336, 341
Ball, R. W. E., 343
Ballard, L. A. T., 221
Bamber, M. K., 419, 421
Bancroft, L., 107
Bandurski, R. S., 308
Banfield, G. L., 385
Baranek, P., 385
Baranov, M. S., 385
Barbat, I., 311
Barber, H. N., 274, 275, 276
Barber, Y. M., 385
Barber, M., 385
Barger, G., 92, 107
Barker, E. P., 347
Barkley, W., 429
Barnard, R. C., 421
Barnes, B., 54, 69
Barnes, E., 64, 69
Barnes, J. M., 301, 308
Barnes, S., 192
Barnes, T. W., 256, 257
Barnette, R. M., 199
Barr, C. G., 192
Barr, H. T., 421
Barrau, J., 276
Barrons, K. C., 292, 308, 385
Bartlett, G. C., 409, 421
Bartlett, H. H., 419, 421
Bartlett, S., 421
Bartley, C., 308
Bartley, T. R., 308
Barton, Lela V., xxvii, 125, 126, 127, 130, 140, 1433, 144, 154, 156, 254
Basinski, J. J., 69
Baskakov, J. A., 284, 311, 345
Bass, S. T., 313
Bateman, Mary Ruth, xxvii
Baten, W. D., 234
Bates, G. H., 336
Bates, J. M., 277
Bateson, A., 221
Bauer, J., 177, 192
Beadle, N. C. W., 125, 154
Beal, J. M., xxvi
Beal, W. J., 6, 129, 154, 192, 221, 286, 308, 421
Bear, F. E., 249, 254
Beath, O. A., 107, 179
Beatty, R. H., 269, 235, 336, 349–50, 385
Beauverie, M. A. Reynaud-. See Reynaud-Beauverie, M. A.
Beck von Mannagetta, G., 61, 62, 70
Becker, H., 221
Becking, R. W., 260, 277
Bedevian, A. K., xviii, 25
Bedford, Duke of, 257
Bedsole, M. R., 192
Beeson, C. F. G., 421
Beetle, A. A., 80, 88
Begue, H., 346
Beimler, R., 337, 348
Belkov, V. P., 385

Bell, A. F., 70
Bell, R. S., 259
Belling, J., 234
Bellini, P., 221
Bellue, Margaret K., 421
Belozerov, P. I., 277
Benedict, H. M., 254
Benjamin, M. S., 421
Bennet, C. W., 108
Bennett, E., 80, 88, 193
Bennett, J. M., 385
Bennetts, H. W., 109
Ber, W., 421
Bercaw, Louise O., xxx
Berezovskii, M. A., 308
Berg, R. Y., 218, 219, 221
Bergeson, E. D., 385
Bernard, R. H., 313
Bernard-Smith, A., 107
Bernhard, M. O., 13, 25
Bernström, P., 234
Berthy, H. P., 386
Bess, H. A., 421
Bessey, C. E., 88
Bewlay, E. W., 420
Bews, J. W., 277
Beyer, R., 46
Beyerinek, W., 425
Beztuzheva, A. A., 160
Bharadwaja, R. C., 277
Bhardwaj, R. B., 400
Bharucha, F. R., 177, 193
Bhuvaneswari, K., 254
Bianchi, D. E., 88, 100, 107
Bianchi, Marissa, xxvii
Bibbey, R. O., 154
Bickley, W. E., 385
Bijl, P. A. van der. See van der Bijl, P. A.
Bilfrey, K., 417, 421
Billings, W. D., 124, 154, 174, 193, 277
Bills, R. W., 107
Bingham, M. T., 277
Birch, W. R., 221
Biriukova, V. S., 399
Birkaia, A. F., 385
Bisset, W. J., 277
Biswas, K., 422
Bizzell, J. A., 176, 197
Black, W. L., 107
Blackman, G. E., xxx, 150, 154, 254, 277, 284, 291, 336
Blackman, G. F., 310
Blair, B. E., 336
Blair, B. O., 277
Blaisdell, J. P., 277, 422
Blake, A. K., 154
Blake, S. F., xvii, 25
Blakeslee, A. F., 88, 234
Blanchard, J. R., 27
Blanchard, M., 70
Blanck, A., 394
Blanck, F. C., 345
Blanco, D. T., 423
Blaser, R. E., 150, 154, 254, 277
Blaxter, K. L., 421
Bleasdale, J. K. A., 254
Blin, H., 70

Blinn, A., 80, 88
Blohm, H., 107
Blom, C., 27
Blommaert, K. L. J., 193
Blondeau, R., 289-90, 346, 395
Blum, A., 213, 212, 277
Blunton, F. S., 108
Boalch, D. H., xxx
Boas, F., 27
Böcher, T. W., 193, 234, 277
Bode, H. R., 251, 254
Bodenheimer, F. S., 422
Boerner, E. G., 225
Boeshore, I., 70
Boewig, H., 70
Boggi, A., 417, 422
Bohme, L., 342
Bohmont, D. W., 107, 170, 193, 400
Bokarev, K. S., 345
Bolar, M. D., 385
Bolley, H. L., 221, 285, 308
Bollow, H., 415, 422
Bolton, J. L., 193
Bonavia, E., 27
Bondarenko, D. D., 302, 308, 386
Bondur, A. I., 386
Böning, K. 415, 422
Bonner, J., 248-9, 251, 252, 254, 256, 308
Bonnet, M., 284
Boodle, L. A., 53, 70
Booth, W. E., 193
Borden, R. J., 422
Borell, A. E., 422
Boriss, H., 154
Börner, H., xxvii, pls. 13, 14, 65, 248, 250-52, 255
Borriel, M., 234
Borthwick, H. A., 141, 155, 160
Bos, J. R., 255
Bosemark, N. O., 234
Boswell, H. H., 200
Boterenbrood, A. J., 166, 277
Botha, P. J., 64, 70
Bottum, F. R., 221
Boughton, I. B., 107
Bouillenne, R., 51
Bouillenne-Walrand, M., 51
Bourgin, R., xxx
Bouriquet, G., 70
Bowden, W. M., 234
Bowen, M. S., 386
Bowen-Jones, J., 255
Bowler, E., 347
Bowman, I., 193
Boyer, B. B., 386
Boyko, H., 221, 277
Boynton, M. F., 221
Boysen-Jensen, P., 285, 342
Bracey, P., 299, 386
Bradbeer, J. W., 155
Bradley, W. B., 179, 193, 255
Bradshaw, A. D., 228, 234
Brady, N. C., 254
Brain, C. K., 64, 70
Bragg, K. K., 386
Bramble, W. C., 386
Brandenburg, M. K., 296, 308

Brandes, E. W., 107
Brandhorst, C. T., 422
Bratley, H. E., 108
Braun, H., 422
Braun-Blanquet, J., 277
Brenchley, W. E., 6, 27, 88, 155, 255, 277, 422
Brendel, F., 27
Bresaloa, M., 70
Brewer, L., 88
Breyer-Brandwijk, M. G., 92, 113
Brian, P. W., 301, 308
Brian, R. C., 288, 308
Briggs, L. J., 180, 193
Brod, F., 416, 422
Brodie, D. A., 27
Brodie, H. J., 221
Brookins, W. W., 386
Brooks, Bettie M., xxviii
Brooks, F. A., 322, 342
Brooks, F. T., 70
Brouwer, W., 27
Brown, B. A., 422
Brown, D., 193
Brown, D. E., 197
Brown, E. C., 155
Brown, H. L., 277
Brown, J. W., 286, 311
Brown, K., 70
Brues, C. T., 105, 108
Bruhn, W. C., xxx
Brun-Hool, J., 437
Bruns, V. F., 155, 373, 386, 391
Brunskill, R. T., 319, 342, 346
Buchholtz, K. P., xxx, 256, 386, 396
Buchli, M., 170, 173, 193, 277
Buckland, D. C., 70
Buckley, T. A., 386
Budd, A. C., 128, 155
Buell, M. F., 200
Bugbee, R. E., 422
Bull, H., 386
Bullock, A. A., 108
Bünning, E., 128, 155
Bunting, A. L., 6
Bunting, L., 422
Burcham, L. T., 421
Burchard, O., 422
Burg, F. W. Zur. See Zur Burg, F. W.
Burger, A. A., 419, 422
Burnham, C. R., 155
Burns, G. P., 422
Burns, P. Y., 368, 396
Bussard, A., 155
Busse, W. F., 155
Butts, J. S., 333-4, 336, 342, 343
Buxton, P. A., 108
Buzacott, J. H., 277, 419, 422
Bychkova, Z., 386
Byrnes, W. R., 386, 394

Cabezon, A. Garcia. See Garcia Cabezon, A.
Cable, D. R., 422
Cacciato, A., xviii, 27
Cady, E. R., 88
Caho, T. T., 387
Cain, S. A., 278, 279

Calderbank, A., 437
Call, L. E., 193
Camargo, R. de, 255
Cameron, E., 411, 422
Cameron, F. K., 258
Campbell, E. G., 82, 88, 178, 193
Campbell, E. M., 6, 7, 27
Campbell, H. W., 108
Campbell, R. S., 386, 396
Campbell, T. G., 436
Cannon, Helen, L., 167, 193, 278
Cannon, J. L., 247
Cannon, W. A., 49, 53, 70, 74, 163-5, 193
Cantwell, L. R., 113
Capitaines, L., 422
Carlson, A. E., 386, 434
Carlson, R. F., 312, 360, 386
Carn, K. G., 221
Carns, H. R., 342, 384
Carpenter, C. W., 422
Carr, P. H., 325-6, 345
Carre, A., 64, 70
Carsner, E., 431
Carson, Rachel, 384, 386
Carter, A. S., 422, 432
Carter, H. H., 417, 421
Carter, W., 108
Carvell, K. L., 308, 386
Carvell, R. L., 41, 46
Cashmore, A. B., 430
Cassady, J. T., 278
Cates, J. S., 200, 282, 419, 423
Cathey, H. M., 383, 387
Chabrolin, C., xxx, 60, 70
Chacko, P. I., 387
Chaiken, L. E., 387
Chalam, G. V., 433
Champness, S. S., 129, 155
Chancellor, A. P., 387
Chancellor, R. J., 222, 371, 389
Chaney, R. W., 130, 155
Chang, xxix
Chapman, J. H., 166, 171, 193
Chapman, V. J., 171, 193
Chater, E. H., 423
Chatin, A., 70
Chatterjee, D., 234
Cheadle, J. N., 158
Cheel, E., 27
Chemin, E., 70
Chepil, W. S., 155
Chernyshova, N. N., 400
Chesalin, G. A., 387
Chestnut, V. K., 80, 83, 88
Chevalier, A., 27, 70, 108
Chilcote, D. O., 391
Childe, V. G., 27
Childress, D. L., 423
Chilton, S. J. P., 398
Chippendale, H. G., 128, 155
Chitwood, H. C., xxvii
Chmora, S., 387
Chodat, F., 193
Chopra, I. C., 82, 88
Chopra, R. N., 82, 88, 108
Chouard, P., xxx, 193
Chow, N. P., 387

Chowdhury, K. A., 13, 25
Chrastil, J., 262, 257
Christiansen, A. M., 346
Christensen, E. M., 278
Christie, J. K., 108
Chu, H. J., 109
Church, T. W., 387
Churchill, B. R., 155, 400
Cifferri, O., 50, 71, 387
Cifferri, R., xxx
Claassen, P. W., 80, 88
Clare, K. E., 387
Clark, A. F., 429
Clark, L. R., 423
Clark, N., 423
Clark, O. R., 185, 193
Clausen, J., 233, 234
Claypole, A., 221
Claypole, E. W., 14, 25
Clegg, H., 92, 112
Clements, F. E., 278
Clendenin, I., 108
Clifford, H. T., 221
Clinch, F. A., 26
Clor, M. A., 308
Clothier, G. L., 223
Clute, W. N., 221
Coban, R., 26
Cobb, G. S., 108
Cocannouer, J. A., 82, 88
Cockayne, A. H., 416, 423
Cockerell, T. D. A., 423
Cocucci, A., 407
Coert, J. H., 71
Coffee, D. R., 343
Coffman, F. A., 160
Colby, W. G., 201, 244-6, 258
Cole, H. E., 193
Coleman, F., 423
Coleman, P. G., 387
Colledge, E., 437
Collinge, W. E., 221
Collins, W., Jr, 423
Condit, I. J., 52, 71
Conrad, P. F., 397
Constable, D. H., 387
Contesse, J. Peter-. See Peter-Contesse, J.
Cook, C. W., 423
Cook, H. H., 194
Cook, J. B., 220-1
Cook, L., 423
Cook, M. T., 108
Cook,, W. H., 309
Cooke, A. R., 309
Cooley, J. S., 108
Coombe, D., 264, 267, 278
Cooper, J. P., 278
Cooper, W. E. Shewell-. See Shewell-Cooper, W. E.
Cooper, W. S., 194
Copeland, E. B., 278
Corbet, A. S., 108
Cords, H. P., 364, 396, 432
Cornelius, D. R., 387
Corner, E. J. H., 278, 423
Cory, E. N., 385
Costa, A. S., 108

Costello, D. F., 79, 88, 221, 435
Costello, E. F., 423
Coster, C., 387
Cotta, A., 387
Cottam, C., 278
Cottam, G., 251, 255
Cottrell-Dormer, W., 70
Couchman, N. R. Fuggles-. *See* Fuggles-Couchman, N. R.
Coulter, J. M., xxvi
Coulter, L. L., 387
Coupland, R. T., 200, 221, 259, 387
Cox, G. E., 277
Coyle, May, xxviii
Cozzi, C., 46
Crafts, A. S., xxx, 284, 287, 291-2, 308, 309, 312, 329-30, 342, 346, 351, 383, 387
Craig, A. L., 398
Crescini, F., 221
Cressler, L., 278
Crocker, W., xxvi, xxvii, 26, 122-7, 130, 140, 143, 154, 156, 285, 309
Croizat, L., xxx
Croker, B. H., 309
Crooks, D. M., 46
Crossan, D. F., 108
Crossley, D. I., 388
Crossman, L., 108
Crovetto, R. M., xxx
Crowdy, S. H., 327-8, 332, 342, 437
Cruz, S. R., 423
Cruzado, H. J., 311
Cumming, B. G., 191, 194
Cunningham, G. H., 423
Cunningham, J. C., 194
Curé, P., 194
Currie, G. A., 423
Currier, H. B., 289, 309, 342
Curtis, J. T., 108, 251, 255
Curtis, L. E., 315, 347
Curtis, R. S., 113
Cutler, H. G., xxvii, pl. 19(a,b), 329
Cutler, W. A., 396
Curtis, R. W., 194

Dabney, T. E., 423
Dadd, C. V., 388, 423
Dahlgren, B. E., 108
Dahlstedt, H., 194
Dammer, W., 278
Danger, L., 71
Danhoff, G. N., 388
Daniel, H. A., 194
Daniel, H. R., 390
Daniels, L. B., 423
Danielson, L. L., 349, 352, 361, 372-4, 378, 381, 388, 393, 397, 437
Dannfelt, H. Julien-. *See* Julien-Dannfelt, H.
Danser, B. H., 57, 71
Dansereau, P., xxx, 123, 159, 214, 215, 221, 241, 266, 278, 279
Darby, G. H., xxxii
Darland, R. W., 283
Darling, L., 53, 71
Darlington, C. D., 22-23, 26, 226, 232, 234, 237, 301, 309

Darlington, H. T., 129, 156, 222
Darrow, R. A., xxx, 388, 398
Darwin, C., 24, 151
Das, A., 57, 73
Das, K., 282, 433
Daskevic, B. N., 108
Datta, R. M., 54, 71
Daubenmire, R. F., 278
David, A. L., 423
David, W. A. L., 222
Davidson, A., 66, 71
Davies, M. E., 348
Davies, W., 388
Davenport, D., xxvi
Davis, A. E. Sanger-. *See* Sanger-Davis, A. E.
Davis, E. F., 252, 255
Davis, F. F., 286, 311
Davis, J. C., 345
Davis, W., 81, 88
Davis, W. E., 124, 126, 156
Dawson, G. W. P., 278
Day, B. E., 388, 309
Day, M. W., 388
Dayton, W. A., 26
DeBach, P., 415, 423
de Camargo, R. *See* Camargo, R. de
De Fato, Joan, xxvii
DeFrance, J. A., 423
de Haan, J. T. *See* Haan, J. T. de
de la Cruz, M., xxix
De Laszlo, H. & Henshaw, P. S. *See* Laszlo, H. De & Henshaw, P. S.
De Peralta, 151
de Peralta, F. *See* Peralta, F. de
DeRose, H. R., 312
De Silva, B. L. T., 194
De Siqueira-Jaçcoud, R. J., 104, 108
de Wildeman, É. *See* Wildeman, É. de
De Vael, W. B., 194
de Vries, D. A., 194
de Vries, D. M., 194, 293
de Vries, O., 194
de Wet, J. M. J., 6, 34, 48
del Gindice, E. *See* Gindice, E. del
Deam, C. C., 209
Dean, H. L., 49, 71
Deatrick, E. P., 388
Decary, R., 423
Defrance, J. A., 388
Degen, A. von, 424
Delouche, J. C., 156
Demiriz, H., xxx
Denfer, D. von. *See* von Denfer, D.
Denisen, E. L., 388
Densmore, F., 80, 88
Dent, T. V., 424
Derkea, W. L., 194
Dersal, W. R. van, 278
Deshpande, V. C., 424
Desmond, Anabelle, 388
Deterre, J., 424
Dewey, L. H., 26, 222
Dexter, S. T., 186, 194
Dice, J. R., 108, 109
Dickerson, L. M., 388
Dieffenbach, E. M., 424
Dietz, S. M., 388

Diglio, A. P. L., 277
Dillman, A. C., 180, 194
Dingle, A. N., 114
Dittmer, H. J., 194
Dioscorides, P., xxviii, pl. 1.
Dirven, J. G. P., 194
Divekar, M. V., 388
Dmitriev, V. A., 240
Dobzhansky, T., 40, 46
Dodd, A. P., xxx, 413, 415, 424
Dodswell, H. E., 275, 276
Doi, Y., 167, 194
Donald, C. M., 255, 437
Donselaar, J. van, 277
Donselaar-Ten Bokkel Huinink, W. E. A. van, 277
Dony, J. G., 222
Doolitle, S. P., 108
Dootjes, E., 388
Dore, W. G., 156
Dorph-Peterson, K., 156
Doughty, J. L., 155
Doull, K. M., 424
Douros, J. D., 342
Dow, R., 53, 71
Dowding, E. S., 55-7, 71
Dox, A. W., 430
Dozier, H. L., 391
Drake, M., 201, 244-6, 258
Drasher, M. L., 81, 88
Dreesen, J., x, 26
Drever, H. R., 309
Drotty, S., 424
Druce, G. C., 16, 27
Du Rietz, G. E. See Rietz, G. E. Du.
du Sablon, M. Leclerc. See Leclerc du Sablon, M.
DuToit, R., 255, 424
Du Toit, E., 424
Dubash, P. J., 193
Duchesne, E. A., xx, 26
Dudgeon, W., 46
Dumbleton, L. J., 429
Duncan, J. F., 194
Duncan, W. H., 194
Dunford, E. G., 194
Dunham, R. S., 419, 432
Dunn, M. S., xxxii
Dunn, S. T., 4, 26
Duperrex, A., 26
Durham, E., 71
Durrell, L. C., 108
Dustin, A., 394
Duthrie, E. C., 392
Duvel, J. T., 129
Dyke, I. J., 297, 336, 341
Dykstra, T. P., 108
Dymond, J. R., 424

Earle, T. T., 374, 391
Earnshaw, F., 233, 240
Eaton, M. E. D., 388
Eaton, R. J., 53, 71
Eaton, S. V., xxvi
Ebbell, B., 26
Eberhardt, C. H., 278

Eberhardt, F., 252, 255
Eberle, G., 201
Eddy, C. O., 400
Edelmann, C. H., 194
Edwards, D. C., 250, 424
Edwards, M., 70
Edwards, Phyllis, xxx
Eeuwens, B. E. P., 194
Eggebrecht, H., 388, 399
Eggeling, W. J., 44, 46
Eggink, H. J., 424
Egginton, G. E., 218, 222, 388, 424
Eggler, W. A., 388
Egler, F. E., 278, 384, 388, 411, 424, 430
Ehrenberg, P., 156
Eichinger, A., 194
Eichhorn, J. A. F., 38
Eklund, O., 156
Elam, F. L., 424
Elford, F. C., 424
Ellenberg, H., 131, 142, 156, 170, 173, 194, 222, 264-5, 267, 278
Elliott, F. C., 424
Ellis, D. E., 57, 71
Ellis, H., 424
Ellis, M. M., 388
Elmendorf, H. B., 184-5, 195
Elton, C. S., 201
Emanuelli, A., 387
Emerson, R. W., 7
Emmart, Emily, xxix, pl. 6(b)
Engelbrecht, H., 237, 240
Engler, A., 13, 26
Ennis, W. B., Jr., xxx, 67, 74, 243, 255, 316, 318-19, 323, 342, 352, 355, 361, 372-4, 378, 381, 388, 393, 397, 437
Everist, S. L., xxx
Felföldy, L. J. M., 195, 222
Eppson, H. F., 179, 255
Erickson, E. C., 394
Erickson, L. C., 108
Erisman, A., 88
Erxleben, H., 344
Es, L. van. See van Es, L.
Esau, K., 194
Espino, R. B., 71
Etter, A. G., 222
Evanari, M., 125, 156, 248, 255
Evans, F. C., 278, 279
Evans, J. W., 411, 424, 425
Evans, M. W., 195
Evans, R. J., 160
Evans, S., 388
Everhart, M., 388
Everson, L. E., 156, 425
Exer, B., 342

Fabian, I., 195
Fabre, R., 342
Fail, H., 425
Farmer, W. H., 386
Fang, S. C., 333-4, 336, 342
Fang, F. C., 343
Farquhar, H. H., 71
Farrar, M. E., 81, 90
Farrer, R. P., 389

Fassett, N. C., 46, 389
Faulks, P. J., 85–6, 88
Fauré, G. O., 415, 435
Fawcett, C. H., 309
Fawcett, H. S., 156
Fedtschenko, B. A., 116, 132, 133, 145, 146, 152, 158
Feinhandler, S., 154
Fellig, J., 334, 336
Fenner, R. L., 421
Fenton, E. W., 109, 192
Ferdinandsen, C., 195
Fernald, M. L., 222
Ferrarini, E., 279
Ferri, M. G., xxx
Fertig, S. N., 389
Fetherston, Mary B., xxviii
Fetvadzhieva, N. Andreeva-. See Andreeva-Fetvadzhieva, N.
Filipiev, I. N., 109
Finn, T. P., xxx, 299, 310
Finney, G. M., 400
Finnerty, D. W., 222, 259
Fischer, H., 26
Fischnich, O., 343
Fisher, C. E. C., 57, 71, 367, 389
Fiske, J. G., 26
Fitch, J. B., 161
Fitzpatrick, H. M., 111
Fitzpatrick, T. J., 202
Flahault, C., 26
Flanagan, T. R., 294, 309
Flay, A. H., 425
Fletcher, A. H., 113
Fletcher, F., 255
Fletcher, H. C., 184–5, 195
Fletcher, P. W., 194
Flint, L. H., 124, 141, 156
Flournoy, R. E., 436
Floyd, V. M., 123, 155
Fogg, J. M., Jr., 273, 279
Fogg, G. E., 290, 309, 320, 343
Foote, M. W., 89
Forbes, R. D., 389
Forster, R., 389
Fox, H. M., 80, 89
Foy, C. L., 342
Franca, C., 109
François, L., 222
Franchini, G., 109
Frank, P. A., 109
Franklin, M. T., 109
Frankton, C., xxx, 200, 204, 222, 227, 241, 243, 254
Franz, J., 425
Frazier, Sir J. G., 86, 89
Frazier, J. C., 195, 389
Frazier, N. W., 109
Frear, D. E. H., xxii, 26
Frederick, A., 28, 223
Frederiksen, H., 343, 327, 351, 389
Freed, V. H., 291, 309, 343, 383, 389
Freeland, R. O., 53, 71
Freeman, E. M., 109
French, G. T., 50, 76
Frey-Wyssling, A., 252, 325, 343
Friesen, H. A., 425

Fritsché, Emma, 51, 71
Frödin, J., 195
Fröst, S., 240
Fryer, J. D., 389
Fryer, J. R., 156
Fryer, M. A., 222
Fryzell, P. A., 222
Fuelleman, R. F., 195, 389
Fuggles-Couchman, N. R., 64, 72
Fukai, G., 80, 89
Fullaway, D. T., 425
Funaioli, A., 195
Funke, G. L., 251–2, 255
Furbush, P. B., 409, 425
Furtick, W. O., 386
Fyfe, R. V., 423, 425

Gaertner, E. E., 72, 425
Gaessler, W. G., 192
Gail, O. E., 199
Gage, 234
Gajic, A., 259
Galil, J., 167, 195
Gallup, A. H., 345
Gallwitz, W., 343
Galston, A. W., 252, 254, 294, 297, 309
Galvimans, E. J. H., 194
Gammon, C., 41, 48
Gams, H., 46
Gancedo, A. P., Garcia. See Garcia Gancedo, A. P.
Ganguli, P. M., 241
Gankin, Olga H., 90
Garcia Cabezon, A., 389
Garcia Gancedo, A. P., 389
Gardiner, Sir A., 1, 26
Gardner, C. A., 109
Gardner, T. R., 425
Garman, H., 62, 72
Garmendia, J. Ortiz. See Ortiz Garmendia, J.
Garner, M. R., xxvi
Garner, W. W., 197
Garrard, A., 156
Garth, R. E., 43, 46
Garthside, S., 423
Gates, F. C., 34, 46, 222, 425
Gäumann, E., xxx
Gay, P. A., 259, 389
Genelly, R., 396
Genkel, P. A., 182, 195
Gentner, W. A., 292, 312, 355, 389, 397
George, J. L., 389
Georgia, A. E., 26
Gerth van Wijk, K. L., xviii, 26
Gervasi, A., 416, 425
Geshele, E. E., 343
Gessner, F., 44, 46
Geyer, J. W., 425
Geysenheyner, L., 46
Gharabaghy, V., 389
Ghikalov, S., 72
Ghosh, S., 13, 27, 108
Gianfagna, A. J., 156
Gibson, A., 425
Gidon, F., 18, 26
Gilbert, B. E., 170, 195

Gilbert, C. S., 195
Giliarov, M. S., 63, 72
Gilkey, Helen M., 3
Gill, L. S., xxx, 54, 72
Gill, N. T., 156
Gillot, X., 26
Gilmore, A. E., 251, 257
Gimingham, C. H., 79, 90, 191, 195, 279
Gindice, E. del, 72
Girsch, A., 425
Glass, E. H., 46
Glastonbury, H. A., 334, 343
Gleason, H. A., xviii, 27, 222
Glendening, G. E., 336
Glimcher, J., 53, 72
Glock, W. S., 195
Godel, G. L., 255
Godfrey, R. K., 112
Godwin, H., 31
Goedewaagen, M. A. J., 170, 195
Goenaga, A., xxvii
Goetze, N., 389
Goiko, A., 72
Golitsyn, S. V., 27
Gonggripj, J., 391
Gonzales, A. J., 389
Gonzales, R. Sosa. See Sosa Gonzales, R.
Good, N. E., 334, 341
Good, R., xxiv, 14, 27, 240, 279
Goodall, D. W., 279
Goodey, J. B., 109
Goodey, T., 109
Goodrum, P. D., 389
Goodyer, J., xxix
Goodwin, R. H., 251, 255, 411, 425
Goor, C. P. van, 389
Goor, G. A. W. van der, 343
Göppert, A. M., 186, 195
Gordon, J. G., 79, 90
Gordon, S. A., 296, 309
Gorter, C. J., 390
Goseco, F., 61, 74
Goss, W. L., 127, 156
Gotaas, H. B., 343
Gourley, J. H., 176, 195
Graber, L. F., 195, 389
Grace, N. H., 81, 89
Grah, R. F., 421
Graham, T. W., 109
Grandfield, C. O., 425
Grano, C. X., 390
Grant, C., 108
Grant, W. F., 240
Graser, H. I., 72, 55
Grassi, M. M., 277
Grau, F. V., 390
Gray, A., 7, 14, 27
Gray, A. P., 255
Gray, R., 252, 256
Green, G. J., 110
Green, K. R., xxx
Greenham, C. G., 343, 381, 390
Greeley, J. R., 390
Gregor, J. W., 233, 234, 240
Gregor, M. J. F., 416, 426
Gregory, P. H., 109
Gregory, Winifred, xxiii, 27

Greig-Smith, P., 279
Greiss, E. A. M., 13, 27
Gressel, J. B., 259
Grieg, J. L., 390
Grieve, B. J., 296, 343
Griffith, W. A., 150, 154, 254, 277
Grigsby, B. H., 109
Grof, B., 72
Groh, H., 46
Grøntved, P., 351, 389
Groot, P. van der, 426
Grosse-Brauckmann, G., 279
Grümmer, G., 248, 251, 256, 259
Grundy, W. M., 399
Gudnason, A., 390
Gudzhabidze, N., 385
Guiljónsson, G., 242
Gunckel, J. E., 296, 343
Gunther, R. T., xxiv, 4, 27
Guppy, H. B., 220, 222, 274, 276, 279
Gustafson, F. G., 195
Gustafsson, Å., 229, 240
Gustafsson, M., 343
Gutenmann, W. H., 437
Guyot, L., 256
Guzman, V. L., 390
Gwirtsman, J. W., xxvii
Gysin, H., 291, 309

Haagen-Smit, A. J., 344
Haan, J. T. de, 59, 72
Haas, T. P., 195
Haasis, F. W., 195
Haccius, B., 343
Hackett, D. P., 390
Hagedorn, H., xxvi, 27
Haider, Z., 66, 69
Haig, I. T., 390
Haines, A., 390
Håkansson, S., 259
Halferdahl, A. C., 284, 309
Hall, C. W., 390
Hall, Elizabeth C., xxiv
Hall, H. M., 234
Hall, T. F., 109, 279, 366-7, 390
Haller, H. L., xx, 27
Halliday, D. J., 336
Halpern, K., 156
Halsted, B. D., 195, 222, 256
Hambler, D. J., 72
Hamblyn, C. J., 416, 426
Hamel, A., 266, 279
Hamilton, K. C., 250, 256
Hamilton, L. S., 390
Hamlin, J. C., 426
Hamm, P. C., 309
Hamner, K. C., xxvi, 347
Hamner, C. L., 286, 302, 309, 310, 312, 313, 345, 347
Hammerton, J. L., 259
Hand, M. E., 161
Hanf, M., xxx, 131, 138, 140, 149, 157, 195, 279, 310
Hanna, L. W., 343
Hannfelt, M. Juhlin, 392
Hansch, C. H., 311, 345

Hansen, A. A., 256, 390
Hansen, H. M., 46
Hansen, J., 54, 72
Hanson, H. C., 109, 278
Hanson, N. S., 238, 390
Hanssen, J., 72
Hanzawa, M., 5, 6, 27
Haq, A., 390
Hara, H., 240
Haramoto, F. H., 421
Hardy, E. A., 195, 426
Hardy, M., 279
Hardy, W. T., 107
Harenbeni, A., 53, 72
Harger, E. M., 394
Harlan, J. L., 6, 34, 48
Harmon, G. W., 157, 222
Haro, S., 358, 392
Harper, H. J., 196, 390
Harper, H. L., 247
Harper, J. L., 127, 152, 157, 225, 235, 238,
    240, 257, 258, 259, 267
Harper, R. L., xxx
Harper, R. M., 7, 14, 27, 46
Harrar, G. J., 112
Harrington, H. D., 47
Harrington, J. B., 257, 426
Harris, B. C., 89
Harris, J. A., 53, 72
Harris, M. R., 109
Harris, P., 415, 426
Harrison, C. J., 53, 72
Harrison, D. S., 398
Hart, G. H., 426
Härtel, O., 72
Hartley, C. W. S., 426
Hartley, G. S., 340, 343, 346
Hartley, W., 240
Harvey, A. D., 222
Harvey, R. B., 109, 196
Harvey, W. A., 284, 309, 342, 394
Harvill, E. K., 192
Harz, C. O., 426
Hash, T. R., 417, 426
Haskell, G., 152, 157, 239, 240
Hatfield, H., Jr., xxviii
Hattingh, I. D., 65, 66, 72, 74, 259
Haudricourt, A. G., 46
Hauman-Merck, L., 72
Hausrath, H.,
Havis, J. R., 310
Hawkes, C. L., 390
Hawksworth, F. S., 56, 71
Hay, J. R., 310
Haymaker, J. W., 301, 309
Haynes, D. W., 387
Häyren, E., 47
Hayward, J. M., 16, 27
Heald, F. D., 50, 72, 428
Healy, A. J., xxx, 220, 222
Hedgecock, G. G., 61, 73
Hédin, L., 47, 279
Heer, O., 11, 27
Hefer, S. R., 73
Hegi, G., 34, 47
Hegner, R., 109
Heim, R., 222

Hein, Alice, 109
Heinen, W., 338, 344
Heinricher, E., 53, 73
Heintze, S. G., 277
Heinze A., 222
Heinze, K., 428
Heiser, C. B., Jr., 232, 240
Helbaek, H., 4, 11, 27, 28, 31
Heldreich, T., 17, 27
Helgeson, E. A., xxi, Pl. 21, 27, 157, 256, 310,
    356–8, 382, 390, 391, 428
Hellwig, F., 27
Helqvist, H., 320–3, 343
Helson, V. A., 289, 345
Hemming, H. G., 308
Hendricks, J. R., 80, 90
Hendricks, S. B., 141, 155, 160
Hendriks, J. A. H., 194
Hendry, G. W., 13, 27
Henkel, A., 81, 89
Henry, A. W., 111
Henshaw, P. S., 81–2, 89
Henslow, G., 62, 73, 223
Herbert, D. A., 40, 47, 73
Herbert, R. A., 303, 310
Hermann, G., 240
Hes, J. W., 391
Heslot, M., xxx
Hess, A. D., 109
Hessler, R., 47
Hewetson, F. N., 41, 47
Hewitt, R., 110
Heydecker, W., 131, 157
Heyne, M., 4
Hickman, K. V., 391
Hiesey, W. M., 234
Hildebrand, F., 223
Hill, E. J., 223
Hill, K. L., 291–2, 311
Hill, R., 291
Hilli, A., 428
Hille, F. J. H. van, 256
Hills, J. L., 428
Hiltner, L., 80, 89
Hilton, J. L., 293, 298, 302, 310
Hinds, T. E., xxx
Hinke, F., 110
Hirata, M., 358, 392
Hirmer, M., 28
Hitchcock, A. E., xxvi, xxvii, Pls. 15, 18(a,b),
    27, 285, 302, 310, 313, 315–18, 345, 374,
    391, 400
Hitchcock, A. S., 148, 152, 157, 223, 285
Hitchcock, J. L. B., 387
Hitrovo, V., 157, 223
Hitzer, K., 223
Hjelmqvist, H., 157
Höck, F.
Hocking, G. M., 27
Hodgon, A. R., 110, 128, 160
Hodgson, J. M., 259, 391, 428
Hoedtke, I., 280
Hoefle, O. M., 428
Høeg, O. A., 280
Hoehne, F. C., 110
Hoffman, J. V., 223
Hoffmann, E., 343

Hoffmann, O. L., 286, 302, 311, 312, 343
Hofsten, C. G. von, xxx, 128, 135–7, 143, 153,
    157, 172–3, 205, 213, 232, 249, 267–9, 344,
    416
Hoagland, 327
Hohendorf, E., 157
Hohn, L. G., 347
Holben, F. J., 202
Holch, A. E., 193
Holekamp, E. R., 428
Holley, R. W., 344
Hollister, B. A., 428
Holloway, J. K., 427, 428
Holly, K., 277, 288, 310, 322, 328, 331–2,
    335, 340, 344, 348
Holm, L. G., 259
Holmberg, O., 73
Holmboe, J., 47, 223
Holmes, G. D., 397
Holmes, R. M., 223
Holmgren, A. H., 110
Holmgren, R. G., 280
Holstun, J. T., 437
Holt, V., 391
Holttum, R. E., 178, 196
Honard, C., 110
Hooker, Sir J., 58
Hoover, M. D., 196
Hope, A., 391
Hopewell, W. W., 347
Hopkins, E. S., 196
Hopkins, H. H., 159
Hopkins, C. M., 249
Hopkins, C. Y., 157
Hopper, W. C., 157
Horn, E. E., 110
Horwitz, W., 383
Hosner, J. F., 391
Hosokawa, T., 44, 47
Hotchkiss, N., 47, 391
Houwink, A. L., 346
Howard, A., 256
Howard, L. O., 427
Howes, F. N., 27
Hoy, J. M., 427
Hoyt, A. S., 427
Hron, F., 351, 391
Hu, Shiu-ying, xxix, xxx, 357
Huber, A., 223
Hubbard, R. A., 391
Hubbard, R. L., 256
Huckenpahler, B. J., 391
Huffaker, C. B., 411, 415–16, 427, 248
Hughes, E. C., 391
Hughes, W. J., 395
Hulbert, H. W., 154
Hulbert, L. C., 280
Hull, H. M., 310, 347
Hull, M. M., 293, 298, 302, 310
Humphrey, R. R., 409, 427
Humphreys, M. E., 159
Hunziker, A. T., 13, 27
Hurry, J. B., 2, 4, 27
Hurst, F., 427
Hurt, R. H., 41, 47
Hurtig, H., 347
Hurtwiz, S., Lachover, D., 223

Huth, E., 223
Hutson, J. C., 427
Hutchinson, Sir J., 31
Hutton, L. D., 112
Huysmans, C. P., 391
Hwang, Tso-chie, 60, 73
Hyde, E. O. C., 427
Hyder, D. N., 391

Ichikawa, C., 196, 247
Ilnicki, R. D., 259
Iltis, H., 28, 223
Imhofe, Barabara, 312
Imms, A. D., 427
Ince, J. W., 196, 247
Ingle, H. D., 275, 276
Ingram, W. M., 392
Innes, T. E. D., 89
Isakova, A. A., 110
Isely, D., 392, 427
Ishikawa, E., 157
Isikawa, S. B., 135–6, 157
Isleib, D., 139
Iurkevich, I. D., 392
Ivanov, P. K., 427
Ivens, G. W., 110, 291, 310
Iversen, J., 10, 28, 402

Jackson, H. W., 392
Jacobs, D. L., 392
Jacques, C., 427
Jacques, H., 223
Jagol, R. B., 392
Jahn, S., 392
Jalas, J., 427
James, N. I., 437
Jannaccone, A., 280
Jansen, L. L., 67, 74, 293, 298, 302, 310
Jarvis, J. M., 392
Jaworski, E. G., 310
Jeffries, C. D., 202
Jenkins, B. C., 392
Jensen, P. Boysen-. See Boysen-Jensen, P.
Jepson, F. P., 427
Jessen, K., 4, 28
Joël, A. H., 196, 280
Johansson, S., 427
John, A., 223
Johnson, D. S., 223
Johnson, E. A., 184, 196
Johnson, E. M., 113
Johnson, Elizabeth W., xxiv
Johnson, L. R., 110
Johnson, O., 392
Johnson, R. H., 343
Johnson, T., 110
Johnston, H., 301, 309
Johnston, M., 392
Johnston, T. H., 196, 428
Johnstone, D. B., 89
Jones, D. R., 327–8, 332, 342
Jones, E. T., 240
Jones E. W., 280
Jones F. D., 287, 310

Jones, G. N., 28
Jones, H. A., 392
Jones, J. Bowen-. *See* Bowen-Jones, J.
Jones, K. L., 188, 196, 223
Jones, K. W., 73, 392
Jones, M. B., 141, 157
Jones, M. D., 110
Joshi, L. M., 392
Josselyn, J., 14, 28
Jovet, P., 267, 280
Judd, S. D., 428
Juhlin-Hannfelt, M., 392
Juhren, G., 161, 258, 434
Juhren, M. C., 161, 258
Juliano, J. B., 73, 157
Julien-Dannfelt, H., xx, 28
Jumalon, F., 423
Junges, W., 196
Justice, O. L., 125, 157

Kadambi, K., 58, 73
Kadry, A. E. R., 63, 73
Kamyshev, N. S., 196
Kalenich, W., 392
Kacperska-Palacz, A. E., 259
Kamensky, K. V., 116, 132, 133, 145, 146, 152, 158
Kamensky, K. W., 428
Kanjilal, U., 57, 73
Kanngiesser, F., 12, 28
Kás, V., 223
Kasahara, Y., xxxi, 158, 280, 358, 392
Kasasian, L., xxxi, 284, 287, 289, 290-3, 313
Kaserer, H., 196
Kassanis, B., 110
Katznelson, H., 256
Kaul, R. N., 256, 428
Kaupp, B. F., 113
Kauter, A., 158
Kavanagh, 251, 255
Kay, B. L., 429
Keays, J. W., 310, 315
Keck, D. D., 234
Keeping, G. S., 428
Keever, C., 251, 256
Keim, F. D., 157, 222
Keller, B. A., 116, 132, 133, 145, 146, 152, 158
Kelley, S. G., 428
Kelly, C. D., 111
Kelton, E., 428
Kempsi, E., 223
Kempton, F. E., 112
Kendrew, W. G., 280
Kennedy, P. B., 28, 89, 223, 392
Kennett, C. E., 427
Kenoyer, L. A., xxxi
Kephart, L. W., 46
Kern, H., xxxi
Kerner von Marilaun, A., 280
Kharitonov, V. N., 73
Khil, G. T., 428
Khrebrov, A. A., 73
Kielhauser, G. E., 280
Kiermayer, O., 344
Kiewnick, L., 259

Kiesselbach, T. A., 181, 196
Kilian, E. M., 256
Kilsheimer, J. A., xxxi
Kinch, D. M., 158
Kinch, R. C., 158
King, C. M., 281, 430
King, D., 429
King, F. H., 249, 256
King, L. J. Pls. 12(a), 19(a,b), 2, 5, 28, 91, 110, 115, 124, 125, 135, 138, 139, 140, 158, 212, 223, 230, 250, 256, 293, 299, 310, 315, 329, 337, 344, 355, 360, 392
King, N. J., 420
Kingdom Ward, F., 53, 73
Kingsbury, J. M., 392
Kinoshita, O., 358, 392
Kinzel, W., 124, 158
Kirchner, O., 280
Kireer, V. N., 427
Kirk, L. E., 139, 158, 223
Kirkpatrick, H., 394, 391, 392
Kishimoto, E., 230, 240
Kivinen, E., 196
Kjaer, A., 158
Klapp, E., 196
Kling, M., 80, 89, 158, 196, 247
Klingman, D. L., xxi, 259, 310, 354, 361, 372-4, 378, 381, 382, 388, 392, 393, 397, 437
Klingman, G. C., 65, 78, 284, 310, 351, 384, 400, 437
Klinkowski, M., 196
Klots, A. B., 110
Knight, L. I., 285, 309
Knoop, F., 298
Knopp, R., 280
Knüsli, E., 291, 309, 310
Kobayashi, T., 196
Koch, L., 73, 252
Koebele, A., 412
Kögl, F., 285, 344
Köhler, E., 73
Koie, G., 428
Kolar, M., 393
Kolev, I. D., 437
Kolk, H., 123, 134, 135, 139, 141, 158
Koller, D., 125, 158
Komarov, V. L., xviii, 28
Kommendahl, T., 259
Kondo, M., 158
König, F., 80, 89
Konik, B., 397
Konzak, R., 256
Koopman, H., 310
Koppikar, H. T., 57, 73
Korobatov, V. A., 393
Korsmo, E., xviii, 28, 32, 47, 196, 257, 351, 393, 428
Korstian, C. F., 73, 158
Kosesan, W. H., 368, 393
Kots, N. N. L., 19, 28
Kott, S. A., 126, 158, 168, 351, 393
Koulechoff, N. H., 76
Kovner, J. A., 196
Kramer, J. A., Jr., 113, 310, 315, 344
Kramer, J. E., xxxii
Kramer, P. J., 327, 344

Kramer, S. N., 1, 28
Krasheninnikov, I. M., 280
Krassulin, V. P., 50, 73, 428
Kraus, E. J., xxvi, 286, 344, 393
Krauss, M. L. H., 428
Kreeb, K., 196
Krefting, L. W., 158
Kreh, W., 280
Kremer, J. C., 203, 205, 223
Krestnikowa-Syssoejwa, A., 421
Kretowitsch, W. L., 250, 256
Krippahl, M., 291
Kristoffersson, K. B., 241
Krochmal, A., 110
Krog, N., 392
Krone, P. R., 360, 386
Krug, H., 158
Krykhanov, L., 393
Krylov, S. V., 408, 428
Krzymowski, R., 28
Kubiena, W. L., 176
Kuckuck, H., 28
Kuhn, J., 241
Kuhn, K., 280
Kuijt, J., 56, 73
Kumar, L. S. S., 73
Kummer, A. P., 147, 152, 158, 280
Kunhikannan, 428
Kunitake, M., 192
Kunkel, L. O., 296, 344
Kupfsov, A. I., 241
Kurochnina, V. F., 308
Kurth, H., 351, 393
Kurup, P. G., 393
Kusano, S., 61, 64, 74
Kust, C, A., 65, 76
Küster E., 293, 344
Kutschera, L., 196
Kwizda, R., xviii
Kzn, P. R., 437

Lacombe, G., 399
Ladonin, V. F., 400
Lakon, G., 428
Lalonde, L. M., 428
Lambert, D. W., 158
Lambertz, P., 326, 344
Lambrech, J. A., 299, 310
Lange, K., 28
Langer, R. H. M., 224
Langille, A. R., 294, 309
Langridge, J., 234
Larmour, R. K., 196
Larson, A. H., 436
Larson, W. H., 393
Laštuvka, Z., 259
Laszlo, H. De, 81–2, 89
Latypov, A. S., 196
Laubach, H. von Solms-. See Solms-Laubach, H. von
Laude, H. M., 158
Lauer, E., 158
Launchbaugh, J. L., 200
Laurence, W., 241
Laus, H., 28

Lauwers, T., 393
Laventiades, G., 110
Lavergne, J., 74
Laviosa Zambotti, P., 298
Lawalree, A., 196
Lawrence, A. A., 5, 28
Lawrence, J. M., 371, 393
Leach, J. G., 111, 428
Lead, L. D., 388
Leasure, J. K., 315, 344, 393
Lebrun, J., 44, 47
Leclerc du Sablon, M., 224
Lee, A., 50, 61, 74
Lee, G. A., 345
Lee, S. B., 109
Lee, W. O., 74, 391, 393
Leeuwen, W. M. D. van. See Leeuwen, W. M. D.
Lefevre, P., 197
Legg, J. W., 193
Leggett, H. W., 428
Lehmann, E., 28, 158
Lehner, E., 89
Lehner, Johanna, 89
Lemaistre. J., 393
Lems, K., 214, 215, 278
Leonard, O. A., 342, 394
Leopold, A. C., 301, 344
Leuchs, F., 259
Levardson, N. O., 394
Lever, R. J. A. W., 428
Levi, E., 344
Levina, R. E. K., 270, 280
Lewis, A. N., 110
Lewis, I. M., 428
Lewis, N. G., 143–4, 158, 428
Lewis, N. R., 394
Lewis, W. A., 398
Li, L. V., 110
Li, Ming-yu, 247, 256
Li, S. C., xxix, 357
Li, T. C., 110
Libby, W. F., 130, 158
Lid, J., 280
Linck, A. J., 310
Lindahl, R. R., 400
Lindberg, H., 224
Lindin, G., 310, 343
Linder, P. J., 345
Lindsay, D. R., 197, 241
Lindsey, A. A., 135, 158, 197, 208
Ling, K. C., 62, 74
Linkola, K., 197
Linkola, L., 18, 28
Linnik, E. F., 394
Linser, H., 344
Linskens, H. F., 338, 344
Linstow, O. von, 197
Lippert, R. D., 159
Lipscomb, B. R., 67, 74
Lipsett, J., 257
Lisk, D. T., 437
Little, B. E., 53, 74
Little, J. E., 89
Lloyd, D. C., 197
Lo, T. T., 62, 74
Lockwood, S., 110, 428

Loehwing, W. F., 256
Loew, E., 280
Lohmeyer, W., 197
Long, H. C., xx, 28, 110, 256
Longchamp, P., xxxi, 394
Longwill, J., 199
Lontz, J. F., 287, 310
Loomis, W. E., xxxi, 319, 325-6, 345, 347, 437
Loos, C. A., 416, 428
Lopinot, A. C., 394, 437
Lorenz, R. W., 385
Loret, V., 28
Lorz, A. See Germany, Federal Republic
Lousley, J. E., 222
Loustalot, A. J., 311
Löve, A., xxvii, 123, 159, 241
Löve, Doris, xxvii, 123, 159, 241
Lovely, W. G., 355, 398
Lowry, O. J., 409, 428
Lubimenko, V. N., 116, 132, 133, 145, 146, 152, 158
Luckwill, L. C., 345
Lund, S., 437
Lunn, W. M., 197
Lush, G. B., 298, 311
Lüstner, G., 54, 74
Luther, H., 197
Lutman, A. S., 428
Lutz, H. J., 47
Lyle, C. C., 428
Lyman, R. J., 394
Lynes, F. F., 394
Lyon, T. L., 176, 197
Lyre, H., 197

MacCallan, S. E. A., xxvii
MacDougal, D. T., 49, 74, 280
McGrawth, H., 67, 74
Mack, G. L., 320, 345
Mackham, B. S., 112
Macleod, D. G., 51, 74, 437
MacMillan, C., 429
MacMullan, R. A., 394
Madaus, G., 280
Mai, W. F., 110
Maitland, V. K., 429
Magee, P. N., 301, 308
Magrou, P., 197
Makarova, V. A., 394
Maki, T. E., 394
Malinga, D. P., 197, 247
Malinowski, M., 87, 89
Mallery, T. D., 159
Malloch, J. G., 107
Malsumura, Y., 47
Malthern, R. O., 89
Malzev, A. I., 116, 132, 133, 145, 146, 152, 158, 437
Manii, A., 394
Manley, K., 394
Mann, H. H., 188, 197, 256, 257
Mann, L. K., 197, 392
Mannagetta, G. Beck von. See Beck von Mannagetta, G.
Manteuffel, K., 197

Manuel, C. G., 429
Marais, A., 257
Marais, S. J. S., 431
Marcovitch, S., 429
Marguez, V. Moreno. See Moreno Marguez, V.
Marie-Victorin, Frère, 14, 28
Marilaun, A. Kerner von. See Kerner von Marilaun, A.
Markle, M. S., xxvi
Marples, E. G., 70
Marshall, E. R., xxvii
Marth, P. C., 286, 311, 383, 387
Marthaler, H., 197
Martin, A. C., 79, 89, 159, 394, 429
Martin, D. J., 429
Martin, G. E., 110
Martin, H. M., xxi, 28, 113, 248, 257
Martin, J. N., 159
Martin, J. T., 329, 345
Martin, P., 257
Martin, R. T., 301, 309
Martin, S. C., 159
Martinez, M., 82, 89
Marudarjan, D., 62, 63, 74
Marzell, H., 77
Masera, M., 394
Massey, A. B., 110
Massey, C. L., 415, 429
Masson, H., 429
Materikina, E., 394
Matheson, H. D., 428
Matheson, R., 394
Mathews, F. P., 110, 111
Mathews, L. J., xxxi
Mathur, A. K., 74
Matic, M., 325, 345
Mattson, S., 197
Mauldin, M. P., 429
Maurizio, A., 224
Mavrodineanu, Simone, xxvii
Maximov, N. A., 180, 197
Maxwell, H., 159
May, W. L., 111
Mayer, F., 345
Mayes, J., 394
Mayne, W. W., 281
Mayton, E. L., 429
McAlister, E. D., 156
McAtee, W. L., 79, 89
McCabe, Catherine, xxviii
McCall, M. A., 7, 28
McCartney, J. E., 197
McCarty, M. K., 362, 394
McConkey, O., 195
McCready, C. C., 288, 331-2, 335, 340, 345, 348
McCreath, J. B., 429
McCullough, J. C., 429
McCully, W. G., 388
McDermott, R. E., 394
MacEwan, J. W. G., 196
McFarland, F. T., 222
McGinnis, H. A., 197
McGrawth, H., 67, 74
McGugan, J. M., 159
McHargue, J. S., 224

McKell, C. M., 429
McLeish, J., 309
McLeod, J. H., 429
McLuckie, J., 60, 74
McNab, J., 254
McNair, J. B., 41, 47, 102, 110
McNaughton, I. H., 259
McNew, G. L., xxvi, xxvii, 28, 311
McWhorter, C. G., 259
McWhorter, F. P., 74
Meadly, G. R., xxxi
Meenakshisun-Dar, 395
Mehl, S., 197
Mehrlich, F. P., 111
Mehta, K. C., 111
Meikle, R. W., 294, 312
Meiklejohn, J., 197, 241, 257
Meinzer, O. E., 197
Melchior, H., 74
Mellini, E., 415, 429
Melnichuk, A. S., 394
Melnikov, N. N., 284, 311, 345
Melo Carvalho, J. C. de, xxxi
Mendizabel, M., 60, 74
Mercer, A. D., 394
Merrill, E. D., 271-3, 281
Merwe, C. R. van der, 429
Meudt, W., 348
Meulen, H. ter, 198
Meusel, H., 281
Meyer, J. E., 89
Meyer, K., 195, 429
Meyers, L., 436
Michiels, A., 394
Miguel, G., 423
Mildner, T., 111
Milić, M., 195
Miller, A. D., 397
Miller, D., 429
Miller, L. P., xxvii, 293, 311, 315-18, 345
Miller, P. M., 74
Miller, P. R., 67, 74
Miller, R. S. B., 394
Mills, H. L., 308
Milthorpe, F. L., 225
Milton, W. E. J., 155, 159
Mimaud, J., 429
Minarik, C. E., 346
Minckler, L. S., 391
Minshall, W. H., 289, 345
Miquel, L., 394
Mirashi, M. V., 38, 47
Mishnev, V. G., 392
Mitchell, A. E., 345
Mitchell, J. W., 286, 311, 344, 345
Mitchell, P., 331
Mitra, S. K., 241
Miuge, S. G., 395
Miyahara, M., 408, 421
Miyawaki, A., 283
Mobley, L., 415, 429
Mode, C., 199
Moiseev, A. D., 429
Moldenke, Alma L., Pl. 6(a), 29, 89
Moldenke, H. N., Pl. 6(a), 29, 89
Molin, N., 395
Molinier, R.

Molisch, H., 248, 257
Möller, I., 281
Monteith, J., 379, 395
Monterrey, A., 395
Montgomery, M. L., 309
Montilla, J. A., 396
Moolani, M. K., 259
Moon, F. E., 195, 247
Moore, Lucy B., 153, 159
Moore, R. J., 241
Moore, R. M., 10, 29, 175, 198, 430
Moore, R. P., 159
Moorhead, G. R., 434
Moreland, D. E., 291-2, 311, 345
Moreno Marguez, 241
Morris, K., 155
Morris, K. R. S., 111
Morris, P. F., 89
Morrow, J., 160
Morrow, R. R., 390
Morton, H. L., 108
Moulton, J. E., 360, 386
Moyle, J., 395
Mueller, I. M., 161, 195
Mueller, L. E., 325-6, 345
Muenscher, W. C., 10, 29, 47
Muir, J., 91, 111, 274, 276, 281, 311, 345, 430
Mukherji, S. K., 195
Müller, W., 415, 430
Müller-Olsen, C., 159
Mulligan, G. A., xxxi, 230, 237, 241
Mullison, W. R., 395
Munerati, O., 74, 159
Munz, P. A., 73
Murbeck, S. V., 241
Murça-Pires, 40, 46
Murdock, H. R., 395
Murley, M. R., 430
Murphy, E. V., 111
Murr, J., 29
Mursil, Albina, F., 159, 430
Muthukrishan, T. S., 423
Muzik, T. J., 311
Myers, A., 159, 430
Myers, L. F., 175, 198, 257

Naguvi, S. B. D., 66, 69
Naib, F., xxxi
Nakausa, M., 114
Napp-Zinn, K., 159
Narasimhan, M. J., 73
Narayana, H. S., 50-51, 73, 74
Narayanan, T. R., 395
Nathanson, A., 198
Naude, T. J., 430
Naumann, A., 80, 89
Naumann, D., 281
Neckel, G., 77
Negi, N. S., 434
Negri, G., 18, 29
Nelson, A. L., 89
Nelson, J. G., 29
Nelson, R. T., 73
Nelson, R. R., 75
Nêmec, B., 293, 345

Netolitzsky, F., 29, 159
Neuweiler, E., 13, 29
Nevens, W. B., 257
Newman, J. E., 158, 197, 208
Newman, L. F., 281
Newman, R. W., 281
Newson, I. E., 108
Newton, G. J. D., 291
Nex, R. W., 345, 438
Nicholas, Nancy, xxviii
Nicholson, A. J., 430
Nicholson, C., 54, 73, 74
Nickell, L. G., 311
Nielsen, E. L., 241
Nielsen, N., 285, 345
Nielsen, N. C., 198
Niering, W. A., xxxi, 425, ,430
Niewoehner, Louise King, xxviii
Nikolskaia, M. N., 430
Noone, J. A., 346
Noordam, D., 111
Noordhoff, L. J., 284, 310, 351, 382
Nordenskiöld, H., 241
Norman, A. G., 284, 311, 342, 346
Norman, A. T., 347
Norman, I. W., 395
Normantas, K., 432
Norris, E. L., 281
Norton, J. B. S., 148, 157
Novitzky, S., 430
Nowinski, M., 430
Nutman, P. S., 286, 346
Nuttonson, M., 198, 211
Nylund, R. E., 395

Oaks, A., 301, 312
Oates, A. V., 430
Oberdorfer, E., 260-1, 263, 281
Oborn, E. T., 395
O'Brien, G. E., 395
O'Connor, B. A., 415, 430
O'Connor, K. F., 281
Offord, H. R., 111
Ogden, E. C., 111, 395
Ohga, I., 130, 159
Oksbjerg, E., 257
Old, A. N., 421
Olesen, C., 281
Olmsted, C. E., xxvi, 190, 191, 198, 234
Olsen, C., 176-7, 198
Olsen, C. Muller, See Müller-Olsen, C.
Olsen, H. K., 395
Olson, H. C., 395
Oosting, H. J., 159, 281
Opatowski, I., 346
Oppenheimer, H. R., 181-2, 198
Orchard, H. E., 111
Ordish, G., 243, 257
Orgell, W. H., Pl. 19(a,b), 311, 325-6, 329, 346
Orlando, A., 111
Orth, H., 437
Ortiz Garmendia, J., 60, 75
Ortman, R., 29
Osborne, D. J., 297

Osman, A., 75
Osol, A., xxxii, 81, 90
Ostapetz, M. L., 75
Ostenfeld, C. H., 241
Ostvold, H., 27
Osvald, H., 249, 250, 254, 257
Otto, J. J., 29
Overbeek, J. van, xxxii, 284, 287, 289, 290, 297, 311, 328, 330, 331, 332, 346, 352, 395
Owen, P. C., xxxi, 137, 159
Ownby, M., 241

Paczosky, I., 166, 198
Padmanathan, 392
Padwick, G. W., 111
Page, T. J., 395
Paine, R. A., 53, 75
Palfy, F., 311
Palhinha, R. T., 56, 75
Palmer, E., 29, 80, 90
Palmer, E. L., 90, 430
Palmér, I., 29
Pammel, L. H., xx, 29, 111, 159, 254, 281, 430
Pande, H. K., 257
Panikkar, M. R., 257
Pantaleon, F. T., 71
Pantalu, V. R., 392
Papadakis, J., 281
Pardini, Dorothy, xxviii
Parish, S. B., 395
Park, F. D. R., 395
Parker, K. W., 107
Parker, R. E., 437
Parkin, A., 346
Parkinson, S. T., 431
Pascoe, T. A., 53, 72
Patrick, Z. A., 252
Patwardhan, G. B., 75
Pauley, S. S., 191, 234, 241
Pavlychenko, T. K., Pl. 9(a,b), 139, 147, 158, 162, 167, 198, 223, 257, 431
Payne, T. M. B., 256
Payne, W. W., 111
Pazold, A., 343
Pearsall, W. H., 159
Pearse, C. K., 395
Pedersen, M. W., 431
Peevy, F. A., 368, 386, 396
Pekoldt, K., xxxi
Pelton, J. F., 281
Pember, F. R., 170, 195
Penfound, W. T., 111, 109, 282
Pengelly, R., 372, 396
Penhallow, R., 431
Penton, A., 198
Peralta, F. de, 257
Perkins, R. C. L., 412, 431
Perry, T. O., 191, 241
Peter-Contesse, J., 53, 75
Peters, B. G., 111
Peters, L., 75
Peters, R. A., 259
Petersen, A. K., 422

Petersen, D., 191, 198, 271
Petersen, H. I., 351, 389
Peterson, D. R., 309, 386, 396
Peterson, K. Dorph-. See Dorph-Peterson, K.
Petit, G., 431
Petrů, E., 252, 257
Pettey, F., 431
Petunova, A. A., 397
Pfeiffer, E., 281
Pfeiffer, R., 346
Phalen, J. M., 111
Phillips, E. P., 431
Phillips, M. R., 281
Phillips, N. E., 47
Phillips, W. M., 404-5, 431
Pickering, S., 249, 257
Piemeisel, Lydia, 180, 200
Piemeisel, R. L., 111, 180, 198, 200, 257, 281, 410, 431
Pierce, D. A., 429
Pierce, G. J., 75
Pierce, W. D., 75
Pieters, A. J., 29
Pietsch, A., 431
Pignatti, S., xxxi, 172, 261-4, 269, 281
Pijl, L. van der, 75
Pijl, P. A. van der, 75
Pillai, A. K., 396
Pinewich, L. M., 75
Pirie, N. W., 396
Plagge, H. H., 198
Plagge, H. N., 192
Plagnat, F., 53, 75
Platt, A. W., 192
Plummer, G. L., 281
Poel, L. W., 171, 199
Poeteren, N. van, 75
Pohl, R. W., 427, 437
Poignant, P., xxxi, 311
Poland, J. L., 392
Polunin, N., xix, xxv, xxviii, 29, 111, 178, 199, 281, 340-41
Poma, M., 51, 71
Pool, R. J., 199
Porsild, M. P., 47, 281
Porter, R. H., 155, 431
Porto, F., 312
Posado, O. L., 396
Potter, G. F., 398
Potter, L. D., 199
Potts, S. F., 316, 346
Potzger, J. E., 199
Poulos, P. L., 311
Powell, T., 431
Prantl, K., 13, 26
Prasad, N., 64, 75
Pratt, E. R., 254
Preston, S. W., 346
Pridham, A. M. S., 156
Priestley, J. H., 325, 346
Primost, E., 344
Prince, F. S., 128, 160
Pringle, W. L., 415, 431
Probst, R., 224
Proebsting, E. L., 251, 257
Puia, I., 311

Pulleng, H., 199
Puttarudriah, M., 346, 432

Quackenbush, F. W., 432
Quadri, S. W. S., 147, 160
Quantin, A., 281
Quastel, J. H., 346
Quinn, L., 367, 389
Quisumbing, E., 62, 75, 82, 90

Rabaté, E., 284, 311
Rabotnov, T., 396
Rademacher, B., xxxi, 29, 199, 248, 251-2, 257, 415, 432
Ragonese, A. E., 111
Ragonese, G. E., xx, 111
Ramakrishna Ayyar, T. V., 432
Ramakrishnan, P. S., 259
Ramirez, Adriana, xxxi
Rao, D., 76
Rao, M. K., 63, 75
Rao, N. L., 60, 75
Rao, P. G., 76
Rao, R. Sashagiri, 50, 54, 75
Rao, V. V., 73
Rasmussen, L. W., 155, 311, 370, 373, 386, 396
Rastorgueva I., 346
Rataj, K., 396
Rather, H. C., 432
Rattray, J. M., 64, 75
Ratzeburg, I. T. E., 29
Rauchfuss, F. L., 281
Raucourt, M., 346
Raunkiaer, C., 34, 47, 191, 281
Rautenshtein, I. I., 346
Ravn, F. K., 224
Ray, P. M., 311
Raymond, L. C., 156
Rayner, H. J. W., 417, 432
Raynor, R. N., 284, 287, 312, 346
Razi, B. A., 68, 75
Rea, H. E., 396
Rechenthin, C. A., 420
Redemann, C. T., 294, 301, 309, 312
Reed, C. F., 75
Reed, P. G., 75
Reeves, R. S., 111
Regilis, K., 432
Rehbein, C. A., 396
Reid, J. J., 342
Reid, V. H., 389
Reigel, A., 422
Reimer, C. A., 396
Reinhart, J. H., 313, 332, 348
Reithel, F. J., 343
Remmert, L. F., 343
Rennerfelt, E., 396
Rensburg, H. J. van, 432
Resühr, B., 224
Reuss, L. A., 396, 432
Revelo, P. M. A., 396

Reynaud-Beauverie, M. A., 282
Rhoads, A. S., 53, 75
Rice, E. L., 282, 312, 322
Richards, P. W., 39, 47
Richens, R. H., 241
Richter, A. A., 75
Rickard, W. H., 308
Ricker, D. W., 427
Riddel, J. A., 315, 317, 335, 347
Riddle, J. E., 2, 31
Ridley, H. N., 130, 276, 282
Riedle, A., 29
Riegel, A., 224
Riepma, P., 396
Ries, S. K., 396
Rietz, G. E. Du, 282
Riley, H. P., 241
Rimbach, A., 167, 199, 282
Rincón, D. J., 396
Rios, P., 396
Rivière, J., 251, 258
Robbins, W. W., 218, 222, 247, 258, 284, 287, 312, 346, 388
Roberts, E. A., 326, 346
Roberts, H. A., 437
Roberts, W. E., 75
Robertson, E. D. S., 109
Robertson, G. W., 223
Robertson, J. H., 364, 396, 432
Robinson, D. W., xxxi
Robinson, E. L., 65, 76
Robinson, R. G., 258, 419, 432
Robinson, T. W., 167, 199
Roche, W., 396
Roe, E. I., 158
Roelofsen, P. A., 326, 346
Roeske, D., 258
Rogenhofer, E., 419, 432
Rogers, C. F., 168-9, 199
Rogers, C. H., 111
Rogers, L. H., 173, 199, 247
Rollins, R. C., xxxi, 227, 241
Romell, L. G., 171, 199
Rominger, J. M., 259
Rose, G. J., 316, 346
Rosenfels, R. S., 224
Roshevitz, R. J., 116, 132, 133, 145, 146, 152, 158
Ross, H., 419, 432
Ross, M. R., 396
Ross, W. C. J., 81, 88
Roth, W., 396
Rothmaler, W., 282
Rouatt, J. W., 256
Roux, E. R., 238
Row, V. V., xxxi, 396
Roxas, M. L., 61, 76
Roy, D. F., 396
Roys, R. L., 90
Rozhkov, A. I., 396
Rübel, E., 282
Rudakov, O., 416, 432
Rudd, R., 396
Rudd, R. L., 48
Rudenko, A., 416, 432
Ruinen, J., 44, 47
Runyon, H. E., 217, 224

Russ, O. G., 401
Russell, Sir E. J., 199, 248, 258, 403, 432
Russell, T. C., 347
Ryan, H. J., 220, 224
Ryker, T. C., 397

Sablon, M. Leclerc du. See Leclerc du Sablon M.
Saburova, P. V., 397
Sadati, H., 432
Sadjiarto, S. D. R., 398
Safra, R., 397
Sagar, G. R., 235, 240, 259
Sakai, K., 242
Sakisaka, M., 229-230
Saldarriaga, V. A., 396
Salisbury, Sir E. J., xxxi, Pl. 11, 115-16, 152, 177, 199, 205, 206, 207, 208, 216, 219, 220, 225, 234, 282
Sallans, B. J., 112
Salzmann, R., 173, 199, 218, 225, 282
Samborski, D. J., 301, 312
Samgin, P. A., 397
Samish, R. M., 199
Sampson, A. W., 397, 432
Sampson, D. R., 236, 242
Samuelsson, G., 47
Sand, P. F., 362, 394
Sanders, H. G., 432
Sands, N. H., 397
Sands, W. N., 43, 44, 47, 59, 76
Sanger-Davis, A. E., 397
Santos, E., 112
Sanzen-Baker, R. G., 54, 76
Sarfatti, G., 282
Sarma, K., 58, 76
Sarospataky, G., 160
Sauer, C. O., 29, 402, 432
Sauer, J. D., 12, 29
Saunders, A. N., 258
Saunders, A. R., 64, 76
Saunders, J. M., 349, 352, 397
Savchenko, E. N., 397
Sawyer, A. M., 76
Sax, K., 282
Saxena, J. S., 432
Sayre, C. B., 199
Sayre, L. E., 192
Sayupatham, T., 419, 432
Schaffner, J. H., 167, 189, 199, 225
Schalow, E., 225
Schaper, P., 432
Scheer, W., 200
Schenck, H., 47
Scherff, R. A., 313, 348
Schieferstein, R. H., 319, 325-6, 347
Schiemann, E., 29, 236-7, 242
Schimper, A. F. W., 43, 48
Schipstra, K., 175, 200
Schisler, L. C., 313
Schmalfuss, K., 169, 200
Schmeling, B. von, 344
Schmelzer, K., 112
Schmitt, L., 200
Schmitz, A., 200

Schmucker, T., 67, 76
Schnelle, F., 200
Schoeman, S. N., 282
Schoene, D. L., 301, 312
Schoenichen, W., 433
Schofield, R. C., 397
Scholl, R., 53, 76
Scholnemann, J. A., 453
Schonland, S., 433
Schramm, G., 200
Schredl, H., 76
Schreiber, M. W., 259
Schroppel, H., 397
Schröter, C., 280, 282
Schultz, A. M., 397, 432
Schulz, O. E., 3, 29
Schwanitz, F., 29, 242
Schwartz, M., 75
Schweinfurth, C., 29
Schweizer, E. E., 437
Schweizer, J., 397
Schwemmin, D. J., 88, 100, 107
Scott, F. M., 325-6, 347
Scott, W. O., 282
Scurti, J., 425
Seale, C. C., 397
Searle, S. A., 200
Sears, P. B., 30
Segadas-Vianna, F., 397
Seidler, L., 201
Sell, H. M., 313
Selleck, G. W., 200, 259, 387
Sellers, W. F., 433
Sen, G., 293, 312
Seo, Y., 196, 247
Seshagiri Rao, R. See Rao, R. Seshagiri, 75
Sernander, R., 213, 218, 225
Setchell, W. A., 200
Severin, H. H., 109, 112
Sewell, N. C., 193, 425
Sexsmith, J. J., 347
Sexton, O. J., 48
Sexton, W. A., 286, 290, 312, 347
Shadbolt, C. A., 258
Shafer, N. E., 397
Shande, W. A., 112
Shantz, H. L., 180, 193, 200
Sharma, S. L., 76
Shaw, F. J. F., 63, 76
Shaw, H. R., 397
Shaw, M., 301, 312
Shaw, R. G., 397
Shaw, R. H., 200
Shaw, W. C., xxxi, 6, 30, 67, 74, 113, 312,
    349, 351, 352, 355, 361, 372-4, 381-2, 388,
    392-3, 397, 437
Shcheglov, I. V., 397
Sheffield, F. M. L., 112
Shell, E. W., 418, 433
Shelmire, B., 112
Shenberger, L. C., 432
Shepherd, H. N., 349, 397
Shevelev, N. I., 433
Shewell-Cooper, W. E., 112, 419, 433
Shields, Lora, M., 296, 308, 312
Shiner, E., 433
Shipinov, N. A., 397

Shiraishi, K., 157
Shishiny, E. E., 160
Shull, A. E., 258
Shull, C. A., xxvi, 122, 140, 160, 242
Shultes, R. E., 86, 90
Shultz, A. M., 200
Shunk, V. D., 176, 195
Siddings, L., 200
Siegel, S. M., 298, 312, 347
Sievers, E., 90
Sifton, H. B., 160, 435
Sijthoff, A. W., xxix
Sikka, S. M., xxxi
Silberbauer, S. F., 91, 113
Silberschmidt, K., 111
Silker, T. H., 398, 433
Silva, B. L. T. De. See De Silva, B. L. T.
Silvestri, F., 433
Simak, M., 159
Simeonov, B., 433
Simmonds, F. J., 433
Simmonds, H. W., 433
Simonart, P., 112
Simpson, A. W., 398
Simpson, G. W., 112
Simpson, J. F. H., 200
Singh, B., 68
Singh, B. N., 173-4, 200, 433
Singh, H. N., 225, 434
Singh, J. P., 432
Singh, L. B., 173-4, 200
Singh, T. C. N., 433
Sinskaia, E. N., 160, 200, 225, 282
Sissingh, G., 282
Sitton, B. G., 398
Skinner, A., 90
Skinner, C. M., 90
Skoog, F., 296, 347
Skoss, J. D., 325, 347
Skrdla, W., 150, 154
Skvortsova, L. A., 312
Slade, R. E., 286, 312, 347
Slater, I. W., 107
Slife, F. W., 282, 297
Small, J., 200, 225
Smirnov, B. M., 433
Smith, A. Bernard-. See Bernard-Smith, A.
Smith, A. D., 80, 90
Smith, A. E., 302, 315, 317, 335, 344, 347,
    348
Smith, B. E., 76
Smith, C. W., 433
Smith, E. V., 398, 399, 429
Smith, F. G., 312
Smith, G., 431
Smith, Gertrude, 2
Smith, H. D., 282
Smith, H. H., 14, 90
Smith, H. S., 433
Smith, J. M., 433, 434
Smith, K. M., 112
Smith, L. B., 45, 46, 48
Smith, L. P., 200
Smith, P. Greig-. See Greig-Smith, P.
Smith, R. C., 434
Smith, T. E., 112
Smith-White, S., 228, 235, 242

Smith, W. N., 384
Snell, K., 160
Sneva, F. A., 391
Snider, H. I., 200
Snijders, J. H., 90
Snog, M., 172, 200
Sokoloff, V. P., 434
Söllner, R., 242
Solms-Laubach, H. von, 76
Solomon, S., 73, 76
Sonvil, W. A., 408, 434
Sonavne, K. M., 160
Somes, H. A., 434
Sorauer, P., 73
Sørensen, T., 242
Sosa Gonzales, R., 398
Sougy, M. P., 160
South, F. W., 398
Southey, J. F., 112
Southwick, L., xxxi
Southwick, M. D., 236, 346
Spankhuizen, J. C. van der L., 398
Sparkes, C. H., 201
Sparrow, A. H., 296, 343
Spears, J. F., 110
Speirs, M. M., 398
Sperlich, A., 76
Sperry, O. E., 160
Speziale, A. J., 309
Spikes, J. D., 347
Spillman, W. J., 200, 282
Spindler, F., 276
Sporne, H. R., 242
Sprague, M. A., 368, 398
Spring, F. G., 48
Springer, P. F., 398
Spurway, C. H., 200
Srinivasan, A. R., 77
Srivastava, T. N., 398
Stadtherr, R., 395
Staehelin, M., 112
Stage, H. H., 289, 312
Stahl, C. A., 434
Stahl, C. F., 113
Stahler, L. M., 112, 258, 417, 434, 436
Stahlin, A., 27
Stahevitch, B. Y., 76
Stakman, E. C., 112
Stamper, E. R., 398
Standley, P. C., 104, 108, 112
Staniforth, D. W., xxxi, 356, 398
Staniland, L. N., 112
Stanton, T. R., 225
Stapel, C., 395
Stapledon, R. G., 282
Stauffer, R. E., 398
Stearn, W. T., xxxi, 10, 30
Stearns, F., 200
Stebbins, G. L., 216, 225
Steenis, J. H., 394, 398
Steinbauer, G. P., 112, 156
Steiner, G., 108
Steinmetz, F. H., 112
Stekhoven, J. H. S., 109
Stelzner, S., 398
Stephens, J. C., 398
Stephens, S. G., 217, 225

Stevens, O. A., 76, 115, 160, 282, 434
Stevenson, Margaret, 343
Stewart, F. C., 50, 76
Stewart, G. S., 112
Stewart, W. S., 41, 48
Steyer, K., 169, 201
Steyn, D. G., 92, 112
Stiles, W. B., 398
Stitt, R. E., 49, 50, 76
Stoa, T. E., 258
Stoddart, L. A., 92, 112
Stoeckler, J. H., 399
Stoesz, H. D., 194
Stoffers, A. L., 338, 344
Stoker, G. L., 160
Stolanova, I., 433
Stone, A. L., 434
Stone, E. C., 201, 434
Stone, G. M., 315, 317, 335, 347
Stone, T. M., 348
Stout, G. L., Pl. 5(a), 76, 391
Stout, M., 125, 160
Stout, O. V. P., 201, 399
Strantz, Elsa, 90
Stratton, R., 90
Streich, A., 408, 434
Strickler, P. E., 349, 352, 397
Struve, V. P., 419, 434
Stryckers, J., 64, 77
Stutzer, A., 201
Suarez, O. R., 282
Subramanian, C. L., 67, 77
Subramanian, T. V., 67, 77, 434
Suggitt, J. W., 399
Suggs, D. D., 419, 434
Suk, A. V., 73
Sulit, M. D., 58, 77, 113
Sulochava, C. B., 254
Summerhayes, V. S., 178, 201
Sund, J. M., 201
Sunk, K. A., 347
Surbur, E. W., 399
Swain, L. C., 399
Swanson, C. R., 113, 312
Swanson, C. P., 232, 242
Swanson, E. P., 347
Swederski, W., 30
Sweet, R. D., 399
Sweet, R. W., xxxi, 359
Sweetman, H. L., 113, 411, 417, 434
Swegey, O. H., 431
Swezey, A. W., 345, 388, 438
Swingle, H. S., 398, 399, 417, 434
Sylvester, S. E., 113
Sylvester, E. P., 221
Symon, D. E., 242
Synerholm, M., 298, 347
Sze, W. B., 387
Szemes, G., 225

Tadros, T. M., 282
Tafuro, A. J., 315, 347
Tajima, S., 283
Takedo, M., 358, 392
Takeuchi, S., 157
Takhtajian, A. L., 90

Talafantova, A., 172, 201
Talbot, M. W., 387
Tallon, G., 283
Tambe, G. C., 434
Tan, J. P., 62, 69
Tannehill, G. F., 434
Tansley, A. G., 281, 283
Tarakanov, K. N., 283
Tarnovich, N. K., 408
Tarzwell, C. M., 392
Tate, P., 77
Tate, H. D., 395
Taubenhaus, J. J., 113
Taylor, A. R. A., 399
Taylor, D. M., 434
Taylor, J., 437
Taylor, T., 150, 154
Taylor, T. H., 154, 254, 277
Taylor, T. P., 419, 432
Tear, J., 395
Tedin, O., 242
Teirlinck, I., 30, 86
Tempany, Sir H. T., 258
Templeman, W. G., 150, 154, 254, 277, 286, 290, 302, 312, 336, 347
ter Meulen, H. See Meulen, H. ter
Tewfic, H., 63, 73
Thakur, C., 434
Thellung, A., 16, 30, 33, 34, 242, 283
Thielebein, M., 343
Thieret, J. W., 434
Thimann, K. V., 285, 313, 347, 348
Thiselton Dyer, T. F., 86, 90
Thoday, D., 54, 77, 160
Thomas, H. E., 113
Thomas, W. L., Jr., 30
Thompson, B. J., 346
Thompson, H. C., 258
Thompson, H. E., 347
Thompson, J. C., 77
Thompson, M. M., 399
Thompson, W. B., xxvi, 27
Thompson, Mrs. William Boyce, xxvi, 30
Thompson, R. C., 1, 30
Thompson, W. R., 434
Thomson, J. R., 409, 435
Thomson, R. B., 435
Thon, H. C. S., 200
Thone, F., 90
Thornton, H. G., 346
Thorp, Elizabeth, xxiv
Thorsteinson, A. J., 113
Thorup, S., 284, 347
Thresh, R., 296, 341
Thurston, Joan M., xxxi, 127, 160, 259
Tibbits, T. W., 347
Tice, L. F., xxxii
Tikhovidova, V. K., 77
Tildesley, W. T., 160, 435
Tillyard, R. J., 435
Timar, L., 201
Timmons, F. L., xxxi, 50, 74, 201, 258, 349, 352, 361, 372-4, 377, 378, 381, 388, 391, 393, 397, 399, 431, 435, 437
Timson, S. D., 77
Tingey, D. C., 160
Tischler, G., 242

Tisdale, E. W., 108
Tisdell, T. F., 92, 113
Tittel, C., 399
Toit, R. Du. See Du Toit, R.
Tokin, B. P., 250, 258
Tolman, B., 125, 160
Tomaselli, R., 283
Toohey, C. L., 77
Tooke, F. G. C., 435
Toole, E. H., 124, 141, 155, 161
Toole, V. K., 141, 155, 161
Torgeson, Kathryn W., xxviii
Toriyama, K., 435
Toyokawa, R., 543
Trabut, M., 77
Train, P., 80, 90
Trautmann, W., 201
Travers, S. J., 435
Trelease, W., 53, 77
Tribe, D. E., 79, 90
Trikojus, V. M., 107
Trivedi, K. N., 76
Tronchet, 51
Troughton, A., 147, 161
Trueblood, H. M., Jr., xxxi
Truhaut, R., 342
Trupin, F., 385
Truscott, F. H., 50, 77
Tryon, E. H., 41, 46
Tryon, H., 435
Tryti, G., 435
Trzciński, W., 161, 225
Tso-chie Hwang. See Hwang, Tso-chie, 77
Tubeuf, K. F. von, 53-4, 77
Tukey, H. B., 302, 309, 310, 312, 347
Tumbelson, M. L., 259
Turesson, G., 242
Turner, G. T., 435
Turner, J. H., 161
Turrill, W. B., xxxi, 15-7, 18, 30, 283
Tutin, T. G., xxxi, 191, 201, 242, 270
Tutin, Winifred, 12, 30
Tutton, S. M., 397
Tüxen, R., 18, 30, 264, 283
Twisselman, C., 435

Ubrizsy, G., 261, 265, 283, 347, 399
Uhlenbroek, J. H., 310
Uhler, F. M., 399
Ulbrich, E., 435
Uphof, J. C. T., 218, 225, 283
Uppal, B. N., xxxi
Urton, N. R., 77
Utiyamada, H., 242
Uttaman, P., 77

Vaartaga, O., 191, 201
Vaas, K. F., 399
Vael, W. B. De. See De Vael, W. B.
Valdes Barry, F., xxxi, 77
Vallance, K. B., 78
Vallez, H., 399
Vallfau, W. D., 113
van der Goor, G. A. W. See Goor, G. A. W. van der.

van der Groot, P. *See* Groot, P. van der.
van der L. van Spankhuizen, J. C. *See* Spankhuizen, J. C. van der L. van
van der Merwe, C. R. *See* Merwe, C. R. van der, 435
Van der Pijl, P. A. *See* Pijl, P. A., Van der.
van der Veen, R., 313
van der Waal, 330
Van Der Zweep, W., 390
van Dersal, W. R. *See* Dersal, W. R. van
Van Engel, W. A., 199
Van Es, L., 113
van Geluwe, J. J. D., 315, 347
Van Goor, C. P., *See* Goor C. P. Van
van Hille, F. J. H. *See* Hille, F. J. H. van
van Leeuwen, W. M. D., 60, 78
van Overbeek, J. *See* Overbeek, J. van
van Poeteren, N. *See* Poeteren, N. van
van Rensburg, H. J. *See* Rensburg, H. J. van, 435
Van Schaack, M. B., 407
Van Spankhuizen, J. C. van der L. *See* Spankhuizen, J. C. van der L. van
van Wijk, H. L. Gerth. *See* Gerth van Wijk, H.
Varenitsa, E. T., 399
Vareschi, V., 48
Varlet, G., 399
Varma, S. C., 151, 161
Vasquez, A., 78
Vassiliev, I. M., 182, 201
Vavilov, N. I., 24, 30, 236, 237, 242
Vegis, A., 201
Velasco, J. R., 399
Velez, I., xxxi, 43, 48, 201
Veloso, H. P., 46, 48
Vengris, J., 161, 201, 244–6, 258
Venkataramani, K. S., 347, 399
Verall, A. F., 113
Verdoorn, I. C., 78
Verma, R. D., 400
Vester, H., 283
Vianna, F. Segadas-. *See* Segadas-Vianna, F.
Victorin, Frère Marie. *See* Marie-Victorin, Frère
Vidme, T, 351, 393
Vigorov, L. I., 247, 258
Viljoen, P. R., 435
Villaneura, 415
Vinogradov, A. P., 201, 247
Virchow, R. N., 80
Visser, T., 161
Vlitos, A. J., xxvii, 296, 299, 300, 337, 348
Voevodin, A. V., 312, 400
Vogel, F., 78
Voitov, P. I., 400
Volkart, A., 64, 78, 172–3, 201, 435
Von Abrams, G. J., 161
von Degen, A. *See* Degen, A. von
von Denfer, D., 201
von Hofsten, C. G. *See* Hofsten, C. G. von
von Linstow, O. *See* Linstow, O. von
Von Mannagetta, G. Beck. *See* Beck Von Mannagetta, G.
von Marilaun, A. Kerner. *See* Kerner von Marilaun, A.
von Solms-Laubach, H. *See* Solms-Laubach, H. von

von Tubeuf, K. F. *See* Tubeuf, K. F. von
Voss, H., 19, 30
Voth, P. D., xxvi
Vries, D. A. de *See* de Vries, D. A..
Vries, D. M. de. *See* de Vries, D. M.
Vries, O., de. *See* de Vries, O.

Wad, Y. D., 434
Wagener, H., 196
Wagener, W. W., 52, 78
Wager, C. A., 416, 435
Wagner, J. S., 113
Wagner, H., 201
Wagner, W. H., Jr., 88, 100, 107, 114
Wagnon, A, Pl. 5(a), 391
Wahlen, F. T., 435,
Wain, R. L., 285, 299, 309, 312, 337–8, 346, 348, 436
Waisel, Y., 183, 201
Waldron, L. R., 139, 161
Walker, A. G., 113
Walker, C. F., 394
Walker, M. N., 113
Wallach, A., 113
Walter, H., xxxi
Walters, M. S., 242
Warbach, O., 48
Warburg, O., 291
Warington, K., 155, 161, 176, 201, 422
Warming, E., 177, 201
Warner, H. H., 78
Warren, T. R., 154
Washburn, R. M., 980, 90
Watt, A. S., 283
Watt, J. M., 92, 113
Waugh, F. A., 31
Weaver, J. E., 161, 202, 278, 283
Weaver, R. J., 312
Webb, P. C. R., 113
Weber, C. R., 398
Weber, G. F., 52–3, 78
Weber, P. W., 436
Weber, R. P., 309
Weed, C. M., 225
Weed, R. M., 315–18, 345
Weeraratina, W. G., 78
Wehsarg, O., 267, 283, 351, 400
Weigert, J., 202
Weight, W. K., 400
Weinstein, I., 113
Weintraub, R. L., 295, 311, 313, 328, 346, 348
Weiser, N. A., 400
Weiser, S., 161
Weisner, J. B., 384, 400
Weiser, I., 90
Weiss, F., 254, 258
Weitzman, S., 400
Weizel, H., 202
Welbank, P. J., 250, 258, 259
Welch, C. E., Jr., 81, 90
Welch, G. B., 436
Weldon, L. W., 391, 400
Weldstra, H., 313
Weller, L. E., 301, 313
Wellman, F. L., 45, 113, 416
Wellman, R. H., xxvii

Wells, P. V., 296, 312
Welton, F. A., 161, 202, 436
Went, F. W., 44, 48, 130, 131, 149, 161, 187, 188, 201, 202, 217, 251, 258, 285, 313, 348, 409
Werner, R., 348
Werth, E., 13, 31, 236, 242
Wessels, J. S. C., 313
West, D. W., 161, 427
West, E., 39, 48
Westman, J. R., 348, 400
Westmoreland, W. G., 400
Whitaker, T. W., 31
White, F. M., xxxii
White, J. T., 2, 31
White, J. W., 202, 436
White, O. E., 202
White, S. Smith-. See Smith-White, S.
White, W. N., 202
Whitehead, E. J., 112
Whiteside, J. S., 339, 348
Whitney, M., 249, 258
Whyte, R. O., 187, 190, 191, 198, 202, 233, 242, 342, 395, 424
Wiant, D. E., 436
Widder, F. J., 242
Widdifield, R. B., 436
Wiehe, P. O., 436
Wightman, E., 309
Wightman, F., 309, 337, 346, 348
Wijk, H. L. Gerth van. See Gerth van Wijk
Wilber, C. P. P., 400
Wild, H., 78, 400
Wildeman, E. de, 152, 161, 248, 253, 258
Wildon, C. E., 313
Wilhelm, S., 113
Willard, C. J., 308, 313, 386, 400, 436
Williams, C. B., 202, 283
Williams, J. H., 400
Williams, J. R., 416, 436
Williams, J. T., 259
Williams, R. E., 358, 460
Williams, R. H., 400
Williams, W. E., 436
Williamson, R. E., 316, 318, 319, 323, 342
Willis, J. C., 242
Willis, S. J., 202
Willmot, F. C., 91, 113
Wilsie, C. P., 20, 31, 234
Wilson, A. C., 436
Wilson, A. M., 429, 436
Wilson, F., 415, 436
Wilson, H. K., 284, 313, 348, 436
Wilson, J. A., xxxi, 1, 2, 31
Wilson Jones, K. See Jones, K. W., 77
Wilson, J. K., 258
Wilson, T. M., 400
Wilson, M., 400
Wiltse, M. G., 400
Winkler, H., 54, 78
Winne, W. T., 400
Winton, A. L., 436
Wisniewski, A. J., 388
Witman, E. D., 291
Wittmack, L., 13, 31, 202, 283
Wodehouse, R. P., 113
Woenig, F., 31

Woestemeyer, V., 436
Wolcott, A. R., 419, 436
Wolcott, G. N., 113
Wolf, D., 384
Wolf, F. A., 113, 416, 437
Wolfe, H. H., 373, 386
Wollenweber, H. W., 47
Woo, M. L., 202
Woodbridge, M. E., 437
Woodford, E. K., xxi, xxxi, 287, 289, 290–3, 312, 313, 331–2, 335, 340, 350–1, 352, 400
Woods, F. W., 239
Woodside, A. M., 114
Wooten, O. B., 437
Worley, D. P., 386
Wormald, H., 114
Worsham, A. D., 65, 78
Wort, D. J., 348
Worzella, W. W., 158
Woytinsky, E. S., xxviii, 31
Woytinsky, W. S., xxvii, 31
Wright, J. M., 239
Wright, M. J., 201
Wright, R., 417, 437
Wright, W. H., 427
Wulf, H. D., 242
Wurgler, W., 401
Wylie, A. P., xix, 26
Wyman, O. L., 112
Wyssling, A. Frey-. See Frey-Wyssling, A.

Yakhontov, V. V., 415, 437
Yamada, T., 203, 225
Yamaguchi, S., 309
Yamasaki, M., 114
Yancey, P. J., 2, 31
Yeo, R. R., 348, 377, 391, 401
Yoder, D. M., xxvii
York, H. H., 53, 78
Young, C. L., 201
Young, P. D., 348
Young, R. S., 437
Younger, R. R., 400
Younkin, S. G., 114
Yue, Z., xxxi
Yuncker, T. G., 49, 78

Zacha, V., 201
Zachartchenko, V., xxvii
Zade, A., 437
Zahariadi, C., 401
Zahl, P. A., 81, 88
Zahloul, M. A., 78
Zahnley, J. W., 161, 348, 401
Zambotti, P. Laviosa. See Laviosa Zambotti, P., 31
Zandstra, K., 194
Zandstra, Z., 283
Zappettini, G., 108
Zaviezo, M. S., 400
Zederbauer, E., 202
Zedler, R. J., xxvii, 310, 315
Zeigler, H., 78
Zeland, M. G., 385
Zeuner, F. E., 13, 31
Zillich, R., 191, 202

Zim, H. S., 89
Zimmerman, F., 31
Zimmerman, P. W., xxvi, Pls. 15, 48, 285, 298, 301, 302, 313, 347, 374, 391, 400
Zimmermann, A., 225
Zinger, N., 31
Zinger, N. *See* Sinskaia & Beztuzheva, 160
Zinger, 117

Zinn, K. Napp-. *See* Napp-Zinn, K.
Zöpfig, F., 53, 78
Zossimovich, V. P., 236, 237, 242,
Zukel, J. W., 313, 315, 317, 335, 347, 348, 400
Zur Burg, F. W., 400
Zurn, F., 202
Zweig, G., 437